M J Neer

INSTRUCTOR'S SOLUTIONS MANUAL FOR

Engineering Mechanics:

STATICS

Second Edition

Andrew Pytel
The Pennsylvania State University

Jaan Kiusalaas
The Pennsylvania State University

BROOKS/COLE PUBLISHING COMPANY
I(T)P® An International Thomson Publishing Company

Pacific Grove · Albany · Belmont · Boston · Cincinnati · Johannesburg · London · Madrid
Melbourne · Mexico City · New York · Scottsdale · Singapore · Tokyo · Toronto

For more information, contact:

BROOKS/COLE PUBLISHING COMPANY
511 Forest Lodge Road
Pacific Grove, CA 93950
USA

International Thomson Publishing Europe
Berkshire House 168-173
High Holborn
London WC1V 7AA
England

Thomas Nelson Australia
102 Dodds Street
South Melbourne, 3205
Victoria, Australia

Nelson Canada
1120 Birchmount Road
Scarborough, Ontario
Canada M1K 5G4

International Thomson Editores
Seneca 53
Col. Polanco
11560 México, D. F., México

International Thomson Publishing GmbH
Königswinterer Strasse 418
53227 Bonn
Germany

International Thomson Publishing Asia
60 Albert Street
#15-01 Albert Complex
Singapore 189969

International Thomson Publishing Japan
Palaceside 5F
1-1-1 Hitotsubashi
Chiyoda-ku, Tokyo 100-0003
Japan

Printed in the United States of America.

5 4 3 2 1

ISBN 0-534-95746-3

1.1

(a) $m = \dfrac{30 \text{ lb}}{5.32 \text{ ft/s}^2} = 5.639 \text{ slugs}$ ◆

(b) $W = mg = (5.639)(32.2) = 181.6 \text{ lb}$ ◆

1.2

$$W = \rho g V = (7850)(9.81)\pi(0.06)^2(0.120) = 104.51 \text{ N}$$

$$\therefore W = 104.51 \text{ N} \times \frac{0.2248 \text{ lb}}{1.0 \text{ N}} = 23.5 \text{ lb}$$ ◆

1.3

(a) $600 \text{ lb/ft}^2 = \dfrac{600 \text{ lb}}{\text{ft}^2} \times \dfrac{4.448 \text{ N}}{1.0 \text{ lb}} \times \dfrac{1.0 \text{ ft}^2}{0.09290 \text{ m}^2} \times \dfrac{1.0 \text{ kN}}{1000 \text{ N}} = 28.73 \text{ kN/m}^2$ ◆

(b) $60 \text{ mi/h} = \dfrac{60 \text{ mi}}{\text{h}} \times \dfrac{5280 \text{ ft}}{1.0 \text{ mi}} \times \dfrac{0.3048 \text{ m}}{1.0 \text{ ft}} \times \dfrac{1.0 \text{ h}}{3600 \text{ s}} = 26.82 \text{ m/s}$ ◆

(c) $10 \text{ Mg} = 10 \times 10^3 \text{ kg} = \left(10 \times 10^3\right) \text{kg} \times \dfrac{0.06852 \text{ slugs}}{1.0 \text{ kg}} = 685.2 \text{ slugs}$ ◆

(d) $14.7 \text{ lb/in}^2 = \dfrac{14.7 \text{ lb}}{\text{in}^2} \times \dfrac{4.448 \text{ N}}{1.0 \text{ lb}} \times \dfrac{1.0 \text{ kN}}{1000 \text{ N}} \times \dfrac{144 \text{ in}^2}{1.0 \text{ ft}^2} \times \dfrac{1.0 \text{ ft}^2}{0.09290 \text{ m}^2} = 101.4 \text{ kN/m}^2$ ◆

1.4

$$I = 20 \text{ kg}\bullet\text{m}^2 = 20 \text{ kg}\bullet\text{m}^2 \times \frac{0.06852 \text{ slugs}}{1.0 \text{ kg}} \times \frac{10.764 \text{ ft}^2}{1.0 \text{ m}^2} = 14.75 \text{ slug}\bullet\text{ft}^2$$

$$\therefore I = 14.75 \frac{\text{lb}\bullet\text{s}^2}{\text{ft}} \bullet \text{ft}^2 = 14.75 \text{ lb}\bullet\text{ft}\bullet\text{s}^2$$ ◆

1.5

$$KE = \frac{1}{2}mv^2 + \frac{1}{2}mk^2\omega^2$$

The first term on the right-hand side gives $[KE] = [m]\left[v^2\right] = [M]\left[\dfrac{L^2}{T^2}\right]$ (1)

Then, the second term on the right-hand side gives

$$[KE] = [M]\left[\frac{L^2}{T^2}\right] = [m]\left[k^2\right]\left[\omega^2\right] = [M]\left[k^2\right]\left[\frac{1}{T^2}\right]$$

Solving gives $\left[k^2\right] = \left[\dfrac{L^2}{T^2}\right]\left[T^2\right]$ or $[k] = [L]$ (2)

(a) In the SI system, Eq. (1) gives $[KE] = [M]\left[\dfrac{L^2}{T^2}\right] = \dfrac{\text{kg}\bullet\text{m}^2}{\text{s}^2}$ ◆

Eq. (2) gives $[k] = [L] = \text{m}$ ◆

(b) In the U.S. system, Eq. (1) gives $[KE] = [M]\left[\dfrac{L^2}{T^2}\right] = \left[\dfrac{FT^2}{L}\right]\left[\dfrac{L^2}{T^2}\right] = [FL] = \text{lb}\bullet\text{ft}$ ◆

Eq. (2) gives $[k] = [L] = \text{ft}$ ◆

1.6

The dimensions of $\dfrac{gkx}{W}$ are: $[g][k][x]\left[\dfrac{1}{W}\right] = \left[\dfrac{L}{T^2}\right]\left[\dfrac{F}{L}\right][L]\left[\dfrac{1}{F}\right] = \left[\dfrac{L}{T^2}\right] = [a]$ Q.E.D.

1.7

The dimensions of $k = \dfrac{F}{x}$ are: $[k] = \left[\dfrac{F}{x}\right] = \left[\dfrac{ML}{T^2}\right]\left[\dfrac{1}{L}\right] = \left[\dfrac{M}{T^2}\right]$ ◆

1.8

(a) $\left[mv^2\right] = \left[\frac{FT^2}{L}\right]\left[\frac{L}{T}\right]^2 = [FL]$ ◆

(b) $[mv] = \left[\frac{FT^2}{L}\right]\left[\frac{L}{T}\right] = [FT]$ ◆

(c) $[ma] = \left[\frac{FT^2}{L}\right]\left[\frac{L}{T^2}\right] = [F]$ ◆

1.9

$y = kx^2$ (where $k = 1.0$)

The dimensions of $k = \frac{y}{x^2}$ are: $\therefore\ [k] = \left[\frac{y}{x^2}\right] = \left[\frac{L}{L^2}\right] = \left[\frac{1}{L}\right]$

$y = x^2$ can be dimensionally correct if the units of the constant 1.0 (not shown explicity) are understood to be in^{-1}.

1.10

(a) $[I] = \left[mR^2\right] = \left[\frac{FT^2}{L}\right]\left[L^2\right] = \left[FLT^2\right]$ ◆

(b) $[I] = \left[mR^2\right] = \left[ML^2\right]$ ◆

1.11

(a) The dimensions of $v^2 = Ax^3 + Bvt$ are: $\left[\frac{L}{T}\right]^2 = [A]\left[L^3\right] + [B]\left[\frac{L}{T}\right][T]$

$\therefore\ [A] = \left[\frac{L}{T}\right]^2\left[\frac{1}{L^3}\right] = \left[T^{-2}L^{-1}\right]$ ◆ $\quad [B] = \left[\frac{L}{T}\right]^2\left[\frac{1}{L}\right] = \left[T^{-2}L\right]$ ◆

(b) The dimensions of $x^3 = Ate^{Bt}$ are: $\left[L^3\right] = [A][T]e^{[B][T]}$

$\therefore\ [B][T] = [1]$ which gives $[B] = \left[T^{-1}\right]$ ◆

and $[A][T] = \left[L^3\right]$ which gives $[A] = \left[L^3T^{-1}\right]$ ◆

1.12

$\left[m\frac{d^2x}{dt^2}\right] = \left[\frac{FT^2}{L}\right]\left[\frac{L}{T^2}\right] = [F]$ Therefore, the dimension of each term is $[F]$.

$\left[c\frac{dx}{dt}\right] = [c]\left[\frac{L}{T}\right] = [F]$ $\qquad \therefore\ [c] = \left[FTL^{-1}\right]$ ◆

$[kx] = [k][L] = [F]$ $\qquad \therefore\ [k] = \left[FL^{-1}\right]$ ◆

$\left[P_0 \sin \omega t\right] = \left[P_0\right]\left[\sin \omega t\right] = [F]$

$\therefore\ \left[P_0\right] = [F]$ ◆

$\left[\omega t\right] = [\omega][T] = [1]$ $\qquad \therefore\ [\omega] = \left[T^{-1}\right]$ ◆

1.13

From Eq. (11.17): $G = \frac{FR^2}{m_A m_B}$ which gives $[G] = \frac{[F]\left[R^2\right]}{\left[m_A\right]\left[m_B\right]}$ (1)

Dim $R^2 = \left[L^2\right]$ (2)

(a) For a gravitational system of units: Dim F = [F] $\quad [m] = \left[\frac{FT^2}{L}\right]$

From Eqs. (1) and (2), we obtain: $[G] = \frac{[F]\left[L^2\right]}{\left[FT^2/L\right]^2} = \left[F^{-1}L^4T^{-4}\right]$ ◆

(b) For an absolute system of units: Dimension $F = \left[\frac{ML}{T^2}\right]$ and $[m] = [M]$

From Eqs. (1) and (2), we obtain $[G] = \left[\frac{ML}{T^2}\right]\left[\frac{\left[L^2\right]}{[M][M]}\right] = \left[M^{-1}L^3T^{-2}\right]$ ◆

1.14

Using $\left[c^2\right]=\left[\frac{L^2}{T^2}\right]$ the dimensions for energy become: $[E]=[m]\left[c^2\right]=[m]\left[\frac{L^2}{T^2}\right]$

(a) For a gravitational system of units: $[m]=\left[\frac{FT^2}{L}\right]$

$$\therefore\ [E]=\left[\frac{FT^2}{L}\right]\left[\frac{L^2}{T^2}\right]=[FL]\quad\blacklozenge$$

(b) For an absolute system of units: $[m]=[M]$

$$\therefore\ [E]=\left[ML^2T^{-2}\right]\quad\blacklozenge$$

1.15

$$F=G\frac{m_Am_B}{R^2}=\left(6.67\times10^{-11}\right)\frac{(10)(10)}{(0.5)^2}=2.668\times10^{-8}\text{ N}$$

$$W=mg=(10)(9.81)=98.1\text{ N}$$

$$\%\text{ of weight}=\frac{F}{W}\times100\%=\frac{2.668\times10^{-8}}{98.1}\times100\%=2.72\times10^{-8}\%\quad\blacklozenge$$

1.16

$$F=G\frac{m_Am_B}{R^2}=\left(3.44\times10^{-8}\right)\frac{\left(\frac{2}{32.2}\right)\left(\frac{2}{32.2}\right)}{(16/12)^2}=7.46\times10^{-11}\text{ lb}\quad\blacklozenge$$

1.17

$$m=\frac{FR^2}{GM_e}=\frac{(2000)(6378+1800)^2(10)^6}{\left(6.67\times10^{-11}\right)\left(5.9742\times10^{24}\right)}=336\text{ kg}\quad\blacklozenge$$

1.18

$$g_m=\frac{GM_m}{R_m^2}\qquad g_e=\frac{GM_e}{R_e^2}$$

$$\therefore\ \frac{g_m}{g_e}=\frac{M_mR_e^2}{M_eR_m^2}=\frac{(0.073483)(6378)^2}{(5.9742)(1738)^2}=0.1656\approx\frac{1}{6}\qquad\text{Q.E.D.}$$

1.19

Shown below is the plot of $g=\frac{GM_e}{R^2}=\frac{\left(6.67\times10^{-11}\right)\left(5.9742\times10^{24}\right)}{(6378+h)^2\left(10^6\right)}$

h (km)	g (m/s^2)
0	9.80
1000	7.32
2000	5.68
3000	4.53
4000	3.70

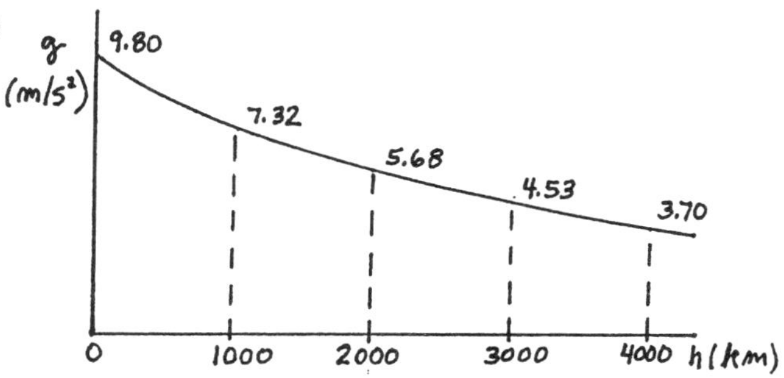

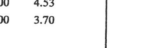

1.20

On earth: $g_e=\frac{GM_e}{R_e^2}$ For a distance h above the earth: $g=\frac{GM_e}{(R_e+h)^2}$

For $g=\frac{1}{2}g_e$: $\frac{GM_e}{(R_e+h)^2}=\frac{1}{2}\frac{GM_e}{R_e^2}$

$$(R_e+h)^2=2R_e^2$$

$(6378+h)^2=2(6378)^2$ which gives $h=2640$ km $\blacklozenge$

1.21

$$R=R_e+R_m+(\text{distance})=6378+1738+\left(384\times10^3\right)=392.1\times10^3\text{ km}=392.1\times10^6\text{ m}$$

$$F=G\frac{M_eM_m}{R^2}=\left(6.67\times10^{-11}\right)\frac{\left(5.9742\times10^{24}\right)\left(0.073483\times10^{24}\right)}{\left(392.1\times10^6\right)^2}=1.905\times10^{20}\text{ N}$$

1.22 (a) By direct measurement,

A + B = 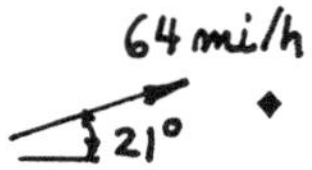 ◆

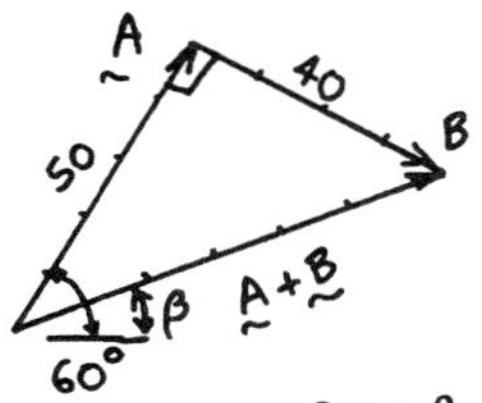

β = 21°

(b) By direct measurement,

A + B + C = 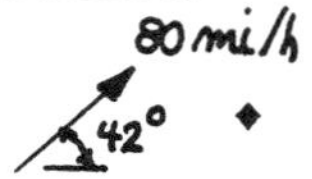 ◆

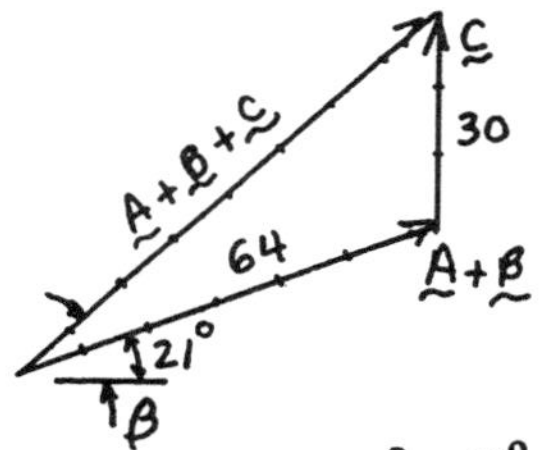

β = 42°

(c) By direct measurement,

A − B =  ◆

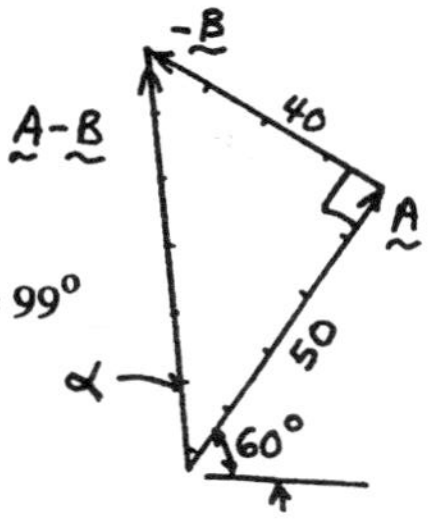

α = 99°

1.23 By direct measurement,

aA = 26 mi/h and bB = − 14.7 mi/h.

Therefore,

$$a = \frac{26}{A} = \frac{26}{50} = 0.52 \;◆$$

$$b = -\frac{14.7}{B} = -\frac{14.7}{40} = -0.37 \;◆$$

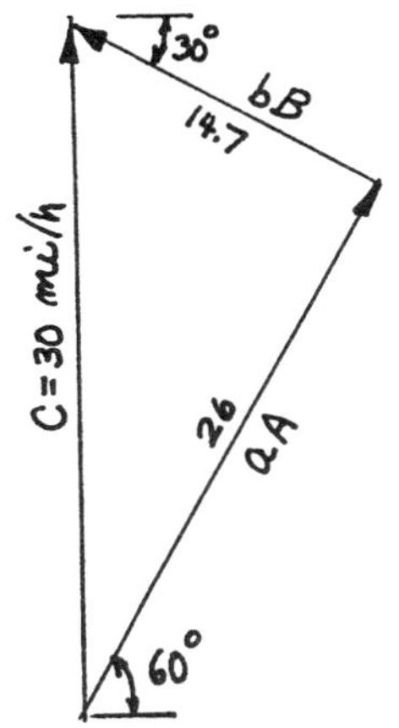

1.24

Horizontal: $H = 6250 \sin 6^{o} = 653$ lb (⟶) ◆

Vertical: $V = 6250 \cos 6^{o} = 6220$ lb (↑) ◆

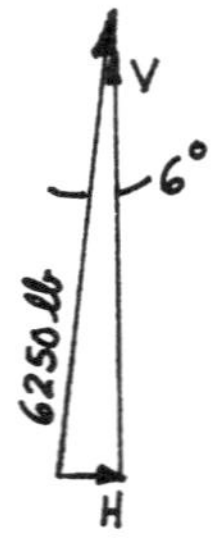

1.25

(a) $F_x = 200 \cos 30^{o} = 173.2$ lb ⟶ ◆ $F_y = 200 \sin 30^{o} = 100.0$ lb ↑ ◆

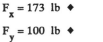

(b) Law of sines: $\frac{200}{\sin 70^{o}} = \frac{F_y}{\sin 50^{o}} = \frac{F_{x'}}{\sin 60^{o}}$

which gives

$$F_y = \frac{200 \sin 50^{o}}{\sin 70^{o}} = 163.0 \text{ lb} \;◆$$

$$F_{x'} = \frac{200 \sin 60^{o}}{\sin 70^{o}} = 184.3 \text{ lb} \;◆$$

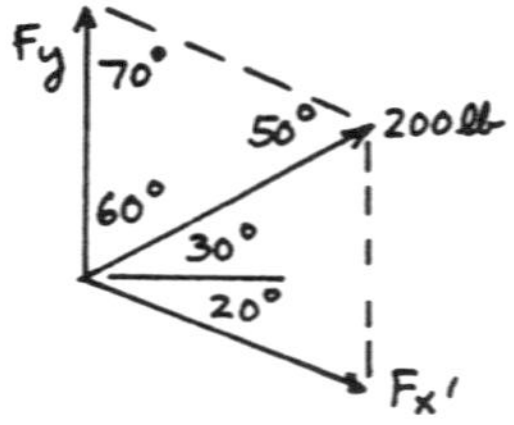

1.26

(a) By direct measurement,

$F_x = 173$ lb ◆

$F_y = 100$ lb ◆

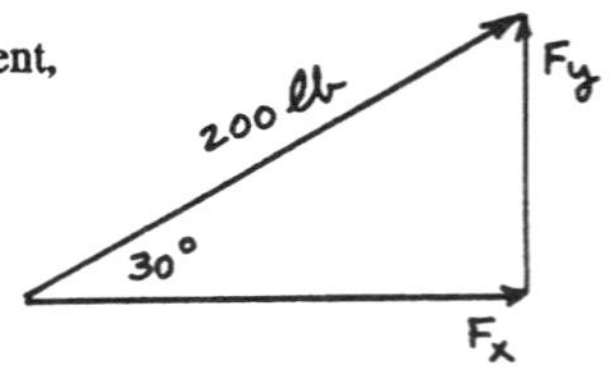

(b) By direct measurement,

$F_{x'} = 184$ lb ◆

$F_y = 163$ lb ◆

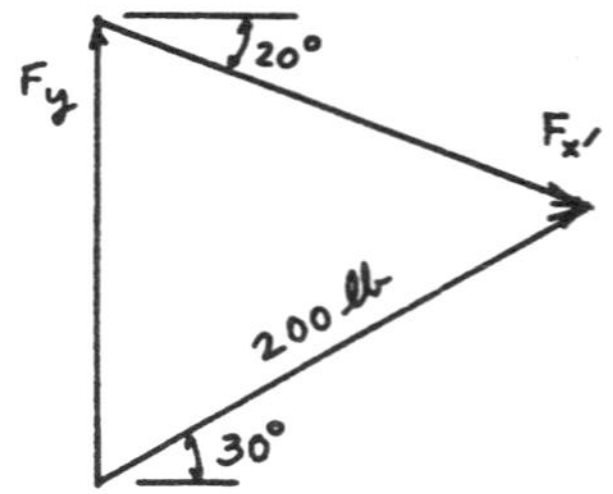

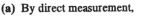

1.27

Geometry: $\alpha = \tan^{-1} 0.5 = 26.57^\circ$

$2\alpha + \gamma = 90^\circ$ from which

$\gamma = 90^\circ - 2(26.57^\circ) = 36.86^\circ$

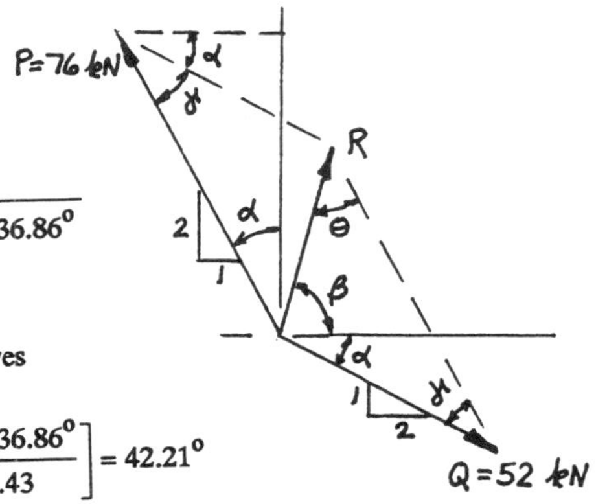

Law of cosines:

$$R = \sqrt{76^2 + 52^2 - 2(76)(52)\cos 36.86^\circ}$$

$\therefore$ R = 46.43 kN

Law of sines : $\dfrac{R}{\sin\gamma} = \dfrac{Q}{\sin\theta}$ which gives

$$\theta = \sin^{-1}\left[\frac{Q\sin\gamma}{R}\right] = \sin^{-1}\left[\frac{52\sin 36.86^\circ}{46.43}\right] = 42.21^\circ$$

Geometry: $\beta = 180^\circ - \theta - \gamma - \alpha$

$= 180^\circ - 42.21^\circ - 36.86^\circ - 26.57^\circ = 74.4^\circ$

Therefore, the resultant of P and Q is:

◆

1.28

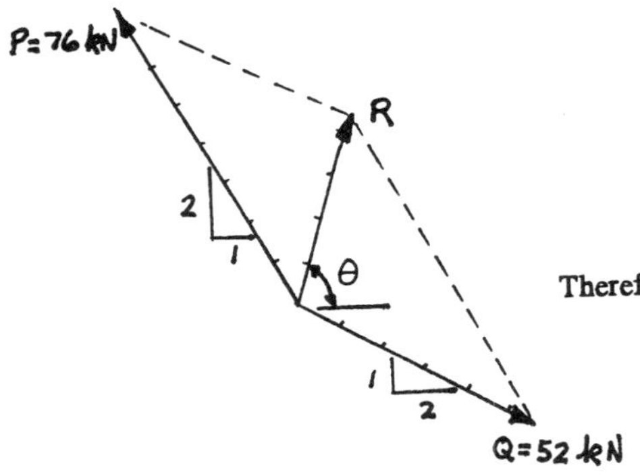

By direct measurement,

R = 46 kN and $\theta = 74^\circ$

Therefore, the resultant of P and Q is:

◆

1.29

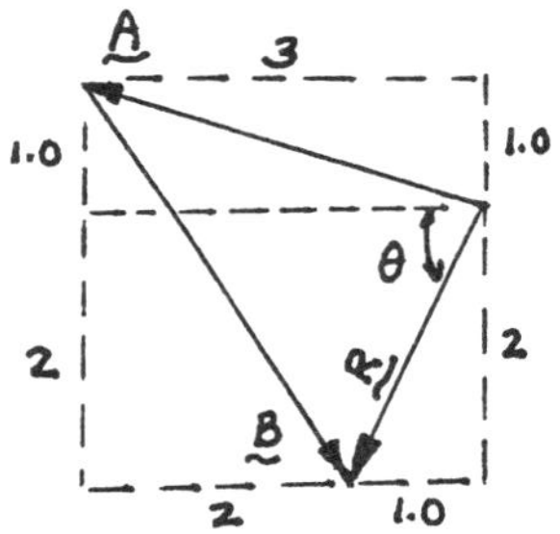

R = A + B

By inspection of the triangle (dimensions in meters)

$R = \sqrt{2^2 + 1.0^2} = 2.24$ m and $\theta = \tan^{-1} 2 = 62.4^\circ$

Therefore, the resultant of **A** and **B** is:

◆

1.30

R = P + Q

$$P = \frac{2000}{\sin 65^\circ} = 2207 \text{ ft}$$

$Q = 3500 - P\cos 65^\circ$

$= 3500 - 2207\cos 65^\circ = 2567$ ft

Therefore, the components are:

2210 ft along OB and 2570 ft along OC ◆

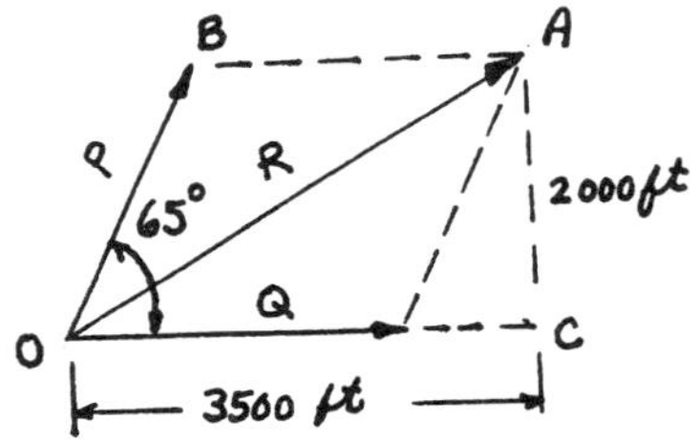

1.31

Law of sines: $\dfrac{360}{\sin 95^\circ} = \dfrac{P_{AB}}{\sin 30^\circ} = \dfrac{P_{AC}}{\sin 55^\circ}$

which gives

$$P_{AB} = \frac{360\sin 30^\circ}{\sin 95^\circ} = 180.7 \text{ lb}$$ ◆

$$P_{AC} = \frac{360\sin 55^\circ}{\sin 95^\circ} = 296 \text{ lb}$$ ◆

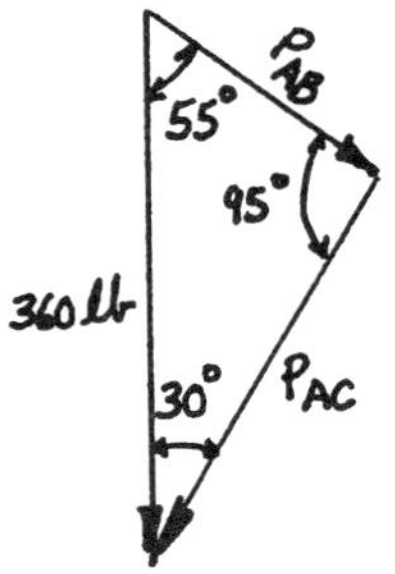

1.32

Law of cosines:

$$200^2 = 360^2 + 185^2 - 2(360)(185)\cos\alpha$$

$\therefore\ \alpha = 21.6^\circ$ ◆

$$185^2 = 360^2 + 200^2 - 2(360)(200)\cos\beta$$

$\therefore\ \beta = 19.9^\circ$ ◆

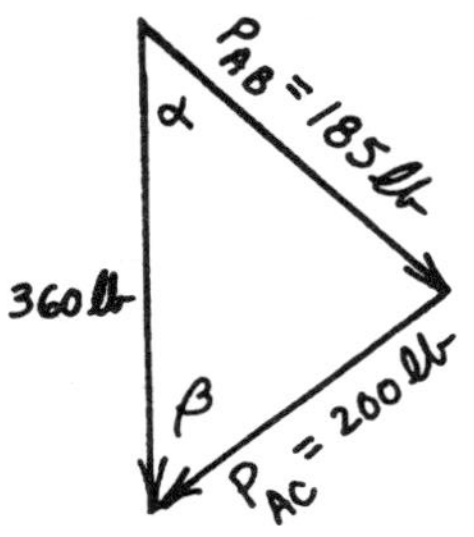

1.33

Law of sines:

$$\frac{P}{\sin 30^\circ} = \frac{5}{\sin 50^\circ}$$

which gives

$$P = \frac{5\sin 30^\circ}{\sin 50^\circ} = 3.26 \text{ kN}$$ ◆

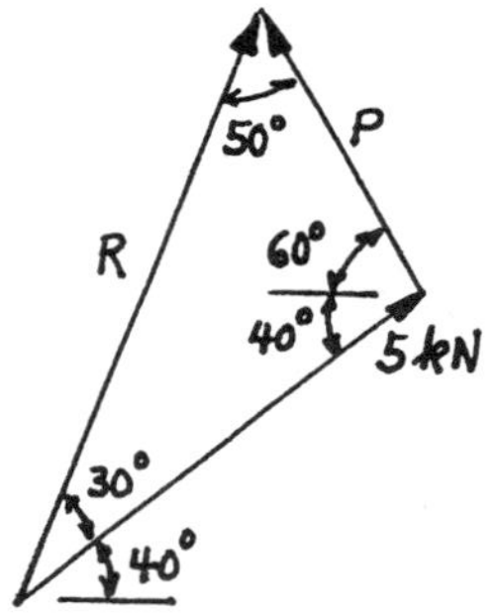

1.34

R = P + Q where R = 650 lb and Q = 500 lb

(a) Law of sines: $\frac{500}{\sin\beta} = \frac{650}{\sin 120^\circ}$

which gives $\beta = 41.77^\circ$ and

$\alpha = 180^\circ - (120^\circ + 41.77^\circ) = 18.23^\circ$

Therefore the direction of the 650-lb resultant is:

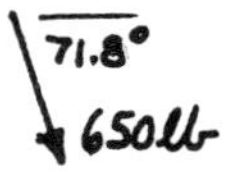

◆

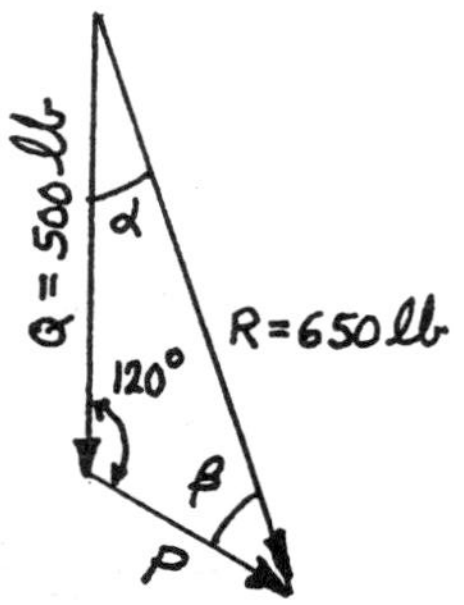

(b) Law of sines: $\frac{P}{\sin\alpha} = \frac{650}{\sin 120^\circ}$ which gives $P = \frac{650\sin 18.23^\circ}{\sin 120^\circ} = 235$ lb ◆

1.35

R = W + T

$T = 2\cos 30^\circ = 1.732$ lb ◆

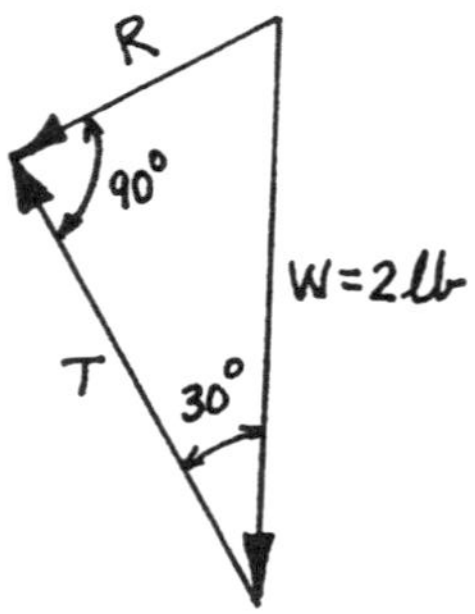

1.36

(a) Law of sines:

$$\frac{5}{\sin 45^\circ} = \frac{P_{OA}}{\sin 105^\circ} = \frac{P_{OB}}{\sin 30^\circ}$$

$P_{OA} = 6.83$ tons; $P_{OB} = 3.54$ tons ◆

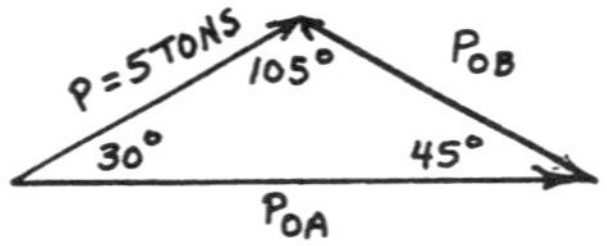

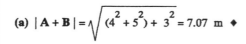

(b) Law of cosines:

$$P_{OB}^2 = 5^2 + 6^2 - 2(5)(6)\cos 30^\circ$$

$\therefore\ P_{OB} = 3.01$ tons ◆

Law of sines:

$$\frac{5}{\sin\theta} = \frac{3.01}{\sin 30^\circ}$$

$\therefore\ \theta = \sin^{-1}(5\sin 30^\circ/3.01) = 56.2^\circ$ ◆

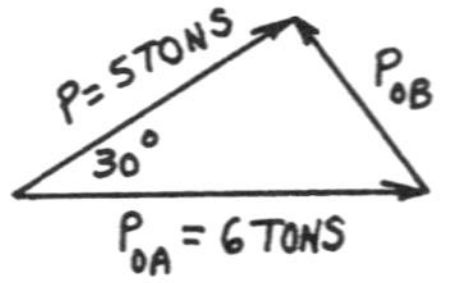

1.37

(a) $|\mathbf{A} + \mathbf{B}| = \sqrt{(4^2 + 5^2) + 3^2} = 7.07$ m ◆

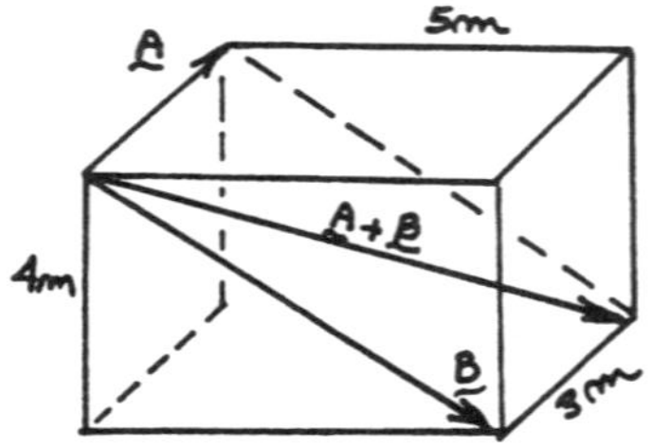

(continued)

(b) $|\mathbf{B}+\mathbf{C}| = \sqrt{3^2+5^2} = 5.83$ m ◆

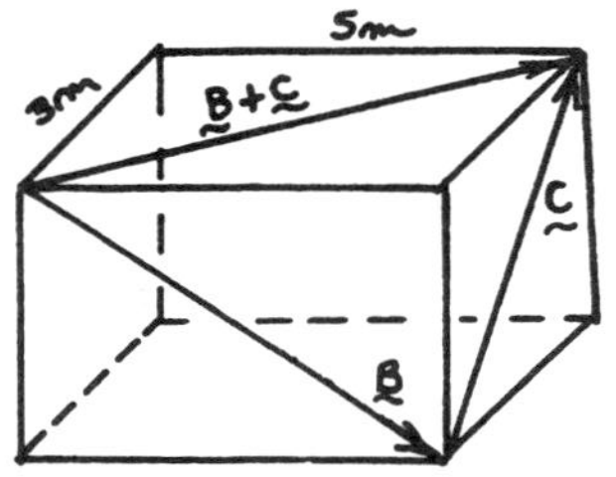

1.38

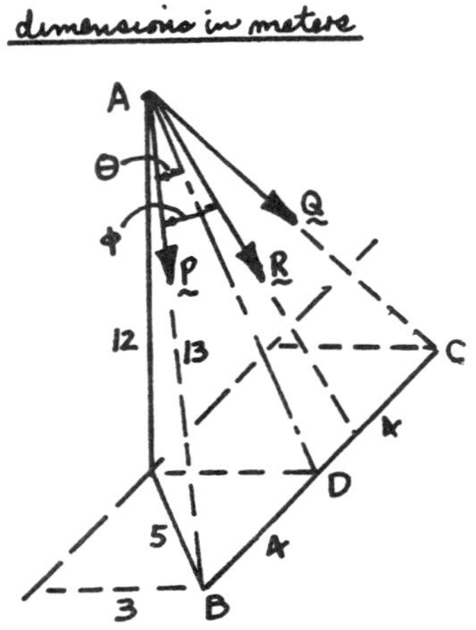

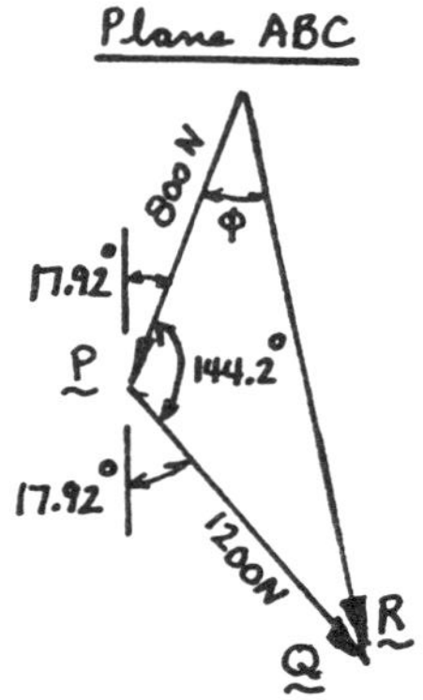

$\theta = \sin^{-1}\frac{4}{13} = 17.92^\circ$

Law of cosines:

$$R = \sqrt{800^2 + 1200^2 - 2(800)(1200)\cos 144.2^\circ} = 1907 \text{ N} \ ◆$$

Law of sines:

$$\frac{1200}{\sin\phi} = \frac{1907}{\sin 144.2^\circ}$$

$$\therefore\ \phi = \sin^{-1}\left(\frac{1200\sin 144.2^\circ}{1907}\right) = 21.6^\circ \ ◆$$

1.39

$\overline{AB} = \overline{AC} = \sqrt{3^2+4^2+12^2} = 13$ m

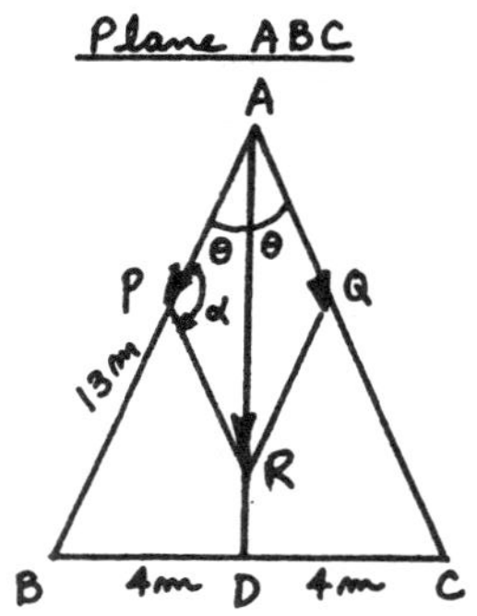

From triangle ABD: $\theta = \sin^{-1}(4/13) = 17.92^\circ$

$\alpha = 180^\circ - 2\theta = 180^\circ - 2(17.92^\circ) = 144.2^\circ$

Law of cosines (using R = 1265 N):

$$1265^2 = P^2 + Q^2 - 2PQ\cos 144.2^\circ$$

(a) $P = Q$

$$1265^2 = P^2 + P^2 - 2P^2\cos 144.2^\circ = 2P^2(1-\cos 144.2^\circ)$$

$\therefore\ P = 665$ N ◆

(b) $Q = 0.5\,P$

$$1265^2 = P^2 + (0.5\,P)^2 - 2P(0.5\,P)\cos 144.2^\circ$$

$\therefore\ P = 881$ N ◆

1.40

$\mathbf{P} = -30\cos 50^\circ \sin 30^\circ\,\mathbf{i} + 30\cos 50^\circ\cos 30^\circ\,\mathbf{j} + 30\sin 50^\circ\,\mathbf{k}$ lb

$\therefore\ \mathbf{P} = -9.64\mathbf{i} + 16.70\mathbf{j} + 22.98\mathbf{k}$ lb ◆

1.41

(a) $\mathbf{r} = 240\sin 40^\circ\cos 50^\circ\,\mathbf{i} + 240\sin 40^\circ\sin 50^\circ\,\mathbf{j} + 240\cos 40^\circ\,\mathbf{k}$ mm

$\therefore\ \mathbf{r} = 99.16\mathbf{i} + 118.2\mathbf{j} + 183.8\mathbf{k}$ mm ◆

(b) $\lambda_x = \frac{r_x}{r} = \frac{99.16}{240} = 0.413 \quad \lambda_y = \frac{r_y}{r} = \frac{118.2}{240} = 0.493 \quad \lambda_z = \frac{r_z}{r} = \frac{183.8}{240} = 0.766$

$\therefore\ \vec{\lambda} = 0.413\mathbf{i} + 0.493\mathbf{j} + 0.766\mathbf{k}$ ◆

1.42

$$\vec{\lambda}_{AB} = \frac{\overrightarrow{AB}}{|\overrightarrow{AB}|} = \frac{24\mathbf{i} - 28\mathbf{j} + 8\mathbf{k}}{37.74} = 0.636\mathbf{i} - 0.742\mathbf{j} + 0.212\mathbf{k}$$

$$\mathbf{v} = 12\,\vec{\lambda}_{AB} = 12(0.636\mathbf{i} - 0.742\mathbf{j} + 0.212\mathbf{k}) = 7.63\mathbf{i} - 8.90\mathbf{j} + 2.54\mathbf{k} \text{ ft/s} \ \blacklozenge$$

1.43

(a) $\overrightarrow{AB} = 7\mathbf{i} + \mathbf{j} + 5\mathbf{k}$ ft $\qquad \therefore |\overrightarrow{AB}| = \sqrt{7^2 + 1^2 + 5^2} = 8.66$ ft ◆

(b) $\vec{\lambda}_{AB} = \frac{\overrightarrow{AB}}{|\overrightarrow{AB}|} = \frac{7\mathbf{i} + \mathbf{j} + 5\mathbf{k}}{8.66} = 0.808\mathbf{i} + 0.115\mathbf{j} + 0.577\mathbf{k}$ ◆

1.44

$$\vec{\lambda}_{AB} = \frac{\overrightarrow{AB}}{|\overrightarrow{AB}|} = \frac{-8\mathbf{i} + 26\mathbf{j} + 12\mathbf{k}}{29.73} = -0.2691\mathbf{i} + 0.8745\mathbf{j} + 0.4036\mathbf{k}$$

$$\mathbf{v} = 6\,\vec{\lambda}_{AB} = 6(-0.2691\mathbf{i} + 0.8745\mathbf{j} + 0.4036\mathbf{k}) = -1.61\mathbf{i} + 5.25\mathbf{j} + 2.42\mathbf{k} \text{ m/s} \ \blacklozenge$$

1.45

$$\vec{\lambda}_{OA} = \frac{\overrightarrow{OA}}{|\overrightarrow{OA}|} = \frac{-4\mathbf{i} + 5\mathbf{j} + 3\mathbf{k}}{7.071} = -0.5657\mathbf{i} + 0.7071\mathbf{j} + 0.4243\mathbf{k}$$

$$\mathbf{F} = F\,\vec{\lambda}_{OA} = 240(-0.5657\mathbf{i} + 0.7071\mathbf{j} + 0.4243\mathbf{k}) = -136\mathbf{i} + 170\mathbf{j} + 102\mathbf{k} \text{ N} \ \blacklozenge$$

1.46

$$\vec{\lambda}_{BA} = \frac{\overrightarrow{BA}}{|\overrightarrow{BA}|} = \frac{18\mathbf{i} - 15\mathbf{j} - 25\mathbf{k}}{34.26} = 0.5254\mathbf{i} - 0.4378\mathbf{j} - 0.7297\mathbf{k}$$

$$\mathbf{F} = F\,\vec{\lambda}_{AB} = 120(0.5254\mathbf{i} - 0.4378\mathbf{j} - 0.7297\mathbf{k}) = 63.0\mathbf{i} - 52.5\mathbf{j} - 87.6\mathbf{k} \text{ lb} \ \blacklozenge$$

1.47

(a) For **A**, the direction cosines are: $\lambda_x = \cos 60^\circ = 0.500$; $\lambda_y = \cos 45^\circ = 0.707$.

Using $\lambda_x^2 + \lambda_y^2 + \lambda_z^2 = 1$, we obtain $\lambda_z = \pm\sqrt{1 - \lambda_x^2 - \lambda_y^2} = \pm 0.500$.

$\therefore \theta_z = \cos^{-1}(\pm 0.500) = 60^\circ$ or 120° ◆

(b) $\mathbf{A} = A\,\vec{\lambda} = 240(0.500\mathbf{i} + 0.707\mathbf{j} \pm 0.500\mathbf{k}) = 120\mathbf{i} + 170\mathbf{j} \pm 120\mathbf{k}$ m ◆

1.48

$$F = \sqrt{1000^2 + 707^2 + 1000^2} = 1581 \text{ lb}$$

$$\vec{\lambda} = \frac{\mathbf{F}}{F} = \frac{1000\mathbf{i} + 707\mathbf{j} - 1000\mathbf{k}}{1581} = 0.6325\mathbf{i} + 0.4472\mathbf{j} - 0.6325\mathbf{k}$$

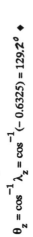

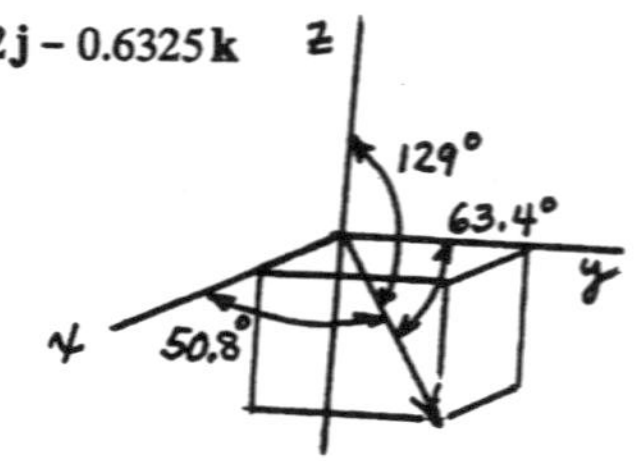

$\theta_x = \cos^{-1}\lambda_x = \cos^{-1}(0.6325) = 50.8^\circ$ ◆

$\theta_y = \cos^{-1}\lambda_y = \cos^{-1}(0.4472) = 63.4^\circ$ ◆

$\theta_z = \cos^{-1}\lambda_z = \cos^{-1}(-0.6325) = 129.2^\circ$ ◆

1.49

$$\mathbf{P}_{OA} = P\,\vec{\lambda}_{OA} = \frac{P(a\mathbf{i} + a\mathbf{j} + a\mathbf{k})}{a\sqrt{3}} = \frac{P}{\sqrt{3}}(\mathbf{i} + \mathbf{j} + \mathbf{k})$$

$$\mathbf{P}_{OB} = P\,\vec{\lambda}_{OB} = \frac{P(a\mathbf{i} + a\mathbf{j})}{a\sqrt{2}} = \frac{P}{\sqrt{2}}(\mathbf{i} + \mathbf{j})$$

$$\therefore \mathbf{R} = \mathbf{P}_{OA} + \mathbf{P}_{OB} = \frac{P}{\sqrt{3}}(\mathbf{i} + \mathbf{j} + \mathbf{k}) + \frac{P}{\sqrt{2}}(\mathbf{i} + \mathbf{j}) = P(1.284\mathbf{i} + 1.284\mathbf{j} + 0.577\mathbf{k}) \ \blacklozenge$$

1.50

(100-lb force) $\mathbf{P} = 100\left(\dfrac{3\mathbf{j} - 5\mathbf{k}}{\sqrt{34}}\right) = 51.45\mathbf{j} - 85.75\mathbf{k}$ lb

(120-lb force) $\mathbf{Q} = 120\left(\dfrac{-4\mathbf{i} + 3\mathbf{j}}{5}\right) = -96.00\mathbf{i} + 72.00\mathbf{j}$ lb

$\mathbf{R} = \mathbf{P} + \mathbf{Q} = (51.45\mathbf{j} - 85.75\mathbf{k}) + (-96.00\mathbf{i} + 72.00\mathbf{j}) = -96.0\mathbf{i} + 123.5\mathbf{j} - 85.8\mathbf{k}$ lb ◆

1.51

$\mathbf{A} = 260\left(\dfrac{12\mathbf{i} + 5\mathbf{j}}{13}\right) = 240\mathbf{i} + 100\mathbf{j}$ m/s

$\mathbf{B} = -100\cos 30^\circ\mathbf{i} + 100\sin 30^\circ\mathbf{j} = -86.60\mathbf{i} + 50.00\mathbf{j}$ m/s

$\mathbf{R} = \mathbf{A} + \mathbf{B} = (240 - 86.60)\mathbf{i} + (100 + 50.00)\mathbf{j} = 153.4\mathbf{i} + 150.0\mathbf{j}$ m/s ◆

1.52

$\mathbf{P} = 120\left(\dfrac{4\mathbf{i} + 3\mathbf{j}}{5}\right) = 96\mathbf{i} + 72\mathbf{j}$ lb $\qquad \mathbf{Q} = 130\left(\dfrac{5\mathbf{i} - 12\mathbf{j}}{13}\right) = 50\mathbf{i} - 120\mathbf{j}$ lb

$\therefore\ \mathbf{P} + \mathbf{Q} = (96\mathbf{i} + 72\mathbf{j}) + (50\mathbf{i} - 120\mathbf{j}) = 146\mathbf{i} - 48\mathbf{j}$ lb ◆

1.53

$\mathbf{P} = 120\left(\dfrac{4\mathbf{i} + 3\mathbf{j}}{5}\right) = 96\mathbf{i} + 72\mathbf{j}$ lb $\qquad \mathbf{Q} = Q\left(\dfrac{5\mathbf{i} - 12\mathbf{j}}{13}\right)$

$\mathbf{R} = \mathbf{P} + \mathbf{Q} = (96\mathbf{i} + 72\mathbf{j}) + Q\left(\dfrac{5\mathbf{i} - 12\mathbf{j}}{13}\right)$

Because the resultant is directed in the positive x-direction, $R = R_x$ and $R_y = 0$.

$R_y = 0$ gives: $\quad 72 - \dfrac{12}{13}Q = 0 \qquad \therefore\ Q = \dfrac{72(13)}{12} = 78$ lb ◆

$R = R_x = 96 + \dfrac{5}{13}Q = 96 + \dfrac{5}{13}(78) = 126$ lb ◆

1.54

$R_x = P_x + Q_x$: $\quad \dfrac{12}{13}(260) = P\cos 25^\circ - Q\cos 50^\circ \quad (1)$

$R_y = P_y + Q_y$: $\quad -\dfrac{5}{13}(260) = P\sin 25^\circ - Q\sin 50^\circ \quad (2)$

Solving (1) and (2) simultaneously yields: $P = 587.2$ lb and $Q = 454.5$ lb ◆

1.55

$R_x = P_x + Q_x$

$\dfrac{4}{5}(200) = 400\cos\theta$ which gives $\quad \theta = \cos^{-1}\left(\dfrac{160}{400}\right) = 66.42^\circ$ ◆

$R_y = P_y + Q_y$

$-\dfrac{3}{5}(200) = 400\sin\theta - Q$ which gives $\quad Q = 400\sin 66.42^\circ + 120 = 487$ lb ◆

1.56

Introduce the x and y-axes as shown: 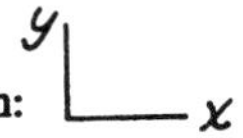

$\therefore\ \mathbf{P} = 76\dfrac{-\mathbf{i} + 2\mathbf{j}}{\sqrt{1^2 + 2^2}} = -33.99\mathbf{i} + 67.98\mathbf{j}$ kN $\qquad \therefore\ \mathbf{Q} = 52\dfrac{2\mathbf{i} - \mathbf{j}}{\sqrt{1^2 + 2^2}} = 46.51\mathbf{i} - 23.26\mathbf{j}$ kN

$\therefore\ \mathbf{R} = \mathbf{P} + \mathbf{Q} = (-33.99\mathbf{i} + 67.98\mathbf{j}) + (46.51\mathbf{i} - 23.26\mathbf{j})$

$= 12.52\mathbf{i} + 44.72\mathbf{j}$ kN

$R = \sqrt{12.52^2 + 44.72^2} = 46.6$ kN

$\theta = \tan^{-1}\dfrac{44.72}{12.52} = 74.4^\circ$

$\therefore$ The resultant of **P** and **Q** is: 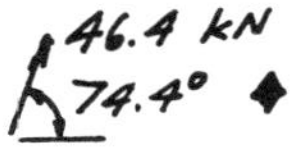 ◆

1.57

(a) $\mathbf{A} \bullet \mathbf{B} = 6(-3) + 9(2) = 0$ ◆ $\qquad$ (b) $\mathbf{A} \bullet \mathbf{B} = 2(6) = 12$ N•m ◆

(c) $\mathbf{A} \bullet \mathbf{B} = 5(-5) + (-6)(8) + (-1)(6) = -79$ m^2 ◆

1.58

(a) $\mathbf{C} = \begin{vmatrix} \mathbf{i} & \mathbf{j} & \mathbf{k} \\ 0 & 6 & 9 \\ 7 & -3 & 2 \end{vmatrix} = 39\mathbf{i} + 63\mathbf{j} - 42\mathbf{k}\ \text{ft}^2$ ◆

(b) $\mathbf{C} = \begin{vmatrix} \mathbf{i} & \mathbf{j} & \mathbf{k} \\ 2 & -3 & 0 \\ 6 & 0 & -13 \end{vmatrix} = 39\mathbf{i} + 26\mathbf{j} + 18\mathbf{k}\ \text{N·m}$ ◆

(c) $\mathbf{C} = \begin{vmatrix} \mathbf{i} & \mathbf{j} & \mathbf{k} \\ 5 & -6 & -1 \\ -5 & 8 & 6 \end{vmatrix} = -28\mathbf{i} - 25\mathbf{j} + 10\mathbf{k}\ \text{m}^2$ ◆

1.59

$$\mathbf{r} \times \mathbf{F} \bullet \vec{\lambda} = \begin{vmatrix} 5 & 4 & 3 \\ 30 & -20 & -10 \\ 0 & 0.6 & 0.8 \end{vmatrix} = -92\ \text{N·m}$$ ◆

$$\vec{\lambda} \times \mathbf{r} \bullet \mathbf{F} = \begin{vmatrix} 0 & 0.6 & 0.8 \\ 5 & 4 & 3 \\ 30 & -20 & -10 \end{vmatrix} = -92\ \text{N·m}$$ ◆

1.60

$\overrightarrow{BA} = 3\mathbf{i} + 4\mathbf{k}$ in. $\quad \overrightarrow{BO} = -5\mathbf{j}$ in. $\quad \overrightarrow{OA} = 3\mathbf{i} + 5\mathbf{j} + 4\mathbf{k}$ in.

$$\overrightarrow{BA} \times \overrightarrow{OA} = \begin{vmatrix} \mathbf{i} & \mathbf{j} & \mathbf{k} \\ 3 & 0 & 4 \\ 3 & 5 & 4 \end{vmatrix} = -20\mathbf{i} + 15\mathbf{k}\ \text{in.}^2$$ ◆

$$\overrightarrow{BO} \times \overrightarrow{OA} = \begin{vmatrix} \mathbf{i} & \mathbf{j} & \mathbf{k} \\ 0 & -5 & 0 \\ 3 & 5 & 4 \end{vmatrix} = -20\mathbf{i} + 15\mathbf{k}\ \text{in.}^2$$ ◆

(Note that ABO is an isosceles triangle with $\overline{AB} = \overline{BO} = 5$ in.)

1.61

$\overrightarrow{BA} = 3\mathbf{i} + 4\mathbf{k}$ in. $\qquad |\overrightarrow{BA}| = \sqrt{3^2 + 4^2} = 5$ in.

$\overrightarrow{OA} = 3\mathbf{i} + 5\mathbf{j} + 4\mathbf{k}$ in. $\qquad |\overrightarrow{OA}| = \sqrt{3^2 + 5^2 + 4^2} = 7.071$ in.

$$\cos\theta = \frac{\overrightarrow{BA} \bullet \overrightarrow{OA}}{|\overrightarrow{BA}||\overrightarrow{OA}|} = \frac{3(3) + 4(4)}{5(7.071)} = 0.7071 \qquad \therefore\ \theta = 45.0^\circ$$ ◆

1.62

$\overline{AC} = 4\sqrt{2}\tan 40^\circ = 4.747$ ft

$\overrightarrow{OA} = 4\mathbf{i} + 4.747\mathbf{j} + 4\mathbf{k}$ ft $\qquad |\overrightarrow{OA}| = \sqrt{4^2 + 4.747^2 + 4^2} = 7.385$ ft

$\overrightarrow{OB} = 4.747\mathbf{j} + 2.50\mathbf{k}$ ft $\qquad |\overrightarrow{OB}| = \sqrt{4.747^2 + 2.50^2} = 5.365$ ft

$$\cos\theta = \frac{\overrightarrow{OA} \bullet \overrightarrow{OB}}{|\overrightarrow{OA}||\overrightarrow{OB}|} = \frac{4.747(4.747) + 4(2.50)}{7.385(5.365)} = 0.8211 \qquad \therefore\ \theta = 34.8^\circ$$ ◆

1.63

Statement (ii) is true. ◆

<u>Proof</u> $\mathbf{A} \times \mathbf{B}$ is perpendicular to **A** and **B**, that is, normal to plane S. Therefore, $\mathbf{C} = \mathbf{A} \times (\mathbf{A} \times \mathbf{B})$ is "normal to the normal" of S. Then **C** lies in plane S. (Note: **C** is also normal to **A**.)

1.64

B is perpendicular to **A** if $\mathbf{A} \bullet \mathbf{B} = 0$.

(a) $\mathbf{A} \bullet \mathbf{B} = 3(5) + (-5)(3) + 2(-2) = -4$
(b) $\mathbf{A} \bullet \mathbf{B} = 3(2) + (-5)(3) + 2(4) = -1$
(c) $\mathbf{A} \bullet \mathbf{B} = 3(1) + (-5)(1) + 2(1) = 0$
(d) $\mathbf{A} \bullet \mathbf{B} = 3(3) + (-5)(1) + 2(-2) = 0$

Therefore, (c) and (d) are perpendicular to **A**. ◆

1.65

$$\mathbf{A}\times\mathbf{B} = \begin{vmatrix} \mathbf{i} & \mathbf{j} & \mathbf{k} \\ 8 & -3 & 2 \\ -6 & 4 & 3 \end{vmatrix} = -17\mathbf{i} - 36\mathbf{j} + 14\mathbf{k}\ \text{ft}^2$$

$$\therefore\ \vec{\lambda} = \frac{\mathbf{A}\times\mathbf{B}}{|\mathbf{A}\times\mathbf{B}|} = \frac{-17\mathbf{i} - 36\mathbf{j} + 14\mathbf{k}}{\sqrt{1781}} = -0.4028\mathbf{i} - 0.8530\mathbf{j} + 0.3317\mathbf{k}$$

Because $\mathbf{B}\times\mathbf{A}$ could also have been used,

$$\vec{\lambda} = \pm(0.403\mathbf{i} + 0.853\mathbf{j} - 0.332\mathbf{k})\ \blacklozenge$$

1.66

$\overrightarrow{AB} = -\mathbf{i} + 4\mathbf{j} - 3\mathbf{k}$ in. $\quad |\overrightarrow{AB}| = \sqrt{1^2 + 4^2 + 3^2} = 5.10$ in.

$\overrightarrow{AC} = 3\mathbf{i} + 2\mathbf{j} - 4\mathbf{k}$ in. $\quad |\overrightarrow{AC}| = \sqrt{3^2 + 2^2 + 4^2} = 5.39$ in.

$$\overrightarrow{AB}\times\overrightarrow{AC} = \begin{vmatrix} \mathbf{i} & \mathbf{j} & \mathbf{k} \\ -1 & 4 & -3 \\ 3 & 2 & -4 \end{vmatrix} = -10\mathbf{i} - 13\mathbf{j} - 14\mathbf{k}\ \text{in.}^2\ \blacklozenge$$

$$\vec{\lambda} = \frac{\overrightarrow{AB}\times\overrightarrow{AC}}{|\overrightarrow{AB}\times\overrightarrow{AC}|} = \frac{-10\mathbf{i} - 13\mathbf{j} - 14\mathbf{k}}{\sqrt{10^2 + 13^2 + 14^2}} = -0.464\mathbf{i} - 0.603\mathbf{j} - 0.649\mathbf{k}$$

Because $\overrightarrow{AC}\times\overrightarrow{AB}$ could also have been used,

$$\vec{\lambda} = \pm(0.464\mathbf{i} + 0.603\mathbf{j} + 0.649\mathbf{k})\ \blacklozenge$$

1.67

$\mathbf{A}\bullet\mathbf{B} = 1(1) + 3(3) + (-5)(2) = 0$ $\quad\therefore$ **A** is perpendicular to **B**

$\mathbf{A}\bullet\mathbf{C} = 1(21) + 3(-7) + (-5)(0) = 0$ $\quad\therefore$ **A** is perpendicular to **C**

$\mathbf{B}\bullet\mathbf{C} = 1(21) + 3(-7) + 2(0) = 0$ $\quad\therefore$ **B** is perpendicular to **C**

Therefore, the three vectors are mutually perpendicular. Q.E.D.

1.68

$$\vec{\lambda}_A = \frac{\mathbf{A}}{A} = \frac{2\mathbf{i} - 3\mathbf{j} + 5\mathbf{k}}{\sqrt{38}} = 0.3244\mathbf{i} - 0.4867\mathbf{j} + 0.8111\mathbf{k}$$

$$F_A = \mathbf{F}\bullet\vec{\lambda}_A = 6(0.3244) + 20(-0.4867) + (-12)(0.8111) = -17.52\ \text{lb}\ \blacklozenge$$

1.69

The unit vectors in the x′ and y′ directions are:

$\mathbf{i}' = \cos 60^\circ\,\mathbf{i} + \sin 60^\circ\,\mathbf{j} = 0.500\mathbf{i} + 0.866\mathbf{j}$

$\mathbf{j}' = -\cos 30^\circ\,\mathbf{i} + \sin 30^\circ\,\mathbf{j} = -0.866\mathbf{i} + 0.500\mathbf{j}$

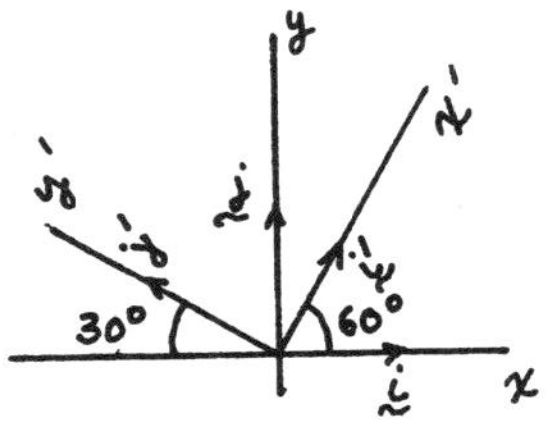

$v_{x'}$ and $v_{y'}$ are the orthogonal projections of $\mathbf{v} = 2\mathbf{i} + \mathbf{j}$ km/h onto the x′ and y′ axes:

$$v_{x'} = \mathbf{v}\bullet\mathbf{i}' = 2(0.500) + 1(0.866) = 1.866\ \text{km/h}\ \blacklozenge$$

$$v_{y'} = \mathbf{v}\bullet\mathbf{j}' = 2(-0.866) + 1(0.500) = -1.232\ \text{km/h}\ \blacklozenge$$

*1.70

$$\vec{\lambda}_B = \frac{\mathbf{B}}{B} = \frac{6\mathbf{i} + 2\mathbf{k}}{\sqrt{6^2 + 2^2}} = 0.9487\mathbf{i} + 0.3162\mathbf{k}$$

The component of **A** parallel to **B** is: $A_B = \mathbf{A}\bullet\vec{\lambda}_B = 3(0.9487) - 4(0.3162) = 1.5813$ in.

$$\therefore\ \mathbf{A}_B = 1.5813(0.9487\mathbf{i} + 0.3162\mathbf{k})\ \text{in.}\ \blacklozenge$$

Letting $\mathbf{A}_C$ be the component of **A** that is perpendicular to **B**, we have

$$\mathbf{A}_C = \mathbf{A} - \mathbf{A}_B$$

$$\mathbf{A}_C = (3\mathbf{i} + 5\mathbf{j} - 4\mathbf{k}) - 1.5813(0.9487\mathbf{i} + 0.3162\mathbf{k}) = 1.500\mathbf{i} + 5.000\mathbf{j} - 4.500\mathbf{k}\ \text{in.}$$

$$\therefore\ A_C = \sqrt{1.500^2 + 5.000^2 + 4.500^2} = 6.892\ \text{in.}$$

The unit vector in the direction of $\mathbf{A}_C$ is

$$\vec{\lambda}_C = \frac{\mathbf{A}_C}{A_C} = \frac{1.500\mathbf{i} + 5.000\mathbf{j} - 4.500\mathbf{k}}{6.892} = 0.2176\mathbf{i} + 0.7255\mathbf{j} - 0.6529\mathbf{k}$$

$$\therefore\ \mathbf{A}_C = 6.892(0.2176\mathbf{i} + 0.7255\mathbf{j} - 0.6529\mathbf{k})\ \text{in.}\ \blacklozenge$$

1.71

(a) $$\mathbf{a} = \pm(\mathbf{b}\times\mathbf{c}) = \pm\begin{vmatrix} \mathbf{i} & \mathbf{j} & \mathbf{k} \\ 0.745 & 0.596 & 0.298 \\ -0.371 & 0.743 & -0.557 \end{vmatrix} = \pm(-0.553\mathbf{i} + 0.304\mathbf{j} + 0.775\mathbf{k}) \ \blacklozenge$$

(b) $v_a = \mathbf{v}\bullet\mathbf{a} = \pm[16(-0.553) + (-24)(0.304) + (-8)(0.775)] = \pm 22.34$ ft/s

$v_b = \mathbf{v}\bullet\mathbf{b} = 16(0.745) + (-24)(0.596) + (-8)(0.298) = -4.77$ ft/s

$v_c = \mathbf{v}\bullet\mathbf{c} = 16(-0.371) + (-24)(0.743) + (-8)(-0.557) = -19.31$ ft/s

$\therefore\ \mathbf{v} = \pm 22.34\mathbf{a} - 4.77\mathbf{b} - 19.31\mathbf{c}$ ft/s ◆

1.72

For the three vectors to lie in the same plane, $\mathbf{A}\times\mathbf{B}\bullet\mathbf{C} = 0$.

$$\mathbf{A}\times\mathbf{B}\bullet\mathbf{C} = \begin{vmatrix} 2 & -1 & 2 \\ 6 & 3 & a \\ 16 & 46 & 7 \end{vmatrix} = 2(21-46a) + 1(42-16a) + 2(276-48) = 0$$

which gives: $540 - 108a = 0 \quad \therefore\ a = 5$ m ◆

*1.73

We first compute a unit vector $\vec{\lambda}$ that is perpendicular to plane ABC:

$\overrightarrow{AB} = -2\mathbf{i} + 5\mathbf{k}$ in. $\qquad \overrightarrow{AC} = -2\mathbf{i} + 6\mathbf{j}$ in.

$$\overrightarrow{AC}\times\overrightarrow{AB} = \begin{vmatrix} \mathbf{i} & \mathbf{j} & \mathbf{k} \\ -2 & 6 & 0 \\ -2 & 0 & 5 \end{vmatrix} = 30\mathbf{i} + 10\mathbf{j} + 12\mathbf{k}\ \text{in.}^2$$

$$\therefore\ \vec{\lambda} = \frac{\overrightarrow{AC}\times\overrightarrow{AB}}{|\overrightarrow{AC}\times\overrightarrow{AB}|} = \frac{30\mathbf{i} + 10\mathbf{j} + 12\mathbf{k}}{\sqrt{30^2 + 10^2 + 12^2}} = 0.8870\mathbf{i} + 0.2957\mathbf{j} + 0.3548\mathbf{k}$$

(continued)

The normal component of $\mathbf{F} = 20\mathbf{i} + 30\mathbf{j} + 50\mathbf{k}$ lb is:

$$F_n = \mathbf{F}\bullet\vec{\lambda} = 20(0.8870) + 30(0.2957) + 50(0.3548)) = 44.15 \text{ lb}$$

$$\mathbf{F}_n = F_n\vec{\lambda} = 44.15(0.8870\mathbf{i} + 0.2957\mathbf{j} + 0.3548\mathbf{k}) = 39.16\mathbf{i} + 13.06\mathbf{j} + 15.66\mathbf{k} \text{ lb}$$

Therefore, the component of $\mathbf{F}$ that lies in plane ABC is:

$$\mathbf{F}_t = \mathbf{F} - \mathbf{F}_n = -19.16\mathbf{i} + 16.94\mathbf{j} + 34.34\mathbf{k} \text{ lb} \ \blacklozenge$$

1.74

Since $\mathbf{a}\times\mathbf{b}$ is perpendicular to the area, it has the correct direction.

Check of magnitude:

$|\mathbf{a}\times\mathbf{b}| = ab\sin\theta = ah = A$ It checks!

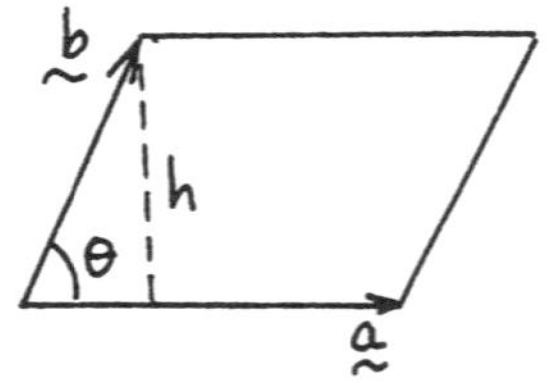

1.75

$|\overrightarrow{AB}\times\overrightarrow{BC}|$ = area of parallelogram ABCD = 2(area of triangle ABC)

$\overrightarrow{AB} = -5\mathbf{i} + 3\mathbf{j} + 3\mathbf{k}$ in. $\qquad \overrightarrow{BC} = 2\mathbf{i} - 2\mathbf{j} + \mathbf{k}$ in.

$$\overrightarrow{AB}\times\overrightarrow{BC} = \begin{vmatrix} \mathbf{i} & \mathbf{j} & \mathbf{k} \\ -5 & 3 & 3 \\ 2 & -2 & 1 \end{vmatrix} = 9\mathbf{i} + 11\mathbf{j} + 4\mathbf{k}\ \text{in.}^2$$

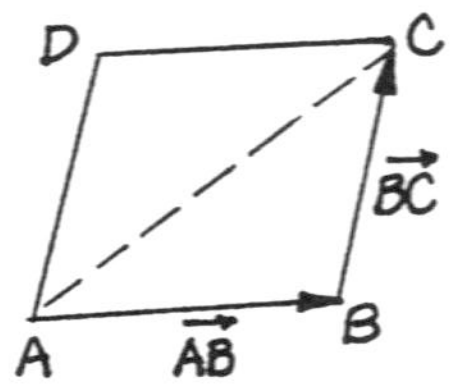

Therefore, area $= \frac{1}{2}|\overrightarrow{AB}\times\overrightarrow{BC}| = \frac{1}{2}\sqrt{9^2 + 11^2 + 4^2} = 14.76\ \text{in.}^2$ ◆

1.76

$|\mathbf{a}\times\mathbf{b}\bullet\mathbf{c}| = |\mathbf{a}\times\mathbf{b}||\mathbf{c}||\cos\theta|$

From Prob. 1.74:

$|\mathbf{a}\times\mathbf{b}|$ = area of base (shown shaded in figure)

Note that $|\mathbf{c}||\cos\theta| = h$

$\therefore\ |\mathbf{a}\times\mathbf{b}\bullet\mathbf{c}|$ = (area of base) x h = vol. of parallelpiped Q.E.D.

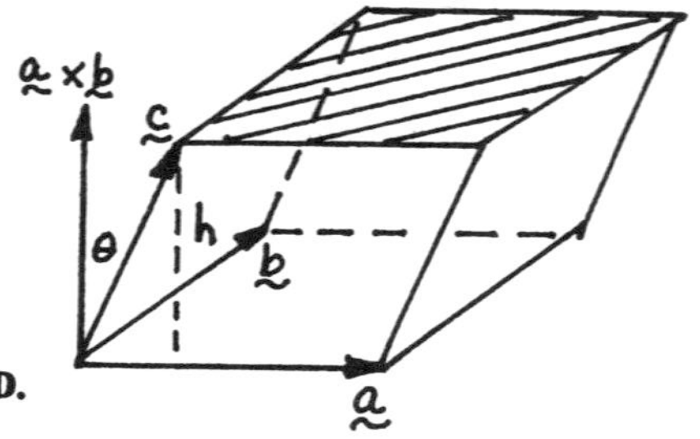

2.1

The sum of each force system is 500 N upward. In addition, each resultant force has the same line of action as the force in (a), except (f) and (h). Therefore, all except (f) and (h) are equivalent to (a). ◆

2.2

$R_x = \Sigma F_x :\ \overset{+}{\rightarrow}\quad R_x = 300\cos 70^\circ + 150\cos 20^\circ = 243.6 \text{ lb}$

$R_y = \Sigma F_y :\ +\uparrow\quad R_y = 300\sin 70^\circ + 150\sin 20^\circ = 333.2 \text{ lb}$

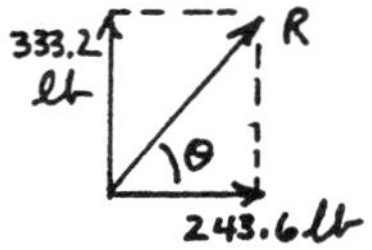

$R = \sqrt{R_x^2 + R_y^2} = \sqrt{243.6^2 + 333.2^2} = 413 \text{ lb}$

$\theta = \tan^{-1}\left(\dfrac{333.2}{243.6}\right) = 53.8^\circ$

R = 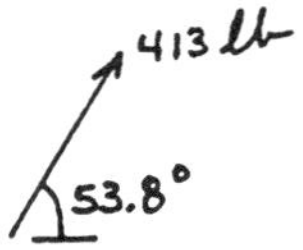 ◆

2.3

$R_x = \Sigma F_x :\ \overset{+}{\rightarrow}\quad -T_1\cos 60^\circ + T_3\cos 40^\circ = 0 \qquad (1)$

$R_y = \Sigma F_y :\ +\uparrow\quad T_1\sin 60^\circ + T_3\sin 40^\circ + 40 = 180 \qquad (2)$

Solving (1) and (2) gives $T_1 = 108.9$ lb and $T_3 = 71.1$ lb ◆

2.4

$R_x = \Sigma F_x :\ \overset{+}{\rightarrow}\quad P\cos\theta + 40\cos 60^\circ - 30 = 90 \qquad \therefore\ P\cos\theta = 100 \text{ kN} \quad (1)$

$R_y = \Sigma F_y :\ +\uparrow\quad P\sin\theta - 40\sin 60^\circ = 0 \qquad \therefore\ P\sin\theta = 34.64 \text{ kN} \quad (2)$

Divide (2) by (1): $\theta = \tan^{-1}\left(\dfrac{34.64}{100}\right) = 19.11^\circ$ ◆

From (1): $P = \dfrac{100}{\cos 19.11^\circ} = 105.8 \text{ kN}$ ◆

2.5

$R_x = \Sigma F_x :\ +\swarrow\quad R_x = 40.0 \text{ N}$

$R_y = \Sigma F_y :\ \overset{+}{\rightarrow}\quad R_y = -60\dfrac{120}{\sqrt{100^2 + 120^2}} = -46.1 \text{ N}$

$R_z = \Sigma F_z :\ +\uparrow\quad R_z = 30 + 60\dfrac{100}{\sqrt{100^2 + 120^2}} = 68.4 \text{ N}$

$\therefore\ \mathbf{R} = 40.0\,\mathbf{i} - 46.1\,\mathbf{j} + 68.4\,\mathbf{k}$ N acting through (0, 120 mm, 0) ◆

2.6

(a) $\mathbf{P}_1 = 110\mathbf{j}$ lb $\quad \mathbf{P}_2 = -200\cos 25^\circ\mathbf{i} + 200\sin 25^\circ\mathbf{j} = -181.26\mathbf{i} + 84.52\mathbf{j}$ lb

$\mathbf{P}_3 = -150\cos 40^\circ\mathbf{i} + 150\sin 40^\circ\mathbf{k} = -114.91\mathbf{i} + 96.42\mathbf{k}$ lb

$\mathbf{R} = \Sigma\mathbf{P} = (-181.26 - 114.91)\mathbf{i} + (110 + 84.52)\mathbf{j} + 96.42\mathbf{k}$

$= -296.17\mathbf{i} + 194.52\mathbf{j} + 96.42\mathbf{k}$ lb

$\therefore\ R = \sqrt{(-296.17)^2 + 194.52^2 + 96.42^2} = 367.2 \text{ lb}$ ◆

(b) $\cos\theta_x = R_x/R = -296.7/367.2 = -0.807$ ◆

$\cos\theta_y = R_y/R = 194.52/367.2 = 0.530$ ◆

$\cos\theta_z = R_z/R = 96.42/367.2 = 0.263$ ◆

(c)

$\dfrac{\overline{AB}_x}{|R_x|} = \dfrac{\overline{AB}_y}{|R_y|} = \dfrac{\overline{AB}_z}{|R_z|} :\quad \dfrac{2}{296.17} = \dfrac{y}{194.52} = \dfrac{z}{96.42}$

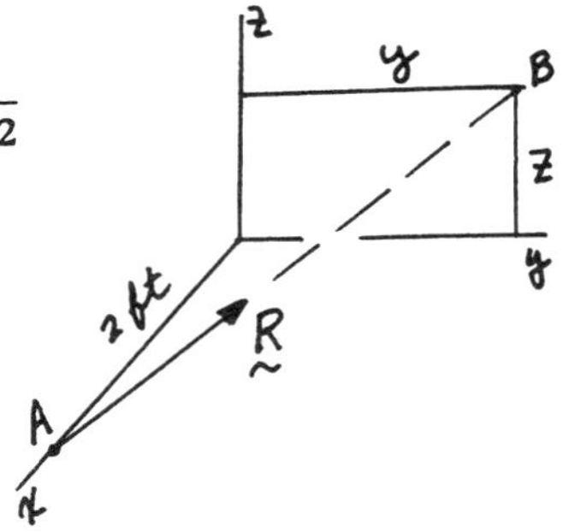

$y = \dfrac{2(194.52)}{296.17} = 1.314 \text{ ft}$

$z = \dfrac{2(96.42)}{296.17} = 0.651 \text{ ft}$

$\therefore$ **R** passes through the point (0, 1.314 ft, 0.651 ft) ◆

2.7

$$\mathbf{R} = (-P_2\cos 25^\circ - P_3\cos 40^\circ)\mathbf{i} + (P_1 + P_2\sin 25^\circ)\mathbf{j} + P_3\sin 40^\circ\mathbf{k}$$
$$= -600\mathbf{i} + 500\mathbf{j} + 300\mathbf{k} \text{ lb}$$

Equating like coefficients:

$$0.9063P_2 + 0.7660P_3 = 600 \text{ lb}$$
$$P_1 + 0.4226P_2 = 500 \text{ lb}$$
$$0.6428P_3 = 300 \text{ lb}$$

Solving gives: $P_1 = 386.9$ lb ◆, $P_2 = 267.6$ lb ◆, $P_3 = 466.7$ lb ◆

2.8

$$\mathbf{P}_1 = 50\left(\frac{4\mathbf{i} - 4\mathbf{j}}{\sqrt{32}}\right) = 35.36\mathbf{i} - 35.36\mathbf{j} \text{ kN}$$

$$\mathbf{P}_2 = 80\left(\frac{2\mathbf{i} - 4\mathbf{j} + 3\mathbf{k}}{\sqrt{29}}\right) = 29.71\mathbf{i} - 59.42\mathbf{j} + 44.57\mathbf{k} \text{ kN}$$

$$\mathbf{P}_3 = 120\left(\frac{4\mathbf{i} - 4\mathbf{j} + 3\mathbf{k}}{\sqrt{41}}\right) = 74.96\mathbf{i} - 74.96\mathbf{j} + 56.22\mathbf{k} \text{ kN}$$

$$\mathbf{R} = \Sigma\mathbf{P} = (35.36 + 29.71 + 74.96)\mathbf{i} - (35.36 + 59.42 + 74.96)\mathbf{j} + (44.57 + 56.22)\mathbf{k}$$

$$\therefore \mathbf{R} = 140.0\mathbf{i} - 169.7\mathbf{j} + 100.8\mathbf{k} \text{ kN}$$ ◆

2.9

$$\mathbf{P}_1 = P_1\left(\frac{4\mathbf{i} - 3\mathbf{j}}{5}\right) = P_1(0.8000\mathbf{i} - 0.6000\mathbf{j})$$

$$\mathbf{P}_2 = P_2\left(\frac{2\mathbf{i} - 3\mathbf{j} + 3\mathbf{k}}{\sqrt{22}}\right) = P_2(0.4264\mathbf{i} - 0.6396\mathbf{j} + 0.6396\mathbf{k})$$

$$\mathbf{P}_3 = P_3\left(\frac{4\mathbf{i} - 3\mathbf{j} + 3\mathbf{k}}{\sqrt{34}}\right) = P_3(0.6860\mathbf{i} - 0.5145\mathbf{j} + 0.5145\mathbf{k})$$

$$\mathbf{R} = \Sigma\mathbf{P} = 200\mathbf{i} - 100\mathbf{j} + 50\mathbf{k} \text{ kN}$$

Equating like coefficients:

$$0.8000P_1 + 0.4264P_2 + 0.6860P_3 = 200$$
$$-0.6000P_1 - 0.6396P_2 - 0.5145P_3 = -100$$
$$0.6396P_2 + 0.5145P_3 = 50$$

Solving gives: $P_1 = 83.33$ kN ◆, $P_2 = -155.4$ kN ◆, $P_3 = 291.5$ kN ◆

2.10

$R_x = \Sigma F_x$: $\overset{+}{\rightarrow}$ $\frac{1}{\sqrt{5}}P_1 + \frac{3}{5}P_2 - 20 = 40\cos 30^\circ$ (1)

$R_y = \Sigma F_y$: $+\uparrow$ $\frac{2}{\sqrt{5}}P_1 - \frac{4}{5}P_2 = 40\sin 30^\circ$ (2)

Solving (1) and (2) gives:

$P_1 = 62.3$ kN ◆

$P_2 = 44.6$ kN ◆

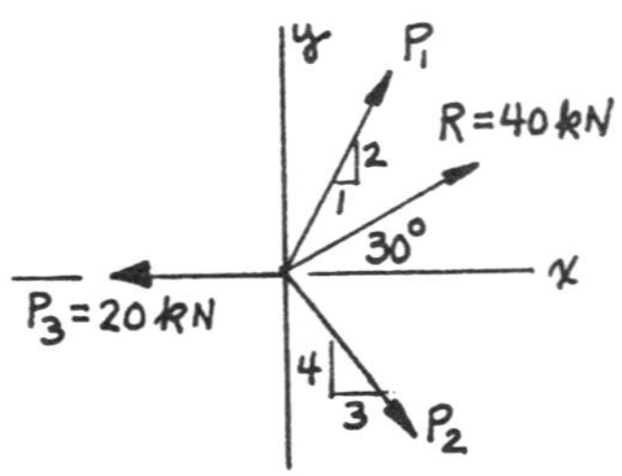

2.11

$R = \sqrt{24^2 + 18^2} = 30$ lb ◆

Using similar triangles:

$\frac{3}{4} = \frac{4}{x}$ $\therefore$ $x = \frac{16}{3} = 5.33$ in. ◆

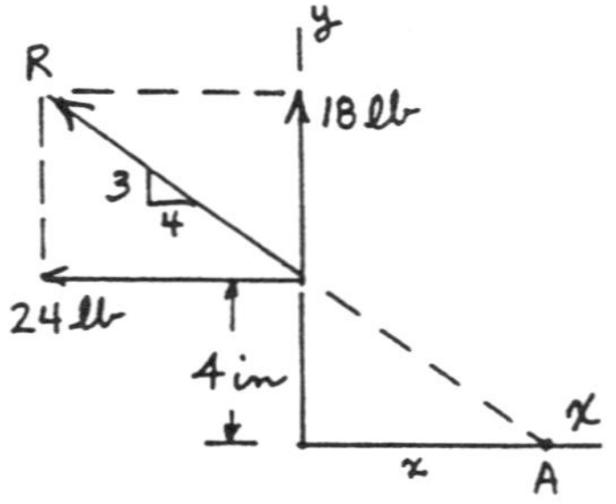

2.12

$\theta = \tan^{-1}(4/16) = 14.04^\circ$

$R_x = \Sigma F_x$: $\overset{+}{\rightarrow}$ $R\cos 14.04^\circ = \frac{4}{5}(25)$

$\therefore$ $R = 20/\cos 14.04^\circ = 20.62$ lb

$R_y = \Sigma F_y$: $+\uparrow$ $20.62\sin 14.04^\circ = \frac{3}{5}(25) - Q$

$\therefore$ $Q = 10.00$ lb ◆

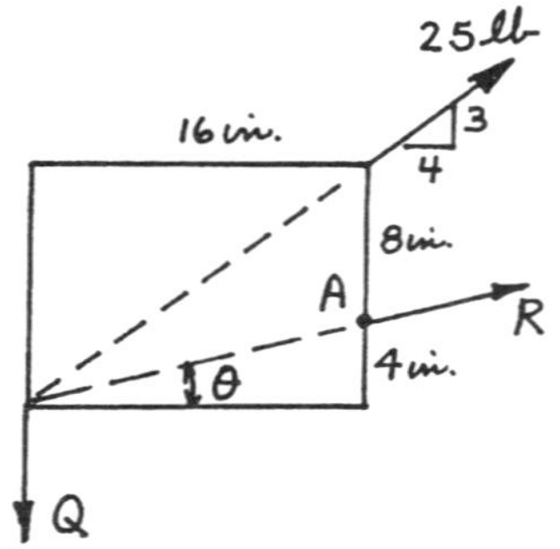

2.13

By inspection:

$R_x = \Sigma F_x = 0$ ♦ $\quad R_y = \Sigma F_y = 0$ ♦

$R_z = \Sigma F_z = (20 + 20 + 15 + 15)\sin 75^\circ = 67.6$ lb ♦

Point on line of action is the center of the plate ♦

2.14

$\mathbf{R} = T\vec{\lambda}_{AB} + T\vec{\lambda}_{AD} + T\vec{\lambda}_{AC}$ where: $\vec{\lambda}_{AB} = -\mathbf{j}$; $\vec{\lambda}_{AD} = -\mathbf{i}$;

$$\vec{\lambda}_{AC} = \left(\frac{-6\mathbf{i} - 4\mathbf{j} + 5\mathbf{k}}{\sqrt{77}}\right) = -0.6838\mathbf{i} - 0.4558\mathbf{j} + 0.5698\mathbf{k}$$

$$\mathbf{R} = T\left[-\mathbf{j} - \mathbf{i} + (-0.6838\mathbf{i} - 0.4558\mathbf{j} + 0.5698\mathbf{k})\right] = T(-1.6838\mathbf{i} - 1.4558\mathbf{j} + 0.5698\mathbf{k})$$

$$\therefore\ R = \sqrt{(-1.6838)^2 + (-1.4558)^2 + 0.5698^2} = 2.30T \ ♦$$

2.15

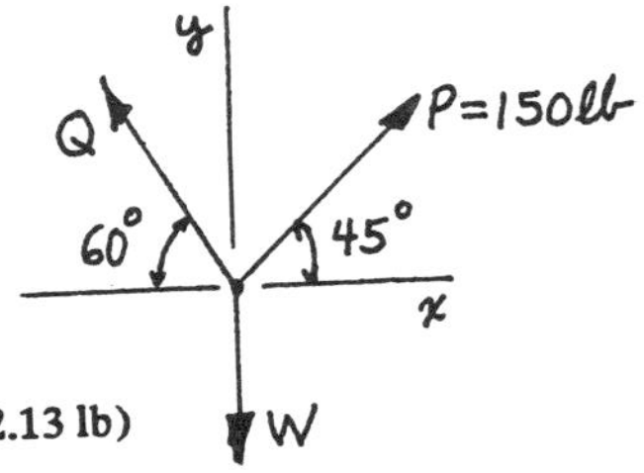

$R_x = \Sigma F_x = 0$

$\overset{+}{\rightarrow}\quad 150\cos 45^\circ - Q\cos 60^\circ = 0 \qquad (1)$

$R_y = \Sigma F_y = 0$

$+\uparrow\quad 150\sin 45^\circ + Q\sin 60^\circ - W = 0 \qquad (2)$

Solving (1) and (2) gives W = 290 lb ♦ (and Q = 212.13 lb)

2.16

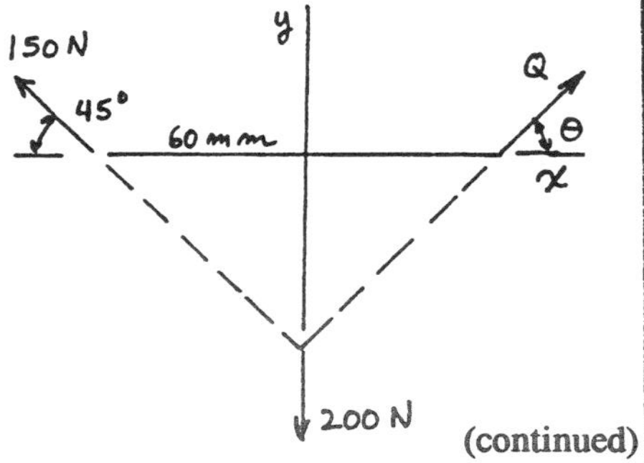

The three forces must be concurrent.

$\Sigma F_x = 0: \quad \overset{+}{\rightarrow}\quad Q\cos\theta - 150\cos 45^\circ = 0$

$Q\cos\theta = 106.1$ N $\qquad (1)$

$\Sigma F_y = 0: \quad +\uparrow\quad Q\sin\theta + 150\sin 45^\circ - 200 = 0$

$Q\sin\theta = 93.93$ N $\qquad (2)$

(continued)

Dividing (2) by (1) gives

$$\theta = \tan^{-1}\left(\frac{93.93}{106.1}\right) = 41.5^\circ \ ♦$$

From (1): $Q = 106.1/\cos 41.5^\circ = 141.7$ N ♦

2.17

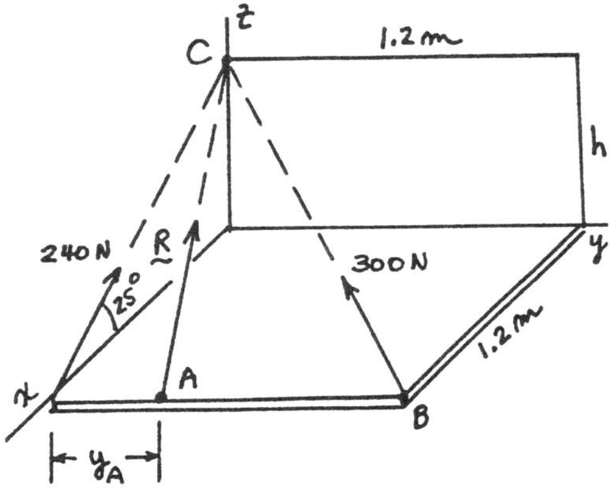

The three forces intersect at C.

$h = 1.2\tan 25^\circ = 0.5596$ m

For the 240-N force :

$-240(\cos 25^\circ\,\mathbf{i} - \sin 25^\circ\,\mathbf{k}) =$

$-217.5\,\mathbf{i} + 101.4\,\mathbf{k}$ N

For the 300-N force $\left(300\ \vec{\lambda}_{BC}\right)$:

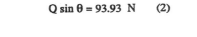

$$300\left(\frac{-1.2\,\mathbf{i} - 1.2\,\mathbf{j} + 0.5596\,\mathbf{k}}{1.787}\right) =$$

$-201.5\,\mathbf{i} - 201.5\,\mathbf{j} + 93.95\,\mathbf{k}$ N

$\mathbf{R} = \Sigma\mathbf{F}$

$= (-217.5 - 201.5)\,\mathbf{i} - 201.5\,\mathbf{j} + (101.4 + 93.95)\,\mathbf{k} = -419.0\,\mathbf{i} - 201.5\,\mathbf{j} + 195.4\,\mathbf{k}$ N ♦

Since **R** acts along $\overline{AC}$: $\dfrac{|R_y|}{y_A} = \dfrac{|R_x|}{1.2} \qquad \therefore\ y_A = \dfrac{|R_y|}{|R_x|}(1.2) = \dfrac{201.5}{419.0}(1.2) = 0.577$ m ♦

2.18

$$T_1 = 200\left(\frac{3\mathbf{i} - 2\mathbf{j} - 6\mathbf{k}}{7}\right) = 85.71\mathbf{i} - 57.14\mathbf{j} - 171.43\mathbf{k} \text{ lb}$$

$$T_2 = 400\left(\frac{3\mathbf{j} - 6\mathbf{k}}{\sqrt{45}}\right) = 178.89\mathbf{j} - 357.77\mathbf{k} \text{ lb}$$

$$T_3 = 350\left(\frac{-4\mathbf{i} - 6\mathbf{k}}{\sqrt{52}}\right) = -194.15\mathbf{i} - 291.22\mathbf{k} \text{ lb}$$

$\mathbf{R} = \Sigma\mathbf{T} = (85.71 - 194.15)\mathbf{i} + (-57.14 + 178.89)\mathbf{j} + (-171.43 - 357.77 - 291.22)\mathbf{k}$

$\therefore\ \mathbf{R} = -108.4\mathbf{i} + 121.8\mathbf{j} - 820.4\mathbf{k}$ lb (acting through point A) ♦

2.19

$R_x = \Sigma F_x$: $R_x = 160 \sin 30^\circ \cos 50^\circ = 51.42$ lb

$R_y = \Sigma F_y$: $\overset{+}{\rightarrow}$ $R_y = -80 \sin 30^\circ + 160 \sin 30^\circ \sin 50^\circ = 21.28$ lb

$R_z = \Sigma F_z$: $+\uparrow$ $R_z = -120 - 80 \cos 30^\circ - 160 \cos 30^\circ = -327.8$ lb

(a) $R = \sqrt{51.42^2 + 21.28^2 + (-327.8)^2} = 332.5$ lb ◆

(b) $\cos\theta_x = 51.42/332.5 = 0.1547$ ◆

$\cos\theta_y = 21.28/332.5 = 0.0640$ ◆

$\cos\theta_z = -327.8/332.5 = -0.9859$ ◆

(c) Note that $\overline{AB}$ has the same direction cosines as **R**.

$\overline{AB} = \dfrac{z}{\cos\theta_z} = \dfrac{-60}{-0.9859} = 60.86$ ft

$x = \overline{AB} \cos\theta_x = 60.86(0.1547) = 9.42$ ft ◆

$y = \overline{AB} \cos\theta_y = 60.86(0.0640) = 3.90$ ft ◆

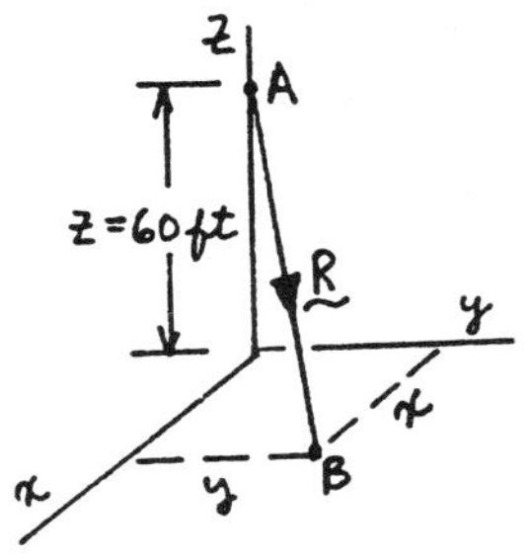

2.20

The three forces intersect at O.

$R_x = \Sigma F_x$:

$\overset{+}{\rightarrow}$ $R_x = 141.4 \cos 45^\circ = 100$ lb

$R_y = \Sigma F_y$:

$+\uparrow$ $R_y = -141.4 \sin 45^\circ - 100 = -200$ lb

(a) $R = \sqrt{100^2 + (-200)^2} = 224$ lb ◆

(b) $\theta = \tan^{-1}(-R_y/R_x) = \tan^{-1}(200/100) = 63.4^\circ$ ◆

(c) $\tan\theta = \dfrac{7}{7-x} = 2$ $\quad\therefore$ $x = 3.5$ ft ◆

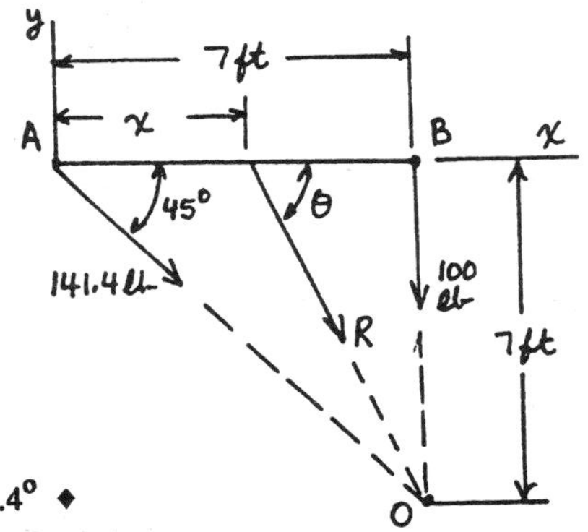

*2.21

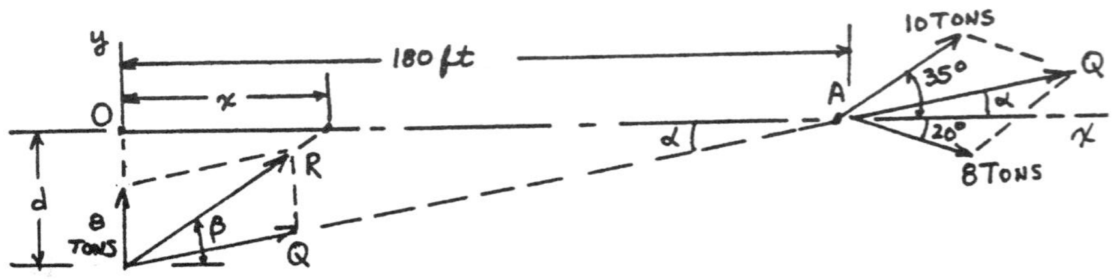

Let **Q** be the resultant of the two forces at A.

$\overset{+}{\rightarrow}$ $Q_x = \Sigma F_x = 10 \cos 35^\circ + 8 \cos 20^\circ = 15.71$ tons

$+\uparrow$ $Q_y = \Sigma F_y = 10 \sin 35^\circ - 8 \sin 20^\circ = 3.00$ tons

$\therefore$ $\tan\alpha = Q_y/Q_x = 3.00/15.71 = 0.1910$

Let **R** be the resultant of **Q** and the 8-ton vertical force.

$\overset{+}{\rightarrow}$ $R_x = \Sigma F_x = Q_x = 15.71$ tons

$+\uparrow$ $R_y = \Sigma F_y = 8 + Q_y = 8 + 3 = 11$ tons

$\therefore$ **R** = 15.71 **i** + 11.00 **j** tons ◆

(Note that $\tan\beta = R_y/R_x = 11.00/15.71 = 0.7002$)

To find x: $d = 180 \tan\alpha = 180(0.1910) = 34.38$ ft

$x = d/\tan\beta = 34.38/0.7002 = 49.1$ ft ◆

2.22

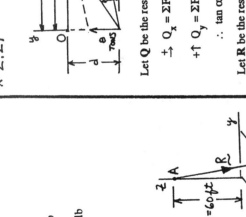

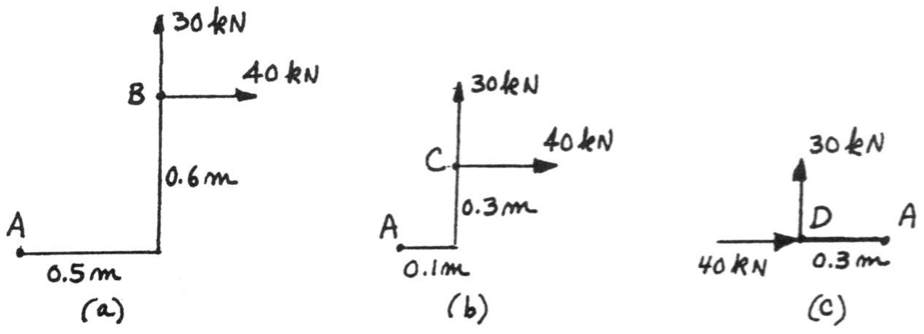

(a) Components at point B

$\overset{+}{\circlearrowleft}$ $M_A = 30(0.5) - 40(0.6) = -9$ kN•m $\quad$ $M_A = 9$ kN•m CW ◆

(continued)

(b) Components at point C

$\circlearrowleft +$ $M_A = 30(0.1) - 40(0.3) = -9$ kN•m $M_A = 9$ kN•m CW ◆

(c) Components at point D

$\circlearrowleft +$ $M_A = -30(0.3) = -9$ kN•m $M_A = 9$ kN•m CW ◆

2.23

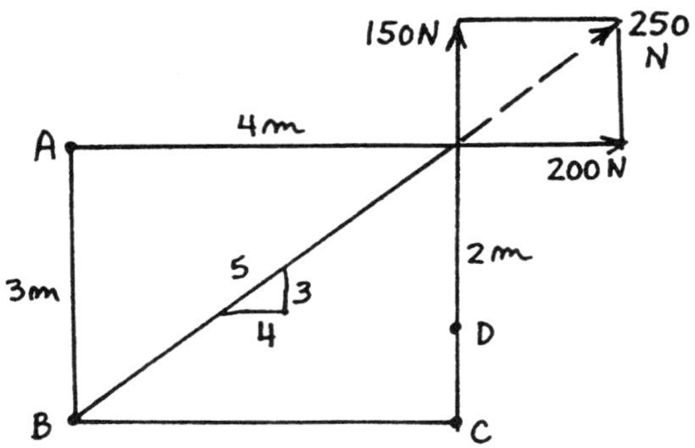

$\circlearrowleft +$ $M_A = 150(4) = 600$ N•m

$\therefore$ $\mathbf{M}_A = 600\,\mathbf{k}$ N•m ◆

$\mathbf{M}_B = \mathbf{0}$ ◆

$\circlearrowleft +$ $M_C = -200(3) = -600$ N•m

$\therefore$ $\mathbf{M}_C = -600\,\mathbf{k}$ N•m ◆

$\circlearrowleft +$ $M_D = -200(2) = -400$ N•m

$\therefore$ $\mathbf{M}_D = -400\,\mathbf{k}$ N•m ◆

2.24

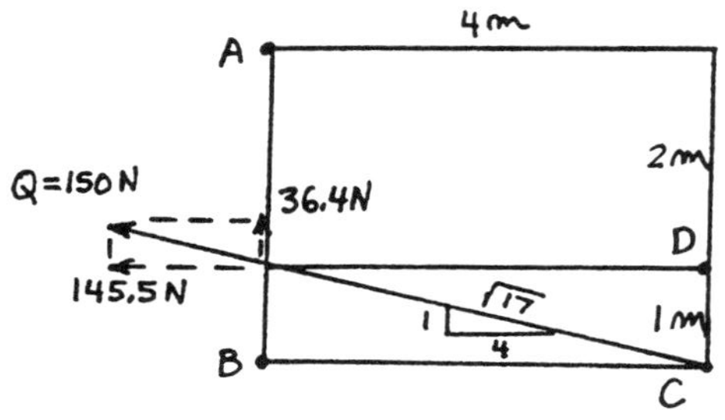

$$Q_x = 150\left(\frac{4}{\sqrt{17}}\right) = 145.5 \text{ N}$$

$$Q_y = 150\left(\frac{1}{\sqrt{17}}\right) = 36.4 \text{ N}$$

$\circlearrowleft +$ $M_A = -145.5(2) = -291$ N•m

$\therefore$ $\mathbf{M}_A = -291\,\mathbf{k}$ N•m ◆

$\circlearrowleft +$ $M_B = 145.5(1) = 145.5$ N•m

$\therefore$ $\mathbf{M}_B = 145.5\,\mathbf{k}$ N•m ◆

$\mathbf{M}_C = \mathbf{0}$ ◆

$\circlearrowleft +$ $M_D = -36.4(4) = -145.6$ N•m

$\therefore$ $\mathbf{M}_D = -145.6\,\mathbf{k}$ N•m ◆

2.25

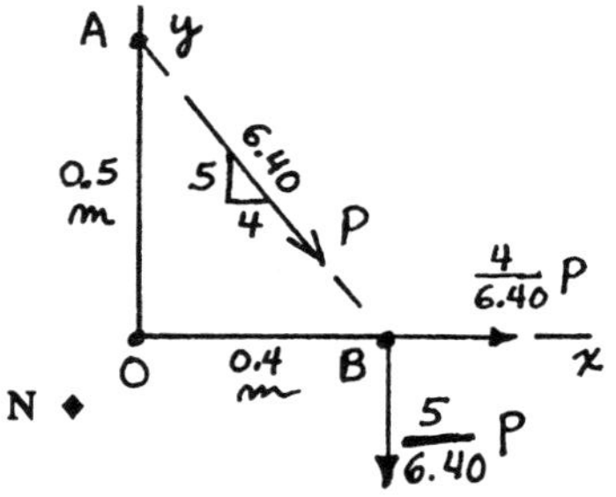

Since M_A and M_B equal zero, the force **P** passes through A and B, as shown.

$\circlearrowleft +$ $M_O = -\dfrac{5}{6.40}P(0.4) = -200$ kN•m

$\therefore$ $P = 640$ N

$$\mathbf{P} = \frac{4}{6.40}(640)\,\mathbf{i} - \frac{5}{6.40}(640)\,\mathbf{j} = 400\mathbf{i} - 500\mathbf{j} \text{ N} ◆$$

2.26

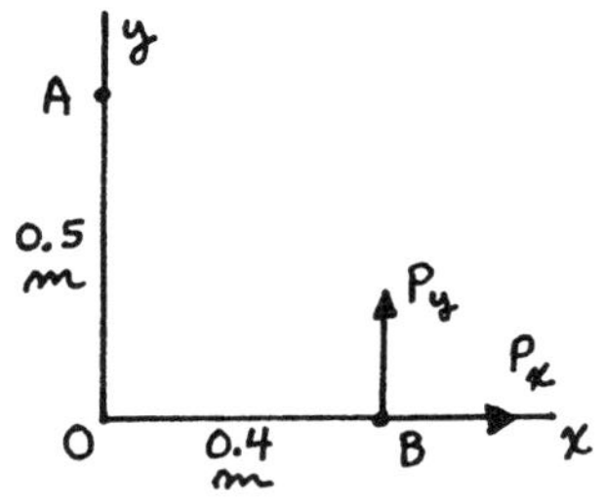

Since $M_B = 0$, **P** passes though B.

$\circlearrowleft +$ $M_O = 0.4\,P_y = 80$ N•m

$P_y = 200$ N

$\circlearrowleft +$ $M_A = 0.4(200) + 0.5\,P_x = -200$ N•m

$P_x = -280/0.5 = -560$ N

$\therefore$ $\mathbf{P} = -560\mathbf{i} + 200\mathbf{j}$ N ◆

2.27

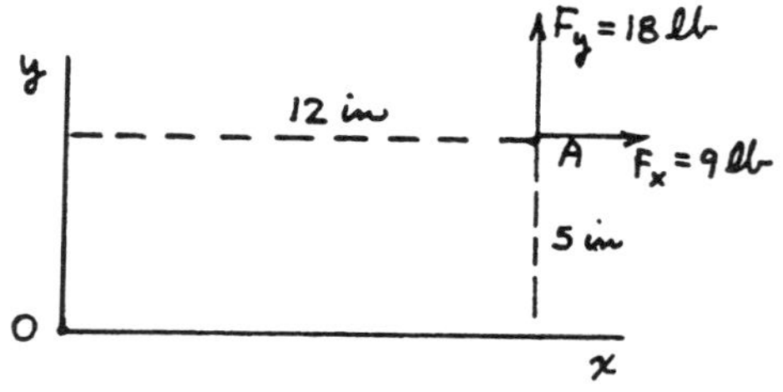

$\mathbf{F} = 9\,\mathbf{i} + 18\,\mathbf{j}$ lb

(a) $$\mathbf{M}_O = \mathbf{r}_{OA} \times \mathbf{F} = \begin{vmatrix} \mathbf{i} & \mathbf{j} & \mathbf{k} \\ 12 & 5 & 0 \\ 9 & 18 & 0 \end{vmatrix}$$

$$= \mathbf{k}\left[18(12) - 5(9)\right] = 171\,\mathbf{k} \text{ lb•in.} ◆$$

(b) $\circlearrowleft +$ $M_O = 18(12) - 9(5) = 171$ lb•in. $\therefore$ $M_O = 171$ lb•in CCW ◆

(continued)

(c) Unit vector perpendicular to OA is

$$\vec{\lambda} = -\frac{5}{13}\mathbf{i} + \frac{12}{13}\mathbf{j}$$

$$F_1 = \mathbf{F}\cdot\vec{\lambda}$$

$$= (9\,\mathbf{i} + 18\,\mathbf{j})\cdot(-\frac{5}{13}\,\mathbf{i} + \frac{12}{13}\,\mathbf{j})$$

$$= \frac{-45+216}{13} = 13.15 \text{ lb}\bullet\text{in.}$$

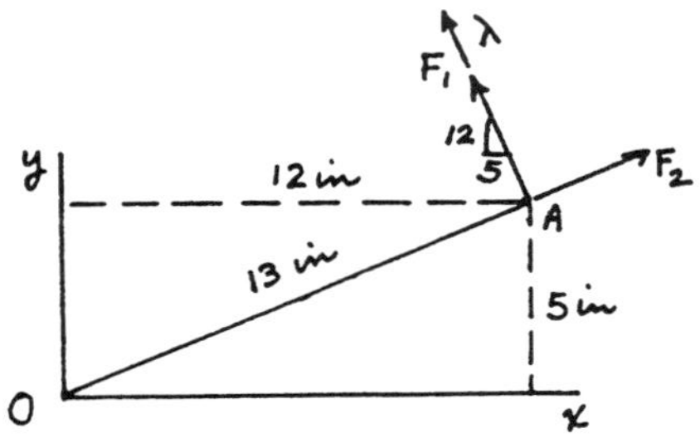

(+) $M_O = 13\,F_1 = 13(13.15) = 171$ lb•in. $\therefore$ $M_O = 171$ lb•in CCW ◆

2.28

(a) For T: (+) $M_B = 20(20) = 400$ kN•m

$\therefore$ $M_B = 400$ kN•m CCW ◆

(b) For W: (+) $M_B = 25(16) = 400$ kN•m

$\therefore$ $M_B = 400$ kN•m CW ◆

(c) For T and W: (+) $\Sigma M_B = +400 - 400 = 0$ ◆

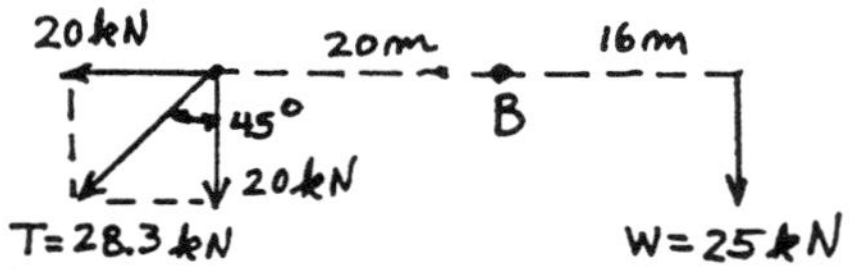

2.29

The moment of **F** about O is maximum when $\theta = 90^o$ ◆

$M_O = F(1.25) = 50$ lb•ft $\quad\therefore\ F = \frac{50}{1.25} = 40$ lb ◆

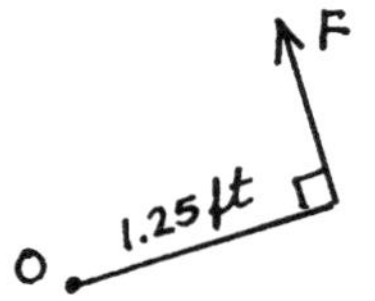

2.30

Since the resultant passes through A, $\Sigma M_A = 0$:

(+) $Q(16) - \frac{4}{5}(25)(8) = 0$

$\therefore$ $Q = 10$ lb ◆

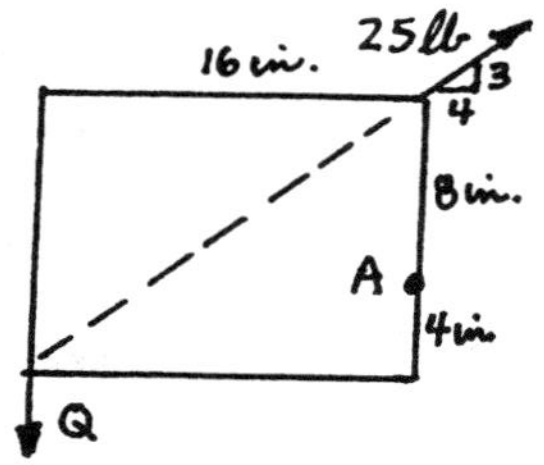

2.31

Because the resultant passes through point A, $\Sigma M_A = 0$.

(+) $24(4) - 18x = 0$ which gives $x = 5.33$ in. ◆

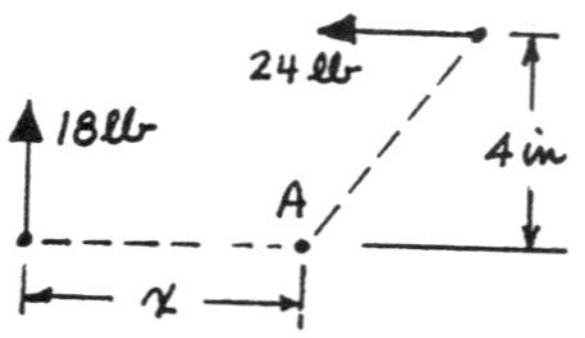

2.32

For no tipping, $\Sigma M_O = 0$:

(+) $6200(8) - 9000(6\cos\theta) = 0$

$\theta = 23.3^o$ ◆

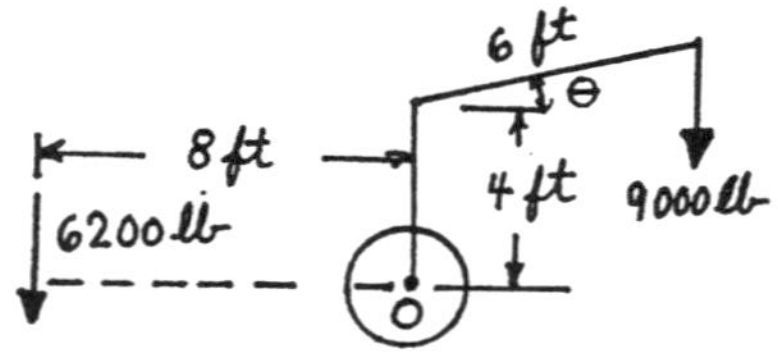

2.33

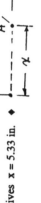

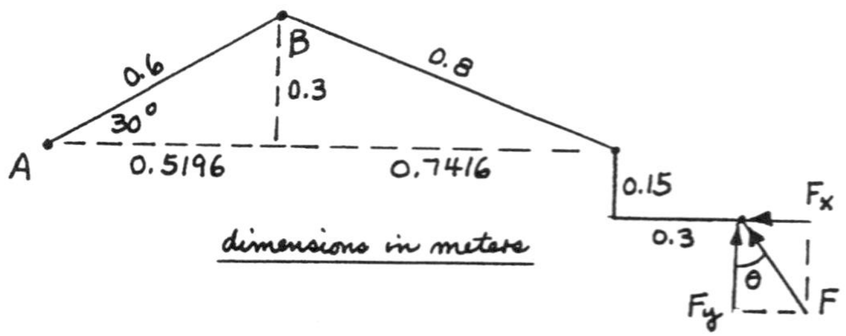

(+) $\Sigma M_A = F_y(0.5196 + 0.7416 + 0.3) - F_x(0.150) = 120$

$1.5612F_y - 0.150F_x = 120 \quad (1)$

(+) $\Sigma M_B = F_y(0.7416 + 0.3) - F_x(0.3 + 0.150) = 60$

$1.0416F_y - 0.450F_x = 60 \quad (2)$

Solving (1) and (2) gives $F_x = 57.34$ N and $F_y = 82.37$ N

Therefore, $F = \sqrt{57.34^2 + 82.37^2} = 100.4$ N ◆ $\quad \theta = \tan^{-1}\left(\frac{57.34}{82.37}\right) = 34.8^o$ ◆

2.34

(a) Valid

(b) Invalid: $\mathbf{r}_2$ has the wrong sense. The result is $-\mathbf{M}_O$.

(c) Invalid: incorrect order of multiplication. The result is $-\mathbf{M}_O$.

(d) Valid: $\mathbf{F}\times\mathbf{r}_2 = -\mathbf{r}_2\times\mathbf{F} = -(-\mathbf{M}_O) = \mathbf{M}_O$

(e) Valid: $-\mathbf{r}_2\times\mathbf{F} = -(-\mathbf{M}_O) = \mathbf{M}_O$

2.35

$$\mathbf{P} = 100\,\vec{\lambda}_{AB} = 100\left(\frac{-0.500\mathbf{i} - 0.600\mathbf{j} + 0.360\mathbf{k}}{0.860}\right) = -58.14\mathbf{i} - 69.77\mathbf{j} + 41.86\mathbf{k}\ \text{N}$$

(a) $\mathbf{M}_O = \mathbf{r}_{OB} \times \mathbf{P}$ $\quad \mathbf{r}_{OB} = 0.360\mathbf{k}$ m $\quad$ ($\mathbf{r}_{OA}$ is also convenient)

$$\therefore\ \mathbf{M}_O = \begin{vmatrix} \mathbf{i} & \mathbf{j} & \mathbf{k} \\ 0 & 0 & 0.360 \\ -58.14 & -69.77 & 41.86 \end{vmatrix} = 25.11\mathbf{i} - 20.93\mathbf{j}\ \text{N·m} \ \blacklozenge$$

(b) $\mathbf{M}_C = \mathbf{r}_{CB} \times \mathbf{P}$ $\quad \mathbf{r}_{CB} = -0.600\mathbf{j}$ m $\quad$ ($\mathbf{r}_{CA}$ is also convenient)

$$\therefore\ \mathbf{M}_C = \begin{vmatrix} \mathbf{i} & \mathbf{j} & \mathbf{k} \\ 0 & -0.600 & 0 \\ -58.14 & -69.77 & 41.86 \end{vmatrix} = -25.12\mathbf{i} - 34.88\mathbf{k}\ \text{N·m} \ \blacklozenge$$

2.36

$$\mathbf{Q} = 250\,\vec{\lambda}_{BD} = 250\left(\frac{-0.500\mathbf{i} + 0.360\mathbf{k}}{0.6161}\right) = -202.9\,\mathbf{i} + 146.1\,\mathbf{k}\ \text{N}$$

(a) $\mathbf{M}_O = \mathbf{r}_{OB} \times \mathbf{Q}$ $\quad \mathbf{r}_{OB} = 0.360\,\mathbf{k}$ m $\quad$ ($\mathbf{r}_{OD}$ is also convenient)

$$\therefore\ \mathbf{M}_O = \begin{vmatrix} \mathbf{i} & \mathbf{j} & \mathbf{k} \\ 0 & 0 & 0.360 \\ -202.9 & 0 & 146.1 \end{vmatrix} = -73.0\mathbf{j}\ \text{N·m} \ \blacklozenge$$

(b) $\mathbf{M}_C = \mathbf{r}_{CB} \times \mathbf{Q}$ $\quad \mathbf{r}_{CB} = -0.600\mathbf{j}$ m $\quad$ ($\mathbf{r}_{CD}$ is also convenient)

$$\therefore\ \mathbf{M}_C = \begin{vmatrix} \mathbf{i} & \mathbf{j} & \mathbf{k} \\ 0 & -0.600 & 0 \\ -202.9 & 0 & 146.1 \end{vmatrix} = -87.7\mathbf{i} - 121.7\mathbf{k}\ \text{N·m} \ \blacklozenge$$

2.37

$\mathbf{M}_O = \mathbf{r}_{OC} \times \mathbf{P}$ $\quad \mathbf{r}_{OC} = 2\mathbf{i} + 4\mathbf{j} - 3\mathbf{k}$ m $\quad \mathbf{P} = P(-\cos 25^\circ\mathbf{i} + \sin 25^\circ\mathbf{k})$

$$\mathbf{M}_O = P\begin{vmatrix} \mathbf{i} & \mathbf{j} & \mathbf{k} \\ 2 & 4 & -3 \\ -\cos 25^\circ & 0 & \sin 25^\circ \end{vmatrix} = P(1.6905\mathbf{i} + 1.8737\mathbf{j} + 3.6252\mathbf{k})$$

(continued)

$$\therefore\ M_O = P\sqrt{1.6905^2 + 1.8737^2 + 3.6252^2} = 4.417P = 200\ \text{kN·m}$$

which gives $P = 200/4.417 = 45.3$ kN $\blacklozenge$

2.38

$$\mathbf{P} = 50(-\cos 25^\circ\mathbf{i} + \sin 25^\circ\mathbf{k}) = -45.32\mathbf{i} + 21.13\mathbf{k}\ \text{kN}$$

(a) $\mathbf{M}_A = \mathbf{r}_{AC} \times \mathbf{P}$ $\quad \mathbf{r}_{AC} = 4\mathbf{j} - 3\mathbf{k}$ m

$$\therefore\ \mathbf{M}_A = \begin{vmatrix} \mathbf{i} & \mathbf{j} & \mathbf{k} \\ 0 & 4 & -3 \\ -45.32 & 0 & 21.13 \end{vmatrix} = 84.52\mathbf{i} + 135.96\mathbf{j} + 181.28\mathbf{k}\ \text{kN·m}$$

(b) $\mathbf{M}_B = \mathbf{r}_{BC} \times \mathbf{P}$ $\quad \mathbf{r}_{BC} = 4\mathbf{j}$ m

$$\therefore\ \mathbf{M}_B = \begin{vmatrix} \mathbf{i} & \mathbf{j} & \mathbf{k} \\ 0 & 4 & 0 \\ -45.32 & 0 & 21.13 \end{vmatrix} = 84.52\mathbf{i} + 181.28\mathbf{k}\ \text{kN·m}$$

2.39

$$\mathbf{Q} = 20\,\vec{\lambda}_{AB} = 20\left(\frac{-3\mathbf{i} + 4\mathbf{j} - 8\mathbf{k}}{9.434}\right) = -6.360\mathbf{i} + 8.480\mathbf{j} - 16.96\mathbf{k}\ \text{lb}$$

(a) $\mathbf{M}_O = \mathbf{r}_{OA} \times \mathbf{Q}$ $\quad \mathbf{r}_{OA} = 8\mathbf{k}$ ft $\quad$ ($\mathbf{r}_{OB}$ is also convenient)

$$\therefore\ \mathbf{M}_O = \begin{vmatrix} \mathbf{i} & \mathbf{j} & \mathbf{k} \\ 0 & 0 & 8 \\ -6.360 & 8.480 & -16.96 \end{vmatrix} = -67.8\mathbf{i} - 50.9\mathbf{j}\ \text{lb·ft} \ \blacklozenge$$

(b) $\mathbf{M}_C = \mathbf{r}_{CB} \times \mathbf{Q}$ $\quad \mathbf{r}_{CB} = -3\mathbf{i}$ ft $\quad$ ($\mathbf{r}_{CA}$ is also convenient)

$$\therefore\ \mathbf{M}_C = \begin{vmatrix} \mathbf{i} & \mathbf{j} & \mathbf{k} \\ -3 & 0 & 0 \\ -6.360 & 8.480 & -16.96 \end{vmatrix} = -50.9\mathbf{j} - 25.4\mathbf{k}\ \text{lb·ft} \ \blacklozenge$$

2.40

$$\mathbf{M}_C = \mathbf{r}_{CF} \times \mathbf{P} + \mathbf{r}_{CD} \times \mathbf{T}$$

$$\mathbf{r}_{CF} = 2\mathbf{i} - 0.8\mathbf{j}\ \text{m};\ \mathbf{r}_{CD} = 1.0\mathbf{i}\ \text{m};\ \ \mathbf{P} = -200\mathbf{k}\ \text{N};\ \mathbf{T} = 300\left(\frac{-\mathbf{i} - 2\mathbf{j} + 0.8\mathbf{k}}{\sqrt{5.64}}\right)\ \text{N}$$

$$\mathbf{M}_C = \begin{vmatrix} \mathbf{i} & \mathbf{j} & \mathbf{k} \\ 2 & -0.8 & 0 \\ 0 & 0 & -200 \end{vmatrix} + \frac{300}{\sqrt{5.64}}\begin{vmatrix} \mathbf{i} & \mathbf{j} & \mathbf{k} \\ 1 & 0 & 0 \\ -1 & -2 & 0.8 \end{vmatrix}$$

$$\mathbf{M}_C = (160\mathbf{i} + 400\mathbf{j}) + \frac{300}{\sqrt{5.64}}(-0.8\mathbf{j} - 2\mathbf{k}) = (160\mathbf{i} + 400\mathbf{j}) + (-101.1\,\mathbf{j} - 252.6\mathbf{k})$$

$$\therefore\ \mathbf{M}_C = 160\mathbf{i} + 299\mathbf{j} - 253\mathbf{k}\ \text{N}\bullet\text{m}\ \blacklozenge$$

2.41

$\mathbf{M}_O = \mathbf{r} \times \mathbf{F}$ $\qquad \mathbf{r} = -8\mathbf{i} + 12\mathbf{j}$ in. $\qquad \mathbf{F} = -120\mathbf{k}$ lb

$$\therefore\ \mathbf{M}_O = \begin{vmatrix} \mathbf{i} & \mathbf{j} & \mathbf{k} \\ -8 & 12 & 0 \\ 0 & 0 & -120 \end{vmatrix} = -1440\mathbf{i} - 960\mathbf{j}\ \text{lb}\bullet\text{in.} = -120\mathbf{i} - 80\mathbf{j}\ \text{lb}\bullet\text{ft}\ \blacklozenge$$

2.42

$\mathbf{P} = -16\cos 40^\circ\mathbf{i} + 16\sin 40^\circ\mathbf{k} = -12.257\mathbf{i} + 10.285\mathbf{k}$ lb $\qquad \mathbf{Q} = -22.00\mathbf{j}$ lb

$$\therefore\ \mathbf{P} + \mathbf{Q} = -12.257\mathbf{i} - 22.00\mathbf{j} + 10.285\mathbf{k}\ \text{lb}$$

$\mathbf{M}_O = \mathbf{r}_{OA} \times (\mathbf{P} + \mathbf{Q})$ $\qquad \mathbf{r}_{OA} = -(3 + 8\cos 40^\circ)\mathbf{i} + (8\sin 40^\circ)\mathbf{k} = -9.128\mathbf{i} + 5.142\mathbf{k}$ in.

$$\mathbf{M}_O = \begin{vmatrix} \mathbf{i} & \mathbf{j} & \mathbf{k} \\ -9.128 & 0 & 5.142 \\ -12.257 & -22.00 & 10.285 \end{vmatrix} = 113.12\mathbf{i} + 30.86\mathbf{j} + 200.82\mathbf{k}\ \text{lb}\bullet\text{in.}$$

$$M_O = \sqrt{113.12^2 + 30.86^2 + 200.82^2} = 232.5\ \text{lb}\bullet\text{in.}\ \blacklozenge$$

$$\cos\theta_x = \frac{113.12}{232.5} = 0.4865;\ \ \cos\theta_y = \frac{30.86}{232.5} = 0.1327;\ \ \cos\theta_z = \frac{200.82}{232.5} = 0.8637\ \blacklozenge$$

2.43

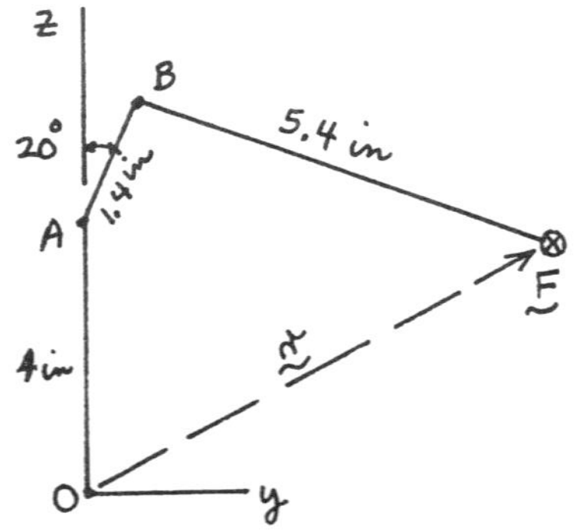

$$r_x = 0$$

$$r_y = 1.4\sin 20^\circ + 5.4\cos 20^\circ = 5.553\ \text{in.}$$

$$r_z = 4 + 1.4\cos 20^\circ - 5.4\sin 20^\circ = 3.469\ \text{in.}$$

$$\mathbf{F} = -36\mathbf{i}\ \text{lb}$$

$$\mathbf{M}_O = \mathbf{r} \times \mathbf{F} = \begin{vmatrix} \mathbf{i} & \mathbf{j} & \mathbf{k} \\ 0 & 5.553 & 3.469 \\ -36 & 0 & 0 \end{vmatrix}$$

$$\therefore\ \mathbf{M}_O = -124.9\mathbf{j} + 199.9\mathbf{k}\ \text{lb}\bullet\text{in.}\ \blacklozenge$$

2.44

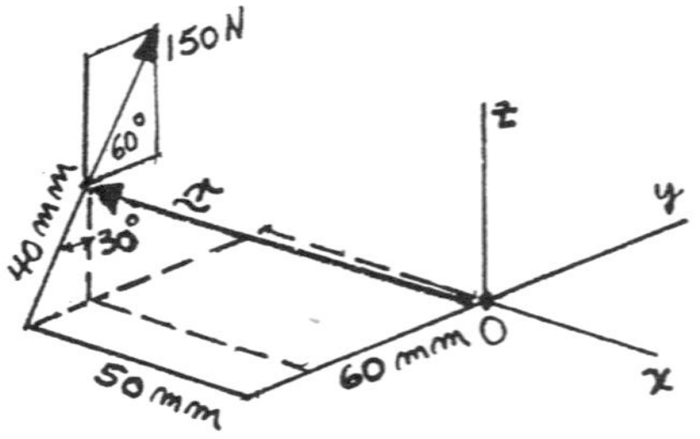

$$\mathbf{r} = -50\mathbf{i} - (60 - 40\sin 30^\circ)\mathbf{j} + 40\cos 30^\circ\mathbf{k}$$
$$= -50.00\mathbf{i} - 40.00\mathbf{j} + 34.64\mathbf{k}\ \text{mm}$$

$$\mathbf{F} = -150\cos 60^\circ\mathbf{j} + 150\sin 60^\circ\mathbf{k}$$
$$= -75.00\mathbf{j} + 129.90\mathbf{k}\ \text{N}$$

$$\mathbf{M}_O = \mathbf{r} \times \mathbf{F} = \begin{vmatrix} \mathbf{i} & \mathbf{j} & \mathbf{k} \\ -50.00 & -40.00 & 34.64 \\ 0 & -75.00 & 129.90 \end{vmatrix}\left(10^{-3}\right) = -2.598\mathbf{i} + 6.495\mathbf{j} - 3.750\mathbf{k}\ \text{N}\bullet\text{m}\ \blacklozenge$$

$$M_O = \sqrt{(-2.598)^2 + (6.495)^2 + (-3.750)^2} = 7.937\ \text{N}\bullet\text{m}\ \blacklozenge$$

$$\cos\theta_x = -\frac{2.598}{7.937} = -0.3273;\ \cos\theta_y = \frac{6.495}{7.937} = 0.8183;\ \cos\theta_z = -\frac{3.750}{7.937} = -0.4725\ \blacklozenge$$

2.45

$\mathbf{P}_1 = \frac{P}{\sqrt{2}}(\mathbf{j} - \mathbf{k})$ $\qquad \mathbf{r}_1 = -d\mathbf{i}$ $\qquad \mathbf{P}_2 = \frac{P}{\sqrt{3}}(\mathbf{i} + \mathbf{j} - \mathbf{k})$ $\qquad \mathbf{r}_2 = (a - d)\mathbf{i}$

$$\mathbf{M}_A = \mathbf{r}_1 \times \mathbf{P}_1 + \mathbf{r}_2 \times \mathbf{P}_2 = \frac{P}{\sqrt{2}}\begin{vmatrix} \mathbf{i} & \mathbf{j} & \mathbf{k} \\ -d & 0 & 0 \\ 0 & 1 & -1 \end{vmatrix} + \frac{P}{\sqrt{3}}\begin{vmatrix} \mathbf{i} & \mathbf{j} & \mathbf{k} \\ (a-d) & 0 & 0 \\ 1 & 1 & -1 \end{vmatrix} = \mathbf{0}$$

(continued)

Canceling P and expanding the determinants gives: $\frac{d}{\sqrt{2}}(-\mathbf{j}-\mathbf{k})+\frac{a-d}{\sqrt{3}}(\mathbf{j}+\mathbf{k})=\mathbf{0}$

Equating either the **j**-components or the **k**-components yields: $\frac{d}{\sqrt{2}}=\frac{a-d}{\sqrt{3}}$

from which we find: $d=\frac{a\sqrt{2}}{\sqrt{2}+\sqrt{3}}=0.449a$ ◆

2.46

Point A: (3 m, 6 m, − 2 m); point D: (0, y m, z m)

$\mathbf{M}_D=\mathbf{r}_{DA}\times\mathbf{F}=\mathbf{0}$ $\quad\mathbf{r}_{DA}=3\,\mathbf{i}+(6-y)\mathbf{j}+(-2-z)\mathbf{k}$ m

$$\mathbf{M}_D=\begin{vmatrix}\mathbf{i}&\mathbf{j}&\mathbf{k}\\3&6-y&-2-z\\10&30&-40\end{vmatrix}$$

$$=\left[(6-y)(-40)-30(-2-z)\right]\mathbf{i}-\left[3(-40)-10(-2-z)\right]\mathbf{j}+\left[3(30)-10(6-y)\right]\mathbf{k}=\mathbf{0}$$

Equating the **j**- and **k**-components to zero, and solving gives: y = − 3 m; z = 10 m.

Therefore, the coordinates of point D are (0, − 3 m, 10 m) ◆

2.47

Part 1

$\mathbf{M}_x=-60(12)=-720$ kN•m ◆

$\mathbf{M}_y=60(3)=180$ kN•m ◆

$\mathbf{M}_z=180(3)-45(12)=0$ ◆

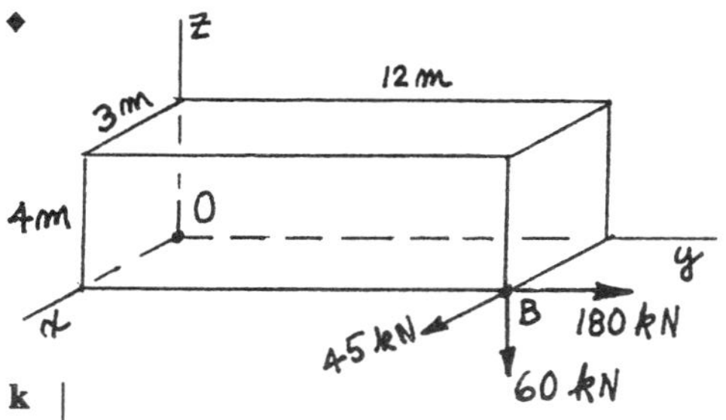

Part 2

$\mathbf{r}_{OB}=3\mathbf{i}+12\mathbf{j}$ m

$\mathbf{F}=45\mathbf{i}+180\mathbf{j}-60\mathbf{k}$ kN

$$\mathbf{M}_O=\mathbf{r}_{OB}\times\mathbf{F}=\begin{vmatrix}\mathbf{i}&\mathbf{j}&\mathbf{k}\\3&12&0\\45&180&-60\end{vmatrix}=-720\mathbf{i}+180\mathbf{j}+0\mathbf{k}\text{ kN•m}$$ ◆

(Note: the answers to Parts 1 and 2 agree, as they should.)

2.48

(a) moment arm is BF $\quad M_{AB}=40(0.9)=36$ kN•m ◆

(b) moment arm is DH $\quad M_{CD}=40(0.9)=36$ kN•m ◆

(c) moment arm is GH $\quad M_{CG}=40(0.8)=32$ kN•m ◆

(d) moment arm is zero $\quad M_{CH}=0$ ◆

(e) force is parallel to EG $\quad M_{EG}=0$ ◆

2.49

$\overline{FG}=\sqrt{9^2+7.5^2}=11.715$ ft

$P_x=400\left(\frac{9}{11.715}\right)=307.3$ lb

$P_z=400\left(\frac{7.5}{11.715}\right)=256.1$ lb

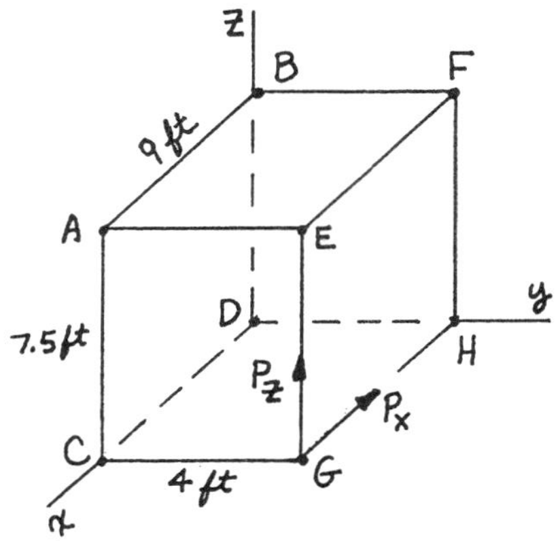

(a) $\mathbf{M}_{AB}=P_z(\overline{AE})\mathbf{i}=256.1(4)\mathbf{i}$
$=1024\mathbf{i}$ lb•ft ◆

(b) $\mathbf{M}_{CD}=P_z(\overline{CG})\mathbf{i}=256.1(4)\mathbf{i}$
$=1024\mathbf{i}$ lb•ft ◆

(c) $\mathbf{M}_{BF}=\mathbf{0}$ (because the force passes through F) ◆

(d) $\mathbf{M}_{DH}=-P_z(\overline{GH})\mathbf{j}=-256.1(9)\mathbf{j}=-2305\mathbf{j}$ lb•ft ◆

(e) $\mathbf{M}_{BD}=P_x(\overline{DH})\mathbf{k}=307.3(4)\mathbf{k}=1229\mathbf{k}$ lb•ft ◆

2.50

The resultant of **P** and **Q** acting at A is:

R = **P** + **Q**

$=(60\mathbf{i}+120\,\mathbf{k})-30\mathbf{k}=60\mathbf{i}+90\mathbf{k}$ N

Note that only the 90-N component has a moment about the x axis.

$\therefore\ \mathbf{M}_x=90(0.4)\mathbf{i}=36\mathbf{i}$ N•m ◆

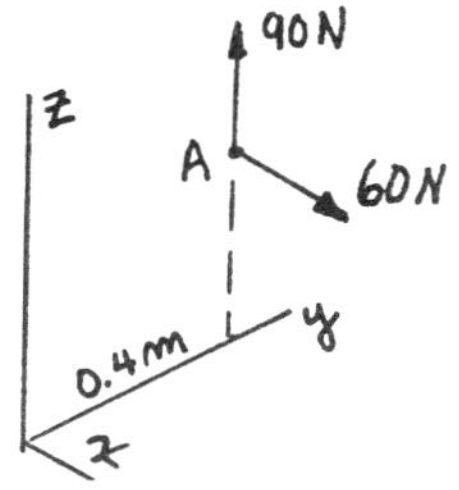

2.51

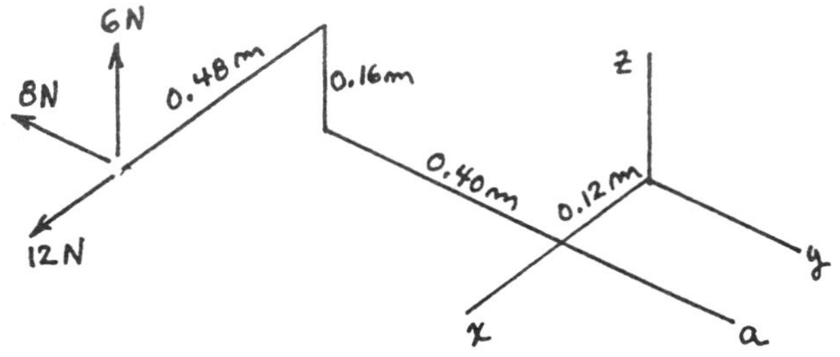

(a) $\mathbf{M}_a = \left[-6(0.480) + 12(0.160)\right]\mathbf{j} = -0.960\,\mathbf{j}$ N•m ◆

(b) $\mathbf{M}_z = \left[-8(0.480 + 0.120) + 12(0.4)\right]\mathbf{k} = \mathbf{0}$ ◆

2.52

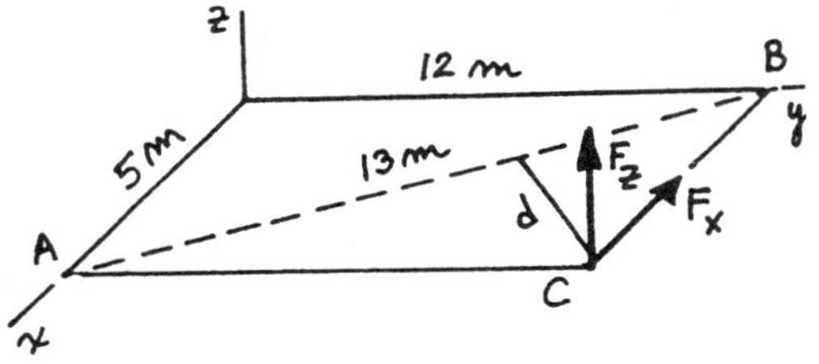

$M_x = 1080 = F_z(\overline{AC})$

$\therefore\ F_z = 1080/12 = 90$ N

$M_{AB} = F_z d$

A convenient way to compute d:

area ABC $= \frac{1}{2}(12)(5) = \frac{1}{2}(13)d$

which gives $d = 4.615$ m

$\therefore\ M_{AB} = 90(4.615) = 415$ N•m ◆

2.53

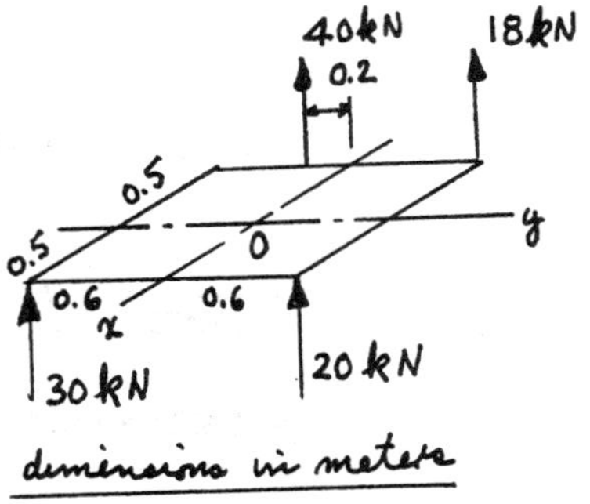

$M_x = (20 + 18)(0.6) - 40(0.2) - 30(0.6)$

$= -3.20$ N•m

$M_y = (40 + 18)(0.5) - (30 + 20)(0.5)$

$= 4.00$ N•m

$\therefore\ \mathbf{M}_O = -3.20\mathbf{i} + 4.00\mathbf{j}$ N•m ◆

2.54

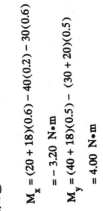

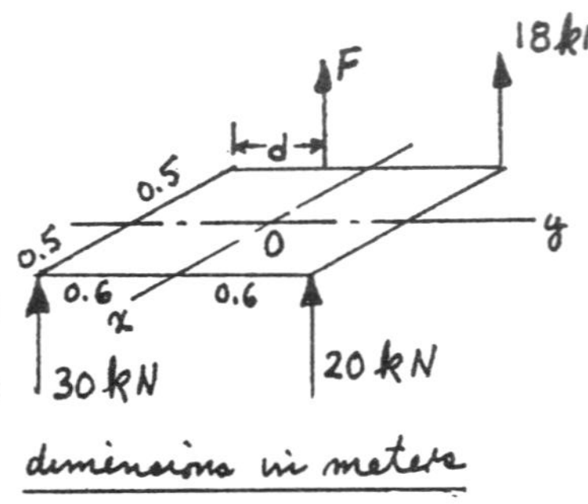

$M_y = (F + 18)(0.5) - (30 + 20)(0.5) = 0$

$\therefore\ F = \dfrac{25 - 9}{0.5} = 32.0$ N ◆

$M_x = (20 + 18)(0.6) - 30(0.6) - F(0.6 - d) = 0$

Substituting F = 32.0 N, and solving for d gives:

$\therefore\ d = \dfrac{-22.8 + 18 + 32.0(0.6)}{32.0} = 0.450$ m ◆

2.55

$M_{aa} = 30(4 - y_0) + 20(6 - y_0) - 40y_0 = 0$ Solving gives: $y_0 = 2.67$ ft ◆

$M_{bb} = (20 + 40)x_0 - 30(6 - x_0) = 0$ Solving gives: $x_0 = 2.00$ ft ◆

2.56

$\mathbf{P} = 60\,\vec{\lambda}_{AH} = 60\left(\dfrac{-0.520\mathbf{j} + 0.480\mathbf{k}}{0.7077}\right) = -44.09\mathbf{j} + 40.70\mathbf{k}$ N

$M_{EG} = \mathbf{r}_{EA} \times \mathbf{P} \cdot \vec{\lambda}_{EG}$ $\quad \mathbf{r}_{EA} = -0.480\mathbf{k}$ m $\quad \vec{\lambda}_{EG} = \dfrac{-0.360\mathbf{i} - 0.520\mathbf{j}}{0.6325}$

$$\therefore\ M_{EG} = \frac{1}{0.6325}\begin{vmatrix} 0 & 0 & -0.480 \\ 0 & -44.09 & 40.70 \\ -0.360 & -0.520 & 0 \end{vmatrix} = 12.05 \text{ N•m}$$

Written in vector form, we have:

$$\mathbf{M}_{EG} = M_{EG}\,\vec{\lambda}_{EG} = 12.05\left(\frac{-0.360\mathbf{i} - 0.520\mathbf{j}}{0.6325}\right) = -6.86\mathbf{i} - 9.91\mathbf{j} \text{ N•m}$$ ◆

2.57

$$\mathbf{P} = 60\,\vec{\lambda}_{AH} = 60\left(\frac{-0.520\mathbf{j} + 0.480\mathbf{k}}{0.7077}\right) = -44.09\mathbf{j} + 40.70\mathbf{k}\ \text{N}$$

$$M_{FD} = \mathbf{r}_{DA} \times \mathbf{P} \bullet \vec{\lambda}_{FD} \qquad \mathbf{r}_{DA} = 0.520\mathbf{j}\ \text{m} \qquad \vec{\lambda}_{FD} = \frac{0.360\mathbf{i} - 0.520\mathbf{j} - 0.480\mathbf{k}}{0.7940}$$

$$\therefore\ M_{FD} = \frac{1}{0.7940}\begin{vmatrix} 0 & 0.520 & 0 \\ 0 & -44.09 & 40.70 \\ 0.360 & -0.520 & -0.480 \end{vmatrix} = 9.596\ \text{N}\bullet\text{m}$$

Written in vector form, we have:

$$\mathbf{M}_{FD} = M_{FD}\vec{\lambda}_{FD} = 9.596\left(\frac{0.360\mathbf{i} - 0.520\mathbf{j} - 0.480\mathbf{k}}{0.7940}\right) = 4.35\mathbf{i} - 6.28\mathbf{j} - 5.80\mathbf{k}\ \text{N}\bullet\text{m}\ \blacklozenge$$

2.58

$$\mathbf{Q} = 120\,\vec{\lambda}_{AG} = 120\left(\frac{-0.360\mathbf{i} - 0.520\mathbf{j} + 0.480\mathbf{k}}{0.7940}\right) = -54.41\mathbf{i} - 78.59\mathbf{j} + 72.54\mathbf{k}\ \text{N}$$

$$M_{EB} = \mathbf{r}_{EA} \times \mathbf{Q} \bullet \vec{\lambda}_{EB}$$

$$\mathbf{r}_{EA} = -0.480\mathbf{k}\ \text{m} \qquad \vec{\lambda}_{EB} = \frac{-0.360\mathbf{i} - 0.480\mathbf{k}}{0.600} = -0.600\mathbf{i} - 0.800\mathbf{k}$$

$$\therefore\ M_{EB} = \begin{vmatrix} 0 & 0 & -0.480 \\ -54.41 & -78.59 & 72.54 \\ -0.600 & 0 & -0.800 \end{vmatrix} = 22.63\ \text{N}\bullet\text{m}$$

Written in vector form, we have

$$\mathbf{M}_{EB} = M_{EB}\vec{\lambda}_{EB} = 22.63(-0.600\mathbf{i} - 0.800\mathbf{k}) = -13.58\mathbf{i} - 18.10\mathbf{k}\ \text{N}\bullet\text{m}\ \blacklozenge$$

2.59

Let the 20-lb force be **Q**:

$$\mathbf{Q} = 20\,\vec{\lambda}_{ED} = 20\left(\frac{-12\mathbf{j} - 4\mathbf{k}}{12.649}\right) = -18.974\mathbf{j} - 6.324\mathbf{k}\ \text{lb}$$

$$\mathbf{P} = P\,\vec{\lambda}_{AF} = P\left(\frac{-4\mathbf{i} + 4\mathbf{k}}{4\sqrt{2}}\right) = P(-0.7071\mathbf{i} + 0.7071\mathbf{k})\ \text{lb}$$

$$M_{GB} = \mathbf{r}_{BE} \times \mathbf{Q} \bullet \vec{\lambda}_{GB} + \mathbf{r}_{BA} \times \mathbf{P} \bullet \vec{\lambda}_{GB} = 0$$

$$\mathbf{r}_{BE} = 4\mathbf{i} + 4\mathbf{k}\ \text{in.} \qquad \mathbf{r}_{BA} = 4\mathbf{i}\ \text{in.} \qquad \vec{\lambda}_{GB} = \frac{12\mathbf{j} - 4\mathbf{k}}{12.649}$$

$$M_{GB} = \frac{1}{12.649}\begin{vmatrix} 4 & 0 & 4 \\ 0 & -18.974 & -6.324 \\ 0 & 12 & -4 \end{vmatrix} + \frac{P}{12.649}\begin{vmatrix} 4 & 0 & 0 \\ -0.7071 & 0 & 0.7071 \\ 0 & 12 & -4 \end{vmatrix} = 0$$

Expanding the determinants gives: $\dfrac{607.1}{12.649} + \dfrac{P}{12.649}(-33.94) = 0 \qquad \therefore\ P = 17.89\ \text{lb}\ \blacklozenge$

2.60

$$M_{BC} = \mathbf{r}_{BA} \times \mathbf{F} \bullet \vec{\lambda}_{BC} = 137.3\ \text{lb}\bullet\text{ft}$$

$$\mathbf{r}_{BA} = 4\mathbf{i}\ \text{ft} \qquad \vec{\lambda}_{BC} = \frac{4\mathbf{j} - 2\mathbf{k}}{4.472} \qquad \mathbf{F} = F\vec{\lambda}_{AD} = F\left(\frac{-2\mathbf{i} + 3\mathbf{j} - 3\mathbf{k}}{4.690}\right)\ \text{lb}$$

$$M_{BC} = \frac{F}{4.690}\,\frac{1}{4.472}\begin{vmatrix} 4 & 0 & 0 \\ -2 & 3 & -3 \\ 0 & 4 & -2 \end{vmatrix} = \frac{F(24)}{4.690(4.472)} = 137.3\ \text{lb}\bullet\text{ft}$$

$\therefore\ F = 120.0\ \text{lb}\ \blacklozenge$

*2.61

Let $\vec{\lambda}$ be a unit vector perpendicular to the plane ABC:

$$\vec{\lambda} = \frac{\vec{AB} \times \vec{AC}}{|\vec{AB} \times \vec{AC}|} \quad \text{where } \vec{AB} = -3\mathbf{j} + 4\mathbf{k} \text{ m and } \vec{AC} = 3\mathbf{i} - 3\mathbf{j} \text{ m}$$

$$\vec{AB} \times \vec{AC} = \begin{vmatrix} \mathbf{i} & \mathbf{j} & \mathbf{k} \\ 0 & -3 & 4 \\ 3 & -3 & 0 \end{vmatrix} = 12\mathbf{i} + 12\mathbf{j} + 9\mathbf{k} \text{ m}^2 \qquad \therefore \vec{\lambda} = \frac{12\mathbf{i} + 12\mathbf{j} + 9\mathbf{k}}{19.21}$$

$$M_\lambda = \mathbf{r}_{OA} \times \mathbf{F} \bullet \vec{\lambda} \qquad \mathbf{r}_{OA} = 3\mathbf{j} \text{ m}$$

$$\mathbf{F} = 250\,\vec{\lambda}_{AB} = 250\left(\frac{-3\mathbf{j} + 4\mathbf{k}}{5}\right) = -150\mathbf{j} + 200\mathbf{k} \text{ N}$$

$$\therefore M_\lambda = \frac{1}{19.21}\begin{vmatrix} 0 & 3 & 0 \\ 0 & -150 & 200 \\ 12 & 12 & 9 \end{vmatrix} = 374.8 \text{ N}\bullet\text{m}$$

Written in vector form, we have:

$$\mathbf{M}_\lambda = M_\lambda \vec{\lambda} = 374.8\left(\frac{12\mathbf{i} + 12\mathbf{j} + 9\mathbf{k}}{19.21}\right) = 234\mathbf{i} + 234\mathbf{j} + 176\mathbf{k} \text{ N}\bullet\text{m} \quad \blacklozenge$$

2.62

$$\mathbf{P} = 240\,\vec{\lambda}_{CE} = 240\left(\frac{-3\mathbf{i} + 2\mathbf{j} - 7\mathbf{k}}{\sqrt{62}}\right) \text{ lb} \qquad \vec{\lambda}_{AD} = \frac{-3\mathbf{i} + 6\mathbf{j} + 7\mathbf{k}}{\sqrt{94}}$$

(a) $\mathbf{r} = \mathbf{r}_{AC} = 6\mathbf{j} + 7\mathbf{k}$ ft

$$M_{AD} = \mathbf{r}_{AC} \times \mathbf{P} \bullet \vec{\lambda}_{AD} = \frac{240}{\sqrt{62}\sqrt{94}}\begin{vmatrix} 0 & 6 & 7 \\ -3 & 2 & -7 \\ -3 & 6 & 7 \end{vmatrix} = \frac{240}{\sqrt{62}\sqrt{94}}(168) = 528 \text{ lb}\bullet\text{ft} \quad \blacklozenge$$

(b) $\mathbf{r} = \mathbf{r}_{DC} = 3\mathbf{i}$ ft

$$M_{AD} = \mathbf{r}_{DC} \times \mathbf{P} \bullet \vec{\lambda}_{AD} = \frac{240}{\sqrt{62}\sqrt{94}}\begin{vmatrix} 3 & 0 & 0 \\ -3 & 2 & -7 \\ -3 & 6 & 7 \end{vmatrix} = \frac{240}{\sqrt{62}\sqrt{94}}(168) = 528 \text{ lb}\bullet\text{ft} \quad \blacklozenge$$

2.63

(a) $M_{OD} = \mathbf{r}_{OA} \times \mathbf{P}_1 \bullet \vec{\lambda}_{OD} + \mathbf{r}_{OC} \times \mathbf{P}_2 \bullet \vec{\lambda}_{OD}$

$\mathbf{P}_1 = -1000\mathbf{k}$ lb; $\mathbf{P}_2 = -2000\mathbf{k}$ lb; $\mathbf{r}_{OA} = 4\mathbf{j}$ ft; $\mathbf{r}_{OC} = 3\mathbf{i} + 8\mathbf{j}$ lb; $\vec{\lambda}_{OD} = 0.6\mathbf{i} + 0.8\mathbf{j}$

$$M_{AD} = \begin{vmatrix} 0 & 4 & 0 \\ 0 & 0 & -1000 \\ 0.6 & 0.8 & 0 \end{vmatrix} + \begin{vmatrix} 3 & 8 & 0 \\ 0 & 0 & -2000 \\ 0.6 & 0.8 & 0 \end{vmatrix} = -2400 - 4800 = -7200 \text{ lb}\bullet\text{ft} \quad \blacklozenge$$

(b) $M_{OD} = -1000(2.4) - 2000(2.4)$

$= -7200$ lb•ft ◆

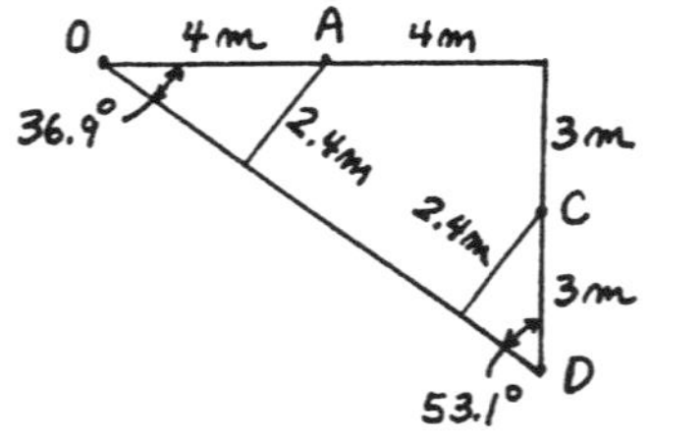

2.64

$$M_{BC} = \mathbf{M}_B \bullet \vec{\lambda}_{BC} = \mathbf{r}_{BD} \times \mathbf{F} \bullet \vec{\lambda}_{BC} = 0 \qquad \mathbf{r}_{BD} = -1.6\mathbf{j} - (1.2 - z_D)\mathbf{k} \text{ m}$$

$$\mathbf{F} = F(0.6\mathbf{i} + 0.8\mathbf{j}) \qquad \vec{\lambda}_{BC} = \frac{\vec{BC}}{|\vec{BC}|} = \frac{1.2\mathbf{i} - 0.6\mathbf{j} - 1.2\mathbf{k}}{1.8}$$

$$\therefore M_{BC} = \frac{F}{1.8}\begin{vmatrix} 0 & -1.6 & -(1.2 - z_D) \\ 0.6 & 0.8 & 0 \\ 1.2 & -0.6 & -1.2 \end{vmatrix} = 0$$

Expanding the determinant: $1.6(0.6)(-1.2) - (1.2 - z_D)(-0.36 - 0.96) = 0$

which gives: $z_D = 0.327$ m ◆

2.65

$$\vec{\lambda}_{AB} = \frac{-3\mathbf{i}+4\mathbf{j}}{5} = -0.600\mathbf{i} + 0.800\mathbf{j}$$

For the pulley at A:

$M_A = M_x = 20(0.5) - 60(0.5) = -20$ kN•m $\quad \therefore \quad \mathbf{M}_A = -20\mathbf{i}$ kN•m

For the pulley at B:

$M_B = M_y = 40(0.8) - 20(0.8) = 16$ kN•m $\quad \therefore \quad \mathbf{M}_B = 16\mathbf{j}$ kN•m

For both pulleys combined:

$$M_{AB} = \left(\mathbf{M}_A + \mathbf{M}_B\right) \bullet \vec{\lambda}_{AB} = (-20\mathbf{i} + 16\mathbf{j}) \bullet (-0.600\mathbf{i} + 0.800\mathbf{j})$$

$$= 12 + 12.8 = 24.8 \text{ kN•m} \ ♦$$

2.66

From the figure at the right:

$x_C = 30 \sin 30^\circ = 15.000$ in.

$y_C = 30 \cos 30^\circ - 24 = 1.981$ in.

$x_D = 18 \sin 30^\circ = 9.000$ in.

$y_D = 24 - 18 \cos 30^\circ = 8.412$ in.

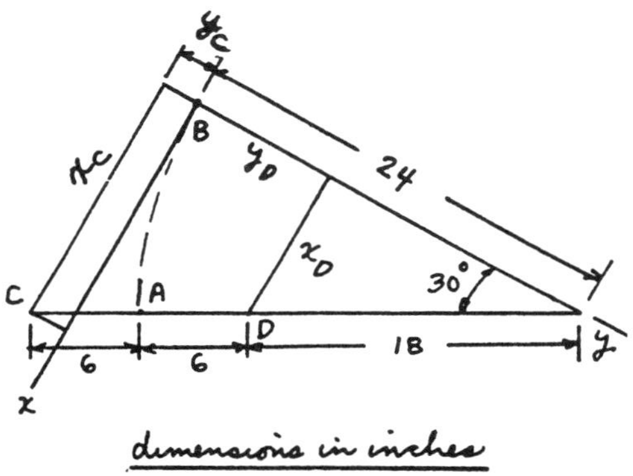

$(M_B)_x = \mathbf{r}_{BC} \times \mathbf{P}_C \bullet \mathbf{i} + \mathbf{r}_{BD} \times \mathbf{P}_D \bullet \mathbf{i}$

$\mathbf{P}_C = 20\mathbf{k}$ lb $\quad \mathbf{P}_D = -20\mathbf{k}$ lb

$\mathbf{r}_{BC} = x_C\mathbf{i} - y_C\mathbf{j} = 15.000\mathbf{i} - 1.981\mathbf{j}$ in.

$\mathbf{r}_{BD} = x_D\mathbf{i} + y_D\mathbf{j} = 9.000\mathbf{i} + 8.412\mathbf{j}$ in.

$$\therefore (M_B)_x = \begin{vmatrix} 15.000 & -1.981 & 0 \\ 0 & 0 & 20 \\ 1 & 0 & 0 \end{vmatrix} + \begin{vmatrix} 9.000 & 8.412 & 0 \\ 0 & 0 & -20 \\ 1 & 0 & 0 \end{vmatrix} = -39.62 - 168.2 = -208 \text{ lb•in}$$

Written in vector form: $(\mathbf{M}_B)_x = (M_B)_x\mathbf{i} = -208\mathbf{i}$ lb•in ♦

2.67

$$\vec{CE} = 160\cos 30^\circ\mathbf{i} - 200\mathbf{j} + (150 - 160\sin 30^\circ)\mathbf{k} = 138.56\mathbf{i} - 200\mathbf{j} + 70\mathbf{k} \text{ mm}$$

$$\vec{\lambda}_{CE} = \frac{\vec{CE}}{|\vec{CE}|} = \frac{138.56\mathbf{i} - 200\mathbf{j} + 70\mathbf{k}}{253.18} = 0.5471\mathbf{i} - 0.7900\mathbf{j} + 0.2765\mathbf{k}$$

$$\mathbf{F} = 30\,\vec{\lambda}_{CE} = 30(0.5471\mathbf{i} - 0.7900\mathbf{j} + 0.2765\mathbf{k}) = 16.413\mathbf{i} - 23.700\mathbf{j} + 8.295\mathbf{k} \text{ kN}$$

$\mathbf{r} = \mathbf{r}_{OE} = 0.150\mathbf{k}$ m $\qquad \vec{\lambda}_{OA} = \sin 60^\circ\mathbf{i} + \cos 60\mathbf{k} = 0.866\mathbf{i} + 0.500\mathbf{k}$

$$M_{OA} = \mathbf{r}_{OE} \times \mathbf{F} \bullet \vec{\lambda}_{OA} = \begin{vmatrix} 0 & 0 & 0.150 \\ 16.413 & -23.700 & 8.295 \\ 0.866 & 0 & 0.500 \end{vmatrix} = 3.08 \text{ kN•m} \ ♦$$

2.68

Assume counterclockwise couples are positive.

(a) $C = -10(0.6) = -6$ N•m

(b) $C = -6$ N•m

(c) $C = -15(0.4) = -6$ N•m

(d) $C = -6$ N•m

(e) $C = 9 - 3 = 6$ N•m

(f) $C = -5(0.6) - 7.5(0.4) = -6$ N•m

(g) $C = -22.5(0.4) + 5(0.6) = -6$ N•m

(h) $C = -5 + 5(0.3) = -3.5$ N•m

(i) $C = 3 - 4 - 6 + 3 = -4$ N•m

Comparing the above results, (b), (c), (d), (f) and (g) are equivalent to (a). ♦

2.69

(a) $\mathbf{C} = -60(5)\mathbf{k} = -300\mathbf{k}$ lb•ft

(b) $\mathbf{C} = -75(4)\mathbf{k} = -300\mathbf{k}$ lb•ft

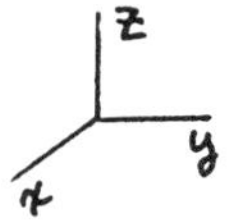

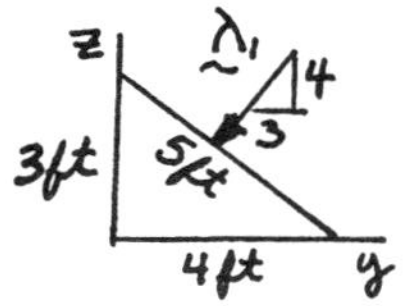

(c) $\mathbf{C}_1 = 75(5)\vec{\lambda}_1 = 375\left(-\frac{3}{5}\mathbf{j} - \frac{4}{5}\mathbf{k}\right) = -225\mathbf{j} - 300\mathbf{k}$ lb•ft

(d) $\mathbf{C} = 100(3)\mathbf{i} = 300\mathbf{i}$ lb•ft

(e) 75-lb forces: $\mathbf{C}_1 = -225\mathbf{j} - 300\mathbf{k}$ lb•ft [as in (c)]

45-lb forces: $\mathbf{C}_2 = 45(5)\mathbf{j} = 225\mathbf{j}$ lb•ft

$\mathbf{C}_1 + \mathbf{C}_2 = -300\mathbf{k}$ lb•ft

(continued)

(f) 45-lb forces: $\mathbf{C}_3 = 45(4)\mathbf{i} = 180\mathbf{i}$ lb•ft

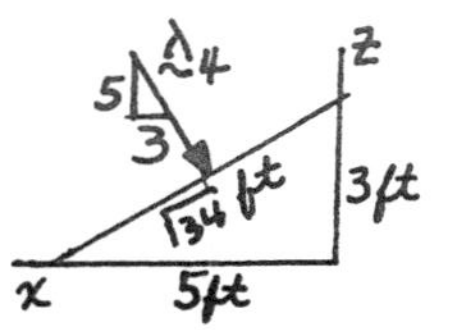

50-lb forces: $\mathbf{C}_4 = 50\left(\sqrt{34}\right)\vec{\lambda}_4$

$$= 50\left(\sqrt{34}\right)\left(\frac{-3\mathbf{i}-5\mathbf{k}}{\sqrt{34}}\right) = -150\mathbf{i} - 250\mathbf{k} \text{ lb•ft}$$

$$\mathbf{C}_3 + \mathbf{C}_4 = 30\mathbf{i} - 250\mathbf{k} \text{ lb•ft}$$

Comparing the above results: (b) and (e) are equivalent to (a). ♦

2.70

(a) The possibilities for the smallest forces are: (1) two forces that act through A and C and are perpendicular to the line AC; or (2) two forces that act through B and D and are perpendicular to the line BD. For either case, the perpendicular distance betwen the forces is: $d = \sqrt{1.2^2 + 1.6^2} = 2$ m. Therefore, $F = \dfrac{80}{2} = 40$ kN ♦

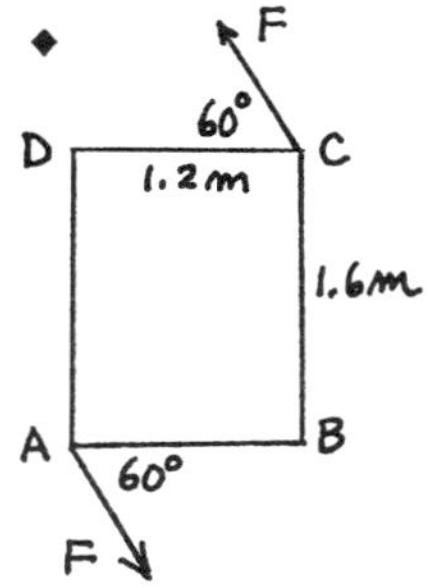

(b) Using the figure at the right,

$$\circlearrowleft + \quad \Sigma M_A = F\sin 60^\circ(1.2) + F\cos 60^\circ(1.6) = 80$$

which gives F = 43.5 kN ♦

2.71

$$\mathbf{C}_1 = 200\vec{\lambda}_{GA} = 200\left(\frac{-6\mathbf{i}-4\mathbf{j}+3\mathbf{k}}{7.810}\right) = -153.65\mathbf{i} - 102.43\mathbf{j} + 76.82\mathbf{k} \text{ N•m}$$

$$\mathbf{C}_2 = 300\vec{\lambda}_{GE} = 300\left(\frac{-4\mathbf{j}+3\mathbf{k}}{5}\right) = -240\mathbf{j} + 180\mathbf{k} \text{ N•m}$$

$$\mathbf{M}_A = \mathbf{C}_1 + \mathbf{C}_2 = -153.65\mathbf{i} - 342.43\mathbf{j} + 256.82\mathbf{k} \text{ N•m}$$

$$\therefore\ M_A = \sqrt{(-153.65)^2 + (-342.43)^2 + 256.82^2} = 455 \text{ N•m} \ ♦$$

(continued)

$$\vec{\lambda}_{GB} = \frac{-6\mathbf{i}+3\mathbf{k}}{6.708} = -0.8944\mathbf{i} + 0.4472\mathbf{k}$$

$$M_{GB} = \mathbf{M}_A \bullet \vec{\lambda}_{GB} = (-153.65\mathbf{i} - 342.43\mathbf{j} + 256.82\mathbf{k}) \bullet (-0.8944\mathbf{i} + 0.4472\mathbf{k})$$

$$= -153.65(-0.8944) + 256.82(0.4472) = 252 \text{ N•m} \ ♦$$

2.72

$$\mathbf{C}_1 = 200\left(\frac{-2\mathbf{i}-5\mathbf{j}+3\mathbf{k}}{6.164}\right) = -64.89\mathbf{i} - 162.23\mathbf{j} + 97.33\mathbf{k} \text{ lb•ft}$$

$\mathbf{C}_2 = 60(2)\mathbf{k} = 120\mathbf{k}$ lb•ft $\qquad \mathbf{C}_3 = -30(5)\mathbf{i} = -150\mathbf{i}$ lb•ft

$$\mathbf{C}^R = \mathbf{C}_1 + \mathbf{C}_2 + \mathbf{C}_3 = -214.89\mathbf{i} - 162.23\mathbf{j} + 217.33\mathbf{k} \text{ lb•ft}$$

$$\therefore\ C^R = \sqrt{(-214.89)^2 + (-162.23)^2 + 217.33^2} = 346 \text{ lb•ft} \ ♦$$

2.73

$$\mathbf{C} = 80\vec{\lambda}_{DB} = 80\left(\frac{0.4\mathbf{i}-0.3\mathbf{j}+0.4\mathbf{k}}{0.6403}\right) = 49.98\mathbf{i} - 37.48\mathbf{j} + 49.98\mathbf{k} \text{ N•m}$$

$\mathbf{P} = -400\mathbf{k}$ N $\qquad \mathbf{r}_{AD} = -0.4\mathbf{i}$ m $\qquad \vec{\lambda}_{AB} = \dfrac{-0.3\mathbf{j}+0.4\mathbf{k}}{0.5} = -0.6\mathbf{j} + 0.8\mathbf{k}$

<u>For Couple C</u>:

$$M_{AB} = \mathbf{C} \bullet \vec{\lambda}_{AB} = (49.98\mathbf{i} - 37.48\mathbf{j} + 49.98\mathbf{k}) \bullet (-0.6\mathbf{j} + 0.8\mathbf{k})$$

$$= (-37.48)(-0.6) + (49.98)(0.8) = 62.47 \text{ N•m}$$

<u>For Force P</u>:

$$M_{AB} = \mathbf{r}_{AD} \times \mathbf{P} \bullet \vec{\lambda}_{AB} = \begin{vmatrix} -0.4 & 0 & 0 \\ 0 & 0 & -400 \\ 0 & -0.6 & 0.8 \end{vmatrix} = -0.4(-240) = 96.00 \text{ N•m}$$

$$\therefore\ \Sigma M_{AB} = 62.47 + 96.00 = 158.5 \text{ N•m} \ ♦$$

*2.74

$C_1 = -200\mathbf{i}$ lb•in. $\quad C_2 = 140\mathbf{k}$ lb•in.

Identify the three points at the corners of the triangle:

A(9 in., 3 in., 6 in.); B(3 in., 7 in., 6 in.); C(9 in., 7 in., 2 in.)

$C_3 = 220\,\vec{\lambda}$ lb•in. where $\vec{\lambda}$ is the unit vector that is perpendicular to triangle ABC, with its sense consistent with the sense of C_3.

$$\vec{\lambda} = \frac{\overrightarrow{AC} \times \overrightarrow{AB}}{\left|\overrightarrow{AC} \times \overrightarrow{AB}\right|} \quad \text{where } \overrightarrow{AC} = 4\mathbf{j} - 4\mathbf{k} \text{ in. and } \overrightarrow{AB} = -6\mathbf{i} + 4\mathbf{j} \text{ in.}$$

$$\overrightarrow{AC} \times \overrightarrow{AB} = \begin{vmatrix} \mathbf{i} & \mathbf{j} & \mathbf{k} \\ 0 & 4 & -4 \\ -6 & 4 & 0 \end{vmatrix} = 16\mathbf{i} + 24\mathbf{j} + 24\mathbf{k} \text{ in.}^2$$

$$\therefore \vec{\lambda} = \frac{16\mathbf{i} + 24\mathbf{j} + 24\mathbf{k}}{37.52} = 0.4264\mathbf{i} + 0.6397\mathbf{j} + 0.6397\mathbf{k}$$

$$C_3 = 220(0.4264\mathbf{i} + 0.6397\mathbf{j} + 0.6397\mathbf{k}) = 93.81\mathbf{i} + 140.73\mathbf{j} + 140.73\mathbf{k} \text{ lb•in.}$$

$$\therefore C^R = C_1 + C_2 + C_3 = -200\mathbf{i} + 140\mathbf{k} + (93.81\mathbf{i} + 140.73\mathbf{j} + 140.73\mathbf{k})$$

$$= -106.2\mathbf{i} + 140.7\mathbf{j} + 280.7\mathbf{k} \text{ lb•in.} \quad \blacklozenge$$

2.75

(a) For the largest couple, place bolts at A and D (maximum moment arm). ◆

(b) $C = P(\overline{AD}) \quad P = 40$ N $\quad \overline{AD} = \sqrt{0.09^2 + 0.120^2} = 0.150$ m

$\therefore C = 40(0.150) = 6.00$ N•m ◆

2.76

$C = 20(12) = 240$ lb•in.

$\therefore \mathbf{M}_x = \mathbf{C}_x = -240 \sin 60^\circ \mathbf{i} = -208\mathbf{i}$ lb•in. ◆

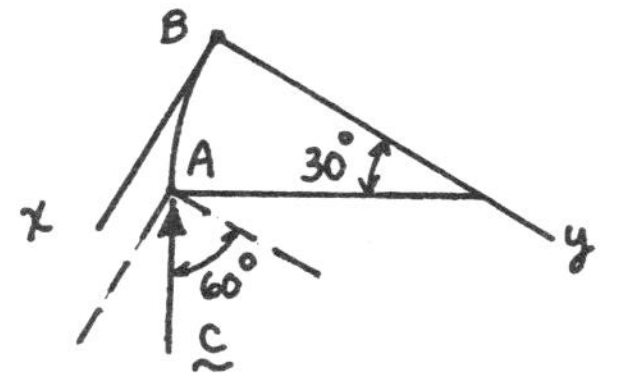

2.77

(a) (+) $C = P \sin\theta\,(0.360) + P\cos\theta\,(0.420) = 10$ N•m

$$\therefore P = \frac{10}{0.360\sin\theta + 0.420\cos\theta} \text{ N} \quad \blacklozenge$$

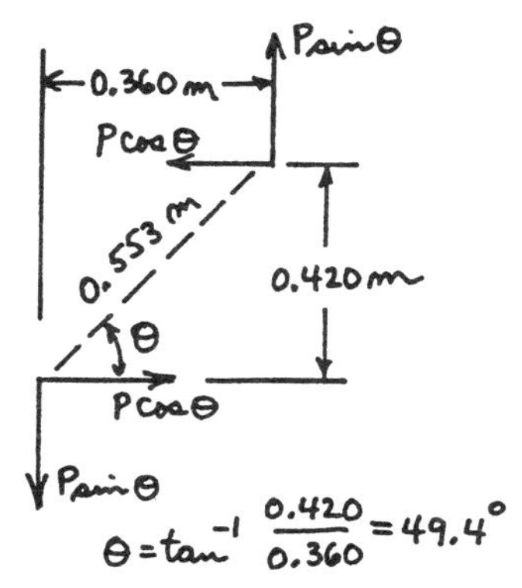

(b)

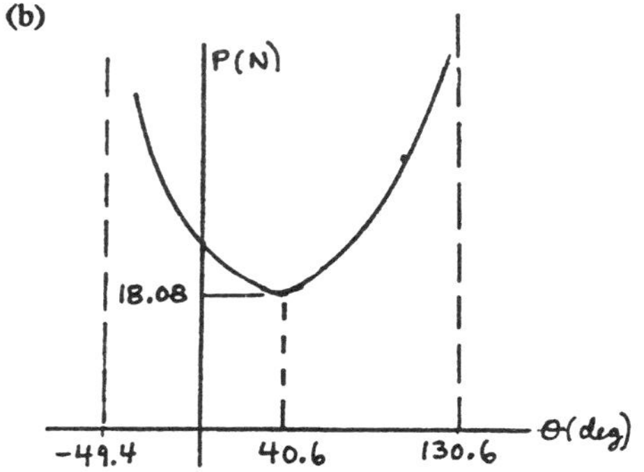

$$P_{min} = \frac{10}{0.553} = 18.08 \text{ N at } \theta = 40.6^\circ$$

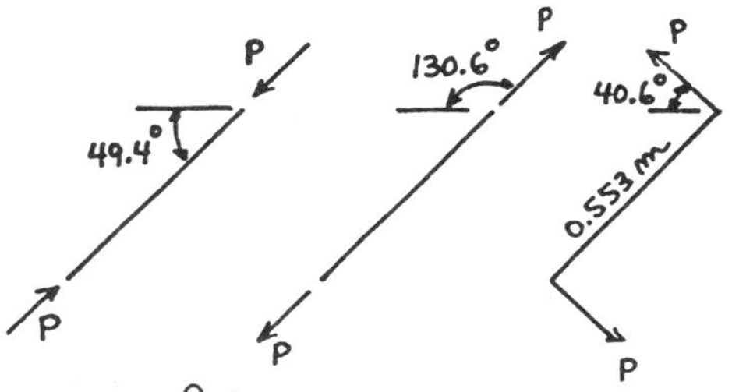

Extremum cases

2.78

$C = -360\cos 30^\circ \mathbf{i} - 360 \sin 30^\circ \mathbf{j} = -311.8\mathbf{i} - 180.0\mathbf{j}$ lb•ft

$\vec{\lambda}_{CD} = -\cos 30^\circ \mathbf{i} - \sin 30^\circ \cos 40^\circ \mathbf{j} + \sin 30^\circ \sin 40^\circ \mathbf{k} = -0.8660\mathbf{i} - 0.3830\mathbf{j} + 0.3214\mathbf{k}$

$\therefore M_{CD} = \mathbf{C} \bullet \vec{\lambda}_{CD} = (-311.8)(-0.8660) + (-180.0)(-0.3830) = 339$ lb•ft ◆

2.79

$\vec{\lambda}_{DC} = \sin 30^\circ \sin 40^\circ \mathbf{i} - \sin 30^\circ \cos 40^\circ \mathbf{j} + \cos 30^\circ \mathbf{k} = 0.3214\mathbf{i} - 0.3830\mathbf{j} + 0.8660\mathbf{k}$

(a) $\mathbf{C} = 52\,\vec{\lambda}_{DC} = 16.71\mathbf{i} - 19.92\mathbf{j} + 45.03\mathbf{k}$ lb•ft ◆

(b) $M_z = C_z = 45.03\mathbf{k}$ lb•ft ◆

2.80

$\mathbf{C}_P = 600(6)\mathbf{i} = 3600\mathbf{i}$ lb•in.

$\mathbf{C}_0 = -C_0 \cos 30^\circ \mathbf{i} + C_0 \sin 30^\circ \mathbf{k}$

$= -0.8660C_0\mathbf{i} + 0.5000C_0\mathbf{k}$ lb•in.

$\mathbf{C}_R = -2R\sin 30^\circ \mathbf{i} - 2R\cos 30^\circ \mathbf{k}$

$= -R\mathbf{i} - 1.7321R\mathbf{k}$ lb•in.

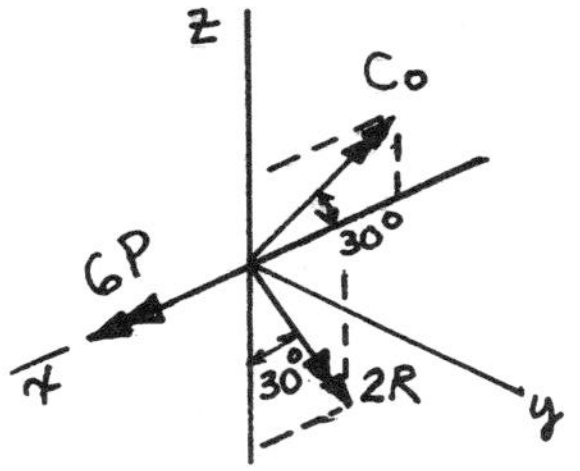

$\therefore\ \Sigma\mathbf{C} = 3600\mathbf{i} + (-0.8660C_0\mathbf{i} + 0.5000C_0\mathbf{k}) + (-R\mathbf{i} - 1.7321R\mathbf{k}) = \mathbf{0}$

Equating like components: (i) $3600 - 0.8660C_0 - R = 0$

(k) $0.5000C_0 - 1.7321R = 0$

Solving gives: $R = 900$ lb ◆ and $C_0 = 3120$ lb•in. ◆

2.81

The system consists of the four couples:

(1) $-1.800\mathbf{k}$ N•m

(2) $-1.800\mathbf{k}$ N•m

(3) $\mathbf{C} = C\cos\theta\,\mathbf{i} + C\sin\theta\,\mathbf{k}$ N•m

(where $C = 0.360F$ N•m)

(4) $-3\cos 25^\circ\mathbf{i} + 3\sin 25^\circ\mathbf{k} =$

$-2.719\mathbf{i} + 1.268\mathbf{k}$ N•m

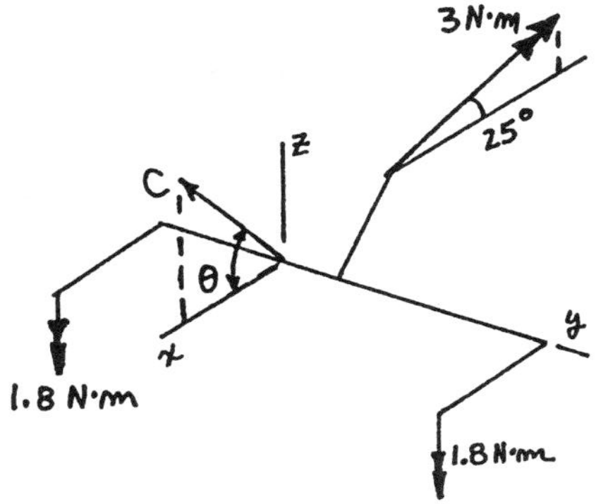

$\Sigma\mathbf{C} = -1.800\mathbf{k} - 1.800\mathbf{k} + (C\cos\theta\,\mathbf{i} + C\sin\theta\,\mathbf{k}) + (-2.719\mathbf{i} + 1.268\mathbf{k}) = \mathbf{0}$

Equating like components: $C\cos\theta - 2.719 = 0$ $[C\cos\theta = 2.719$ (i)$]$

$-3.600 + C\sin\theta + 1.268 = 0$ $[C\sin\theta = 2.332$ (ii)$]$

(continued)

Dividing (ii) by (i) gives $\theta = \tan^{-1}\left(\dfrac{2.332}{2.719}\right) = 40.6^\circ$ ◆

From (i) we find $C = \dfrac{2.719}{\cos 40.6^\circ} = 0.360F$ $\therefore F = 9.95$ N ◆

2.82

Represent each of the systems by an eqivalent force-couple system with the force acting at the upper left corner of the figure.

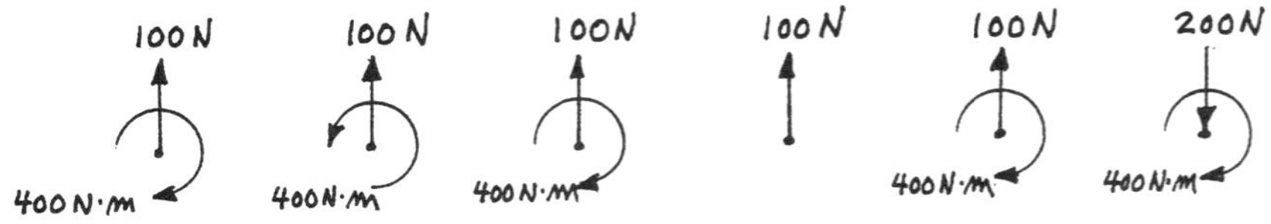

(a) (b) (c) (d) (e) (f)

By inspection, the systems in (c) and (e) are equivalent to the system in (a). ◆

2.83

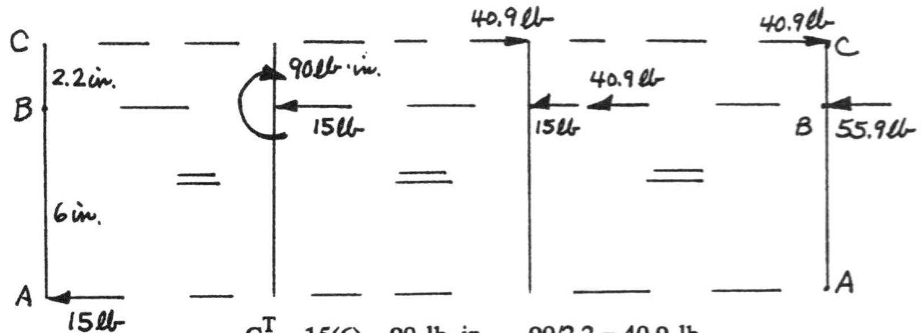

$C^T = 15(6) = 90$ lb•in. $90/2.2 = 40.9$ lb

Original system — (i) Equivalent system with force at B. — (ii) Equivalent system: one force at B and one force at C.

(a) Fig. (i): A 15-lb force acting to the left at B, and a 90 lb-in. clockwise couple. ◆

(b) Fig. (ii): A 55.9-lb force acting to the left at B, and a 40.9-lb force acting to the right at C. ◆

2.84

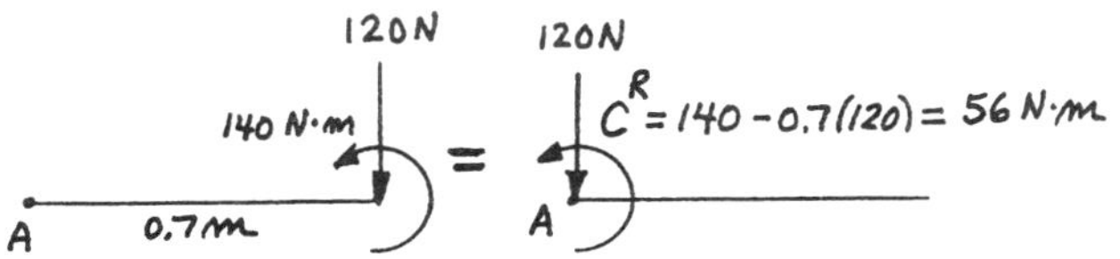

(a) From above figure: a 120-N downward force at A, and a 56 N•m CCW couple. ◆

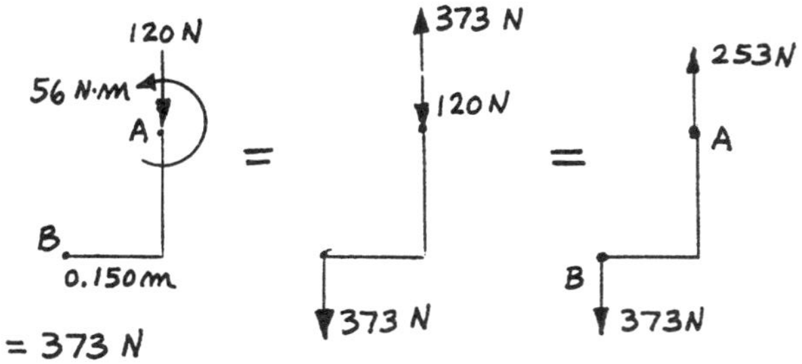

$$\frac{56}{0.150} = 373 \text{ N}$$

(b) From above figure: a 253-N upward force at A, and a 373-N downward force at B. ◆

2.85

Moving the three forces to A:

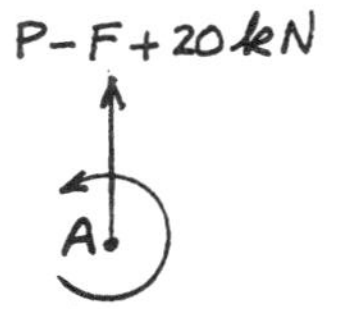

$$C^R = 2P - 5F + 7(20) \text{ kN·m}$$

Therefore,

$$P - F + 20 = 50 \text{ N} \qquad (1)$$

$$2P - 5F + 140 = 170 \text{ kN•m} \qquad (2)$$

Solving (1) and (2) gives

$P = 40$ kN and $F = 10$ kN ◆

2.86

Move the two forces to O.

$$\mathbf{R} = 50\cos 60^\circ \mathbf{i} - (90 + 50\sin 60^\circ)\mathbf{j}$$

$$= 25\mathbf{i} - 133.3\mathbf{j} \text{ lb}$$

$$C^R = 4T_2 - 2T_1 = 4(50) - 2(90) = 20 \text{ lb•in.}$$

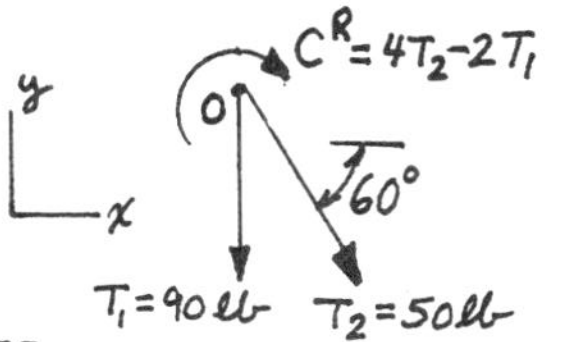

Therefore, the force-couple system with the force acting at O is -- Force: $25\mathbf{i} - 133.3\mathbf{j}$ lb; Couple: 20 lb•in. clockwise ◆

2.87

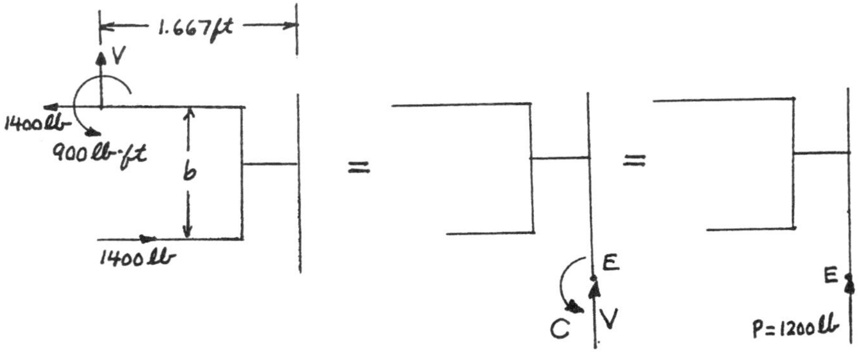

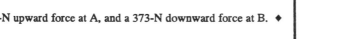

(a) Original system (b) Move force system as shown (c) Final system

Compare Figs. (b) and (c): Force: $V = P = 1200$ lb

Couple : $C = 900 + 1400b - V(1.667) = M_E = 0$

$$\therefore\ b = \frac{1200(1.667) - 900}{1400} = 0.7860 \text{ ft} = 9.43 \text{ in.} ◆$$

2.88

Transferring force from O to A gives

force = 100 **k** N ◆

$(C^T)_x = 60$ N•m; $(C^T)_y = -50$ N•m

$\therefore\ \mathbf{C}^R = 60\,\mathbf{i} - 50\,\mathbf{j}$ N•m ◆

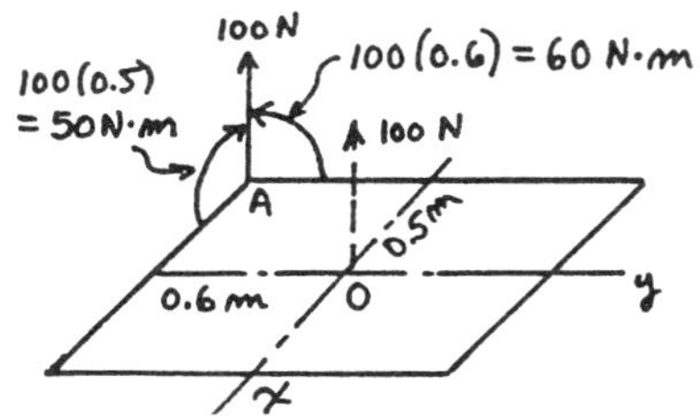

2.89

The force acting at O equals **F**, and the couple equals the moment about O.

$$\mathbf{F} = 160\,\vec{\lambda}_{AB} = 160\left(\frac{-2.2\mathbf{i} + 2.0\mathbf{j} - 2.0\mathbf{k}}{3.583}\right) = -98.24\mathbf{i} + 89.31\mathbf{j} - 89.31\mathbf{k} \text{ kN} ◆$$

$$\mathbf{C}^R = \mathbf{M}_O = \mathbf{r}_{OB} \times \mathbf{F} = \begin{vmatrix} \mathbf{i} & \mathbf{j} & \mathbf{k} \\ 0 & 2 & 0 \\ -98.24 & 89.31 & -89.31 \end{vmatrix} = -178.6\mathbf{i} + 196.5\mathbf{k} \text{ kN•m} ◆$$

2.90

The force acting at O equals **P**.

$$\mathbf{P} = 200\,\vec{\lambda}_{AB} = 200\left(\frac{-6\mathbf{i}+4\mathbf{k}}{\sqrt{52}}\right) = -166.41\mathbf{i} + 110.94\mathbf{k}\ \text{lb}$$

The couple $\mathbf{C}^R$ equals the combined moment of **C** and **P** about O.

For **C**: $\mathbf{M}_O = \mathbf{C} = 1200\,\vec{\lambda}_{AO} = 1200\left(\frac{-6\mathbf{i}-8\mathbf{j}}{10}\right) = -720\mathbf{i} - 960\mathbf{j}\ \text{lb}\bullet\text{ft}$

For **P**: $\mathbf{M}_O = \mathbf{r}_{OA}\times\mathbf{P}$ $\quad \mathbf{r}_{OA} = 4\mathbf{i}+8\mathbf{j}$ ft

$$\mathbf{M}_O = \mathbf{r}_{OA}\times\mathbf{P} = \begin{vmatrix} \mathbf{i} & \mathbf{j} & \mathbf{k} \\ 4 & 8 & 0 \\ -166.41 & 0 & 110.94 \end{vmatrix} = 887.5\mathbf{i} - 443.8\mathbf{j} + 1332\mathbf{k}\ \text{lb}\bullet\text{ft}$$

$$\therefore\ \mathbf{C}^R = (-720\mathbf{i}-960\mathbf{j}) + (887.5\mathbf{i} - 443.8\mathbf{j} + 1332\mathbf{k}) = 167.5\mathbf{i} - 1404\mathbf{j} + 1332\mathbf{k}\ \text{lb}\bullet\text{ft}$$

The equivalent force-couple system with the force acting at O is:

Force: $-166.41\mathbf{i} + 110.94\mathbf{k}$ lb; Couple: $167.5\mathbf{i} - 1404\mathbf{j} + 1332\mathbf{k}$ lb•ft ◆

* 2.91

(a) $\mathbf{R} = \mathbf{F} = 2500\mathbf{i} + 4000\mathbf{j} + 3000\mathbf{k}$ lb ◆

$$\mathbf{C}^R = \mathbf{r}_{OA}\times\mathbf{P} = \begin{vmatrix} \mathbf{i} & \mathbf{j} & \mathbf{k} \\ 10 & 5 & -4 \\ 2500 & 4000 & 3000 \end{vmatrix} = 31{,}000\mathbf{i} - 40{,}000\mathbf{j} + 27{,}500\mathbf{k}\ \text{lb}\bullet\text{in.}\ ◆$$

(b) Normal component of force: $P = R_y = 4000$ lb ◆

Shear component of force: $V = \sqrt{R_x^2 + R_z^2} = \sqrt{2500^2 + 3000^2} = 3910$ lb ◆

(c) Torque: $T = C_y^R = 40{,}000$ lb•in. ◆

Bending component: $M = \sqrt{(C_x^R)^2 + (C_z^R)^2} = \sqrt{31{,}000^2 + 27{,}500^2} = 41{,}400$ lb•in. ◆

2.92

$$\vec{\lambda}_{DC} = \sin 30^\circ \sin 40^\circ\,\mathbf{i} - \sin 30^\circ \cos 40^\circ\,\mathbf{j} + \cos 30^\circ\,\mathbf{k}$$
$$= 0.3214\mathbf{i} - 0.3830\mathbf{j} + 0.8660\mathbf{k}$$

The force at O equals the original force:

(continued)

$$\mathbf{F} = 9.8\,\vec{\lambda}_{DC} = 9.8(0.3214\mathbf{i} - 0.3830\mathbf{j} + 0.8660\mathbf{k}) = 3.150\mathbf{i} - 3.753\mathbf{j} + 8.487\mathbf{k}\ \text{lb}$$

The given couple is:

$$\mathbf{C} = 52\,\vec{\lambda}_{DC} = 52(0.3214\mathbf{i} - 0.3830\mathbf{j} + 0.8660\mathbf{k}) = 16.71\mathbf{i} - 19.92\mathbf{j} + 45.03\mathbf{k}\ \text{lb}\bullet\text{ft}$$

Moving the force to O, and letting $\mathbf{C}^R$ be the resultant couple, we have: $\mathbf{C}^R = \mathbf{C} + \mathbf{M}_O$

$\mathbf{M}_O = \mathbf{r}_{OD}\times\mathbf{F}$ $\qquad \mathbf{r}_{OD} = -4.2\sin 40^\circ\,\mathbf{i} + 4.2\cos 40^\circ\,\mathbf{j} + 2.800\mathbf{k}$

$= -2.700\mathbf{i} + 3.217\mathbf{j} + 2.800\mathbf{k}$ ft

$$\mathbf{M}_O = \begin{vmatrix} \mathbf{i} & \mathbf{j} & \mathbf{k} \\ -2.700 & 3.217 & 2.800 \\ 3.150 & -3.753 & 8.487 \end{vmatrix} = 37.81\mathbf{i} + 31.73\mathbf{j}\ \text{lb}\bullet\text{ft}$$

$$\therefore\ \mathbf{C}^R = \mathbf{C} + \mathbf{M}_O = (16.71\mathbf{i} - 19.92\mathbf{j} + 45.03\mathbf{k}) + (37.81\mathbf{i} + 31.73\mathbf{j})$$
$$= 54.52\mathbf{i} + 11.81\mathbf{j} + 45.03\mathbf{k}\ \text{lb}\bullet\text{ft}$$

The equivalent force-couple system with the force acting at O is:

Force: $3.150\mathbf{i} - 3.753\mathbf{j} + 8.487\mathbf{k}$ lb; Couple: $54.52\mathbf{i} + 11.81\mathbf{j} + 45.03\mathbf{k}$ lb•ft ◆

2.93

The force at O equals the original force:

$$\mathbf{F} = 140\,\vec{\lambda}_{AC} = 140\left(\frac{-1.5\mathbf{i}+2.0\mathbf{j}}{2.50}\right) = -84.0\mathbf{i} + 112.0\mathbf{j}\ \text{N}\ ◆$$

The original couple is: $\mathbf{C} = 220\,\vec{\lambda}_{AB} = 220\left(\frac{-1.5\mathbf{i}+2.0\mathbf{k}}{2.50}\right) = -132.0\mathbf{i} + 176.0\mathbf{k}$ N•m

When the force is moved to O, the resultant couple is: $\mathbf{C}^R = \mathbf{C} + \mathbf{M}_O$

where $\mathbf{M}_O = \mathbf{r}_{OA}\times\mathbf{F}$ and $\mathbf{r}_{OA} = 1.5\mathbf{i}$ m

$$\mathbf{M}_O = \mathbf{r}_{OA}\times\mathbf{F} = \begin{vmatrix} \mathbf{i} & \mathbf{j} & \mathbf{k} \\ 1.5 & 0 & 0 \\ -84.0 & 112.0 & 0 \end{vmatrix} = 168.0\mathbf{k}\ \text{N}\bullet\text{m}$$

$$\therefore\ \mathbf{C}^R = \mathbf{C} + \mathbf{M}_O = (-132.0\mathbf{i} + 176.0\mathbf{k}) + 168.0\mathbf{k} = -132\mathbf{i} + 344\mathbf{k}\ \text{N}\bullet\text{m}\ ◆$$

2.94

$\mathbf{M}_{AB} = \mathbf{r}_{AO} \times \mathbf{P} \bullet \vec{\lambda}_{AB} = 600 \text{ lb}\bullet\text{ft}$

$\mathbf{r}_{AO} = -8\mathbf{j} \text{ ft} \qquad \mathbf{P} = P\cos 20^\circ \mathbf{i} + P\sin 20^\circ \mathbf{k} \qquad \vec{\lambda}_{AB} = -\cos 30^\circ \mathbf{i} + \sin 30^\circ \mathbf{k}$

$$\therefore M_{AB} = \begin{vmatrix} 0 & -8 & 0 \\ P\cos 20^\circ & 0 & P\sin 20^\circ \\ -\cos 30^\circ & 0 & \sin 30^\circ \end{vmatrix} = 8(P\cos 20^\circ \sin 30^\circ + P\sin 20^\circ \cos 30^\circ) = 600 \text{ lb}\bullet\text{ft}$$

Solving for P gives: $P = 97.9$ lb ◆

2.95

$\mathbf{C}_1 = 220\,\vec{\lambda}_{AC} = 220\left(\dfrac{-6\mathbf{i} + 8\mathbf{j}}{10}\right) = -132\mathbf{i} + 176\mathbf{j} \text{ N}\bullet\text{m}$

$\mathbf{C}_2 = 180\,\vec{\lambda}_{BD} = 180\left(\dfrac{-3\mathbf{i} - 4\mathbf{j} + 8\mathbf{k}}{\sqrt{89}}\right) = -57.24\mathbf{i} - 76.32\mathbf{j} + 152.64\mathbf{k} \text{ N}\bullet\text{m}$

which gives $\mathbf{C}_1 + \mathbf{C}_2 = -189.24\mathbf{i} + 99.68\mathbf{j} + 152.64\mathbf{k} \text{ N}\bullet\text{m}$

$M_{AD} = (\mathbf{C}_1 + \mathbf{C}_2)\bullet\vec{\lambda}_{AD} = (-189.24\mathbf{i} + 99.68\mathbf{j} + 152.64\mathbf{k})\bullet(-0.6\mathbf{i} + 0.8\mathbf{k})$

$= (-189.24)(-0.6) + 152.64(0.8) = 235.7 \text{ N}\bullet\text{m}$

Written in vector form,

$\mathbf{M}_{AD} = 235.7\,\vec{\lambda}_{AD} = 235.7(-0.6\,\mathbf{i} + 0.8\,\mathbf{k}) = -141.4\mathbf{i} + 188.6\mathbf{k} \text{ N}\bullet\text{m}$ ◆

2.96

$\mathbf{T}_1 = T_1\,\vec{\lambda}_{AB} = T_1\left(\dfrac{-10\mathbf{j} - 12\mathbf{k}}{\sqrt{244}}\right) = T_1(-0.6402\mathbf{j} - 0.7682\mathbf{k})$

$\mathbf{T}_2 = T_2\,\vec{\lambda}_{AC} = T_2\left(\dfrac{6\mathbf{i} - 12\mathbf{k}}{\sqrt{180}}\right) = T_2(0.4472\mathbf{i} - 0.8944\mathbf{k})$

$\mathbf{T}_3 = T_3\,\vec{\lambda}_{AD} = T_3\left(\dfrac{-4\mathbf{i} + 3\mathbf{j} - 12\mathbf{k}}{13}\right) = T_3(-0.3077\mathbf{i} + 0.2308\mathbf{j} - 0.9231\mathbf{k})$

$\mathbf{R} = \mathbf{T}_1 + \mathbf{T}_2 + \mathbf{T}_3$ Equating like components gives:

(i-components) $\quad 0.4472T_2 - 0.3077T_3 = 0$

(j-components) $\quad -0.6402T_1 \quad 0.2308T_3 = 0$

(k-components) $\quad -0.7682T_1 - 0.8944T_2 - 0.9231T_3 = -400$

Solving yields: $T_1 = 79.4$ N; $T_2 = 151.6$ N; $T_3 = 220.3$ N ◆

2.97

Letting point O be the origin of the rectangular coordinate system, we have

$\mathbf{M}_O = M_x\mathbf{i} + 400\mathbf{j} + M_z\mathbf{k} = \mathbf{r}_{OA} \times \mathbf{F} \qquad (\mathbf{r}_{OA} = x\mathbf{i} + 3\mathbf{j} + 5\mathbf{k} \text{ m})$

$$\therefore \mathbf{M}_O = M_x\mathbf{i} + 400\mathbf{j} + M_z\mathbf{k} = \begin{vmatrix} \mathbf{i} & \mathbf{j} & \mathbf{k} \\ x & 3 & 5 \\ 20 & -30 & -60 \end{vmatrix}$$

Expanding the determinant, and equating like components gives

(i-components) $\quad M_x = -30 \qquad M_x = -30\mathbf{i} \text{ N}\bullet\text{m}$ ◆

(j-components) $\quad 400 = 60x + 100 \qquad x = 5.00 \text{ m}$ ◆

(k-components) $\quad M_z = -30x - 60 \qquad M_z = -210\mathbf{k} \text{ N}\bullet\text{m}$ ◆

2.98

$M_{CD} = \mathbf{r}_{CA} \times \mathbf{P} \bullet \vec{\lambda}_{CD} = 50 \text{ lb}\bullet\text{in.}$

$\mathbf{r}_{CA} = 6\mathbf{i} - 2\mathbf{j} \text{ in.} \qquad \mathbf{P} = P\vec{\lambda}_{AB} = P\left(\dfrac{-3\mathbf{i} - 2\mathbf{j} + 5\mathbf{k}}{\sqrt{38}}\right) \text{ lb} \qquad \vec{\lambda}_{CD} = \dfrac{-4\mathbf{j} + 5\mathbf{k}}{\sqrt{41}}$

Using the determinant form of the scalar triple product:

$$M_{CD} = \frac{P}{\sqrt{38}\sqrt{41}}\begin{vmatrix} 6 & -2 & 0 \\ -3 & -2 & 5 \\ 0 & -4 & 5 \end{vmatrix} = \frac{P}{\sqrt{38}\sqrt{41}}\left[6(-10 + 20) + 2(-15)\right] = 50 \text{ lb}\bullet\text{in.}$$

Solving for P gives: $P = \dfrac{50\sqrt{38}\sqrt{41}}{30} = 65.8$ lb ◆

2.99

The resultant couple is: (+ CCW) $C^R = \Sigma M_O = 400 + 120 - 320 = 200 \text{ N}\bullet\text{m}$ (CCW)

For the two forces shown at the right:

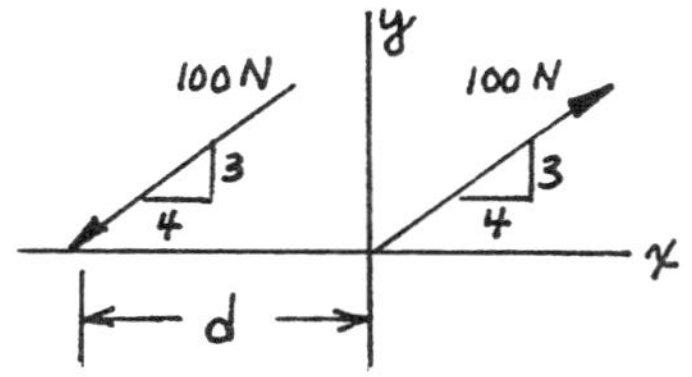

(+ CCW) $\Sigma M_O = 60d = 200 \text{ N}\bullet\text{m}$

$\therefore d = 3.33$ m

Therefore, the second force intersects the x axis at the point with coordinates are: (− 3.33 m, 0). ◆

2.100

(a) $\mathbf{M}_O = \mathbf{r}_{OA} \times \mathbf{P} + \mathbf{C}$

$\mathbf{r}_{OA} = 4\mathbf{k}$ ft $\quad \mathbf{P} = P\vec{\lambda}_{AB} = 500\left(\frac{3\mathbf{i} - 4\mathbf{k}}{5}\right) = 300\mathbf{i} - 400\mathbf{k}$ lb $\quad \mathbf{C} = 1200\mathbf{k}$ lb•ft

$$\therefore \mathbf{M}_O = \begin{vmatrix} \mathbf{i} & \mathbf{j} & \mathbf{k} \\ 0 & 0 & 4 \\ 300 & 0 & -400 \end{vmatrix} + 1200\mathbf{k} = 1200\mathbf{j} + 1200\mathbf{k} \text{ lb•ft} \ ◆$$

The magnitude of the moment about O is: $M_O = \sqrt{1200^2 + 1200^2} = 1697$ lb•ft

(b) $M_{OF} = \mathbf{M}_O \bullet \vec{\lambda}_{OF} = (1200\mathbf{j} + 1200\mathbf{k}) \bullet \left(\frac{3\mathbf{i} + 12\mathbf{j} + 4\mathbf{k}}{13}\right)$

$$= \frac{1200(12)}{13} + \frac{1200(4)}{13} = 1477 \text{ lb•ft} \ ◆$$

2.101

$\overset{+}{\rightarrow}\ R_x = \Sigma F_x = T_1 \sin 45^\circ - T_3 \sin 30^\circ = 0 \qquad (1)$

$+\uparrow\ R_y = \Sigma F_y = T_1 \cos 45^\circ + T_3 \cos 30^\circ + 300 = 500$ lb $\qquad (2)$

Solving (1) and (2) simultaneously gives: $T_1 = 103.5$ lb and $T_3 = 146.4$ lb ◆

2.102

(a) $\mathbf{F} \bullet \mathbf{C} = 200(-400) + 100(300) + 250(200) = 0$

Because **F** and **C** are perpendicular, they can be reduced to a single force. Q.E.D.

(b) Let A(x, y, 0) be the point in the xy plane where the combined moment of **F** and **C** is zero, and let O be the origin of the coordinate system. Since F acts at O, we have:

$\mathbf{M}_A = \mathbf{r}_{AO} \times \mathbf{F} + \mathbf{C} = \mathbf{0}$ (where $\mathbf{r}_{AO} = -x\mathbf{i} - y\mathbf{j}$ in.).

$$\therefore \mathbf{M}_A = \begin{vmatrix} \mathbf{i} & \mathbf{j} & \mathbf{k} \\ -x & -y & 0 \\ 200 & 100 & 250 \end{vmatrix} + (-400\mathbf{i} + 300\mathbf{j} + 200\mathbf{k})$$

$$= (-250y)\mathbf{i} + (250x)\mathbf{j} + (-100x + 200y)\mathbf{k} - 400\mathbf{i} + 300\mathbf{j} + 200\mathbf{k} = \mathbf{0}$$

(continued)

Equating the **i**- and **j**-components to zero gives:

$-250y - 400 = 0 \qquad 250x + 300 = 0$

$y = -1.60$ in. $\qquad x = -1.20$ in.

Check using **k**-components:

$-100(-1.2) + 200(-1.6) + 200 = 0$ it checks!

Therefore, the coordinates of point A are $(-1.2$ in., -1.6 in., $0)$ ◆

2.103

$\mathbf{P}_1 = 100\vec{\lambda}_{AO} = 100\left(\frac{-4\mathbf{i} - 3\mathbf{k}}{5}\right) = -80\mathbf{i} - 60\mathbf{k}$ N

$\mathbf{P}_2 = 500\vec{\lambda}_{DE} = 500\left(\frac{4\mathbf{i} + 3\mathbf{k}}{5}\right) = 400\mathbf{i} + 300\mathbf{k}$ N $\qquad \mathbf{P}_3 = 300\mathbf{j}$ N

$\mathbf{R} = \mathbf{P}_1 + \mathbf{P}_2 + \mathbf{P}_3 = 320\mathbf{i} + 300\mathbf{j} + 240\mathbf{k}$ N

$\therefore R = \sqrt{320^2 + 300^2 + 240^2} = 500$ N ◆

$\mathbf{C} = \Sigma \mathbf{M}_F = \mathbf{r}_{FO} \times \mathbf{P}_1 + \mathbf{r}_{FE} \times \mathbf{P}_2 \qquad \mathbf{r}_{FO} = -4\mathbf{i} - 8\mathbf{j}$ m $\qquad \mathbf{r}_{FE} = 3\mathbf{k}$ m

$$\mathbf{C} = \begin{vmatrix} \mathbf{i} & \mathbf{j} & \mathbf{k} \\ -4 & -8 & 0 \\ -80 & 0 & -60 \end{vmatrix} + \begin{vmatrix} \mathbf{i} & \mathbf{j} & \mathbf{k} \\ 0 & 0 & 3 \\ 400 & 0 & 300 \end{vmatrix} = (480\mathbf{i} - 240\mathbf{j} - 640\mathbf{k}) + 1200\mathbf{j}$$

$\therefore \mathbf{C} = 480\mathbf{i} + 960\mathbf{j} - 640\mathbf{k}$ N•m $\qquad \therefore C = \sqrt{480^2 + 960^2 + (-640)^2} = 1250$ N•m ◆

2.104

$\overset{+}{\rightarrow}\ R_x = \Sigma F_x = P - P = 0$

$+\uparrow\ R_y = \Sigma F_y = P$

Therfore, the force acting at A is R = P (acting upward) ◆

Because **R** passes through point A, the moment of the three forces about A is zero.

$\circlearrowleft{+}\ \Sigma M_A = P(L - x) - P(L/2) = 0$ which gives $x = L/2$ ◆

2.105

Because the resultant force passes through O and there is no resultant couple, the combined moment of the two forces about O is zero.

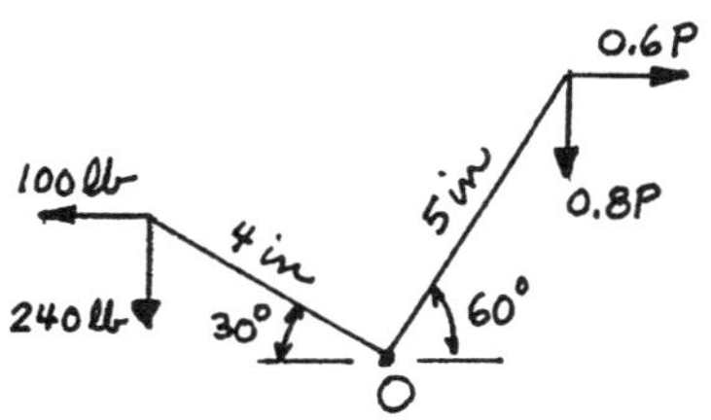

$\circlearrowleft + \; \Sigma M_O = 240(4\cos 30^\circ) + 100(4\sin 30^\circ) - 0.8P(5\cos 60^\circ) - 0.6P(5\sin 60^\circ) = 0$

Solving for P gives: P = 224 lb ♦

2.106

$\overrightarrow{BA} = -3\mathbf{i} - 3\cos 20^\circ \mathbf{j} + (4 - 3\sin 20^\circ)\mathbf{k} = -3\mathbf{i} - 2.819\mathbf{j} + 2.974\mathbf{k}$ lb

$\overrightarrow{CA} = 2\mathbf{i} - 2.819\mathbf{j} + 2.974\mathbf{k}$ lb

$$\mathbf{T}_1 = 30\vec{\lambda}_{BA} = 30\left(\frac{-3\mathbf{i} - 2.819\mathbf{j} + 2.974\mathbf{k}}{5.0785}\right) = -17.722\mathbf{i} - 16.653\mathbf{j} + 17.568\mathbf{k} \text{ lb}$$

$$\mathbf{T}_2 = 90\vec{\lambda}_{CA} = 90\left(\frac{2\mathbf{i} - 2.819\mathbf{j} + 2.974\mathbf{k}}{4.5600}\right) = 39.474\mathbf{i} - 55.638\mathbf{j} + 58.697\mathbf{k} \text{ lb}$$

$\mathbf{R} = \mathbf{T}_1 + \mathbf{T}_2 = 21.752\mathbf{i} - 72.291\mathbf{j} + 76.265\mathbf{k}$ lb

$\therefore \; R = \sqrt{21.752^2 + (-72.291)^2 + 76.265^2} = 107.3$ lb ♦

2.107

$\mathbf{P} = -300\mathbf{i} + 200\mathbf{j} + 150\mathbf{k}$ lb $\qquad \mathbf{C} = C\vec{\lambda}_{BE} = C(-0.6\mathbf{j} + 0.8\mathbf{k})$ lb•ft

$\mathbf{r}_{DA} = 3\mathbf{j}$ ft $\qquad \vec{\lambda}_{DE} = -0.6\mathbf{i} + 0.8\mathbf{k}$

<u>For **P**</u>: $M_{DE} = \mathbf{r}_{DA} \times \mathbf{P} \cdot \vec{\lambda}_{DE} = \begin{vmatrix} 0 & 3 & 0 \\ -300 & 200 & 150 \\ -0.6 & 0 & 0.8 \end{vmatrix} = -3(-240 + 90) = 450$ lb•ft

<u>For **C**</u>: $M_{DE} = \mathbf{C} \cdot \vec{\lambda}_{DE} = C(-0.6\mathbf{j} + 0.8\mathbf{k}) \cdot (-0.6\mathbf{i} + 0.8\mathbf{k}) = 0.640C$

<u>Combined moment of **P** and **C**</u>: $\Sigma M_{DE} = 450 + 0.640C = 800$ lb•ft

which gives: C = 547 lb•ft ♦

2.108

On AB: $\mathbf{C}_1 = -40(0.2)\mathbf{k} = -8\mathbf{k}$ N•m $\qquad$ On CD: $\mathbf{C}_2 = -P(0.4)\mathbf{k} = -0.4P\mathbf{k}$ N•m

For $\mathbf{C}_1 = \mathbf{C}_2$: $-8 = -0.4P$ which gives: P = 20 N ♦

3.1

Let point A be the point where the 10 lb force is applied in Fig. (a).

(a): $\overset{+}{\rightarrow} R_x = \Sigma F_x = 0.8(10) = 8$ lb ; $+\uparrow R_y = \Sigma F_y = 0.6(10) = 6$ lb ;

$\circlearrowleft + \; \Sigma M_A = -50$ lb•ft

(b): $\overset{+}{\rightarrow} R_x = \Sigma F_x = 8$ lb ; $+\uparrow R_y = \Sigma F_y = 10 - 4 = 6$ lb ;

$\circlearrowleft + \; \Sigma M_A = -10(5) = -50$ lb•ft

(c): $\overset{+}{\rightarrow} R_x = \Sigma F_x = 0.8(10) = 8$ lb ; $+\uparrow R_y = \Sigma F_y = 0.6(10) = 6$ lb ;

$\circlearrowleft + \; \Sigma M_A = -50 - 0.6(10)(1) = -56$ lb•ft

(d): $\overset{+}{\rightarrow} R_x = \Sigma F_x = 8$ lb ; $+\uparrow R_y = \Sigma F_y = 10 - 4 = 6$ lb ;

$\circlearrowleft + \; \Sigma M_A = -24 - 10(5) + 8(3) = -50$ lb•ft

(e): $\overset{+}{\rightarrow} R_x = \Sigma F_x = 8$ lb ; $+\uparrow R_y = \Sigma F_y = 6$ lb ;

$\circlearrowleft + \; \Sigma M_A = -80 - 6(5) + 36 + 8(3) = -50$ lb•ft

(f): $\overset{+}{\rightarrow} R_x = \Sigma F_x = 8$ lb ; $+\uparrow R_y = \Sigma F_y = 5$ lb ;

$\circlearrowleft + \; \Sigma M_A = -5(5) = -25$ lb•ft

Comparing the above results, we see that (b), (d), and (e) are equivalent to (a). ♦

3.2

(a) $R = \Sigma F_y$: $\quad +\uparrow \; R = 16 - 20 - 14 = -18$ kN

$C^R = \Sigma M_A$: $\circlearrowleft + \; C^R = -48 + 16(7) - 14(5) - 20(2) = -46$ kN•m

Therefore the equivalent force-couple system with the force acting at A is

R = − 18**j** kN; C^R = 46 kN•m CW ♦

(b) As in part (a), R = − 18 kN

$C^R = \Sigma M_B$: $\circlearrowleft + \; C^R = -48 + 14(2) + 20(5) = 80$ kN•m

Therefore the equivalent force-couple system with the force acting at B is

R = − 18**j** kN: C^R = 80 kN•m CCW ♦

3.3

$C^R = \Sigma M_C = 0 \quad \circlearrowleft\!+ \quad C^R = -48 + 16(7 - x) - 14(5 - x) + 20(x - 2) = 0$

Solving gives: $x = 2.56$ m ◆

3.4

$R = \Sigma F: \quad +\uparrow \quad R = 18 + 30 + 46 + 60 = 154$ lb

$C^R = \Sigma M_O: \quad \circlearrowleft\!+ \quad C^R = 60(3.2) - 46(3.5 - 3.2) - 30(8.0 - 3.2) - 18(11.5 - 3.2)$

$= -115.2$ lb•in.

Therefore, the equivalent force-couple system with the force acting at O is

$R = 154$ lb $\uparrow$; $C^R = 115.2$ lb•in. CW ◆

3.5

$R_x = \Sigma F_x: \quad \overset{+}{\rightarrow} \quad R_x = 300 - 210.67 = 89.3$ N

$R_y = \Sigma F_y: \quad +\uparrow \quad R_y = 561.80 + 400 = 961.8$ N

$C^R = \Sigma M_O: \quad \circlearrowleft\!+ \quad C^R = (561.80 + 400)(0.3) - 300(0.2)$

$= 228.54$ N•m

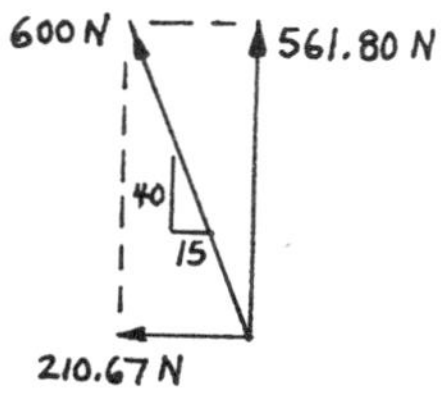

Therefore, the equivalent force-couple system with the force acting at O is

$\mathbf{R} = 89.3\mathbf{i} + 961.8\mathbf{j}$ N; $C^R = 228.5$ N•m CW ◆

3.6

$R_x = \Sigma F_x: \quad \overset{+}{\rightarrow} \quad 90 = P_x + 166.41 - 300$

$P_x = 223.6$ lb

$R_y = \Sigma F_y: \quad +\uparrow \quad 300 = P_y + 110.94 + 60$

$P_y = 129.1$ lb

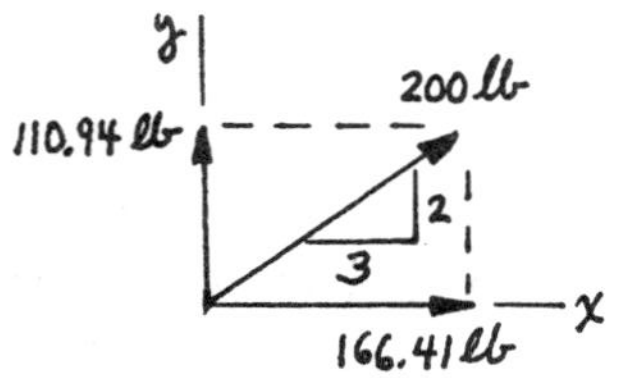

Therefore, the force **P** is: $\mathbf{P} = 223.6\mathbf{i} + 129.1\mathbf{j}$ lb ◆

$\Sigma M_O' = 0: \quad \circlearrowleft\!+ \quad 300(8) + 60(4) - 223.6y - 166.41(4) = 0$

Solving gives: $y = 8.83$ in. ◆

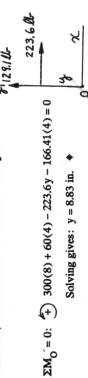

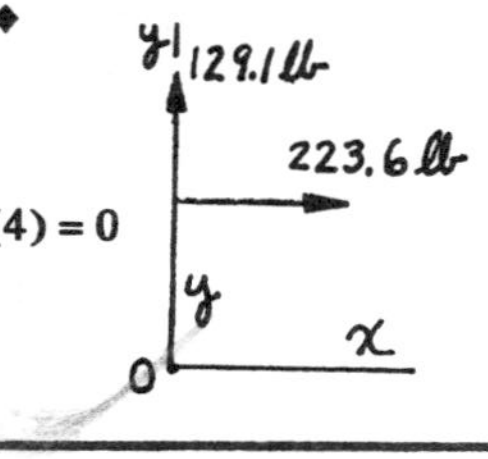

3.7

The force-couple system with the force acting at O is:

$\mathbf{R} = \Sigma\mathbf{F} = (20 + 40 + 50)\mathbf{k} = 110\mathbf{k}$ kN ◆

$\mathbf{C}^R = \Sigma\mathbf{M}_O = (4\mathbf{j} \times 50\mathbf{k}) + (3\mathbf{i} \times 20\mathbf{k}) = 200\mathbf{i} - 60\mathbf{j}$ kN•m ◆

3.8

$\mathbf{R} = \Sigma\mathbf{F} = (-320 + 200 + 240)\mathbf{k} = 120\mathbf{k}$ lb ◆

$\mathbf{C}^R = \Sigma\mathbf{M}_D = [\mathbf{r}_{DO} \times (-320\mathbf{k})] + (\mathbf{r}_{DB} \times 200\mathbf{k}) + (\mathbf{r}_{DA} \times 240\mathbf{k})$

$\mathbf{r}_{DO} = -6\cos 30^\circ\mathbf{i} - 6\sin 30^\circ\mathbf{j} = -5.196\mathbf{i} - 3.000\mathbf{j}$ ft

$\mathbf{r}_{DB} = -6\cos 30^\circ\mathbf{i} + (6 - 6\sin 30^\circ)\mathbf{j} = -5.196\mathbf{i} + 3.000\mathbf{j}$ ft

$\mathbf{r}_{DA} = (6 - 6\cos 30^\circ)\mathbf{i} - 6\sin 30^\circ\mathbf{j} = 0.8039\mathbf{i} - 3.000\mathbf{j}$ ft

$$\mathbf{C}^R = \begin{vmatrix} \mathbf{i} & \mathbf{j} & \mathbf{k} \\ -5.196 & -3.000 & 0 \\ 0 & 0 & -320 \end{vmatrix} + \begin{vmatrix} \mathbf{i} & \mathbf{j} & \mathbf{k} \\ -5.196 & 3.000 & 0 \\ 0 & 0 & 200 \end{vmatrix} + \begin{vmatrix} \mathbf{i} & \mathbf{j} & \mathbf{k} \\ 0.8039 & -3.000 & 0 \\ 0 & 0 & 240 \end{vmatrix}$$

$\therefore \mathbf{C}^R = (960\mathbf{i} - 1662\mathbf{j}) + (600\mathbf{i} + 1039\mathbf{j}) + (-720\mathbf{i} - 192.9\mathbf{j}) = 840\mathbf{i} - 815\mathbf{j}$ lb•ft ◆

3.9

$\mathbf{C}^R = \Sigma\mathbf{M}_D = \mathbf{0} = [\mathbf{r}_{DO} \times (-P\mathbf{k})] + (\mathbf{r}_{DB} \times 200\mathbf{k}) + (\mathbf{r}_{DA} \times 240\mathbf{k})$

$\mathbf{r}_{DO} = -6\cos\theta\mathbf{i} - 6\sin\theta\mathbf{j}$ ft $\qquad \mathbf{r}_{DB} = -6\cos\theta\mathbf{i} + (6 - 6\sin\theta)\mathbf{j}$ ft

$\mathbf{r}_{DA} = (6 - 6\cos\theta)\mathbf{i} - 6\sin\theta\mathbf{j}$ ft

$$\therefore \mathbf{C}^R = (6)\begin{vmatrix} \mathbf{i} & \mathbf{j} & \mathbf{k} \\ -\cos\theta & -\sin\theta & 0 \\ 0 & 0 & -P \end{vmatrix} + (6)\begin{vmatrix} \mathbf{i} & \mathbf{j} & \mathbf{k} \\ -\cos\theta & 1 - \sin\theta & 0 \\ 0 & 0 & 200 \end{vmatrix}$$

$$+ (6)\begin{vmatrix} \mathbf{i} & \mathbf{j} & \mathbf{k} \\ 1 - \cos\theta & -\sin\theta & 0 \\ 0 & 0 & 240 \end{vmatrix} = \mathbf{0}$$

(continued)

Expanding the determinants gives:

$$(P\sin\theta\mathbf{i} - P\cos\theta\mathbf{j}) + [200(1-\sin\theta)\mathbf{i} + 200\cos\theta\mathbf{j}] + [-240\sin\theta\mathbf{i} - 240(1-\cos\theta)\mathbf{j}] = 0$$

Equating like components and simplifying, we obtain:

(i-components): $P\sin\theta + 200 - 200\sin\theta - 240\sin\theta = 0$

which gives: $\sin\theta(P - 440) = -200$ lb (1)

(j-components): $-P\cos\theta + 200\cos\theta - 240 + 240\cos\theta = 0$

which gives: $\cos\theta(P - 440) = -240$ lb (2)

Dividing (1) by (2) yields: $\dfrac{\sin\theta}{\cos\theta} = \tan\theta = \dfrac{200}{240}$ $\therefore\ \theta = 39.8^{\circ}$ ◆

Using (1), we get: $P = -\dfrac{200}{\sin 39.8^{\circ}} + 440 = 127.6$ lb ◆

3.10

$\mathbf{R} = \Sigma\mathbf{F}$ and $\mathbf{C}^R = \Sigma\mathbf{M}_A$

(a) $\mathbf{R} = 2\mathbf{i} + 6\mathbf{j}$ lb; $\mathbf{C}^R = -6\mathbf{j}$ lb•in. (b) $\mathbf{R} = 4\mathbf{i} + 6\mathbf{j} + 3\mathbf{k}$ lb; $\mathbf{C}^R = 0$

(c) $\mathbf{R} = 2\mathbf{i} + 6\mathbf{j}$ lb; $\mathbf{C}^R = -6\mathbf{j}$ lb•in.

(d) $\mathbf{R} = 0$; $\mathbf{C}^R = -15\mathbf{i} + (9 + 12 - 13)\mathbf{j} = -15\mathbf{i} + 8\mathbf{j}$ lb•in.

(e) $\mathbf{R} = 0$; $\mathbf{C}^R = -15\mathbf{i} + 8\mathbf{j}$ lb•in. (f) $\mathbf{R} = 0$; $\mathbf{C}^R = (25 - 25)\mathbf{i} + (16 - 16)\mathbf{j} = 0$

Comparing the above results: (a) and (c) are equivalent; (d) and (e) are equivalent. ◆

3.11

$\mathbf{R} = \mathbf{P} + \mathbf{Q}$: $8\mathbf{j} = \mathbf{P} + 10\mathbf{i}$ $\therefore\ \mathbf{P} = -10\mathbf{i} + 8\mathbf{j}$ lb ◆

$\Sigma\mathbf{M}_O = \mathbf{C}^R$: $(x\mathbf{i}\times\mathbf{P}) + [(8\mathbf{j} - z\mathbf{k})\times\mathbf{Q}] = -72\mathbf{j}$ lb•in.

$$\begin{vmatrix} \mathbf{i} & \mathbf{j} & \mathbf{k} \\ x & 0 & 0 \\ -10 & 8 & 0 \end{vmatrix} + \begin{vmatrix} \mathbf{i} & \mathbf{j} & \mathbf{k} \\ 0 & 8 & -z \\ 10 & 0 & 0 \end{vmatrix} = -72\mathbf{j} \text{ lb•in.}$$

Expanding the determinants and equating like components gives:

(j-components): $-10z = -72$ lb•in. $\therefore\ z = 7.2$ in. ◆

(k-components): $8x - 80 = 0$ $\therefore\ x = 10$ in. ◆

3.12

$$\mathbf{T}_1 = 50\vec{\lambda}_{AD} = 50\left(\frac{-3\mathbf{i} - 4\mathbf{j} + 3\mathbf{k}}{\sqrt{34}}\right) = -25.72\mathbf{i} - 34.30\mathbf{j} + 25.72\mathbf{k} \text{ kN}$$

$$\mathbf{T}_2 = 20\vec{\lambda}_{AC} = 20\left(\frac{3\mathbf{i} - 4\mathbf{j}}{5}\right) = 12\mathbf{i} - 16\mathbf{j} \text{ kN}$$

$\therefore\ \mathbf{R} = \mathbf{T}_1 + \mathbf{T}_2 = -13.72\mathbf{i} - 50.30\mathbf{j} + 25.72\mathbf{k}$ kN ◆

$\mathbf{C}^R = \Sigma\mathbf{M}_O = \left[\mathbf{r}_{OA}\times\left(\mathbf{T}_1 + \mathbf{T}_2\right)\right] + \mathbf{C}$ Note: $\mathbf{r}_{OA} = 4\mathbf{j}$ m and $\mathbf{C} = 150.0\mathbf{j}$ kN•m

$\mathbf{C}^R = 4\mathbf{j}\times(-13.72\mathbf{i} - 50.30\mathbf{j} + 25.72\mathbf{k}) + 150\mathbf{j} = (54.88\mathbf{k} + 102.88\mathbf{i}) + 150.0\mathbf{j}$

$\therefore\ \mathbf{C}^R = 102.9\mathbf{i} + 150.0\mathbf{j} + 54.9\mathbf{k}$ kN•m ◆

3.13

$$\mathbf{P} = 120\vec{\lambda}_{AD} = 120\left(\frac{-1.5\mathbf{i} + 2.0\mathbf{j}}{2.5}\right) = -72.0\mathbf{i} + 96.0\mathbf{j} \text{ N} \qquad \mathbf{Q} = 92.0\mathbf{j} - 50.0\mathbf{k} \text{ N}$$

$\therefore\ \mathbf{R} = \mathbf{P} + \mathbf{Q} = -72.0\mathbf{i} + 188.0\mathbf{j} - 50.0\mathbf{k}$ N ◆

$$\mathbf{C} = 180\vec{\lambda}_{AB} = 180\left(\frac{-1.5\mathbf{i} + 2.0\mathbf{k}}{2.5}\right) = -108.0\mathbf{i} + 144.0\mathbf{k} \text{ N•m}$$

$\mathbf{C}^R = \Sigma\mathbf{M}_C = (\mathbf{r}_{CD}\times\mathbf{P}) + (\mathbf{r}_{CB}\times\mathbf{Q}) + \mathbf{C}$

$$= \begin{vmatrix} \mathbf{i} & \mathbf{j} & \mathbf{k} \\ 0 & 0 & -2 \\ -72.0 & 96.0 & 0 \end{vmatrix} + \begin{vmatrix} \mathbf{i} & \mathbf{j} & \mathbf{k} \\ 0 & -2 & 0 \\ 0 & 92.0 & -50.0 \end{vmatrix} + (-108.0\mathbf{i} + 144.0\mathbf{k})$$

$= (192.0\mathbf{i} + 144.0\mathbf{j}) + (100\mathbf{i}) + (-108.0\mathbf{i} + 144.0\mathbf{k})$ N•m

$\therefore\ \mathbf{C}^R = 184.0\mathbf{i} + 144.0\mathbf{j} + 144.0\mathbf{k}$ N•m ◆

3.14

$$\mathbf{R} = \Sigma\mathbf{F} = \left[-12 - \frac{12}{13}(26)\right]\mathbf{i} + 0\mathbf{j} + \left[\frac{5}{13}(26) - 32 - 8\right] = -36\mathbf{i} - 30\mathbf{k} \text{ lb} \quad \blacklozenge$$

$\mathbf{C}^R = \Sigma\mathbf{M}_D$

$$C_x^R = \Sigma M_{Dx} = 32(1.5) + 8(1.5) - \frac{5}{13}(26)(4.5) = 15 \text{ lb}\cdot\text{ft}$$

$$C_y^R = \Sigma M_{Dy} = 32(0.75) - 8(0.75) - 12(1.0) + 26(1.0) - 32 = 0$$

$$C_z^R = \Sigma M_{Dz} = -\frac{12}{13}(26)(4.5) - 12(4.5) = -162 \text{ lb}\cdot\text{ft}$$

$$\therefore \mathbf{C}^R = 15\mathbf{i} - 162\mathbf{k} \text{ lb}\cdot\text{ft} \quad \blacklozenge$$

3.15

$\mathbf{P}_1 = 20(-\cos 35^\circ\mathbf{i} + \sin 35^\circ\mathbf{k}) = -16.383\mathbf{i} + 11.472\mathbf{k}$ N; $\mathbf{P}_2 = 14\mathbf{k}$ N

$\therefore \mathbf{R} = \mathbf{P}_1 + \mathbf{P}_2 = -16.38\mathbf{i} + 25.47\mathbf{k}$ N $\blacklozenge$

$\mathbf{C}^R = \Sigma\mathbf{M}_A = (\mathbf{r}_{AC} \times \mathbf{P}_1) + (\mathbf{r}_{AB} \times \mathbf{P}_2) + \mathbf{C}$

$\mathbf{r}_{AC} = -0.300\mathbf{i} + 0.250\mathbf{j}$ m; $\mathbf{r}_{AB} = 0.250\mathbf{j}$ m

$\mathbf{C} = 6(\cos 55^\circ\mathbf{i} + \sin 55^\circ\mathbf{k}) = 3.441\mathbf{i} + 4.915\mathbf{k}$ N·m

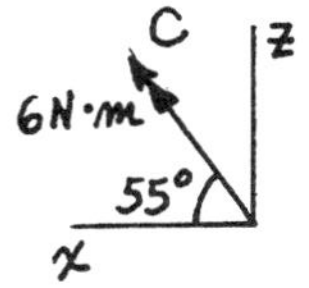

$$\mathbf{C}^R = \begin{vmatrix} \mathbf{i} & \mathbf{j} & \mathbf{k} \\ -0.300 & 0.250 & 0 \\ -16.383 & 0 & 11.472 \end{vmatrix} + \begin{vmatrix} \mathbf{i} & \mathbf{j} & \mathbf{k} \\ 0 & 0.250 & 0 \\ 0 & 0 & 14 \end{vmatrix} + (3.441\mathbf{i} + 4.915\mathbf{k})$$

$$= (2.868\mathbf{i} + 3.442\mathbf{j} + 4.096\mathbf{k}) + (3.500\mathbf{i}) + (3.441\mathbf{i} + 4.915\mathbf{k})$$

$$\therefore \mathbf{C}^R = 9.81\mathbf{i} + 3.44\mathbf{j} + 9.01\mathbf{k} \text{ N}\cdot\text{m} \quad \blacklozenge$$

3.16

(1) $\circlearrowleft + \; \Sigma M_O = -300d = -900$ lb·in.

$\therefore d = 3$ in.

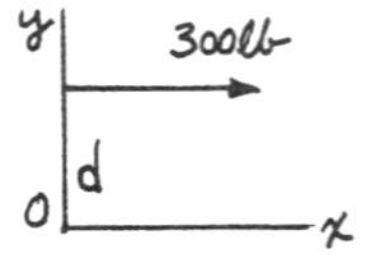

$\mathbf{R} = 300\mathbf{i}$ lb intersecting the y axis at y = 3 in. $\blacklozenge$

(2) $R = \sqrt{200^2 + 200^2} = 283$ N

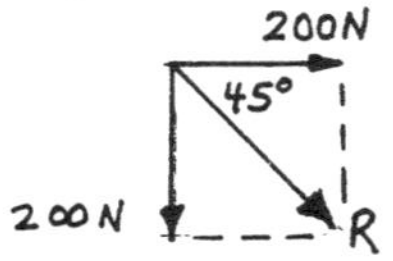

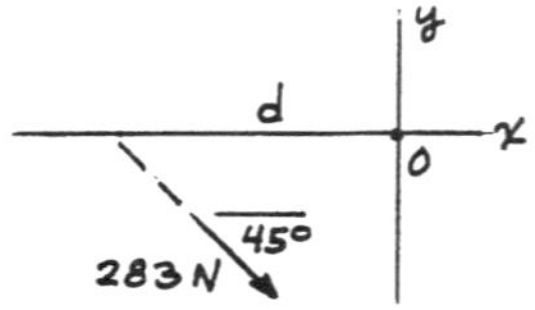

$\circlearrowleft + \; \Sigma M_O = 200d = 800$ N·m $\quad \therefore d = 4.00$ m

$\mathbf{R} = 200\mathbf{i} - 200\mathbf{j}$ N intersecting the x axis at x = −4 m $\blacklozenge$

(3) $R = \sqrt{600^2 + 400^2} = 721$ kN

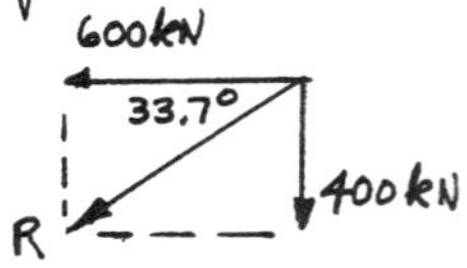

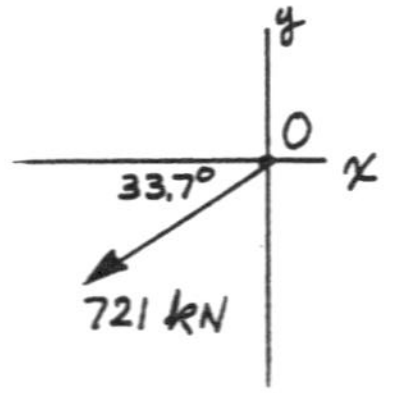

Because $\Sigma M_O = 0$, **R** passes through O.

$\mathbf{R} = -600\mathbf{i} - 400\mathbf{j}$ kN passing through the origin O $\blacklozenge$

(4) $R = \sqrt{600^2 + 800^2} = 1000$ lb

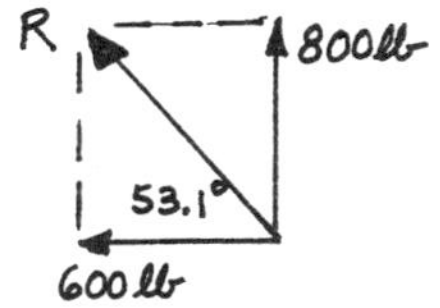

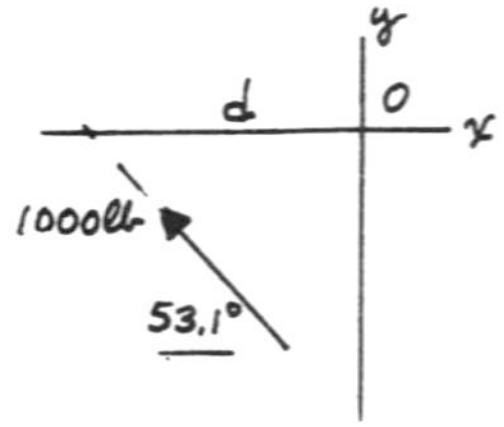

$\circlearrowleft + \; \Sigma M_O = -800d = -24\,000$ lb·ft $\quad \therefore d = 30$ ft

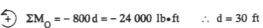

$\mathbf{R} = -600\mathbf{i} + 800\mathbf{j}$ lb intersecting the x axis at x = −30 ft $\blacklozenge$

3.17

$R_x = \Sigma F_x$: $\quad \xrightarrow{+} \; R_x = -100\cos 50^\circ + 400\cos 35^\circ = 263$ lb

$R_y = \Sigma F_y$: $\quad +\uparrow \; R_y = -100\sin 50^\circ - 400\sin 35^\circ - 200 = -506$ lb

$\therefore \mathbf{R} = 263\mathbf{i} - 506\mathbf{j}$ lb acting through point O $\blacklozenge$

3.18

$R_y = \Sigma F_y$: $+\uparrow$ $800 = 900 \sin\theta + \frac{3}{5}(500)$ which gives: $\theta = 33.75^o$ ◆

$R_x = \Sigma F_x$: $\underrightarrow{+}$ $0 = -900 \cos\theta + \frac{4}{5}(500) + P$

$\therefore$ $P = 900 \cos 33.75^o - 400 = 348$ lb ◆

3.19

(a) $R = \Sigma F$ $+\downarrow$ $R = 200 + 120 + 300 + 500 = 1120$ kN

$\Sigma M_A = Rd$ (using x = 5 m):

(+) $300(2) + 120(10) + 200(14) + 500(5) = 1120d$ kN•m

$\therefore$ $d = 6.34$ m ◆

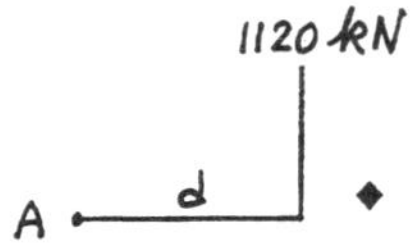

(b) $\Sigma M_A = Rd$ (using R = 1120 kN and d = 17/2 = 8.50 m):

(+) $300(2) + 120(10) + 200(14) + 500x = 1120(8.50)$ kN•m

$\therefore$ $x = 9.84$ m ◆

3.20

(a) P = 120 lb

$R_x = \Sigma F_x$: $\underrightarrow{+}$ $R_x = 360 - 360 = 0$

$R_y = \Sigma F_y$: $+\uparrow$ $R_y = -150 + 70 + 120 = 40$ lb

$\Sigma M_O = Rd$: (+) $-150(4) - 360(3) + 70(8) + 120(11) = 40d$ lb•ft

$\therefore$ $d = 5.00$ ft

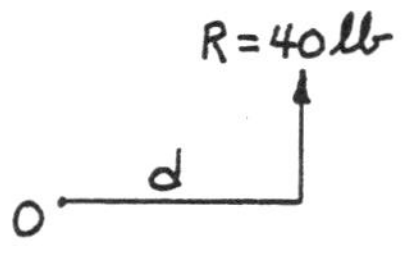

The resultant is a 40 lb upward force acting 5.00 ft to the right of point O. ◆

(b) P = 80 lb

$R_x = \Sigma F_x$: $\underrightarrow{+}$ $R_x = 360 - 360 = 0$

$R_y = \Sigma F_y$: $+\uparrow$ $R_y = -150 + 70 + 80 = 0$

(+) $\Sigma M_O = -150(4) - 360(3) + 70(8) + 80(11) = -240$ lb•ft

The resultant is a 240 lb•ft clockwise couple. ◆

3.21

(a): $R_x = \Sigma F_x = 0$; $+\uparrow$ $R_y = \Sigma F_y = 21$ kN; $\Sigma M_A = 0$

(b): $R_x = \Sigma F_x = 0$; $+\uparrow$ $R_y = \Sigma F_y = 6 + 15 = 21$ kN; (+) $\Sigma M_A = 15(0.6) - 6(1.5) = 0$

(c): $R_x = \Sigma F_x = 0$; $+\uparrow$ $R_y = \Sigma F_y = 15 + 6 = 21$ kN;

(+) $\Sigma M_A = 6(0.6) - 15(1.5) + 18.9 = 0$

(d): $\underrightarrow{+}$ $R_x = \Sigma F_x = \frac{4}{5}(10) - \frac{8}{17}(17) = 0$; $+\uparrow$ $R_y = \Sigma F_y = \frac{3}{5}(10) + \frac{15}{17}(17) = 21$ kN;

(+) $\Sigma M_A = \frac{3}{5}(10)(0.6) - \frac{4}{5}(10)(1.575) - \frac{15}{17}(17)(1.5) = -31.5$ kN•m

(e): $\underrightarrow{+}$ $R_x = \Sigma F_x = 8 - 8 = 0$; $+\uparrow$ $R_y = \Sigma F_y = 21$ kN; (+) $\Sigma M_A = 21(0.6) - 8(1.575) = 0$

(f): $\underrightarrow{+}$ $R_x = \Sigma F_x = 8 - 6 = 2$ kN; $+\uparrow$ $R_y = \Sigma F_y = 6 + 15 = 21$ kN;

(+) $\Sigma M_A = 15(0.6) - 8(1.575) - 6(1.5) + 12.6 = 0$

Comparing the above results, we see that (b), (c), and (e) are equivalent to (a). ◆

3.22

$R_x = \Sigma F_x$: $\underrightarrow{+}$ $R_x = 2F \sin\theta - F$

$R_y = \Sigma F_y$: $+\uparrow$ $R_y = F \cos\theta - F \cos\theta = 0$

(+) $\Sigma M_O = 3rF$

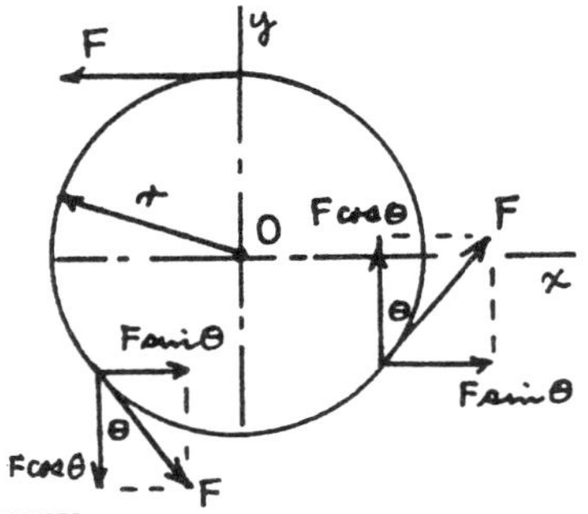

(a) $\theta = 30^o$:

$R_x = 2F \sin 30^o - F = 0$; $R_y = 0$; $\Sigma M_O = 3rF$ CCW

The resultant is a CCW couple of magnitude 3rF. ◆

(b) $\theta = 45^o$:

$R_x = 2F \sin 45^o - F = 0.414F$; $R_y = 0$

(+) $\Sigma M_O = 3rF = (0.414F)d$

which gives: $d = 7.25r$

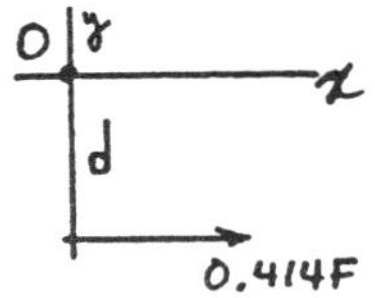

The resultant is the force **R** = 0.414F **i** intersecting the y axis at y = −7.25r. ◆

3.23

$R_x = \Sigma F_x$: $\overset{+}{\rightarrow}$ $R_x = \frac{3}{5}(100) = 60$ lb $R_y = \Sigma F_y$: $+\uparrow$ $R_y = \frac{4}{5}(100) - 400 = -320$ lb

(+) $\Sigma M_A = 2000 - 400(4) + \frac{4}{5}(100)(9) = -320d$

which gives $d = -3.50$ ft

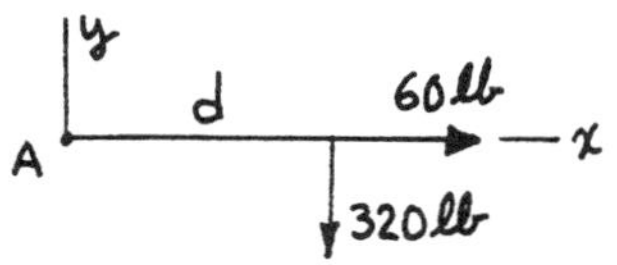

Therefore, the resultant is: **R** = 60**i** – 320**j** lb passing through the point (– 3.50 ft, 0) ◆

3.24

$R_x = \Sigma F_x$: $\overset{+}{\rightarrow}$ $R_x = -\frac{3}{5}(150) - \frac{5}{13}(130) + 80 = -60$ N

$R_y = \Sigma F_y$: $+\uparrow$ $R_y = -\frac{4}{5}(150) + \frac{12}{13}(130) = 0$

$\Sigma M_O = Rd$: (+) $\Sigma M_O = C + \frac{3}{5}(150)(2.4) - \frac{4}{5}(150)(2.8) + \frac{5}{13}(130)(2.4) = C$

Therefore, **R** = – 60**i** N and $\Sigma M_O = C$ (CCW) for both parts (a) and (b).

(a) <u>C = 0</u>: **R** = – 60**i** N $\Sigma M_O = C = 0$

The resultant is: **R** = – 60**i** N acting through O. ◆

(b) <u>C = 90 N•m</u> **R** = – 60**i** N $\Sigma M_O = C = 90$ N•m (CCW)

(+) $\Sigma M_O = 90 = 60d$ N•m which gives d = 1.5 m

The resultant is: **R** = – 60**i** N intersecting y-axis at y = 1.5 m. ◆

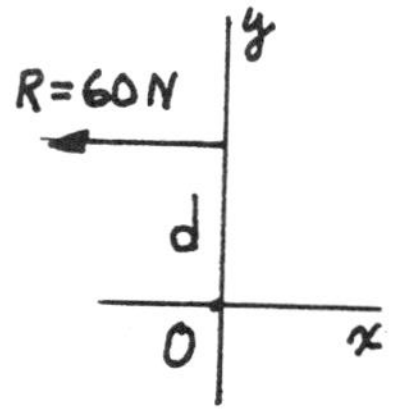

3.25

Since **R** passes through B, the sum of the moments about B is zero.

(+) $\Sigma M_B = 30.5(3) - 36(1.5) - \frac{5}{13}F(2.5) = 0$ which gives F = 39.0 lb ◆

$R_x = \Sigma F_x$: $\overset{+}{\rightarrow}$ $R_x = -30.5 - \frac{12}{13}(39.0) = -66.5$ lb

$R_y = \Sigma F_y$: $+\uparrow$ $R_y = 36 - \frac{5}{13}(39.0) = 21.0$ lb

∴ **R** = – 66.5**i** + 21.0**j** lb ◆

3.26

$R_x = \Sigma F_x$: $\overset{+}{\rightarrow}$ $R_x = -20\cos 30^\circ = -17.32$ N

$R_y = \Sigma F_y$: $+\uparrow$ $R_y = 20\sin 30^\circ - 60 = -50.0$ N

∴ **R** = – 17.32**i** – 50.0**j** N

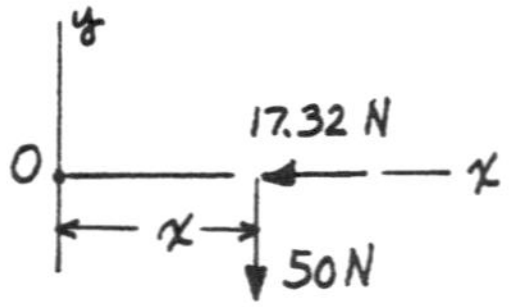

$\Sigma M_O = R_y x$:

(+) $50x = -20\cos 30^\circ(0.5) - 20\sin 30^\circ(1.0) + 12 + 60(0.5) = 23.34$ N•m

∴ x = 0.467 m

The resultant is: **R** = – 17.32**i** – 50.0**j** N, intersecting the x axis at x = 0.467 m. ◆

3.27

$\overset{+}{\rightarrow}$ $R_x = \Sigma F_x = -\frac{2}{\sqrt{13}}P_1 - P_2 + \frac{4}{5}P_3 = 0$

$+\uparrow$ $R_y = \Sigma F_y = \frac{3}{\sqrt{13}}P_1 - \frac{3}{5}P_3 = 0$

(+) $\Sigma M_B = 3\left(\frac{3}{\sqrt{13}}P_1\right) + 2\left(\frac{2}{\sqrt{13}}P_1\right) = 150$ lb•ft

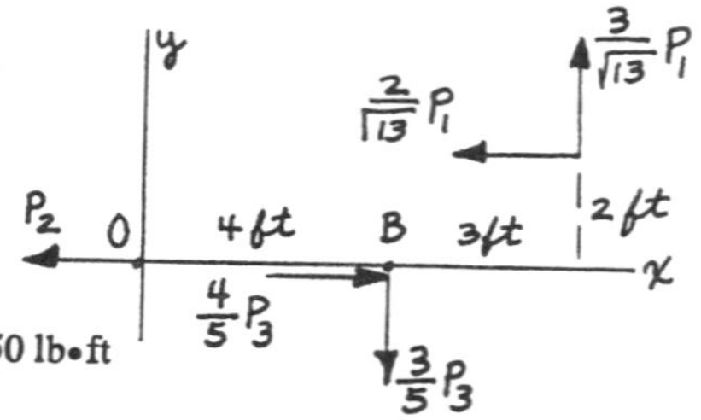

Solving gives: $P_1 = 41.60$ lb, $P_2 = 23.08$ lb, $P_3 = 57.69$ lb ◆

3.28

$R_x = \Sigma F_x$: $\overset{+}{\rightarrow}$ $0 = P_1\sin 30^\circ - P_2$ (1)

$R_y = \Sigma F_y$: $+\uparrow$ $-R = -P_1\cos 30^\circ - 100$ (2)

$\Sigma M_B = 0$:

(+) $2(100) + 1.5P_2$

$- P_1\sin 30^\circ(3) - P_1\cos 30^\circ(2) = 0$ (3)

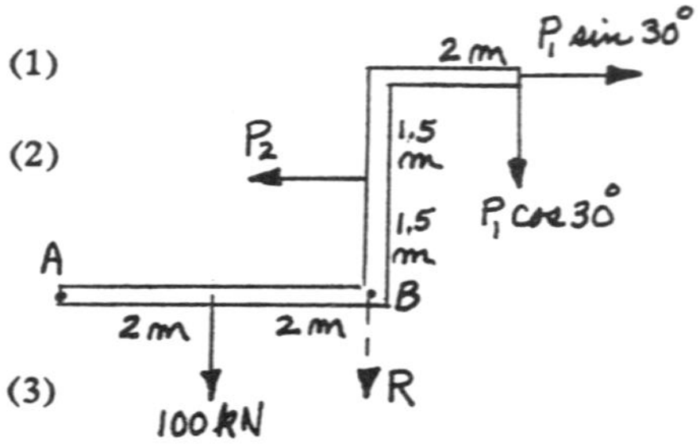

Solving (1), (2) and (3) gives:

$P_1 = 80.6$ kN, $P_2 = 40.3$ kN, R = 169.8 kN ◆

*3.29

$R_x = \Sigma F_x = 0$: $\overset{+}{\rightarrow}$ $P_1 \sin 30^\circ - 50 = 0$ (1)

$R_y = \Sigma F_y = 0$: $+\uparrow$ $P_1 \cos 30^\circ + P_2 - 300 = 0$ (2)

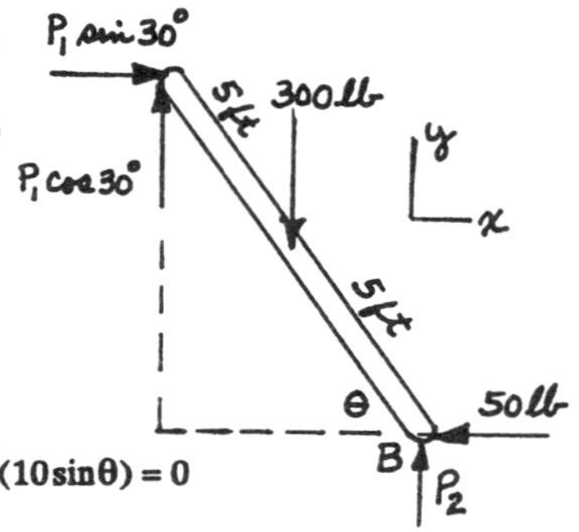

Solving (1) and (2) gives:

$P_1 = 100$ lb, $P_2 = 213.40$ lb ◆

$\Sigma M_B = 0$:

$(+)$ $300(5\cos\theta) - P_1 \cos 30^\circ(10\cos\theta) - P_1 \sin 30^\circ(10\sin\theta) = 0$

$$300(5\cos\theta) - 100\cos 30^\circ(10\cos\theta) - 100\sin 30^\circ(10\sin\theta) = 0$$

$$1500\cos\theta - 866.03\cos\theta - 500\sin\theta = 0$$

$$633.97\cos\theta = 500\sin\theta$$

$\tan\theta = \sin\theta/\cos\theta = 633.97/500 = 1.2679$ $\quad\therefore\ \theta = 51.7^\circ$ ◆

3.30

(a) $R = \Sigma F_z = -80$ lb

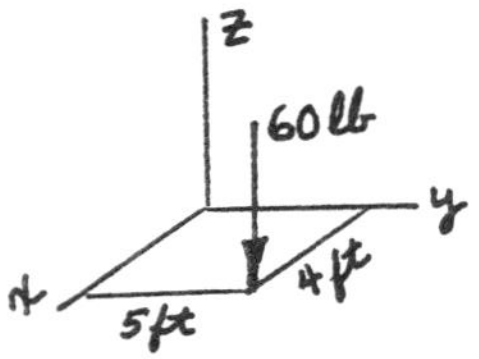

$\Sigma M_x = Ry$: $\quad -400 = -80y$ gives $y = 5$ ft

$\Sigma M_y = -Rx$ $\quad 320 = -(-80)x$ gives $x = 4$ ft

$\therefore$ $\mathbf{R} = -80\,\mathbf{k}$ lb passing through the point (4 ft, 5 ft, 0) ◆

(b) $R = \Sigma F_z = 50$ kN

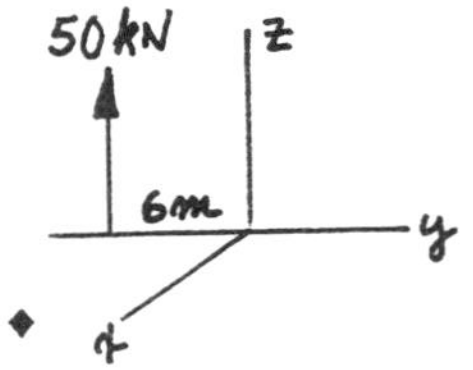

$\Sigma M_x = Ry$: $\quad -300 = 50y$ gives $y = -6$ m

$\Sigma M_y = -Rx$ $\quad 0 = -50x$ gives $x = 0$

$\therefore$ $\mathbf{R} = 50\,\mathbf{k}$ kN passing through the point (0, – 6 m, 0) ◆

(continued)

(c) $R = \Sigma F_z = 400$ lb

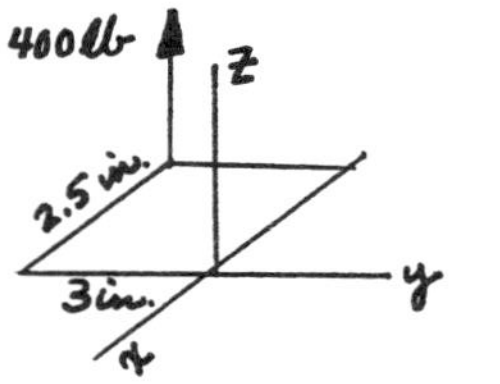

$\Sigma M_x = Ry$: $\quad -1200 = 400y$ gives $y = -3$ in.

$\Sigma M_y = -Rx$ $\quad 1000 = -400x$ gives $x = -2.5$ in.

$\therefore$ $\mathbf{R} = 400\,\mathbf{k}$ lb passing through the point (– 2.5 in., – 3 in., 0) ◆

(d) $R = \Sigma F_z = 25$ N

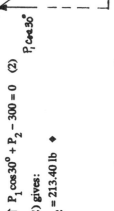

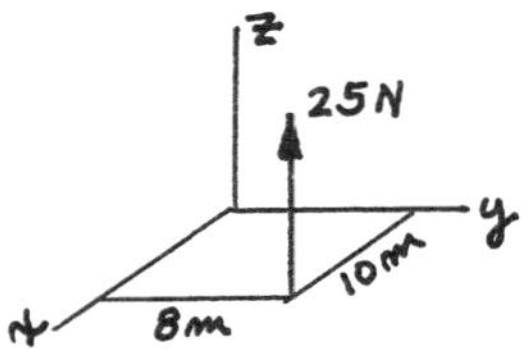

$\Sigma M_x = Ry$: $\quad 200 = 25y$ gives $y = 8$ m

$\Sigma M_y = -Rx$ $\quad -250 = -25x$ gives $x = 10$ m

$\therefore$ $\mathbf{R} = 25\,\mathbf{k}$ N passing through the point (10 m, 8 m, 0) ◆

3.31

(a): The given forces are concurrent. Therefore, the resultant is a force. ◆

(b): $\quad \mathbf{R} = \left[\frac{3}{5}(15) - \frac{3}{5}(15)\right]\mathbf{i} + \left[\frac{4}{5}(15) + \frac{4}{5}(15) - 24\right]\mathbf{j} = 0$

Because **R** = 0, the resultant is not a force. The 24-kN force and one of the 15-kN forces intersect. The sum of the moments about this point of intersection is not zero. Therefore, the resultant is a couple. ◆

(c): The 25-kN force is perpendicular to the couple-vector that is equivalent to the two 20-kN forces. This force and couple-vector can be reduced to a single force. Therfore, the resultant is a force. ◆

(d): The 16 kN-force is not perpendicular to the couple-vector that is equivalent to the two 12-kN forces. Therefore, the resultant is a wrench. ◆

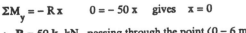

(e): $\quad$ The given force is $\mathbf{F} = 15\left(-\frac{3}{5}\mathbf{i} + \frac{4}{5}\mathbf{j}\right) = -9\mathbf{i} + 12\mathbf{j}$ kN.

The sum of the two couples is $\mathbf{C} = 400\mathbf{i} + 300\mathbf{j}$ kN. Since **F** and **C** are perpendicular (they have negative reciprocal slopes), they can be reduced to a single force. Therefore, the resultant is a force. ◆

3.32

$$\mathbf{T}_1 = 900\,\vec{\lambda}_1 = 900\left(\frac{3\mathbf{i} - 8\mathbf{j} + 4\mathbf{k}}{\sqrt{89}}\right) = 286.2\mathbf{i} - 763.2\mathbf{j} + 381.6\mathbf{k} \text{ lb}$$

$$\mathbf{T}_2 = 500\,\vec{\lambda}_2 = 500\left(\frac{-4\mathbf{i} - 8\mathbf{j} + 4\mathbf{k}}{\sqrt{96}}\right) = -204.1\mathbf{i} - 408.2\mathbf{j} + 204.1\mathbf{k} \text{ lb}$$

$$\mathbf{T}_3 = 300\,\vec{\lambda}_3 = 300\left(\frac{-8\mathbf{j} - 6\mathbf{k}}{10}\right) = -240.0\mathbf{j} - 180.0\mathbf{k} \text{ lb}$$

$\therefore\ \mathbf{R} = \mathbf{T}_1 + \mathbf{T}_2 + \mathbf{T}_3 = 82.1\mathbf{i} - 1411\mathbf{j} + 406\mathbf{k}$ lb, acting through the point of concurrency ◆

3.33

$$\mathbf{T}_1 = \mathrm{T}_1\vec{\lambda}_1 = \mathrm{T}_1\left(\frac{3\mathbf{i} - 8\mathbf{j} + 4\mathbf{k}}{\sqrt{89}}\right) = \mathrm{T}_1(0.3180\mathbf{i} - 0.8480\mathbf{j} + 0.4240\mathbf{k}) \text{ lb}$$

$$\mathbf{T}_2 = \mathrm{T}_2\vec{\lambda}_2 = 980\left(\frac{-4\mathbf{i} - 8\mathbf{j} + 4\mathbf{k}}{\sqrt{96}}\right) = -400.1\mathbf{i} - 800.2\mathbf{j} + 400.1\mathbf{k} \text{ lb}$$

$$\mathbf{T}_3 = \mathrm{T}_3\vec{\lambda}_3 = \mathrm{T}_3\left(\frac{-8\mathbf{j} - 6\mathbf{k}}{10}\right) = \mathrm{T}_3(-0.8\mathbf{j} - 0.6\mathbf{k}) \text{ lb}$$

$\mathbf{R} = \mathrm{R}\mathbf{j} = \mathbf{T}_1 + \mathbf{T}_2 + \mathbf{T}_3$ Equating like components gives:

(i-components): $0 = 0.3180\mathrm{T}_1 - 400.1$ (1)

(j-components): $\mathrm{R} = -0.8480\mathrm{T}_1 - 800.2 - 0.8\mathrm{T}_3$ (2)

(k-components): $0 = 0.4240\mathrm{T}_1 + 400.1 - 0.6\mathrm{T}_3$ (3)

Solving (1) and (3) yields: $\mathrm{T}_1 = 1258$ lb; $\mathrm{T}_3 = 1556$ lb ◆

3.34

$$\mathbf{P}_1 = \mathrm{P}_1\vec{\lambda}_{AD} = \mathrm{P}_1\left(\frac{-0.8\mathbf{i} + 0.9\mathbf{j} + 2\mathbf{k}}{\sqrt{5.450}}\right) = \mathrm{P}_1(-0.3427\mathbf{i} + 0.3855\mathbf{j} + 0.8567\mathbf{k}) \text{ kN}$$

$$\mathbf{P}_2 = \mathrm{P}_2\vec{\lambda}_{BD} = \mathrm{P}_2\left(\frac{-0.8\mathbf{i} - 1.4\mathbf{j} + 2\mathbf{k}}{\sqrt{6.600}}\right) = \mathrm{P}_2(-0.3114\mathbf{i} - 0.5450\mathbf{j} + 0.7785\mathbf{k}) \text{ kN}$$

$$\mathbf{P}_3 = \mathrm{P}_3\vec{\lambda}_{CD} = \mathrm{P}_3\left(\frac{1.5\mathbf{i} + 2\mathbf{k}}{2.50}\right) = \mathrm{P}_3(0.600\mathbf{i} + 0.800\mathbf{k}) \text{ kN}$$

$\mathbf{R} = 200\mathbf{k} = \mathbf{P}_1 + \mathbf{P}_2 + \mathbf{P}_3$ Equating like components gives:

(continued)

(i-components): $0 = -0.3427\mathrm{P}_1 - 0.3114\mathrm{P}_2 + 0.600\mathrm{P}_3$ (1)

(j-components): $0 = 0.3855\mathrm{P}_1 - 0.5450\mathrm{P}_2$ (2)

(k-components): $200 = 0.8567\mathrm{P}_1 + 0.7785\mathrm{P}_2 + 0.800\mathrm{P}_3$ (3)

Solving (1), (2), and (3) yields: $\mathrm{P}_1 = 92.68$ kN; $\mathrm{P}_2 = 65.56$ kN; $\mathrm{P}_3 = 86.96$ kN ◆

3.35

$\Sigma\mathbf{F} = \mathbf{0}$: $\mathbf{P} - 80\mathbf{i} - 120\mathbf{j} + 90\mathbf{k} = \mathbf{0}$ $\therefore\ \mathbf{P} = 80\mathbf{i} + 120\mathbf{j} - 90\mathbf{k}$ N ◆

Choosing point O as the moment center (any point could be used):

$$\mathbf{C}^R = \Sigma\mathbf{M}_O = 90(0.3)\,\mathbf{i} + 120(0.2)\,\mathbf{i} = 51.0\mathbf{i} \text{ N}\bullet\text{m}$$ ◆

3.36

$\mathrm{R} = \Sigma\mathrm{F}_z$ $+\uparrow$ $\mathrm{R} = -20 + 80 - 60 = 0$ Therefore, the resultant is not a force.

$\Sigma\mathrm{M}_x = -20(0.8) + 80(0.8) - 60(0.5) = 18$ kN•m

$\Sigma\mathrm{M}_y = -80(0.6) + 60(0.6) = -12$ kN•m $\Sigma\mathrm{M}_z = 0$

The resultant is the couple: $18\mathbf{i} - 12\mathbf{j}$ kN•m ◆

3.37

$\mathrm{R} = \Sigma\mathrm{F}_z$: $+\uparrow$ $\mathrm{R} = 80 + 72 + 70 + 64 = 286$ lb

$\Sigma\mathrm{M}_x = \mathrm{R}\,y$: $70(2) + (72 + 64)(6) = 286y$ $y = 3.343$ ft

$\Sigma\mathrm{M}_y = -\mathrm{R}\,x$: $-(70 + 64)(6) = -286x$ $x = 2.811$ ft

The resultant is the force: $\mathbf{R} = 286\mathbf{k}$ lb passing through the point (2.81 ft, 3.34 ft, 0) ◆

3.38

$R = \Sigma F_z$: $+\uparrow$ $12 = P_1 + P_2$ (1)

$\Sigma M_x = 12(20) = P_2(5) + \frac{3}{5}C$ (2)

$\Sigma M_y = -12(15) = -P_2(15) - \frac{4}{5}C$ (3)

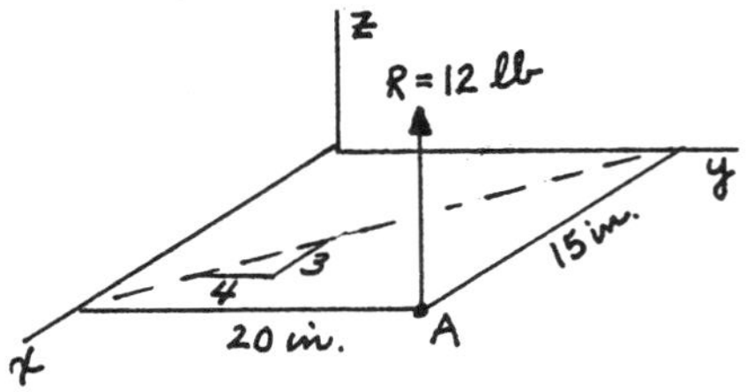

Solving (1), (2), and (3) gives: $P_1 = 28.8$ lb; $P_2 = -16.8$ lb; $C = 540$ lb•in. ◆

3.39

$R = \Sigma F_z$: $+\uparrow$ $R = P_1 + P_2 = 20 + 30 = 50$ lb

$\Sigma M_x = Ry$: $P_2(5) + 0.6C = Ry$

$$y = \frac{5P_2 + 0.6C}{R} = \frac{5(30) + 0.6(100)}{50} = 4.20 \text{ in.}$$

$\Sigma M_y = -Rx$: $-15P_2 - 0.8C = -Rx$

$$x = \frac{15P_2 + 0.8C}{R} = \frac{15(30) + 0.8(100)}{50} = 10.60 \text{ in.}$$

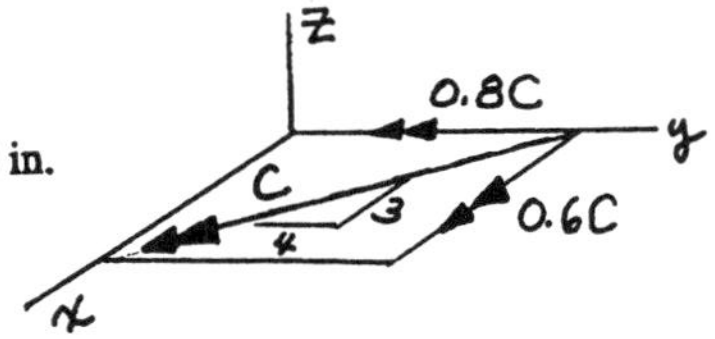

The resultant is the force: $\mathbf{R} = 50\mathbf{k}$ lb passing through the point (10.60 in., 4.20 in., 0) ◆

3.40

$R_x = \Sigma F_x = 0$

$R_y = \Sigma F_y$:

$\xrightarrow{+}$ $R_y = 300 + 80 + 200 = 580$ lb

$R_z = \Sigma F_z = 0$

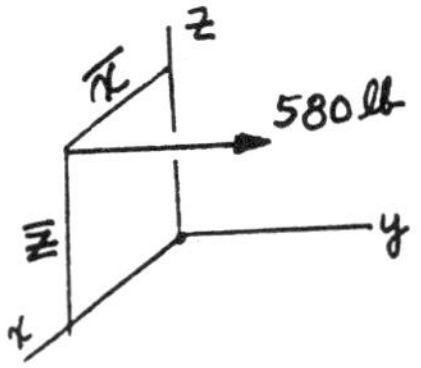

$\Sigma M_x = -580z$ $\quad -300(3) - 80(3\cos 30^o) + 500\cos 45^o = -580z$ $\quad \therefore\ z = 1.301$ ft

$\Sigma M_z = 580x$ $\quad 80(3\sin 30^o) + 200(3) + 500\sin 45^o = 580x$ $\quad \therefore\ x = 1.851$ ft

The resultant is $\mathbf{R} = 580\mathbf{j}$ lb acting through the point (1.851 ft, 0, 1.301 ft). ◆

3.41

$$\mathbf{P} = P\vec{\lambda}_{BC} = P\left(\frac{-4.0\mathbf{i} - 1.5\mathbf{j} + 2.0\mathbf{k}}{\sqrt{22.25}}\right) = P(-0.8480\mathbf{i} - 0.3180\mathbf{j} + 0.4240\mathbf{k})\text{ N}$$

$\mathbf{Q} = Q\vec{\lambda}_{BD} = Q(-0.8480\mathbf{i} + 0.3180\mathbf{j} + 0.4240\mathbf{k})$ N ; $\mathbf{W} = -100\mathbf{k}$ N ; $\mathbf{F} = -20\mathbf{j}$ N

Because **R** acts at point O, $\Sigma \mathbf{M}_O = \mathbf{0}$.

$(\mathbf{r}_{OB} \times \mathbf{P}) + (\mathbf{r}_{OB} \times \mathbf{Q}) + [\mathbf{r}_{OA} \times (\mathbf{W} + \mathbf{F})] = \mathbf{0}$ $\quad \mathbf{r}_{OB} = 4\mathbf{i}$ m ; $\mathbf{r}_{OA} = 6\mathbf{i}$ m

$$(P)\begin{vmatrix} \mathbf{i} & \mathbf{j} & \mathbf{k} \\ 4 & 0 & 0 \\ -0.8480 & -0.3180 & 0.4240 \end{vmatrix} + (Q)\begin{vmatrix} \mathbf{i} & \mathbf{j} & \mathbf{k} \\ 4 & 0 & 0 \\ -0.8480 & 0.3180 & 0.4240 \end{vmatrix} + \begin{vmatrix} \mathbf{i} & \mathbf{j} & \mathbf{k} \\ 6 & 0 & 0 \\ 0 & -20 & -100 \end{vmatrix} = \mathbf{0}$$

Expanding the determinants, and equating like components:

(j-components): $-1.696P - 1.696Q + 600 = 0$ (1)

(k-components): $-1.272P + 1.272Q - 120 = 0$ (2)

Solving (1) and (2) gives: $P = 129.7$ N ; $Q = 224.1$ N ◆

$\mathbf{R} = \mathbf{P} + \mathbf{Q} + \mathbf{W} + \mathbf{F} = 129.7(-0.8480\mathbf{i} - 0.3180\mathbf{j} + 0.4240\mathbf{k})$
$\quad + 224.1(-0.8480\mathbf{i} + 0.3180\mathbf{j} + 0.4240\mathbf{k}) - 100\mathbf{k} - 20\mathbf{j}$ N

$\therefore\ \mathbf{R} = -300\mathbf{i} + 10\mathbf{j} + 50\mathbf{k}$ N ◆

3.42

$$\mathbf{P} = P\vec{\lambda}_{AB} = P\left(\frac{-28\mathbf{i} - 80\mathbf{j} - 69\mathbf{k}}{\sqrt{28^2 + 80^2 + 69^2}}\right) = P(-0.2562\mathbf{i} - 0.7320\mathbf{j} - 0.6313\mathbf{k})\text{ lb}$$

$$\mathbf{Q} = Q\vec{\lambda}_{AC} = Q\left(\frac{32\mathbf{i} - 76\mathbf{j} - 69\mathbf{k}}{\sqrt{32^2 + 76^2 + 69^2}}\right) = Q(0.2976\mathbf{i} - 0.7068\mathbf{j} - 0.6417\mathbf{k})\text{ lb}$$

$\mathbf{W} = -2400\mathbf{k}$ lb (intersects the y axis at y = 20 ft)

Because **R** acts at point O, $\Sigma \mathbf{M}_O = \mathbf{0}$.

(continued)

$(\mathbf{r}_{OA} \times \mathbf{P}) + (\mathbf{r}_{OA} \times \mathbf{Q}) + (20\,\mathbf{j} \times \mathbf{W}) = 0 \qquad \mathbf{r}_{OA} = 40\mathbf{j} + 69\mathbf{k}$ ft

$$(P)\begin{vmatrix} \mathbf{i} & \mathbf{j} & \mathbf{k} \\ 0 & 40 & 69 \\ -0.2562 & -0.7320 & -0.6313 \end{vmatrix} + (Q)\begin{vmatrix} \mathbf{i} & \mathbf{j} & \mathbf{k} \\ 0 & 40 & 69 \\ 0.2976 & -0.7068 & -0.6417 \end{vmatrix} + \begin{vmatrix} \mathbf{i} & \mathbf{j} & \mathbf{k} \\ 0 & 20 & 0 \\ 0 & 0 & -2400 \end{vmatrix} = 0$$

Expanding the determinants, and equating like components:

(i-components): $25.26P + 23.10Q = 48\,000$ (1)

(j-components): $-17.68P + 20.53Q = 0$ (2)

(k-components): $10.25P - 11.90Q = 0$ (3)

Solving (1) and (2) gives: $P = 1063$ lb ; $Q = 915$ lb ◆

$\mathbf{R} = \mathbf{P} + \mathbf{Q} + \mathbf{W}$

$= 1063(-0.2562\mathbf{i} - 0.7320\mathbf{j} - 0.6313\mathbf{k}) + 915(0.2976\mathbf{i} - 0.7068\mathbf{j} - 0.6417\mathbf{k}) - 2400\mathbf{k}$

$\therefore\ \mathbf{R} = -1425\mathbf{j} - 3660\mathbf{k}$ lb ◆

3.43

The unit vector in the direction of **R** is

$$\vec{\lambda} = \frac{\mathbf{R}}{R} = \frac{600\mathbf{i} + 1400\mathbf{j} + 700\mathbf{k}}{1676} = 0.3580\mathbf{i} + 0.8353\mathbf{j} + 0.4177\mathbf{k}$$

The component of $\mathbf{C}^R$ that is in the direction of $\vec{\lambda}$ is:

$$C_t^R = \mathbf{C}^R \cdot \vec{\lambda} = (-800\mathbf{i} + 500\mathbf{j} + 600\mathbf{k}) \cdot (0.3580\mathbf{i} + 0.8353\mathbf{j} + 0.4177\mathbf{k})$$

$$= -800(0.3580) + 500(0.8353) + 600(0.4177) = 381.9 \text{ lb}\cdot\text{ft}$$

$$\mathbf{C}_t^R = 381.9\,\vec{\lambda}$$

$$= 381.9(0.3580\mathbf{i} + 0.8353\mathbf{j} + 0.4177\mathbf{k}) = 136.7\mathbf{i} + 319.0\mathbf{j} + 159.5\mathbf{k} \text{ lb}\cdot\text{ft}$$

The component of $\mathbf{C}^R$ that is normal to $\vec{\lambda}$ is:

$$\mathbf{C}_n^R = \mathbf{C}^R - \mathbf{C}_t^R = (-800\mathbf{i} + 500\mathbf{j} + 600\mathbf{k}) - (136.7\mathbf{i} + 319.0\mathbf{j} + 159.5\mathbf{k})$$

$$= -936.7\mathbf{i} + 181.0\mathbf{j} + 440.5\mathbf{k} \text{ lb}\cdot\text{ft}$$

Let A be the point where the axis of the wrench passes through the yz plane:

$\mathbf{r}_{OA} = y\mathbf{j} + z\mathbf{k}$ ft.

(continued)

$\mathbf{r}_{OA} \times \mathbf{R} = \mathbf{C}_n^R$ becomes:

$$\begin{vmatrix} \mathbf{i} & \mathbf{j} & \mathbf{k} \\ 0 & y & z \\ 600 & 1400 & 700 \end{vmatrix} = -936.7\mathbf{i} + 181.0\mathbf{j} + 440.5\mathbf{k} \text{ lb}\cdot\text{ft}$$

Expanding the determinant, and equating like components gives:

(j-components): $600z = 181.0$ lb•ft which gives: $z = 0.302$ ft

(k-components): $-600y = 440.5$ lb•ft which gives: $y = -0.734$ ft

Wrench: force $= 600\mathbf{i} + 1400\mathbf{j} + 700\mathbf{k}$ lb ; couple $= 136.7\mathbf{i} + 319.0\mathbf{j} + 159.5\mathbf{k}$ lb•ft ;

wrench axis passes through (0, − 0.734 ft, 0.302 ft) ◆

3.44

The unit vector in the direction of **R** is

$$\vec{\lambda} = \frac{\mathbf{R}}{R} = \frac{300\mathbf{i} + 400\mathbf{j} - 500\mathbf{k}}{707.1} = 0.4243\mathbf{i} + 0.5657\mathbf{j} - 0.7071\mathbf{k}$$

The component of $\mathbf{C}^R$ that is in the direction of $\vec{\lambda}$ is:

$$C_t^R = \mathbf{C}^R \cdot \vec{\lambda} = (1400\mathbf{i} + 800\mathbf{j} + 600\mathbf{k}) \cdot (0.4243\mathbf{i} + 0.5657\mathbf{j} - 0.7071\mathbf{k})$$

$$= 1400(0.4243) + 800(0.5657) + 600(-0.7071) = 622.3 \text{ N}\cdot\text{m}$$

$$\mathbf{C}_t^R = 622.3\,\vec{\lambda}$$

$$= 622.3(0.4243\mathbf{i} + 0.5657\mathbf{j} - 0.7071\mathbf{k}) = 264.0\mathbf{i} + 352.0\mathbf{j} - 440.0\mathbf{k} \text{ N}\cdot\text{m}$$

The component of $\mathbf{C}^R$ that is normal to $\vec{\lambda}$ is:

$$\mathbf{C}_n^R = \mathbf{C}^R - \mathbf{C}_t^R = (1400\mathbf{i} + 800\mathbf{j} + 600\mathbf{k}) - (264.0\mathbf{i} + 352.0\mathbf{j} - 440.0\mathbf{k})$$

$$= 1136.0\mathbf{i} + 448.0\mathbf{j} + 1040.0\mathbf{k} \text{ N}\cdot\text{m}$$

Let A be the point where the axis of the wrench passes through the xy plane:

$\mathbf{r}_{OA} = x\mathbf{i} + y\mathbf{j}$ m.

$\mathbf{r}_{OA} \times \mathbf{R} = \mathbf{C}_n^R$ becomes:

$$\begin{vmatrix} \mathbf{i} & \mathbf{j} & \mathbf{k} \\ x & y & 0 \\ 300 & 400 & -500 \end{vmatrix} = 1136.0\mathbf{i} + 448.0\mathbf{j} + 1040.0\mathbf{k} \text{ N}\cdot\text{m}$$

(continued)

Expanding the determinant, and equating like components gives:

(i-components): $-500y = 1136.0$ N•m which gives: $y = -2.272$ m

(j-components): $500x = 448.0$ N•m which gives: $x = 0.896$ m

Wrench: force = $300\mathbf{i} + 400\mathbf{j} - 500\mathbf{k}$ N ; couple = $264\mathbf{i} + 352\mathbf{j} - 440\mathbf{k}$ N•m ; wrench axis passes through (0.896 m, − 2.272 m, 0) ◆

3.45

(a) $\mathbf{R} = 12\mathbf{j} - 12\mathbf{j} + 16\mathbf{k} = 16\mathbf{k}$ kN ◆

$\mathbf{C}^R = \Sigma\mathbf{M}_O = -12(15)\mathbf{i} + 12(9)\mathbf{k} = -180\mathbf{i} + 108\mathbf{k}$ kN•m ◆

(b) The unit vector in the direction of **R** is **k**.

The component of $\mathbf{C}^R$ that is in the direction of $\vec{\lambda}$ (= **k**) is:

$C_t^R = \mathbf{C}^R \cdot \vec{\lambda} = (-180\mathbf{i} + 108\mathbf{k}) \cdot \mathbf{k} = 108$ kN•m $\quad \therefore\ \mathbf{C}_t^R = 108\mathbf{k}$ kN•m

The component of $\mathbf{C}^R$ that is normal to $\vec{\lambda}$ is:

$\mathbf{C}_n^R = \mathbf{C}^R - \mathbf{C}_t^R = (-180\mathbf{i} + 108\mathbf{k}) - 108\mathbf{k} = -180\mathbf{i}$ kN•m

Let A be the point where the axis of the wrench crosses the xy plane:

$\mathbf{r}_{OA} = x\mathbf{i} + y\mathbf{j}$ m.

$\mathbf{r}_{OA} \times \mathbf{R} = \mathbf{C}_n^R$ becomes:
$$\begin{vmatrix} \mathbf{i} & \mathbf{j} & \mathbf{k} \\ x & y & 0 \\ 0 & 0 & 16 \end{vmatrix} = -180\mathbf{i} \text{ kN•m}$$

Expanding the determinant, and equating like components gives:

(i-components): $16y = -180$ kN•m which gives: $y = -11.25$ m

(j-components): $-16x = 0$ which gives: $x = 0$

Wrench: force = $16\mathbf{k}$ kN ; couple = $108\mathbf{k}$ kN•m;

wrench axis passes through (0, − 11.25 m, 0) ◆

3.46

Area of stop sign: $A = 32(32) - 4(0.5)(10)(10) = 824\ \text{in}^2 = 5.722\ \text{ft}^2$

$R = pA = 2.3(5.722) = 13.2$ lb

The resultant is a 13.2 lb normal force, acting at the center of the stop sign. ◆

3.47

R = volume under the load surface = 0.5(58.9)(32)(6) = 5650 kN

The resultant is a 5650 kN normal force, acting at $\bar{x} = 16$ m, $\bar{z} = 2$ m (the centroid of the load volume). ◆

3.48

$P_1 = 0.5(4)(300) = 600$ lb

$\bar{x}_1 = 3 + (2/3)4 = 5.667$ ft

$P_2 = 500(7) = 3500$ lb

$\bar{x}_2 = 0.5(7) = 3.5$ ft

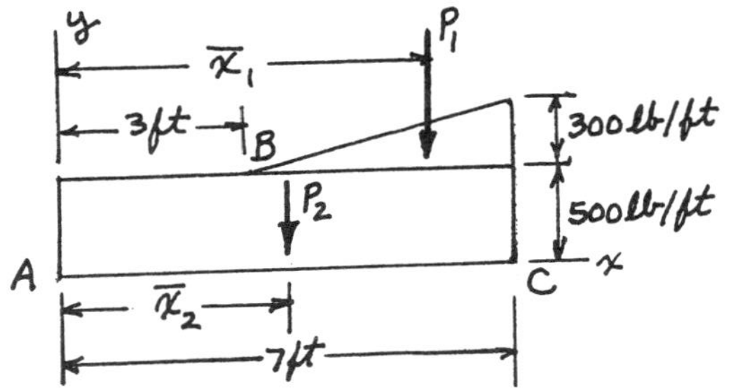

$R = \Sigma F_y$:

$+\uparrow\ R = -P_1 - P_2 = -600 - 3500 = -4100$ lb

$\Sigma M_A = R\bar{x}$: $\circlearrowleft +\ \ -P_1\bar{x}_1 - P_2\bar{x}_2 = R\bar{x}$

$-3500(3.5) - 600(5.667) = -4100\bar{x}$ which gives $\bar{x} = 3.817$ ft

The resultant is $\mathbf{R} = -4100\mathbf{k}$ lb acting through the point (3.82 ft, 0). ◆

3.49

$P = 0.5(3)w_0 = 1.5w_0$ kN

$d = 1.5 + 2[2/3(3)] = 5.5$ m

Noting that C = Pd, we get

$60 = 1.5w_0(5.5)$

$\therefore\ w_0 = 7.27$ kN/m ◆

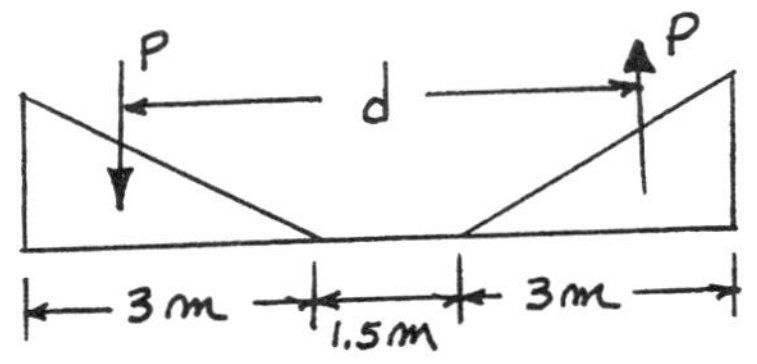

3.50

$R_x = \Sigma F_x$

$\xrightarrow{+}\ R_x = -\dfrac{w_0 L}{4}$

$R_y = \Sigma F_y$

$+\uparrow\ R_y = -\dfrac{w_0 L}{2} + \dfrac{w_0 L}{4} = -\dfrac{w_0 L}{4}$

$\therefore\ \mathbf{R} = -\dfrac{w_0 L}{4}(\mathbf{i}+\mathbf{j})$

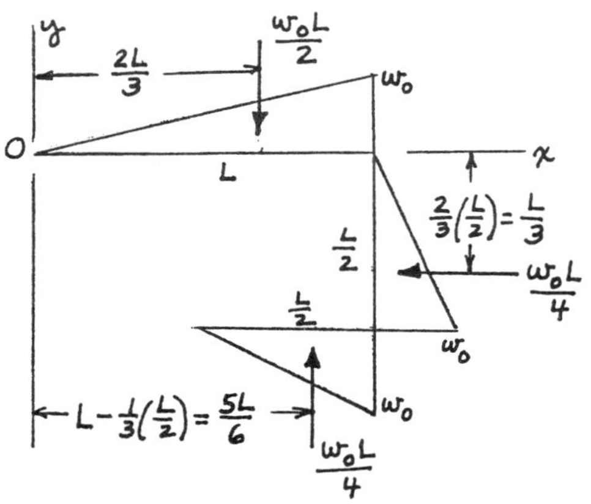

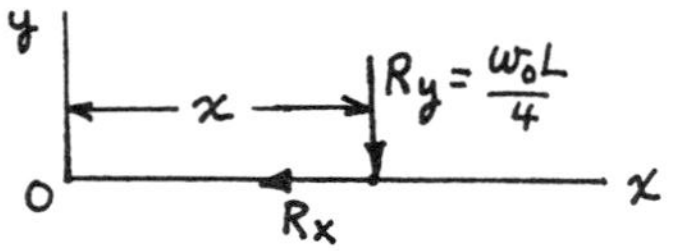

$\Sigma M_O = R_y x$:

$$-\frac{w_0 L}{2}\left(\frac{2L}{3}\right) - \frac{w_0 L}{4}\left(\frac{L}{3}\right) + \frac{w_0 L}{4}\left(\frac{5L}{6}\right) = -\frac{w_0 L}{4}x$$

which gives: $\quad x = 4L\left(\dfrac{1}{3} + \dfrac{1}{12} - \dfrac{5}{24}\right) = 0.8333L$

The resultant is $\mathbf{R} = -\dfrac{w_0 L}{4}(\mathbf{i}+\mathbf{j})$ intersecting the x axis at $x = 0.833L$ ◆

3.51

By symmetry, $\bar{x} = 0.4$ m.

Using the fact that the length of the loading along the x axis is 0.8 m:

$P_1 = 80(1.5)(0.8) = 96$ kN

$P_2 = 0.5(40)(1.5)(0.8) = 24$ kN

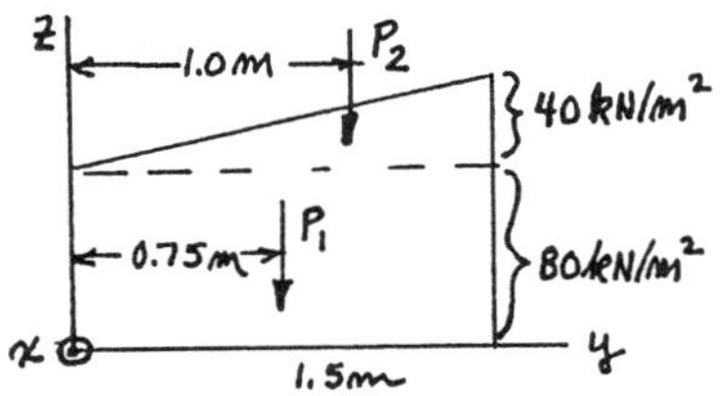

$R_z = \Sigma F_z$:

$+\uparrow\ R = -P_1 - P_2 = -96 - 24 = -120$ kN

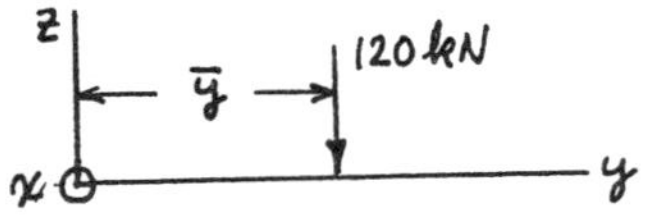

$\Sigma M_x = R\bar{y}$: $\quad -96(0.75) - 24(1.0) = -120\bar{y}$

which gives $\bar{y} = 0.800$ m

The resultant is the force $\mathbf{R} = -120\mathbf{k}$ kN passing through the point (0.4 m, 0.8 m, 0)

3.52

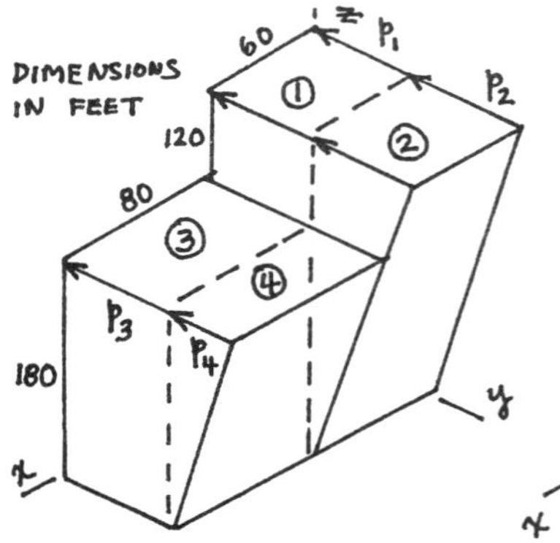

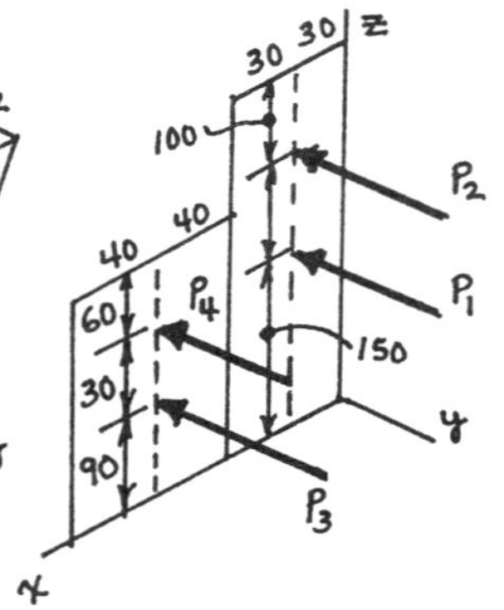

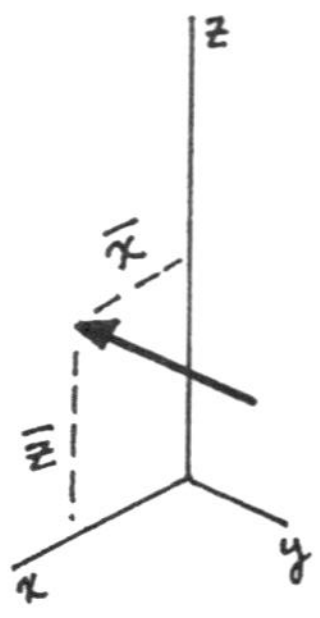

$p_1 = p_3 = 1.8$ lb/ft^2 ; $p_2 = 1.4$ lb/ft^2

By similar triangles, the pressure p_4 is given by: $\quad p_4/180 = p_2/300$

which gives $p_4 = (180/300)1.4 = 0.84$ lb/ft^2

$P_1 = 1.8(60)(300) = 32\,400$ lb

$P_2 = 0.5(1.4)(60)(300) = 12\,600$ lb

$P_3 = 1.8(80)(180) = 25\,920$ lb

$P_4 = 0.5(0.84)(80)(180) = 6050$ lb

$R = \Sigma P$: $\quad R = 32\,400 + 12\,600 + 25\,920 + 6050 = 76\,970$ lb

$\Sigma M_x = R\,\bar{z} \quad P_1(150) + P_2(200) + P_3(90) + P_4(120) = 76\,970\,\bar{z}$

Substituting the values for the P's and solving gives: $\bar{z} = 135.6$ ft

$\Sigma M_z = R\,\bar{x} \quad (P_1 + P_2)30 + (P_3 + P_4)100 = 76\,970\,\bar{x}$

Substituting the values for the P's and solving gives: $\bar{x} = 59.1$ ft

The resultant is $\mathbf{R} = -76\,970\,\mathbf{j}$ lb acting through the point: (59.1 ft, 0, 135.6 ft). ◆

3.53

$R_1 = 10(2.4) = 24$ MN

$d_1 = 0.5(2.4) = 1.2$ m

$R_2 = 6(1.25) = 7.5$ MN

$d_2 = 0.75 + 0.5(1.25)$

$= 1.375$ m

$R_3 = 0.5(4)(1.25) = 2.5$ MN

$d_3 = 0.75 + (2/3)(1.25)$

$= 1.583$ m

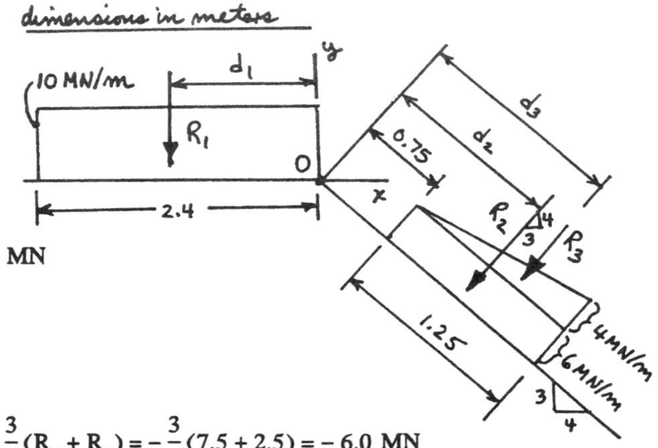

$R_x = \Sigma F_x$: $\overset{+}{\rightarrow}$ $R_x = -\frac{3}{5}(R_2 + R_3) = -\frac{3}{5}(7.5 + 2.5) = -6.0$ MN

$R_y = \Sigma F_y$: $+\uparrow$ $R_y = -R_1 - \frac{4}{5}(R_2 + R_3) = -24 - \frac{4}{5}(7.5 + 2.5) = -32.0$ MN

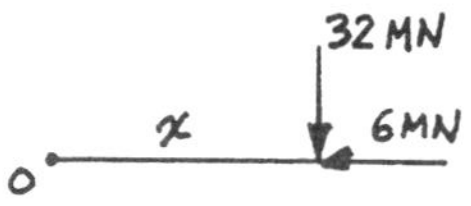

$\Sigma M_O = Rd$: (+↺) $-R_1 d_1 + R_2 d_2 + R_3 d_3 = 32x$

$\therefore x = \frac{1}{32}\left[-24(1.2) + 7.5(1.375) + 2.5(1.583)\right] = -0.454$ m

The resultant is $\mathbf{R} = -6\mathbf{i} - 32\mathbf{j}$ MN intersecting the x axis at $x = -0.454$ m. ◆

3.54

$R_1 = 0.5(750)(20)\sqrt{6^2 + 12^2}$

$= 100.6$ kips

$R_2 = 750(20)(7.5)$

$= 112.5$ kips

$R_3 = 0.5(7.5)(467)(20)$

$= 35.0$ kips

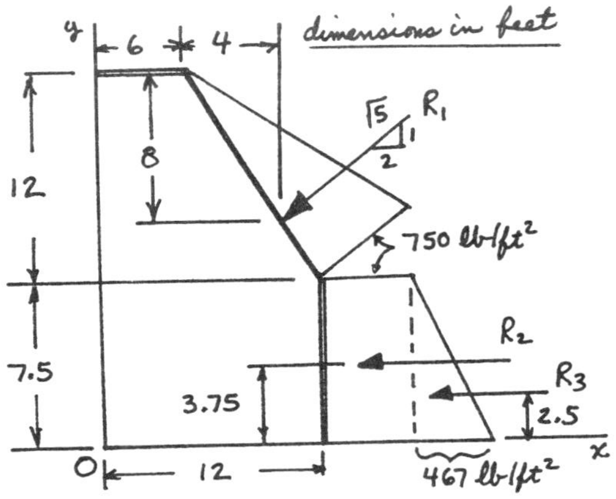

(continued)

$R_x = \Sigma F_x$:

$\overset{+}{\rightarrow}$ $R_x = -\frac{2}{\sqrt{5}}R_1 - R_2 - R_3 = \left[-\frac{2}{\sqrt{5}}(100.6) - 112.5 - 35.0\right] \times 10^3 = -237 \times 10^3$ lb

$R_y = \Sigma F_y$: $+\uparrow$ $R_y = -\frac{1}{\sqrt{5}}R_1 = -\frac{1}{\sqrt{5}}(100.6 \times 10^3) = -45.0 \times 10^3$ lb

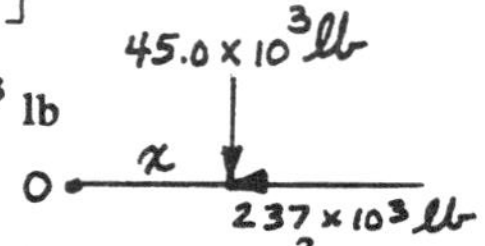

$\Sigma M_O = Rd$: (+↺) $\frac{1}{\sqrt{5}}R_1(10) - \frac{2}{\sqrt{5}}R_1(11.5) - R_2(3.75) - R_3(2.5) = (45.0 \times 10^3)x$

$x = \frac{1}{45}\left[\frac{1}{\sqrt{5}}(100.6)(10) - \frac{2}{\sqrt{5}}(100.6)(11.5) - 112.5(3.75) - 35.0(2.5)\right] = -24.3$ ft

The resultant force is $\mathbf{R} = (-237 \times 10^3)\mathbf{i} - (45.0 \times 10^3)\mathbf{j}$ lb acting through the point: (– 24.3 ft, 0). ◆

3.55

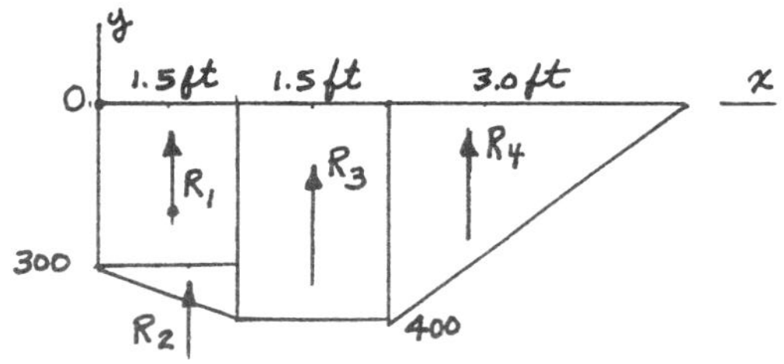

$R_1 = 1.5(300) = 450$ lb $\bar{x}_1 = 0.5(1.5) = 0.75$ ft

$R_2 = 0.5(1.5)(100) = 75$ lb $\bar{x}_2 = (2/3)(1.5) = 1.00$ ft

$R_3 = 1.5(400) = 600$ lb $\bar{x}_3 = 1.5 + 0.5(1.5) = 2.25$ ft

$R_4 = 0.5(3.0)(400) = 600$ lb $\bar{x}_4 = 3 + (1/3)(3) = 4.00$ ft

$\therefore R = \Sigma F_y$: $+\uparrow$ $R = 450 + 75 + 600 + 600 = 1725$ lb

$\Sigma M_O = Rd$: (+↺) $450(0.75) + 75(1.00) + 600(2.25) + 600(4.00) = 1725x$

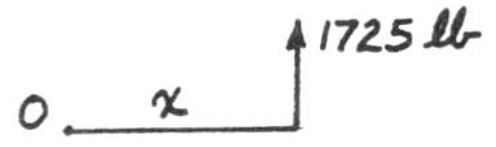

$\therefore x = \frac{4162.5}{1725} = 2.413$ ft

The resultant is $\mathbf{R} = 1725\mathbf{j}$ lb acting through the point: (2.41 ft, 0). ◆

3.56

$R_x = \Sigma F_x$: $\overset{+}{\rightarrow}$ $400\cos 30^\circ = T_1 \cos 50^\circ + T_2 \cos 20^\circ - 95$ (1)

$R_y = \Sigma F_y$: $+\uparrow$ $400\sin 30^\circ = T_1 \sin 50^\circ - T_2 \sin 20^\circ$ (2)

Solving (1) and (2) gives: $T_1 = 361$ lb and $T_2 = 223$ lb ◆

3.57

$R_x = \Sigma F_x = 0$: $\overset{+}{\rightarrow}$ $0.6P - 0.8Q = 0$ (1)

$R_y = \Sigma F_y = 0$: $+\uparrow$ $0.8P - 0.6Q - 20 = 0$ (2)

Solving (1) and (2) gives: $P = 57.1$ lb and $Q = 42.9$ lb ◆

$C^R = \Sigma M_{origin}$ (+↺) $50 = C - 0.6P(3) - 0.6Q(4) - 20(2)$

$\therefore$ $C = 296$ lb•ft ◆

3.58

$\mathbf{R} = -600\mathbf{k}$ kN $x = 3$ m $y = 2$ m

$R = \Sigma F_y$ $+\uparrow$ $-600 = -P - Q - 50$ (1)

$\Sigma M_x = R\bar{y}$ $-Qd = -600(2)$ (2)

$\Sigma M_y = -R\bar{x}$ $P(4) = -(-600)(3)$ (3)

Solving (1), (2), and (3) gives: $P = 450$ N; $Q = 100$ N; and $d = 12.0$ m ◆

3.59

$\mathbf{T}_1 = T_1 \vec{\lambda}_{AB} = T_1(-0.6\mathbf{i} - 0.8\mathbf{j})$ $\mathbf{T}_2 = T_2 \vec{\lambda}_{AC} = T_2(-\cos 30^\circ \mathbf{j} + \sin 30^\circ \mathbf{k})$

$\mathbf{T}_3 = T_3 \vec{\lambda}_{AD} = T_3\left(\frac{4\mathbf{i} - 8\mathbf{j}}{\sqrt{80}}\right)$

$\mathbf{R} = \mathbf{T}_1 + \mathbf{T}_2 + \mathbf{T}_3 + 60\mathbf{j} - 20\mathbf{k} = \mathbf{0}$

(continued)

Equating each of the components to zero, we obtain:

(i-component) $-0.6T_1 + \frac{4}{\sqrt{80}}T_3 = 0$ (1)

(j-component) $-0.8T_1 - \cos 30^\circ T_2 - \frac{8}{\sqrt{80}}T_3 + 60 = 0$ (2)

(k-component) $\sin 30^\circ T_2 - 20 = 0$ (3)

Solving (1), (2), and (3) gives:

$T_1 = 12.68$ kN ; $T_2 = 40.00$ kN ; $T_3 = 17.01$ kN ◆

3.60

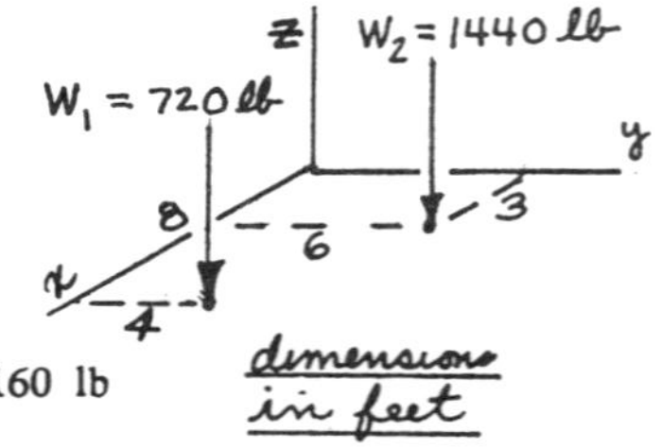

$W_1 = 20(0.5)(12)(6) = 720$ lb

$W_2 = 20(6)(12) = 1440$ lb

$R = \Sigma F_z$

$+\uparrow$ $R = -W_1 - W_2 = -720 - 1440 = -2160$ lb

$\Sigma M_x = R\bar{y}$ $-720(4) - 1440(6) = -2160\bar{y}$ $\therefore$ $\bar{y} = 5.33$ ft

$\Sigma M_y = -R\bar{x}$ $720(8) + 1440(3) = -(-2160)\,\bar{x}$ $\therefore$ $\bar{x} = 4.67$ ft

The coordinates of the point where R intersects the plate are (4.67 ft, 5.33 ft, 0) ◆

3.61

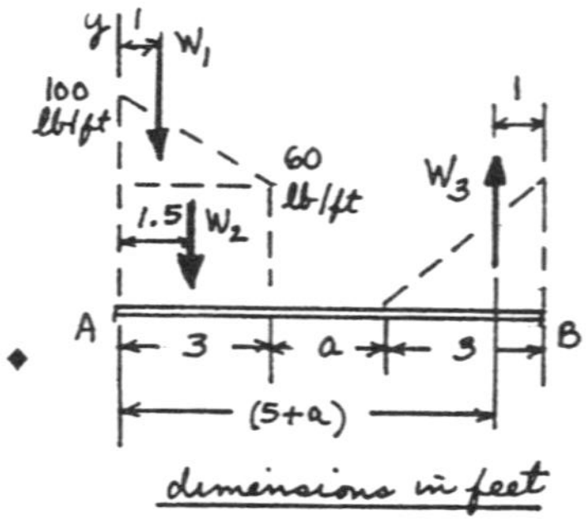

$W_1 = 0.5(3)(40) = 60$ lb

$W_2 = 3(60) = 180$ lb

$W_3 = 0.5(3)(w) = 1.5\,w$ lb

$R = \Sigma F_y = 0$

$+\uparrow$ $-60 - 180 + 1.5\,w = 0$ $\therefore$ $w = 160$ lb/ft ◆

$\Sigma M_A = 1200$ lb•ft (CCW):

(+↺) $1200 = -60(1) - 180(1.5) + 1.5\,w(5 + a)$

Substituting $w = 160$ lb/ft, and solving gives $a = 1.375$ ft ◆

3.62

(a) $\mathbf{R} = \Sigma\mathbf{F} = -200\mathbf{i} + 300\mathbf{j} + (200 + 250 - 300)\mathbf{k} = -200\mathbf{i} + 300\mathbf{j} + 150\mathbf{k}$ lb ◆

$\mathbf{C}^R = \Sigma\mathbf{M}_O = 250(5)\mathbf{i} + 300(2)\mathbf{j} + 200(5)\mathbf{k} = 1250\mathbf{i} + 600\mathbf{j} + 1000\mathbf{k}$ lb•ft ◆

(b) The unit vector in the direction of **R** is

$$\vec{\lambda} = \frac{\mathbf{R}}{R} = \frac{-200\mathbf{i} + 300\mathbf{j} + 150\mathbf{k}}{390.5} = -0.5122\mathbf{i} + 0.7683\mathbf{j} + 0.3841\mathbf{k}$$

The component of $\mathbf{C}^R$ that is in the direction of $\vec{\lambda}$ is:

$$C_t^R = \mathbf{C}^R \bullet \vec{\lambda} = (1250\mathbf{i} + 600\mathbf{j} + 1000\mathbf{k}) \bullet (-0.5122\mathbf{i} + 0.7683\mathbf{j} + 0.3841\mathbf{k})$$

$$= 1250(-0.5122) + 600(0.7683) + 1000(0.3841) = 204.83 \text{ lb•ft}$$

$$\mathbf{C}_t^R = 204.83\,\vec{\lambda}$$

$$= 204.83(-0.5122\mathbf{i} + 0.7683\mathbf{j} + 0.3841\mathbf{k}) = -104.91\mathbf{i} + 157.37\mathbf{j} + 78.68\mathbf{k} \text{ lb•ft}$$

The component of $\mathbf{C}^R$ that is normal to $\vec{\lambda}$ is:

$$\mathbf{C}_n^R = \mathbf{C}^R - \mathbf{C}_t^R = (1250\mathbf{i} + 600\mathbf{j} + 1000\mathbf{k}) - (-104.91\mathbf{i} + 157.37\mathbf{j} + 78.68\mathbf{k})$$

$$= 1354.91\mathbf{i} + 442.63\mathbf{j} + 921.32\mathbf{k} \text{ lb•ft}$$

Let A be the point where the axis of the wrench passes through the xy plane:

$\mathbf{r}_{OA} = x\mathbf{i} + y\mathbf{j}$ m.

$$\mathbf{r}_{OA} \times \mathbf{R} = \mathbf{C}_n^R \text{ becomes: } \begin{vmatrix} \mathbf{i} & \mathbf{j} & \mathbf{k} \\ x & y & 0 \\ -200 & 300 & 150 \end{vmatrix} = 1354.91\mathbf{i} + 442.63\mathbf{j} + 921.32\mathbf{k} \text{ lb•ft}$$

Expanding the determinant, and equating like components gives:

(i-components): $150y = 1354.91$ lb•ft which gives: $y = 9.033$ ft

(j-components): $-150x = 442.63$ lb•ft which gives: $x = -2.951$ ft

Wrench: force = $-200\mathbf{i} + 300\mathbf{j} + 150\mathbf{k}$ lb; couple = $-104.9\mathbf{i} + 157.4\mathbf{j} + 78.7\mathbf{k}$ lb•ft

wrench axis passes through (− 2.95 ft, 9.03 ft, 0) ◆

3.63

$R_z = \Sigma F_z$: $+\uparrow$ $30 = T_1 + T_2 + T_3 = 6 + 14 + T_3$ $\therefore T_3 = 30 - 20 = 10$ lb ◆

$\Sigma M_x = 0$: $T_1(2) - T_2(3) + T_3 y = 0$

$6(2) - 14(3) + 10y = 0$ $\therefore y = 30/10 = 3.00$ in. ◆

$\Sigma M_y = 0$: $T_1(6) - T_2(2) - T_3 x = 0$

$6(6) - 14(2) - 10x = 0$ $\therefore x = 8/10 = 0.80$ in. ◆

3.64

$R_y = \Sigma F_y$: $+\uparrow$ $R_y = 100\sin 30^\circ - 50 = 0$ (1)

$R_x = \Sigma F_x$: $\overset{+}{\rightarrow}$ $R_x = P + 100\cos 30^\circ$ (2)

$\Sigma M_O = Rd$

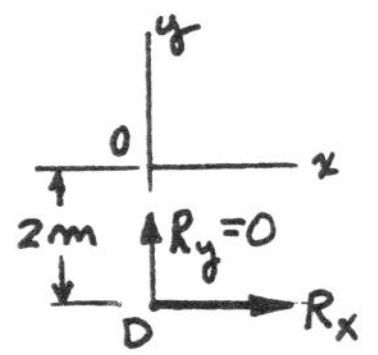

$\circlearrowleft +$ $100(4) - P(4) + 50(4) - 140 = R_x(2)$ (3)

Solving (2) and (3) gives: $P = 47.8$ kN ◆ and $R_x = 134.4$ kN $\therefore \mathbf{R} = 134.4\mathbf{i}$ kN ◆

3.65

$R = \Sigma F_z$: $+\uparrow$ $R = -40 - 25 - 35 = -100$ kN

$\Sigma M_x = Ry$: $35(4) + 25(4\sin 40^\circ) - 40(4\sin 30^\circ) = -100y$ $\therefore y = -1.243$ m ◆

$\Sigma M_y = -Rx$: $25(4\cos 40^\circ) - 40(4\cos 30^\circ) = -(-100)x$ $\therefore x = -0.620$ m ◆

3.66

$$\mathbf{F}_1 = 260\,\vec{\lambda}_{AB} = 260\left(\frac{4\mathbf{i} + 12\mathbf{j} - 3\mathbf{k}}{13}\right) = 80\mathbf{i} + 240\mathbf{j} - 60\mathbf{k} \text{ N};\ \mathbf{F}_2 = 300\mathbf{k} \text{ N}$$

$\therefore \mathbf{R} = \mathbf{F}_1 + \mathbf{F}_2 = 80\mathbf{i} + 240\mathbf{j} + 240\mathbf{k}$ N ◆

$$\mathbf{C} = 780\,\vec{\lambda}_{BA} = 780\left(\frac{-4\mathbf{i} - 12\mathbf{j} + 3\mathbf{k}}{13}\right) = -240\mathbf{i} - 720\mathbf{j} + 180\mathbf{k} \text{ N•m}$$

$\mathbf{C}^R = \Sigma\mathbf{M}_E = (\mathbf{r}_{EB} \times \mathbf{F}_1) + \mathbf{C}$ where $\mathbf{r}_{EB} = 12\mathbf{j}$ m

$$\mathbf{C}^R = \begin{vmatrix} \mathbf{i} & \mathbf{j} & \mathbf{k} \\ 0 & 12 & 0 \\ 80 & 240 & -60 \end{vmatrix} + (-240\mathbf{i} - 720\mathbf{j} + 180\mathbf{k})$$

$\therefore \mathbf{C}^R = (-720\mathbf{i} - 960\mathbf{k}) + (-240\mathbf{i} - 720\mathbf{j} + 180\mathbf{k}) = -960\mathbf{i} - 720\mathbf{j} - 780\mathbf{k}$ N•m ◆

3.67

(a) $R_x = \Sigma F_x$: $\overset{+}{\rightarrow}$ $R_x = 200 - (3/5)150 - (4/5)90 = 38$ lb

$R_y = \Sigma F_y$: $+\uparrow$ $R_y = (4/5)150 - (3/5)90 = 66$ lb

$C^R = \Sigma M_O$: $\circlearrowleft +$ $C^R = 800 + 150(2.5) = 1175$ lb•ft

Therefore, the equivalent force-couple system with the force acting at point O is:

$\mathbf{R} = 38\mathbf{i} + 66\mathbf{j}$ lb; $C^R = 1175$ lb•ft CCW ◆

(b) The force acting at point A is the same **R** that was found in part (a).

$C^R = \Sigma M_A$: $\circlearrowleft +$ $C^R = 800 + 200(3) - 150(2.5) = 1025$ lb•ft

Therefore, the equivalent force-couple system with the force acting at point A is:

$\mathbf{R} = 38\mathbf{i} + 66\mathbf{j}$ lb; $C^R = 1025$ lb•ft CCW ◆

3.68

$R_x = \Sigma F_x$: $\overset{+}{\rightarrow}$ $R_x = 300\cos 60^\circ + 100 + 200\cos 30^\circ = 423.2$ lb

$R_y = \Sigma F_y$: $+\uparrow$ $R_y = 300\sin 60^\circ - 200\sin 30^\circ = 159.8$ lb

$\therefore\ R = \sqrt{423.2^2 + 159.8^2} = 452$ lb ◆

3.69

$$\mathbf{P} = 120\vec{\lambda}_{AC} = 120\left(\frac{-1.5\mathbf{i} + 2\mathbf{j}}{2.5}\right) = 120(-0.6\mathbf{i} + 0.8\mathbf{j}) = -72.0\mathbf{i} + 96.0\mathbf{j}\text{ N}$$

$$\mathbf{C}^R = 180\vec{\lambda}_{AB} = 180\left(\frac{-1.5\mathbf{i} + 2\mathbf{k}}{2.5}\right) = -108.0\mathbf{i} + 144.0\mathbf{k}\text{ N·m}$$

The component of $\mathbf{C}^R$ that is in the direction of $\vec{\lambda}_{AC}$ is:

$$C_t^R = \mathbf{C}^R \cdot \vec{\lambda}_{AC} = (-108.0\mathbf{i} + 144.0\mathbf{k})\cdot(-0.6\mathbf{i} + 0.8\mathbf{j}) = -108.0(-0.6) = 64.80\text{ N·m}$$

$$\mathbf{C}_t^R = 64.80\vec{\lambda}_{AC} = 64.80(-0.6\mathbf{i} + 0.8\mathbf{j}) = -38.88\mathbf{i} + 51.84\mathbf{j}\text{ N·m}$$

(continued)

The component of $\mathbf{C}^R$ that is normal to $\vec{\lambda}_{AC}$ is:

$$\mathbf{C}_n^R = \mathbf{C}^R - \mathbf{C}_t^R = (-108.0\mathbf{i} + 144.0\mathbf{k}) - (-38.88\mathbf{i} + 51.84\mathbf{j})$$
$$= -69.12\mathbf{i} - 51.84\mathbf{j} + 144.0\mathbf{k}\text{ N·m}$$

Let D be the point where the axis of the wrench passes through the yz plane:

$\mathbf{r}_{AD} = (x_D - 1.5)\mathbf{i} + z_D\mathbf{k}$ m

$$\mathbf{r}_{AD}\times\mathbf{P} = \mathbf{C}_n^R \text{ becomes: } \begin{vmatrix} \mathbf{i} & \mathbf{j} & \mathbf{k} \\ x_D - 1.5 & 0 & z_D \\ -72.0 & 96.0 & 0 \end{vmatrix} = -69.12\mathbf{i} - 51.84\mathbf{j} + 144.0\mathbf{k}\text{ N·m}$$

Expanding the determinant, and equating like components gives:

(**i**-components): $-96.0z_D = -69.12$ N•m which gives: $z_D = 0.720$ m

(**k**-components): $96.0(x_D - 1.5) = 144.0$ N•m which gives: $x_D = 3.00$ m

Wrench: force $= -72.0\mathbf{i} + 96.0\mathbf{j}$ N; couple $= -38.88\mathbf{i} + 51.84\mathbf{j}$ N•m

wrench axis passes through (3.00 m, 0, 0.720 m) ◆

3.70

$$\mathbf{T}_1 = T_1\vec{\lambda}_1 = T_1\left(\frac{3\mathbf{i} - 2\mathbf{j} - 8\mathbf{k}}{\sqrt{77}}\right) = T_1(0.3419\mathbf{i} - 0.2279\mathbf{j} - 0.9117\mathbf{k})\text{ N}$$

$$\mathbf{T}_2 = T_2\vec{\lambda}_2 = T_2\left(\frac{3\mathbf{j} - 8\mathbf{k}}{\sqrt{73}}\right) = T_2(0.3511\mathbf{j} - 0.9363\mathbf{k})\text{ N}$$

$$\mathbf{T}_3 = T_3\vec{\lambda}_3 = 500\left(\frac{-4\mathbf{i} - 8\mathbf{k}}{\sqrt{80}}\right) = -223.6\mathbf{i} - 447.2\mathbf{k}\text{ N}$$

$\mathbf{R} = R\mathbf{k} = \mathbf{T}_1 + \mathbf{T}_2 + \mathbf{T}_3$

Equating like components gives:

(**i**-component) $0 = 0.3419T_1 - 223.6$ (1)

(**j**-component) $0 = -0.2279T_1 + 0.3511T_2$ (2)

(**k**-component) $R = -0.9117T_1 - 0.9363T_2 - 447.2$ (3)

Solving (1), (2), and (3) gives: $T_1 = 654$ N; $T_2 = 425$ N; $R = -1441$ N ◆

4.1

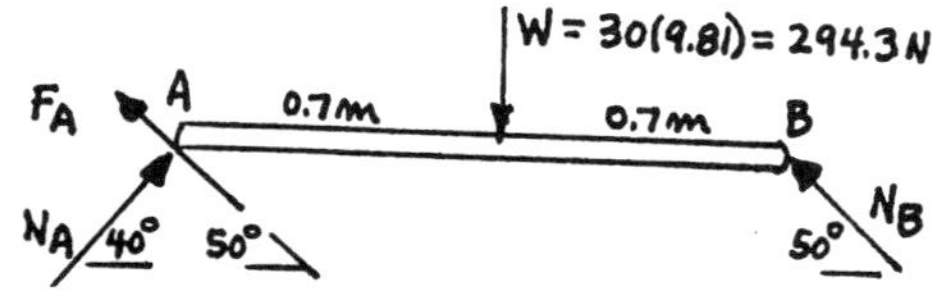

3 unknowns ◆
(N_A, F_A, N_B)

4.2

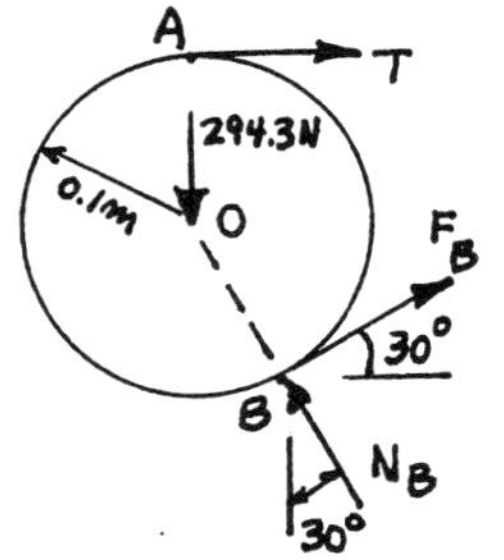

W = 30(9.81) = 294.3 N
3 unknowns ◆
(N_B, F_B, T)

4.3

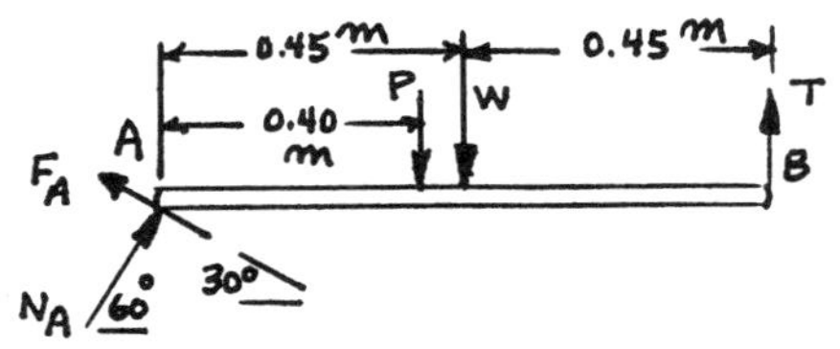

W = 30(9.81) = 294.3 N
P = 0.5(0.6)(800) = 240 N
3 unknowns ◆
(N_A, F_A, T)

4.4

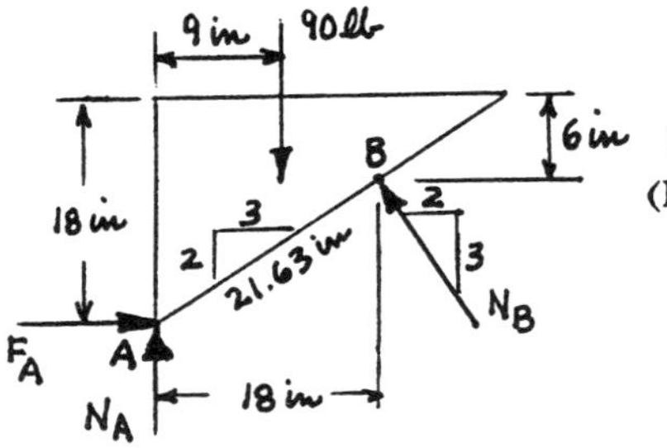

3 unknowns ◆
(N_A, F_A, N_B)

4.5

(a)

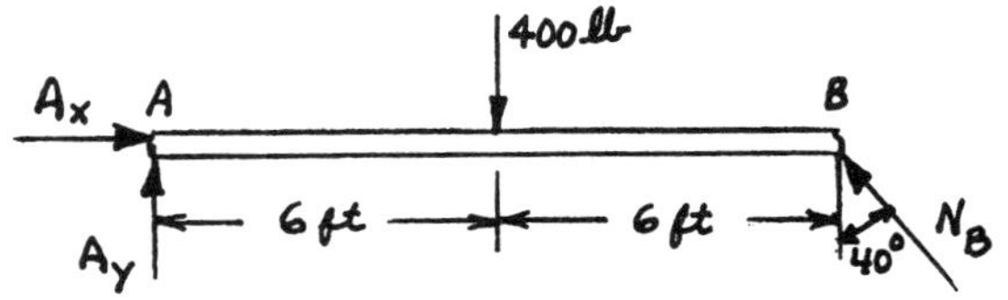

3 unknowns ◆
(A_x, A_y, N_B)

(b)

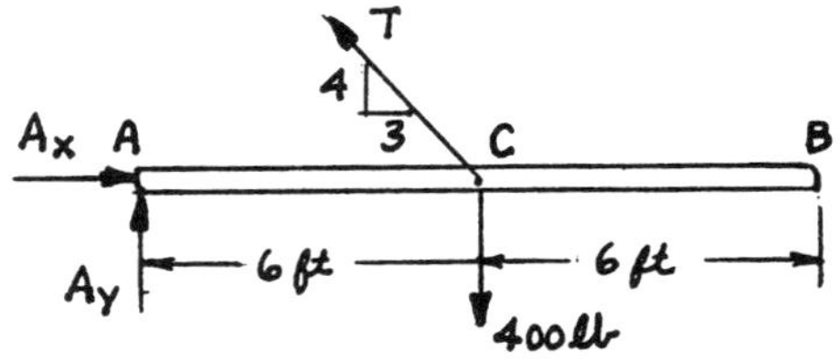

3 unknowns ◆
(A_x, A_y, T)

(c)

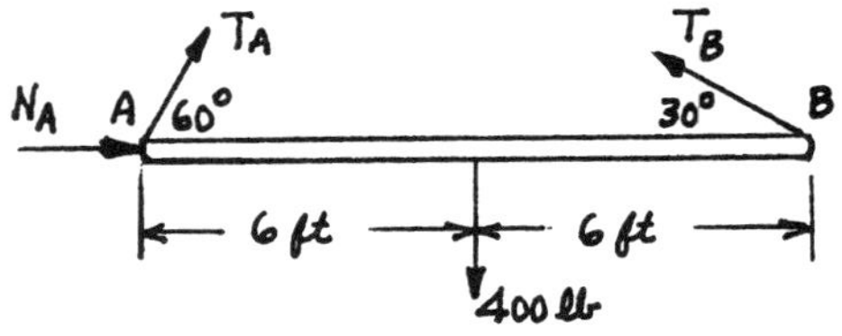

3 unknowns ◆
(N_A, T_A, T_B)

(d)

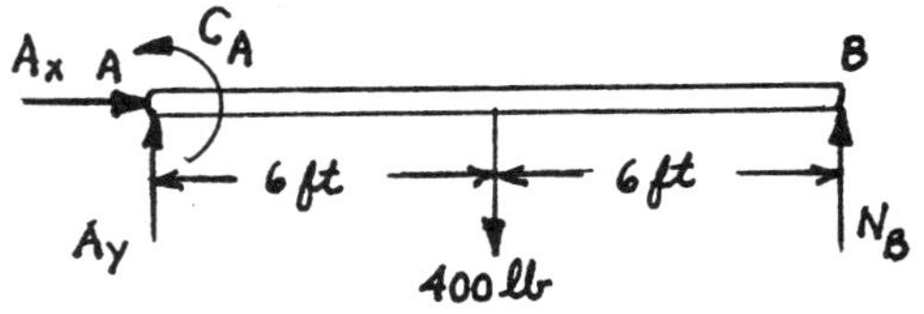

4 unknowns ◆
(A_x, A_y, N_B, C_A)

4.6

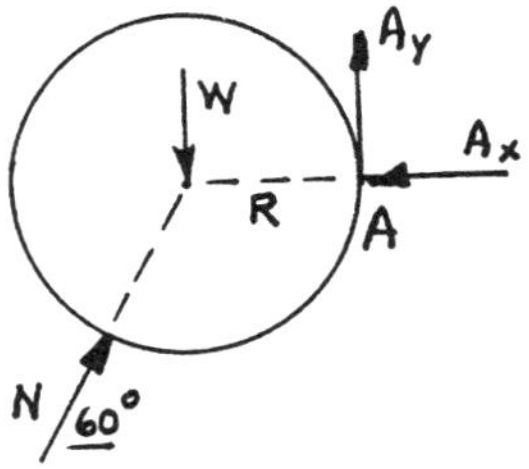

(a)
3 unknowns ◆
(A_x, A_y, N)

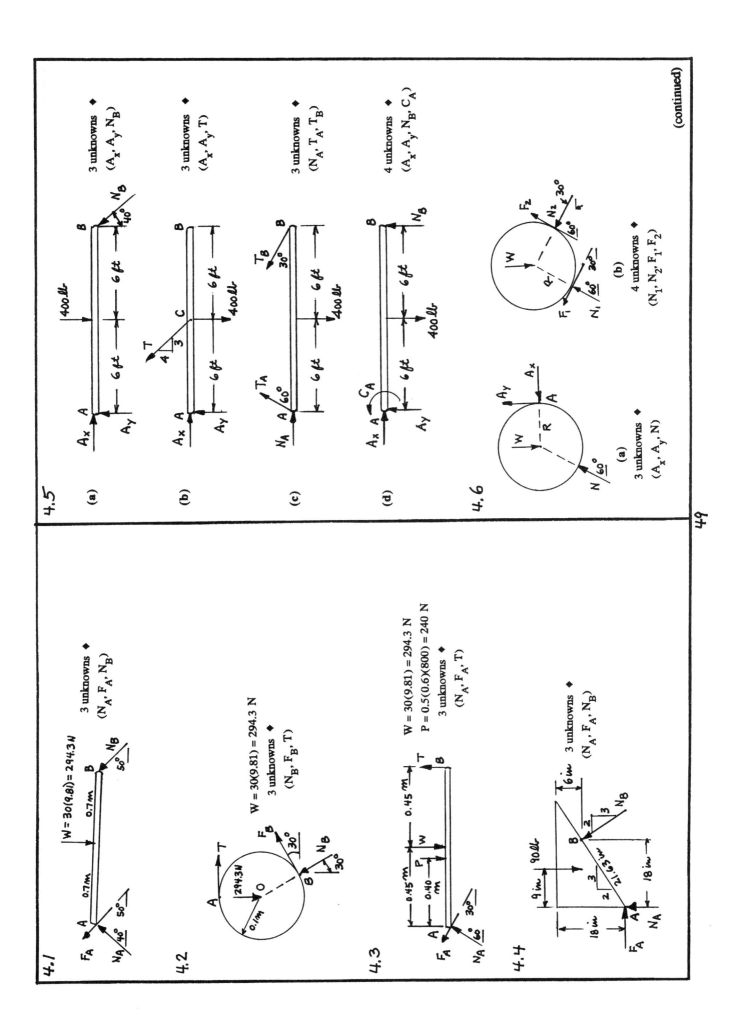

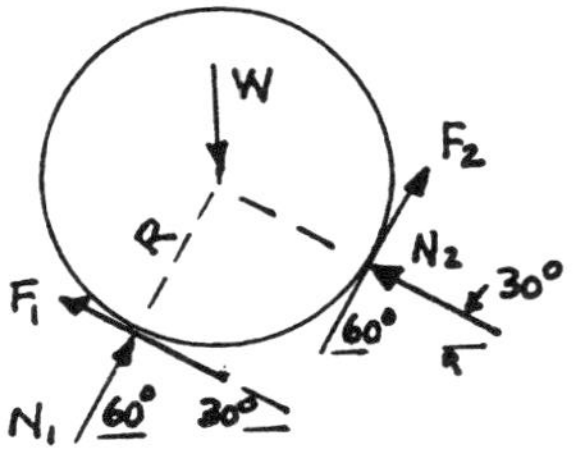

(b)
4 unknowns ◆
(N_1, N_2, F_1, F_2)

(continued)

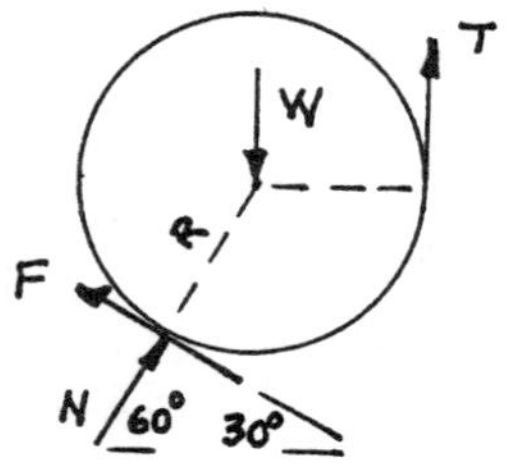

(c)

3 unknowns ◆

(N, F, T)

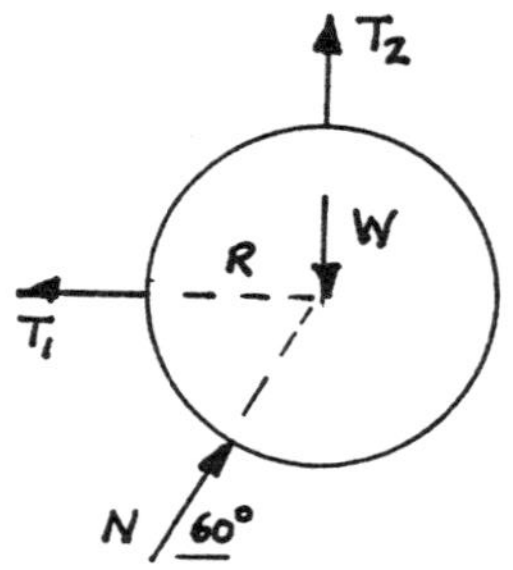

(d)

3 unknowns ◆

(T_1, T_2, N)

4.7

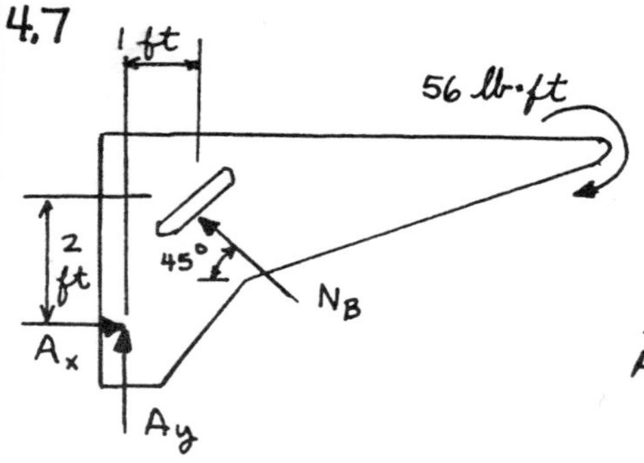

(a)

3 unknowns ◆

(A_x, A_y, N_B)

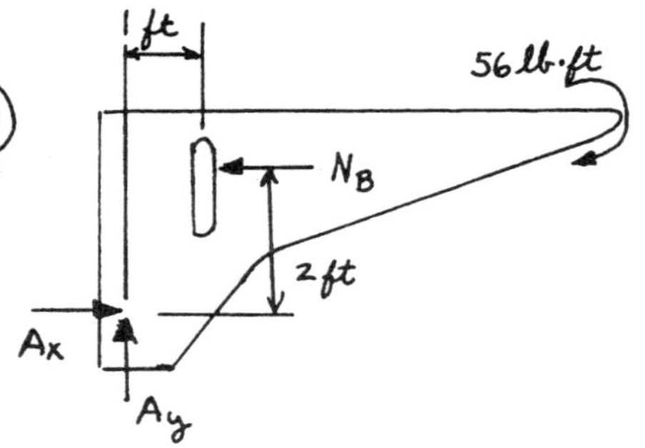

(b)

3 unknowns ◆

(A_x, A_y, N_B)

4.8

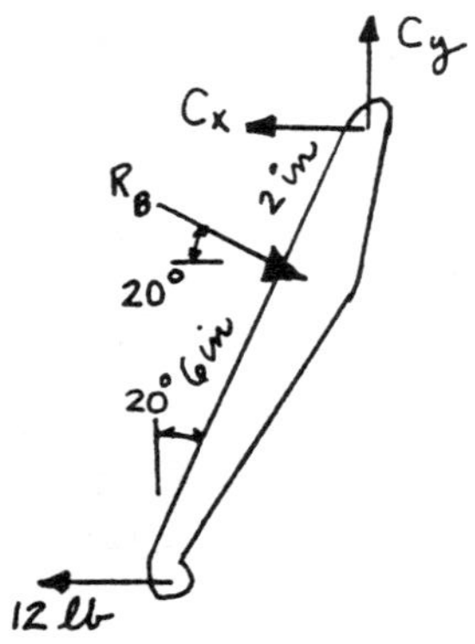

3 unknowns ◆

(C_x, C_y, R_B)

4.9

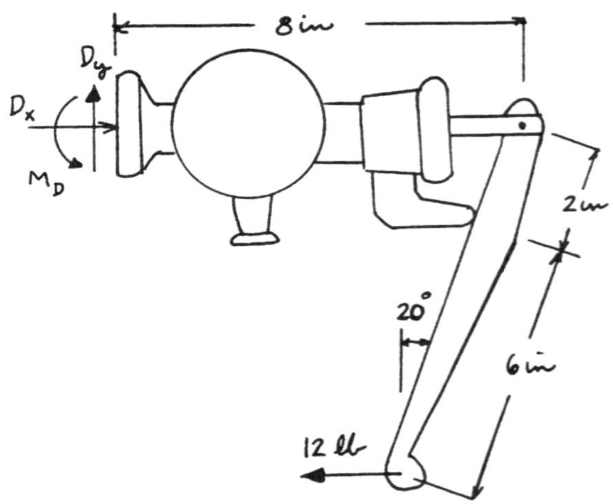

3 unknowns ◆

(D_x, D_y, M_D)

4.10

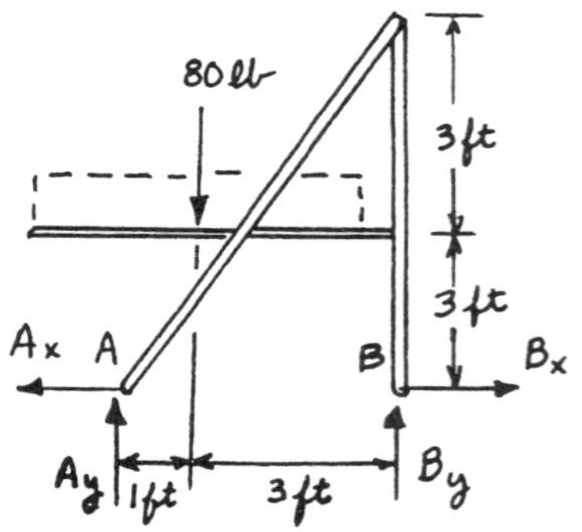

4 unknowns ◆

(A_x, A_y, B_x, B_y)

4.11

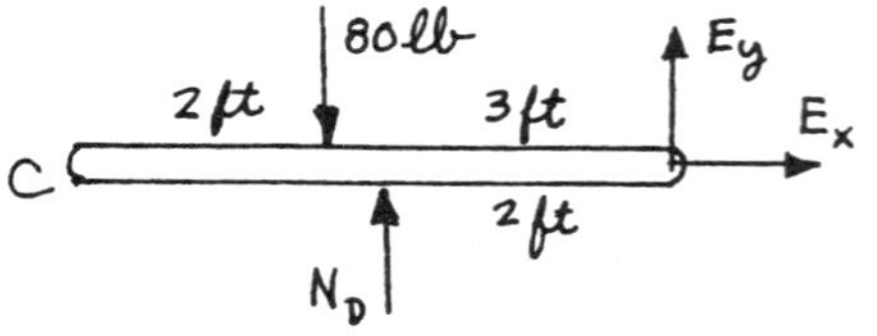

3 unknowns ◆

(E_x, E_y, N_D)

4.12

Refer to the given FBD. Let the x-axis be parallel to the inclined plane and the y-axis be perpendicular to the inclined plane.

$\Sigma F_x = 0$: $+\nearrow$ $N_A - W\sin\theta = 0$ $\qquad N_A = W\sin\theta \qquad (1)$

$\Sigma F_y = 0$: $\nwarrow +$ $N_B - W\cos\theta = 0$ $\qquad N_B = W\cos\theta \qquad (2)$

Dividing (1) by (2): $\dfrac{\sin\theta}{\cos\theta} = \tan\theta = \dfrac{N_A}{N_B}$. Using $N_B = 1.5\,N_A$, $\theta = \tan^{-1}(1/1.5) = 33.7^\circ$ ◆

$N_A = W\sin 33.7^\circ = 0.555\,W$ ◆ $\qquad N_B = W\cos 33.7^\circ = 0.832\,W$ ◆

4.13

Refer to the given FBD.

$\Sigma M_A = 0$: (+ ↻) $4P - 120(4\sin 20^\circ) = 0$ $\qquad \therefore P = 120\sin 20^\circ = 41.0$ lb ◆

4.14

Refer to the given FBD.

$\Sigma M_A = 0$: (+ ↻) $P\cos 20^\circ(4\cos 20^\circ) - P\sin 20^\circ(4\sin 20^\circ) - 120(4\sin 20^\circ) = 0$

$$P = \frac{120\sin 20^\circ}{\cos^2 20^\circ - \sin^2 20^\circ} = 53.6 \text{ lb}$$ ◆

4.15

Refer to the given FBD.

$\Sigma M_D = 0$: (+ ↺) $T_C(3 + 4\tan 30^\circ) - 200(2) = 0$ $\qquad \therefore T_C = 75.34$ lb ◆

$\Sigma F_x = 0$: $\overset{+}{\rightarrow}$ $T_C - T_B\cos 30^\circ = 0$ $\qquad \therefore T_B = \dfrac{T_C}{\cos 30^\circ} = \dfrac{75.34}{\cos 30^\circ} = 87.00$ lb ◆

$\Sigma F_y = 0$: $+\uparrow$ $T_A + T_B\sin 30^\circ - 200 = 0$

$\therefore T_A = 200 - T_B\sin 30^\circ = 200 - 87.00\sin 30^\circ = 156.5$ lb ◆

4.16

Refer to the given FBD.

$\Sigma M_A = 0$: (+ ↻) $C_A + 0.8(10\sin 16^\circ) + 0.8(20\sin 16^\circ - 10) + 2(20\sin 16^\circ - 24) = 0$

$\therefore C_A = 38.4$ lb•in ◆

4.17

Refer to the given FBD.

$\Sigma M_A = 0$: (+ ↻) $0.8(10\sin\theta) + 0.8(20\sin\theta - 10) + 2(20\sin\theta - 24) = 0$

$8\sin\theta + (16\sin\theta - 8) + (40\sin\theta - 48) = 0$

$\therefore \theta = \sin^{-1}(56/64) = 61.0^\circ$ ◆

4.18

Refer to the given FBD.

$\Sigma M_A = 0$: (+ ↺) $2500(2/\cos\theta) - 3730(4\sin\theta) = 0$

$\sin\theta\cos\theta = (1/2)\sin 2\theta = 0.3351$ $\qquad \therefore \theta = 21.0^\circ$ ◆

4.19

Refer to the given FBD. Let the x-axis be horizontal, and the y-axis be vertical.

$\Sigma M_A = 0$: (+ ↺) $\dfrac{8}{17}T(15) - 480(8) + C_A = 0$ $\qquad \therefore C_A = 8\left(480 - \dfrac{15}{17}T\right)$ lb•ft

$\Sigma F_x = 0$: $\overset{+}{\rightarrow}$ $A_x - \dfrac{8}{17}T = 0$ $\qquad \therefore A_x = \dfrac{8}{17}T$ lb

$\Sigma F_y = 0$: $+\uparrow$ $A_y - 480 - \dfrac{15}{17}T = 0$ $\qquad \therefore A_y = 480 + \dfrac{15}{17}T$ lb

(a) $T = 544$ lb

$C_A = 8\left[480 - \dfrac{15}{17}(544)\right] = 0$ ◆

$A_x = \dfrac{8}{17}(544) = 256$ lb ◆ $\qquad A_y = 480 + \dfrac{15}{17}(544) = 960$ lb ◆

(b) $T = 0$

$C_A = 8(480) = 3840$ lb•ft ◆ $\qquad A_x = 0$ ◆ $\qquad A_y = 480$ lb ◆

4.20

Refer to the given FBD.

$\Sigma M_D = 0$: $\circlearrowleft +$ $40(19.5\sin\theta) - 120(12\cos\theta) = 0$

$\tan\theta = (120)(12)/(40)(19.5) = 1.8462 \qquad \therefore\ \theta = 61.56^\circ$ ◆

4.21

Refer to the given FBD. Let the x-axis be horizontal, and the y-axis be vertical.

$\Sigma M_A = 0$ $\circlearrowleft +$ $N_C \sin 50^\circ(0.45 - 0.4\cos 40^\circ) - N_C \cos 50^\circ(0.4\sin 40^\circ) - 2.4 - 3(0.75) = 0$

$\therefore\ N_C = -84.12\ \text{kN}$ ◆

$\Sigma F_x = 0$: $\overset{+}{\rightarrow}$ $A_x + N_C \cos 50^\circ = 0 \qquad \therefore\ A_x = -(-84.12\cos 50^\circ) = 54.07\ \text{kN}$

$\Sigma F_y = 0$: $+\uparrow$ $A_y - 3 + N_C \sin 50^\circ = 0 \qquad \therefore\ A_y = 3 - (-84.12\sin 50^\circ) = 67.44\ \text{kN}$

$\therefore\ A = \sqrt{54.07^2 + 67.44^2} = 86.4\ \text{kN}$ ◆

4.22

Refer to the given FBD. Let the x-axis be horizontal, and the y-axis be vertical. (The force T in the inclined portion of the rope will be considered to be acting at point C.)

$\Sigma M_A = 0$: $\circlearrowleft +$ $245(2.4) + 883(3) - T(4.8) + T\sin 20^\circ(2.8) - T\cos 20^\circ(4.8) = 0$

$\therefore\ T = 387.5\ \text{N}$ ◆

$\Sigma F_x = 0$: $\overset{+}{\rightarrow}$ $-A_x + T\sin 20^\circ = 0 \qquad \therefore\ A_x = 387.5\sin 20^\circ = 132.5\ \text{N}$ ◆

$\Sigma F_y = 0$: $+\uparrow$ $A_y + T + T\cos 20^\circ - 245 - 883 = 0$

$\therefore\ A_y = 1128 - 387.5(1 + \cos 20^\circ) = 376.4\ \text{N}$ ◆

4.23

Refer to the given FBD. Let the x axis be horizontal, and the y-axis be vertical.

$\Sigma F_x = 0$: $\overset{+}{\rightarrow}$ $388\cos 70^\circ - F_D = 0 \qquad \therefore\ F_D = 132.7\ \text{N}$ ◆

$\Sigma F_y = 0$: $+\uparrow$ $N_D - 883 + 388\sin 70^\circ = 0 \qquad \therefore\ N_D = 518\ \text{N}$ ◆

$\Sigma M_D = 0$: $\circlearrowleft +$ $883b + 388\sin 70^\circ(0.8 - b) - 388\cos 70^\circ(1.2) = 0$

$\therefore\ b = -0.255\ \text{m}$ ◆

4.24

Refer to the given FBD.

$\Sigma F_x = 0$: $\overset{+}{\rightarrow}$ $T\cos 35^\circ - N\cos 30^\circ = 0 \qquad \therefore\ N = 0.9459T \quad (1)$

$\Sigma F_y = 0$: $+\uparrow$ $T\sin 35^\circ + N\sin 30^\circ - 70 = 0 \quad (2)$

Substituting (1) into (2) gives: $T\sin 35^\circ + (0.9459T)\sin 30^\circ = 70 \qquad \therefore\ T = 66.89\ \text{lb}$

$\Sigma M_B = 0$: $\circlearrowleft +$ $60(2) + 10x - T\sin 35^\circ(4) = 0$

$$\therefore\ x = \frac{66.89\sin 35^\circ(4) - 120}{10} = 3.35\ \text{ft}$$ ◆

4.25

Refer to the given FBD. Let the y-axis be vertical.

$\Sigma F_y = 0$: $+\uparrow$ $2N_B + N_B - \frac{W}{5} - \frac{4W}{5} - 6000 = 0 \qquad \therefore\ 3N_B = 6000 + W\ \text{lb} \quad (1)$

$\Sigma M_B = 0$: $\circlearrowleft +$ $\frac{W}{5}(248) + \frac{4W}{5}(152) + 6000(60) - N_A(200) = 0$

Using $N_A = 2N_B$, and simplifying: $\qquad N_B = 0.4280W + 900\ \text{lb} \quad (2)$

Solving (1) and (2) gives: $W = 11\,620\ \text{lb}$ ◆

4.26

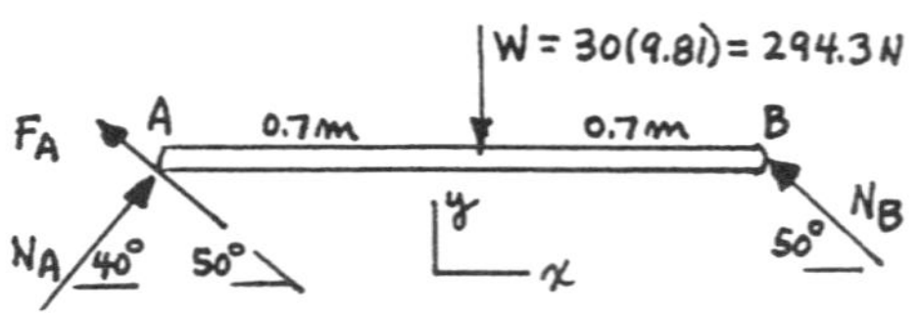

$\Sigma M_A = 0$: $\circlearrowleft +$ $N_B \sin 50^\circ(1.4)$

$- 294.3(0.7) = 0$

$\therefore\ N_B = 192.1\ \text{N}$

$\Sigma F_x = 0$: $\overset{+}{\rightarrow}$ $N_A \cos 40^\circ$

$- F_A \cos 50^\circ - N_B \cos 50^\circ = 0 \quad (1)$

$\Sigma F_y = 0$: $+\uparrow$ $N_A \sin 40^\circ + F_A \sin 50^\circ + N_B \sin 50^\circ - 294.3 = 0 \quad (2)$

(continued)

Solving (1) and (2) gives: $N_A = 189.18$ N and $F_A = 33.36$ N

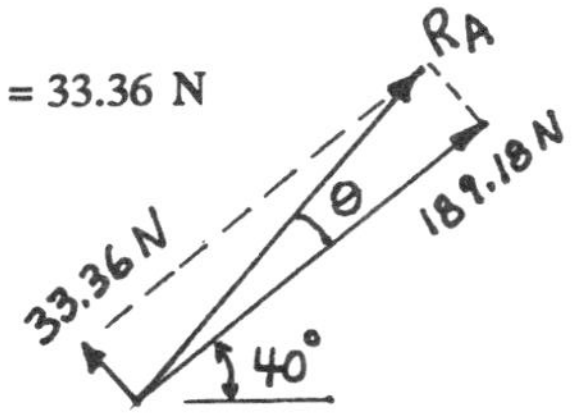

$$R_A = \sqrt{189.18^2 + 33.36^2} = 192.1 \text{ N}$$

$$\theta = \tan^{-1}\left(\frac{33.36}{189.18}\right) = 10.0^\circ$$

Therefore, the forces acting on the body at A and B are:

$R_A = 192.1$ N at 50° and $R_B = 192.1$ N at 50° ◆

4.27

$W = 30(9.81) = 294.3$ N

$\Sigma M_B = 0$:

$$294.3(0.1\sin30^\circ) - T_A(0.1 + 0.1\cos30^\circ) = 0$$

$$\therefore\ T_A = 78.86 \text{ N} \quad ◆$$

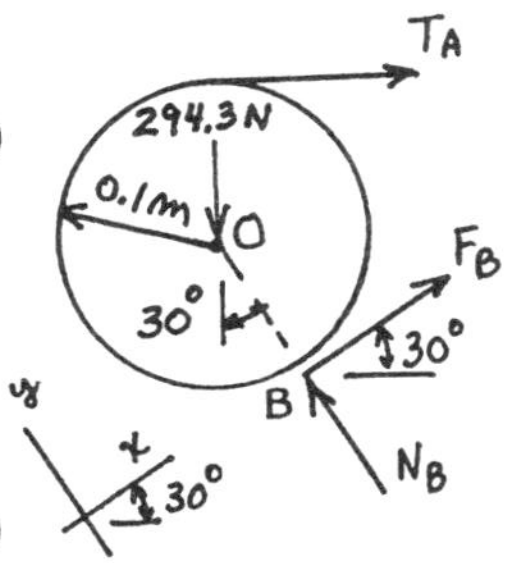

$$\Sigma M_O = 0: \quad F_B(0.1) - T_A(0.1) = 0$$

$$\therefore\ F_B = T_A = 78.86 \text{ N}$$

$$\Sigma F_y = 0: \quad N_B - 294.3\cos30^\circ - T_A \sin 30^\circ = 0$$

$$\therefore\ N_B = 294.3\cos30^\circ + 78.86\sin30^\circ = 294.3\text{N}$$

$$R_B = \sqrt{294.3^2 + 78.86^2} = 304.6 \text{ N} \qquad \theta = \tan^{-1}\left(\frac{294.3}{78.86}\right) = 75.0^\circ$$

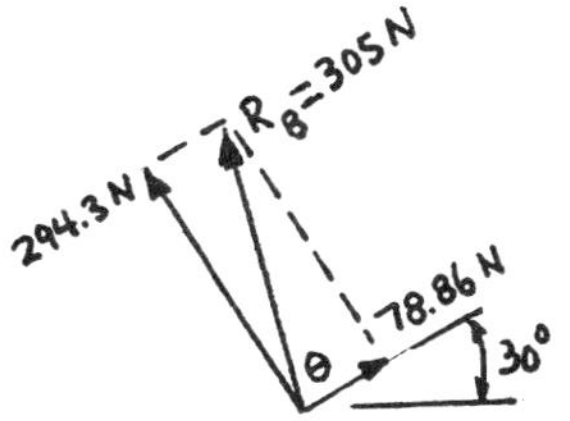

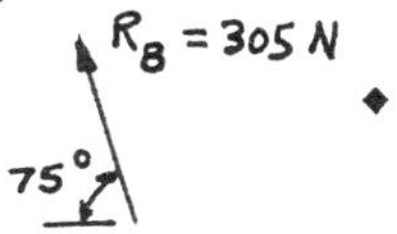

◆

4.28

$W = 30(9.81) = 294.3$ N; $P = 0.5(0.6)(800) = 240$ N

$\Sigma M_A = 0$:

$$T(0.9) - 294.3(0.45) - 240(0.40) = 0$$

$$\therefore\ T = 253.8 \text{ N} \qquad (1)$$

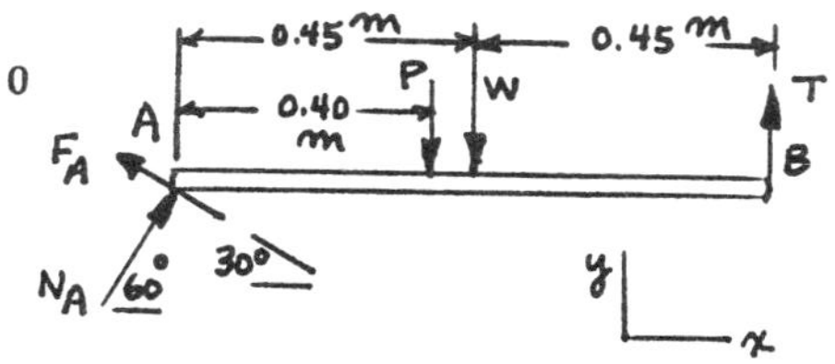

$$\Sigma F_x = 0: \quad N_A\cos60^\circ - F_A\cos30^\circ = 0$$

$$\therefore\ F_A = 0.5774 N_A \qquad (2)$$

$$\Sigma F_y = 0: \quad +\uparrow\ N_A\sin60^\circ + F_A\sin30^\circ - 294.3 - 240 + T = 0 \qquad (3)$$

Substituting (1) and (2) into (3):

$$N_A\sin60^\circ + (0.5774N_A)\sin30^\circ = 294.3 + 240 - 253.8$$

$$\therefore\ N_A = 242.9 \text{ N} \qquad F_A = 0.5774(242.9) = 140.3 \text{ N}$$

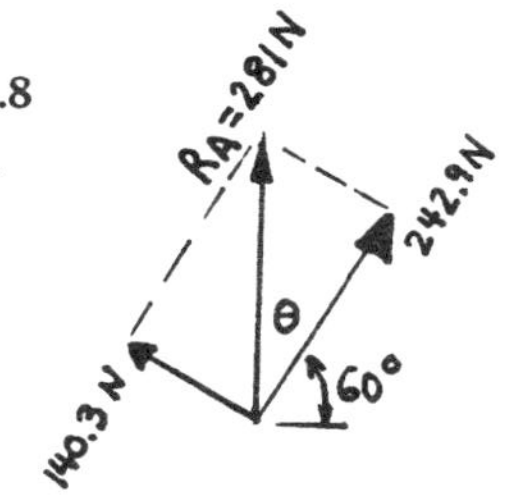

$$R_A = \sqrt{242.9^2 + 140.3^2} = 281 \text{ N}$$

$$\theta = \tan^{-1}\left(\frac{140.3}{242.9}\right) = 30.0^\circ$$

Therefore, the forces acting on the body at A and B are:

$R_A = 281$ N ↑ and $R_B = 254$ N ↑ ◆

4.29

$$\Sigma M_A = 0: \quad N_B(21.63) - 90(9) = 0$$

$$\therefore\ N_B = 37.45 \text{ lb}$$ (slope 3, 2) ◆

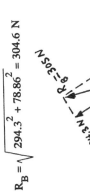

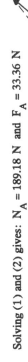

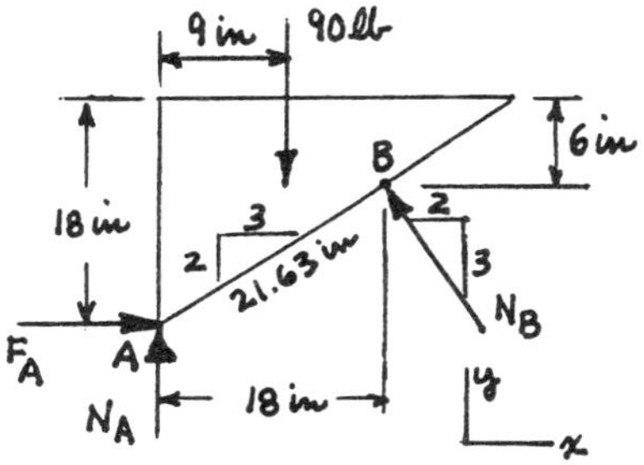

$$\Sigma F_x = 0: \quad F_A - \frac{2}{\sqrt{13}}N_B = 0$$

$$\therefore\ F_A = \frac{2}{\sqrt{13}}(37.45) = 20.77 \text{ lb}$$

$$\Sigma F_y = 0: \quad +\uparrow\ N_A - 90 + \frac{3}{\sqrt{13}}N_B = 0$$

$$\therefore\ N_A = 90 - \frac{3}{\sqrt{13}}(37.45) = 58.84 \text{ lb}$$

(continued)

$R_A = \sqrt{58.84^2 + 20.77^2} = 62.4$ lb $\qquad \theta = \tan^{-1}\left(\frac{58.84}{20.77}\right) = 70.6^\circ$

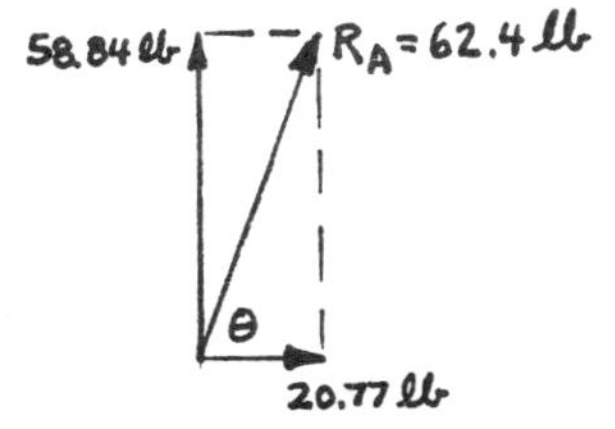

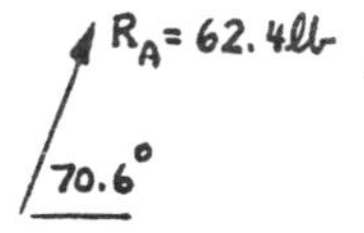

◆

4.30

$\Sigma M_A = 0$:

$\circlearrowleft\!+\;\; P(6\sin 40^\circ + 24) - T\cos 20^\circ(6\sin 40^\circ)$

$\qquad - T\sin 20^\circ(6\cos 40^\circ) = 0$

$\therefore\; T = \dfrac{(6\sin 40^\circ + 24)P}{6(\sin 40^\circ\cos 20^\circ + \cos 40^\circ\sin 20^\circ)} = 5.36P$ ◆

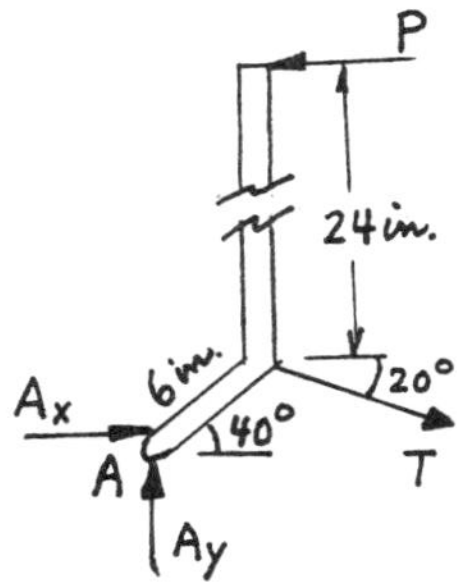

4.31

$A_1 = 6(12) = 72$ ft^2

$W_1 = 72(82) = 5904$ lb

$A_2 = 2(9) = 18$ ft^2

$W_2 = 18(82) = 1476$ lb

$A_3 = 0.5(9)(4) = 18$ ft^2

$W_3 = 18(82) = 1476$ lb

$\Sigma M_C = 0$:

$\circlearrowleft\!+\;\; 5904(6 - x) + 1476(15 - x)$

$\qquad + 1476(16.5 - x) = 0$

$\therefore\; x = 9.25$ ft ◆

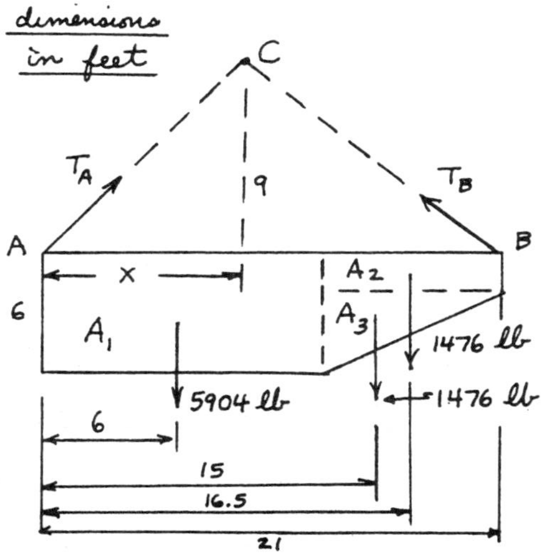

(continued)

The tensions have the following slopes:

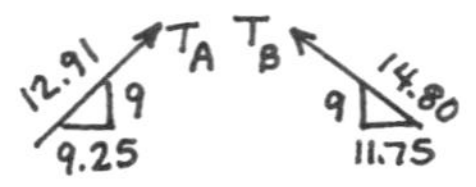

$\Sigma M_A = 0$: $\;\circlearrowleft\!+\;\; \dfrac{9}{14.80} T_B(21) - 5904(6) - 1476(15 + 16.5) = 0$

$\therefore\; T_B = 6415$ lb ◆

$\Sigma F_y = 0$: $\;+\uparrow\;\; \dfrac{9}{12.91} T_A + \dfrac{9}{14.80} T_B - 5904 - 2(1476) = 0$

Substituting $T_B = 6415$ lb and solving gives: $T_A = 7108$ lb ◆

4.32

$\Sigma F_x = 0$: $\;B_x = 0$ ◆

$\Sigma M_B = 0$:

$\circlearrowright\!+\;\; 12A_y + 2(9) - 12 - 3(2) = 0$

$\therefore\; A_y = 0$

$\Sigma F_y = 0$: $\;+\uparrow\;\; B_y + 2 - 3 = 0$

$\therefore\; B_y = 1.0$ kN

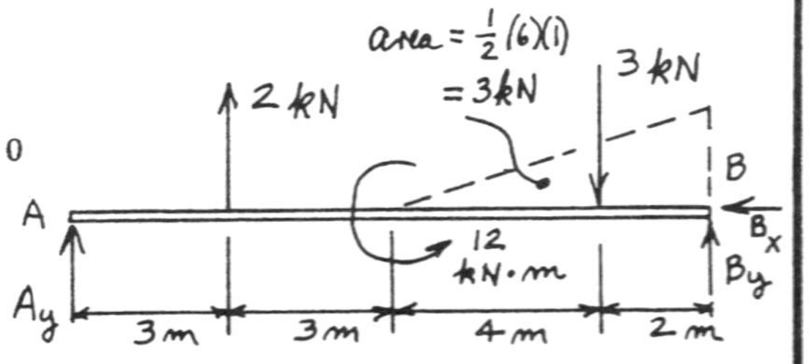

Therefore, the reactions are: $R_A = 0$ ◆ ; $R_B = 1.0$ kN ↑ ◆

4.33

$\Sigma F_x = 0$:

$\overset{+}{\rightarrow}\;\; \dfrac{5.6}{6.093} T_{BC} - \dfrac{2.2}{6.017} T_{BA} = 0$

$\therefore\; T_{BC} = 0.3978\, T_{BA} \qquad (1)$

$\Sigma F_y = 0$:

$+\uparrow\;\; \dfrac{5.6}{6.017} T_{BA} - \dfrac{2.4}{6.093} T_{BC} - 1200(9.81) = 0 \qquad (2)$

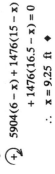

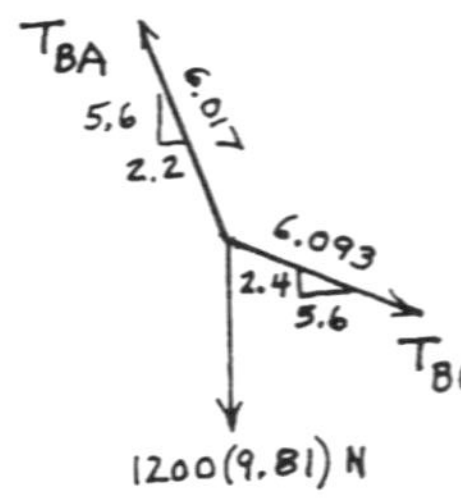

Solving (1) and (2) gives: $T_{BA} = 15\,210$ N ◆ ; $T_{BC} = 6050$ N ◆

4.34

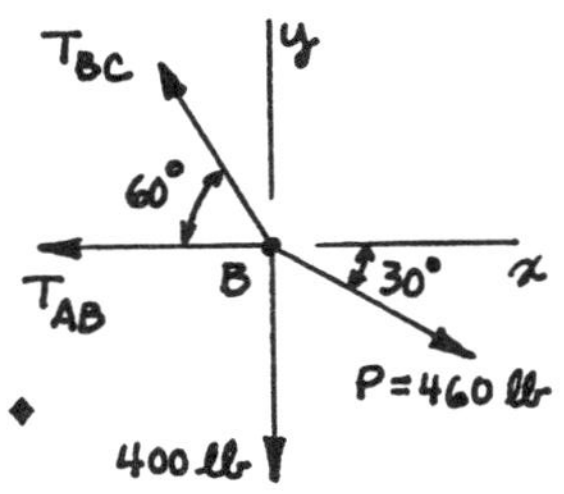

$\Sigma F_y = 0$: $+\uparrow$ $T_{BC}\sin 60^\circ - 400 - 460\sin 30^\circ = 0$

$\therefore$ $T_{BC} = 727.46$ lb ◆

$\Sigma F_x = 0$: $\overset{+}{\rightarrow}$ $460\cos 30^\circ - T_{AB} - T_{BC}\cos 60^\circ = 0$

$\therefore$ $T_{AB} = 460\cos 30^\circ - 727.46\cos 60^\circ = 34.6$ lb ◆

4.35

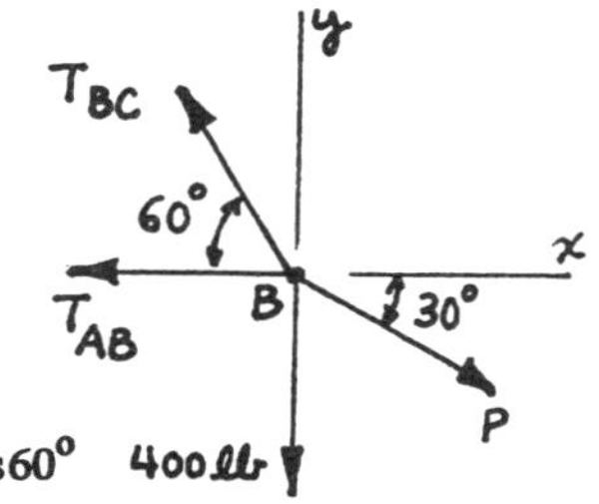

$\Sigma F_y = 0$: $+\uparrow$ $T_{BC}\sin 60^\circ - 400 - P\sin 30^\circ = 0$

$\therefore$ $T_{BC} = 461.9 + 0.5774P$ lb

Note that T_{BC} is always positive.

$\Sigma F_x = 0$: $\overset{+}{\rightarrow}$ $P\cos 30^\circ - T_{AB} - T_{BC}\cos 60^\circ = 0$

$\therefore$ $T_{AB} = P\cos 30^\circ - (461.9 + 0.5774P)\cos 60^\circ$

$T_{AB} = -231.0 + 0.5773P$ lb

Note that T_{AB} is positive only if $P > \dfrac{231.0}{0.5773} = 400$ lb

Therefore, $P_{min} = 400$ lb ◆

4.36

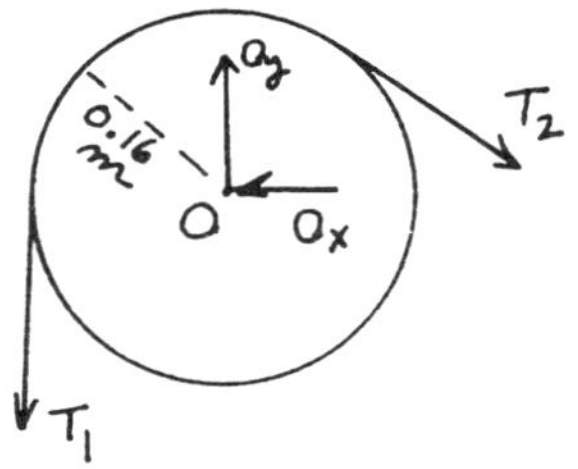

(a) $\Sigma M_O = 0$: $\circlearrowleft +$ $T_1(0.16) - T_2(0.16) = 0$

$\therefore$ $T_1 = T_2$ Q.E.D.

(continued)

(b) $\Sigma M_O = 0$: $\circlearrowleft +$ $T_1(0.16) - T_2(0.16) + C = 0$

$\therefore$ $C = (T_2 - T_1)(0.16) = 200(0.16) = 32.0$ N•m ◆

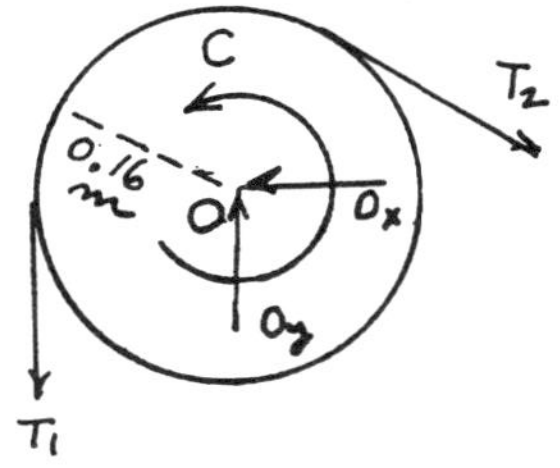

4.37

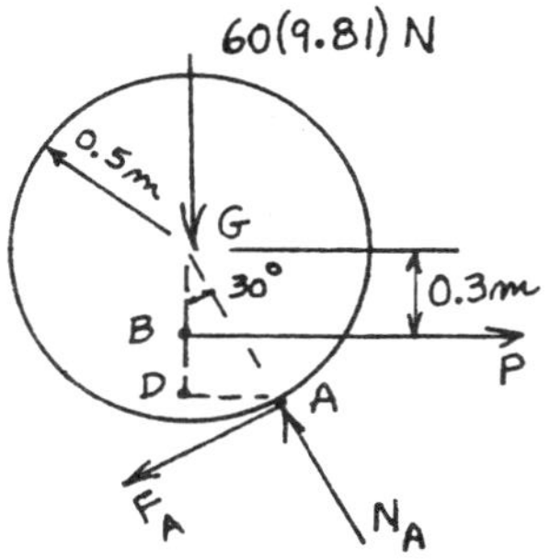

(a) $\Sigma M_A = 0$:

$\circlearrowleft +$ $60(9.81)(\overline{DA}) - P(\overline{BD}) = 0$

Note: $\overline{DA} = 0.5\sin 30^\circ = 0.250$ m

$\overline{BD} = 0.5\cos 30^\circ - 0.3 = 0.1330$ m

$\therefore$ $60(9.81)(0.250) - P(0.1330) = 0$

which gives: $P = 1106$ N ◆

(b) If the inclined surface were smooth ($F_A = 0$), the moment equation $\Sigma M_G = 0$ could not be satisfied. Therefore, equilibrium would not be possible. ◆

4.38

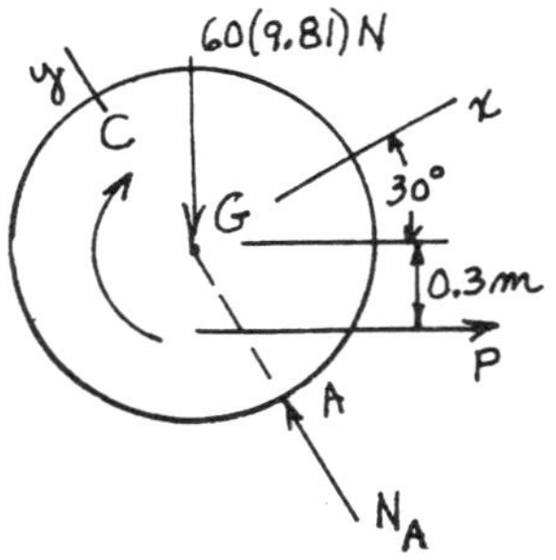

$\Sigma F_x = 0$: $+\nearrow$ $P\cos 30^\circ - 60(9.81)\sin 30^\circ = 0$

$\therefore$ $P = 339.8$ N ◆

$\Sigma M_G = 0$: $\circlearrowleft +$ $P(0.3) - C = 0$

$\therefore$ $C = 0.3(339.8) = 101.9$ N•m ◆

4.39

(a) $\Sigma M_B = 0$: $\circlearrowleft +$ $392.4(1.0) - C = 0$

$\therefore C = 392.4$ N•m ◆

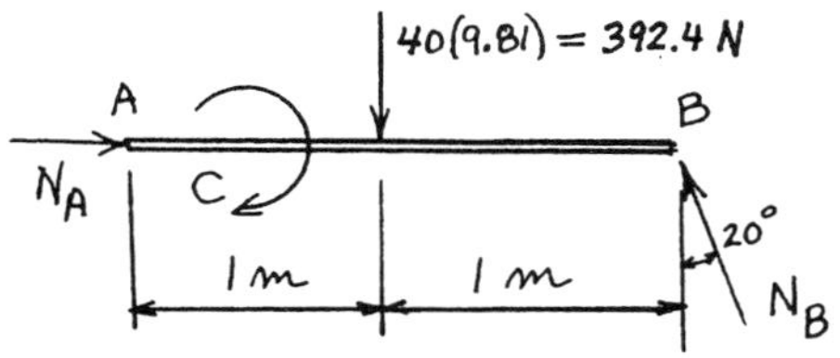

(b) $\Sigma F_y = 0$: $+\uparrow$ $N_B \cos 20^\circ - 392.4 = 0$

$\therefore N_B = 417.6$ N ◆

$\Sigma M_A = 0$: $\circlearrowleft +$ $-392.4(1.0 \cos 54^\circ) - C$

$+ N_B \cos 20^\circ (2 \cos 54^\circ)$

$- N_B \sin 20^\circ (2 \sin 54^\circ) = 0$

Substituting $N_B = 417.6$ N and solving gives: $C = 0$ ◆

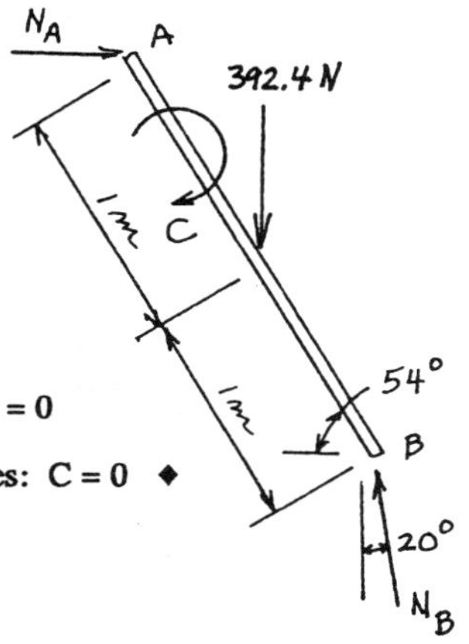

4.40

$\Sigma M_A = 0$:

$\circlearrowleft +$ $F_B \cos 28^\circ (0.18 \cos 18^\circ)$

$- F_B \sin 28^\circ (0.18 \sin 18^\circ) - 120 = 0$

$\therefore F_B = 959.7$ N ◆

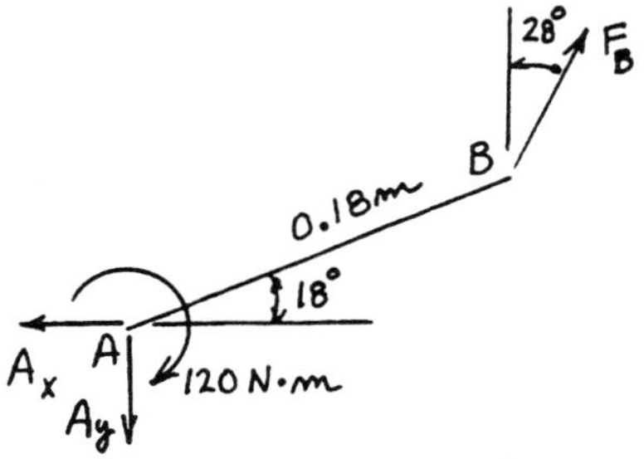

$\Sigma F_x = 0$:

$\overset{+}{\rightarrow}$ $-A_x + 959.7 \sin 28^\circ = 0$ gives: $A_x = 450.6$ N

$\Sigma F_y = 0$:

$+\uparrow$ $-A_y + 959.7 \cos 28^\circ = 0$ gives: $A_y = 847.4$ N

$\therefore R_A = \sqrt{450.6^2 + 847.4^2} = 960$ N ◆

4.41

(a) $\Sigma M_B = 0$:

$\circlearrowleft +$ $3000 \cos 12^\circ (6)$

$- 3000 \sin 12^\circ (2.2)$

$- N_A(9) = 0$

$\therefore N_A = 1803.8$ lb ◆

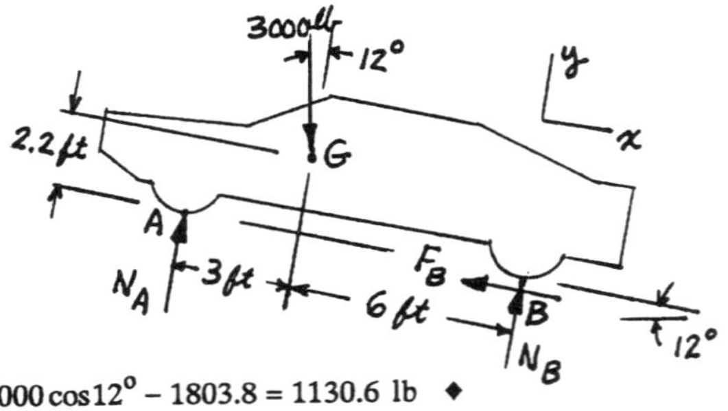

$\Sigma F_y = 0$:

$N_B = 3000 \cos 12^\circ - N_A = 3000 \cos 12^\circ - 1803.8 = 1130.6$ lb ◆

(b) $\Sigma F_x = 0$: $F_B = 3000 \sin 12^\circ = 624$ lb ◆

4.42

$\Sigma F_y = 0$: $+\uparrow$ $(T_A + T_B)\cos 20^\circ - 17.66 = 0$

$\therefore T_A + T_B = 18.79$ kN

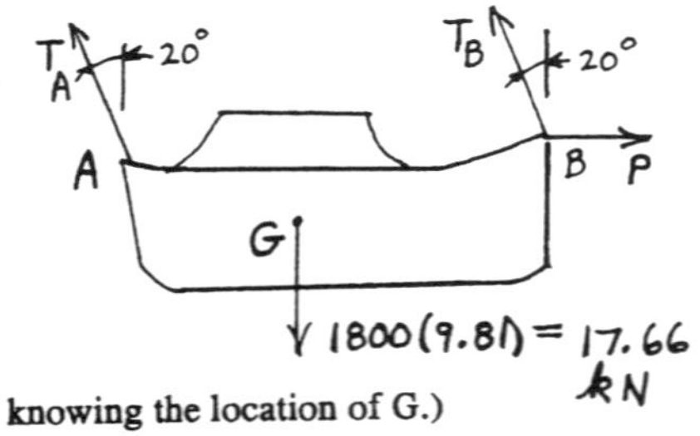

$\Sigma F_x = 0$: $\overset{+}{\rightarrow}$ $(T_A + T_B)\sin 20^\circ - P = 0$

$\therefore P = 18.79 \sin 20^\circ = 6.43$ kN ◆

(Note that T_A and T_B cannot be found without knowing the location of G.)

4.43

$\Sigma M_B = 0$: $\circlearrowleft +$ $800(9) - N_A(3) = 0$

$\therefore N_A = 2400$ lb ◆

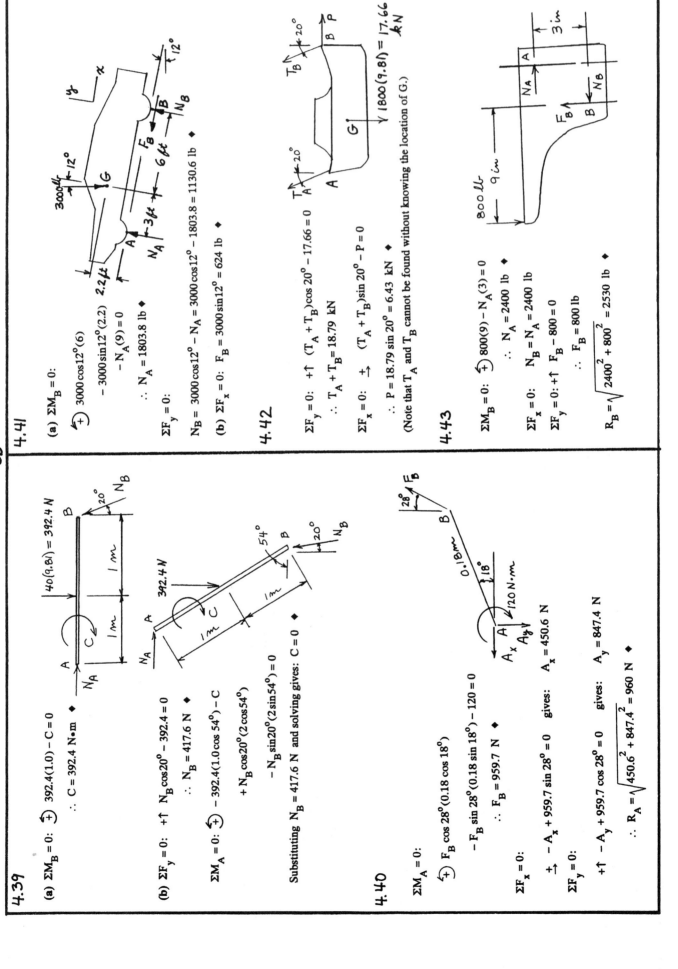

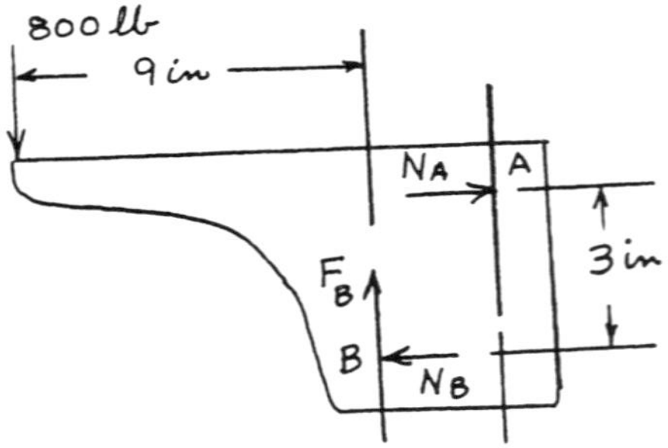

$\Sigma F_x = 0$: $N_B = N_A = 2400$ lb

$\Sigma F_y = 0$: $+\uparrow$ $F_B - 800 = 0$

$\therefore F_B = 800$ lb

$R_B = \sqrt{2400^2 + 800^2} = 2530$ lb ◆

4.44

$\Sigma M_A = 0$:

$$\circlearrowleft + \quad T_{BC}\sin\theta\left(\frac{2L}{3}\cos\theta\right) + T_{BC}\cos\theta\left(\frac{2L}{3}\sin\theta\right) - W\left(\frac{L}{2}\sin\theta\right) = 0$$

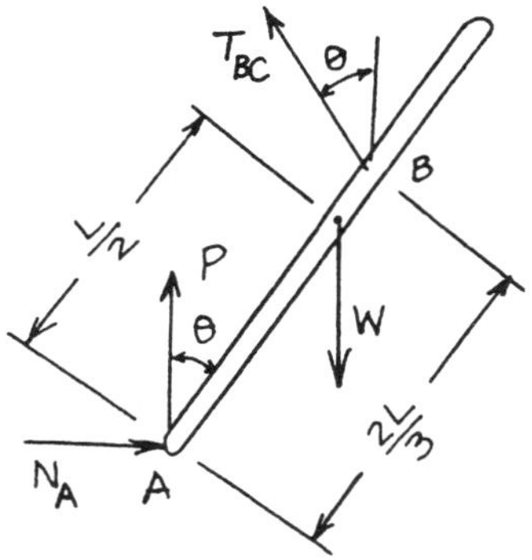

which simplifies as $T_{BC} = \dfrac{3W}{8\cos\theta}$

$\Sigma F_y = 0$: $+\uparrow$ $P + T_{BC}\cos\theta - W = 0$

$$P = W - \frac{3W}{8} = \frac{5W}{8} \qquad \therefore \text{ P is independent of } \theta. \quad \text{Q.E.D.}$$

4.45

$\Sigma M_A = 0$:

$$\circlearrowleft + \quad 330\sin\theta\left(\frac{2L}{3}\cos\theta\right) + 330\cos\theta\left(\frac{2L}{3}\sin\theta\right) - 40\left(\frac{L}{2}\sin\theta\right) = 0$$

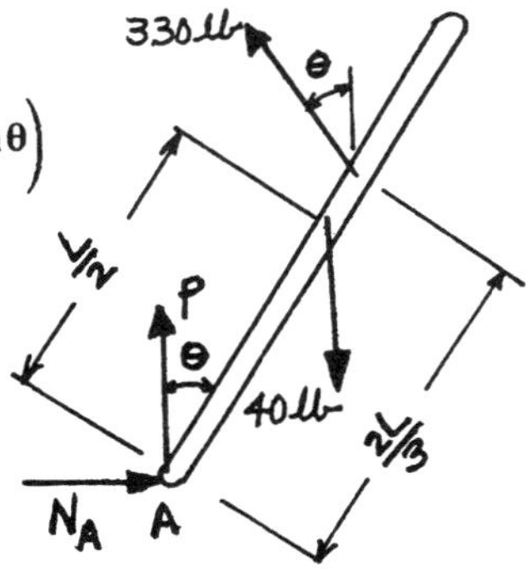

which gives: $220\cos\theta + 220\cos\theta = 20$

$$\therefore \ \theta = \cos^{-1}\left(\frac{20}{440}\right) = 87.4^\circ \ \blacklozenge$$

4.46

(a) $x = 1.5$ m

$\Sigma M_A = 0$:

$$\circlearrowleft + \quad -N_B(2) + 90(9.81)(1.5) + 20(9.81)(2) = 0$$

$$\therefore \ N_B = 858.4 \text{ N} \ \blacklozenge$$

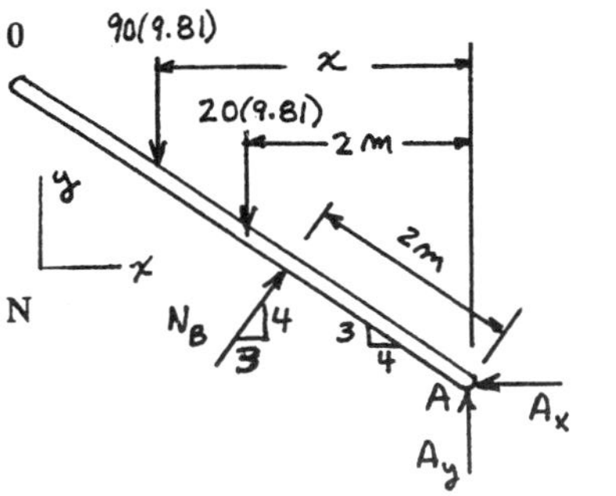

$\Sigma F_y = 0$: $+\uparrow$ $A_y + \frac{4}{5}N_B - 110(9.81) = 0$

$$\therefore \ A_y = 110(9.81) - \frac{4}{5}(858.4) = 392.4 \text{ N}$$

$\Sigma F_x = 0$: $A_x = \frac{3}{5}N_B = \frac{3}{5}(858.4) = 515.0$ N

$$R_A = \sqrt{515.0^2 + 392.4^2} = 647 \text{ N} \ \blacklozenge$$

(continued)

(b) The ladder is ready to fall when $A_y = 0$.

$\Sigma F_y = 0$: $+\uparrow$ $\frac{4}{5}N_B - 110(9.81) = 0 \qquad \therefore \ N_B = 1349$ N

$\Sigma M_A = 0$: $\circlearrowleft +$ $90(9.81)x + 20(9.81)(2) - N_B(2) = 0$

$$\therefore \ x = \frac{-20(9.81)(2) + 1349(2)}{90(9.81)} = 2.61 \text{ m} \ \blacklozenge$$

4.47

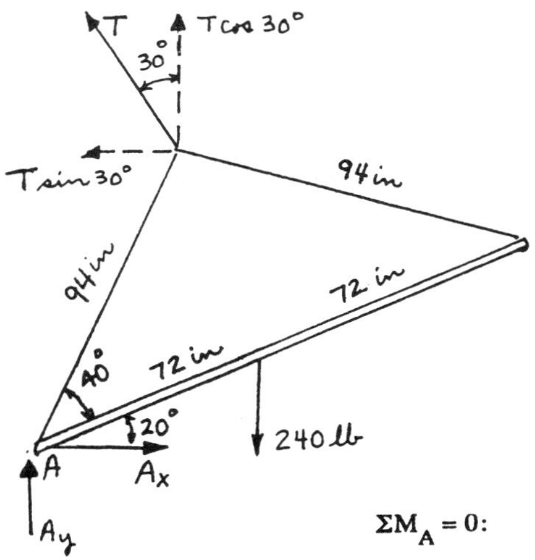

$\Sigma M_A = 0$:

$$\circlearrowleft + \quad -240(72\cos 20^\circ) + T\sin 30^\circ(94\sin 60^\circ) + T\cos 30^\circ(94\cos 60^\circ) = 0$$

$$\therefore \ T = 199.5 \text{ lb} \ \blacklozenge$$

$\Sigma F_x = 0$: $A_x = T\sin 30^\circ = 199.5\sin 30^\circ = 99.75$ lb

$\Sigma F_y = 0$:

$+\uparrow$ $A_y - 240 + T\cos 30^\circ = 0$

$$A_y = 240 - 199.5\cos 30^\circ = 67.23 \text{ lb}$$

$$\therefore \ R_A = \sqrt{99.75^2 + 67.23^2} = 120.3 \text{ lb} \ \blacklozenge$$

4.48

$\Sigma M_A = 0$:

$\circlearrowleft + \quad T(20) - T(120) + 14(120) - 0.40(9.81)(80) = 0$

$\therefore \; T = 13.66 \text{ N}$ ◆

$\Sigma F_x = 0: \quad A_x = T = 13.66 \text{ N}$

$\Sigma F_y = 0: \quad +\uparrow \; T - A_y + 14 - 0.40(9.81) = 0$

$A_y = 13.66 + 14 - 0.40(9.81) = 23.74 \text{ N}$

$\therefore \; R_A = \sqrt{13.66^2 + 23.74^2} = 27.4 \text{ N}$ ◆

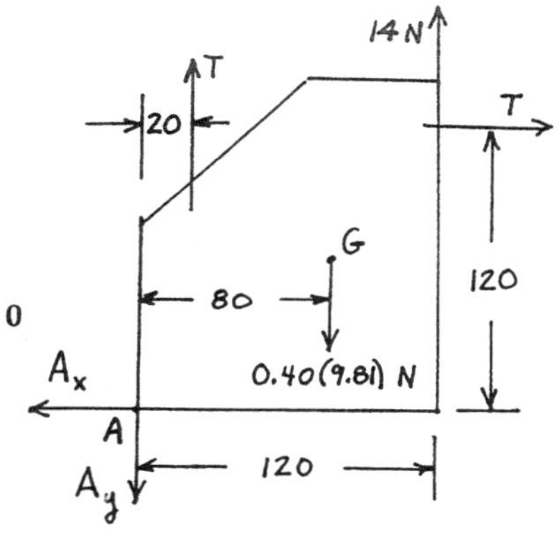

4.49

$\Sigma M_B = 0$:

$\circlearrowleft + \quad 300(9.81)(331.7) - P(600 + 500) = 0$

$\therefore \; P = 887 \text{ N}$ ◆

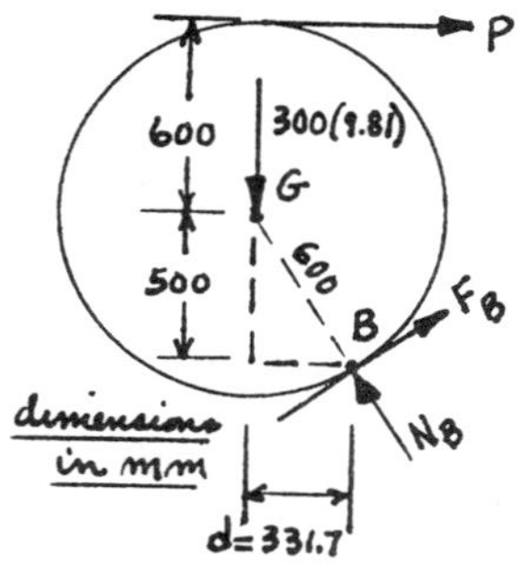

4.50

$\Sigma F_y = 0$:

$+\uparrow \; B_y - 1500 - 12(9.81) = 0$

$B_y = 1618 \text{ N}$ ◆

$\Sigma M_B = 0$:

$\circlearrowleft + \quad A_x(0.250) - 240 = 0$

$A_x = 960 \text{ N}$ ◆

$\Sigma F_x = 0: \quad B_x = A_x = 960 \text{ N}$ ◆

$\therefore \; R_A = \sqrt{960^2 + 1500^2} = 1781 \text{ N}$ ◆

and $R_B = \sqrt{960^2 + 1618^2} = 1881 \text{ N}$ ◆

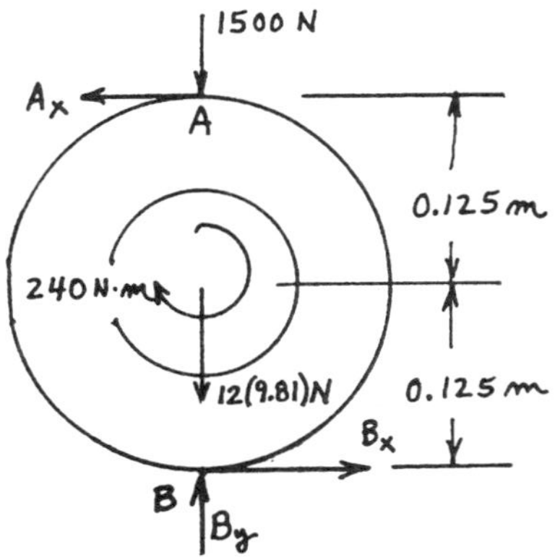

4.51

$\Sigma F_x = 0: \quad A_x = 0$

$\Sigma M_A = 0$:

$\circlearrowleft + \quad N_C(19) - 360(5.5) - 144(15) - 250(9.5) = 0$

$\therefore \; N_C = 342.9 \text{ lb}$

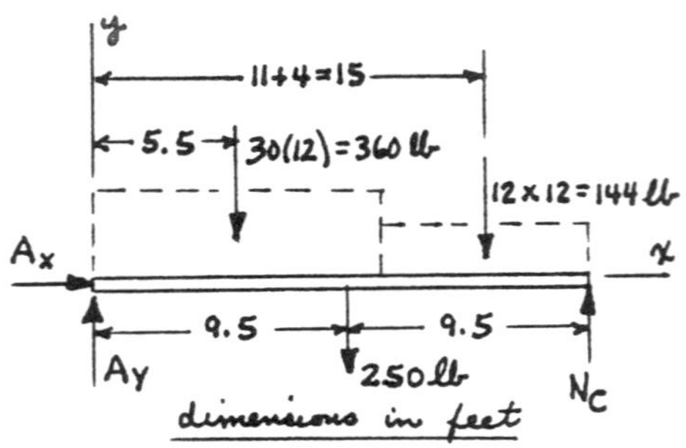

$\Sigma F_y = 0$:

$+\uparrow \; A_y - 360 - 144 - 250 + N_C = 0$

$\therefore \; A_y = 360 + 144 + 250 - 342.9 = 411 \text{ lb}$

Therefore the reactions at A and C are: $\mathbf{A} = 411\,\mathbf{j}$ lb and $\mathbf{N}_C = 343\,\mathbf{j}$ lb ◆

4.52

weight of water per unit area:

$$\frac{1500}{480 + 180} = 2.273 \text{ lb/in}^2$$

$W_1 = 2.273(480) = 1091 \text{ lb}$

$W_2 = 2.273(180) = 409 \text{ lb}$

$\Sigma M_A = 0$:

$\circlearrowleft + \quad R_B \sin 50^\circ(30) - 1091(10) - 409(25) = 0$

$\therefore \; R_B = 919.7 \text{ lb}$ ◆

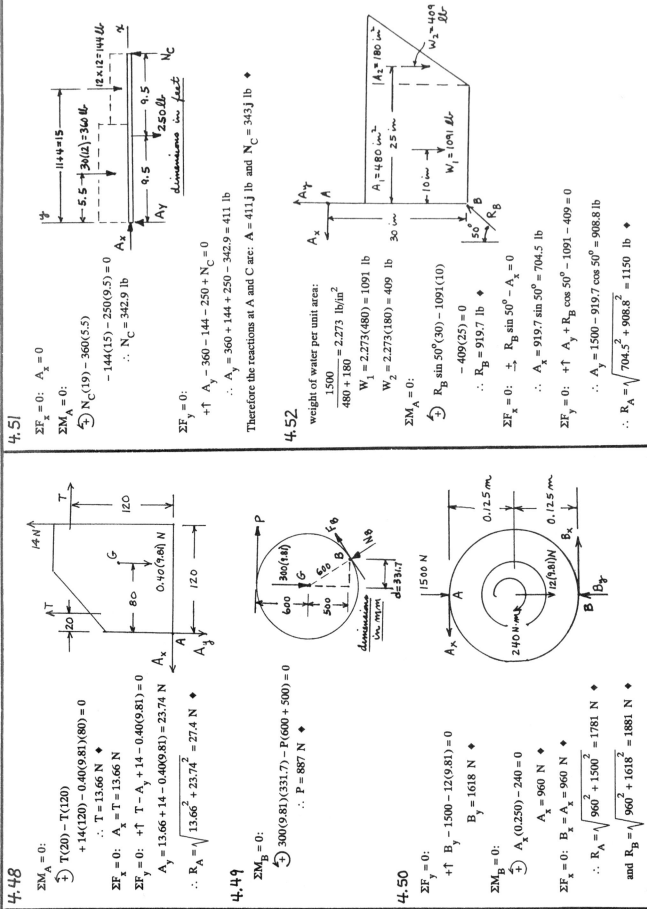

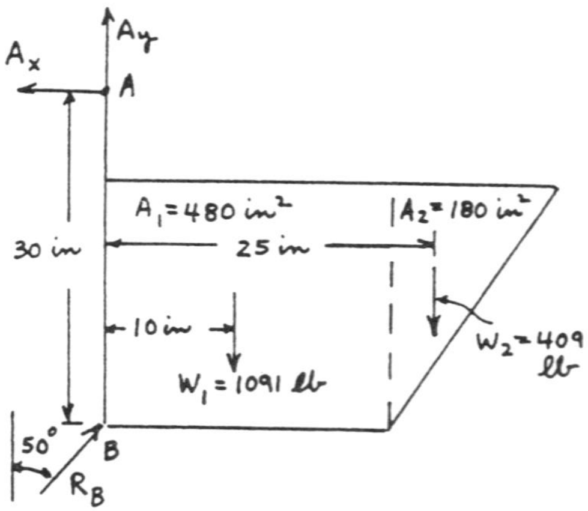

$\Sigma F_x = 0: \quad \overset{+}{\rightarrow} \; R_B \sin 50^\circ - A_x = 0$

$\therefore \; A_x = 919.7 \sin 50^\circ = 704.5 \text{ lb}$

$\Sigma F_y = 0: \quad +\uparrow \; A_y + R_B \cos 50^\circ - 1091 - 409 = 0$

$\therefore \; A_y = 1500 - 919.7 \cos 50^\circ = 908.8 \text{ lb}$

$\therefore \; R_A = \sqrt{704.5^2 + 908.8^2} = 1150 \text{ lb}$ ◆

4.53

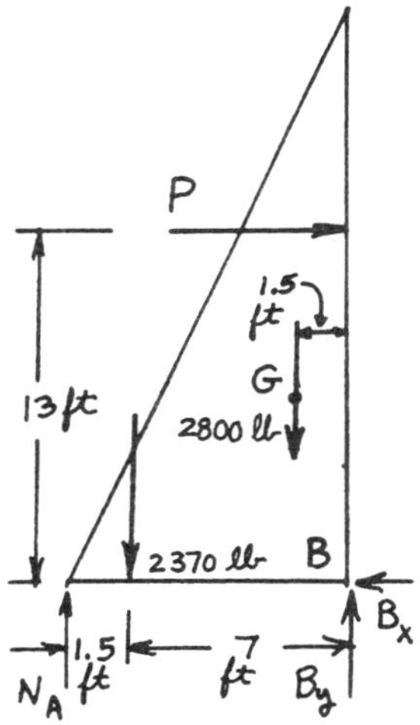

(a) $P = 1200$ lb

$\Sigma M_B = 0$:

$\circlearrowleft + \; -N_A(8.5) + 2370(7) + 2800(1.5) - 1200(13) = 0$

$\therefore\; N_A = 611$ lb ◆

$\Sigma F_x = 0$: $B_x = P = 1200$ lb

$\Sigma F_y = 0$: $+\uparrow\; N_A + B_y - 2370 - 2800 = 0$

$\therefore\; B_y = 5170 - N_A = 5170 - 611 = 4559$ lb

$\therefore\; R_B = \sqrt{1200^2 + 4559^2} = 4710$ lb ◆

(b) $P = 10\,q_{min}$ and $N_A = 0$ (for impending tipping)

$\Sigma M_B = 0$: $\circlearrowleft +\; 2370(7) + 2800(1.5) - 10\,q_{min}(13) = 0$ $\quad\therefore\; q_{min} = 160$ lb/ft ◆

4.54

When h = 6 ft, the contact force at C is zero.

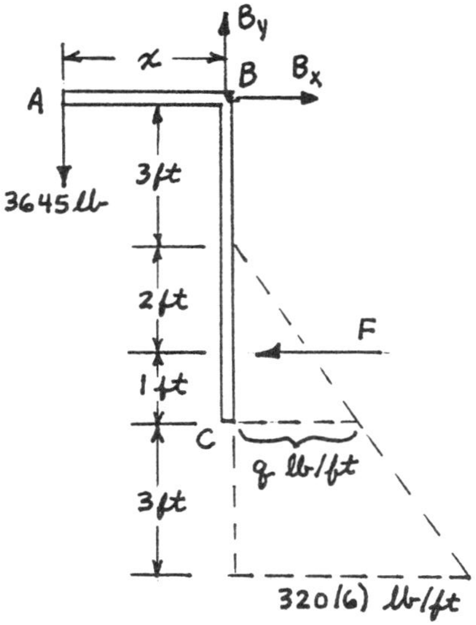

Using similar triangles:

$$\frac{q}{3} = \frac{320(6)}{6}$$

$\therefore\; q = 960$ lb/ft

$F = 0.5(3)(960) = 1440$ lb

$\Sigma M_B = 0$:

$\circlearrowleft +\; 3645\,x - 1440(5) = 0$

$\therefore\; x = 1.975$ ft ◆

4.55

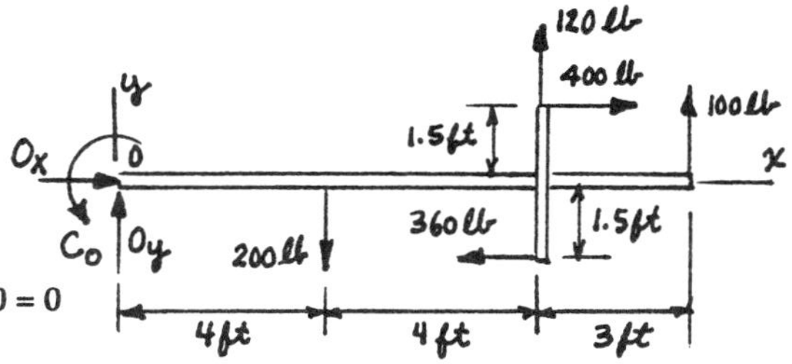

$\Sigma F_x = 0$:

$\overset{+}{\rightarrow}\; O_x + 400 - 360 = 0$

$\therefore\; O_x = -40$ lb

$\Sigma F_y = 0$:

$+\uparrow\; O_y - 200 + 120 + 100 = 0$

$\therefore\; O_y = -20$ lb

$\Sigma M_O = 0$: $\circlearrowleft +\; C_O - 200(4) + 120(8) - 400(1.5) - 360(1.5) + 100(11) = 0$

$\therefore\; C_O = -120$ lb•ft

Therefore, the reactions at O are: $\mathbf{C}_O = -120\mathbf{k}$ lb•ft and $\mathbf{O} = -40\mathbf{i} - 20\mathbf{j}$ lb ◆

*4.56

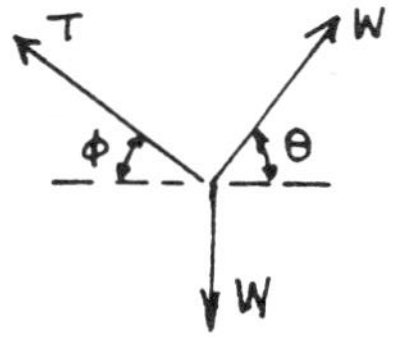

Equilibrium

$\Sigma F_x = 0$: $\overset{+}{\rightarrow}\; W\cos\theta - T\cos\phi = 0$

$\therefore\; T = W(\cos\theta/\cos\phi) \qquad (1)$

$\Sigma F_y = 0$: $+\uparrow\; T\sin\phi + W\sin\theta - W = 0$

Using (1): $W\cos\theta\tan\phi + W\sin\theta - W = 0$ or $\cos\theta\tan\phi + \sin\theta - 1 = 0 \qquad (2)$

Geometry

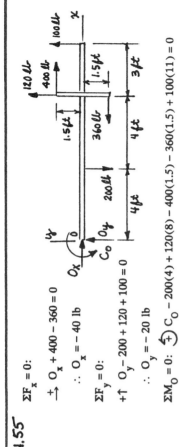

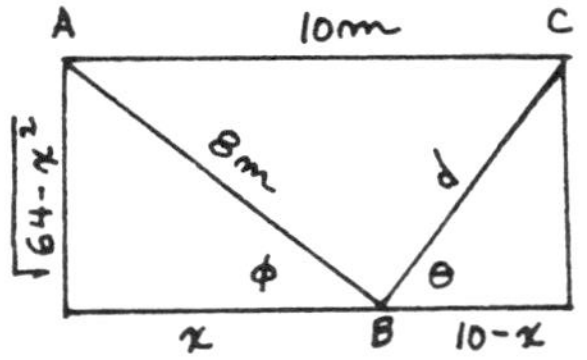

$$d = \sqrt{(10-x)^2 + (64 - x^2)} = \sqrt{164 - 20x} \qquad (3)$$

$$\tan\phi = \frac{\sqrt{64 - x^2}}{x}\;;\quad \cos\theta = \frac{10 - x}{d}\;;$$

$$\sin\theta = \frac{\sqrt{64 - x^2}}{d}$$

Solution

Substituting the expressions for $\tan\phi$, $\cos\theta$, and $\sin\theta$ into (2) gives:

$$\frac{10 - x}{d}\,\frac{\sqrt{64 - x^2}}{x} + \frac{\sqrt{64 - x^2}}{d} - 1 = 0 \quad \text{which reduces to} \quad 10\sqrt{64 - x^2} = x\,d \qquad (4)$$

Squaring both sides of (4) and substituting d from (3):

$$100(64 - x^2) = x^2(164 - 20x) \quad \text{which becomes:} \quad 20x^3 - 264x^2 + 6400 = 0$$

Solving by Newton's method gives: $x = 7.48$ m ◆

*4.57

<u>Geometry</u> $s_1 + s_2 = 120$ m (1)

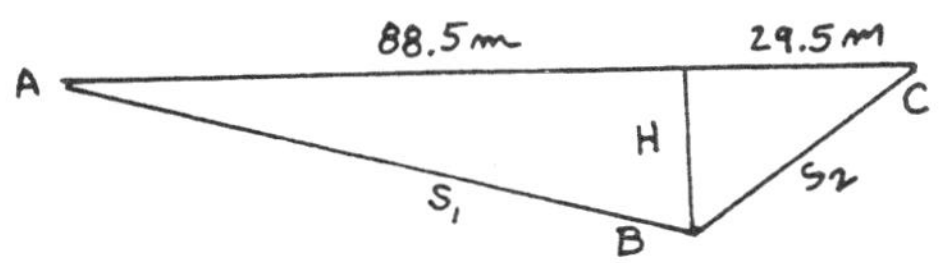

$H^2 = s_1^2 - 88.5^2 = s_2^2 - 29.5^2$ (2)

$\therefore\ s_1^2 - s_2^2 = 6962\ m^2$

$(s_1 - s_2)(s_1 + s_2) = (s_1 - s_2)(120) = 6962\ m^2$

which gives: $(s_1 - s_2) = 6962/120 = 58.017$ m (3)

Solving (1), (2) and (3):

$s_1 = 89.008$ m ; $s_2 = 30.992$ m ; H = 9.50 m

<u>Equilibrium</u>

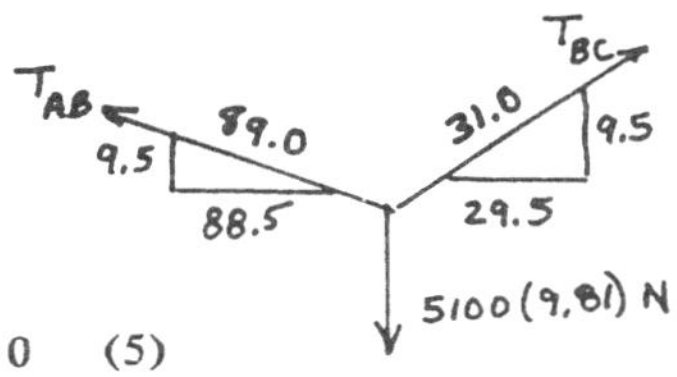

$\Sigma F_x = 0$: $\overset{+}{\rightarrow}$ $\frac{29.5}{31.0}T_{BC} - \frac{88.5}{89.0}T_{AB} = 0$

$\therefore\ T_{BC} = 1.045\,T_{AB}$ (4)

$\Sigma F_y = 0$: $+\uparrow$ $\frac{9.5}{89.0}T_{AB} + \frac{9.5}{31.0}T_{BC} - 5100(9.81) = 0$ (5)

Solving (4) and (5) gives: $T_{AB} = 117.2$ kN ◆ ; $T_{BC} = 122.4$ kN ◆

4.58

$\Sigma M_B = 0$:

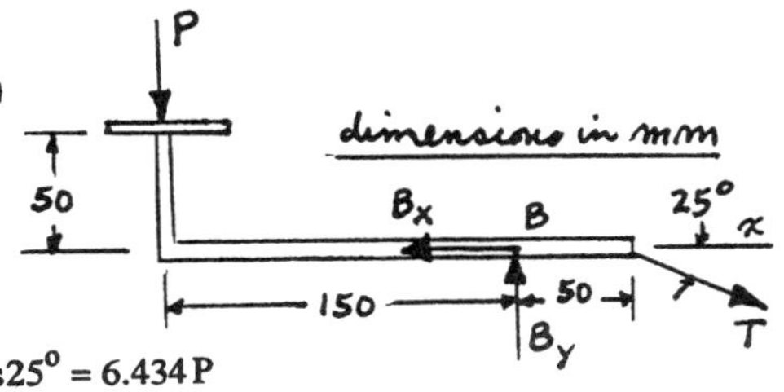

$\circlearrowleft\!+$ $P(0.150) - T\sin 25^\circ(0.05) = 0$

$T = 7.0986P$

$\Sigma F_x = 0$: $\overset{+}{\rightarrow}$ $T\cos 25^\circ - B_x = 0$

$B_x = T\cos 25^\circ = (7.0986P)\cos 25^\circ = 6.434P$

$\Sigma F_y = 0$: $+\uparrow$ $B_y - P - T\sin 25^\circ = 0$

$B_y = P + T\sin 25^\circ = P + (7.0986P)\sin 25^\circ = 4.000P$

$\therefore\ B = \sqrt{B_x^2 + B_y^2} = P\sqrt{6.434^2 + 4.000^2} = 7.576P = 1800$ N gives P = 238 N ◆

*4.59

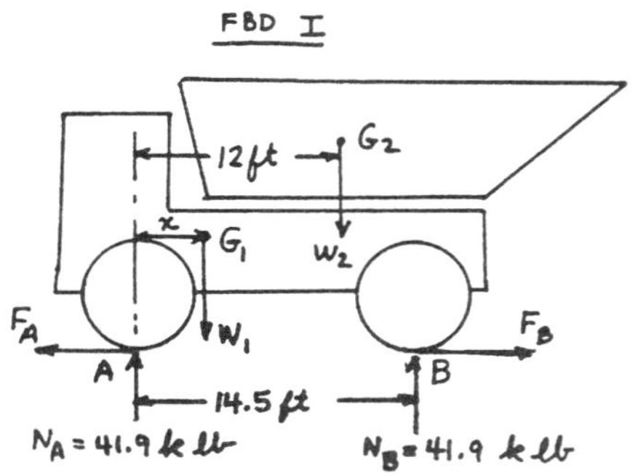

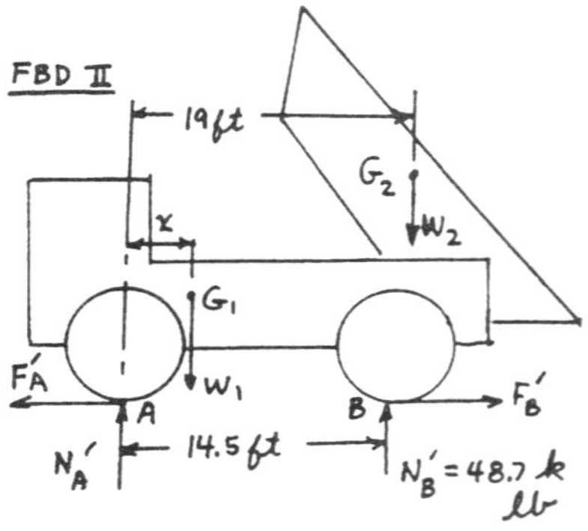

<u>FBD I</u> $\Sigma M_A = 0$: $\circlearrowleft\!+$ $W_1x + W_2(12) - 41.9(14.5) = 0$ (1)

<u>FBD II</u> $\Sigma M_A = 0$: $\circlearrowleft\!+$ $W_1x + W_2(19) - 48.7(14.5) = 0$ (2)

<u>FBD I</u> $\Sigma F_y = 0$: $+\uparrow$ $2(41.9) - W_1 - W_2 = 0$ (3)

Solving (1), (2) and (3) gives: x = 6.29 ft ◆ ; $W_1 = 69.7$ kips ◆ ; $W_2 = 14.1$ kips ◆

*4.60

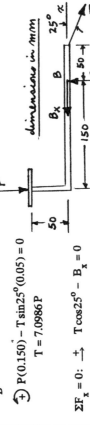

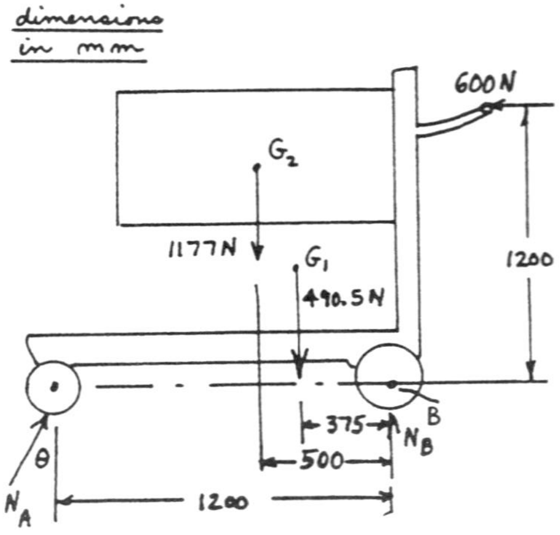

$W_1 = 50(9.81) = 490.5$ N

$W_2 = 120(9.81) = 1177$ N

<u>Find the largest acceptable value of θ</u>

$\Sigma F_x = 0$: $N_A\sin\theta = 600$ (1)

$\Sigma M_B = 0$:

$\circlearrowleft\!+$ $N_A\cos\theta(1200) - 1177(500)$

$- 490.5(375) - 600(1200) = 0$

$\therefore\ N_A\cos\theta = 1244$ (2)

Dividing (1) by (2) gives: $\theta = \tan^{-1}(600/1244) = 25.75^\circ$

(continued)

Check tipping

$\Sigma F_y = 0$: $+\uparrow$ $N_A \cos\theta + N_B - 1177 - 490.5 = 0$ $\therefore$ $N_B = 1177 + 490.5 - 1244 = 423.5$ N

Because N_B is not negative, the truck will not tip.

Find R

$R - R\cos\theta = 5$ mm

which gives: $R = \dfrac{5}{1 - \cos 25.75^\circ} = 50.4$ mm ◆

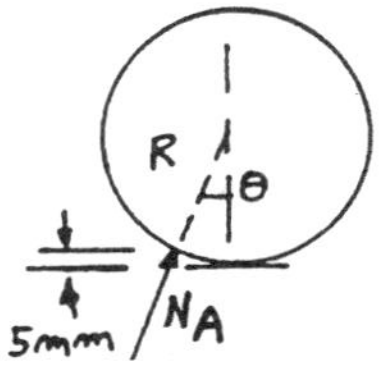

4.61

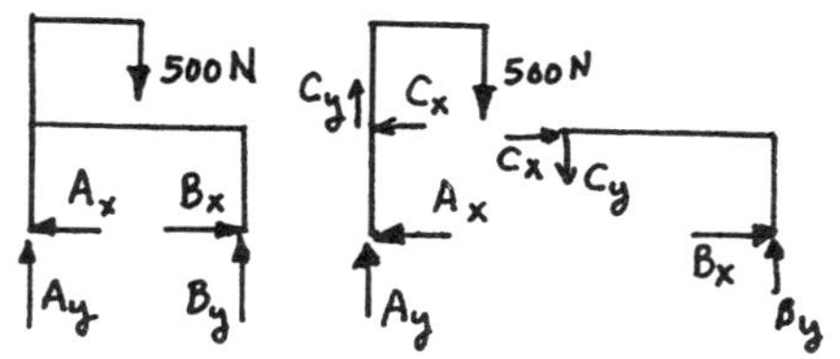

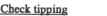

(a) 6 unknowns, 6 independent equations ◆

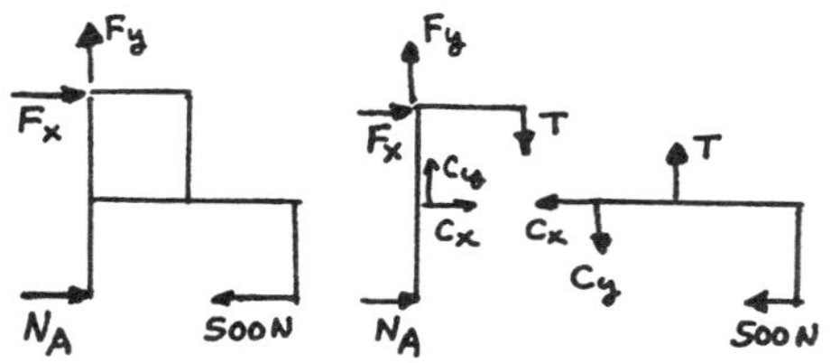

(b) 6 unknowns, 6 independent equations ◆

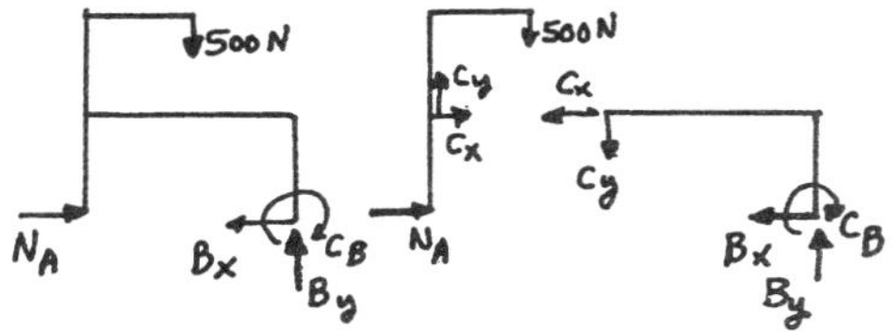

(c) 6 unknowns, 6 independent equations ◆

4.62

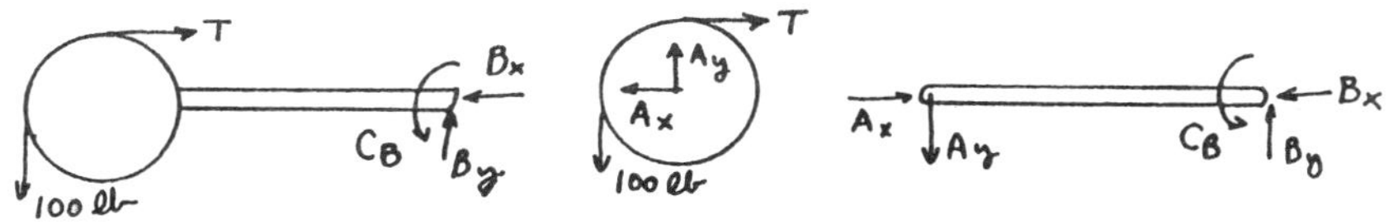

(a) 6 unknowns, 6 independent equations ◆

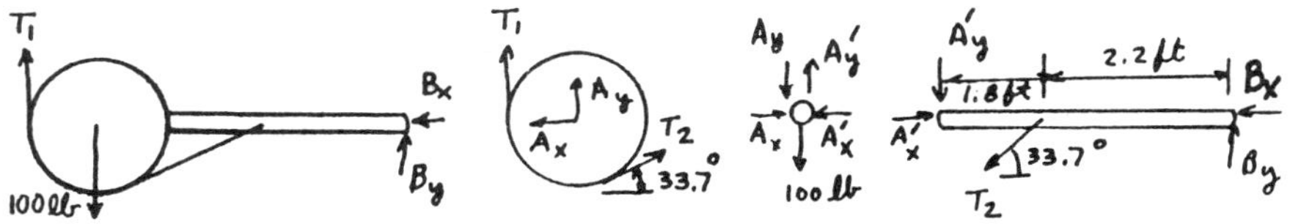

(b) 8 unknowns, 8 independent equations ◆

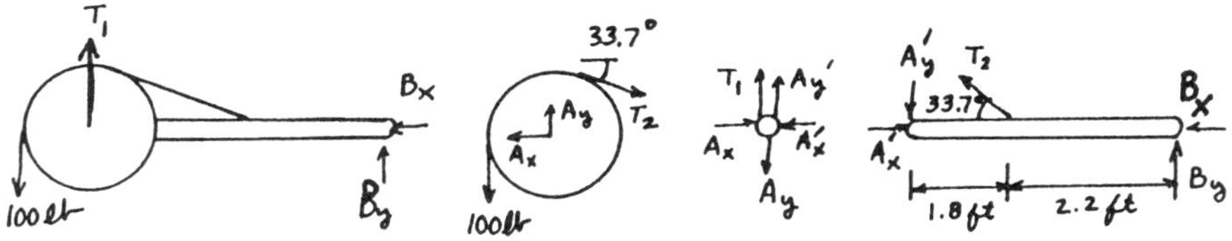

(c) 8 unknowns, 8 independent equations ◆

4.63

$\dfrac{w_0}{1.8} = \dfrac{3}{3}$ $\therefore w_0 = 1.8$ kN/m

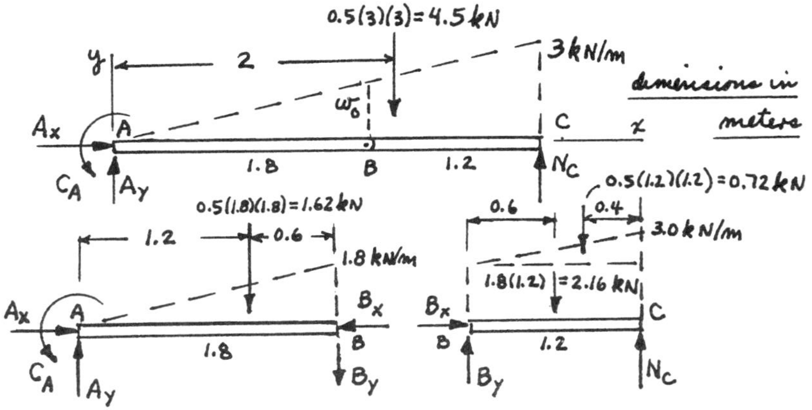

6 unknowns, 6 independent equations ◆

4.64

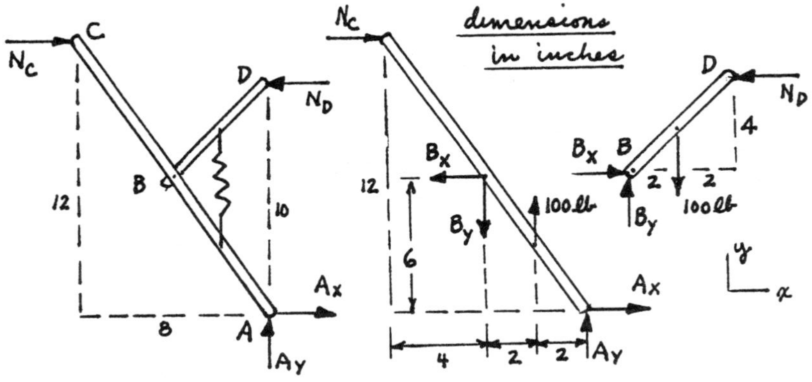

6 unknowns, 6 independent equations ◆

4.65

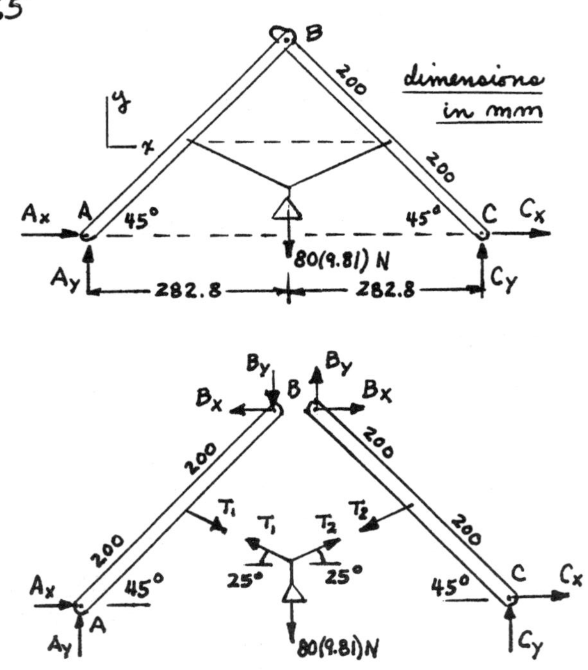

8 unknowns, 8 independent equations ◆

4.66

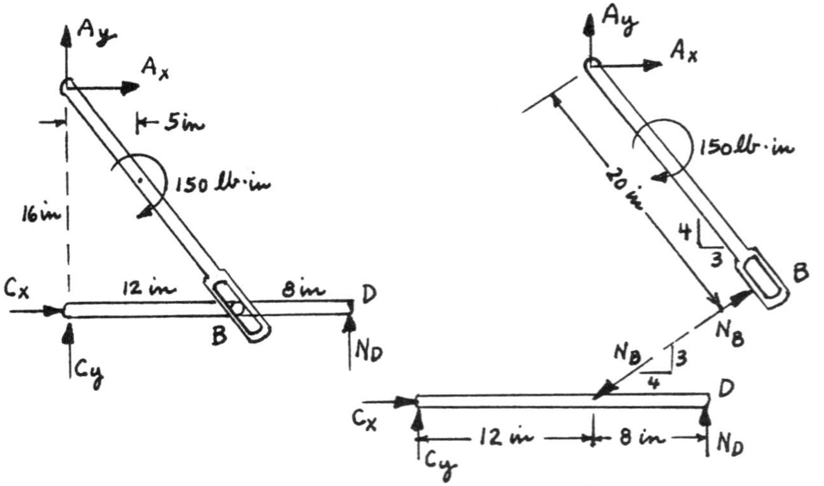

6 unknowns, 6 independent equations ◆

4.67

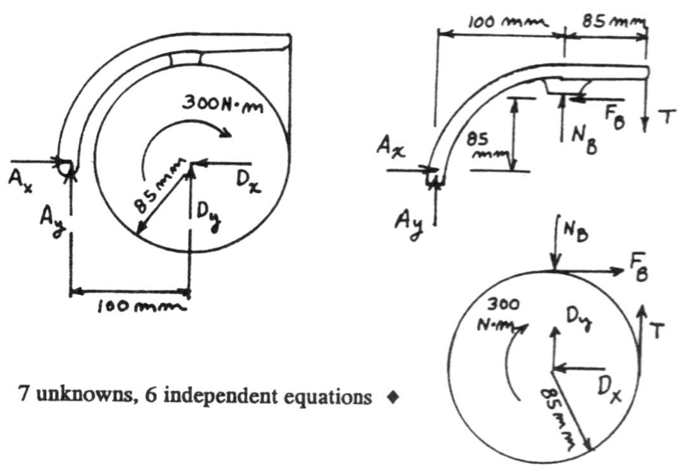

7 unknowns, 6 independent equations ◆

4.68

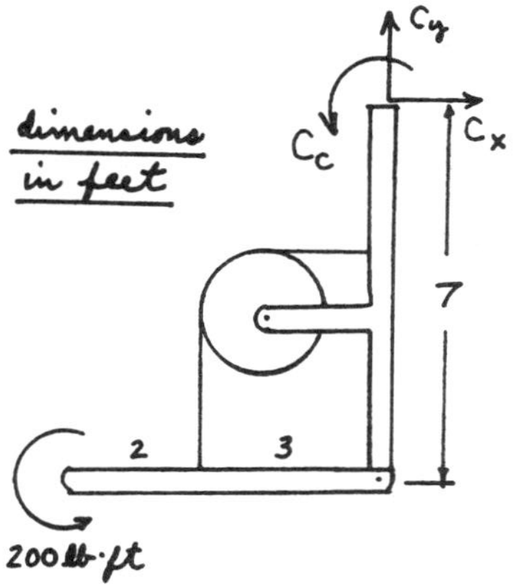

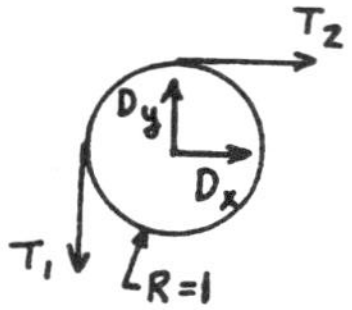

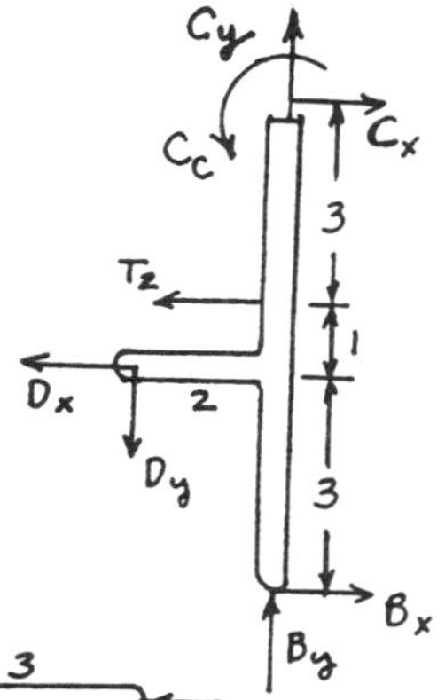

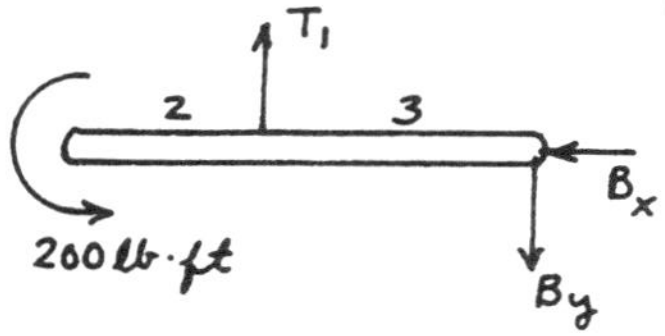

9 unknowns, 9 independent equations ◆

4.69

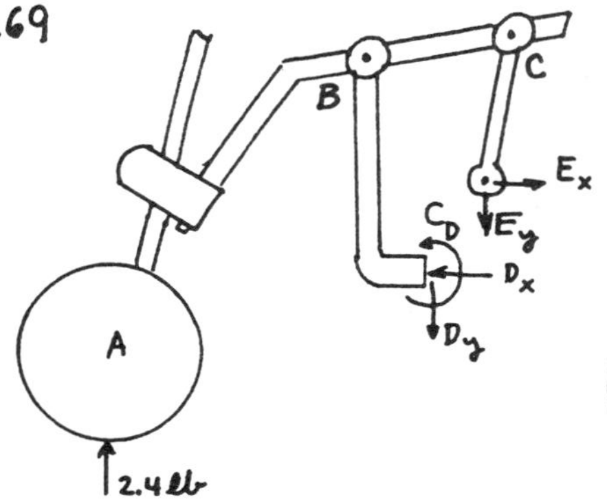

Entire assembly

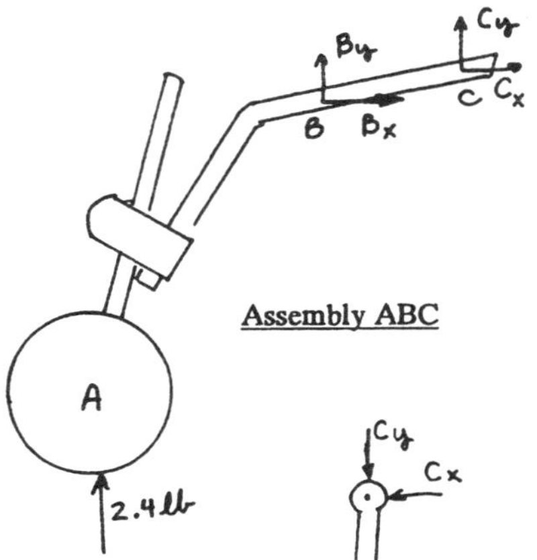

Assembly ABC

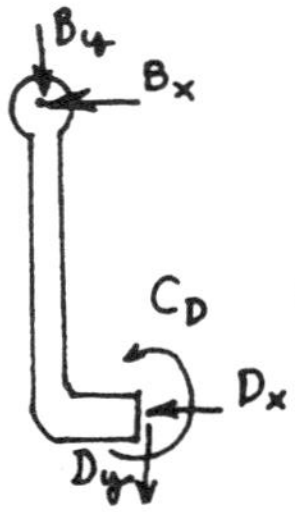

Arm BD

Link CE

4.70

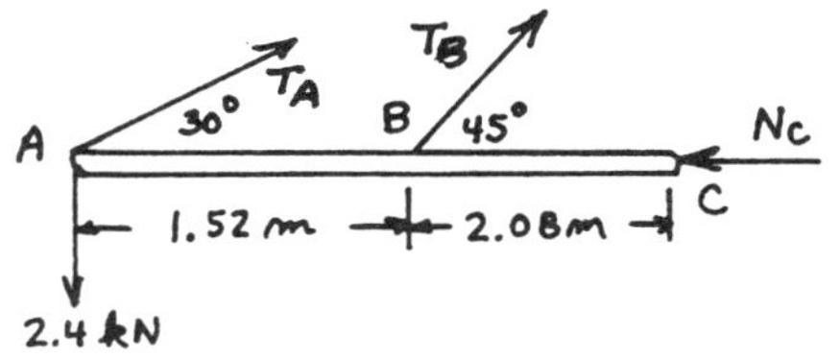

(a) Bar ABC with pin A in bar ABC

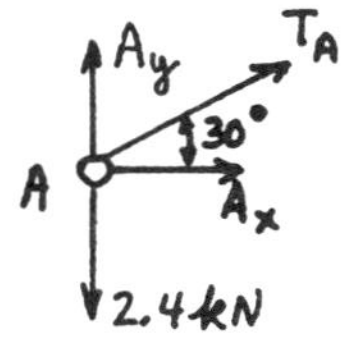

(c) Pin A

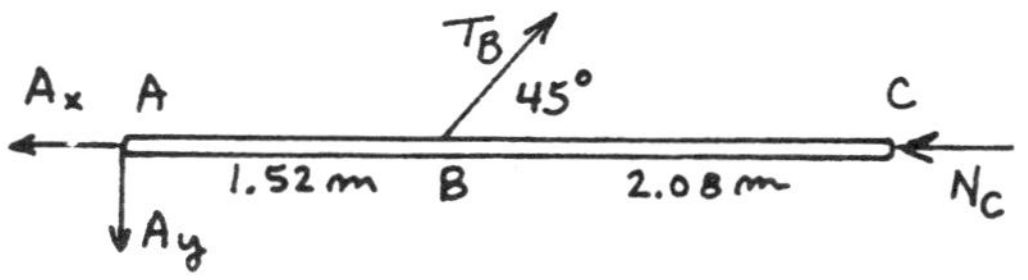

(b) Bar ABC with pin A removed

4.71

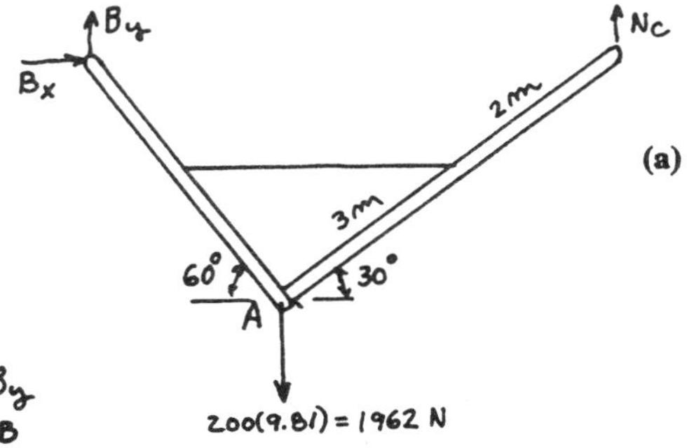

(a) Entire structure

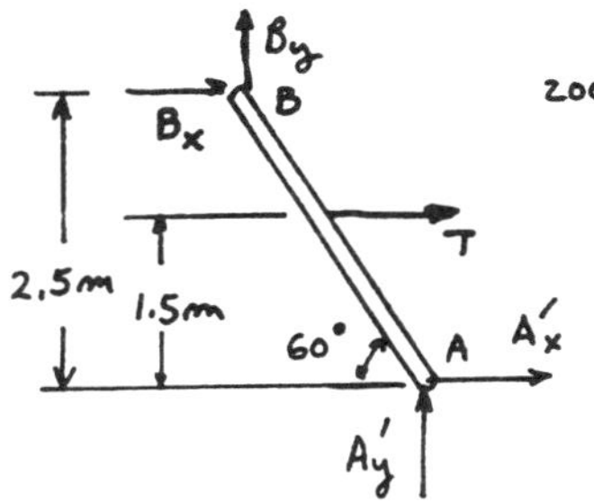

(c) Bar BA with pin A removed

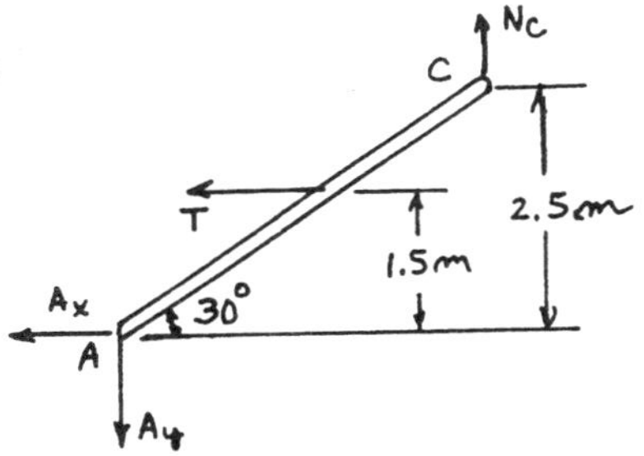

Bar AC with pin A removed

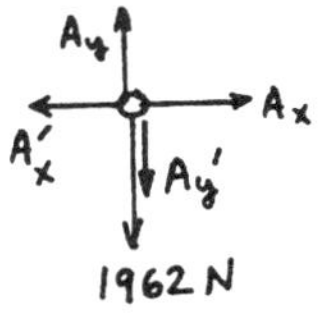

(b) Pin A

4.72

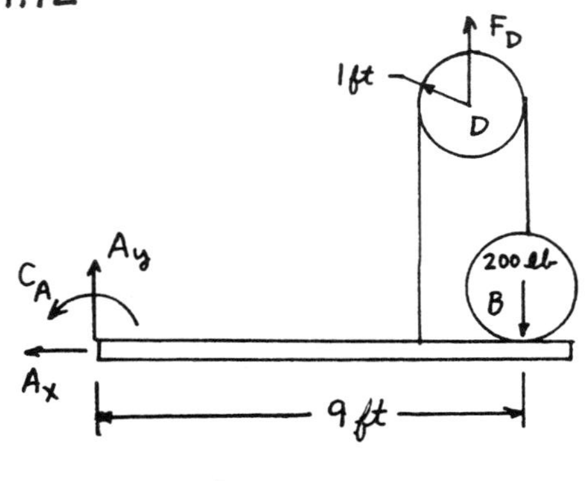

(a) Entire assembly

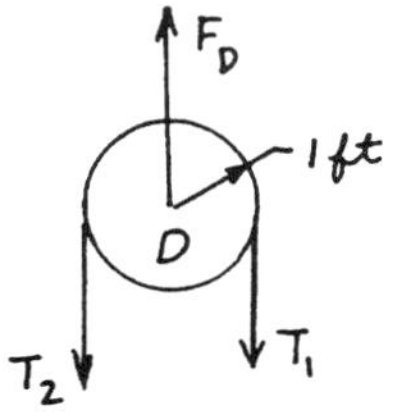

(b) Pulley

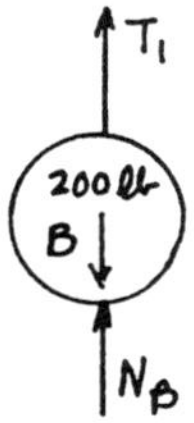

(c) Ball

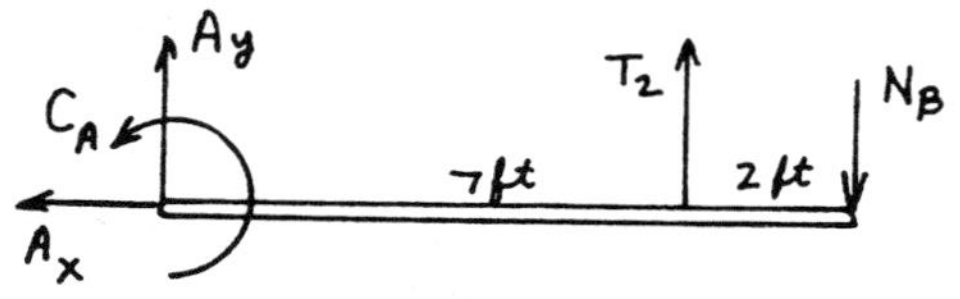

(d) Beam

4.73

Using the FBD of entire beam, similar triangles gives: $\frac{w_0}{1.8} = \frac{3}{3}$ $\quad \therefore \; w_0 = 1.8$ kN/m

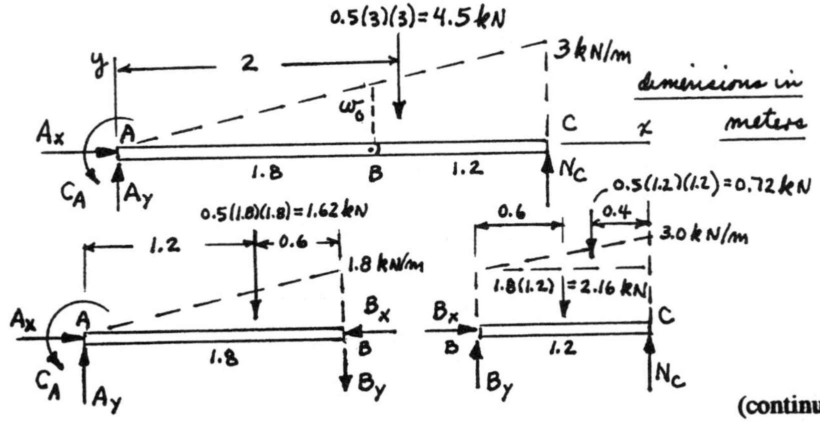

(continued)

FBD of segment BC

$\Sigma M_C = 0$: $\circlearrowleft +$ $0.72(0.4) + 2.16(0.6) - B_y(1.2) = 0$ $\quad \therefore \; B_y = 1.32$ kN

$\Sigma F_x = 0$: $\quad B_x = 0$ ◆

FBD of segment AB

$\Sigma F_x = 0$: $\quad A_x = B_x = 0$ ◆

$\Sigma F_y = 0$: $\quad +\uparrow \; A_y - B_y - 1.62 = 0$ $\quad \therefore \; A_y = 1.32 + 1.62 = 2.92$ kN ◆

$\Sigma M_A = 0$: $\circlearrowleft +$ $C_A - 1.62(1.2) - B_y(1.8) = 0$

$\therefore \; C_A = 1.62(1.2) + 1.32(1.8) = 4.32$ kN•m ◆

(Note: In the above analysis, the FBD of the entire beam ABC was not used.)

4.74

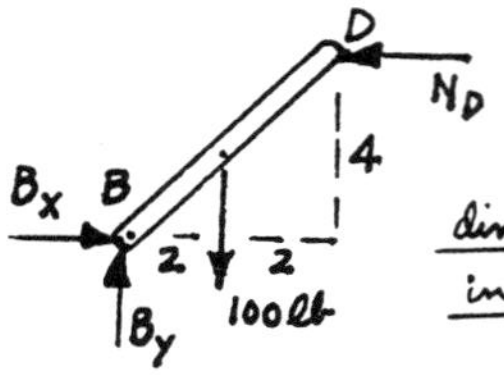

dimensions in inches

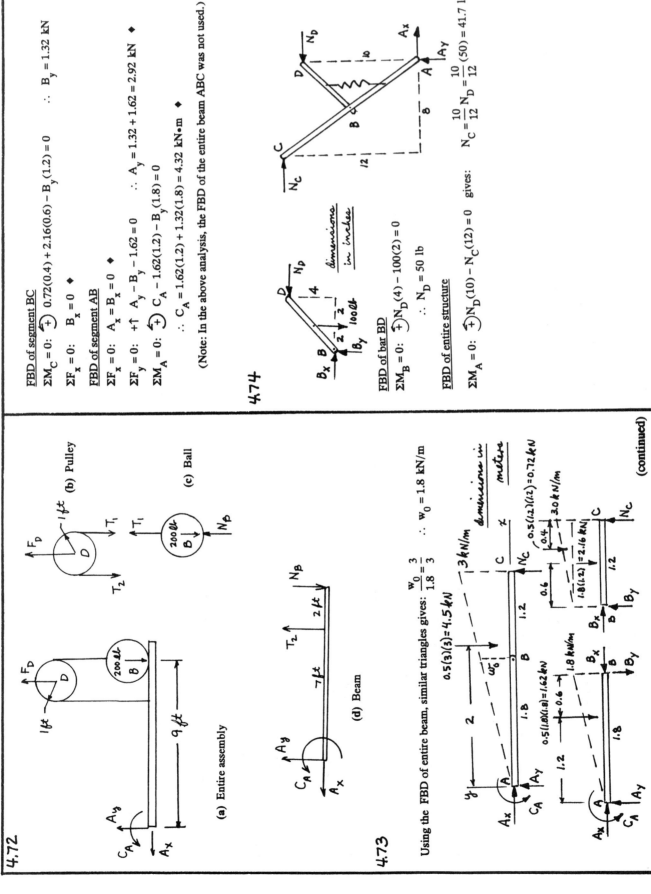

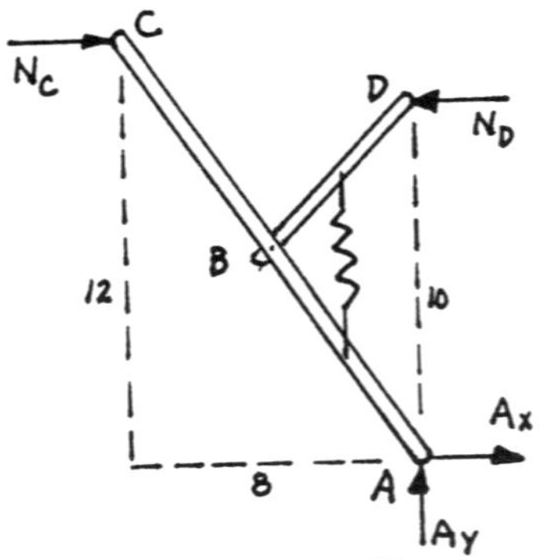

FBD of bar BD

$\Sigma M_B = 0$: $\circlearrowleft +$ $N_D(4) - 100(2) = 0$

$\therefore \; N_D = 50$ lb

FBD of entire structure

$\Sigma M_A = 0$: $\circlearrowleft +$ $N_D(10) - N_C(12) = 0$ gives: $\quad N_C = \frac{10}{12} N_D = \frac{10}{12}(50) = 41.7$ lb ◆

4.75

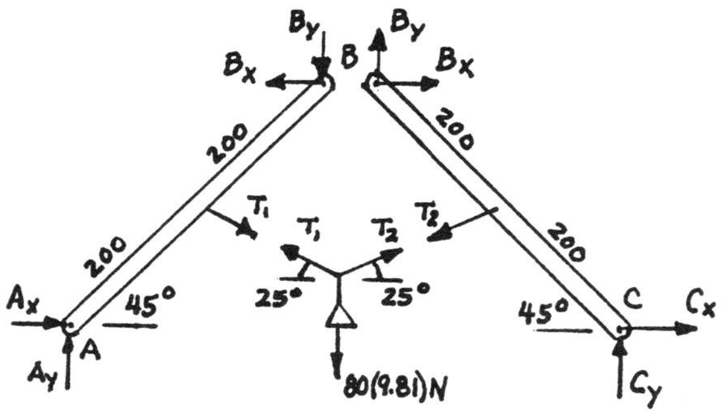

FBD of entire system (not shown here): Symmetry gives $A_y = C_y = \dfrac{80(9.81)}{2} = 392.4$ N

FBD of the small mass: $\Sigma F_x = 0$: $T_1 = T_2$

$$\Sigma F_y = 0: \; +\uparrow \; T_1 \sin 25^\circ + T_2 \sin 25^\circ - 80(9.81) = 0$$

$$\therefore \; 2T_2 \sin 25^\circ = 80(9.81) \quad \text{which gives} \quad T_2 = 928.5 \text{ N}$$

FBD of bar BC

$$\Sigma M_B = 0: \; \circlearrowleft + \; C_x(400 \sin 45^\circ) + C_y(400 \cos 45^\circ)$$

$$- T_2 \cos 25^\circ (200 \sin 45^\circ) - T_2 \sin 25^\circ (200 \cos 45^\circ) = 0$$

Substituting $C_y = 392.4$ N and $T_2 = 928.5$ N and solving for C_x gives: $C_x = 224.6$ N

Therefore, the magnitude of the pin reaction at C is

$$C = \sqrt{C_x^2 + C_y^2} = \sqrt{224.6^2 + 392.4^2} = 453 \text{ N} \; \blacklozenge$$

(Note that the FBD of bar AB was not used in the above analysis.)

4.76

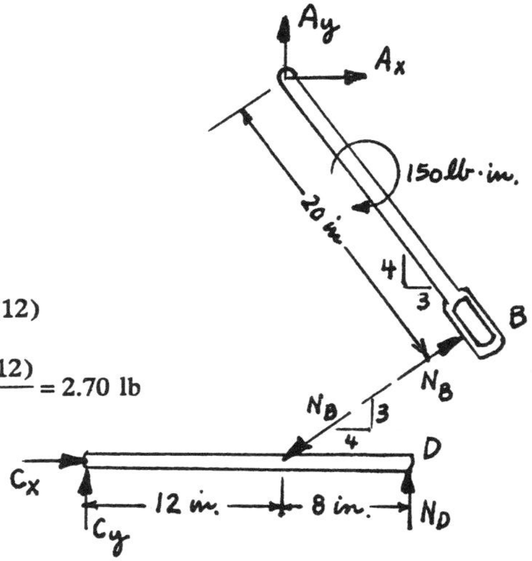

FBD of bar AB

$$\Sigma M_A = 0: \; 150 = N_B(20)$$

$$\therefore \; N_B = 7.5 \text{ lb}$$

FBD of bar CD

$$\Sigma M_C = 0: \; N_D(20) = \frac{3}{5} N_B(12)$$

$$\therefore \; N_D = \frac{0.6(7.5)(12)}{20} = 2.70 \text{ lb}$$

4.77

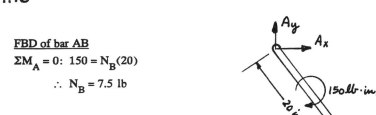

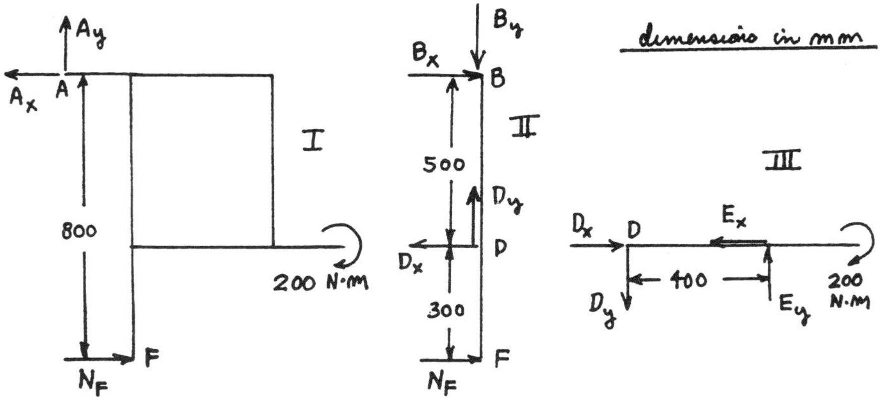

FBD I	$\Sigma M_A = 0$: $\circlearrowleft + \; 0.8 N_F - 200 = 0$	$\therefore N_F = 250$ N
FBD II	$\Sigma M_B = 0$: $\circlearrowleft + \; 0.8 N_F - 0.5 D_x = 0$	$\therefore D_x = 400$ N
FBD III	$\Sigma M_E = 0$: $\circlearrowleft + \; 0.4 D_y - 200 = 0$	$\therefore D_y = 500$ N

$$D = \sqrt{400^2 + 500^2} = 640 \text{ N} \; \blacklozenge$$

4.78

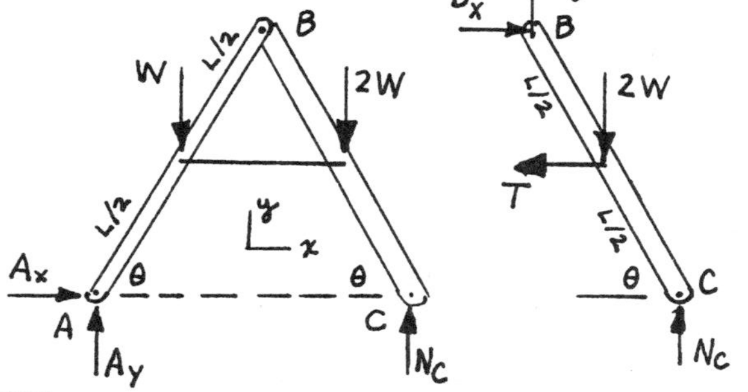

FBD of entire structure

$\Sigma M_A = 0$: $\circlearrowleft +$ $N_C(2L\cos\theta) - W\left(\frac{L}{2}\cos\theta\right) - 2W\left(\frac{3L}{2}\cos\theta\right) = 0$ gives: $N_C = \frac{7W}{4}$

FBD of bar BC

$\Sigma M_B = 0$: $\circlearrowleft +$ $N_C(L\cos\theta) - 2W\left(\frac{L}{2}\cos\theta\right) - T\left(\frac{L}{2}\sin\theta\right) = 0$

$\therefore \frac{7W}{4}\cos\theta - W\cos\theta = \frac{T}{2}\sin\theta$ which gives: $T = 1.5W\cot\theta$ ◆

4.79

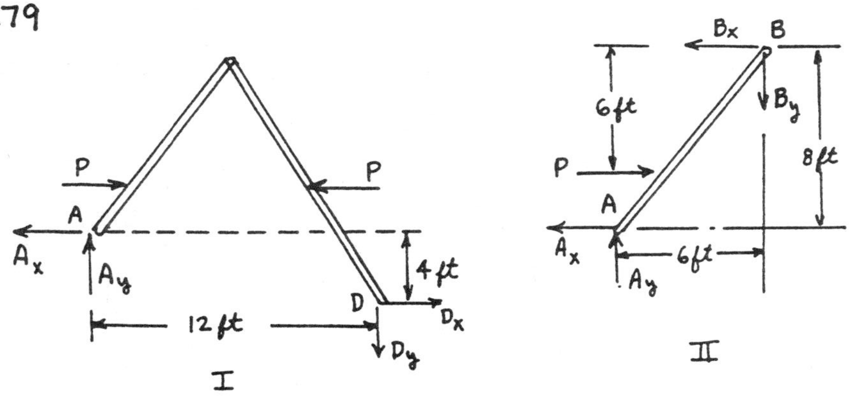

FBD I $\Sigma M_D = 0$: $\circlearrowleft +$ $A_x(4) - A_y(12) = 0$ $\therefore A_x = 3A_y$

FBD II $\Sigma M_B = 0$: $\circlearrowleft +$ $P(6) - A_y(6) - A_x(8) = 0$

$P(6) - A_y(6) - 3A_y(8) = 0$ $\therefore A_y = 0.2P$ $(A_x = 0.6P)$

$R_A = P\sqrt{0.2^2 + 0.6^2} = 0.632P$ ◆

4.80

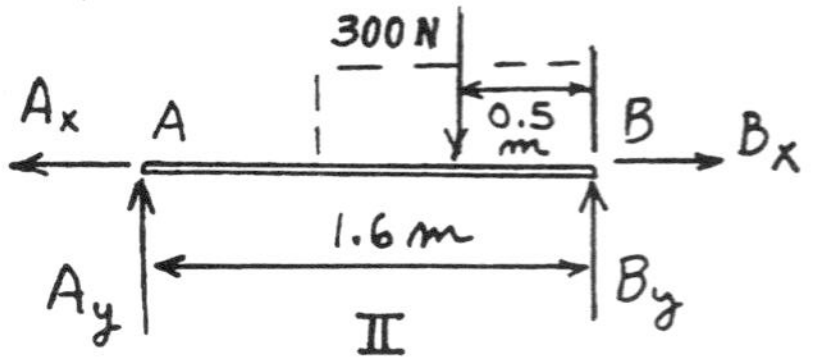

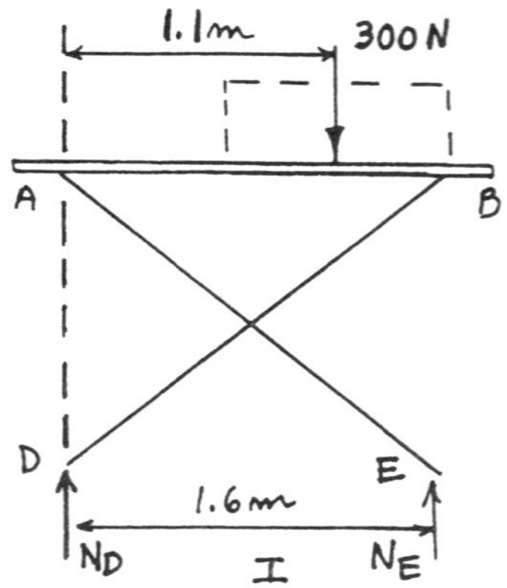

FBD I $\Sigma M_D = 0$:

$\circlearrowleft +$ $N_E(1.6) - 300(1.1) = 0$

$\therefore N_E = 206.25$ N

FBD II $\Sigma M_B = 0$:

$\circlearrowleft +$ $300(0.5) - A_y(1.6) = 0$

$\therefore A_y = 93.75$ N

FBD III $\Sigma M_C = 0$:

$\circlearrowleft +$ $93.75(0.8) + 206.25(0.8) - A_x(0.6) = 0$

$\therefore A_x = 400$ N

$\Sigma F_y = 0$: $+\uparrow$ $C_y - 93.75 + 206.25 = 0$

$\therefore C_y = -112.5$ N

$\Sigma F_x = 0$: $\xrightarrow{+}$ $A_x - C_x = 0$ $\therefore C_x = A_x = 400$ N

$R_A = \sqrt{93.75^2 + 400^2} = 410.8$ N ◆

$R_C = \sqrt{112.5^2 + 400^2} = 415.5$ N ◆

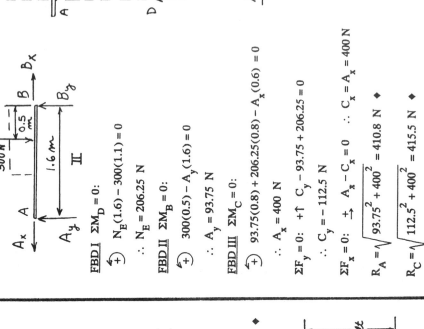

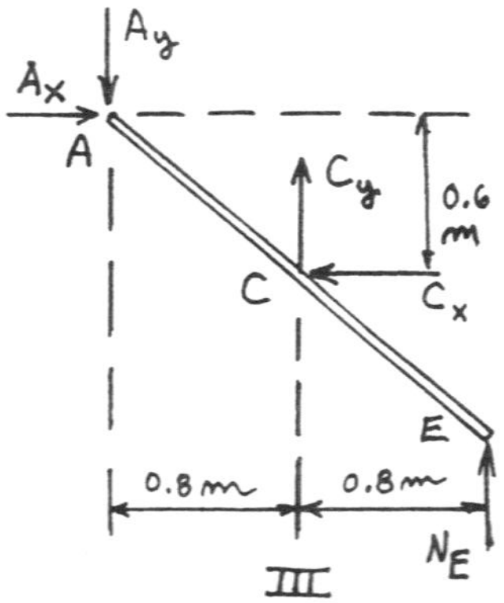

4.81

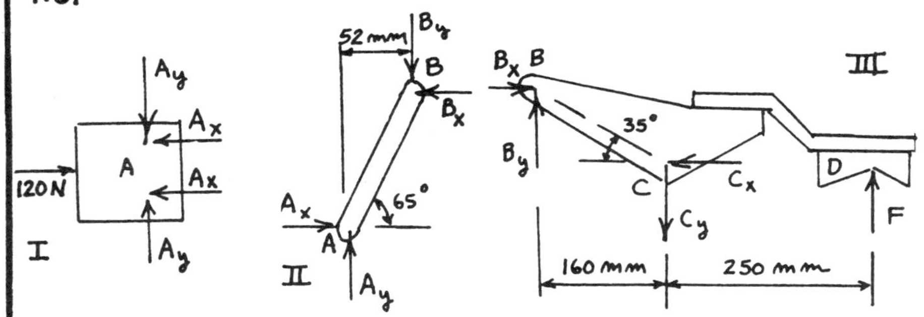

FBD I $\Sigma F_x = 0$: $\overset{+}{\rightarrow}$ $120 - 2A_x = 0$ $\quad \therefore A_x = 60$ N

FBD II $\Sigma F_x = 0$: $\overset{+}{\rightarrow}$ $A_x - B_x = 0$ $\quad \therefore B_x = A_x = 60$ N

$\Sigma M_A = 0$: $\circlearrowleft +$ $B_x(52 \tan 65^o) - B_y(52) = 0$

$\therefore B_y = B_x \tan 65^o = 60 \tan 65^o = 128.7$ N

FBD III $\Sigma M_C = 0$: $\circlearrowleft +$ $F(250) - B_y(160) - B_x(160 \tan 35^o) = 0$

$\therefore F = (1/250)[128.7(160) + 60(160 \tan 35^o)] = 109.3$ N ◆

4.82

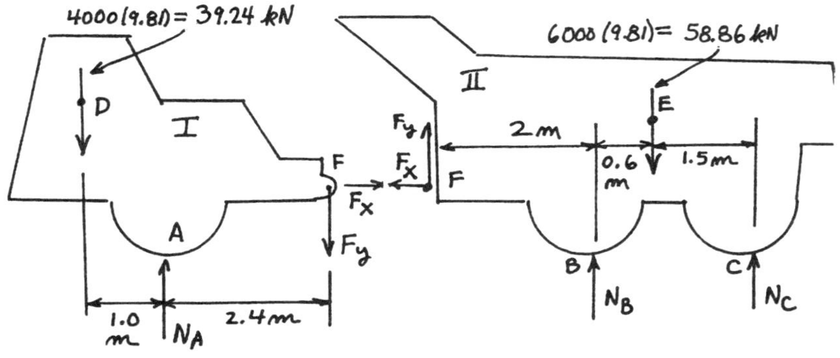

(continued)

FBD I $\Sigma M_F = 0$: $\circlearrowleft +$ $39.24(3.4) - N_A(2.4) = 0$ $\quad \therefore N_A = 55.59$ kN ◆

$\Sigma F_x = 0$: $F_x = 0$

$\Sigma F_y = 0$: $+\uparrow$ $N_A - 39.24 - F_y = 0$ $\quad \therefore F_y = 55.59 - 39.24 = 16.35$ kN ◆

FBD II $\Sigma M_B = 0$: $\circlearrowleft +$ $N_C(2.1) - 58.86(0.6) - F_y(2) = 0$ (since $F_x = 0$)

$N_C = (1/2.1)[58.86(0.6) + 16.35(2)] = 32.39$ kN ◆

$\Sigma F_y = 0$: $+\uparrow$ $N_B + N_C + F_y - 58.86 = 0$

$N_B = -N_C - F_y + 58.86 = -32.39 - 16.35 + 58.86 = 10.12$ kN ◆

4.83

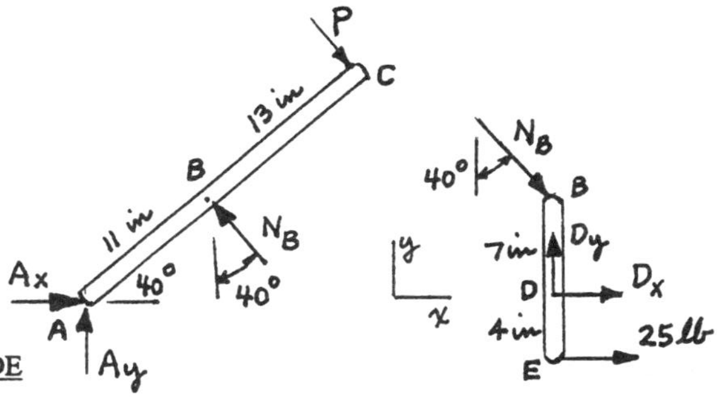

FBD of bar BDE

$\Sigma M_D = 0$: $\circlearrowleft +$ $25(4) - N_B \sin 40^o(7) = 0$ $\quad \therefore N_B = 22.22$ lb

FBD of bar ABC

$\Sigma M_A = 0$: $\circlearrowleft +$ $N_B(11) - P(24) = 0$ $\quad \therefore P = (11/24)N_B = (11/24)(22.22) = 10.19$ lb ◆

4.84

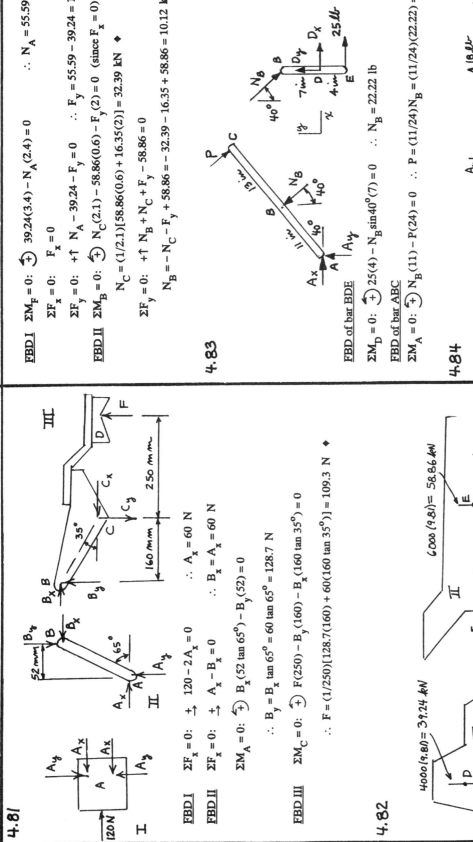

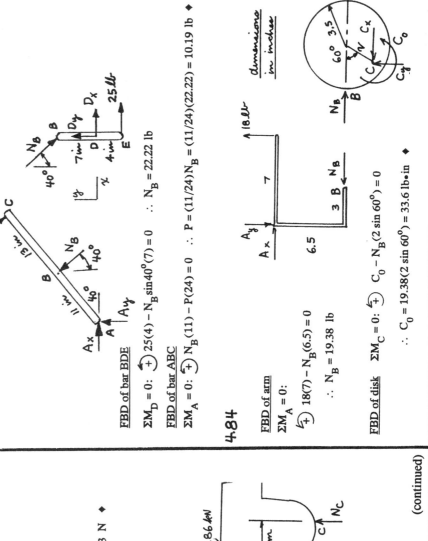

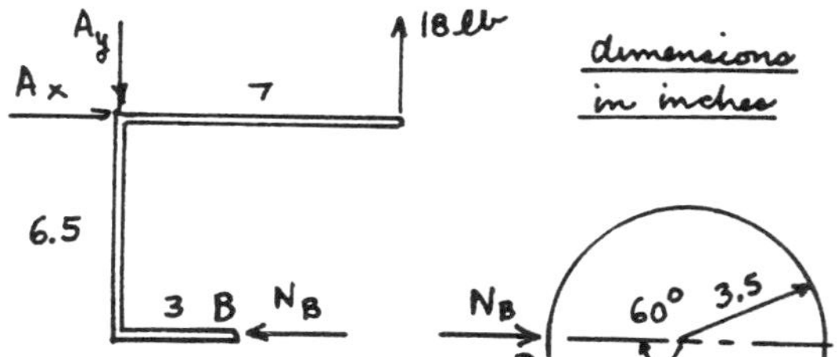

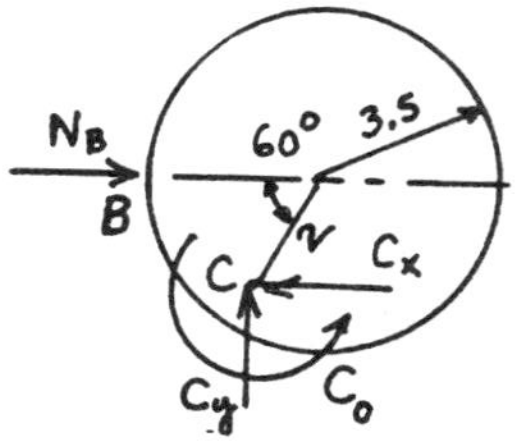

FBD of arm

$\Sigma M_A = 0$:

$\circlearrowleft +$ $18(7) - N_B(6.5) = 0$

$\therefore N_B = 19.38$ lb

FBD of disk $\Sigma M_C = 0$: $\circlearrowleft +$ $C_0 - N_B(2 \sin 60^o) = 0$

$\therefore C_0 = 19.38(2 \sin 60^o) = 33.6$ lb•in ◆

4.85

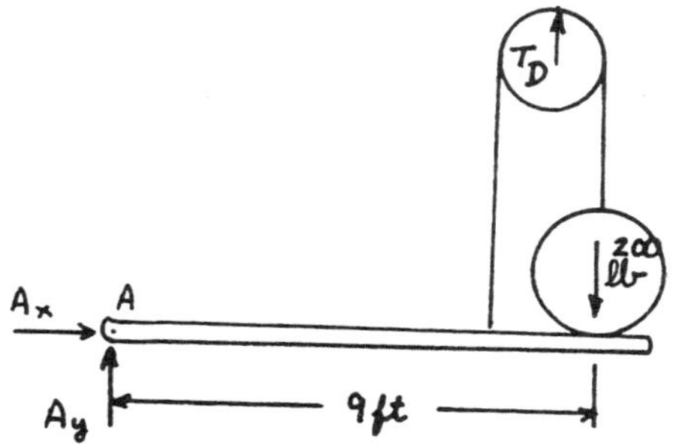

$\Sigma M_A = 0$:

(+) $T_D(8) - 200(9) = 0$

$\therefore\ T_D = 225$ lb

$\Sigma F_x = 0$: $A_x = 0$

$\Sigma F_y = 0$: $+\uparrow$ $A_y + T_D - 200 = 0$

$\therefore\ A_y = -225 + 200 = -25$ lb

$R_A = \sqrt{A_x^2 + A_y^2} = 25$ lb ◆

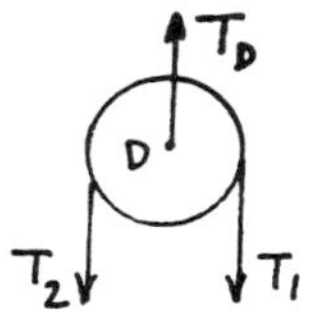

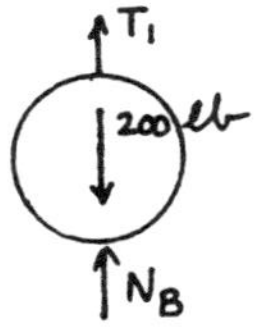

$\Sigma M_D = 0$: $T_1 = T_2$

$\Sigma F_y = 0$: $+\uparrow$ $T_D - T_1 - T_2 = 0$

$\therefore\ T_1 = 0.5\,T_D = 0.5(225) = 112.5$ lb

$\Sigma F_y = 0$: $+\uparrow$ $T_1 + N_B - 200 = 0$

$\therefore\ N_B = 200 - T_1$

$= 200 - 112.5 = 87.5$ lb ◆

4.86

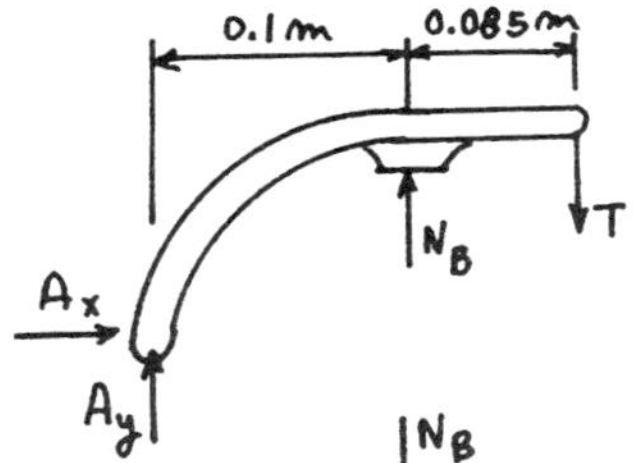

FBD of arm

$\Sigma M_A = 0$: (+) $N_B(0.1) - T(0.185) = 0$

$\therefore\ N_B = 1.85\,T$

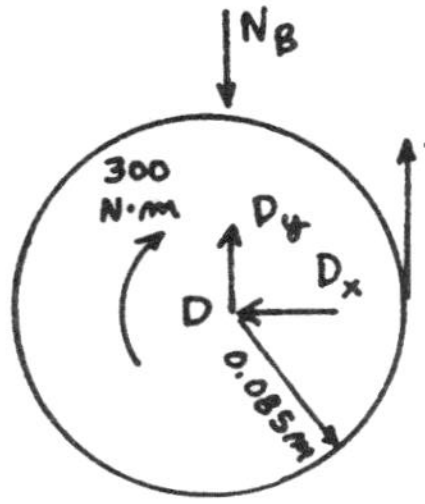

FBD of cylinder

$\Sigma M_D = 0$: (+) $T(0.085) - 300 = 0$

$\therefore\ T = 3530$ N ◆

Therefore, $N_B = 1.85(3530) = 6531$ N ◆

4.87

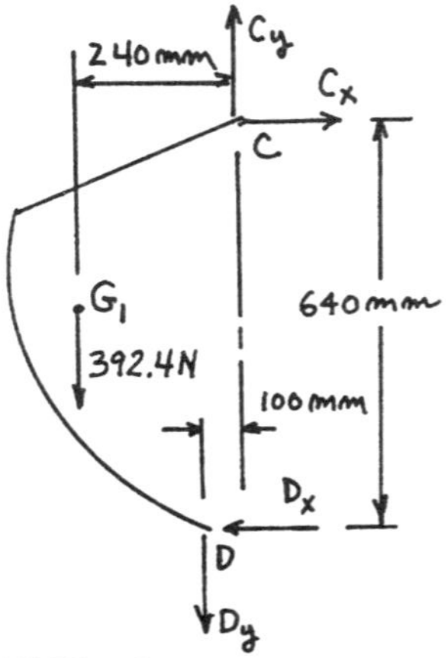

$W_{CD} = 40(9.81) = 392.4$ N

$W_B = 60(9.81) = 588.6$ N

FBD of B

$\Sigma M_B = 0$: $D_y = E_y$

$\Sigma F_y = 0$:

$+\uparrow$ $D_y + E_y - 588.6 = 2\,D_y - 588.6 = 0$

$\therefore\ D_y = 588.6/2 = 294.3$ N

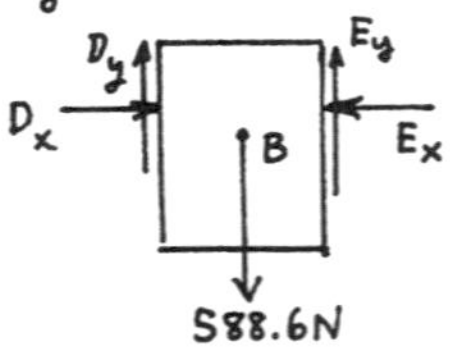

FBD of CD

$\Sigma M_C = 0$: (+) $D_y(100) - D_x(640) + 392.4(240) = 0$

$\therefore\ D_x = (1/640)[294.3(100) + 392.4(240)] = 193.1$ N

$D = \sqrt{D_x^2 + D_y^2} = \sqrt{193.1^2 + 294.3^2} = 352$ N ◆

4.88

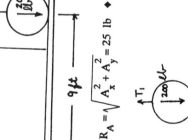

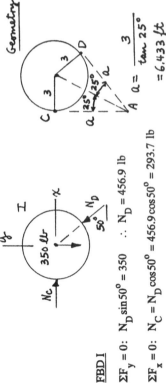

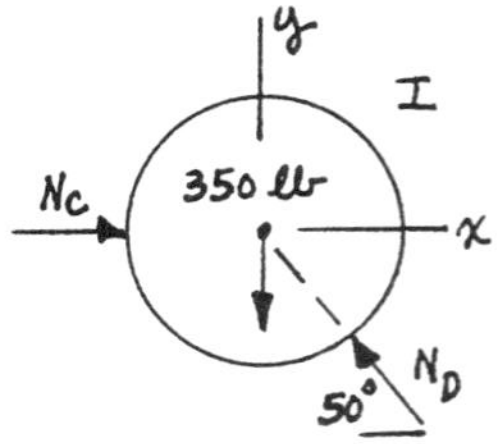

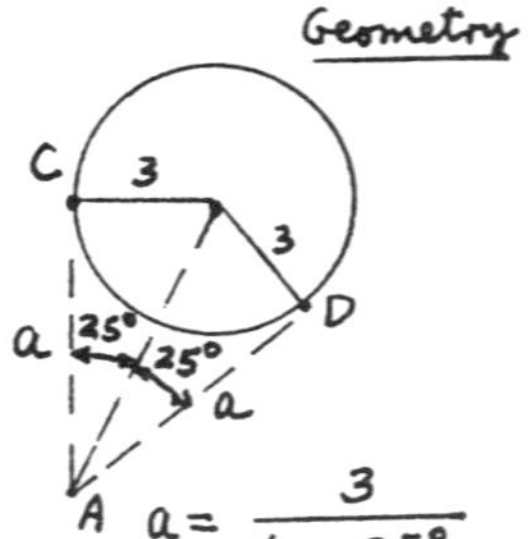

$a = \dfrac{3}{\tan 25^\circ}$

$= 6.433$ ft

FBD I

$\Sigma F_y = 0$: $N_D \sin 50^\circ = 350$ $\therefore\ N_D = 456.9$ lb

$\Sigma F_x = 0$: $N_C = N_D \cos 50^\circ = 456.9 \cos 50^\circ = 293.7$ lb

(continued)

FBD II

(Using the above geometry, we have found that the vertical distance between point A and the line of action of N_C is 6.433 ft.)

$\Sigma M_A = 0$:

$\circlearrowleft + \; T(10.5) - 350(3) - N_C(6.433) = 0$

$$\therefore\ T = \frac{350(3) + 293.7(6.433)}{10.5} = 280 \text{ lb} \ \blacklozenge$$

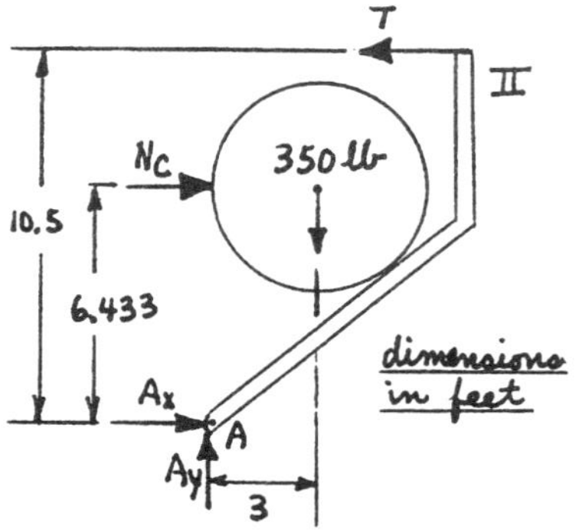

4.89

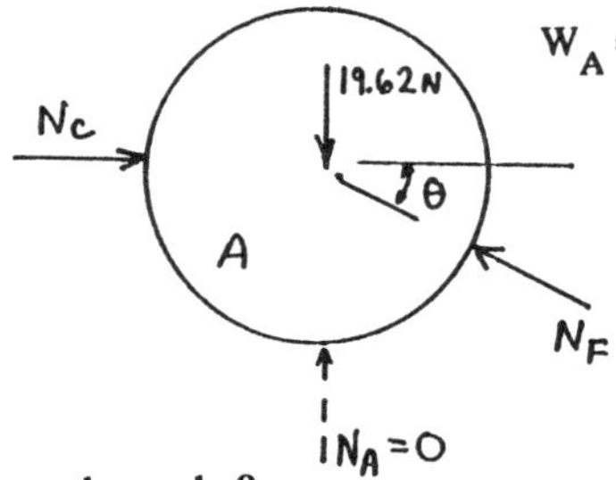

$W_A = 2(9.81) = 19.62$ N $\quad W_B = 1(9.81) = 9.81$ N

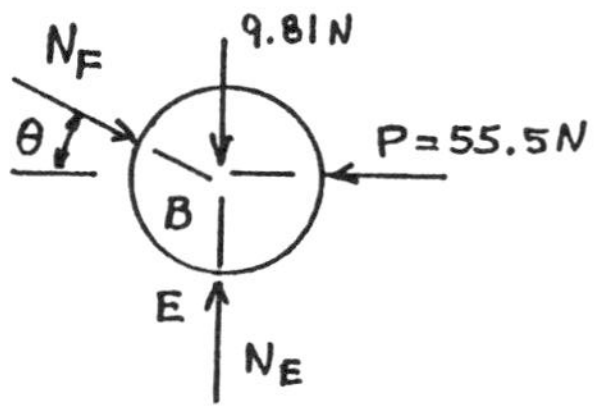

Compute the angle θ

FBD of A $\quad \Sigma F_y = 0$: $+\uparrow$ $\quad N_F \sin\theta - 19.62 = 0 \qquad N_F \sin\theta = 19.62 \quad (1)$

FBD of B $\quad \Sigma F_x = 0$: $\overset{+}{\rightarrow}$ $\quad N_F \cos\theta - 55.5 = 0 \qquad N_F \cos\theta = 55.5 \quad (2)$

Divide (1) by (2): $\sin\theta/\cos\theta = \tan\theta = 19.62/55.5 \quad \therefore\ \theta = 19.47^\circ$

Geometry

$$\tan 19.47^\circ = \frac{20 - R}{20 + R}$$

Solving gives: $R = 9.55$ mm $\blacklozenge$

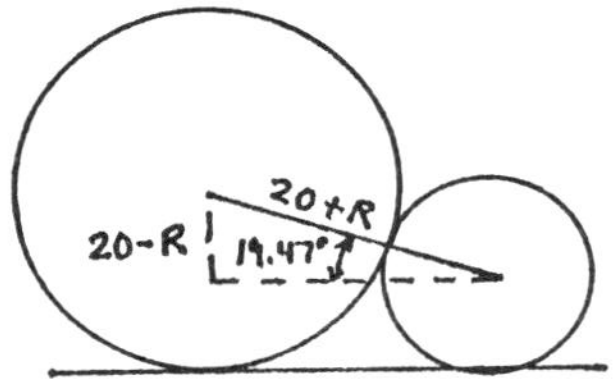

4.90

FBD of entire structure

$\Sigma M_E = 0$: $\circlearrowleft + \; F_y(30) - F_x(6) - 3600(9) = 0$

$\therefore\ F_x = 5F_y - 5400 \quad (1)$

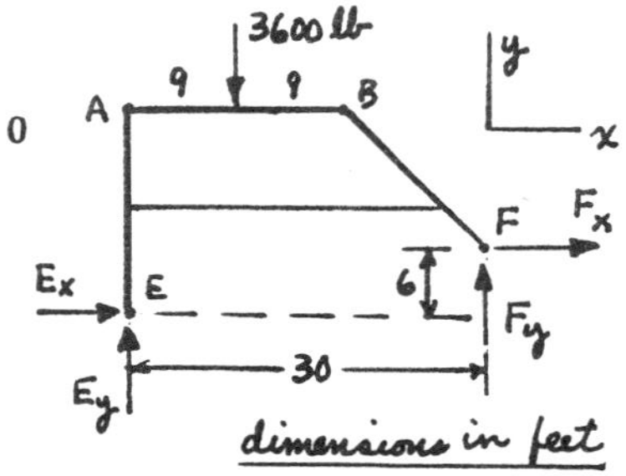

FBD of AB $\quad \Sigma M_A = 0$: $\quad B_y = 1800$ lb

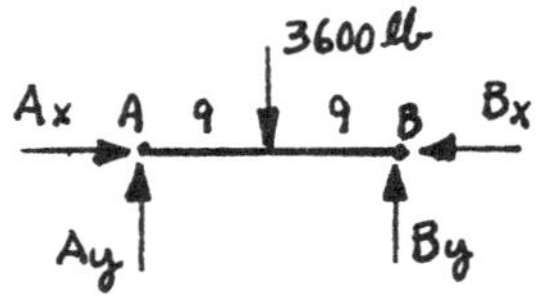

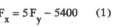

FBD of BF

$\Sigma F_y = 0$: $\quad F_y = B_y = 1800$ lb

Substituting $F_y = 1800$ lb into (1) gives:

$F_x = 5(1800) - 5400 = 3600$ lb

$\Sigma M_B = 0$: $\circlearrowleft + \; F_y(12) + F_x(12) - T(9) = 0$

$$\therefore\ T = \frac{12(1800 + 3600)}{9} = 7200 \text{ lb} \ \blacklozenge$$

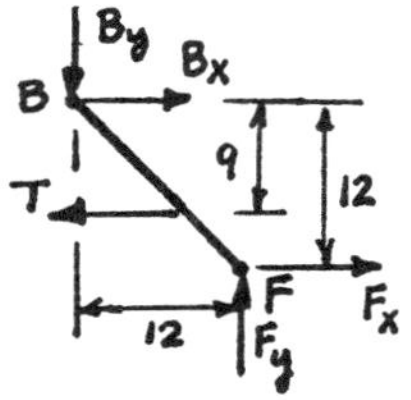

4.91

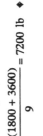

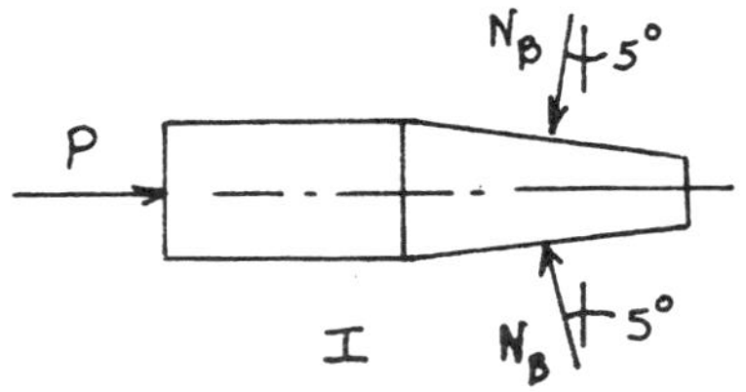

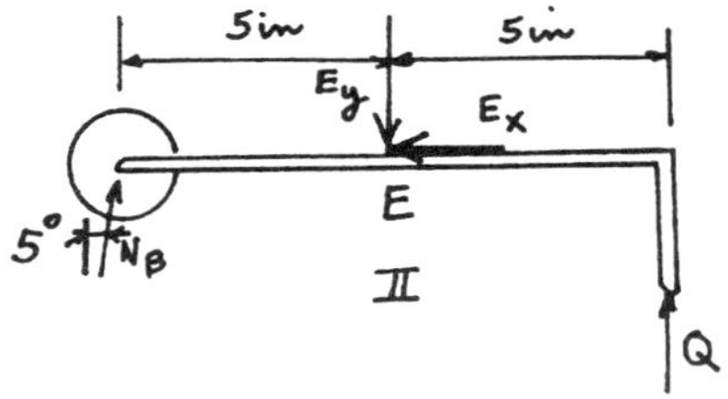

FBD I $\quad \Sigma F_x = 0$: $\overset{+}{\rightarrow}$ $\quad P - 2N_B \sin 5^\circ = 0 \qquad \therefore\ N_B = 5.737\,P$

FBD II $\quad \Sigma M_E = 0$: $\circlearrowleft + \; Q(5) - N_B \cos 5^\circ (5) = 0$

$\therefore\ Q = N_B \cos 5^\circ = 5.737\,P \cos 5^\circ = 5.72\,P \ \blacklozenge$

4.92

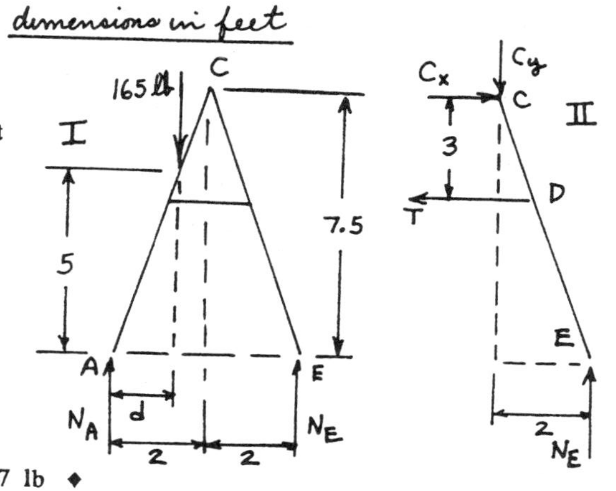

FBD I

Using similar triangles:

$$\frac{d}{5} = \frac{2}{7.5} \quad \text{or} \quad d = 4/3 \text{ ft}$$

$\Sigma M_A = 0$:

$\circlearrowleft + \quad N_E(4) - 165(4/3) = 0$

$\therefore \quad N_E = 55.00$ lb

FBD II

$\Sigma M_C = 0$:

$\circlearrowleft + \quad N_E(2) - T(3) = 0$

$\therefore \quad T = (2/3)55.00 = 36.7$ lb ◆

4.93

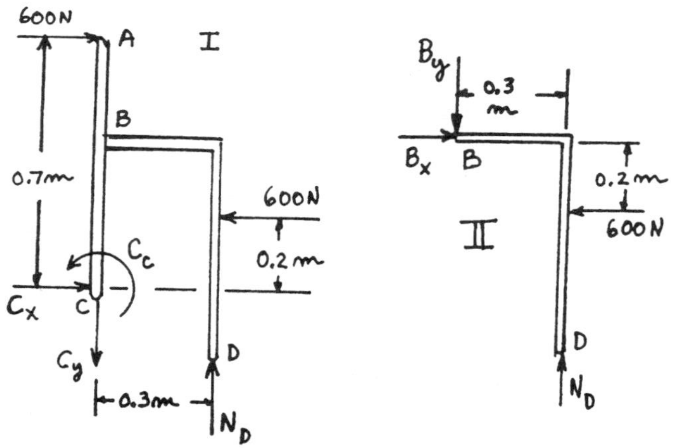

FBD II $\quad \Sigma M_B = 0$: $\circlearrowleft + \quad N_D(0.3) - 600(0.2) = 0 \quad \therefore \quad N_D = 400$ N

FBD I $\quad \Sigma M_C = 0$: $\circlearrowleft + \quad C_C + N_D(0.3) + 600(0.2) - 600(0.7) = 0$

$\therefore \quad C_C = -400(0.3) - 600(0.2) + 600(0.7) = 180.0$ N•m ◆

$\Sigma F_x = 0$: $\quad \overset{+}{\rightarrow} \quad C_x - 600 + 600 = 0 \quad \therefore \quad C_x = 0$ ◆

$\Sigma F_y = 0$: $\quad +\uparrow \quad N_D - C_y = 0 \quad \therefore \quad C_y = N_D = 400$ N ◆

4.94

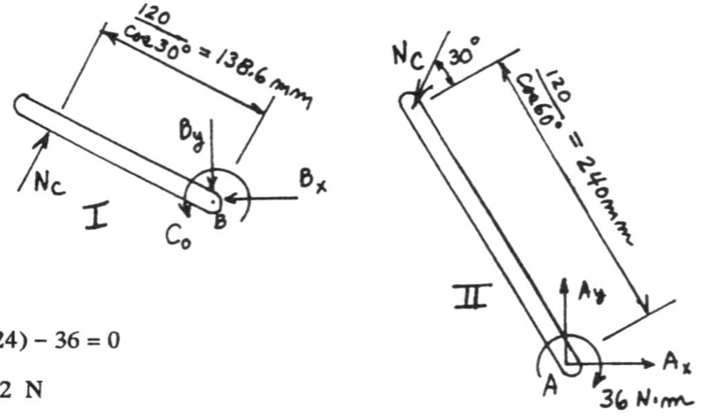

FBD II $\quad \Sigma M_A = 0$:

$\circlearrowleft + \quad N_C \cos 30^\circ(0.24) - 36 = 0$

$\therefore \quad N_C = 173.2$ N

FBD I $\quad \Sigma M_B = 0$:

$\circlearrowleft + \quad C_0 - N_C(0.1386) = 0$

$\therefore \quad C_0 = 24.0$ N•m ◆

4.95

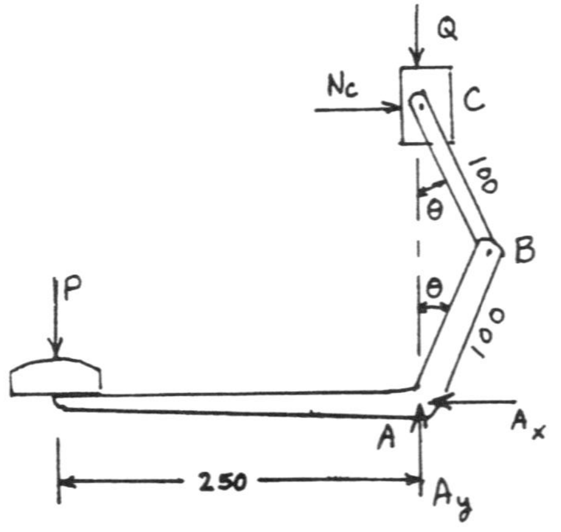

$\Sigma M_A = 0$:

$\circlearrowleft + \quad P(250) - N_C(200 \cos\theta) = 0$

$$\therefore \quad N_C = \frac{1.25\,P}{\cos\theta}$$

$\Sigma M_B = 0$: $\circlearrowleft + \quad Q(100 \sin\theta) - N_C(100 \cos\theta) = 0$

$$\therefore \quad Q \sin\theta = N_C \cos\theta = \frac{1.25\,P}{\cos\theta} \cos\theta \quad \text{or} \quad \frac{Q}{P} = \frac{1.25}{\sin\theta}$$

Using $Q/P = 4$, $\quad \theta = \sin^{-1}\left(\frac{1.25}{4}\right) = 18.2^\circ$ ◆

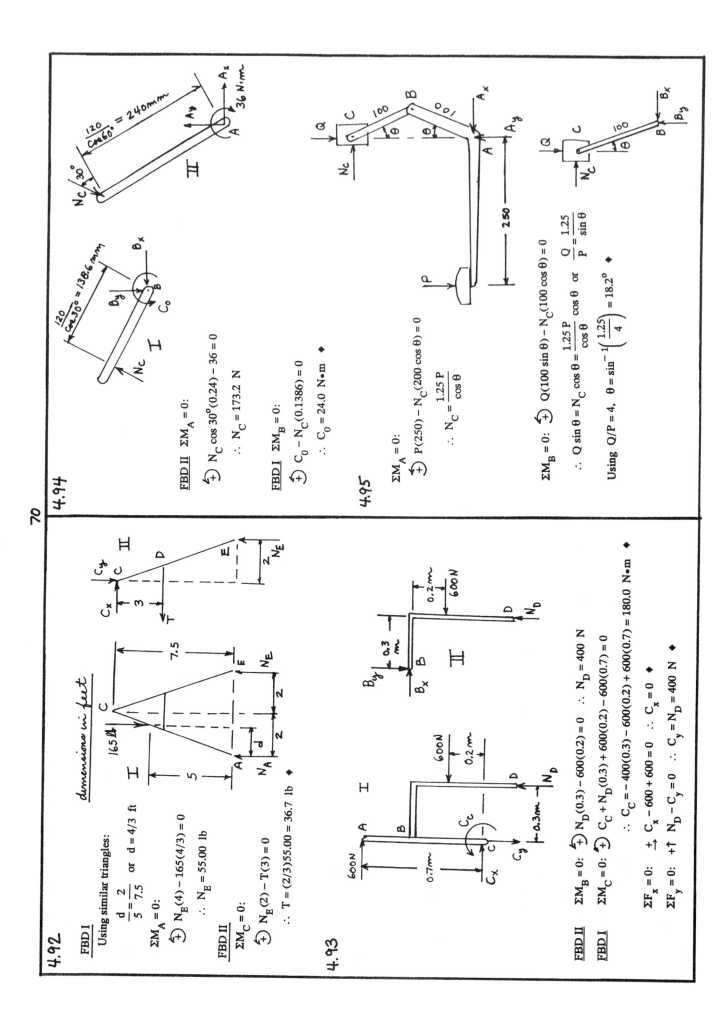

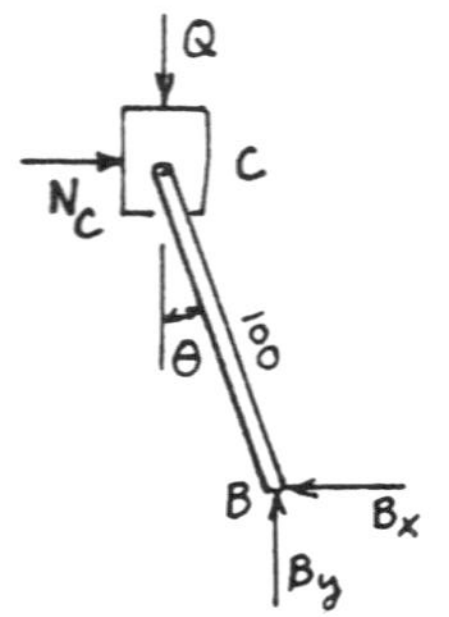

4.96

(a) <u>FBD of entire system</u>

$\Sigma F_y = 0 \quad +\uparrow\ 2T_A + 2T_B - 390 = 0$

$\therefore\ T_A + T_B = 195 \text{ lb} \qquad (1)$

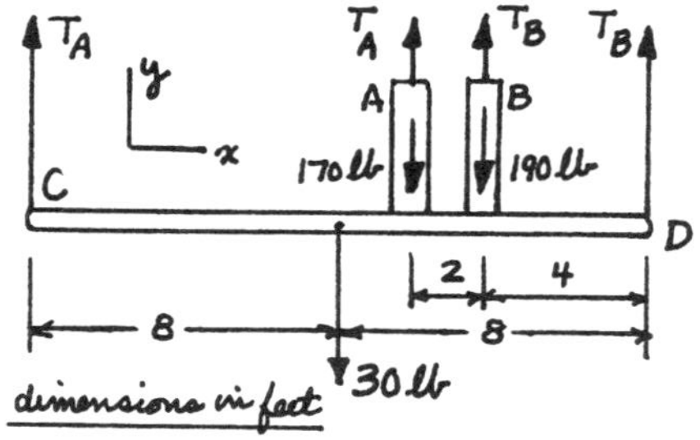

$\Sigma M_D = 0$:

$\circlearrowleft + \quad 30(8) + 170(6) + 190(4)$
$\quad - T_A(16) - T_A(6) - T_B(4) = 0 \quad (2)$

Solving (1) and (2) gives:

$T_A = 68.9 \text{ lb and } T_B = 126.1 \text{ lb}$ ◆

(b) <u>FBD of man A</u>

$\Sigma F_y = 0 \quad N_A = 170 - T_A = 170 - 68.9 = 101.1 \text{ lb}$ ◆

<u>FBD of man B</u>

$\Sigma F_y = 0 \quad N_B = 190 - T_B = 190 - 126.1 = 63.9 \text{ lb}$ ◆

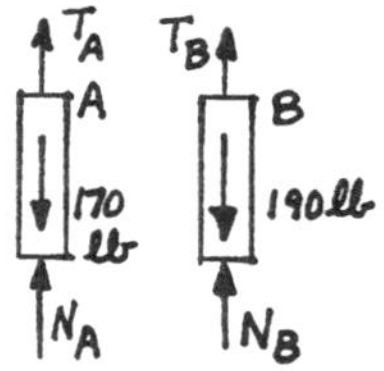

4.97

$\Sigma M_D = 0$:

$\circlearrowleft + \quad T_{CD}(3) - 3200(15.59) = 0$

$\therefore\ T_{CD} = 16630 \text{ lb}$ ◆

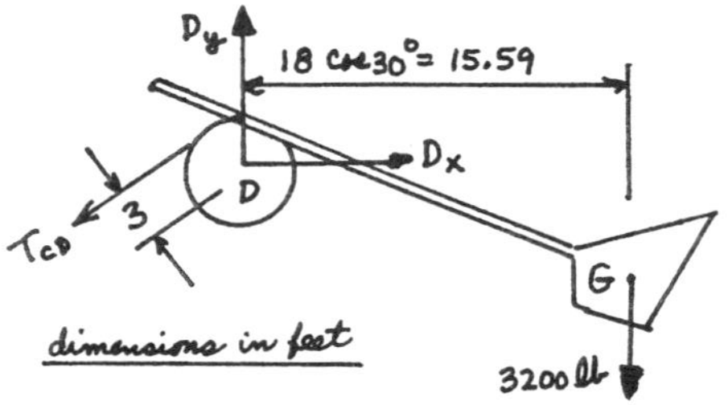

$\Sigma M_E = 0$:

$\circlearrowleft + \quad 3T_{CD} + T_{AB}(21.21)$
$\quad - 3200(27.08) = 0$

which gives:

$21.21\, T_{AB} = -3(16630)$
$\quad + 3200(27.08)$

$\therefore\ T_{AB} = 1733 \text{ lb}$ ◆

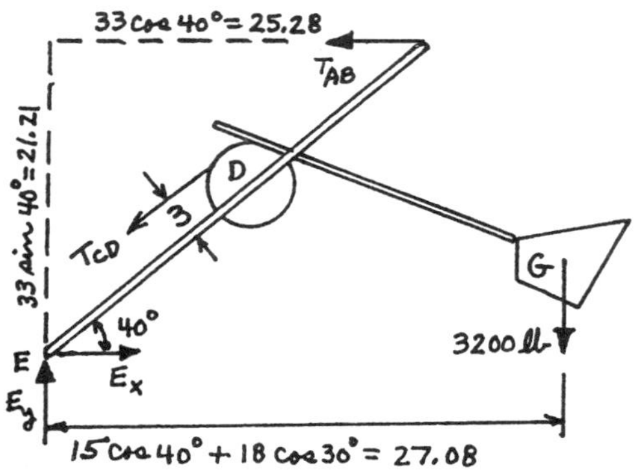

4.98

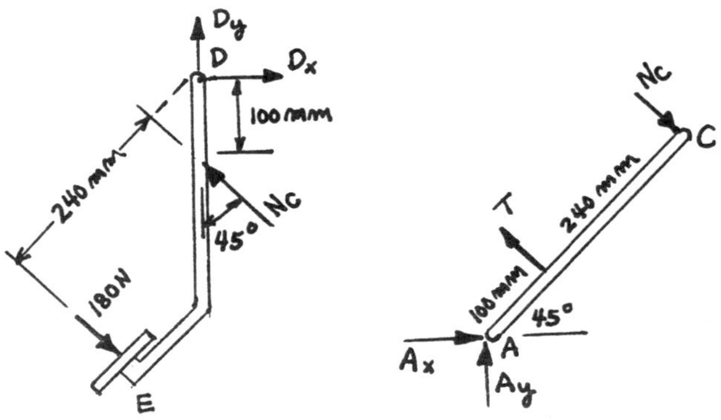

<u>FBD I</u> $\quad \Sigma M_D = 0: \quad \circlearrowleft + \ 180(240 + 100\sin 45^\circ) - N_C \sin 45^\circ(100) \qquad \therefore\ N_C = 790.9 \text{ N}$

<u>FBD II</u> $\quad \Sigma M_A = 0: \quad \circlearrowleft + \ T(100) - N_C(340) = 0 \qquad \therefore\ T = (340/100)(790.9) = 2690 \text{ N}$ ◆

4.99

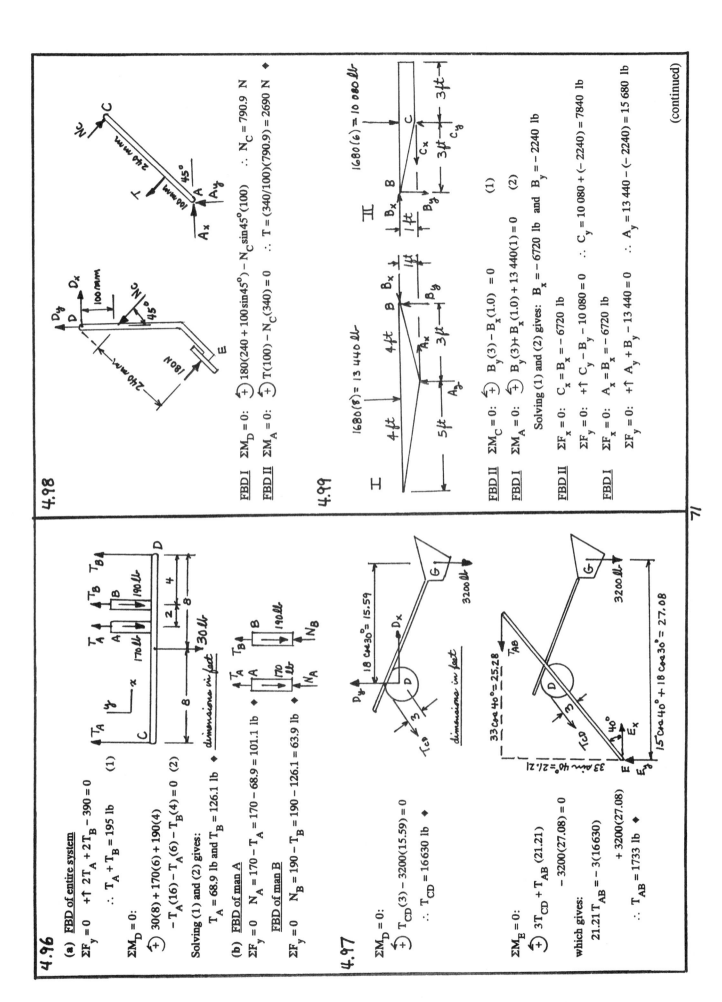

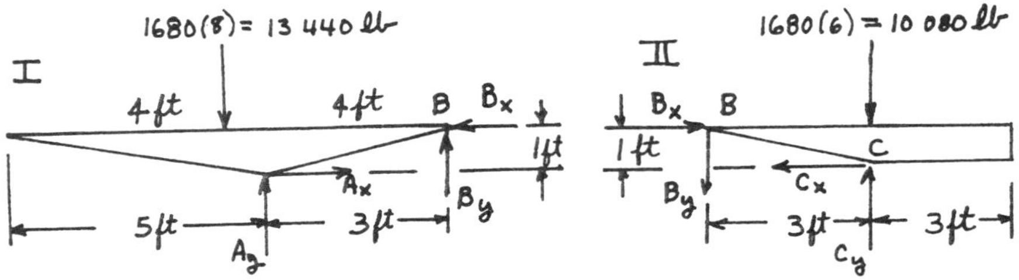

<u>FBD II</u> $\quad \Sigma M_C = 0: \quad \circlearrowleft + \ B_y(3) - B_x(1.0) = 0 \qquad (1)$

<u>FBD I</u> $\quad \Sigma M_A = 0: \quad \circlearrowleft + \ B_y(3) + B_x(1.0) + 13\,440(1) = 0 \qquad (2)$

Solving (1) and (2) gives: $B_x = -6720$ lb and $B_y = -2240$ lb

<u>FBD II</u> $\quad \Sigma F_x = 0: \quad C_x = B_x = -6720 \text{ lb}$

$\Sigma F_y = 0: \quad +\uparrow\ C_y - B_y - 10\,080 = 0 \qquad \therefore\ C_y = 10\,080 + (-2240) = 7840 \text{ lb}$

<u>FBD I</u> $\quad \Sigma F_x = 0: \quad A_x = B_x = -6720 \text{ lb}$

$\Sigma F_y = 0: \quad +\uparrow\ A_y + B_y - 13\,440 = 0 \qquad \therefore\ A_y = 13\,440 - (-2240) = 15\,680 \text{ lb}$

(continued)

$$R_A = \sqrt{(-6720)^2 + (15\,680)^2} = 17.06 \text{ kips} \ \blacklozenge$$

$$R_B = \sqrt{(-6720)^2 + (-2240)^2} = 7.08 \text{ kips} \ \blacklozenge$$

$$R_C = \sqrt{(-6720)^2 + 7840^2} = 10.33 \text{ kips} \ \blacklozenge$$

4.100

CD is a two-force member.

dimensions in meters

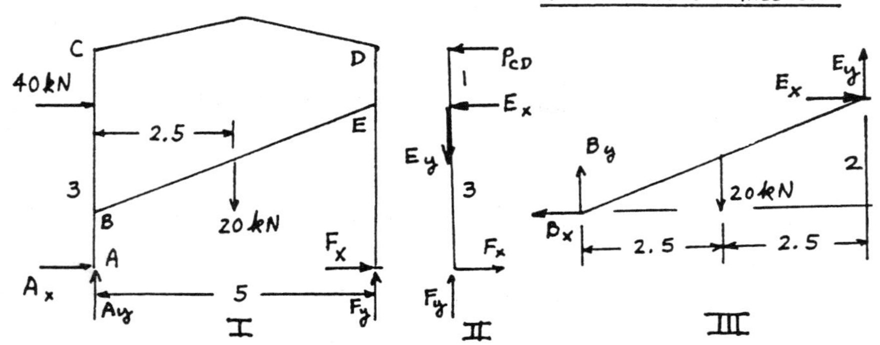

FBD I

$\Sigma M_A = 0$: $\circlearrowleft+$ $F_y(5) - 40(3) - 20(2.5) = 0$ $\quad \therefore F_y = 34$ kN ◆

$\Sigma F_y = 0$: $+\uparrow$ $A_y + F_y - 20 = 0$ $\quad \therefore A_y = -34 + 20 = -14$ kN ◆

FBD II $\quad \Sigma F_y = 0$: $E_y = F_y = 34$ kN

FBD III

$\Sigma M_B = 0$: $\circlearrowleft+$ $E_y(5) - E_x(2) - 20(2.5) = 0$ $\quad \therefore E_x = (1/2)[34(5) - 50] = 60$ kN

FBD II

$\Sigma M_F = 0$: $\circlearrowleft+$ $E_x(3) + P_{CD}(4) = 0$ $\quad \therefore P_{CD} = (-3/4)(60) = -45$ kN ◆

$\Sigma F_x = 0$: $\overset{+}{\rightarrow}$ $F_x - E_x - P_{CD} = 0$ $\quad \therefore F_x = 60 + (-45) = 15$ kN ◆

FBD I $\quad \Sigma F_x = 0$: $\overset{+}{\rightarrow}$ $A_x + F_x + 40 = 0$ $\quad \therefore A_x = -15 - 40 = -55$ kN ◆

4.101

AC and AD are two-force members.

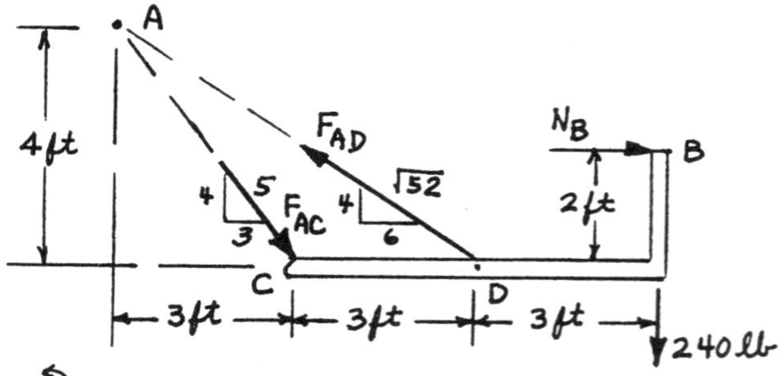

$\Sigma M_A = 0$: $\circlearrowleft+$ $N_B(2) - 240(9) = 0$ $\quad \therefore N_B = 1080$ lb ◆

$\Sigma M_C = 0$: $\circlearrowleft+$ $\dfrac{4}{\sqrt{52}} F_{AD}(3) - 240(6) - N_B(2) = 0$

$\therefore F_{AD} = \left(\sqrt{52}/12\right)[240(6) + 1080(2)] = 2160$ lb ◆

$\Sigma M_D = 0$: $\circlearrowleft+$ $\dfrac{4}{5} F_{AC}(3) - N_B(2) - 240(3) = 0$

$\therefore F_{AC} = (5/12)[1080(2) + 240(3)] = 1200$ lb ◆

4.102

BE is a two-force member.

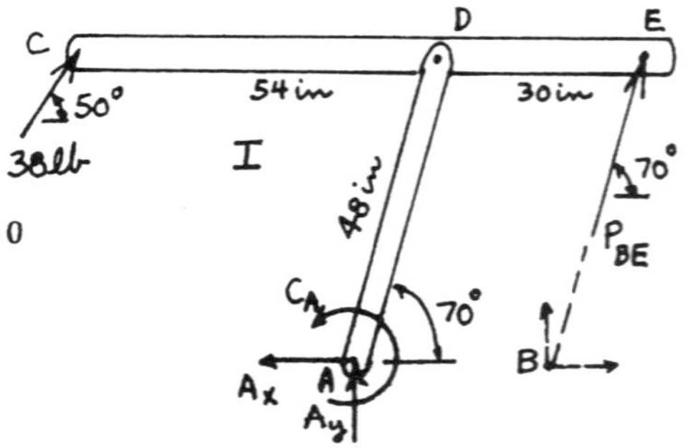

FBD II $\quad \Sigma M_D = 0$:

$\circlearrowleft+$ $P_{BE} \sin 70^\circ(30) - 38 \sin 50^\circ(54) = 0$

$\therefore P_{BE} = 55.8$ lb

FBD I $\quad \Sigma M_A = 0$:

$\circlearrowleft+$ $P_{BE} \sin 70^\circ(30) + C_A$

$- 38 \cos 50^\circ(48 \sin 70^\circ)$

$- 38 \sin 50^\circ(54 - 48 \cos 70^\circ) = 0$

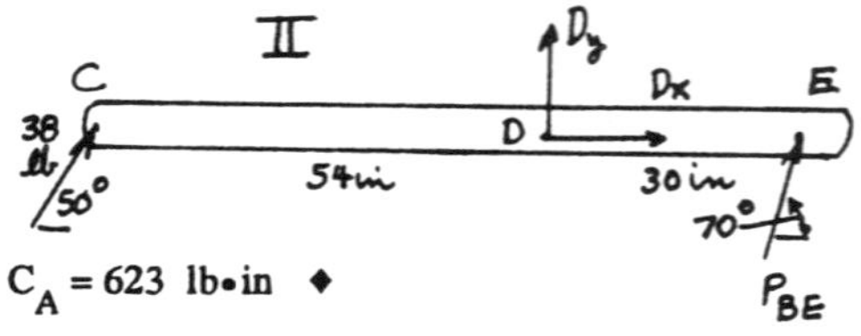

Substituting for P_{BE} and solving gives: $C_A = 623$ lb•in ◆

4.103

AB is a two-force member.

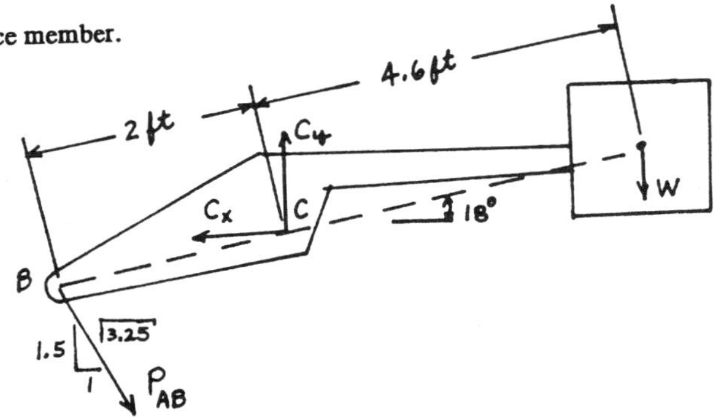

$\Sigma M_C = 0$: $\circlearrowleft\!+$ $\frac{1.5}{\sqrt{3.25}} P_{AB}(2\cos 18^\circ) + \frac{1}{\sqrt{3.25}} P_{AB}(2\sin 18^\circ) - W(4.6\cos 18^\circ) = 0$

$\therefore\ P_{AB} = 2.272\ W$ The pin reaction at B equals 2.27 W ◆

$\Sigma F_x = 0$: $C_x = \frac{1}{\sqrt{3.25}} P_{AB} = \frac{1}{\sqrt{3.25}}(2.272)\,W = 1.260\ W$

$\Sigma F_y = 0$: $+\uparrow\ C_y - W - \frac{1.5}{\sqrt{3.25}} P_{AB} = 0$ $\therefore\ C_y = W + \frac{1.5}{\sqrt{3.25}}(2.272\ W) = 2.890\ W$

The pin reaction at C equals $W\sqrt{1.260^2 + 2.890^2} = 3.15\ W$ ◆

4.104

AB is a two-force member.

$$\theta = \tan^{-1}\left(\frac{20.10}{375}\right) = 3.068^\circ$$

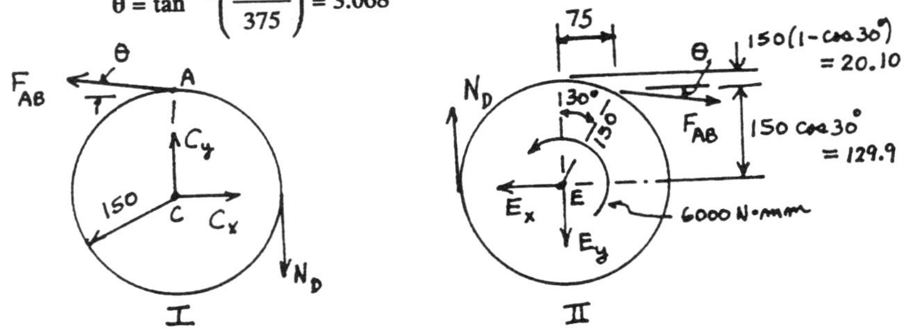

<u>FBD I</u>

$\Sigma M_C = 0$: $\circlearrowleft\!+$ $F_{AB}\cos 3.068^\circ(150) - N_D(150) = 0$ $\therefore\ N_D = 0.9986\,F_{AB}$ (1)

<u>FBD II</u>

$\Sigma M_E = 0$: $\circlearrowleft\!+$ $6000 - N_D(150) - F_{AB}\cos 3.068^\circ(129.9) - F_{AB}\sin 3.068^\circ(75) = 0$

$\therefore\ N_D = 40.0 - 0.8915\,F_{AB}$ (2)

Solving (1) and (2) gives: $F_{AB} = 21.2$ N The pin reaction at A is 21.2 N ◆

4.105

All bars are two-force members.

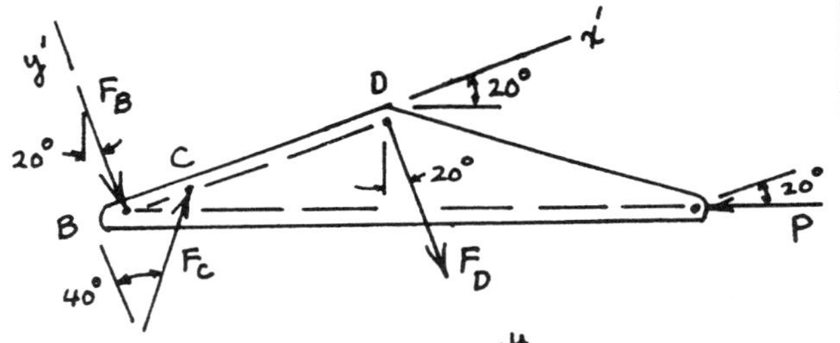

$\Sigma F_{x'} = 0$:

$+\nearrow$ $F_C \sin 40^\circ - P\cos 20^\circ = 0$

$\therefore\ F_C = 1.462\ P$

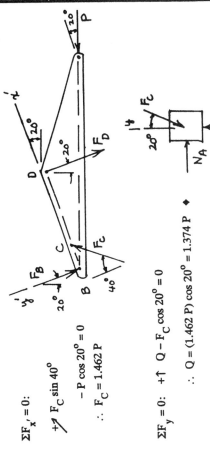

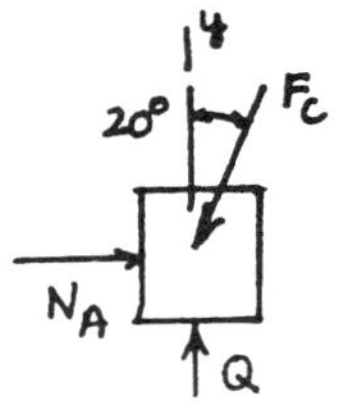

$\Sigma F_y = 0$: $+\uparrow$ $Q - F_C\cos 20^\circ = 0$

$\therefore\ Q = (1.462\ P)\cos 20^\circ = 1.374\ P$ ◆

4.106

BC is a two-force member.

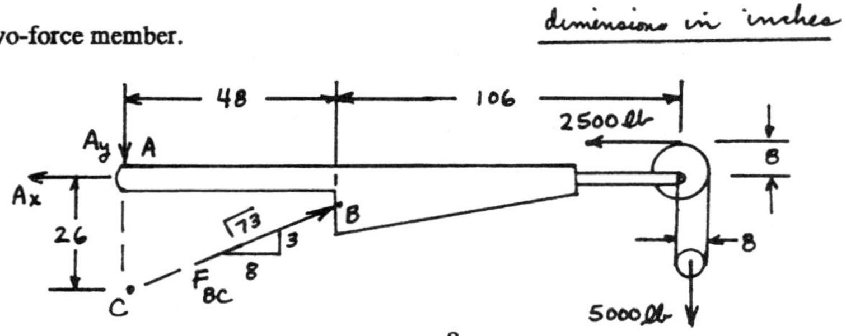

$\Sigma M_A = 0$: $\circlearrowleft +$ $2500(8) - 5000(48 + 106 + 4) + \frac{8}{\sqrt{73}} F_{BC}(26) = 0$

$\therefore\ F_{BC} = 31\,630$ lb   The pin reaction at C equals 31.6 kips. ◆

$\Sigma F_x = 0$: $\xrightarrow{+}$ $\frac{8}{\sqrt{73}}(31\,630) - A_x - 2500 = 0$ $\therefore\ A_x = 27\,120$ lb

$\Sigma F_y = 0$: $+\uparrow$ $\frac{3}{\sqrt{73}}(31\,630) - A_y - 5000 = 0$ $\therefore\ A_y = 6106$ lb

The pin reaction at A equals $\sqrt{(27\,120)^2 + 6106^2} = 27.8$ kips ◆

4.107

AB is a two-force member.

$\Sigma M_C = 0$:

$\circlearrowleft +$ $\frac{3}{\sqrt{10}} F_{AB}(5) - 780(10) = 0$

$\therefore\ F_{AB} = 1644$ lb ◆

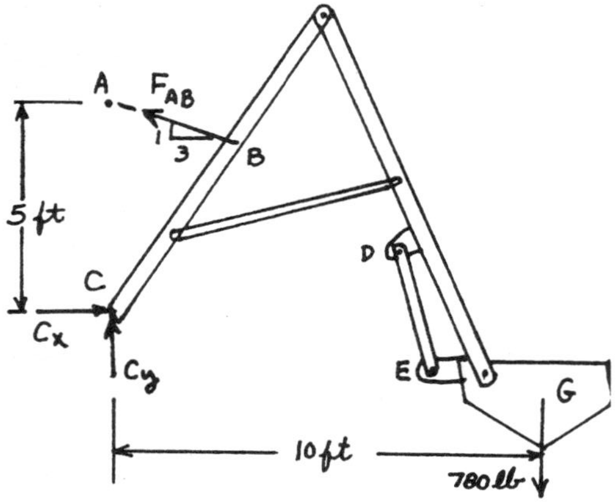

4.108

DE is a two-force member.

$\Sigma M_F = 0$:

$\circlearrowleft +$ $\frac{10}{\sqrt{109}} F_{DE}(1.0) - 780(1.5) = 0$

$\therefore\ F_{DE} = 1222$ lb

The pin reaction at E on the scoop is

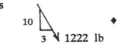

10, 3 (slope) 1222 lb ◆

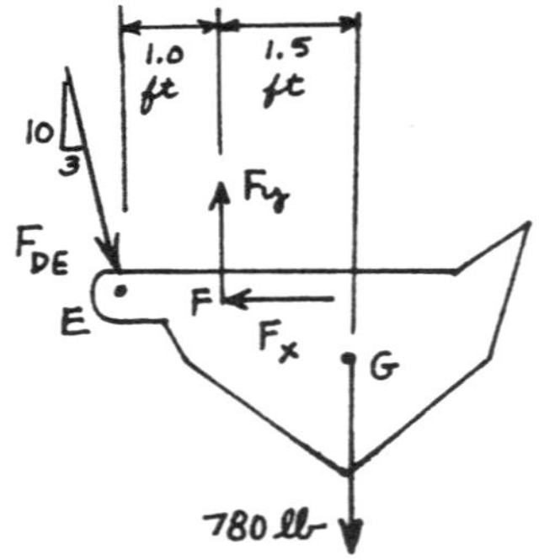

$\Sigma F_x = 0$: $\xrightarrow{+}$ $\frac{3}{\sqrt{109}}(1222) - F_x = 0$

$\therefore\ F_x = 351$ lb ←

$\Sigma F_y = 0$: $+\uparrow$ $F_y - \frac{10}{\sqrt{109}}(1222) - 780 = 0$

$\therefore\ F_y = 1950$ lb ↑

$R_F = \sqrt{351^2 + 1950^2} = 1981$ lb ; $\theta = \tan^{-1}(1950/351) = 79.8^\circ$

The pin reaction on the scoop at F is 1981 lb ◆ (79.8°)

4.109

AB is a two-force member.

$\Sigma M_C = 0$:

$\circlearrowleft +$ $F_{AB}(0.6) - 20(3) = 0$

$\therefore\ F_{AB} = 100$ lb

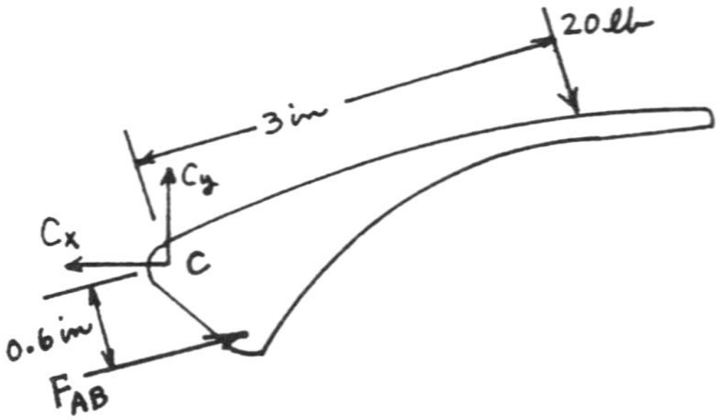

$\Sigma F_x = 0$: $\xrightarrow{+}$ $P - F_{AB}\cos 15^\circ = 0$

$\therefore\ P = 100 \cos 15^\circ = 96.6$ lb ◆

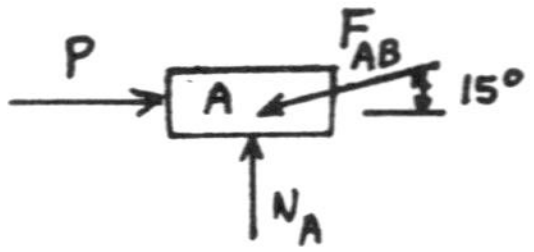

4.110

AD is a two-force member.

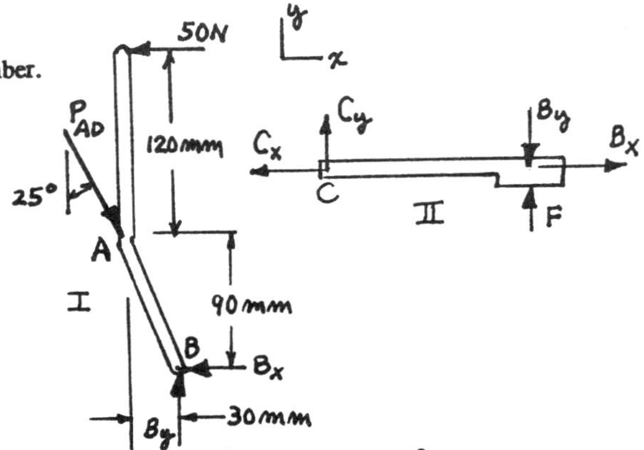

FBD I: $\Sigma M_B = 0$: $\circlearrowleft +$ $50(210) + P_{AD}\cos25^\circ(30) - P_{AD}\sin25^\circ(90) = 0$ $\quad \therefore\ P_{AD} = 968.1$ N

$\Sigma F_y = 0$: $\quad B_y = P_{AD}\cos25^\circ = 968.1\cos25^\circ = 877.4$ N

FBD II: $\Sigma M_C = 0$: $F = B_y = 877.4$ N ◆

4.111

BC is a two-force member.

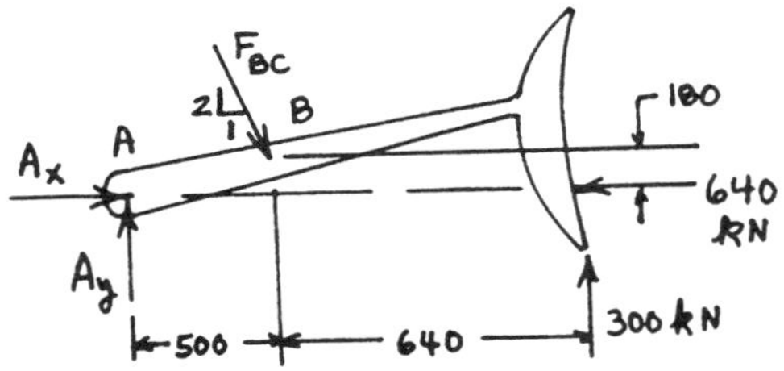

$\Sigma M_A = 0$:

$\circlearrowleft +$ $300(1140) - \frac{2}{\sqrt{5}} F_{BC}(500)$

$- \frac{1}{\sqrt{5}} F_{BC}(180) = 0$

$\therefore\ F_{BC} = 648$ kN

The pin reactions at B and C each equal 648 kN ◆

$\Sigma F_x = 0$: $\overset{+}{\rightarrow}$ $A_x + \frac{1}{\sqrt{5}} F_{BC} - 640 = 0$ $\qquad \therefore\ A_x = -\frac{1}{\sqrt{5}}(648) + 640 = 350.2$ kN

$\Sigma F_y = 0$: $+\uparrow$ $A_y - \frac{2}{\sqrt{5}} F_{BC} + 300 = 0$ $\qquad \therefore\ A_y = \frac{2}{\sqrt{5}}(648) - 300 = 279.6$ kN

The pin reaction at A is $\sqrt{350.2^2 + 279.6^2} = 448$ kN ◆

4.112

Each of the three bars is a two-force member.

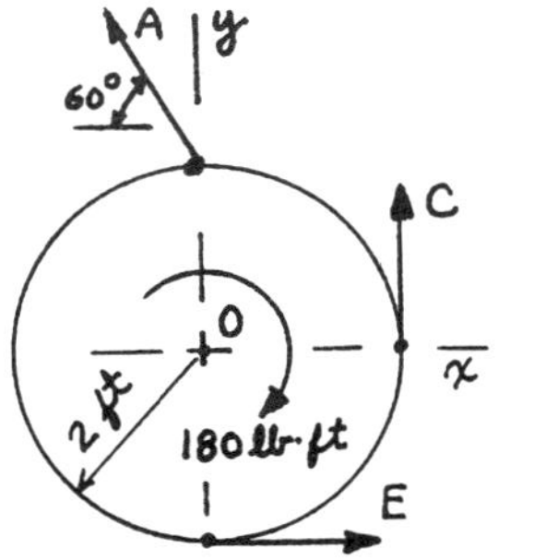

$\Sigma F_y = 0$: $+\uparrow$ $A\sin60^\circ + C = 0 \quad (1)$

$\Sigma F_x = 0$: $\overset{+}{\rightarrow}$ $E - A\cos60^\circ = 0 \quad (2)$

$\Sigma M_O = 0$: $\circlearrowleft +$ $A\cos60^\circ(2) + C(2) + E(2) - 180 = 0 \quad (3)$

Solving (1), (2) and (3) gives:

A = 671.8 lb; C = − 581.8 lb; and E = 335.9 lb

Therefore, the magnitudes of the pin reactions are:

A = 672 lb; C = 582 lb; and E = 336 lb ◆

4.113

AB and CD are two-force members.

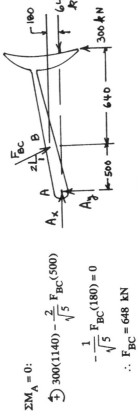

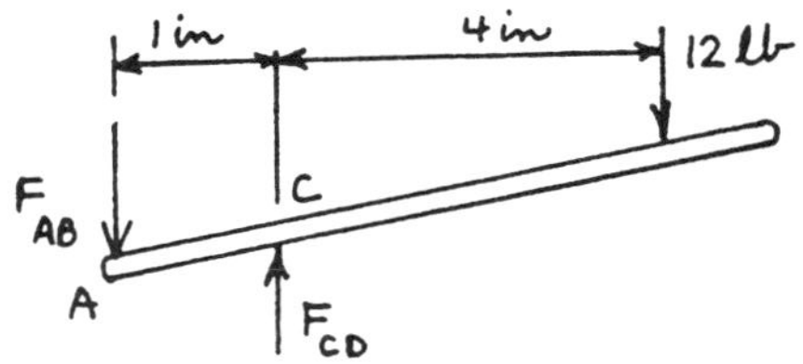

$\Sigma M_A = 0$:

$\circlearrowleft +$ $F_{CD}(1) - 12(5) = 0$

$\therefore\ F_{CD} = 60$ lb

The force at C and the force at D are each equal to 60 lb ◆

4.114

Since the body is acted upon by only two forces, G must be directly under A. (The FBD has been rotated for convenience.)

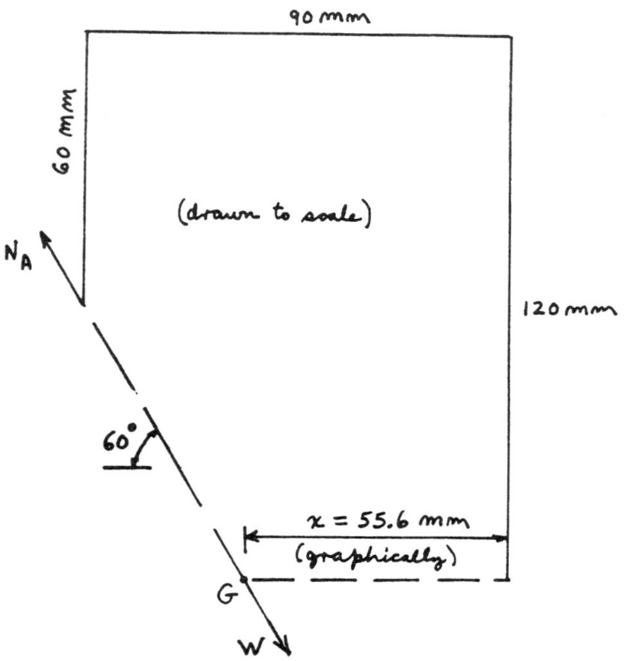

$\therefore\ x = 55.6$ mm ◆

4.115

The wheel is a two-force member.

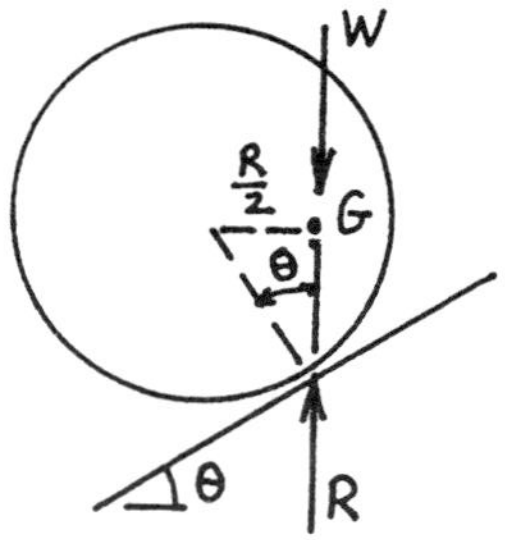

$\sin\theta = \frac{R/2}{R} = 0.5 \qquad \therefore\ \theta = 30^\circ$ ◆

4.116

E and BD are two-force members.

dimensions in inches

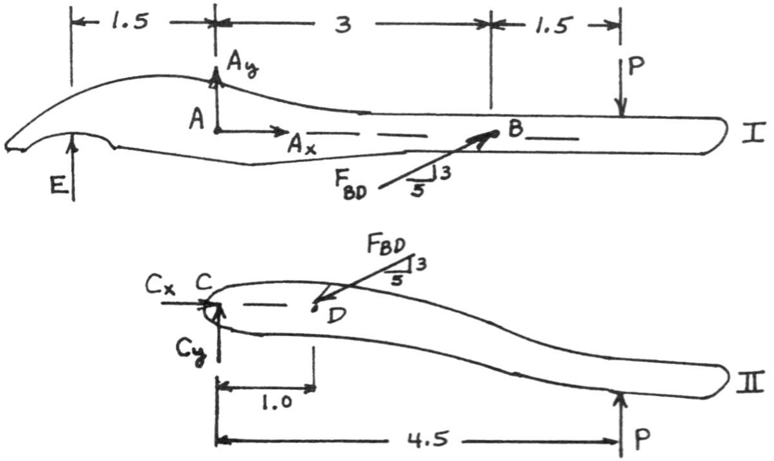

FBD II $\Sigma M_C = 0$: $\circlearrowleft^{+}$ $P(4.5) - \frac{3}{\sqrt{34}} F_{BD}(1.0) = 0 \qquad \therefore\ F_{BD} = \frac{3}{2}\sqrt{34}\,P$

FBD I $\Sigma M_A = 0$: $\circlearrowleft^{+}$ $\frac{3}{\sqrt{34}} F_{BD}(3) - E(1.5) - P(4.5) = 0$

$\therefore\ \frac{27}{2} P - E(1.5) - P(4.5) = 0 \qquad$ Solving gives $E = 6\,P$ ◆

4.117

Both bars are two-force members.

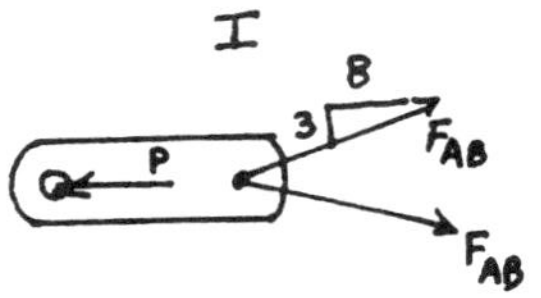

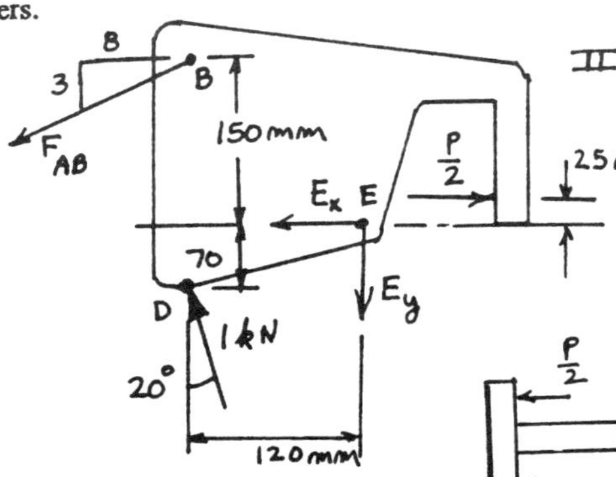

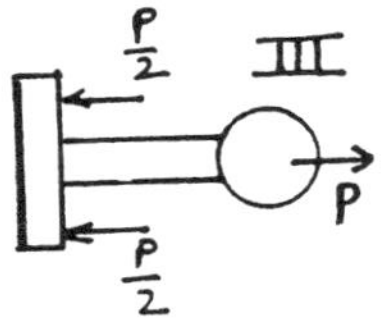

<u>FBD I</u> $\Sigma F_x = 0$:

$$\overset{+}{\rightarrow}\ 2\left(\frac{8}{\sqrt{73}} F_{AB}\right) - P = 0$$

$\therefore\ F_{AB} = 0.5340\ P$

<u>FBD II</u> $\Sigma M_E = 0$:

$$\circlearrowleft\!+\ \frac{8}{\sqrt{73}} F_{AB}(150) + \frac{3}{\sqrt{73}} F_{AB}(120) - \frac{P}{2}(25) - (1 \cos 20^{\circ})(120) - (1 \sin 20^{\circ})(70) = 0$$

Substituting $F_{AB} = 0.5340\ P$ and solving gives $P = 1.611$ kN ◆

4.118

BD is a two-force member.

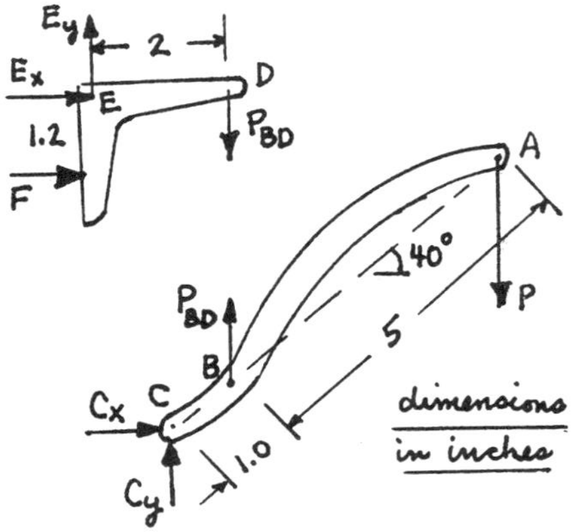

<u>FBD of arm ABC</u>

$\Sigma M_C = 0$: $\circlearrowleft\!+\ [P_{BD}(1.0) - 6P]\cos 40^{\circ} = 0$

$\therefore\ P_{BD} = 6P$

<u>FBD of blade ED</u>

$\Sigma M_E = 0$: $\circlearrowleft\!+\ F(1.2) - P_{BD}(2) = 0$

$$\therefore\ F = \frac{6P(2)}{1.2} = 10P\ ◆$$

∗ 4.119

CG and AD are two-force members.

dimensions in inches

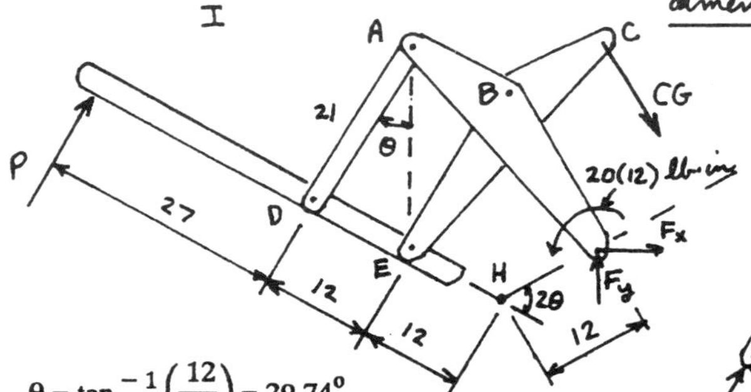

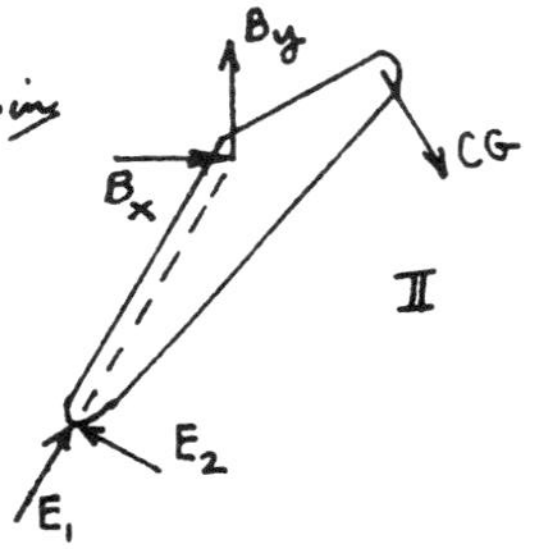

$$\theta = \tan^{-1}\left(\frac{12}{21}\right) = 29.74^{\circ}$$

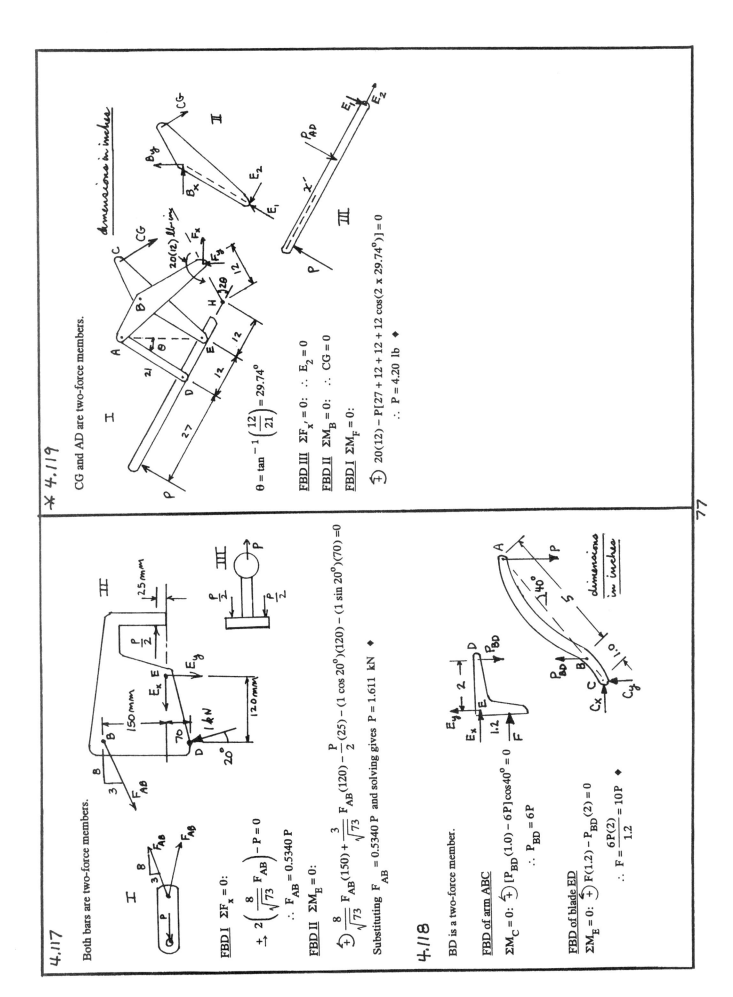

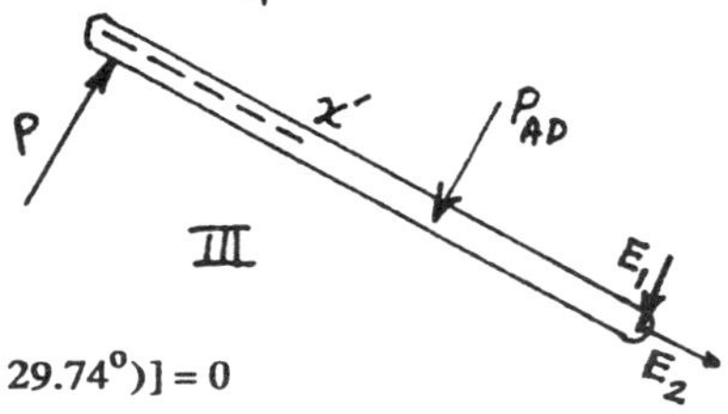

<u>FBD III</u> $\Sigma F_{x'} = 0$: $\therefore\ E_2 = 0$

<u>FBD II</u> $\Sigma M_B = 0$: $\therefore\ CG = 0$

<u>FBD I</u> $\Sigma M_F = 0$:

$$\circlearrowleft\!+\ 20(12) - P[27 + 12 + 12 + 12\cos(2 \times 29.74^{\circ})] = 0$$

$\therefore\ P = 4.20$ lb ◆

*4.120

The four shorter links are two-force members. *dimensions in inches*

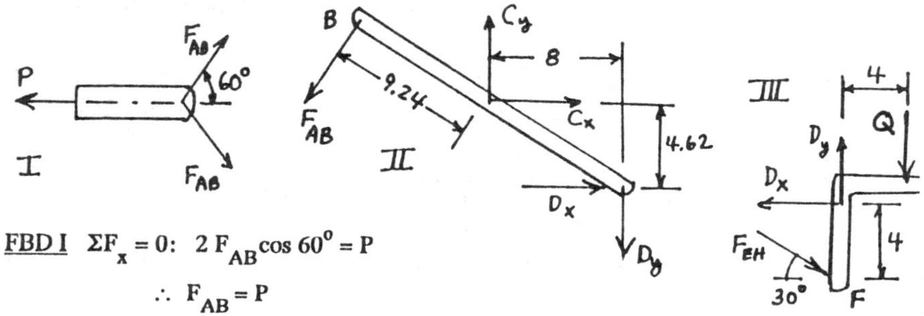

<u>FBD I</u> $\Sigma F_x = 0$: $2F_{AB}\cos 60^\circ = P$

$\therefore F_{AB} = P$

<u>FBD III</u>

$\Sigma M_F = 0$: (+) $D_x(4) - Q(4) = 0$ $\therefore D_x = Q$

$\Sigma F_x = 0$: $\overset{+}{\rightarrow}$ $F_{EH}\cos 30^\circ - D_x = 0$ $\therefore F_{EH} = D_x/\cos 30^\circ = 1.155\,Q$

$\Sigma F_y = 0$: $+\uparrow$ $D_y - Q - F_{EH}\sin 30^\circ = 0$ $\therefore D_y = Q + (1.155\,Q)\sin 30^\circ = 1.578\,Q$

<u>FBD II</u>

$\Sigma M_C = 0$: (+) $F_{AB}(9.24) + D_x(4.62) - D_y(8) = 0$

$\therefore P = (1/9.24)[-Q(4.62) + (1.578\,Q)8] = 0.866\,Q$ ◆

4.121

The links are two-force bodies.
Let F_A and F_B be the force in the links,
and let R_A be the resultant force acting at A.
Because the plate is a three-force body,
R_A and F_B intersect at the mass center G of the plate.

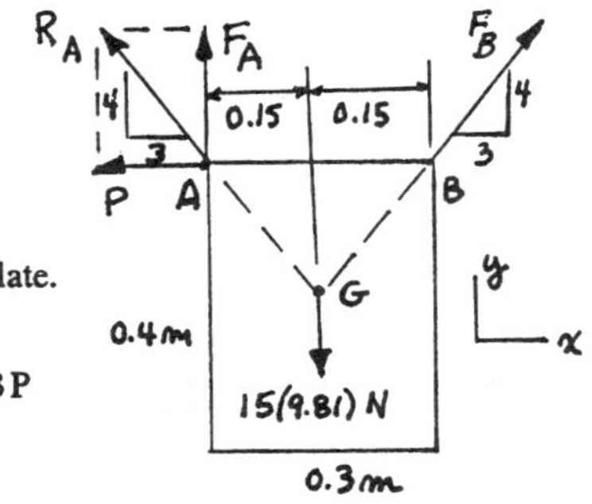

From the slope of R_A: $\dfrac{F_A}{P} = \dfrac{4}{3}$ $\therefore F_A = 1.333P$

$\Sigma M_B = 0$: (+) $15(9.81)(0.15) - F_A(0.3) = 0$

which gives: $1.333P(0.3) = 15(9.81)(0.15)$ $\therefore P = 55.2$ N ◆

4.122

The bracket is a three-force member. Therefore, the 800-lb force, N_A and R_B intersect at O.

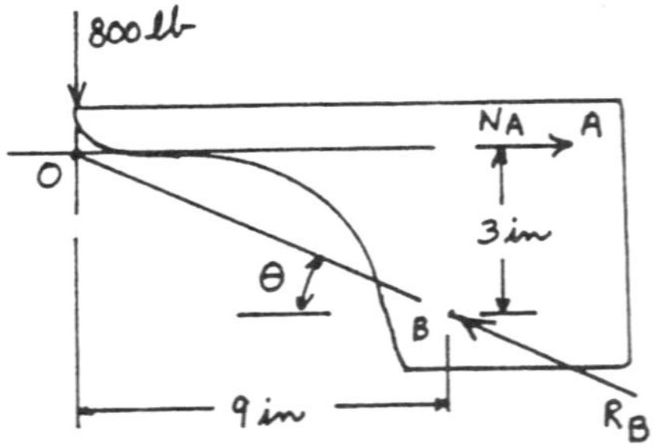

$\theta = \tan^{-1}\left(\dfrac{3}{9}\right) = 18.43^\circ$

$\Sigma F_y = 0$: $+\uparrow$ $R_B \sin 18.43^\circ - 800 = 0$

$\therefore R_B = 2530$ lb ◆

$\Sigma F_x = 0$:

$\overset{+}{\rightarrow}$ $N_A - R_B\cos 18.43^\circ = 0$

$\therefore N_A = 2530\cos 18.43^\circ = 2400$ lb ◆

4.123

Bar ACB is a three-force body. Let O refer to the point of intersection of the three forces.

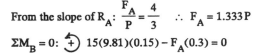

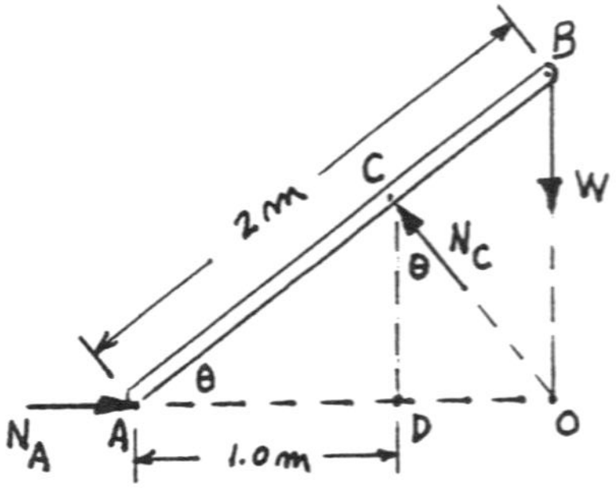

$\overline{AD} = 1.0$ m $\quad \overline{AB} = 2.0$ m

$\overline{CD} = \overline{AD}\tan\theta = 1.0\tan\theta$ m

$\overline{DO} = \overline{CD}\tan\theta = \tan^2\theta$ m

By geometry: $\overline{AD} + \overline{DO} = \overline{AB}\cos\theta$
which gives:

$1 + \tan^2\theta = 2\cos\theta$

$1 + \dfrac{\sin^2\theta}{\cos^2\theta} = 2\cos\theta$

$\cos^2\theta + \sin^2\theta = 2\cos^3\theta$

$1 = 2\cos^3\theta$

$\therefore \cos^3\theta = 1/2$ which gives $\theta = 37.5^\circ$ ◆

4.124

When the car is about to mount the curb, all wheels are two force members. Therefore, the reactions pass through the axles. The car is a three force body.

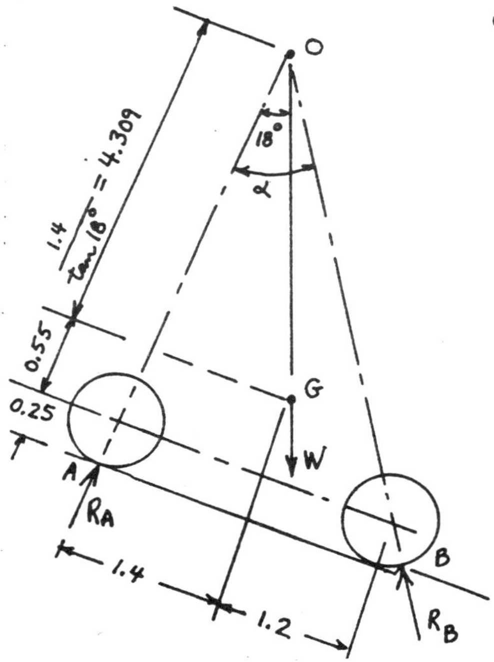

$$\alpha = \tan^{-1}\left(\frac{2.6}{4.309 + 0.550}\right) = 28.15^{\circ}$$

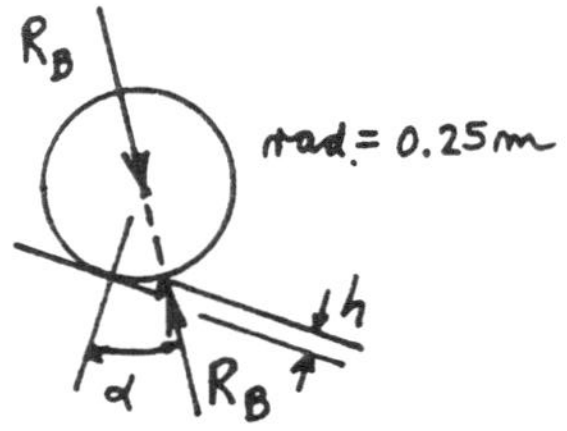

$$\cos \alpha = \frac{0.25 - h}{0.25}$$

$$\therefore \ h = 0.25(1 - \cos 28.15^{\circ}) = 0.0296 \ \text{m} = 29.6 \ \text{mm} \ \blacklozenge$$

4.125

The bar is a three-force member. Therefore, N_A, N_B and P intersect at O.

$$\overline{OE} = x \tan 60^{\circ} = (L - x)\tan 30^{\circ}$$

$$\therefore \ \frac{x}{L-x} = \frac{\tan 30^{\circ}}{\tan 60^{\circ}} = \frac{1}{3}$$

which gives: $3x = L - x$

or $x = L/4$

Note that triangles AOE and EOC are similar. $\therefore \ \theta = 30^{\circ}$ ◆

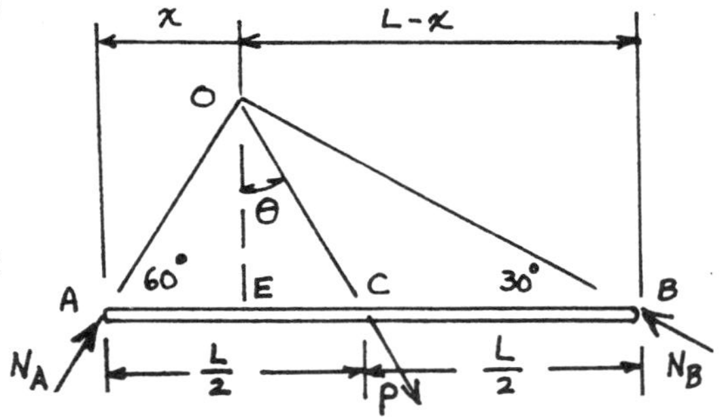

4.126

The bar is a three-force member. Therefore, N_A, N_B and W intersect at O.

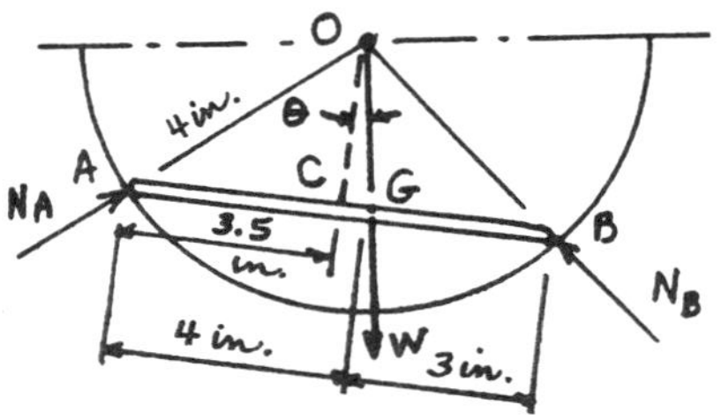

From triangle COG,

$$\tan \theta = \frac{\overline{CG}}{\overline{CO}}$$

Note that $\overline{CG} = 4.0 - 3.5 = 0.5$ in. and from triangle AOC, we have

$$\overline{CO} = \sqrt{4^2 - 3.5^2} = 1.936 \ \text{in.} \qquad \therefore \ \theta = \tan^{-1}\left(\frac{0.5}{1.936}\right) = 14.48^{\circ} \ \blacklozenge$$

4.127

The rocket is a three-force member. Therefore, T_A, T_B and W intersect at O.

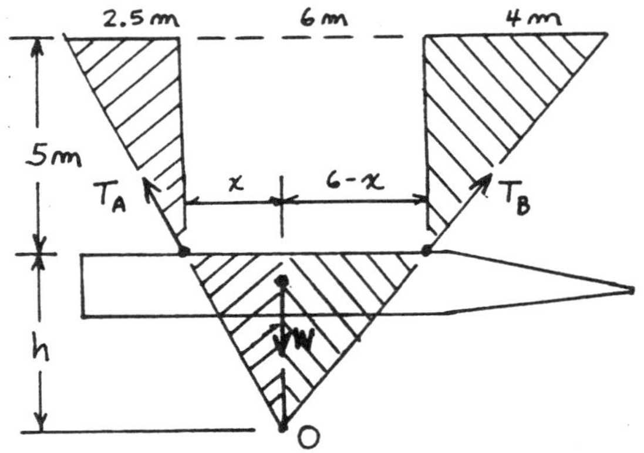

Using similar triangles,

$$\frac{2.5}{5} = \frac{x}{h} \quad \therefore \ h = 2x$$

Also,

$$\frac{4}{5} = \frac{6-x}{h} = \frac{6-x}{2x}$$

Solving gives: $x = 2.31$ m ◆

4.128

BD is a two-force member.
ABD is a three-force member.

Therefore, the three forces acting on ABD intersect at point E.

From similar triangles: $\frac{70}{35} = \frac{35}{d}$

$\therefore\ d = 17.5$ mm ◆

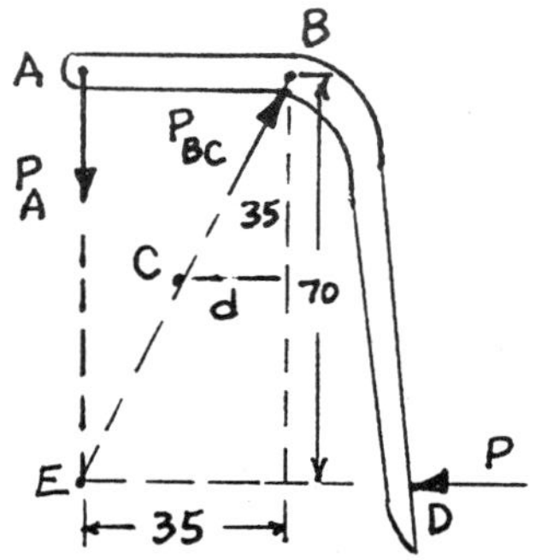

4.129

Bar AB is a three-force body. Let O refer to the point of intersection of the three forces.

$\overline{OF} = \overline{BE} = 18\sin 40^\circ$ ft $\quad \overline{AF} = 9\cos 40^\circ$ ft

$\therefore\ \alpha = \tan^{-1}\frac{\overline{OF}}{\overline{AF}} = \tan^{-1}\left(\frac{18\sin 40^\circ}{9\cos 40^\circ}\right) = 59.21^\circ$

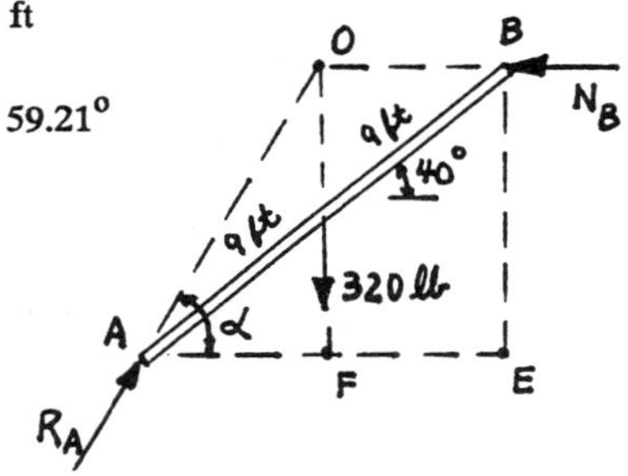

FBD of bar AB

$\Sigma F_y = 0 \quad +\uparrow\ R_A \sin\alpha - 320 = 0$

$\therefore\ R_A = \frac{320}{\sin 59.21^\circ} = 372.5$ lb

R_A is the resultant of the normal force N_A and the tension T. Referring to the figure below:

$R_{Ax} = R_A \cos 59.21^\circ = T\cos 55^\circ$

$\therefore\ T = \frac{372.5\cos 59.21^\circ}{\cos 55^\circ} = 332$ lb ◆

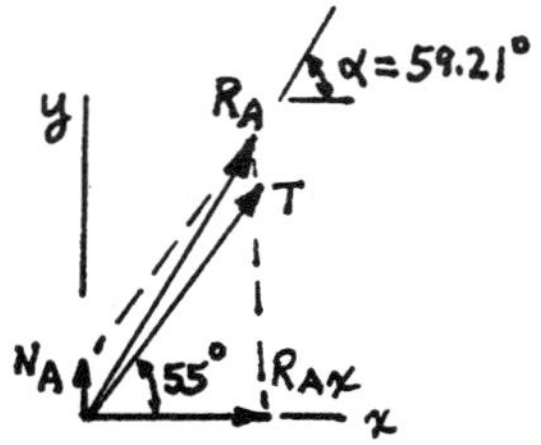

(Note: It is more convenient to find the tension by re-drawing the FBD of bar AB, ignoring the fact that it is a three-force body. One solution would involve writing and solving the equilibrium equations $\Sigma M_A = 0$ and $\Sigma F_x = 0$.)

4.130

In both cases, the roller is a three-force member. Therefore, P, R_B and the 80-lb force intersect at O. $\quad \therefore\ \alpha = \cos^{-1}(21/24) = 28.96^\circ$

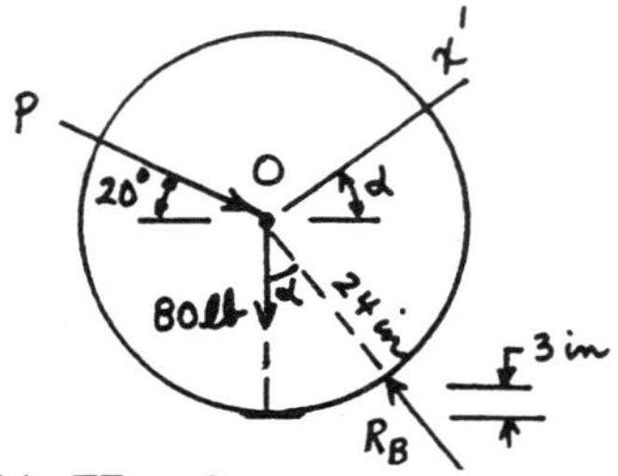

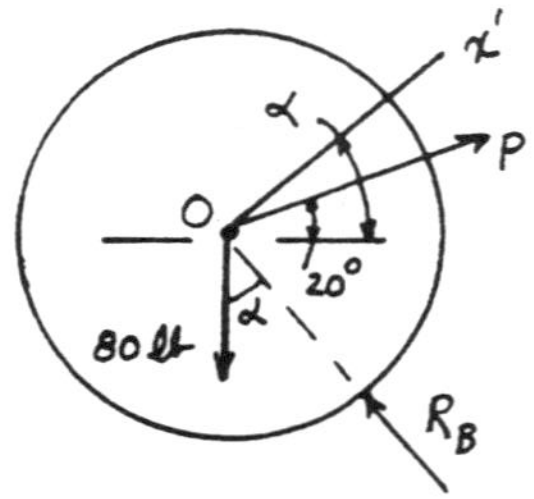

(a) $\Sigma F_{x'} = 0$:

$+\nearrow\ P\cos(28.96^\circ + 20^\circ) - 80\sin 28.96^\circ = 0$

$\therefore\ P = 59.0$ lb ◆

(b) $\Sigma F_{x'} = 0$:

$+\nearrow\ P\cos(28.96^\circ - 20^\circ) - 80\sin 28.96^\circ = 0$

$\therefore\ P = 39.2$ lb ◆

4.131

FBD of joint A

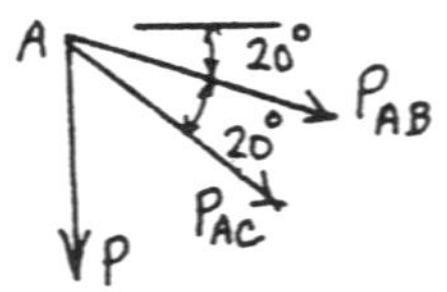

$\Sigma F_x = 0: \quad \overset{+}{\rightarrow}\ P_{AB}\cos 20^\circ + P_{AC}\cos 40^\circ = 0$

$\therefore\ P_{AC} = -1.2267\,P_{AB} \qquad (1)$

$\Sigma F_y = 0: \quad +\downarrow\ P + P_{AB}\sin 20^\circ + P_{AC}\sin 40^\circ = 0 \qquad (2)$

Substituting (1) into (2) gives:

$P + P_{AB}\sin 20^\circ + (-1.2267\,P_{AB})\sin 40^\circ = 0$

$\therefore\ P_{AB} = 2.24\,P = 2.24\,P$ (T) ◆ and $P_{AC} = -1.2267(2.24) = -2.75\,P = 2.75\,P$ (C) ◆

4.132

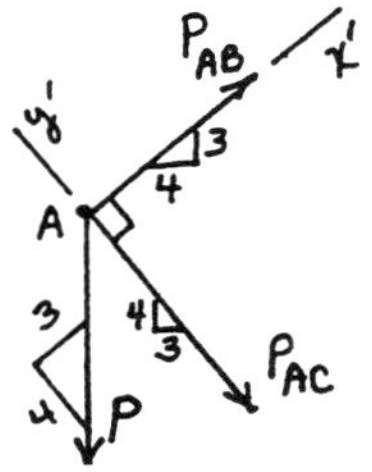

FBD of joint A

$\Sigma F_{x'} = 0$: $P_{AB} = 0.6\,P = 0.6\,P$ (T) ◆

$\Sigma F_{y'} = 0$: $P_{AC} = -0.8\,P = 0.8\,P$ (C) ◆

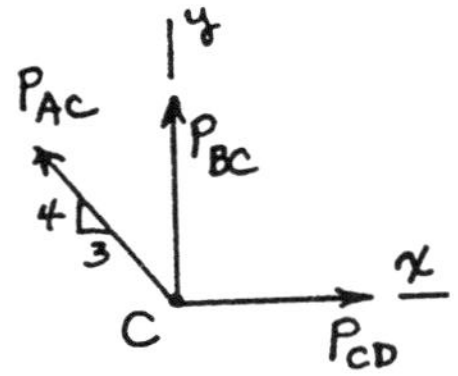

FBD of joint C

$\Sigma F_y = 0$: $P_{BC} = -0.8\,P_{AC}$

$= -0.8(-0.8\,P) = 0.64\,P = 0.64\,P$ (T) ◆

$\Sigma F_x = 0$: $P_{CD} = 0.6\,P_{AC} = 0.6(-0.8P)$

$= -0.48\,P = 0.48\,P$ (C) ◆

4.133

From the FBD of the entire truss (not shown here), $D_x = 0$ and $D_y = N_H = 1.5\,P\uparrow$.

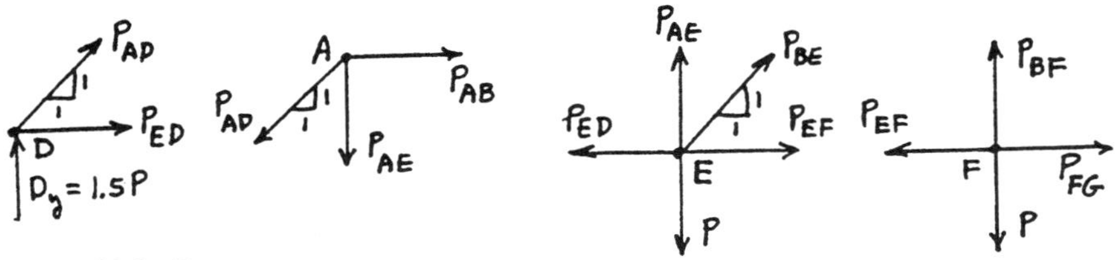

FBD of joint D

$\Sigma F_y = 0$: $+\uparrow\ (1/\sqrt{2})P_{AD} + 1.5\,P = 0$ $\quad\therefore\ P_{AD} = -\sqrt{2}\,(1.5\,P) = 2.121\,P$ (C) ◆

$\Sigma F_x = 0$: $\overset{+}{\rightarrow}\ (1/\sqrt{2})P_{AD} + P_{ED} = 0$ $\quad\therefore\ P_{ED} = -(1/\sqrt{2})P_{AD} = 1.5\,P = 1.5\,P$ (T) ◆

FBD of joint A

$\Sigma F_x = 0$: $\overset{+}{\rightarrow}\ P_{AB} - (1/\sqrt{2})P_{AD} = 0$ $\quad\therefore\ P_{AB} = (1/\sqrt{2})P_{AD} = -1.5\,P = 1.5\,P$ (C) ◆

$\Sigma F_y = 0$: $+\uparrow\ -P_{AE} - (1/\sqrt{2})P_{AD} = 0$ $\quad\therefore\ P_{AE} = -(1/\sqrt{2})P_{AD} = 1.5\,P = 1.5\,P$ (T) ◆

(continued)

FBD of joint E

$\Sigma F_y = 0$: $+\uparrow\ P_{AE} + (1/\sqrt{2})P_{BE} - P = 0$

$\therefore\ P_{BE} = \sqrt{2}\,(P - P_{AE}) = \sqrt{2}\,(P - 1.5\,P) = -0.707\,P = 0.707\,P$ (C) ◆

$\Sigma F_x = 0$: $\overset{+}{\rightarrow}\ P_{EF} + (1/\sqrt{2})P_{BE} - P_{ED} = 0$

$\therefore\ P_{EF} = P_{ED} - (1/\sqrt{2})P_{BE} = 1.5\,P - (1/\sqrt{2})(-0.707\,P) = 2.00\,P = 2.00\,P$ (T) ◆

FBD of joint F: $\Sigma F_y = 0$: $P_{BF} = P = P$ (T) ◆

By symmetry, $P_{CH} = P_{AD}$; $P_{GH} = P_{ED}$; $P_{CB} = P_{AB}$; $P_{CG} = P_{AE}$; $P_{BG} = P_{BE}$; $P_{GF} = P_{EF}$. ◆

4.134

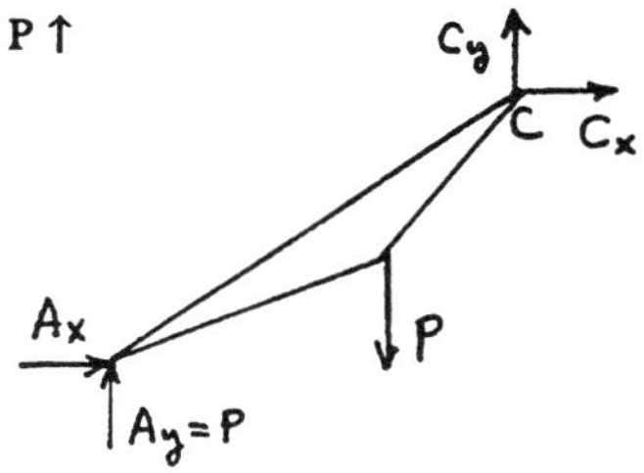

FBD of entire truss (not shown here): $A_y = E_y = P\uparrow$

FBD of left half of truss:

$\Sigma M_C = 0$: $+\ \ P(4) - A_y(12) + A_x(8) = 0$

$A_x = (1/8)[-P(4) + P(12)] = P$

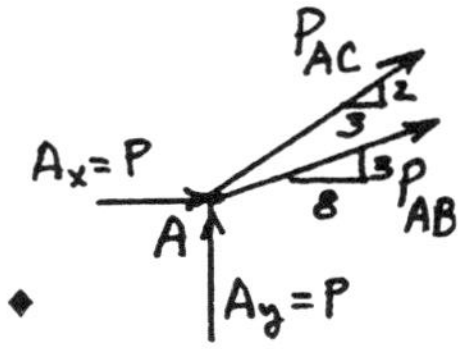

FBD of joint A

$\Sigma F_x = 0$: $\overset{+}{\rightarrow}\ \dfrac{8}{\sqrt{73}}P_{AB} + \dfrac{3}{\sqrt{13}}P_{AC} + P = 0$ (1)

$\Sigma F_y = 0$: $+\uparrow\ \dfrac{3}{\sqrt{73}}P_{AB} + \dfrac{2}{\sqrt{13}}P_{AC} + P = 0$ (2)

Solving (1) and (2) gives: $P_{AB} = 1.220\,P = 1.220\,P$ (T) ◆

$P_{AC} = -2.575\,P = 2.575\,P$ (C) ◆

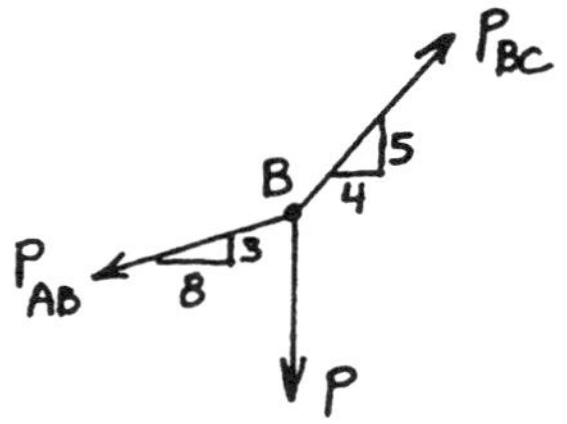

FBD of joint B

$\Sigma F_x = 0$: $\overset{+}{\rightarrow}\ \dfrac{4}{\sqrt{41}}P_{BC} - \dfrac{8}{\sqrt{73}}P_{AB} = 0$

$\therefore\ P_{BC} = \dfrac{\sqrt{41}}{4}\left(\dfrac{8}{\sqrt{73}}\right)(1.220\,P)$

$= 1.829\,P = 1.829\,P$ (T) ◆

By symmetry: $P_{DC} = P_{BC} = 1.829\,P$ (T) ◆

$P_{ED} = P_{AB} = 1.220\,P$ (T) ◆

$P_{EC} = P_{AC} = 2.575\,P$ (C) ◆

4.135

<u>FBD of entire truss</u> (not shown here)

$\Sigma M_A = 0$: $N_D(16) = 1.5P(8\sin 35^\circ)$ $\therefore$ $N_D = 0.4302P$ (↑)

$\Sigma F_x = 0$: $A_x = 2.5P\cos 35^\circ = 2.0479P$ (⟶)

$\Sigma F_y = 0$: $A_y = 2.5P\sin 35^\circ - N_D = 2.5P\sin 35^\circ - 0.4302P = 1.004P$ (↑)

<u>FBD of joint A</u>

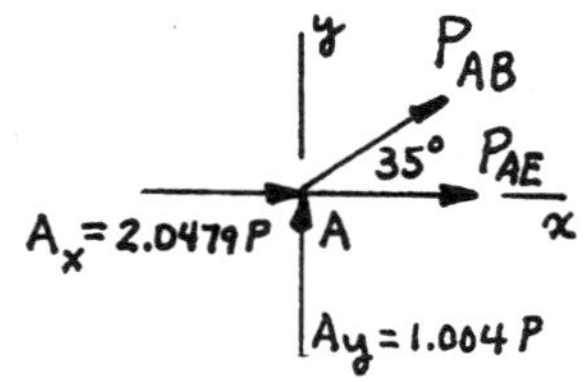

$\Sigma F_y = 0$: $+\uparrow$ $P_{AB}\sin 35^\circ + 1.004P = 0$

$\therefore$ $P_{AB} = -1.750P = 1.750P$ (C) ◆

$\Sigma F_x = 0$: $\overset{+}{\rightarrow}$ $2.0479P + P_{AE} + P_{AB}\cos 35^\circ = 0$

$\therefore$ $P_{AE} = -2.0479P - (-1.750P\cos 35^\circ)$

$= -0.6144P = 0.6144P$ (C) ◆

<u>FBD of joint D</u>

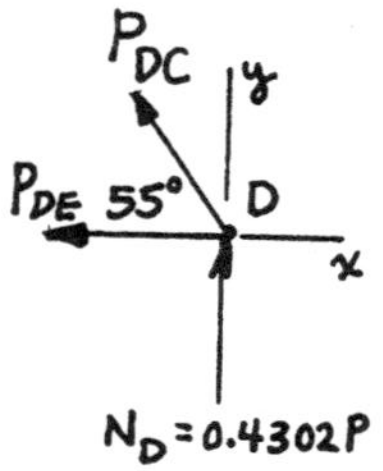

$\Sigma F_y = 0$: $+\uparrow$ $0.4302P + P_{DC}\sin 55^\circ = 0$

$\therefore$ $P_{DC} = -0.5252P = 0.5252P$ (C) ◆

$\Sigma F_x = 0$: $\overset{+}{\rightarrow}$ $-P_{DC}\cos 55^\circ - P_{DE} = 0$

$\therefore$ $P_{DE} = -(-0.5252P)\cos 55^\circ = 0.3012P$ (T) ◆

<u>FBD of joint C</u>

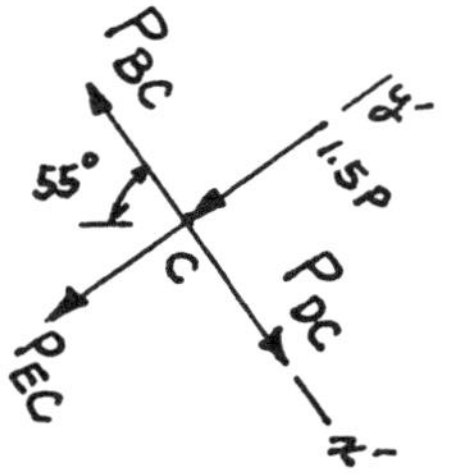

$\Sigma F_{y'} = 0$: $P_{EC} = -1.5P = 1.5P$ (C) ◆

$\Sigma F_{x'} = 0$: $P_{BC} = P_{DC} = -0.5252P = 0.5252P$ (C) ◆

<u>FBD of joint B</u>

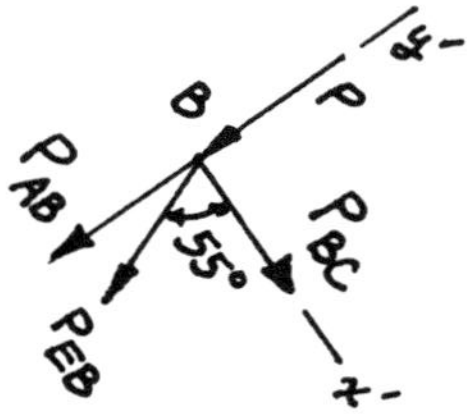

$\Sigma F_{y'} = 0$: $+\nearrow$ $-P - P_{AB} - P_{EB}\sin 55^\circ = 0$

$\therefore$ $P_{EB} = (1/\sin 55^\circ)[-P - (-1.750P)] = 0.9156P$ (T) ◆

4.136

<u>FBD of joint A</u> $\Sigma F_y = 0$: $\left(1/\sqrt{5}\right)P_{AD} = P$

$\therefore$ $P_{AD} = \sqrt{5}\,P = 2.236\,P = 2.236\,P$ (T) ◆

$\Sigma F_x = 0$: $P_{AB} = -\left(2/\sqrt{5}\right)P_{AD}$

$= -\left(2/\sqrt{5}\right)\left(\sqrt{5}\,P\right) = -2\,P = 2\,P$ (C) ◆

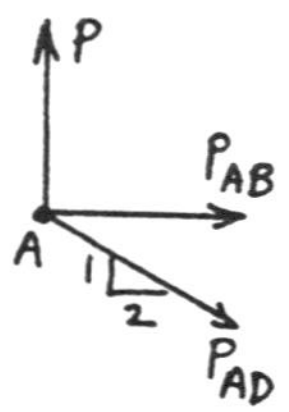

<u>FBD of joint B</u> $\Sigma F_x = 0$: $P_{BC} = P_{AB} = -2\,P = 2\,P$ (C) ◆

$\Sigma F_y = 0$: $P_{BD} = P = P$ (T) ◆

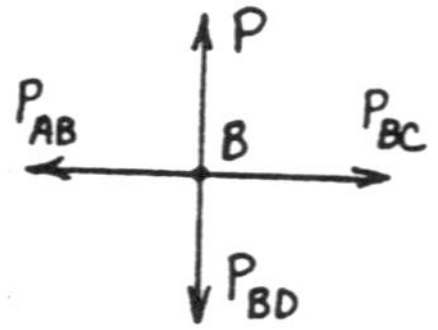

<u>FBD of joint D</u>

$\Sigma F_x = 0$: $\overset{+}{\rightarrow}$ $\dfrac{2}{\sqrt{5}}P_{DE} - \dfrac{2}{\sqrt{5}}P_{AD} + \dfrac{2}{\sqrt{5}}P_{CD} = 0$

$\therefore$ $P_{DE} - 2.236\,P + P_{CD} = 0$ (1)

$\Sigma F_y = 0$: $+\uparrow$ $\dfrac{1}{\sqrt{5}}P_{AD} + P_{BD} + \dfrac{1}{\sqrt{5}}P_{CD} - \dfrac{1}{\sqrt{5}}P_{DE} = 0$

$2.236\,P + \sqrt{5}\,P + P_{CD} - P_{DE} = 0$

$\therefore$ $P_{CD} - P_{DE} + 4.472\,P = 0$ (2)

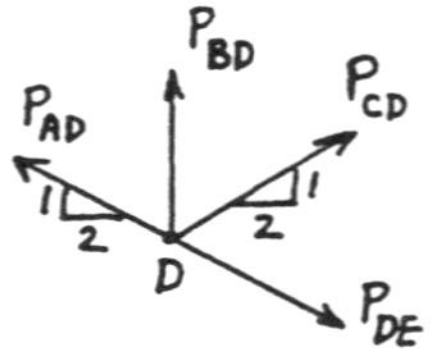

Solving (1) and (2) gives: $P_{CD} = -1.118\,P = 1.118\,P$ (C) ◆

$P_{DE} = 3.354\,P = 3.354\,P$ (T) ◆

<u>FBD of joint C</u> $\Sigma F_y = 0$: $+\downarrow$ $P_{CE} + \left(1/\sqrt{5}\right)P_{CD} = 0$

$\therefore$ $P_{CE} = -\left(1/\sqrt{5}\right)\left(-1.118\,P\right) = 0.500\,P = 0.500\,P$ (T) ◆

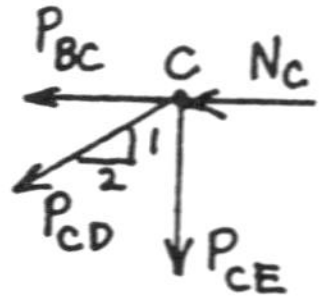

4.137

<u>FBD of entire truss</u> (not shown here)

$\Sigma M_A = 0$: $3000\cos 40^\circ(6) = N_D(8)$ $\therefore$ $N_D = 1724$ lb (↑)

$\Sigma F_y = 0$: $A_y = 3000\sin 40^\circ - N_D = 3000\sin 40^\circ - 1724 = 204.4$ lb (↑)

$\Sigma F_x = 0$: $A_x = 3000\cos 40^\circ = 2298$ lb (⟵)

(continued)

FBD of joint B

$\Sigma F_x = 0$: $P_{BC} = -3000\cos 40^{\circ}$

$= -2298 \text{ lb} = 2298 \text{ lb (C)}$ ◆

$\Sigma F_y = 0$: $P_{AB} = -3000\sin 40^{\circ}$

$= -1928 \text{ lb} = 1928 \text{ lb (C)}$ ◆

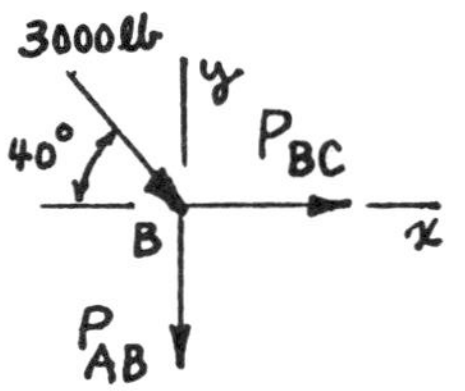

FBD of joint A

$\Sigma F_y = 0$: $+\uparrow \ \frac{3}{\sqrt{13}} P_{AC} + P_{AB} + 204.4 = 0$

$\therefore \ P_{AC} = \frac{\sqrt{13}}{3}(-P_{AB} - 204.4)$

$= \frac{\sqrt{13}}{3}(1928 - 204.4) = 2072 \text{ lb (T)}$ ◆

$\Sigma F_x = 0$: $\underrightarrow{+} \ P_{AD} + \frac{2}{\sqrt{13}} P_{AC} - 2298 = 0$

$\therefore \ P_{AD} = -\frac{2}{\sqrt{13}}(2072) + 2298 = 1149 \text{ lb (T)}$ ◆

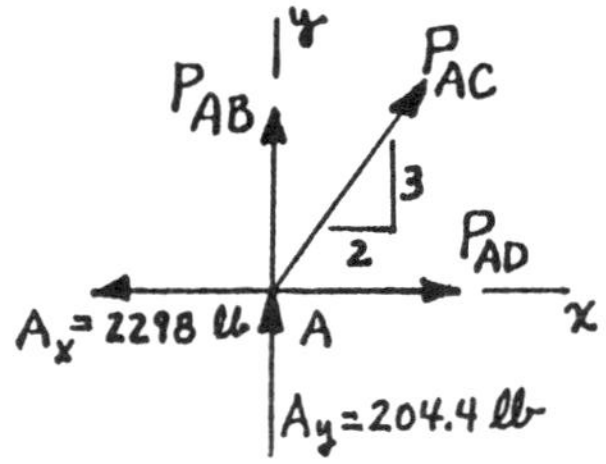

FBD of joint D

$\Sigma F_y = 0$: $+\uparrow \ \frac{3}{\sqrt{13}} P_{CD} + 1724 = 0$

$\therefore \ P_{CD} = -\frac{\sqrt{13}}{3}(1724) = -2072 \text{ lb} = 2072 \text{ lb (C)}$ ◆

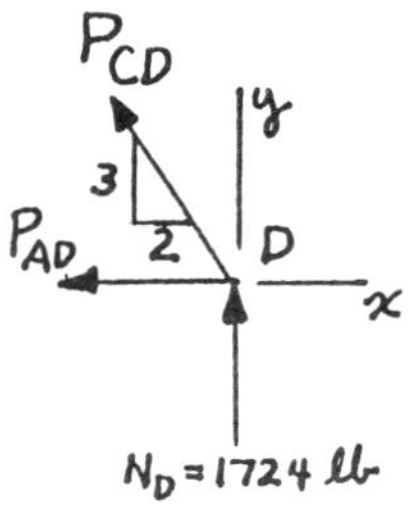

4.138

From the FBD of the entire truss (not shown here), $A_x = 0$; $A_y = 2$ kN ↑ and $N_C = 3$ kN ↑

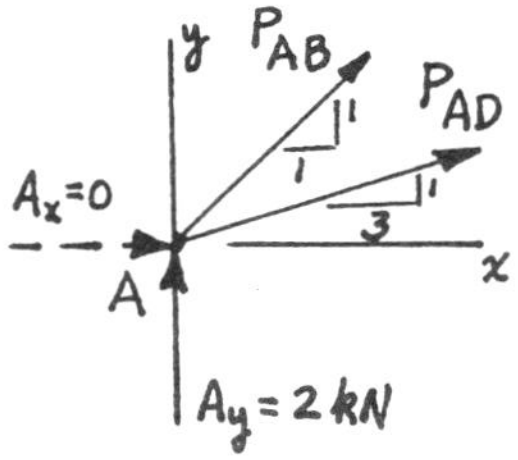

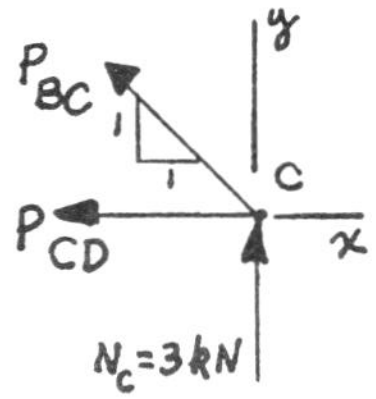

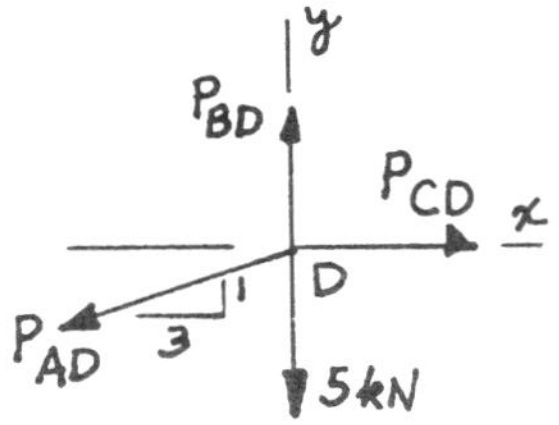

(continued)

FBD of joint A

$\Sigma F_x = 0$: $\underrightarrow{+} \ \left(1/\sqrt{2}\right) P_{AB} + \left(3/\sqrt{10}\right) P_{AD} = 0 \qquad (1)$

$\Sigma F_y = 0$: $+\uparrow \ \left(1/\sqrt{2}\right) P_{AB} + \left(1/\sqrt{10}\right) P_{AD} + 2 = 0 \qquad (2)$

Solving (1) and (2) simultaneously gives:

$P_{AB} = -4.243 \text{ kN} = 4.24 \text{ kN (C)}$ ◆ and $P_{AD} = 3.162 \text{ kN} = 3.16 \text{ kN (T)}$ ◆

FBD of joint C

$\Sigma F_y = 0$: $+\uparrow \ \left(1/\sqrt{2}\right) P_{BC} + 3 = 0 \qquad \therefore \ P_{BC} = -3\sqrt{2} \text{ kN} = 4.24 \text{ kN (C)}$ ◆

$\Sigma F_x = 0$: $\underrightarrow{+} \ -P_{CD} - \left(1/\sqrt{2}\right) P_{BC} = 0 \qquad \therefore \ P_{CD} = -\left(1/\sqrt{2}\right)\left(-3\sqrt{2}\right) = 3.0 \text{ kN (T)}$ ◆

FBD of joint D

$\Sigma F_y = 0$: $+\uparrow \ P_{BD} - \left(1/\sqrt{10}\right) P_{AD} - 5 = 0 \qquad \therefore \ P_{BD} = 5 + \left(1/\sqrt{10}\right)(3.162) = 6.0 \text{ kN (T)}$ ◆

4.139

FBD of entire truss (not shown here) $A_y = C_y = 100$ kN (↑) and $A_x = 0$

FBD of joint A

$\Sigma F_y = 0$: $+\uparrow \ 100 + P_{AB}\sin 30^{\circ} = 0$

$\therefore \ P_{AB} = -200 \text{ kN} = 200 \text{ kN (C)}$ ◆

$\Sigma F_x = 0$: $\underrightarrow{+} \ P_{AB}\cos 30^{\circ} + P_{AD} = 0$

$\therefore \ P_{AD} = -P_{AB}\cos 30^{\circ} = -(-200)\cos 30^{\circ} = 173.2 \text{ kN (T)}$ ◆

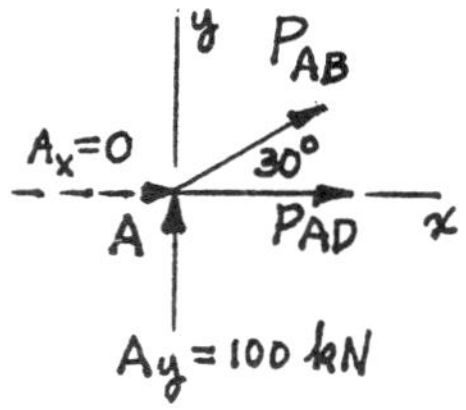

FBD of joint B

$\Sigma F_{y'} = 0$: $+\nwarrow \ -200\cos 30^{\circ} - P_{BD} = 0$

$\therefore \ P_{BD} = -173.2 \text{ kN} = 173.2 \text{ kN (C)}$ ◆

$\Sigma F_{x'} = 0$: $+\nearrow \ P_{BC} - P_{AB} - 200\sin 30^{\circ} = 0$

$\therefore \ P_{BC} = -200 + 100 = -100 \text{ kN} = 100 \text{ kN (C)}$ ◆

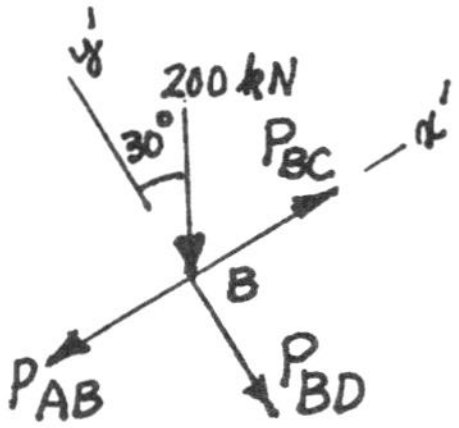

FBD of joint D

$\Sigma F_y = 0$: $+\uparrow \ P_{CD}\sin 60^{\circ} + P_{BD}\sin 60^{\circ} = 0$

$\therefore \ P_{CD} = -P_{BD} = -(-173.2) = 173.2 \text{ kN (T)}$ ◆

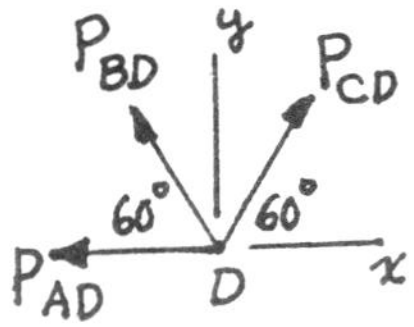

4.140

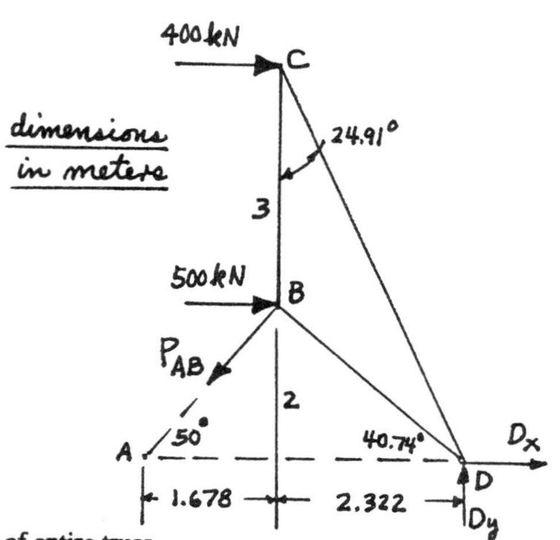

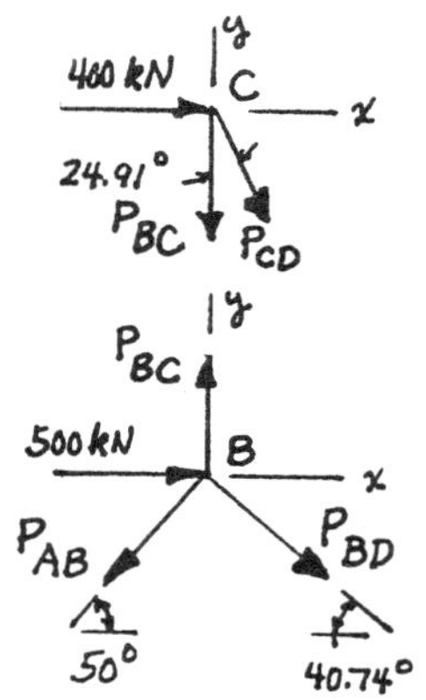

FBD of entire truss

$\Sigma M_D = 0$: $\circlearrowleft +$ $P_{AB}\sin 50^\circ(4) - 500(2) - 400(5) = 0$ $\quad \therefore\ P_{AB} = 979.1 \text{ kN} = 979 \text{ kN (T)}$ ◆

FBD of joint B

$\Sigma F_x = 0$: $\overset{+}{\rightarrow}$ $500 + P_{BD}\cos 40.74^\circ - P_{AB}\cos 50^\circ = 0$

$\therefore\ P_{BD} = (1/\cos 40.74^\circ)(979.1\cos 50^\circ - 500) = 170.7 \text{ kN} = 171 \text{ kN (T)}$ ◆

$\Sigma F_y = 0$: $+\uparrow$ $P_{BC} - P_{AB}\sin 50^\circ - P_{BD}\sin 40.74^\circ$

$\therefore\ P_{BC} = 979.1\sin 50^\circ + 170.7\sin 40.74^\circ = 861.4 \text{ kN} = 861 \text{ kN (T)}$ ◆

FBD of joint C

$\Sigma F_x = 0$: $\overset{+}{\rightarrow}$ $P_{CD}\sin 24.91^\circ + 400 = 0$

$\therefore\ P_{CD} = -400/\sin 24.91^\circ = -949.7 \text{ kN} = 950 \text{ kN (C)}$ ◆

4.141

If the load P acting at B is removed:

Prob. 4.134: AB and BC are zero-force members.

Prob. 4.135: There are no zero-force members.

Prob. 4.136: BD, CD and CE are zero-force members.

4.142

FBD of joint B

$\Sigma F_y = 0$: $P_{BD} = 185 \text{ lb}$

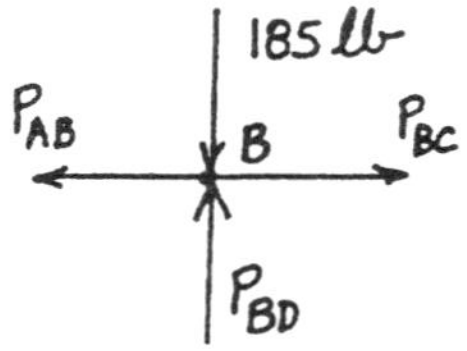

FBD of joint D

$$\Sigma F_y = 0:\quad +\uparrow\quad 2(500)\frac{L}{\sqrt{L^2+64}} = P_{BD}$$

$$\therefore\ \frac{L}{\sqrt{L^2+64}} = \frac{P_{BD}}{1000} = 0.185$$

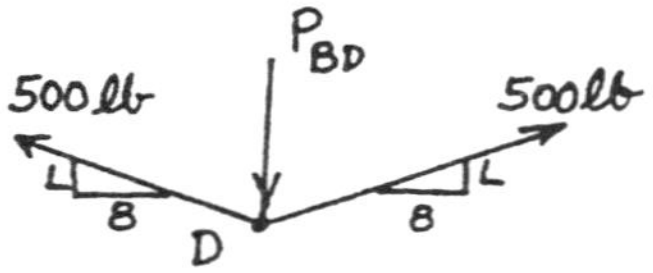

Solving for L gives: $L = 1.506$ ft ◆

4.143

FBD of pulley

$\Sigma M_A = 0$: $T = 42$ kN

$\Sigma F_x = 0$: $A_x = T = 42$ kN

$\Sigma F_y = 0$: $A_y = 42$ kN

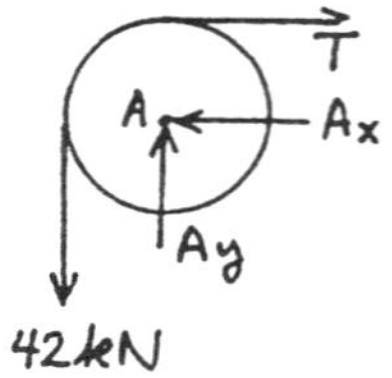

FBD of joint A

$$\Sigma F_x = 0:\quad \overset{+}{\rightarrow}\quad \frac{12}{13}P_{AB} + \frac{12}{13}P_{AC} + 42 = 0$$

$$\therefore\ P_{AB} + P_{AC} + 45.50 = 0 \qquad (1)$$

$$\Sigma F_y = 0:\quad +\uparrow\quad \frac{5}{13}P_{AB} - \frac{5}{13}P_{AC} - 42 = 0$$

$$\therefore\ P_{AB} - P_{AC} - 109.2 = 0 \qquad (2)$$

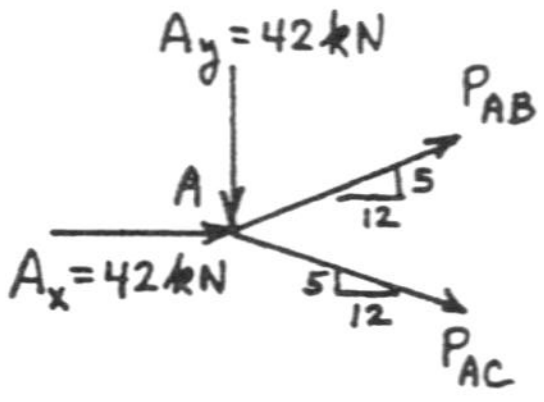

Solving (1) and (2) gives:

$P_{AB} = 31.85 \text{ kN} = 31.85 \text{ kN (T)}$ ◆

$P_{AC} = -77.35 \text{ kN} = 77.35 \text{ kN (C)}$ ◆

FBD of joint B

$$\Sigma F_x = 0:\quad \overset{+}{\rightarrow}\quad \frac{12}{13}P_{BD} - \frac{12}{13}P_{AB} - 42 = 0$$

$$\therefore\ P_{BD} = P_{AB} + 45.50 = 31.85 + 45.50$$

$$= 77.35 \text{ kN} = 77.35 \text{ kN (T)}$$ ◆

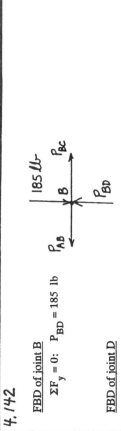

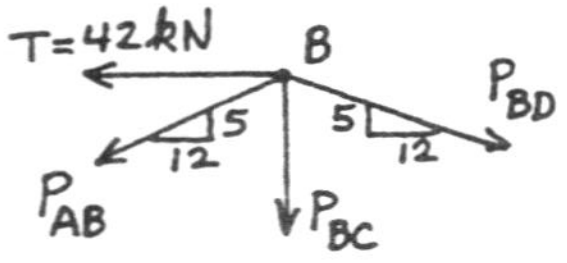

4.144

FBD of joint D

$\Sigma F_y = 0$: $P_{DH} = -P$

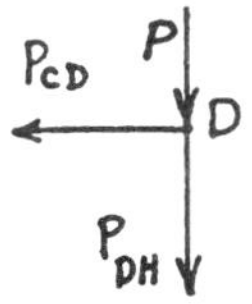

FBD of joint H $\quad \Sigma F_x = 0$: $P_{HC} = -P_{HG}$ (1)

$\Sigma F_y = 0$: $+\uparrow$ $P_{DH} + \frac{2}{\sqrt{13}} P_{HC} - \frac{2}{\sqrt{13}} P_{HG} = 0$

$\therefore -P + \frac{2}{\sqrt{13}}\left(P_{HC} - P_{HG}\right) = 0$ (2)

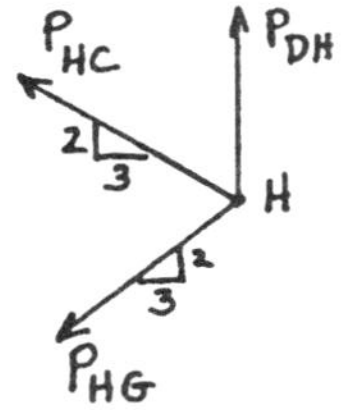

Solving (1) and (2) gives: $P_{HC} = 0.901\,P = 0.901\,P$ (T) ◆

$P_{HG} = -P_{HC} = -0.901\,P = 0.901\,P$ (C) ◆

4.145

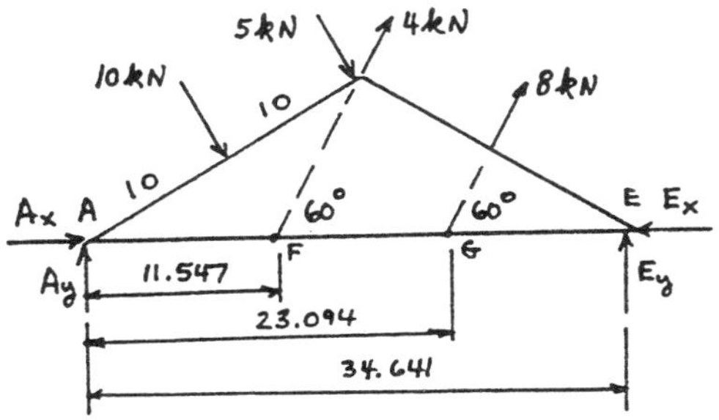

dimensions in meters

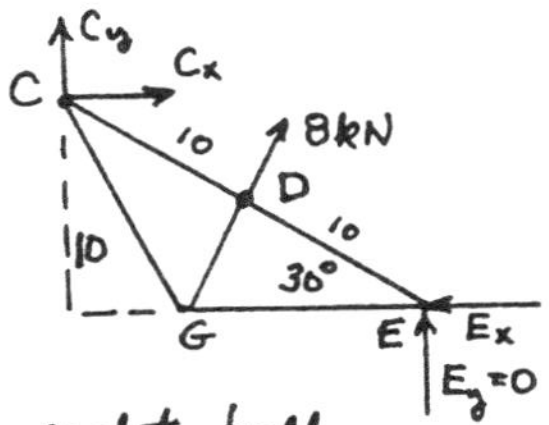

right half

FBD of entire truss $\quad \Sigma M_A = 0$:

$\circlearrowleft\!+$ $-10(10) - 5(20) + 4\sin 60^\circ(11.547) + 8\sin 60^\circ(23.094) + E_y(34.641) = 0$

$\therefore E_y = 0$

FBD of right half of truss $\quad \Sigma M_C = 0$: $\quad 8(10) = E_x(10) \quad \therefore E_x = 8$ kN

The reaction at E is: $R_E = 8$ kN $\leftarrow$ ◆

(continued)

FBD of joint E

$\Sigma F_y = 0$: $P_{DE} = 0$ ◆

$\Sigma F_x = 0$: $P_{EG} = -8$ kN $= 8$ kN (C) ◆

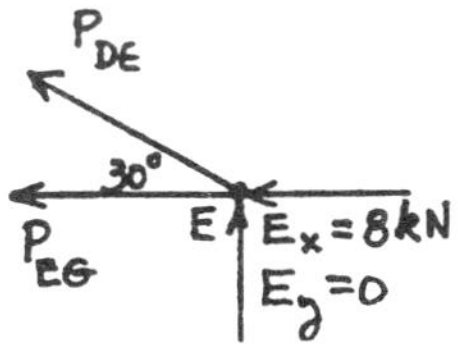

FBD of joint D

$\Sigma F_{y'} = 0$: $P_{DG} = 8$ kN $= 8$ kN (T) ◆

$\Sigma F_{x'} = 0$: $P_{CD} = P_{DE} = 0$ ◆

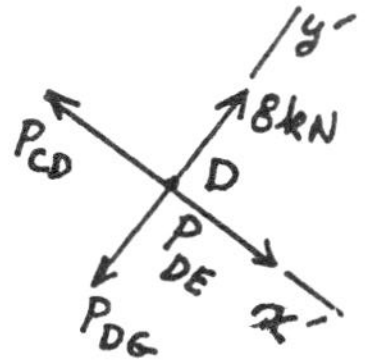

FBD of joint G

$\Sigma F_y = 0$: $P_{CG} = -P_{DG} = -8$ kN $= 8$ kN (C) ◆

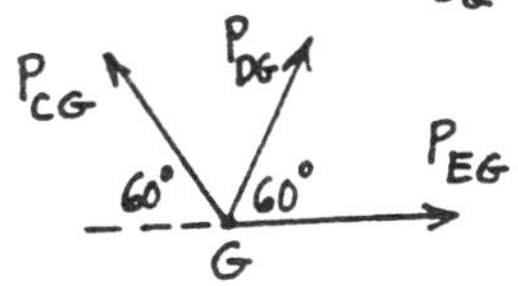

4.146

From the FBD of the entire truss (not shown here): $A_x = 0$; $A_y = N_D = 8000$ lb $\uparrow$

FBD of joint B

$\Sigma F_x = 0$: $\overset{+}{\rightarrow}$ $\frac{1}{\sqrt{2}} P_{BE} - \frac{1}{\sqrt{17}} P_{AB} = 0 \quad \therefore P_{BE} = \frac{\sqrt{2}}{\sqrt{17}} P_{AB}$

$\Sigma F_y = 0$: $+\uparrow$ $-8000 - \frac{4}{\sqrt{17}} P_{AB} - \frac{1}{\sqrt{2}} P_{BE} = 0$

$-8000 - \frac{4}{\sqrt{17}} P_{AB} - \frac{1}{\sqrt{17}} P_{AB} = 0$

$\therefore P_{AB} = -6597$ lb

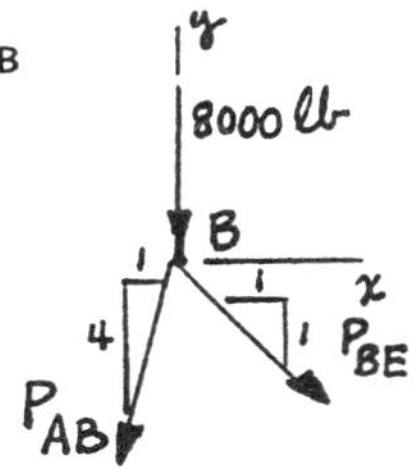

FBD of jointA

$\Sigma F_y = 0$: $+\uparrow$ $8000 + \frac{4}{\sqrt{17}} P_{AB} + \frac{1}{\sqrt{2}} P_{AE} = 0$

$8000 + \frac{4}{\sqrt{17}}(-6597) + \frac{1}{\sqrt{2}} P_{AE} = 0$

which gives: $P_{AE} = -2263$ lb

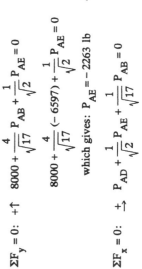

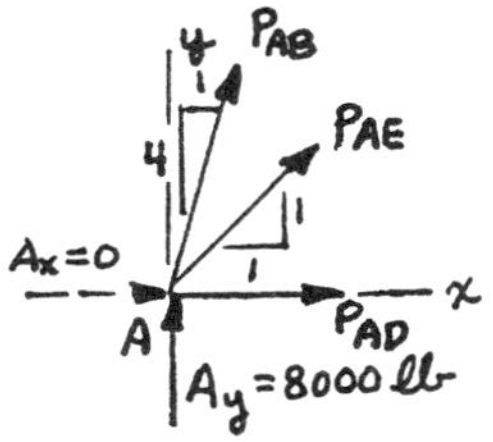

$\Sigma F_x = 0$: $\overset{+}{\rightarrow}$ $P_{AD} + \frac{1}{\sqrt{2}} P_{AE} + \frac{1}{\sqrt{17}} P_{AB} = 0$

$\therefore P_{AD} = -\frac{1}{\sqrt{2}}(-2263) - \frac{1}{\sqrt{17}}(-6597) = 3200$ lb (T) ◆

4.147

From the FBD of the entire truss (not shown here):

$A_x = 300$ kN →; $A_y = 600$ kN ↑; $D_y = 200$ kN ↓

FBD of joint A

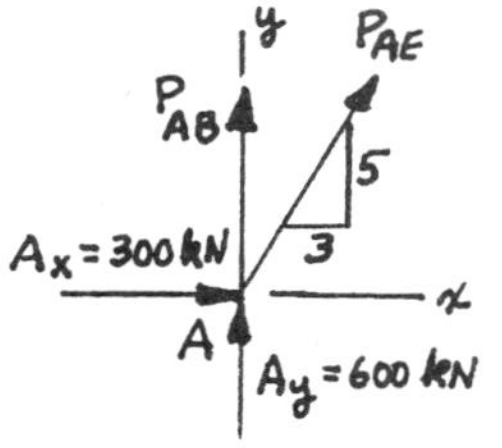

$\Sigma F_x = 0$: $\xrightarrow{+}$ $\frac{3}{\sqrt{34}} P_{AE} + 300 = 0$

$\therefore P_{AE} = -\frac{300\sqrt{34}}{3}$

$= -583.1$ kN $= 583.1$ kN (C) ◆

$\Sigma F_y = 0$: $+\uparrow$ $P_{AB} + \frac{5}{\sqrt{34}} P_{AE} + 600 = 0$

$\therefore P_{AB} = -\frac{5}{\sqrt{34}}(-583.1) - 600 = -100$ kN $= 100$ kN (C) ◆

FBD of joint B

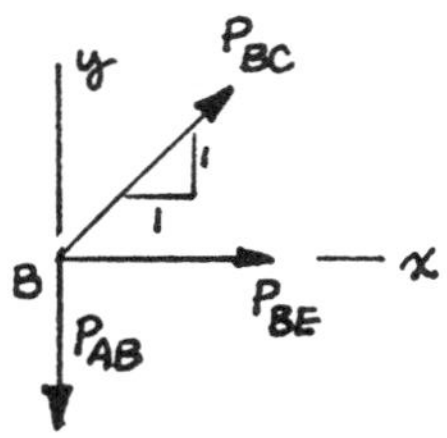

$\Sigma F_y = 0$: $+\uparrow$ $\frac{1}{\sqrt{2}} P_{BC} - P_{AB} = 0$

$\therefore P_{BC} = \sqrt{2}\, P_{AB} = \sqrt{2}\,(-100)$

$= -141.4$ kN $= 141.4$ kN (C) ◆

$\Sigma F_x = 0$: $\xrightarrow{+}$ $P_{BE} + \frac{1}{\sqrt{2}} P_{BC} = 0$

$\therefore P_{BE} = -\frac{1}{\sqrt{2}}(-141.4) = 100$ kN (T) ◆

4.148

FBD of a section to the right of a vertical cut

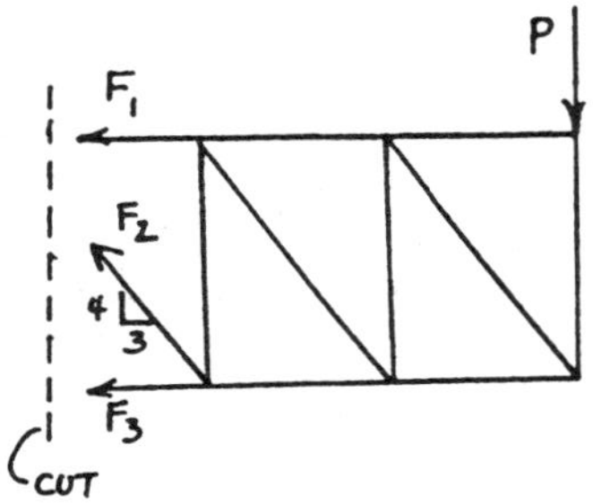

$\Sigma F_y = 0$: $\frac{4}{5} F_2 = P$

$\therefore F_2 = 1.25\,P = 1.25\,P$ (T) ◆

Since the FBD is the same regardless of the panel in which the cut is made, all diagonal members carry the same force: 1.25 P (T). ◆

4.149

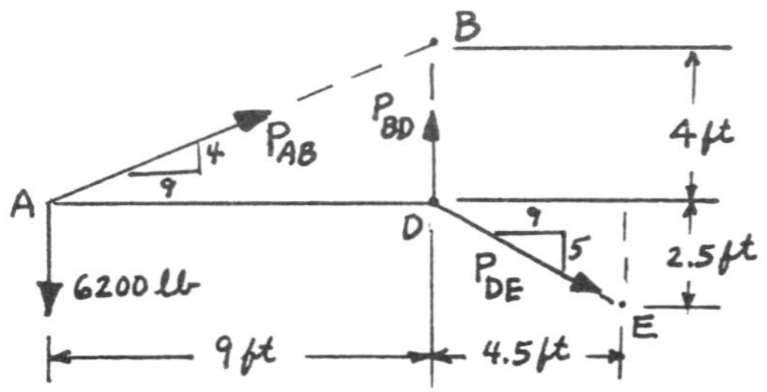

$\Sigma M_B = 0$: $\circlearrowleft +$ $6200(9) + \frac{9}{\sqrt{106}} P_{DE}(4) = 0$ $\therefore P_{DE} = -15\,960$ lb $= 15\,960$ lb (C) ◆

$\Sigma M_D = 0$: $\circlearrowleft +$ $6200(9) - \frac{4}{\sqrt{97}} P_{AB}(9) = 0$ $\therefore P_{AB} = 15\,270$ lb (T) ◆

$\Sigma F_y = 0$: $+\uparrow$ $-6200 + \frac{4}{\sqrt{97}} P_{AB} - \frac{5}{\sqrt{106}} P_{DE} + P_{BD} = 0$

$-6200 + 6200 + 7750 + P_{BD} = 0$ $\therefore P_{BD} = -7750$ lb $= 7750$ lb (C) ◆

4.150

From the FBD of the entire truss (not shown here):

$A_x = 0$, $A_y = 8000$ lb ↑, $N_E = 10000$ lb ↑

$\Sigma M_B = 0$: $\circlearrowleft +$ $P_{FG}(4) - 8000(8) = 0$ $\therefore P_{FG} = 16000$ lb (T) ◆

$\Sigma M_G = 0$: $\circlearrowleft +$ $4000(8) - 8000(16) - \frac{1}{\sqrt{5}} P_{BC}(16) = 0$

$\therefore P_{BC} = -13\,420$ lb $= 13\,420$ lb (C) ◆

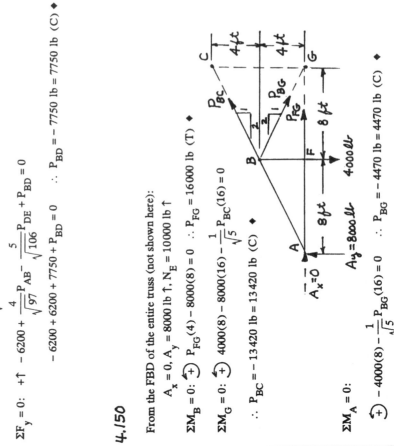

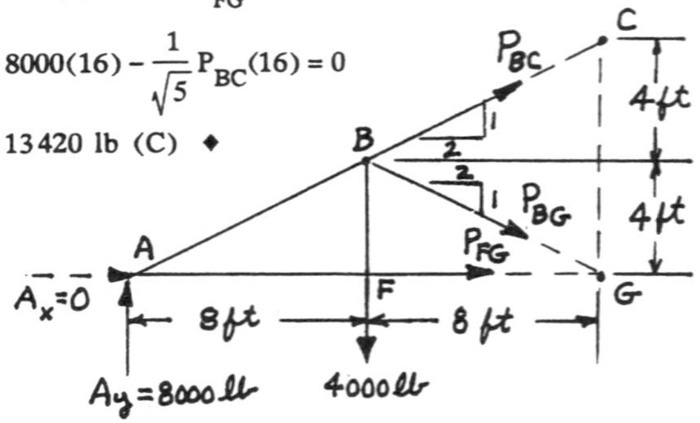

$\Sigma M_A = 0$:

$\circlearrowleft +$ $-4000(8) - \frac{1}{\sqrt{5}} P_{BG}(16) = 0$ $\therefore P_{BG} = -4470$ lb $= 4470$ lb (C) ◆

4.151

$\Sigma M_A = 0$:

$$\circlearrowleft + \quad \frac{3}{\sqrt{13}} P_{CE}(6) - 20(4) = 0$$

$$\therefore \; P_{CE} = \frac{80\sqrt{13}}{18} = 16.02 \text{ kN (T)}$$

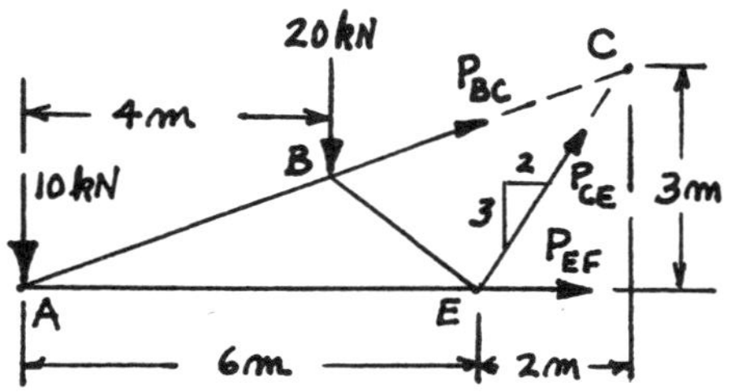

4.152

<u>FBD of the entire truss</u> (not shown here)

$\Sigma M_J = 0$: $\circlearrowleft +$ $N_R(40) - 300(10) = 0 \quad \therefore \; N_R = 75$ kN

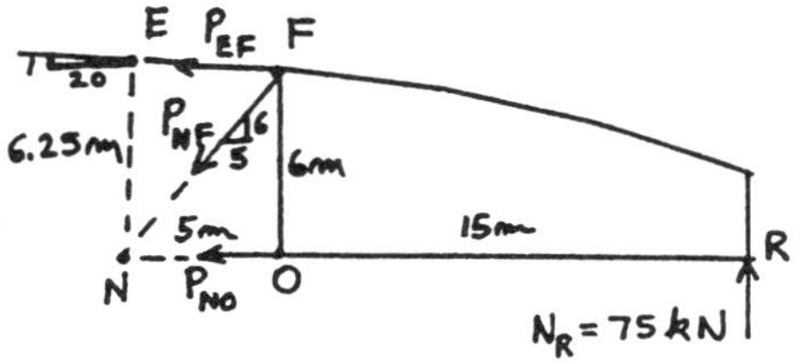

<u>FBD of the section shown</u>

$\Sigma M_F = 0$: $\circlearrowleft +$ $75(15) - P_{NO}(6) = 0 \qquad \therefore \; P_{NO} = 187.5 \text{ kN} = 187.5 \text{ kN (T)}$ ◆

$\Sigma M_N = 0$: $\circlearrowleft +$ $75(20) + \dfrac{20}{\sqrt{401}} P_{EF}(6.25) = 0 \quad \therefore \; P_{EF} = -240.3 \text{ kN} = 240.3 \text{ kN (C)}$ ◆

$\Sigma F_y = 0$: $+\uparrow \; 75 - \dfrac{6}{\sqrt{61}} P_{NF} + \dfrac{1}{\sqrt{401}} P_{EF} = 0$

$$\therefore \; P_{NF} = \frac{\sqrt{61}}{6}\left[75 + \frac{1}{\sqrt{401}}(-240.3)\right] = 82.0 \text{ kN} = 82.0 \text{ kN (T)} \; ◆$$

4.153

<u>FBD of the entire truss</u> (not shown here)

$\Sigma M_J = 0$: $\circlearrowleft +$ $N_R(40) - 300(25) = 0 \quad \therefore \; N_R = 187.5$ kN

(continued)

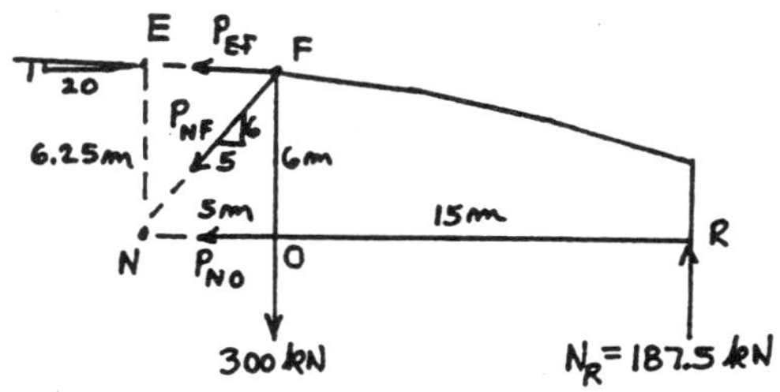

<u>FBD of the section shown</u>

$\Sigma M_F = 0$: $\circlearrowleft +$ $187.5(15) - P_{NO}(6) = 0 \qquad \therefore \; P_{NO} = 468.8 \text{ kN} = 468.8 \text{ kN (T)}$ ◆

$\Sigma M_N = 0$: $\circlearrowleft +$ $187.5(20) - 300(5) + \dfrac{20}{\sqrt{401}} P_{EF}(6.25) = 0$

$\therefore \; P_{EF} = -360.4 \text{ kN} = 360.4 \text{ kN (C)}$ ◆

$\Sigma F_y = 0$: $+\uparrow \; 187.5 - 300 - \dfrac{6}{\sqrt{61}} P_{NF} + \dfrac{1}{\sqrt{401}} P_{EF} = 0$

$$\therefore \; P_{NF} = \frac{\sqrt{61}}{6}\left[187.5 - 300 + \frac{1}{\sqrt{401}}(-360.4)\right] = -169.9 \text{ kN} = 169.9 \text{ kN (C)} \; ◆$$

4.154

From the analysis of the FBD of the entire truss (not shown here), we obtain

$$A_x = 0, \; A_y = 0.250 \text{ P} \uparrow, \text{ and } E_y = 0.750 \text{ P} \uparrow$$

<u>FBD of section shown</u>

$\Sigma F_y = 0$: $P_{BG} = 0.250 \text{ P} = 0.250 \text{ P (T)}$ ◆

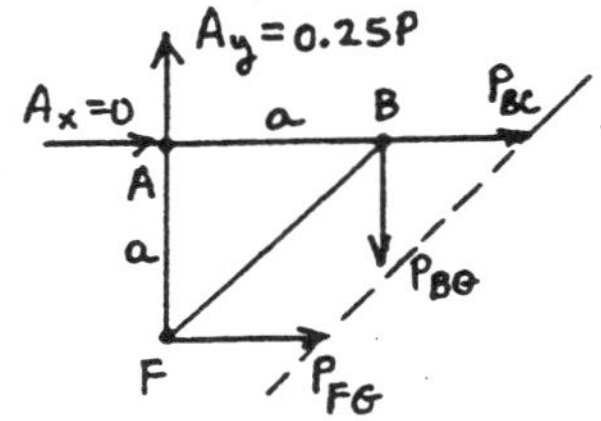

<u>FBD of section shown</u>

$\Sigma F_y = 0$: $+\uparrow \; 0.75 \text{ P} - \text{P} + \left(1/\sqrt{2}\right) P_{CI} = 0$

$\therefore \; P_{CI} = \sqrt{2}\,(\text{P} - 0.750 \text{ P}) = 0.354 \text{ P} = 0.354 \text{ P (T)}$ ◆

$\Sigma M_I = 0$: $\circlearrowleft +$ $0.750 \text{ P}(a) + P_{CD}(a) = 0$

$\therefore \; P_{CD} = -0.750 \text{ P} = 0.750 \text{ P (C)}$ ◆

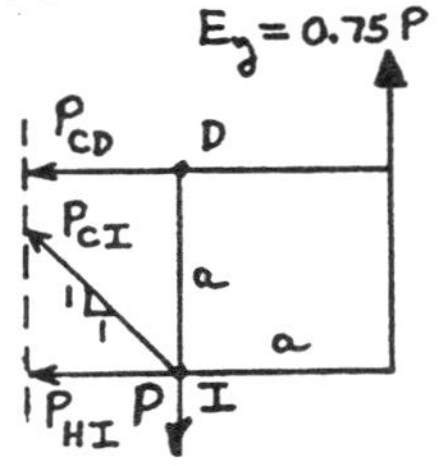

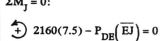

4.155

From the analysis of the entire truss (not shown here), the vertical reaction at E depends on the location of P as follows: P at J: $E_y = P$; P at I: $E_y = 0.750\,P$; P at H: $E_y = 0.500\,P$;

P at G: $E_y = 0.250\,P$; P at F: $E_y = 0$. (In each case, E_y is directed upward.)

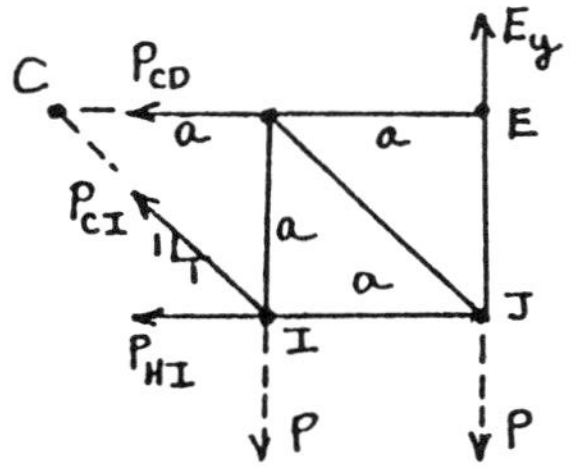

FBD of the section shown

If P acts at J ($E_y = P$)

$\Sigma F_y = 0$ gives $P_{CI} = 0$

$\Sigma M_C = 0$ gives $P_{HI} = 0$

If P acts at I ($E_y = 0.750\,P$)

$\Sigma F_y = 0$: $+\uparrow\ E_y - P + \left(1/\sqrt{2}\right)P_{CI} = 0$

$\therefore\ P_{CI} = \sqrt{2}\left(P - E_y\right) = \sqrt{2}\left(P - 0.750\,P\right) = 0.3536\,P = 0.3536\,P\ \text{(T)}$

$\Sigma M_C = 0$: $\circlearrowleft +$ $E_y(2a) - P(a) - P_{HI}(a) = 0$

$\therefore\ P_{HI} = 2(0.750)P - P = 0.500\,P = 0.500\,P\ \text{(T)}$

If P acts at H, G or F

$\Sigma F_y = 0$: $+\uparrow\ E_y + \left(1/\sqrt{2}\right)P_{CI} = 0 \quad \therefore\ P_{CI} = -\sqrt{2}\,E_y = \sqrt{2}\,E_y\ \text{(C)}$

$\Sigma M_C = 0$: $\circlearrowleft +$ $E_y(2a) - P_{HI}(a) = 0 \quad \therefore\ P_{HI} = 2E_y = 2E_y\ \text{(T)}$

(a) The maximum tension occurs in HI when P acts at H ($E_y = 0.500\,P$).

$\therefore$ Max tension in HI $= 2E_y = 2(0.500\,P) = P = 48$ kips ◆

(b) The maximum compression in CI occurs when P acts at H ($E_y = 0.500\,P$).

$\therefore$ Max compression in CI $= \sqrt{2}\,E_y = \sqrt{2}\,(0.500\,P) = \sqrt{2}\,(0.500)(48) = 33.9$ kips ◆

(c) The maximum tension in CI occurs when P acts at I.

$\therefore$ Max tension in CI $= 0.3536\,P = 0.3536(48) = 16.97$ kips ◆

4.156

From the FBD of joint G, we see that the force in CG is zero.

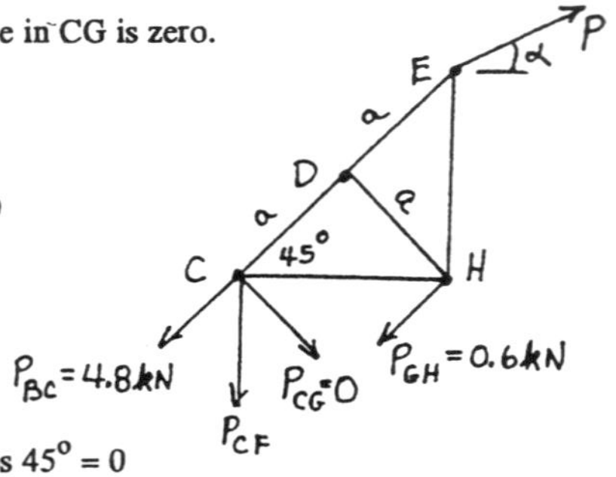

FBD of the section shown

$\Sigma M_C = 0$: $\circlearrowleft +$ $0.6(a) + P\cos\alpha(2a\sin 45^\circ)$

$- P\sin\alpha(2a\cos 45^\circ) = 0$

$\therefore\ P\sin\alpha - P\cos\alpha = 0.4243 \quad (1)$

$\Sigma F_x = 0$: $\xrightarrow{+}$ $P\cos\alpha - 4.8\cos 45^\circ - 0.6\cos 45^\circ = 0$

$\therefore\ P\cos\alpha = 3.8184\ \text{kN} \quad (2)$

Substituting (2) into (1) gives:

$P\sin\alpha = 3.8184 + 0.4243 = 4.2427\ \text{kN} \quad (3)$

Dividing (3) by (2), we obtain

$\dfrac{\sin\alpha}{\cos\alpha} = \tan\alpha = \dfrac{4.2427}{3.8184}$ which gives $\alpha = 48.01^\circ$ ◆

From (2), $P = \dfrac{3.8184}{\cos 48.01^\circ} = 5.708\ \text{kN}$ ◆

4.157

Geometry: $\dfrac{\overline{EJ} - 2}{9} = \dfrac{\overline{FK} - \overline{BG}}{12} = \dfrac{4-2}{12} = \dfrac{1}{6} \qquad \therefore\ \overline{EJ} = 3.5\ \text{ft}$

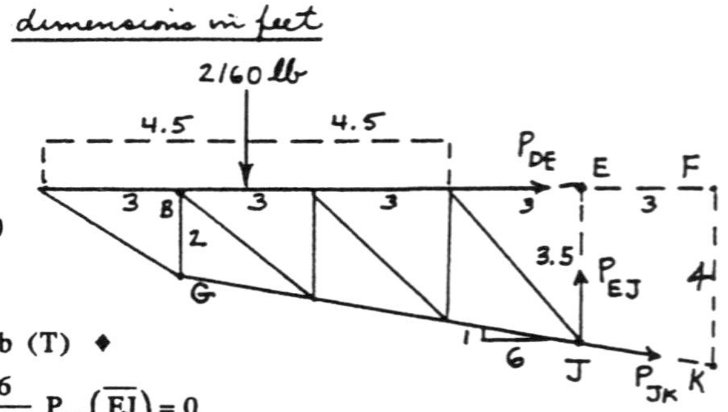

FBD of section shown

$\Sigma M_J = 0$:

$\circlearrowleft +$ $2160(7.5) - P_{DE}\left(\overline{EJ}\right) = 0$

$\therefore\ P_{DE} = 2160(7.5)/3.5$

$= 4630\ \text{lb} = 4630\ \text{lb (T)}$ ◆

$\Sigma M_E = 0$: $\circlearrowleft +$ $2160(7.5) + \dfrac{6}{\sqrt{37}}P_{JK}\left(\overline{EJ}\right) = 0$

$\therefore\ P_{JK} = -\dfrac{\sqrt{37}}{6(3.5)}(2160)(7.5) = -4692\ \text{lb} = 4692\ \text{lb (C)}$ ◆

(continued)

$$\Sigma F_y = 0: \quad +\uparrow \quad -2160 + P_{EJ} - \frac{1}{\sqrt{37}} P_{JK} = 0$$

$$\therefore \; P_{EJ} = 2160 + \frac{1}{\sqrt{37}}(-4692) = 1389 \text{ lb} = 1389 \text{ lb (T)} \; \blacklozenge$$

4.158

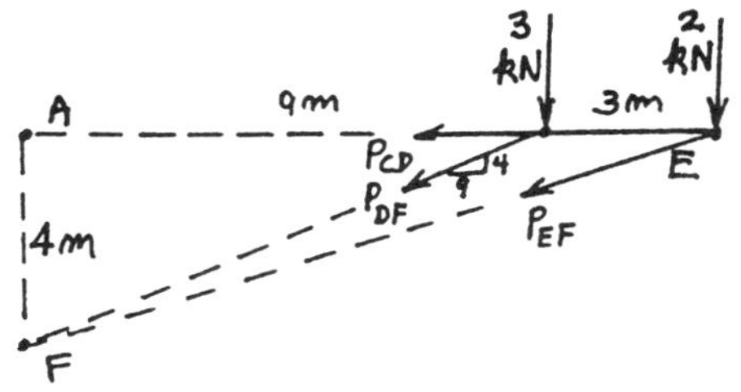

FBD of section shown

$\Sigma M_F = 0$:

$$(+)\; P_{CD}(4) - 3(9) - 2(12) = 0$$

$$\therefore \; P_{CD} = 12.75 \text{ kN} = 12.75 \text{ kN (T)} \; \blacklozenge$$

$\Sigma M_E = 0$:

$$(+)\; \frac{4}{\sqrt{97}} P_{DF}(3) + 3(3) = 0$$

$$\therefore \; P_{DF} = -7.39 \text{ kN} = 7.39 \text{ kN (C)} \; \blacklozenge$$

4.159

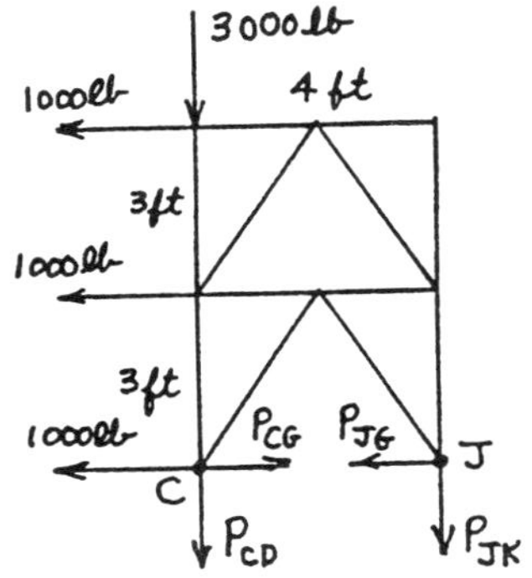

FBD of section shown

$\Sigma M_J = 0$:

$$(+)\; P_{CD}(4) + 3000(4) + 1000(6) + 1000(3) = 0$$

$$\therefore \; P_{CD} = -5250 \text{ lb} = 5250 \text{ lb (C)} \; \blacklozenge$$

$\Sigma M_C = 0$:

$$(+)\; -P_{JK}(4) + 1000(6) + 1000(3) = 0$$

$$\therefore \; P_{JK} = 2250 \text{ lb} = 2250 \text{ lb (T)} \; \blacklozenge$$

4.160

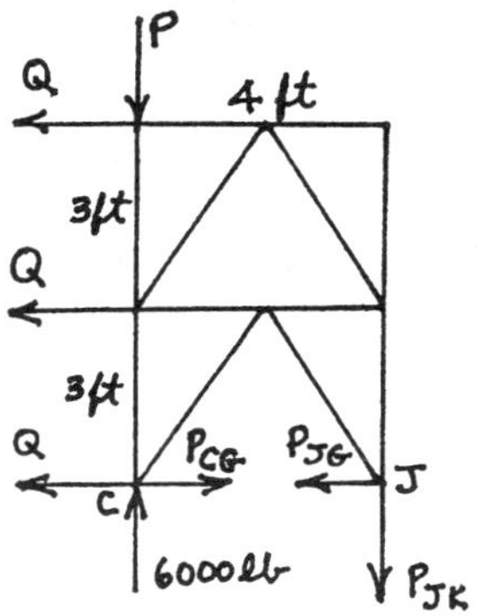

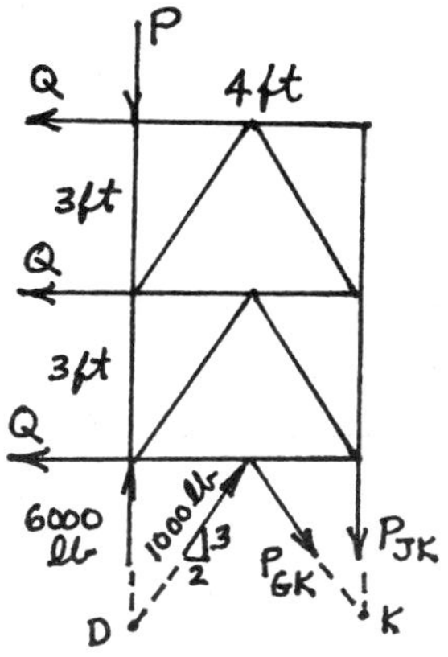

FBD of section shown above

$\Sigma M_J = 0$:

$$(+)\; P(4) + Q(3 + 6) - 6000(4) = 0$$

$$\therefore \; 4P + 9Q = 24\,000 \text{ lb}\cdot\text{ft} \quad (1)$$

FBD of section shown above

$\Sigma M_K = 0$:

$$(+)\; P(4) + Q(3 + 6 + 9) - 6000(4) - \frac{3}{\sqrt{13}}(1000)(4) = 0$$

$$\therefore \; 4P + 18Q = 27\,328 \text{ lb}\cdot\text{ft} \quad (2)$$

Solving (1) and (2) gives:

$$P = 5170 \text{ lb} \; \blacklozenge \quad \text{and} \quad Q = 370 \text{ lb} \; \blacklozenge$$

4.161

FBD of section shown

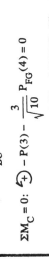

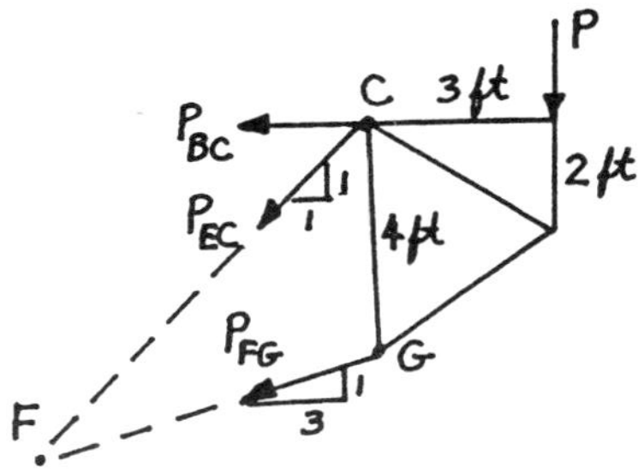

$$\Sigma M_F = 0: \quad (+)\; P_{BC}(6) - P(9) = 0$$

$$\therefore \; P_{BC} = 1.500\,P = 1.500\,P \text{ (T)} \; \blacklozenge$$

$$\Sigma M_C = 0: \quad (+)\; -P(3) - \frac{3}{\sqrt{10}} P_{FG}(4) = 0$$

$$\therefore \; P_{FG} = -0.7906\,P = 0.7906\,P \text{ (C)} \; \blacklozenge$$

$$\Sigma F_y = 0: \quad +\downarrow \quad P + \frac{1}{\sqrt{2}} P_{EC} + \frac{1}{\sqrt{10}} P_{FG} = 0$$

$$\therefore \; P_{EC} = \sqrt{2}\left[-P - \left(-\frac{0.7906\,P}{\sqrt{10}}\right)\right] = -1.061\,P = 1.061\,P \text{ (C)} \; \blacklozenge$$

4.162

Extreme cases occur when P = 200 kN acts at I, and when P = 0.

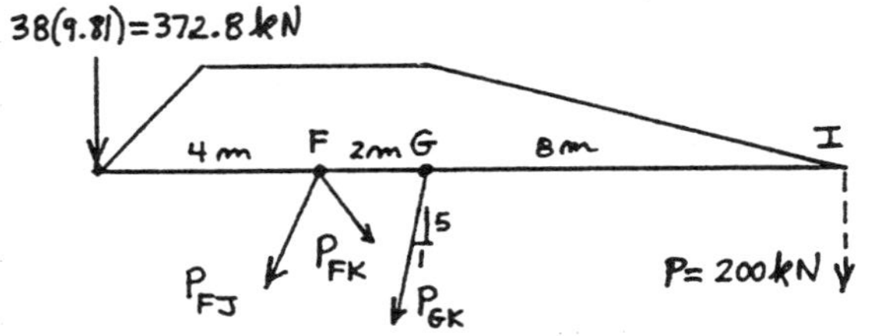

FBD of section shown (with P = 200 kN acting at I)

$$\Sigma M_F = 0: \quad (+)\ 372.8(4) - 200(10) - \frac{5}{\sqrt{26}} P_{GK}(2) = 0$$

$$\therefore\ P_{GK} = -259 \text{ kN} = 259 \text{ kN (C)} \ ◆$$

FBD of section shown (with P = 0)

$$\Sigma M_F = 0: \quad (+)\ 372.8(4) - \frac{5}{\sqrt{26}} P_{GK}(2) = 0$$

$$\therefore\ P_{GK} = 760 \text{ kN} = 760 \text{ kN (T)} \ ◆$$

4.163

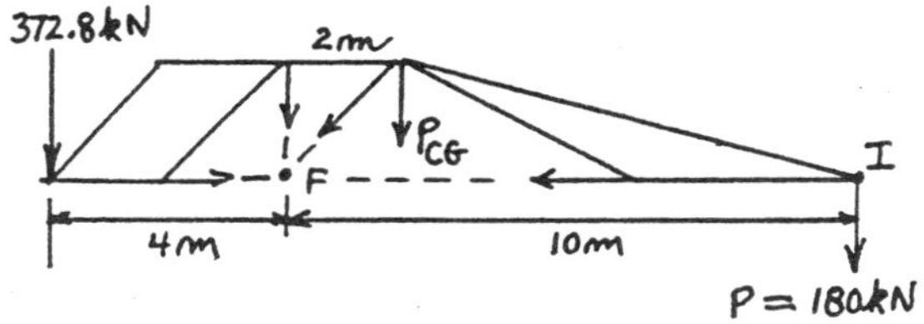

(a) FBD of section shown (with P = 180 kN acting at I)

$$\Sigma M_F = 0: \quad (+)\ 372.8(4) - 180(10) - P_{CG}(2) = 0$$

$$\therefore\ P_{CG} = -154.4 \text{ kN} = 154.4 \text{ kN (C)} \ ◆$$

(b) FBD of section shown (assuming that P is removed)

$$\Sigma M_F = 0: \quad (+)\ 372.8(4) - P_{CG}(2) = 0$$

$$\therefore\ P_{CG} = 746 \text{ kN} = 746 \text{ kN (T)} \ ◆$$

4.164

From the FBD of the entire truss (not shown here): $A_x = 0$ and $A_y = 2.5\,P \uparrow$

FBD of joint N

$\Sigma F_x = 0: \quad P_{NJ} = -P_{ND}$

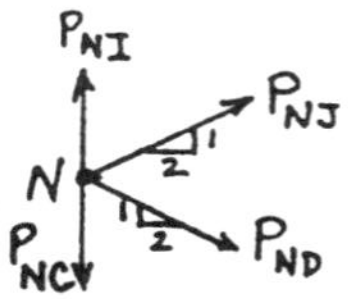

FBD of section shown

$\Sigma F_y = 0:$

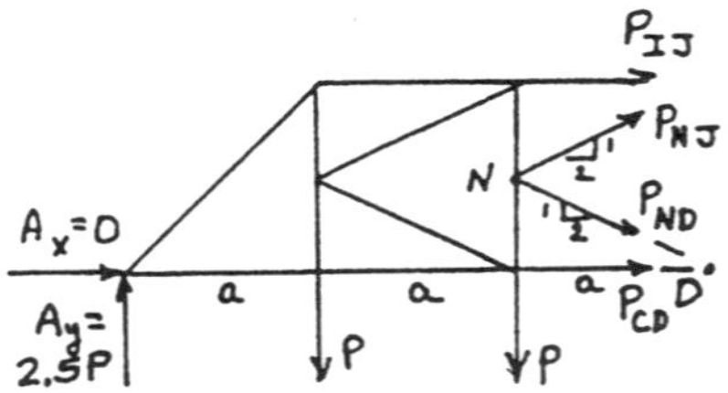

$$+\uparrow \quad 2.5\,P - P - P + \frac{1}{\sqrt{5}}(P_{NJ} - P_{ND}) = 0$$

$$0.5\,P + \frac{1}{\sqrt{5}}(2\,P_{NJ}) = 0$$

$$\therefore\ P_{NJ} = -0.559\,P = 0.559\,P \text{ (C)} \ ◆ \quad \text{and} \quad P_{ND} = 0.559\,P = 0.559\,P \text{ (T)}$$

$$\Sigma M_D = 0: \quad (+)\ P(2a) + P(a) - 2.5\,P(3a) - P_{IJ}(a) - \frac{1}{\sqrt{5}} P_{NJ}(a) - \frac{2}{\sqrt{5}} P_{NJ}\left(\frac{a}{2}\right) = 0$$

$$\therefore\ -4.5\,P - P_{IJ} - \frac{2}{\sqrt{5}} P_{NJ} = 0$$

which gives: $P_{IJ} = -4.5\,P - \frac{2}{\sqrt{5}}(-0.559\,P) = -4.00\,P = 4.00\,P \text{ (C)}$ ◆

$$\Sigma M_N = 0: \quad (+)\ P(a) - 2.5\,P(2\,a) - P_{IJ}\left(\frac{a}{2}\right) + P_{CD}\left(\frac{a}{2}\right) = 0$$

$$\therefore\ P_{CD} = 2[-P + 5\,P + 0.5(-4.00\,P)] = 4.00\,P = 4.00\,P \text{ (T)} \ ◆$$

4.165

FBD of entire truss

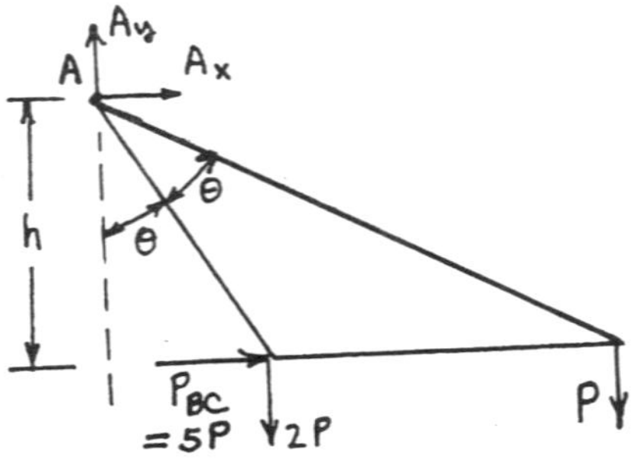

$\Sigma M_A = 0:$

$$(+)\ 5\,P(h) - 2\,P(h \tan\theta) - P(h \tan 2\theta) = 0$$

which can be simplified as

$$\tan 2\theta + 2\tan\theta - 5 = 0$$

Solving by Newton's method gives

$$\theta = 0.6460 \text{ rad} = 37.0^\circ \ ◆$$

4.166

From the FBD of the entire truss (not shown here): $A_x = 0$, $A_y = N_E = 1.5P \uparrow$

$\Sigma M_G = 0$: $\circlearrowleft +$ $P(L) - 1.5P(2L) - \frac{1}{\sqrt{5}} P_{BC}(L) = 0$

$\therefore P_{BC} = -2\sqrt{5}\,P = 4.470P$ (C) ◆

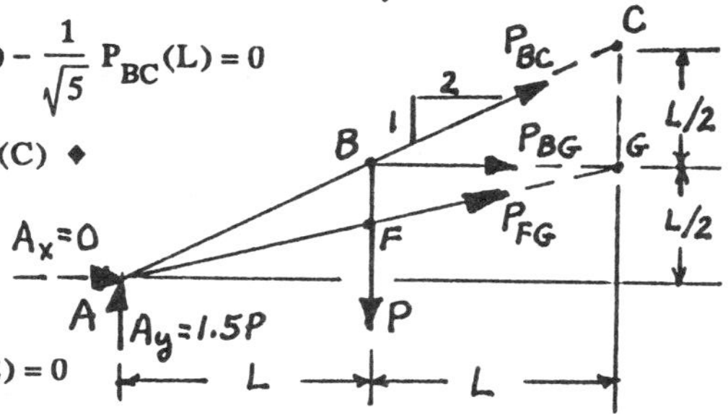

$\Sigma M_A = 0$: $\circlearrowleft +$ $-PL - P_{BG}(L/2) = 0$

$\therefore P_{BG} = -2.0P = 2.0P$ (C) ◆

4.167

From FBD of entire truss (not shown here): $F_y = G_y = 20000$ lb $\uparrow$

<u>FBD of section shown</u>

$\Sigma M_B = 0$

$\circlearrowleft +$ $20000(16) - 12000(16) - G_x(14) = 0$

$\therefore G_x = \frac{8000(16)}{14} = 9142$ lb ◆

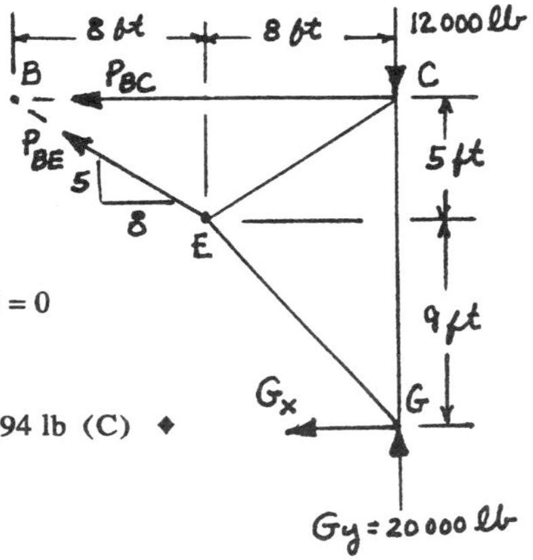

$\Sigma F_y = 0$: $+\uparrow$ $\frac{5}{\sqrt{89}} P_{BE} + 200000 - 12000 = 0$

$\therefore P_{BE} = -\frac{8000\sqrt{89}}{5} = -15094$ lb $= 15094$ lb (C) ◆

$\Sigma F_x = 0$: $\xrightarrow{+}$ $-P_{BC} - \frac{8}{\sqrt{89}} P_{BE} - G_x = 0$

$\therefore P_{BC} = -\frac{8}{\sqrt{89}}(-15094) - 9142 = 3658$ lb (T) ◆

4.168

$\Sigma M_L = 0$:

$\circlearrowleft +$ $W(2\sqrt{2}\,L) - W(L) - P_{EF}(L) = 0$

$\therefore P_{EF} = (2\sqrt{2} - 1)W = 1.828\,W$ (T) ◆

$\Sigma M_E = 0$:

$\circlearrowleft +$ $W(2\sqrt{2}\,L) + P_{KL}(L) = 0$

$\therefore P_{KL} = -2\sqrt{2}\,W = 2.83\,W$ (C) ◆

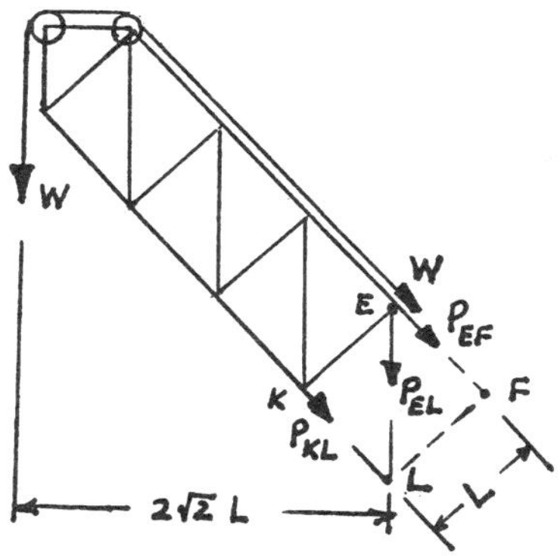

4.169

$\Sigma M_A = 0$: $\circlearrowleft +$ $B(0.5) - 20(9.81)(0.6) = 0$

$\therefore B = 235.4$ N ◆

$\Sigma F_x = 0$: $A_x = B = 235.4$ N

$\Sigma F_y = 0$: $A_y = 20(9.81) = 196.2$ N

$\therefore A = \sqrt{235.4^2 + 196.2^2} = 306$ N ◆

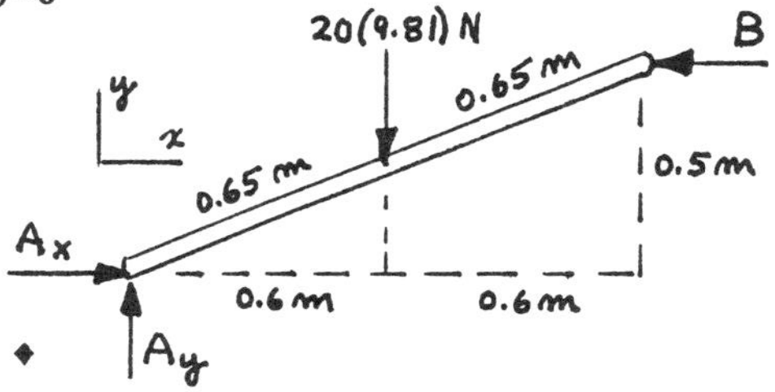

4.170

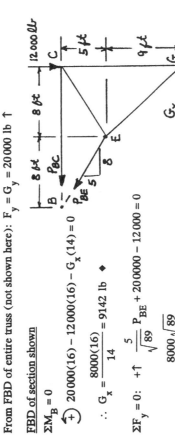

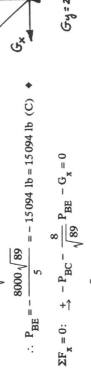

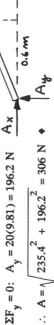

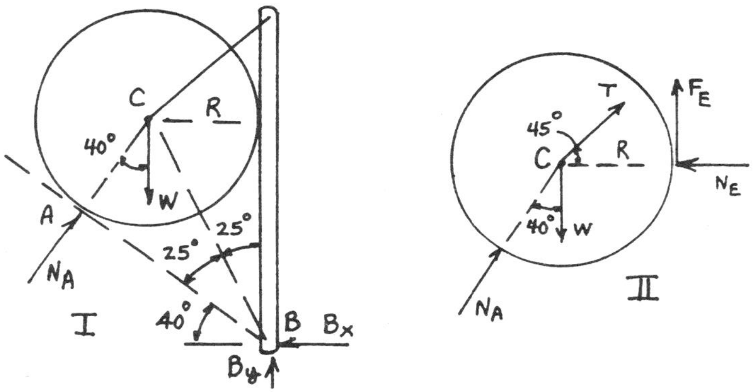

<u>FBD I</u> $\Sigma M_B = 0$: $\circlearrowleft +$ $WR - N_A(\overline{AB}) = 0$ (From the figure: $\overline{AB} = R/\tan 25^\circ$)

$\therefore N_A = \frac{WR}{R/\tan 25^\circ} = 0.4663\,W$ ◆

(continued)

FBD II $\Sigma M_C = 0$: $F_E = 0$ ◆

$\Sigma F_y = 0$: $+\uparrow$ $N_A \cos 40^\circ - W + T \sin 45^\circ = 0$

$\therefore\ T = \dfrac{W}{\sin 45^\circ}[1 - 0.4663 \cos 40^\circ] = 0.9090\ W$ ◆

$\Sigma F_x = 0$: $\underset{\rightarrow}{+}$ $N_A \sin 40^\circ + T \cos 45^\circ - N_E = 0$

$\therefore\ N_E = W[0.4663 \sin 40^\circ + 0.9090 \cos 45^\circ] = 0.9425\ W$ ◆

4.171

$\Sigma M_A = 0$: $\circlearrowleft +$ $N_C \sin 65^\circ(4) + N_C \cos 65^\circ(2.5) - 5(2) = 0$

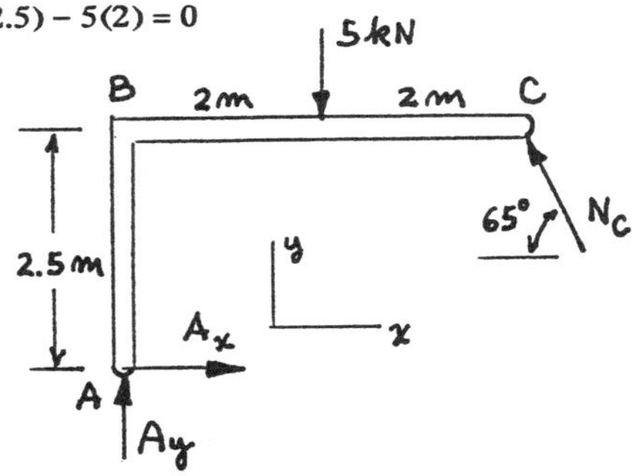

$\therefore\ N_C = \dfrac{10}{4\sin 65^\circ + 2.5\cos 65^\circ} = 2.136\ \text{kN}$

$\Sigma F_x = 0$:

$A_x = N_C \cos 65^\circ$

$= 2.136 \cos 65^\circ = 0.9027\ \text{kN}$

$\Sigma F_y = 0$:

$A_y = 5 - N_C \sin 65^\circ = 5 - 2.136 \sin 65^\circ = 3.064\ \text{kN}$

$\therefore\ A = \sqrt{0.9027^2 + 3.064^2} = 3.19\ \text{kN}$ ◆

4.172

$\Sigma M_A = 0$:

$\circlearrowleft +$ $T\cos 30^\circ(L) + 20(L) - 20(L\tan\theta) = 0$

$\therefore\ T = \dfrac{20(\tan\theta - 1)}{\cos 30^\circ} = 23.1(\tan\theta - 1)\ \text{kN}$ ◆

When $\theta = 45^\circ$, $T = 0$ ◆

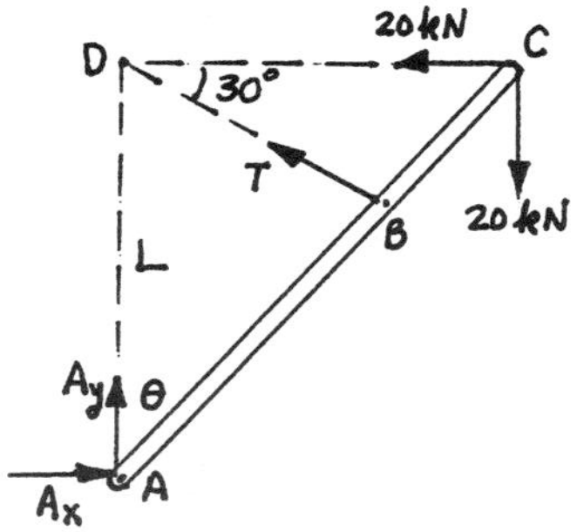

4.173

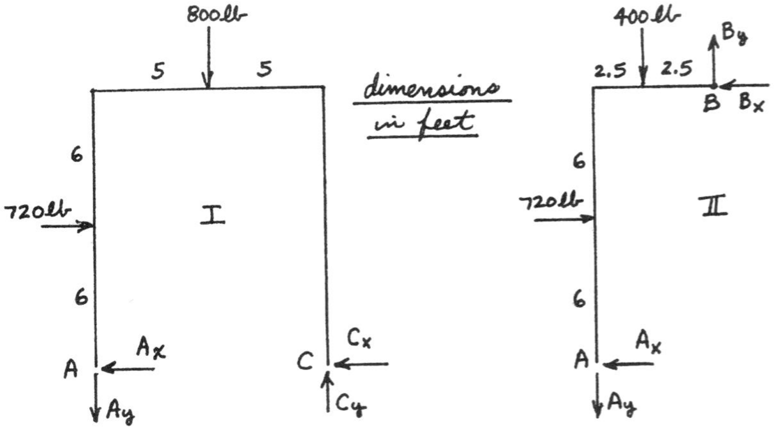

FBD I

$\Sigma M_A = 0$: $\circlearrowleft +$ $C_y(10) - 720(6) - 800(5) = 0$ $\therefore\ C_y = 832\ \text{lb}$

$\Sigma F_y = 0$: $+\uparrow$ $C_y - A_y - 800 = 0$ $\therefore\ A_y = C_y - 800 = 832 - 800 = 32\ \text{lb}$

FBD II

$\Sigma M_B = 0$: $\circlearrowleft +$ $400(2.5) + 720(6) + A_y(5) - A_x(12) = 0$

$\therefore\ A_x = (1/12)[400(2.5) + 720(6) + 32(5)] = 456.7\ \text{lb}$

$\Sigma F_x = 0$: $\underset{\rightarrow}{+}$ $720 - A_x - B_x = 0$ $\therefore\ B_x = 720 - A_x = 720 - 456.7 = 263.3\ \text{lb}$

$\Sigma F_y = 0$: $+\uparrow$ $B_y - 400 - A_y = 0$ $\therefore\ B_y = A_y + 400 = 32 + 400 = 432\ \text{lb}$

FBD I

$\Sigma F_x = 0$: $\underset{\rightarrow}{+}$ $720 - A_x - C_x = 0$ $\therefore\ C_x = 720 - A_x = 720 - 456.7 = 263.3\ \text{lb}$

Therefore, the magnitudes of the pin reactions at A, B and C are:

$A = \sqrt{A_x^2 + A_y^2} = \sqrt{456.7^2 + 32^2} = 458\ \text{lb}$ ◆

$B = \sqrt{B_x^2 + B_y^2} = \sqrt{263.3^2 + 432^2} = 506\ \text{lb}$ ◆

$C = \sqrt{C_x^2 + C_y^2} = \sqrt{263.3^2 + 832^2} = 873\ \text{lb}$ ◆

4.174

From the FBD of the entire structure assuming N_E acts upward (not shown here):

$\Sigma M_A = 0$: $N_E(4) = 6(1.6)$ $N_E = 2.40$ kN

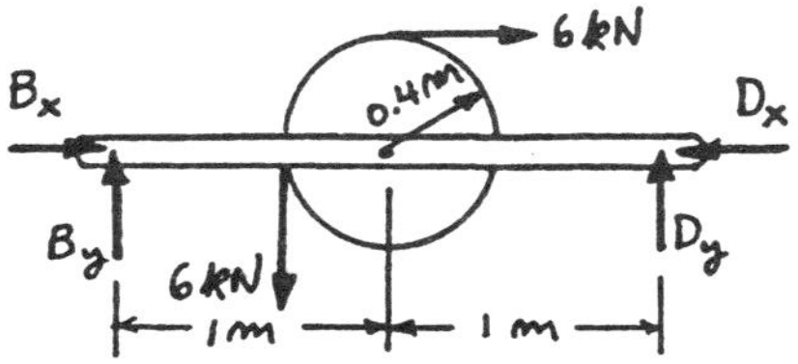

$\Sigma M_B = 0$:

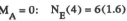

$\circlearrowleft +$ $D_y(2) - 6(0.4) - 6(0.6) = 0$

$\therefore$ $D_y = 3.00$ kN

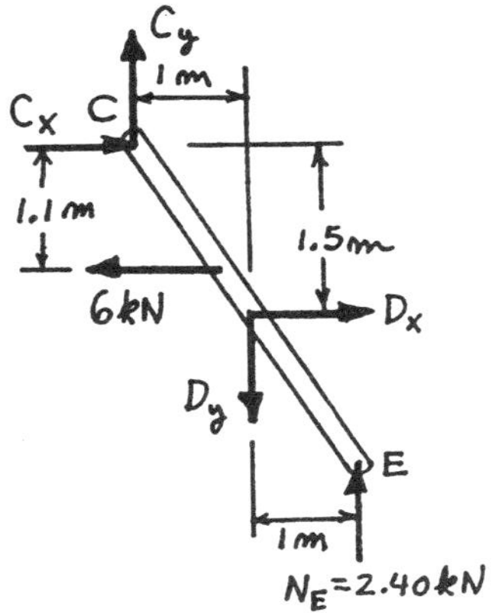

$\Sigma M_C = 0$:

$\circlearrowleft +$ $2.40(2) + D_x(1.5) - D_y(1) - 6(1.1) = 0$

Substituting $D_y = 3.00$ kN, and solving

gives: $D_x = 3.20$ kN

The magnitude of the pin reaction at D is

$$D = \sqrt{3.20^2 + 3.00^2} = 4.39 \text{ kN} \blacklozenge$$

4.175

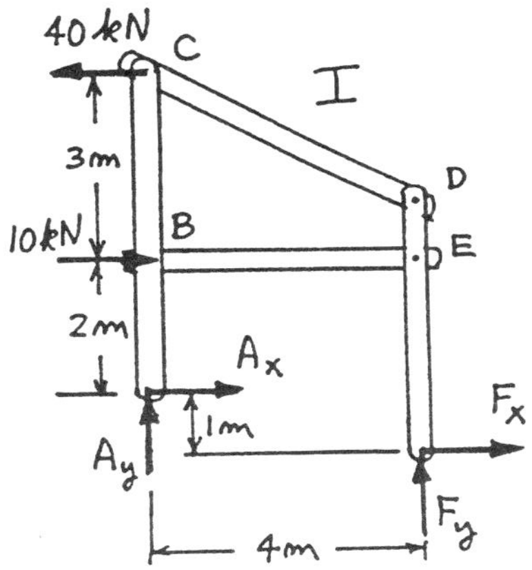

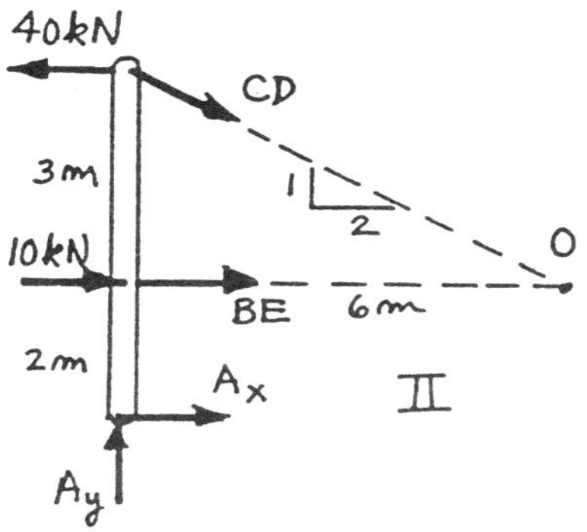

(continued)

CD and BE are two-force members.

FBD I

$\Sigma M_F = 0$: $\circlearrowleft +$ $40(6) - 10(3) - A_x(1) - A_y(4) = 0$

$A_x + 4A_y = 210$ kN•m (1)

FBD II

$\Sigma M_O = 0$: $\circlearrowleft +$ $40(3) + A_x(2) - A_y(6) = 0$

$A_x - 3A_y = -60$ kN•m (2)

FBD I

$\Sigma F_x = 0$: $\xrightarrow{+}$ $F_x + A_x + 10 - 40 = 0$

$\therefore$ $F_x = -25.72$ kN

$\Sigma F_y = 0$: $F_y = -A_y = -38.57$ kN

The magnitude of the pin reaction at F is

$$F = \sqrt{(-25.72)^2 + 38.57^2} = 46.4 \text{ kN} \blacklozenge$$

Solving (1) and (2) gives:

$A_x = 55.72$ kN and $A_y = 38.57$ kN

The magnitude of the pin reaction at A is

$$A = \sqrt{55.72^2 + 38.57^2} = 67.8 \text{ kN} \blacklozenge$$

4.176

FBD of entire frame:

$\Sigma M_D = 0$: $\circlearrowleft +$ $20 - 20 - A_x(2) - A_y(6) = 0$

$A_x = -3A_y$ (1)

FBD of bar AB:

$\Sigma M_B = 0$: $\circlearrowleft +$ $A_x(4) - A_y(3) - 20 = 0$ (2)

Solving (1) and (2) gives:

$A_x = 4.00$ kN and $A_y = -1.333$ kN

$$\therefore A = \sqrt{4.00^2 + (-1.333)^2} = 4.22 \text{ kN} \blacklozenge$$

FBD of entire frame:

$\Sigma F_x = 0$: $D_x = -A_x = -4.00$ kN

$\Sigma F_y = 0$: $D_y = -A_y = 1.333$ kN

Therefore, $D = A = 4.22$ kN $\blacklozenge$

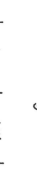

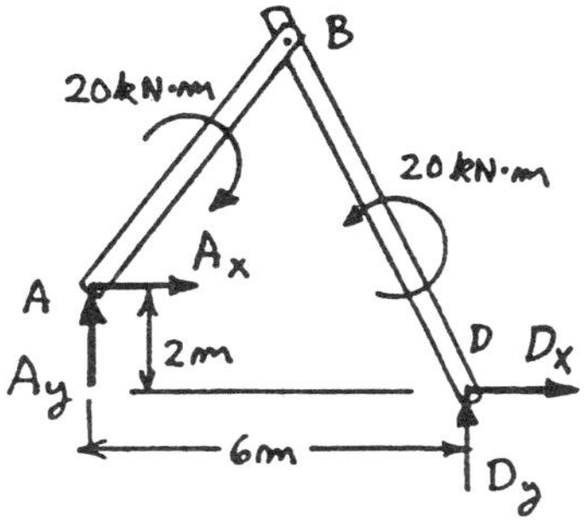

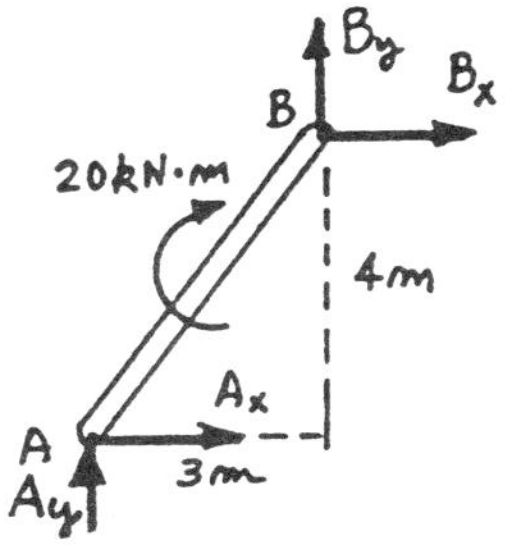

4.177

From FBD of entire truss (not shown here), reactions are $A_x = 0$, $A_y = G_y = 3000$ lb ↑.

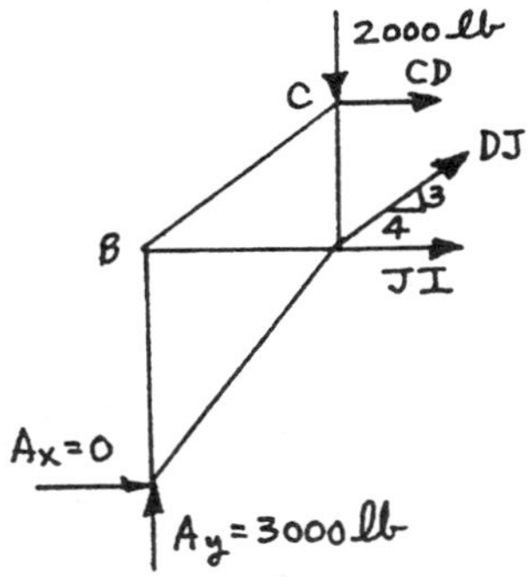

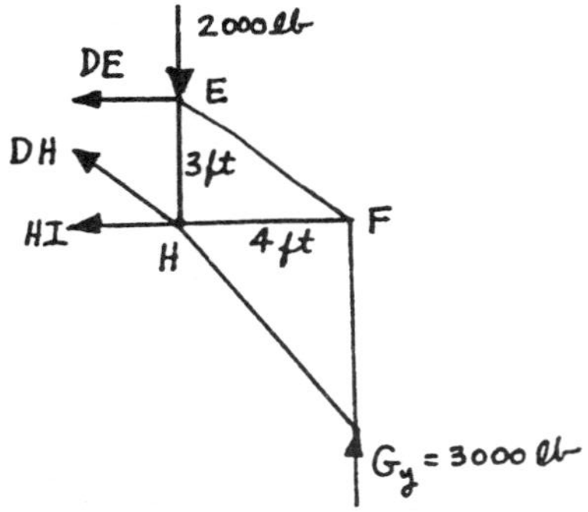

(a) FBD of section shown above

$\Sigma F_y = 0$:

$+\uparrow \quad 0.6DJ - 2000 + 3000 = 0$

$\therefore \quad DJ = -1667 \text{ lb} = 1667 \text{ lb (C)}$ ◆

(b) FBD of section shown above

$\Sigma M_H = 0$

$\circlearrowleft + \quad 3000(4) + DE(3) = 0$

$\therefore \quad DE = -4000 \text{ lb} = 4000 \text{ lb (C)}$ ◆

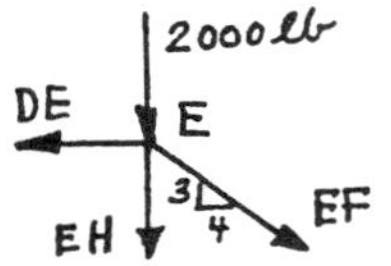

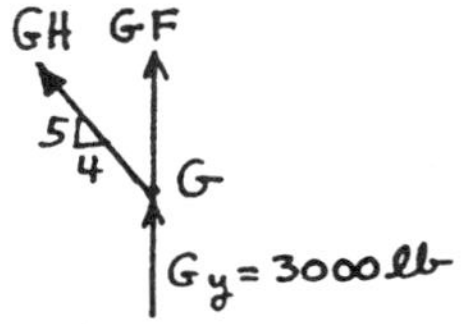

(c) FBD of joint E

$\Sigma F_x = 0$: $\quad \overset{+}{\rightarrow} \quad 0.8EF - DE = 0$

$\therefore \quad EF = DE/0.8 = -4000/0.8$

$= -5000 \text{ lb} = 5000 \text{ lb (C)}$ ◆

(d) FBD of joint G

$\Sigma F_x = 0$: $\quad GH = 0$ ◆

4.178

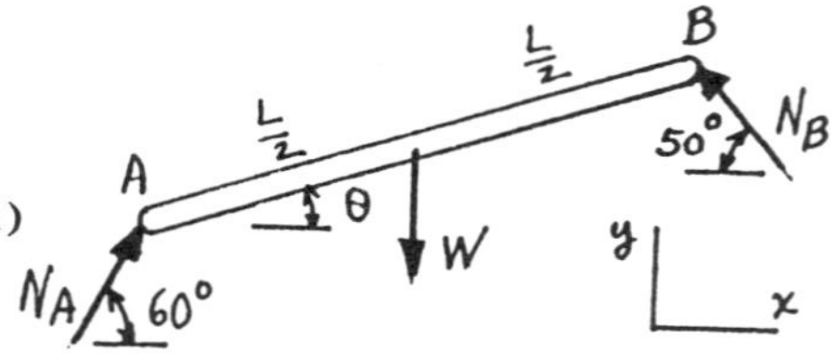

$\Sigma F_x = 0$:

$\overset{+}{\rightarrow} \quad N_A \cos 60^\circ - N_B \cos 50^\circ = 0 \qquad (1)$

$\Sigma F_y = 0$:

$+\uparrow \quad N_A \sin 60^\circ + N_B \sin 50^\circ - W = 0 \qquad (2)$

Solving (1) and (2) gives: $N_A = 0.6840$ W and $N_B = 0.5321$ W

$\Sigma M_A = 0: \quad + \quad N_B \sin 50^\circ(L \cos\theta) + N_B \cos 50^\circ(L \sin\theta) - W(L/2)\cos\theta = 0$

Substituting $N_B = 0.5321$ W, and simplifying gives

$0.3420 \sin\theta = 0.0924 \cos\theta \quad$ from which $\theta = \tan^{-1}(0.0924/0.3420) = 15.12^\circ$ ◆

4.179

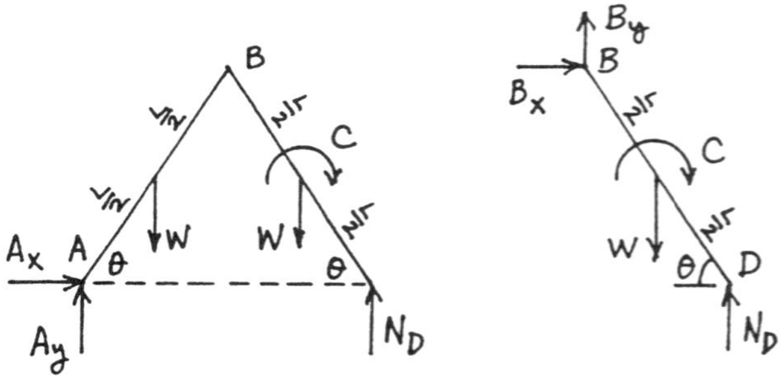

FBD of entire structure

$\Sigma M_A = 0$: $\circlearrowleft + \quad N_D(2 L \cos\theta) - W(L/2)\cos\theta - W(3L/2)\cos\theta - C = 0 \qquad (1)$

FBD of bar BD

$\Sigma M_B = 0$: $\circlearrowleft + \quad N_D L \cos\theta - W(L/2)\cos\theta - C = 0 \qquad (2)$

Solving (1) and (2) gives: $C = WL \cos\theta$ ◆

4.180

(a) FBD I $\Sigma M_B = 0$:

$$\circlearrowleft + \quad \frac{3}{\sqrt{13}} P_{DE}(4) + 200(6) = 0$$

$\therefore\ P_{DE} = -360.5\ \text{kN} = 360.5\ \text{kN (C)}$ ◆

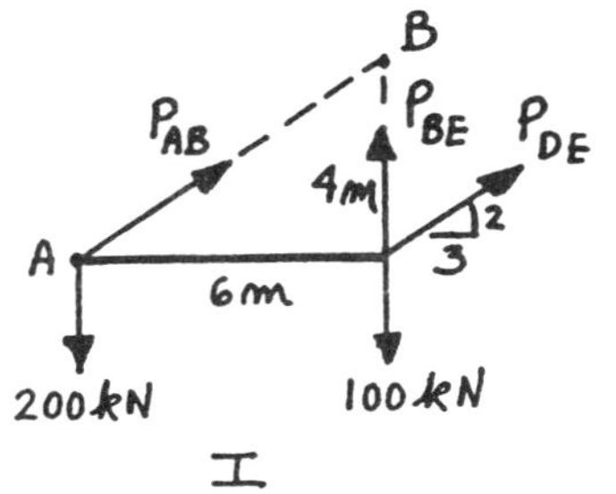

(b) FBD I $\Sigma M_A = 0$:

$$\circlearrowleft + \quad \frac{2}{\sqrt{13}} P_{DE}(6) + P_{BE}(6) - 100(6) = 0$$

$\therefore\ P_{BE} = 100 - \frac{2}{\sqrt{13}} P_{DE} = 100 - \frac{2}{\sqrt{13}}(-360.5) = 300\ \text{kN (T)}$

(c) FBD II $\Sigma M_D = 0$:

$$\circlearrowleft + \quad 200(9) + 100(3) - \frac{3}{\sqrt{13}} P_{BC}(4) = 0$$

$\therefore\ P_{BC} = 631\ \text{kN (T)}$ ◆

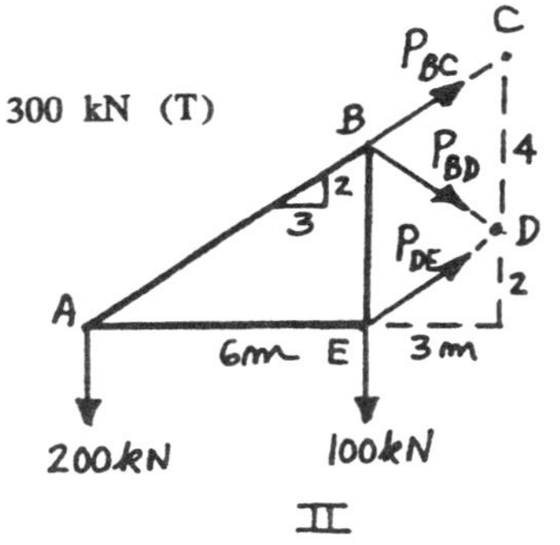

4.181

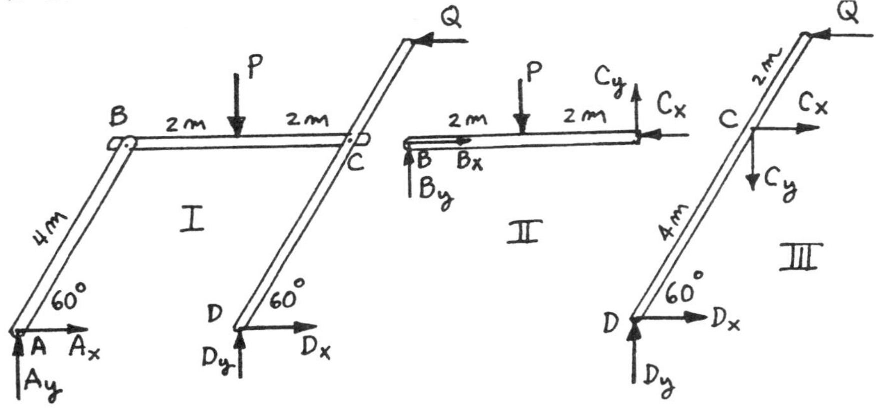

FBD I $\Sigma M_A = 0$: $\circlearrowleft +\ D_y(4) - P(4\cos 60^\circ + 2) + Q(6\sin 60^\circ) = 0$

$D_y = P - 1.299\,Q$ (1)

(continued)

FBD II $\Sigma M_B = 0$: $\circlearrowleft +\ C_y(4) - P(2) = 0$ $\therefore\ C_y = \frac{P}{2}$ (2)

FBD III $\Sigma F_y = 0$: $D_y = C_y$ (3)

Combining (1), (2), and (3): $\frac{P}{2} = P - 1.299\,Q$ which gives $P = 2.60\,Q$ ◆

4.182

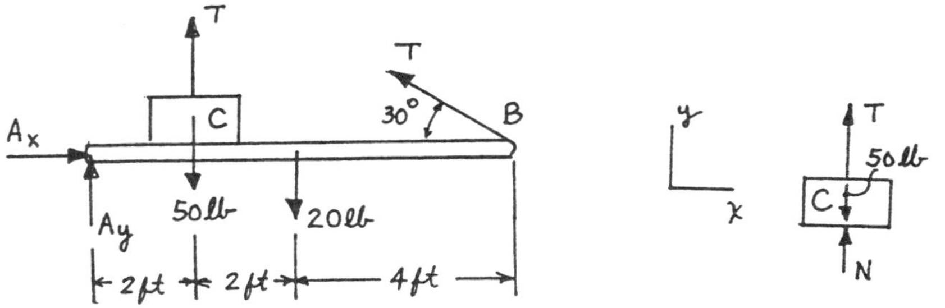

$\Sigma M_A = 0$:

$\circlearrowleft +\ T\sin 30^\circ(8) + T(2) - 50(2) - 20(4) = 0$

$T = 30.0$ lb

$\Sigma F_y = 0$: $+\uparrow$ $T - 50 + N = 0$

$N = 50 - T = 50 - 30 = 20$ lb ◆

4.183

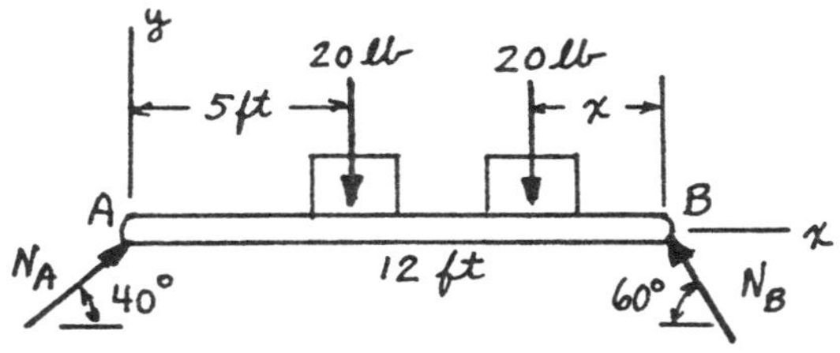

$\Sigma F_x = 0$: $\overset{+}{\rightarrow}$ $N_A\cos 40^\circ - N_B\cos 60^\circ = 0$ $\therefore\ N_A = 0.6527\,N_B$ (1)

$\Sigma F_y = 0$: $+\uparrow$ $N_A\sin 40^\circ + N_B\sin 60^\circ - 40 = 0$ (2)

Solving (1) and (2) gives: $N_A = 20.308$ lb and $N_B = 31.115$ lb

$\Sigma M_B = 0$: $\circlearrowleft +\ 20(7) + 20x - N_A\sin 40^\circ(12) = 0$

$$\therefore\ x = \frac{20.308\sin 40^\circ(12) - 140}{20} = 0.832\ \text{ft}$$ ◆

4.184

From the FBD of the entire truss (not shown here), the reactions acting on the truss are:

$A_x = 1500$ lb ← ; $A_y = 1500$ lb ↑ ; $N_E = 6500$ lb ↑

(a) The FBD of the section shown contains three unknowns: P_{BC}, P_{BF}, and P_{AF}. Let O be the point where P_{BC} and P_{AF} intersect. From geometry, the distances $\overline{AG}$ and $\overline{OG}$ are related by:

$$\frac{4+\overline{AG}}{\overline{OG}} = \frac{4+\frac{2}{3}(\overline{OG})}{\overline{OG}} = \frac{4}{3}$$

which gives $\overline{AG} = 4$ ft and $\overline{OG} = 6$ ft.

$\Sigma M_O = 0$:

$\circlearrowleft + \; 1500(6) + 1500(4) - 1500(8) - P_{BF}(8) = 0$

$\therefore P_{BF} = 375$ lb (T) ◆

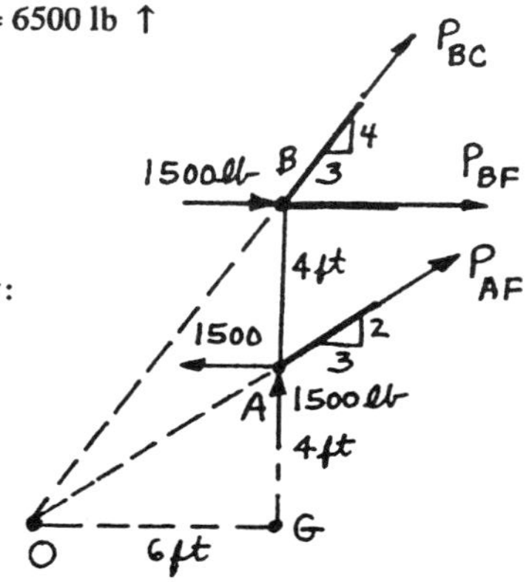

(b) FBD of joint E

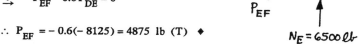

$\Sigma F_y = 0$: $+\uparrow$ $6500 + 0.8P_{DE} = 0$ $\therefore P_{DE} = -8125$ lb

$\Sigma F_x = 0$: $\overset{+}{\rightarrow}$ $-P_{EF} - 0.6P_{DE} = 0$

$\therefore P_{EF} = -0.6(-8125) = 4875$ lb (T) ◆

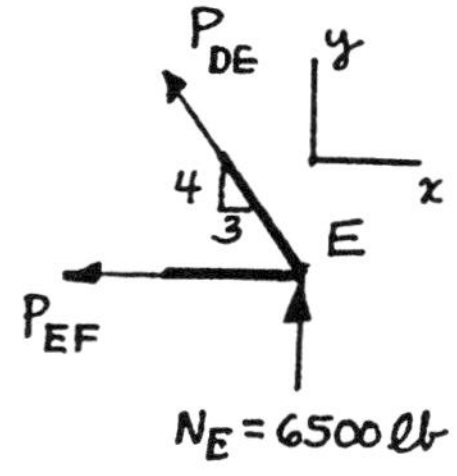

4.185

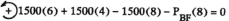

$\Sigma M_B = 0$: $\circlearrowleft +$ $200 \sin 30^{\circ}(2) - T_A(6) = 0$

$T_A = 33.3$ lb ◆

$\Sigma M_A = 0$: $\circlearrowleft +$ $T_B(6) - 200 \sin 30^{\circ}(4) = 0$

$T_B = 66.7$ lb ◆

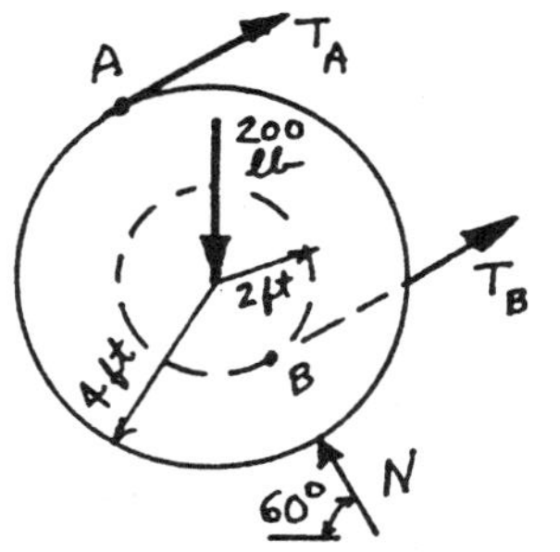

4.186

FBD of entire stool (not shown here)

$\Sigma M_E = 0$:

$\circlearrowleft +$ $W(12) - N_A(18) = 0$

$N_A = 2W/3$

FBD of seat CD

$\Sigma M_D = 0$:

$\circlearrowleft +$ $N_C(18) - W(6) = 0$

$N_C = W/3$

FBD of bar ABC

$\Sigma M_B = 0$:

$\circlearrowleft +$ $400(4) - N_A(9) - N_C(9) = 0$

$1600 - (2W/3)(9) - (W/3)(9) = 0$

which gives $W = 178$ lb ◆

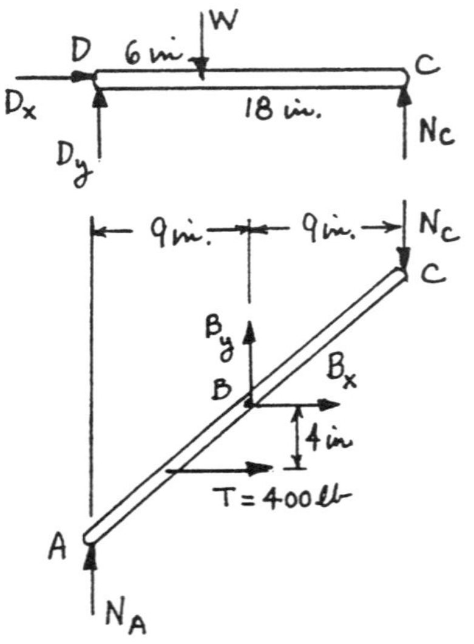

4.187

From the FBD of the entire truss (not shown here):

$D_x = 0$ and $D_y = 30$ kN ↑

(a) FBD of section shown

$\Sigma M_F = 0$:

$\circlearrowleft +$ $20(4) - 30(8) - (0.6)P_{BD}(8) = 0$

$\therefore P_{BD} = -33.33$ kN = 33.33 kN (C) ◆

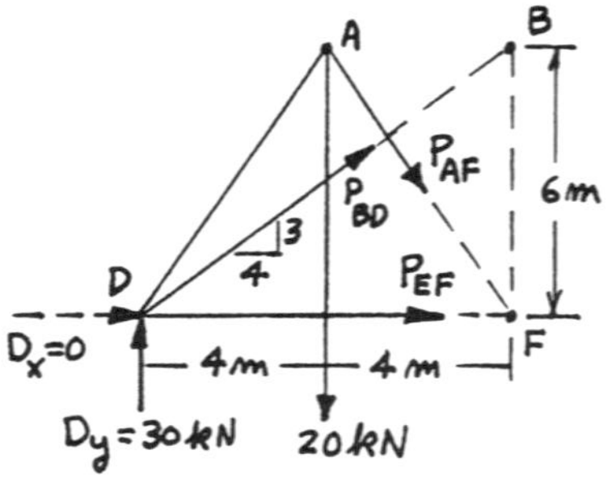

(b) FBD of pin B

$\Sigma F_x = 0$: $P_{BD} = P_{BH}$

$\Sigma F_y = 0$: $+\uparrow$ $-0.6P_{BD} - P_{BF} - 0.6P_{BH} = 0$

$\therefore P_{BF} = -2(0.6P_{BD})$

$= -2(0.6)(-33.33) = 40.0$ kN (T) ◆

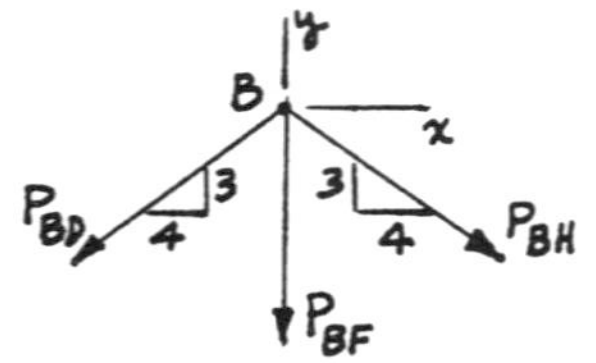

4.188

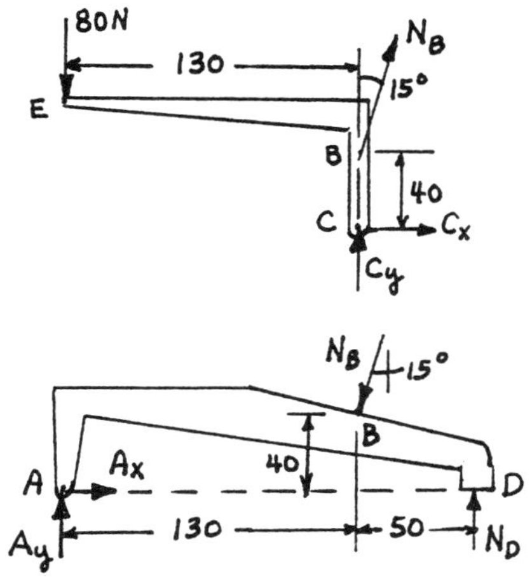

FBD of CBE

$\Sigma M_C = 0$:

$\circlearrowleft + \; 80(130) - N_B \sin 15^\circ (40) = 0$

$\therefore \; N_B = 1004.6 \text{ N}$

FBD of AD

$\Sigma M_A = 0$:

$\circlearrowleft + \; N_D(180) - N_B \cos 15^\circ (130)$

$+ N_B \sin 15^\circ (40) = 0$

$$\therefore \; N_D = \frac{1004.6(130\cos 15^\circ - 40\sin 15^\circ)}{180} = 643 \text{ N} \; ◆$$

5.1

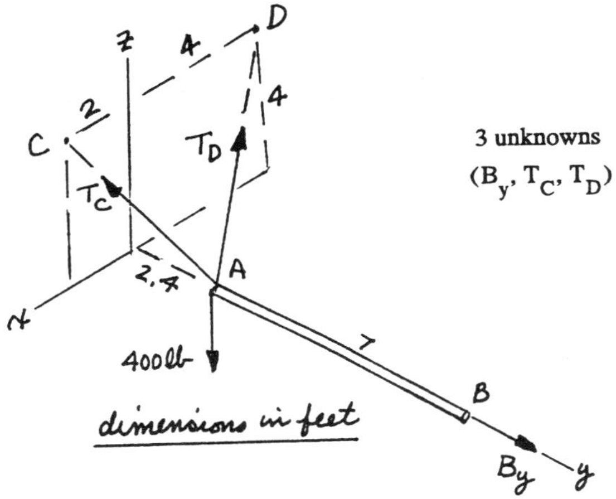

3 unknowns ◆

(B_y, T_C, T_D)

5.2

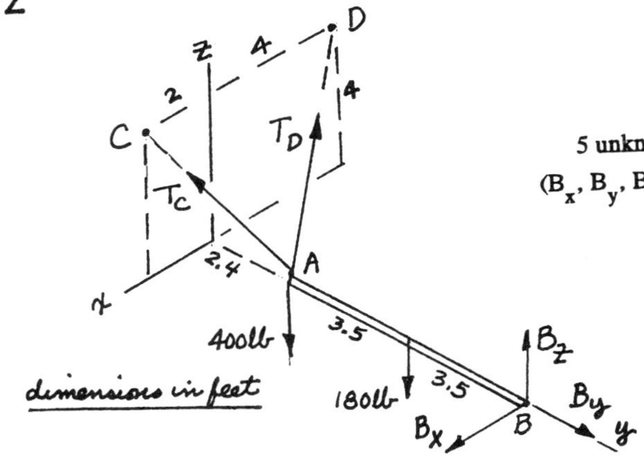

5 unknowns ◆

$(B_x, B_y, B_z, T_C, T_D)$

5.3

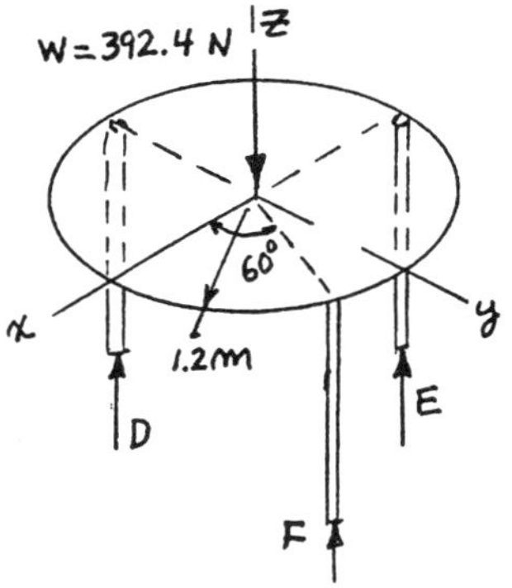

$W = 40(9.81) = 392.4 \text{ N}$

3 unknowns ◆

(D, E, F)

5.4

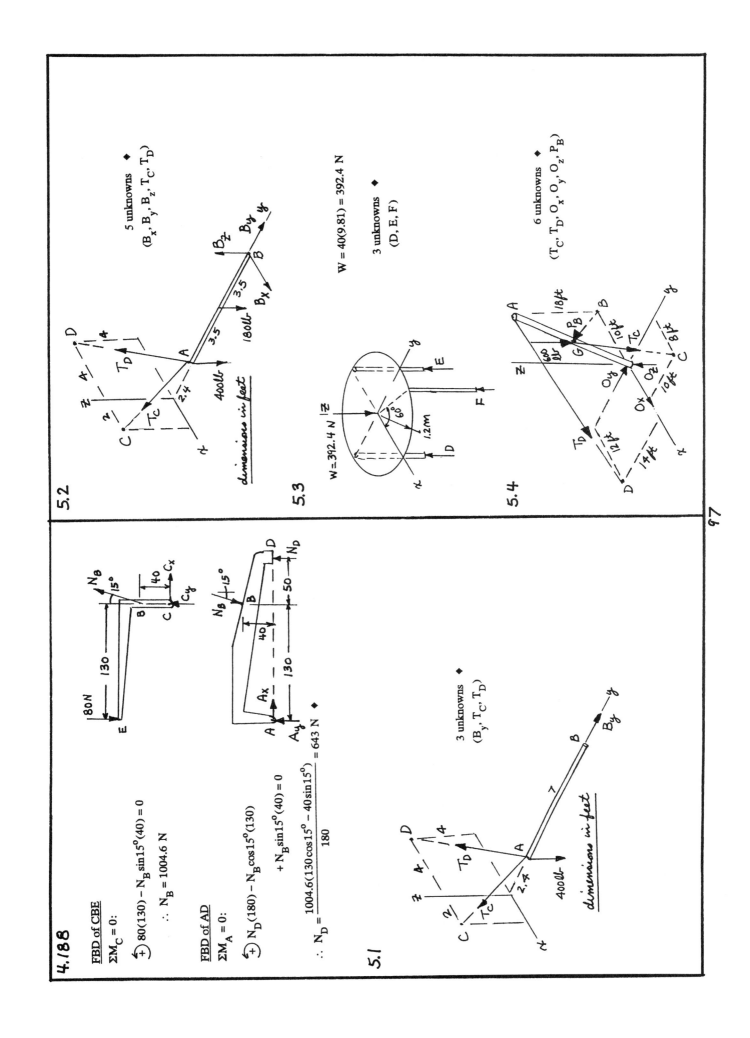

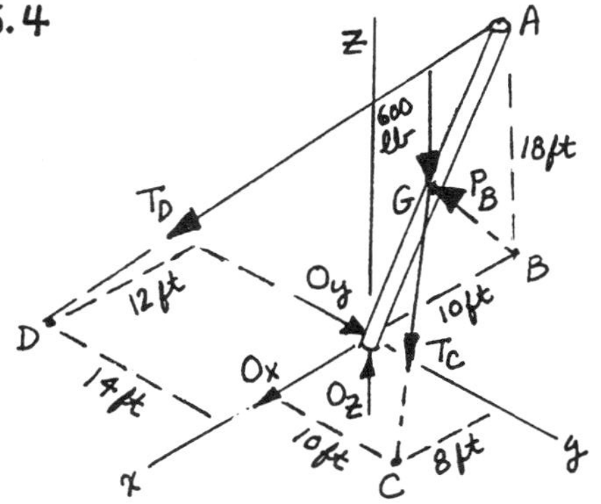

6 unknowns ◆

$(T_C, T_D, O_x, O_y, O_z, P_B)$

5.5

Mass/length = 40 kg/4 m = 10 kg/m

$m_{AO} = 10(2.5) = 25$ kg; $m_{AB} = 15$ kg

$W_{AO} = 25(9.81) = 245.3$ N

$W_{AB} = 15(9.81) = 147.2$ N

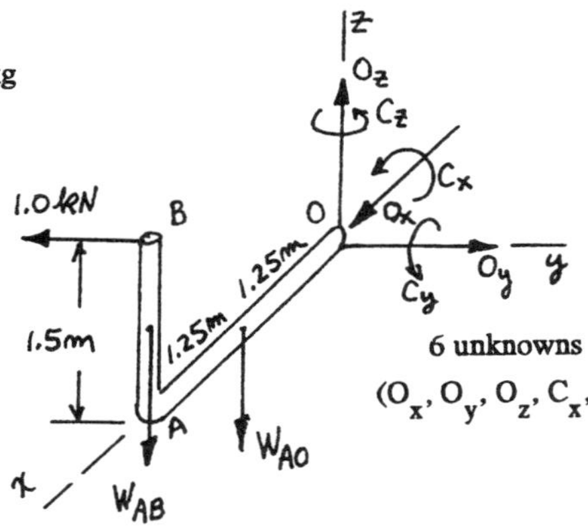

6 unknowns ◆

$(O_x, O_y, O_z, C_x, C_y, C_z)$

5.6

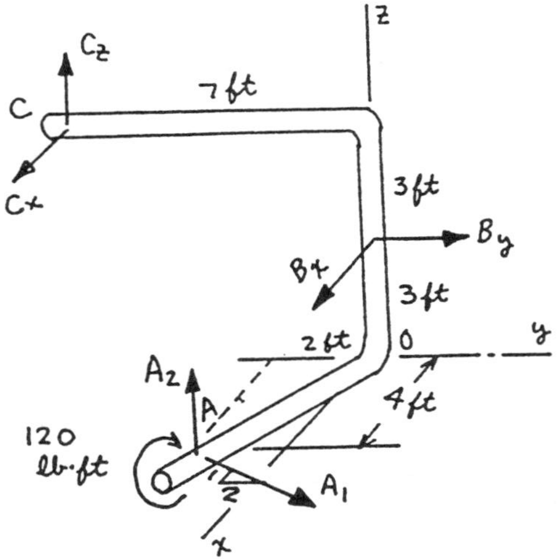

6 unknowns ◆

$(A_1, A_2, B_x, B_y, C_x, C_z)$

5.7

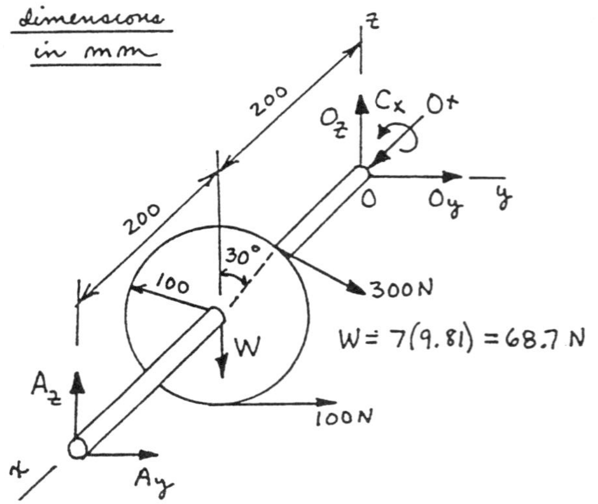

6 unknowns ◆

$(O_x, O_y, O_z, C_x, A_y, A_z)$

5.8

6 unknowns ◆

$(B_x, B_y, B_z, A_x, A_y, T_{CD})$

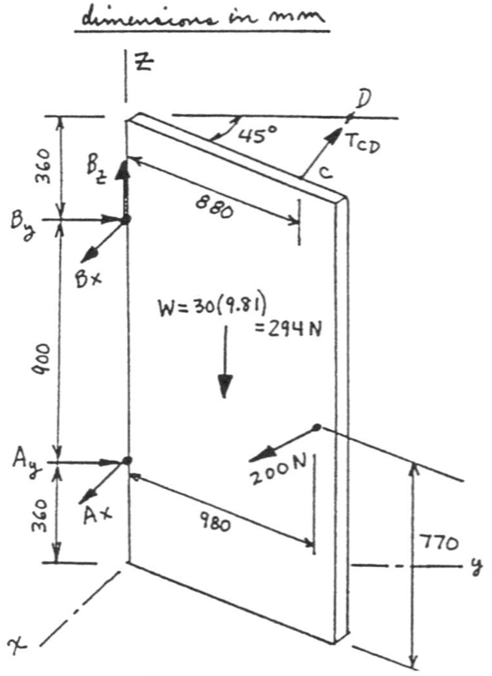

5.9

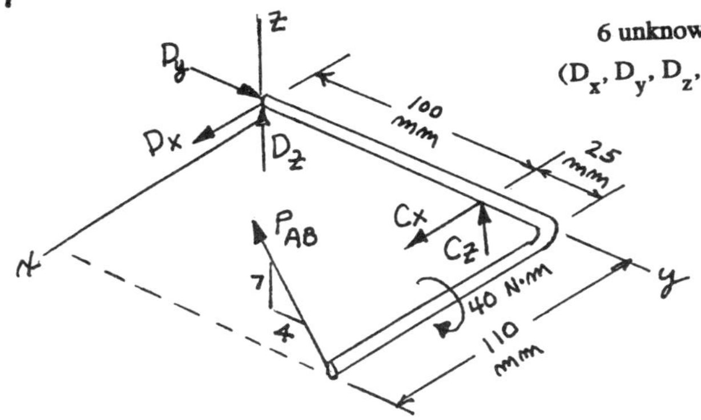

6 unknowns ◆
(D_x, D_y, D_z, C_x, C_z, P_{AB})

5.10

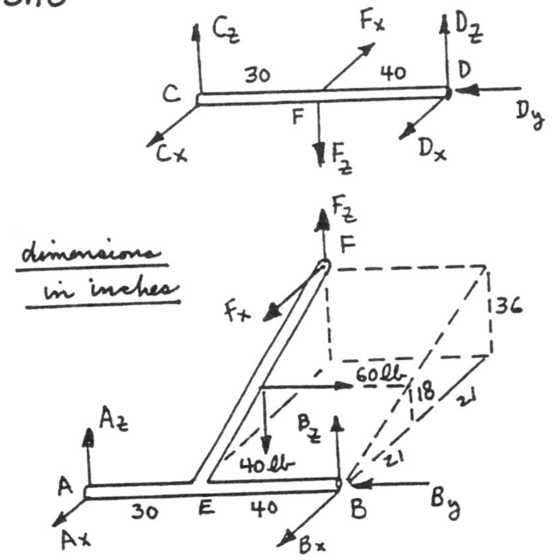

12 unknowns ◆
(A_x, A_z, B_x, B_y, B_z,
C_x, C_z, D_x, D_y, D_z, F_x, F_z)

5.11

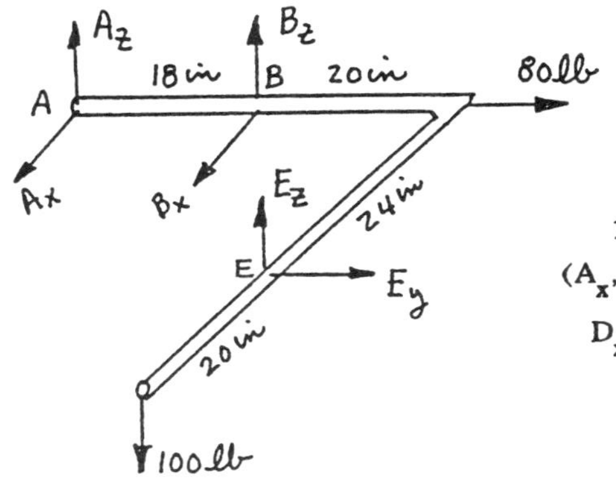

12 unknowns ◆
(A_x, A_z, B_x, B_z, E_y, E_z,
D_x, D_y, D_z, C_x, C_y, C_z)

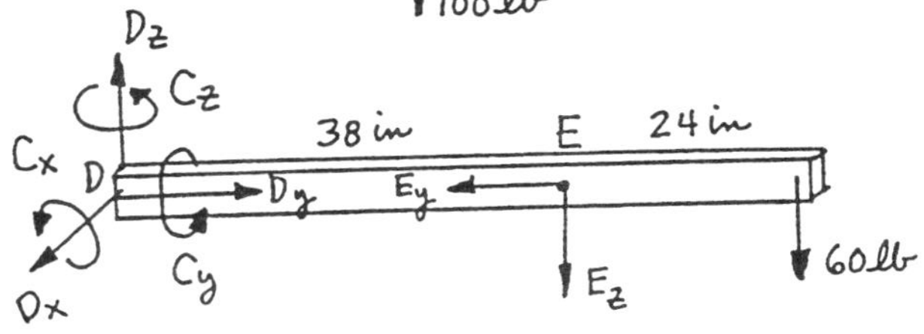

5.12

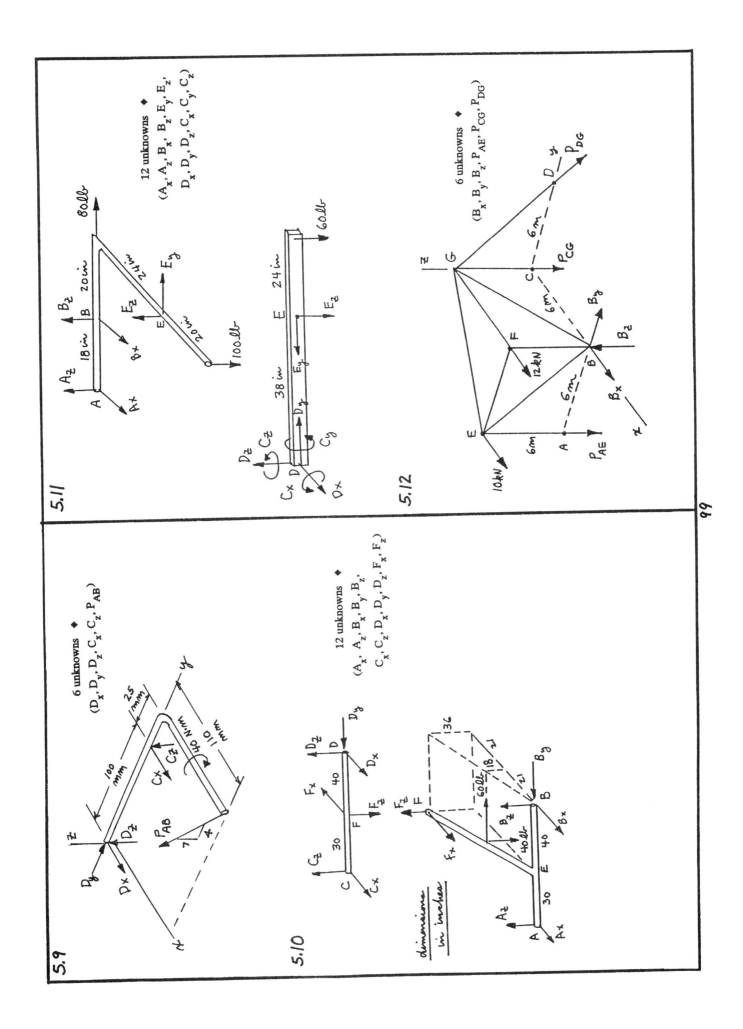

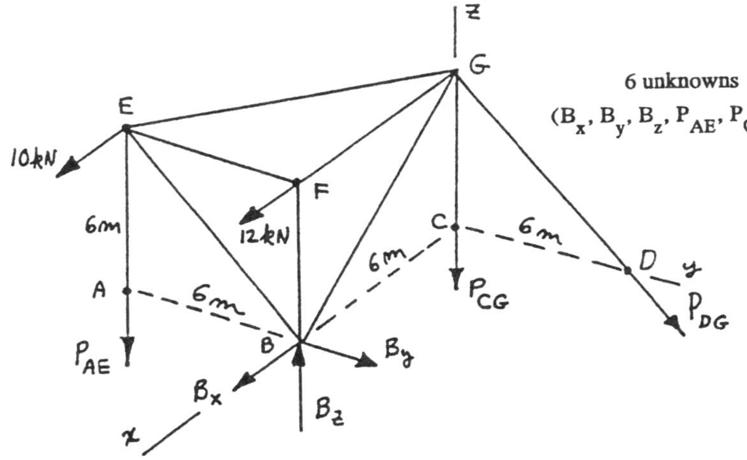

6 unknowns ◆
(B_x, B_y, B_z, P_{AE}, P_{CG}, P_{DG})

5.13

$$\Sigma M_{DB} = \left(\mathbf{r}_{BA} \times \mathbf{T}_{AC} \bullet \vec{\lambda}_{DB}\right) + \left(\mathbf{r}_{BA} \times \mathbf{W} \bullet \vec{\lambda}_{DB}\right) = 0 \quad \text{(gives } T_{AC}\text{)}$$

$$\mathbf{r}_{BA} = -2\mathbf{i} - 2.5\mathbf{k}\ \text{m} \qquad \mathbf{W} = -1500\mathbf{k}\ \text{kN} \qquad \vec{\lambda}_{DB} = \frac{2\mathbf{i} - 1.5\mathbf{j}}{2.5}$$

$$\mathbf{T}_{AC} = T_{AC}\left(\frac{-3\mathbf{i} - 1.2\mathbf{j} + 2.5\mathbf{k}}{4.085}\right) = T_{AC}(-0.7344\mathbf{i} - 0.2938\mathbf{j} + 0.6120\mathbf{k})$$

$$\therefore\ \Sigma M_{DB} = \frac{T_{AC}}{2.5}\begin{vmatrix} -2 & 0 & -2.5 \\ -0.7344 & -0.2938 & 0.6120 \\ 2 & -1.5 & 0 \end{vmatrix} + \frac{1}{2.5}\begin{vmatrix} -2 & 0 & -2.5 \\ 0 & 0 & -1500 \\ 2 & -1.5 & 0 \end{vmatrix} = 0$$

Cancelling 2.5, and expanding the determinants: $-6.059T_{AC} + 4500 = 0$

which gives $T_{AC} = 743$ kN ◆

5.14

$$\Sigma M_{BC} = \left(\mathbf{r}_{BA} \times \mathbf{T}_{AD} \bullet \vec{\lambda}_{BC}\right) + \left(\mathbf{r}_{BA} \times \mathbf{W} \bullet \vec{\lambda}_{BC}\right) = 0 \quad \text{(gives } T_{AD}\text{)}$$

$$\mathbf{r}_{BA} = -2\mathbf{i} - 2.5\mathbf{k}\ \text{m} \qquad \mathbf{W} = -1500\mathbf{k}\ \text{kN} \qquad \vec{\lambda}_{BC} = \frac{-5\mathbf{i} - 1.2\mathbf{j}}{5.142}$$

$$\mathbf{T}_{AD} = T_{AD}\left(\frac{1.5\mathbf{j} + 2.5\mathbf{k}}{2.915}\right) = T_{AD}(0.5146\mathbf{j} + 0.8576\mathbf{k})$$

$$\therefore\ \Sigma M_{BC} = \frac{T_{AD}}{5.142}\begin{vmatrix} -2 & 0 & -2.5 \\ 0 & 0.5146 & 0.8576 \\ -5 & -1.2 & 0 \end{vmatrix} + \frac{1}{5.142}\begin{vmatrix} -2 & 0 & -2.5 \\ 0 & 0 & -1500 \\ -5 & -1.2 & 0 \end{vmatrix} = 0$$

Cancelling 5.142, and expanding the determinants: $-8.491\,T_{AD} + 3600 = 0$

which gives $T_{AD} = 424$ kN ◆

5.15

$$\Sigma M_{OE} = \left(\mathbf{r}_{OA} \times \mathbf{T}_{AD} \bullet \vec{\lambda}_{OE}\right) + \left(\mathbf{r}_{OB} \times \mathbf{P} \bullet \vec{\lambda}_{OE}\right) = 0 \quad \text{(gives } T_{AD}\text{)}$$

$$\mathbf{r}_{OA} = 3\mathbf{j}\ \text{ft} \qquad \mathbf{r}_{OB} = 5\mathbf{j}\ \text{ft} \qquad \mathbf{P} = -8000\mathbf{k}\ \text{lb} \qquad \vec{\lambda}_{OE} = \frac{-3.5\mathbf{i} + 3\mathbf{k}}{4.610}$$

$$\mathbf{T}_{AD} = T_{AD}\left(\frac{2.5\mathbf{i} - 3\mathbf{j} + 3\mathbf{k}}{4.924}\right) = T_{AD}(0.5077\mathbf{i} - 0.6093\mathbf{j} + 0.6093\mathbf{k})$$

$$\therefore\ \Sigma M_{OE} = \frac{T_{AD}}{4.610}\begin{vmatrix} 0 & 3 & 0 \\ 0.5077 & -0.6093 & 0.6093 \\ -3.5 & 0 & 3 \end{vmatrix} + \frac{1}{4.610}\begin{vmatrix} 0 & 5 & 0 \\ 0 & 0 & -8000 \\ -3.5 & 0 & 3 \end{vmatrix} = 0$$

Cancelling 4.610, and expanding the determinants: $-10.97T_{AD} + 140\,000 = 0$

which gives $T_{AD} = 12\,760$ lb ◆

5.16

$$\Sigma M_{OD} = \left(\mathbf{r}_{OC} \times \mathbf{T}_{CE} \bullet \vec{\lambda}_{OD}\right) + \left(\mathbf{r}_{OB} \times \mathbf{P} \bullet \vec{\lambda}_{OD}\right) = 0 \quad \text{(gives } T_{CE}\text{)}$$

$$\mathbf{r}_{OC} = 6\mathbf{j}\ \text{ft} \qquad \mathbf{r}_{OB} = 5\mathbf{j}\ \text{ft} \qquad \mathbf{P} = -8000\mathbf{k}\ \text{lb} \qquad \vec{\lambda}_{OD} = \frac{2.5\mathbf{i} + 3\mathbf{k}}{3.905}$$

$$\mathbf{T}_{CE} = T_{CE}\left(\frac{-3.5\mathbf{i} - 6\mathbf{j} + 3\mathbf{k}}{7.566}\right) = T_{CE}(-0.4626\mathbf{i} - 0.7930\mathbf{j} + 0.3965\mathbf{k})$$

$$\therefore\ \Sigma M_{OE} = \frac{T_{CE}}{3.905}\begin{vmatrix} 0 & 6 & 0 \\ -0.4626 & -0.7930 & 0.3965 \\ 2.5 & 0 & 3 \end{vmatrix} + \frac{1}{3.905}\begin{vmatrix} 0 & 5 & 0 \\ 0 & 0 & -8000 \\ 2.5 & 0 & 3 \end{vmatrix} = 0$$

Cancelling 3.905, and expanding the determinants: $14.27T_{CE} - 100\,000 = 0$

which gives $T_{CE} = 7010$ lb ◆

5.17

$\Sigma M_{DE} = 0$ (gives O_y)

$-8000(5) + O_y(3) = 0 \qquad \therefore\ O_y = 13\,330$ lb ◆

5.18

$$\Sigma M_{AC} = (\mathbf{r}_{AB} \times T_B \bullet \vec{\lambda}_{AC}) + (\mathbf{r}_{AG} \times \mathbf{W} \bullet \vec{\lambda}_{AC}) = 0 \qquad \text{(gives } T_B\text{)}$$

$\mathbf{r}_{AB} = -3.6\mathbf{i} + 0.8\mathbf{j}$ m $\qquad \mathbf{r}_{AG} = -2.4\mathbf{i} + 1.0\mathbf{j}$ m $\qquad \mathbf{W} = -60\mathbf{k}$ kN

$\vec{\lambda}_{AC} = \dfrac{-3.6\mathbf{i} + 3.0\mathbf{j}}{4.686} \qquad \mathbf{T}_B = T_B\mathbf{k}$ kN

$$\therefore\ \Sigma M_{AC} = \frac{T_B}{4.686}\begin{vmatrix} -3.6 & 0.8 & 0 \\ 0 & 0 & 1 \\ -3.6 & 3 & 0 \end{vmatrix} + \frac{1}{4.686}\begin{vmatrix} -2.4 & 1.0 & 0 \\ 0 & 0 & -60 \\ -3.6 & 3 & 0 \end{vmatrix} = 0$$

Cancelling 4.686, and expanding the determinants: $\quad 7.920T_B - 216 = 0$

which gives $\quad T_B = 27.3$ kN ◆

5.19

$$\Sigma M_{AB} = (\mathbf{r}_{AC} \times T_C \bullet \vec{\lambda}_{AB}) + (\mathbf{r}_{AG} \times \mathbf{W} \bullet \vec{\lambda}_{AB}) = 0 \qquad \text{(gives } T_C\text{)}$$

$\mathbf{r}_{AC} = -3.6\mathbf{i} + 3.0\mathbf{j}$ m $\qquad \mathbf{r}_{AG} = -2.4\mathbf{i} + 1.0\mathbf{j}$ m $\qquad \mathbf{W} = -60\mathbf{k}$ kN

$\vec{\lambda}_{AB} = \dfrac{-3.6\mathbf{i} + 0.8\mathbf{j}}{3.688} \qquad \mathbf{T}_C = T_C\mathbf{k}$ kN

$$\therefore\ \Sigma M_{AB} = \frac{T_C}{3.688}\begin{vmatrix} -3.6 & 3.0 & 0 \\ 0 & 0 & 1 \\ -3.6 & 0.8 & 0 \end{vmatrix} + \frac{1}{3.688}\begin{vmatrix} -2.4 & 1.0 & 0 \\ 0 & 0 & -60 \\ -3.6 & 0.8 & 0 \end{vmatrix} = 0$$

Cancelling 3.688, and expanding the determinants: $\quad -7.920T_C + 100.8 = 0$

which gives $\quad T_C = 12.73$ kN ◆

5.20

$$\Sigma M_{OD} = (\mathbf{r}_{OA} \times T_{AE} \bullet \vec{\lambda}_{OD}) + (\mathbf{r}_{OB} \times \mathbf{P} \bullet \vec{\lambda}_{OD}) + (\mathbf{C} \bullet \vec{\lambda}_{OD}) = 0 \qquad \text{(gives } T_{AE}\text{)}$$

$\mathbf{r}_{OA} = 4\mathbf{i}$ ft $\qquad \mathbf{r}_{OB} = 4\mathbf{i} + 2\mathbf{j}$ ft $\qquad \vec{\lambda}_{OD} = \dfrac{4\mathbf{i} + 7\mathbf{j} + 2\mathbf{k}}{8.307}$

$\mathbf{P} = -2000\mathbf{k}$ lb $\qquad \mathbf{C} = -6000\mathbf{k}$ lb•ft

$$\mathbf{T}_{AE} = T_{AE}\left(\frac{-4\mathbf{i} + 7\mathbf{j} + 4\mathbf{k}}{9}\right) = T_{AE}(-0.4444\mathbf{i} + 0.7778\mathbf{j} + 0.4444\mathbf{k})$$

$$\therefore\ \Sigma M_{OD} = \frac{T_{AE}}{8.307}\begin{vmatrix} 4 & 0 & 0 \\ -0.4444 & 0.7778 & 0.4444 \\ 4 & 7 & 2 \end{vmatrix}$$

$$+ \frac{1}{8.307}\begin{vmatrix} 4 & 2 & 0 \\ 0 & 0 & -2000 \\ 4 & 7 & 2 \end{vmatrix} + (-6000\mathbf{k}) \bullet \left(\frac{4\mathbf{i} + 7\mathbf{j} + 2\mathbf{k}}{8.307}\right) = 0$$

Cancelling 8.307, and expanding: $\quad -6.221T_{AE} + 40\,000 - 12\,000 = 0$

which gives $\quad T_{AE} = 4500$ lb ◆

5.21

$\Sigma M_x = 0$: $\quad 4P_{BC} - 2W = 0 \qquad \therefore\ P_{BC} = W/2 = 60/2 = 30$ lb ◆

$\Sigma M_z = 0$: $\quad 4A_y = 0 \qquad \therefore\ A_y = 0$ ◆

$\Sigma F_y = 0$: $\quad A_y + O_y = 0 \qquad \therefore\ O_y = 0$ ◆

$\Sigma M_y = 0$: $\quad -4A_z + 2W - 1.5P_{BC} = 0 \qquad \therefore\ A_z = (1/4)[2(60) - 1.5(30)] = 18.75$ lb ◆

$\Sigma F_z = 0$: $\quad O_z + A_z - W + P_{BC} = 0 \qquad \therefore\ O_z = -18.75 + 60 - 30 = 11.25$ lb ◆

$\Sigma F_x = 0$: $\quad O_x = 0$ ◆

5.22

Since the force system is concurrent: $\Sigma \mathbf{F} = \mathbf{T}_{BC} + \mathbf{T}_{BD} + \mathbf{R}_A + \mathbf{P} = \mathbf{0}$

$$\mathbf{T}_{BC} = T_{BC}\left(\frac{2\mathbf{i} - 6\mathbf{j} + 6\mathbf{k}}{8.718}\right) = T_{BC}(0.2294\mathbf{i} - 0.6882\mathbf{j} + 0.6882\mathbf{k})$$

$$\mathbf{T}_{BD} = T_{BD}\left(\frac{-4\mathbf{i} - 6\mathbf{j} + 2\mathbf{k}}{7.483}\right) = T_{BD}(-0.5345\mathbf{i} - 0.8018\mathbf{j} + 0.2673\mathbf{k})$$

$$\mathbf{R}_A = R_A\left(\frac{-2\mathbf{i} + 6\mathbf{j} + 3\mathbf{k}}{7}\right) = R_A(-0.2857\mathbf{i} + 0.8571\mathbf{j} + 0.4286\mathbf{k})$$

$$\mathbf{P} = 12\mathbf{i} - 16\mathbf{k}\ \text{kN}$$

$$\Sigma F_x = 0: \quad 0.2294T_{BC} - 0.5345T_{BD} - 0.2857R_A + 12 = 0 \qquad (1)$$

$$\Sigma F_y = 0: \quad -0.6882T_{BC} - 0.8018T_{BD} + 0.8571R_A = 0 \qquad (2)$$

$$\Sigma F_z = 0: \quad 0.6882T_{BC} + 0.2673T_{BD} + 0.4286R_A - 16 = 0 \qquad (3)$$

Solving (1), (2) and (3) simultaneously gives

$$T_{BC} = 5.82\ \text{kN}; \quad T_{BD} = 14.95\ \text{kN}; \quad R_A = 18.66\ \text{kN}\ \blacklozenge$$

5.23

$$\Sigma \mathbf{M}_O = (\mathbf{r}_{OA} \times \mathbf{T}_{AD}) + (\mathbf{r}_{OB} \times \mathbf{T}_{BC}) + (\mathbf{r}_{OA} \times \mathbf{W}) = \mathbf{0}$$

$$\mathbf{r}_{OA} = 2\mathbf{j}\ \text{ft} \quad \mathbf{r}_{OB} = 4\mathbf{j}\ \text{ft} \quad \mathbf{W} = -120\mathbf{k}\ \text{lb}$$

$$\mathbf{T}_{AD} = T_{AD}\left(\frac{-3\mathbf{i} - 2\mathbf{j} + 2\mathbf{k}}{\sqrt{17}}\right) \qquad \mathbf{T}_{BC} = T_{BC}\left(\frac{3\mathbf{i} - 4\mathbf{j}}{5}\right) = T_{BC}(0.6\mathbf{i} - 0.8\mathbf{j})\ \text{lb}$$

$$\Sigma \mathbf{M}_O = \frac{T_{AD}}{\sqrt{17}}\begin{vmatrix} \mathbf{i} & \mathbf{j} & \mathbf{k} \\ 0 & 2 & 0 \\ -3 & -2 & 2 \end{vmatrix} + T_{BC}\begin{vmatrix} \mathbf{i} & \mathbf{j} & \mathbf{k} \\ 0 & 4 & 0 \\ 0.6 & -0.8 & 0 \end{vmatrix} + \begin{vmatrix} \mathbf{i} & \mathbf{j} & \mathbf{k} \\ 0 & 2 & 0 \\ 0 & 0 & -120 \end{vmatrix} = \mathbf{0}$$

Expanding the determinants, and equating like components gives:

(i-components) $\quad \dfrac{4T_{AD}}{\sqrt{17}} - 240 = 0 \qquad \therefore\ T_{AD} = 247.4\ \text{lb}\ \blacklozenge$

(k-components) $\quad \dfrac{6T_{AD}}{\sqrt{17}} - 2.4T_{BC} = 0 \qquad \therefore\ T_{BC} = \dfrac{6(247.4)}{2.4\sqrt{17}} = 150.0\ \text{lb}\ \blacklozenge$

5.24

$$(\Sigma M_B)_x = 0: \ -A_y(0.3) + C_z(1.0) + 600(0.5) = 0 \qquad (1)$$

$$(\Sigma M_B)_y = 0: \ -A_z(0.8) - C_x(0.5) + 600(0.3) = 0 \qquad (2)$$

$$(\Sigma M_B)_z = 0: \ A_y(0.8) - C_x(1.0) = 0 \qquad (3) \qquad \Sigma F_z = 0: \ A_z + C_z = 0 \qquad (4)$$

Solving (1)-(4) gives: $A_y = -375$ N; $A_z = 412.5$ N; $C_x = -300$ N; $C_z = -412.5$ N

$$\Sigma F_x = 0: \ B_x + C_x + 600 = 0 \qquad \therefore\ B_x = -600 - C_x = -600 - (-300) = -300\ \text{N}$$

$$\Sigma F_y = 0 \ \ A_y + B_y + 600 = 0 \qquad \therefore\ B_y = -600 - A_y = -600 - (-375) = -225\ \text{N}$$

$$A = \sqrt{A_y^2 + A_z^2} = \sqrt{(-375)^2 + 412.5^2} = 557\ \text{N}\ \blacklozenge$$

$$B = \sqrt{B_x^2 + B_y^2} = \sqrt{(-300)^2 + (-225)^2} = 375\ \text{N}\ \blacklozenge$$

$$C = \sqrt{C_x^2 + C_z^2} = \sqrt{(-300)^2 + (-412.5)^2} = 510\ \text{N}\ \blacklozenge$$

5.25

$$\mathbf{W} = -784.8\mathbf{k}\ \text{N}$$

$$\mathbf{T}_A = T_A\left(\frac{-1.4\mathbf{i} + 1.8\mathbf{k}}{\sqrt{5.2}}\right) = T_A(-0.6139\mathbf{i} + 0.7894\mathbf{k})$$

$$\mathbf{T}_E = T_E\left(\frac{1.4\mathbf{i} + 1.8\mathbf{k}}{\sqrt{5.2}}\right) = T_E(0.6139\mathbf{i} + 0.7894\mathbf{k})$$

$$\mathbf{T}_B = T_B\left(\frac{-1.4\mathbf{i} - 2.0\mathbf{j} + 1.8\mathbf{k}}{\sqrt{9.2}}\right) = T_B(-0.4616\mathbf{i} - 0.6594\mathbf{j} + 0.5934\mathbf{k})$$

$$\mathbf{T}_D = T_D\left(\frac{1.4\mathbf{i} - 2.0\mathbf{j} + 1.8\mathbf{k}}{\sqrt{9.2}}\right) = T_D(0.4616\mathbf{i} - 0.6594\mathbf{j} + 0.5934\mathbf{k})$$

$$\Sigma M_x = 0: \ \left[(T_B)_z + (T_D)_z\right](2.0) - W(1.0) = 0$$

$$2(0.5934T_B)(2.0) - 784.8(1.0) = 0 \qquad \therefore\ T_B = T_D = 330.6\ \text{N}\ \blacklozenge$$

$$\Sigma F_y = 0: \ (T_B)_y + (T_D)_y + T_C = 0$$

$$2(-0.6594)(330.6) + T_C = 0 \qquad \therefore\ T_C = 436.0\ \text{N}\ \blacklozenge$$

$$\Sigma F_z = 0: \ (T_A)_z + (T_E)_z + (T_B)_z + (T_D)_z - W = 0$$

$$2(0.7894T_A) + 2(0.5934)(330.6) - 784.8 = 0 \qquad \therefore\ T_A = T_E = 248.6\ \text{N}\ \blacklozenge$$

5.26

$\Sigma \mathbf{M}_{OB} = (\mathbf{r}_{AC} \times \mathbf{P} \bullet \vec{\lambda}_{OB}) + (\mathbf{r}_{AD} \times \mathbf{W} \bullet \vec{\lambda}_{OB}) = 0$ (contains only θ as an unknown)

$\mathbf{r}_{AC} = a\mathbf{j}$; $\mathbf{r}_{AD} = 2a\mathbf{j}$; $\mathbf{W} = -W\mathbf{k}$; $\mathbf{P} = -(W/2)\mathbf{i}$; $\vec{\lambda}_{OB} = \sin\theta\,\mathbf{i} + \cos\theta\,\mathbf{k}$

$$\Sigma M_{OB} = \begin{vmatrix} 0 & a & 0 \\ -W/2 & 0 & 0 \\ \sin\theta & 0 & \cos\theta \end{vmatrix} + \begin{vmatrix} 0 & 2a & 0 \\ 0 & 0 & -W \\ \sin\theta & 0 & \cos\theta \end{vmatrix} = 0$$

Expanding the determinants, and simplifying gives: $\dfrac{\cos\theta}{2} = 2\sin\theta$

$\therefore \dfrac{\sin\theta}{\cos\theta} = \tan\theta = \dfrac{1}{4}$ which yields $\theta = 14.04^\circ$ ◆

5.27

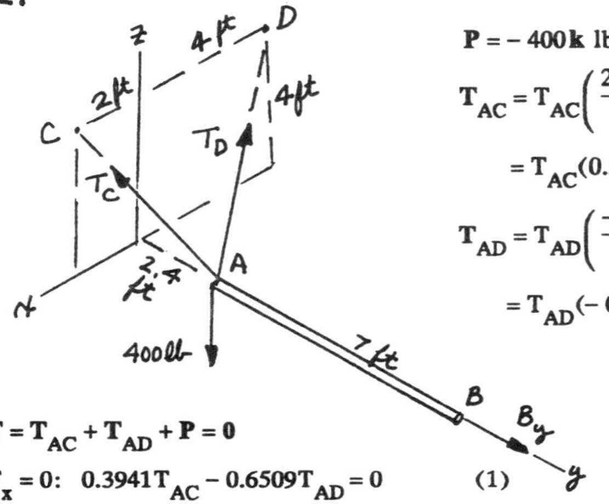

$\mathbf{P} = -400\mathbf{k}$ lb

$\mathbf{T}_{AC} = T_{AC}\left(\dfrac{2\mathbf{i} - 2.4\mathbf{j} + 4\mathbf{k}}{\sqrt{25.76}}\right)$

$= T_{AC}(0.3941\mathbf{i} - 0.4729\mathbf{j} + 0.7881\mathbf{k})$

$\mathbf{T}_{AD} = T_{AD}\left(\dfrac{-4\mathbf{i} - 2.4\mathbf{j} + 4\mathbf{k}}{\sqrt{37.76}}\right)$

$= T_{AD}(-0.6509\mathbf{i} - 0.3906\mathbf{j} + 0.6509\mathbf{k})$

$\Sigma \mathbf{F} = \mathbf{T}_{AC} + \mathbf{T}_{AD} + \mathbf{P} = \mathbf{0}$

$\Sigma F_x = 0$: $0.3941T_{AC} - 0.6509T_{AD} = 0$ (1)

$\Sigma F_z = 0$: $0.7881T_{AC} + 0.6509\,T_{AD} - 400 = 0$ (2)

Adding (1) and (2): $1.1822T_{AC} - 400 = 0$ which gives: $T_{AC} = \dfrac{400}{1.1822} = 338.4$ lb ◆

$\therefore T_{AD} = \dfrac{0.3941(338.4)}{0.6509} = 204.9$ lb ◆

$\Sigma M_{CD} = 0$: $B_y(4) - 2.4(400) = 0$ $\therefore B_y = 240.0$ lb ◆

5.28

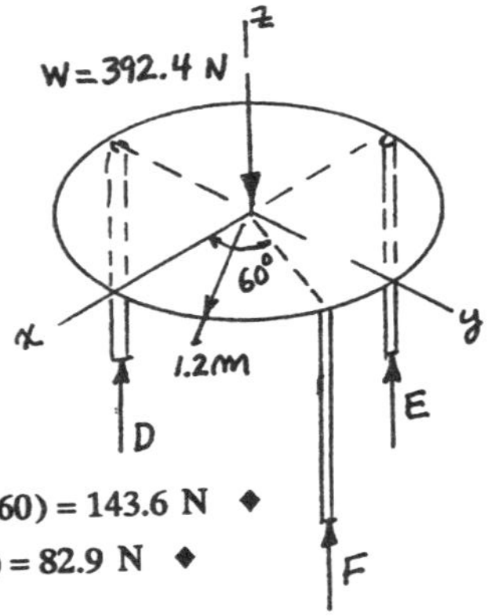

$W = 40(9.81) = 392.4$ N

$\Sigma M_x = 0$: $F(R\sin 60^\circ) - DR = 0$

$0.8660F = D$

$\Sigma M_y = 0$: $ER - F(R\cos 60^\circ) = 0$

$0.5F = E$

$\Sigma F_z = 0$: $D + E + F - W = 0$

$(0.8660 + 0.5 + 1.0)F - 392.4 = 0$

$\therefore F = 165.85$ N ◆ $D = 165.85(0.8660) = 143.6$ N ◆

$E = 0.5(165.85) = 82.9$ N ◆

5.29

mass/length = 40/10 = 10 kg/m

$W_{AB} = 1.5(10)(9.81) = 147.15$ N

$W_{AO} = 2.5(10)(9.81) = 245.25$ N

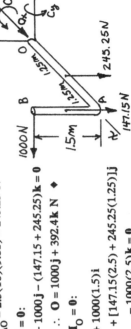

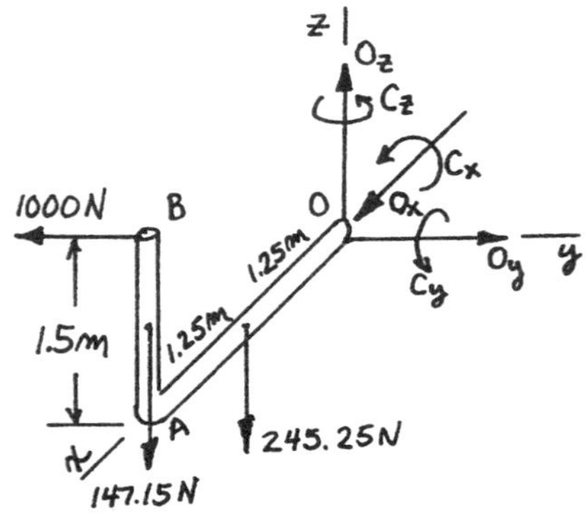

$\Sigma \mathbf{F} = \mathbf{0}$:

$\mathbf{O} - 1000\mathbf{j} - (147.15 + 245.25)\mathbf{k} = \mathbf{0}$

$\therefore \mathbf{O} = 1000\mathbf{j} + 392.4\mathbf{k}$ N ◆

$\Sigma \mathbf{M}_O = \mathbf{0}$:

$\mathbf{C} + 1000(1.5)\mathbf{i}$

$+ [147.15(2.5) + 245.25(1.25)]\mathbf{j}$

$- 1000(2.5)\mathbf{k} = \mathbf{0}$

$\therefore \mathbf{C} = -1500\mathbf{i} - 674\mathbf{j} + 2500\mathbf{k}$ N•m ◆

5.30

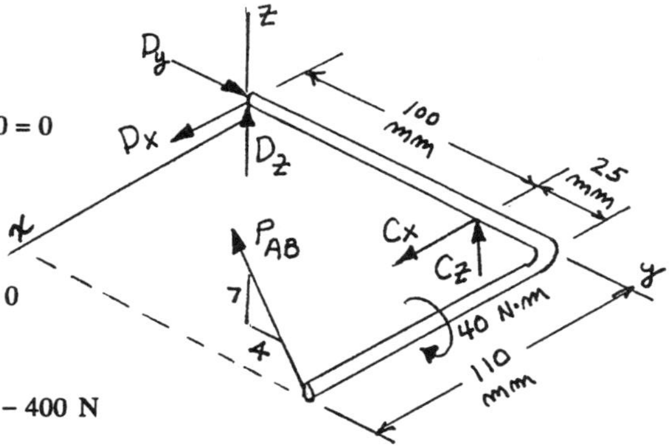

$\Sigma M_y = 0$: $P_{AB} = 0$

$\Sigma M_x = 0$: $C_z(0.1) - 40 = 0$

$\therefore\ C_z = 400$ N

$\Sigma M_z = 0$: $C_x = 0$

$\Sigma F_x = 0$: $D_x = -C_x = 0$

$\Sigma F_y = 0$: $D_y = 0$

$\Sigma F_z = 0$: $D_z = -C_z = -400$ N

Therefore, the reactions at C and D are:

$\mathbf{C} = 400\mathbf{k}$ N; $\mathbf{D} = -400\mathbf{k}$ N ◆

5.31

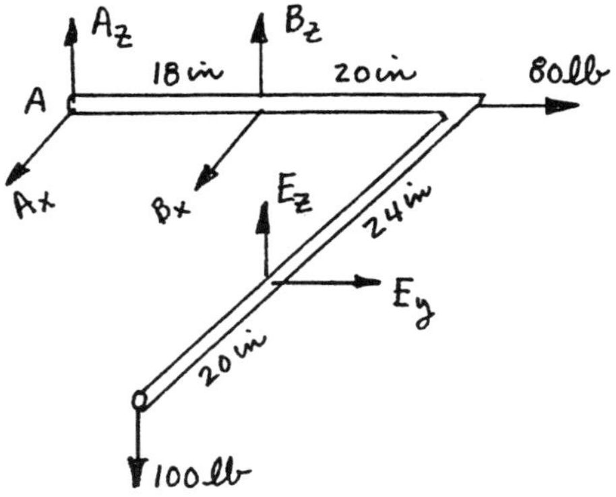

<u>On bar ABE</u>

$\Sigma F_y = 0$: $E_y = -80$ lb

$\Sigma M_{AB} = 0$: $E_z(24) = 100(44)$

$\therefore\ E_z = 183.3$ lb

<u>On bar DE</u>

$\Sigma F_y = 0$: $D_y = E_y = -80$ lb

$\Sigma F_z = 0$: $D_z - E_z - 60 = 0$

$\therefore\ D_z = 60 + 183.3 = 243$ lb

$\Sigma F_x = 0$: $D_x = 0$

Therefore, the force at D is

$\mathbf{D} = -80\mathbf{j} + 243\mathbf{k}$ lb ◆

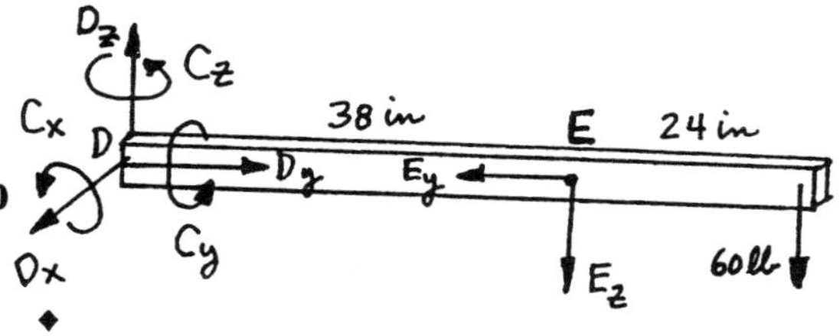

$\Sigma M_C = 0$:

$\mathbf{C} + [-E_z(38) - 60(62)]\mathbf{i} = \mathbf{0}$

Therefore the couple at D is

$\mathbf{C} = 10685\mathbf{i}$ lb•in = $890\mathbf{i}$ lb•ft ◆

5.32

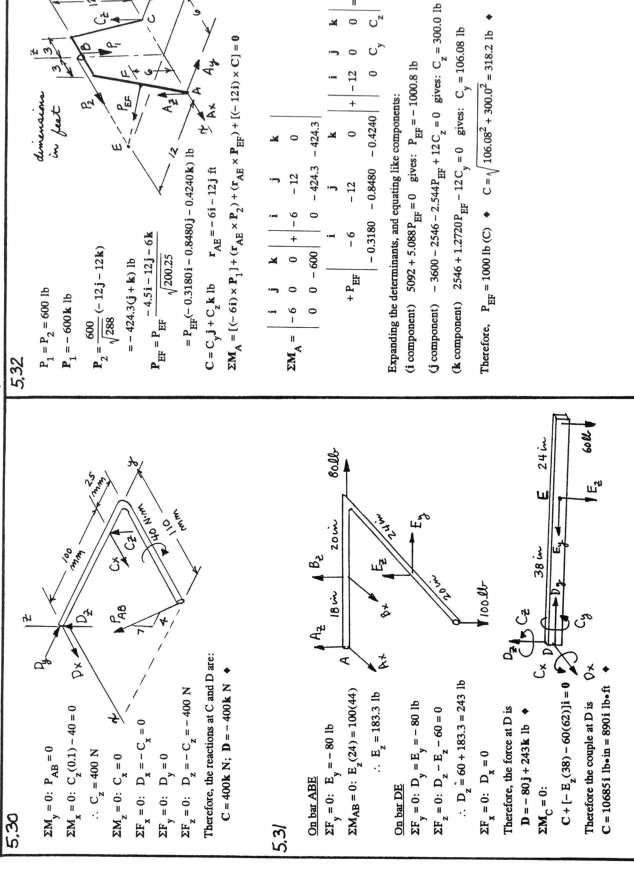

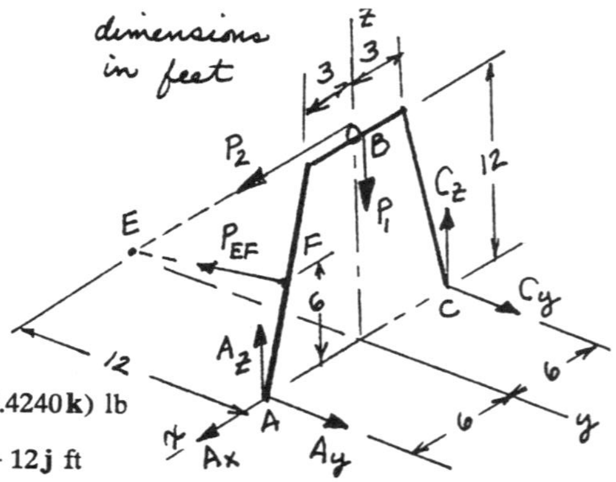

$P_1 = P_2 = 600$ lb

$\mathbf{P}_1 = -600\mathbf{k}$ lb

$$\mathbf{P}_2 = \frac{600}{\sqrt{288}}(-12\mathbf{j} - 12\mathbf{k})$$

$$= -424.3(\mathbf{j} + \mathbf{k}) \text{ lb}$$

$$\mathbf{P}_{EF} = P_{EF}\frac{-4.5\mathbf{i} - 12\mathbf{j} - 6\mathbf{k}}{\sqrt{200.25}}$$

$$= P_{EF}(-0.3180\mathbf{i} - 0.8480\mathbf{j} - 0.4240\mathbf{k}) \text{ lb}$$

$\mathbf{C} = C_y\mathbf{j} + C_z\mathbf{k}$ lb $\mathbf{r}_{AE} = -6\mathbf{i} - 12\mathbf{j}$ ft

$$\Sigma \mathbf{M}_A = [(-6\mathbf{i}) \times \mathbf{P}_1] + (\mathbf{r}_{AE} \times \mathbf{P}_2) + (\mathbf{r}_{AE} \times \mathbf{P}_{EF}) + [(-12\mathbf{i}) \times \mathbf{C}] = \mathbf{0}$$

$$\Sigma \mathbf{M}_A = \begin{vmatrix} \mathbf{i} & \mathbf{j} & \mathbf{k} \\ -6 & 0 & 0 \\ 0 & 0 & -600 \end{vmatrix} + \begin{vmatrix} \mathbf{i} & \mathbf{j} & \mathbf{k} \\ -6 & -12 & 0 \\ 0 & -424.3 & -424.3 \end{vmatrix}$$

$$+ P_{EF}\begin{vmatrix} \mathbf{i} & \mathbf{j} & \mathbf{k} \\ -6 & -12 & 0 \\ -0.3180 & -0.8480 & -0.4240 \end{vmatrix} + \begin{vmatrix} \mathbf{i} & \mathbf{j} & \mathbf{k} \\ -12 & 0 & 0 \\ 0 & C_y & C_z \end{vmatrix} = \mathbf{0}$$

Expanding the determinants, and equating like components:

(**i** component) $5092 + 5.088P_{EF} = 0$ gives: $P_{EF} = -1000.8$ lb

(**j** component) $-3600 - 2546 - 2.544P_{EF} + 12C_z = 0$ gives: $C_z = 300.0$ lb

(**k** component) $2546 + 1.2720P_{EF} - 12C_y = 0$ gives: $C_y = 106.08$ lb

Therefore, $P_{EF} = 1000$ lb (C) ◆ $C = \sqrt{106.08^2 + 300.0^2} = 318.2$ lb ◆

5.33

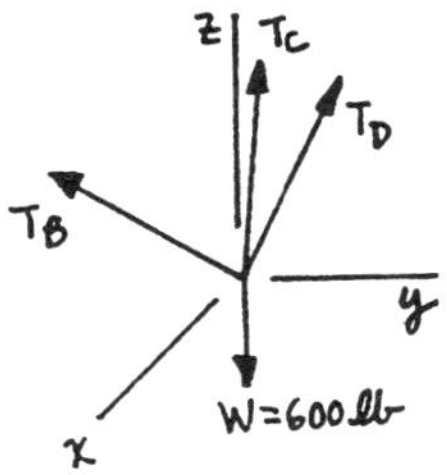

$$\Sigma\mathbf{F} = T_B\vec{\lambda}_{AB} + T_C\vec{\lambda}_{AC} + T_D\vec{\lambda}_{AD} + \mathbf{W} = 0$$

$$\vec{\lambda}_{AB} = \frac{4\,\mathbf{i} - 4\,\mathbf{j} + 7\,\mathbf{k}}{9} = 0.4444\,\mathbf{i} - 0.4444\,\mathbf{j} + 0.7778\,\mathbf{k}$$

$$\vec{\lambda}_{AC} = \frac{-4\,\mathbf{i} - 2\,\mathbf{j} + 7\,\mathbf{k}}{8.307} = -0.4815\,\mathbf{i} - 0.2408\,\mathbf{j} + 0.8427\,\mathbf{k}$$

$$\vec{\lambda}_{AD} = \frac{1.6\,\mathbf{i} + 4\,\mathbf{j} + 7\,\mathbf{k}}{8.219} = 0.1947\,\mathbf{i} + 0.4867\,\mathbf{j} + 0.8517\,\mathbf{k}$$

$$\mathbf{W} = -600\,\mathbf{k}\ \text{lb}$$

$$\Sigma F_x = 0: \quad 0.4444\,T_B - 0.4815\,T_C + 0.1947\,T_D = 0$$

$$\Sigma F_y = 0: \quad -0.4444\,T_B - 0.2408\,T_C + 0.4867\,T_D = 0$$

$$\Sigma F_z = 0: \quad 0.7778\,T_B + 0.8427\,T_C + 0.8517\,T_D - 600 = 0$$

Solving simultaneously gives: $T_B = 167$ lb ; $T_C = 269$ lb ; $T_D = 285$ lb ◆

5.34

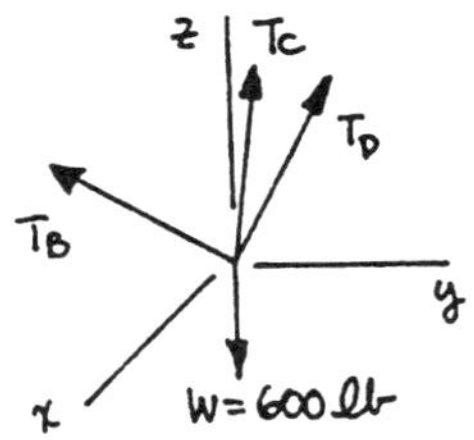

$$\Sigma M_{BC} = \left(\mathbf{r}_{BA} \times \mathbf{T}_D \bullet \vec{\lambda}_{BC}\right) + \left(\mathbf{r}_{BA} \times \mathbf{W} \bullet \vec{\lambda}_{BC}\right) = 0 \qquad (\text{gives } T_D)$$

$$\mathbf{r}_{BA} = -4\,\mathbf{i} + 4\,\mathbf{j} - 7\,\mathbf{k}\ \text{ft}$$

$$\vec{\lambda}_{BC} = \frac{-8\,\mathbf{i} + 2\,\mathbf{j}}{8.246}$$

$$\mathbf{W} = -600\,\mathbf{k}\ \text{lb}$$

$$\mathbf{T}_D = T_D\left(\frac{1.6\,\mathbf{i} + 4\,\mathbf{j} + 7\,\mathbf{k}}{8.219}\right)$$

$$= T_D(0.1947\,\mathbf{i} + 0.4867\,\mathbf{j} + 0.8517\,\mathbf{k})$$

$$\therefore\ \Sigma M_{BC} = \frac{T_D}{8.246}\begin{vmatrix} -4 & 4 & -7 \\ 0.1947 & 0.4867 & 0.8517 \\ -8 & 2 & 0 \end{vmatrix} + \frac{1}{8.246}\begin{vmatrix} -4 & 4 & -7 \\ 0 & 0 & -600 \\ -8 & 2 & 0 \end{vmatrix} = 0$$

Cancelling 8.246, and expanding the determinants: $-50.42\,T_D + 14\,400 = 0$

which gives $T_D = 286$ lb ◆

5.35

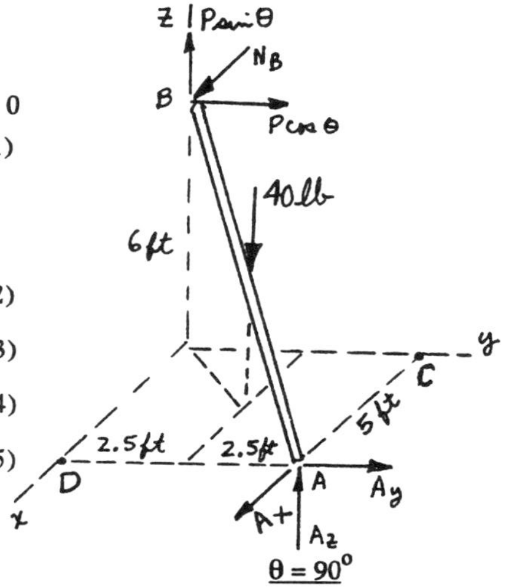

$$\Sigma M_{AC} = 0:$$

$$-P\cos\theta(6) - P\sin\theta(5) + 40(2.5) = 0$$

$$\therefore\ 6P\cos\theta + 5P\sin\theta = 100 \qquad (1)$$

$$\Sigma M_{AD} = 0:$$

$$P\sin\theta(5) + N_B(6) - 40(2.5) = 0$$

$$\therefore\ 5P\sin\theta + 6N_B = 100 \qquad (2)$$

$$\Sigma F_x = 0: \quad A_x = -N_B \qquad (3)$$

$$\Sigma F_y = 0: \quad A_y = -P\cos\theta \qquad (4)$$

$$\Sigma F_z = 0: \quad A_z = 40 - P\sin\theta \qquad (5)$$

<u>$\theta = 0$</u>

(1) gives $6P = 100$ $\quad\therefore\ P = 16.67$ lb ◆

(2) gives $6N_B = 100$ $\quad\therefore\ N_B = 16.67$ lb ◆

(3) gives $A_x = -N_B = -16.67$ lb

(4) gives $A_y = -P = -16.67$ lb

(5) gives $A_z = 40$ lb

$\therefore\ \mathbf{A} = -16.67\mathbf{i} - 16.67\mathbf{j} + 40\mathbf{k}$ lb ◆

<u>$\theta = 90°$</u>

(1) gives $5P = 100$ $\quad\therefore\ P = 20$ lb ◆

(2) gives $5P + 6N_B = 100$

$\therefore\ N_B = (1/6)[100 - 5(20)] = 0$ ◆

(3) gives $A_x = 0$

(4) gives $A_y = 0$

(5) gives $A_z = 40 - P = 20$ lb

$\therefore\ \mathbf{A} = 20\mathbf{k}$ lb ◆

5.36

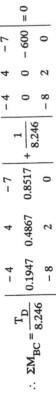

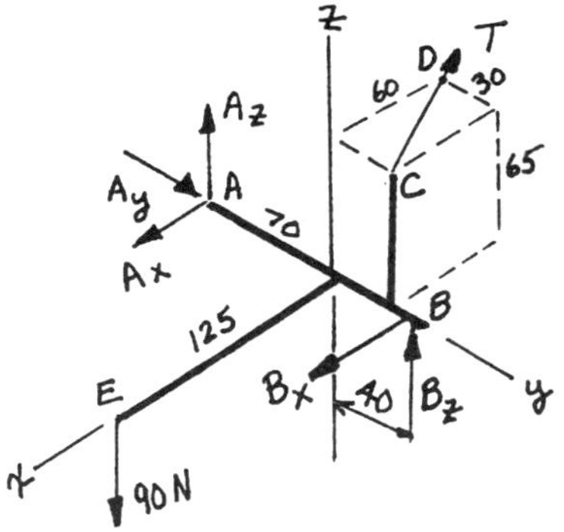

$$\mathbf{T} = T\left(\frac{-60\,\mathbf{i} - 30\,\mathbf{j}}{\sqrt{4500}}\right)$$

$$= T(-0.8944\,\mathbf{i} - 0.4472\,\mathbf{j})$$

$$\mathbf{r}_{AC} = 100\,\mathbf{j} + 65\,\mathbf{k}\ \text{mm}$$

$$\mathbf{r}_{AE} = 125\,\mathbf{i} + 70\,\mathbf{j}\ \text{mm}$$

$$\mathbf{r}_{AB} = 110\,\mathbf{j}\ \text{mm}$$

$$\mathbf{B} = B_x\,\mathbf{i} + B_z\,\mathbf{k} \qquad \mathbf{P} = -90\,\mathbf{k}\ \text{N}$$

(continued)

$$\Sigma M_A = (\mathbf{r}_{AC} \times \mathbf{T}) + (\mathbf{r}_{AE} \times \mathbf{P}) + (\mathbf{r}_{AB} \times \mathbf{B}) = 0$$

$$\Sigma M_A = T\begin{vmatrix} \mathbf{i} & \mathbf{j} & \mathbf{k} \\ 0 & 100 & 65 \\ -0.8944 & -0.4472 & 0 \end{vmatrix} + \begin{vmatrix} \mathbf{i} & \mathbf{j} & \mathbf{k} \\ 125 & 70 & 0 \\ 0 & 0 & -90 \end{vmatrix} + \begin{vmatrix} \mathbf{i} & \mathbf{j} & \mathbf{k} \\ 0 & 110 & 0 \\ B_x & 0 & B_z \end{vmatrix} = 0$$

Expanding the determinants, and equating like components:

(**i** component) $29.07T - 6300 + 110B_z = 0$ (1)

(**j** component) $-58.14T + 11250 = 0$ (2)

(**k** component) $89.44T - 110B_x = 0$ (3)

Solving (1), (2) and (3) gives: $T = 193.50$ N; $B_x = 157.33$ N; $B_z = 6.14$ N

$\Sigma F_x = A_x + B_x + T_x = 0 \quad \therefore A_x = -B_x - T_x = -157.33 - (-0.8944)(193.50) = 15.74$ N

$\Sigma F_y = A_y + T_y = 0 \quad \therefore A_y = -T_y = -(-0.4472)(193.5) = 86.53$ N

$\Sigma F_z = A_z + B_z - 90 = 0 \quad \therefore A_z = 90 - B_z = 90 - 6.14 = 83.86$ N

Therefore, $T = 193.5$ N; $\mathbf{A} = 15.7\mathbf{i} + 86.5\mathbf{j} + 83.9\mathbf{k}$ N; $\mathbf{B} = 157.3\mathbf{i} + 6.14\mathbf{k}$ N ◆

5.37

$\Sigma F_y = 0: \quad \therefore B_y = 0; \; \Sigma M_z = 0: \quad \therefore B_x = 0$

$\Sigma M_x = 0: \; 800B_z = 400W \quad \therefore B_z = 0.5W$

Therefore, $\mathbf{B} = 0.5W\mathbf{k}$ ◆

$\Sigma F_z = 0: \; T_A \cos 20^\circ - W + B_z = 0$

$\therefore T_A = W(1 - 0.5)/\cos 20^\circ$

$= 0.5321\,W$ ◆

$\Sigma F_x = 0: \; P - T_A \sin 20^\circ = 0$

$\therefore P = (0.5321\,W)\sin 20^\circ$

$= 0.1820\,W$ ◆

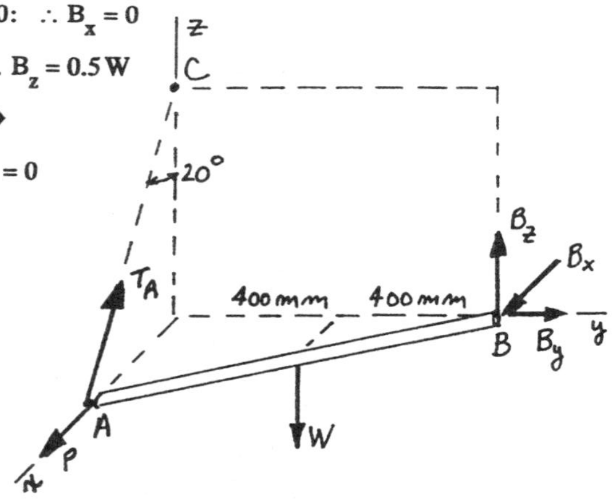

5.38

$P_A = P_O = P_B = \dfrac{1470(9.81)}{3} = 4807$ N

$W_1 = (4/7)(1470)(9.81) = 8240$ N

$W_2 = (3/7)(1470)(9.81) = 6180$ N

$\Sigma M_y = 0: \; P_A(a) = W_1(2)$

$\therefore a = \dfrac{2W_1}{P_A} = \dfrac{2(8240)}{4807} = 3.43$ m ◆

$\Sigma M_x = 0: \; P_B(b) = W_2(1.5)$

$\therefore b = \dfrac{1.5W_2}{P_B} = \dfrac{1.5(6180)}{4807} = 1.93$ m ◆

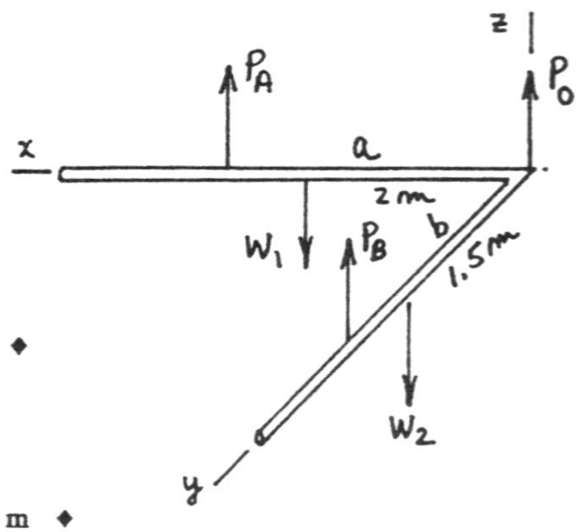

5.39

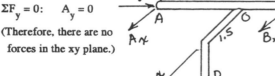

$\Sigma M_{A_z} = 0: \; B_x = 0$

$\Sigma F_x = 0: \quad A_x = 0$

$\Sigma F_y = 0: \quad A_y = 0$

(Therefore, there are no forces in the xy plane.)

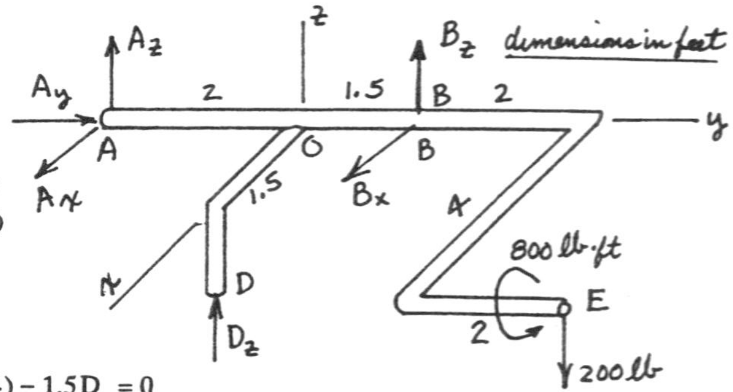

$\Sigma M_y = 0: \; 800 + 200(4) - 1.5D_z = 0$

$\therefore D_z = 1066.7$ lb

$\Sigma M_{B_x} = 0: \; -3.5A_z - 1.5D_z - 200(4) = 0$

$-3.5A_z = 200(4) + 1.5(1066.7) \quad \therefore A_z = -685.7$ lb

$\Sigma F_z = 0: \; A_z + B_z + D_z - 200 = 0 \quad \therefore B_z = 200 - (-685.7) - 1066.7 = -181.0$ lb

Therefore, the reactions are

$\mathbf{A} = -686\mathbf{k}$ lb; $\mathbf{B} = -181.0\mathbf{k}$ lb; $\mathbf{D} = 1067\mathbf{k}$ lb ◆

5.40

$\Sigma M_y = 0$: $120(12) - 28P = 0 \quad \therefore\ P = 51.43$ lb

$\Sigma M_x = 0$:

$120(24) + 50(28)$
$\quad + P(71) - B_z(59) = 0$

$\therefore\ B_z = 134.43$ lb

$\Sigma M_z = 0 \quad \therefore\ B_x = 0$

$\Sigma F_x = 0$: $\quad A_x + B_x = 0$

$\therefore\ A_x = 0$

$\Sigma F_y = 0$: $\quad A_y = 0$

$\Sigma F_z = 0$: $\quad A_z + B_z - 120 - 50 - P = 0$

$\therefore\ A_z = 120 + 50 + 51.43 - 134.43 = 87.00$ lb

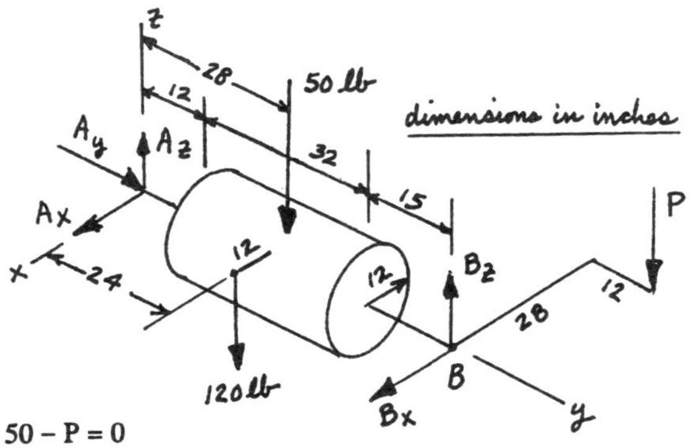

Therefore, the answers are: $P = 51.4$ lb; $\mathbf{A} = 87.0\mathbf{k}$ lb; $\mathbf{B} = 134.4\mathbf{k}$ lb ◆

5.41

Note that OA is a two-force body.

$\Sigma \mathbf{M}_B = \mathbf{0}$ gives O_x and T_{CD}.

$$\mathbf{T}_{CD} = T_{CD}\left(\frac{-1.8\mathbf{i} - 1.6\mathbf{j} + 2\mathbf{k}}{3.131}\right)$$

$$= T_{CD}(-0.5749\mathbf{i} - 0.5110\mathbf{j} + 0.6388\mathbf{k})$$

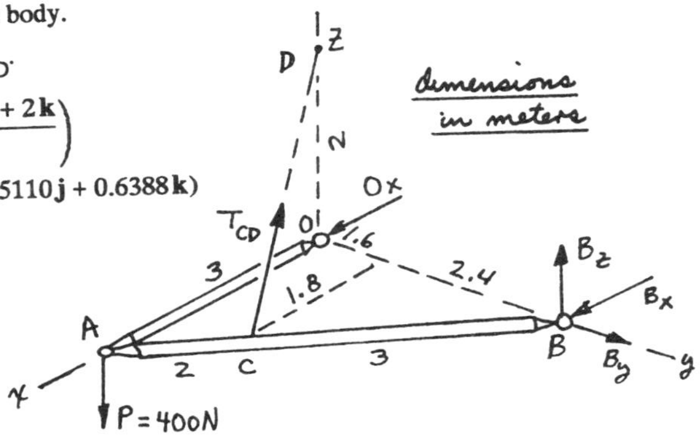

$\Sigma M_{B_y} = 0$: $\quad 400(3) - (T_{CD})_z(1.8) = 0$

$1200 = 0.6388\,T_{CD}(1.8) \qquad \therefore\ T_{CD} = 1044$ N ◆

$\Sigma M_{B_z} = 0$: $\quad O_x(4) - (T_{CD})_x(2.4) - (T_{CD})_y(1.8) = 0$

$O_x(4) - (0.5749)(1044)(2.4) - (0.5110)(1044)(1.8) = 0$

$\therefore\ O_x = 600$ N which gives $\mathbf{O}_x = 600\mathbf{i}$ N ◆

5.42

$$\Sigma \mathbf{M}_A = \left(\mathbf{r}_{AD} \times \mathbf{P}_{CD}\right) + \left[\mathbf{r}_{AG} \times (-54\mathbf{j} - 64\mathbf{k})\right] + \left(\mathbf{r}_{AB} \times \mathbf{B}\right) = \mathbf{0}$$

$\mathbf{P}_{CD} = P_{CD}(\sin 30^\circ\,\mathbf{j} + \cos 30^\circ\,\mathbf{k})$

$\quad = P_{CD}(0.5000\mathbf{j} + 0.8660\mathbf{k})$

$\mathbf{r}_{AD} = 1.00\mathbf{i} + 6.24\mathbf{k}$ ft ; $\mathbf{r}_{AB} = -3\mathbf{i}$ ft

$\mathbf{r}_{AG} = -1.5\mathbf{i} + 4.5\mathbf{k}$ ft

$\mathbf{B} = B_y\mathbf{j} + B_z\mathbf{k}$

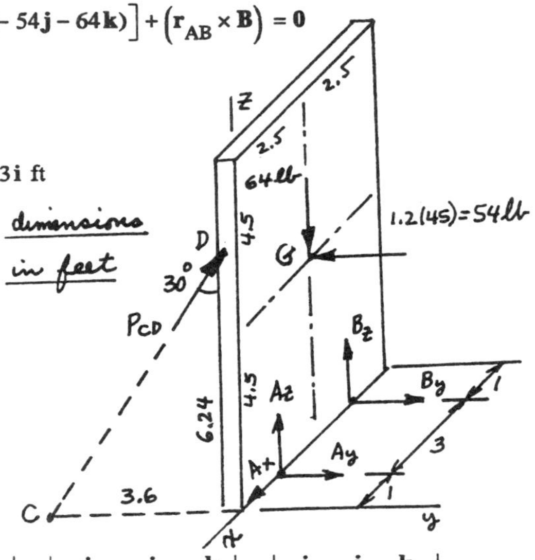

$$\Sigma \mathbf{M}_A = P_{CD}\begin{vmatrix} \mathbf{i} & \mathbf{j} & \mathbf{k} \\ 1.00 & 0 & 6.24 \\ 0 & 0.5000 & 0.8660 \end{vmatrix} + \begin{vmatrix} \mathbf{i} & \mathbf{j} & \mathbf{k} \\ -1.5 & 0 & 4.5 \\ 0 & -54 & -64 \end{vmatrix} + \begin{vmatrix} \mathbf{i} & \mathbf{j} & \mathbf{k} \\ -3 & 0 & 0 \\ 0 & B_y & B_z \end{vmatrix} = \mathbf{0}$$

Expanding the determinants, the components of the moment equation are:

(**i** component) $\quad -3.120P_{CD} + 243.0 = 0 \quad (1)$

(**j** component) $\quad -0.8660P_{CD} - 96.0 + 3B_z = 0 \quad (2)$

(**k** component) $\quad 0.5000P_{CD} + 81.0 - 3B_y = 0 \quad (3)$

Solving (1) - (3) simultaneously gives: $P_{CD} = 77.9$ lb ◆

$B_y = 40.0$ lb ; $B_z = 54.49$ lb $\qquad \therefore\ \mathbf{B} = 40.0\mathbf{j} + 54.5\mathbf{k}$ lb ◆

$\Sigma F_x = 0$: $\quad A_x = 0 \qquad \Sigma F_y = 0$: $\quad A_y = -40.0 - 77.9\sin 30^\circ + 54 = -25.0$ lb

$\Sigma F_z = 0$: $\quad A_z = -54.49 - 77.9\cos 30^\circ + 64 = -58.0$ lb $\qquad \therefore\ \mathbf{A} = -25.0\mathbf{j} - 58.0\mathbf{k}$ lb ◆

5.43

$$\mathbf{P} = P_{BD}\vec{\lambda}_{DB} = P_{BD}\left(\frac{5\mathbf{i} + 2\mathbf{j} - 5\mathbf{k}}{7.348}\right)$$

$$= P_{BD}(0.6805\mathbf{i} + 0.2722\mathbf{j} - 0.6805\mathbf{k})$$

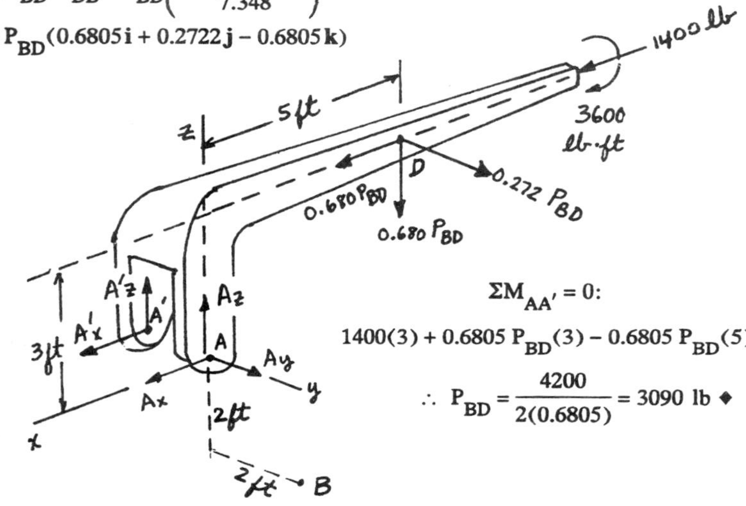

$\Sigma M_{AA'} = 0$:

$$1400(3) + 0.6805\,P_{BD}(3) - 0.6805\,P_{BD}(5) = 0$$

$$\therefore\ P_{BD} = \frac{4200}{2(0.6805)} = 3090 \text{ lb} \blacklozenge$$

5.44

$\Sigma M_x = 0$:

$$\frac{4}{5}P_{BD}(3) = \frac{1}{\sqrt{2}}P_{BE}(4)$$

$$\therefore\ P_{BD} = 1.179\,P_{BE} \qquad (1)$$

$\Sigma M_{C_y} = 0$:

$$P(10) = 4\left(\frac{4}{5}P_{BD} + \frac{1}{\sqrt{2}}P_{BE}\right)$$

$$10\,P = 3.200\,P_{BD} + 2.828\,P_{BE} \qquad (2)$$

Solving (1) and (2) simultaneously gives:

$P_{BE} = 1.515\,P$; $P_{BD} = 1.786\,P$ ◆

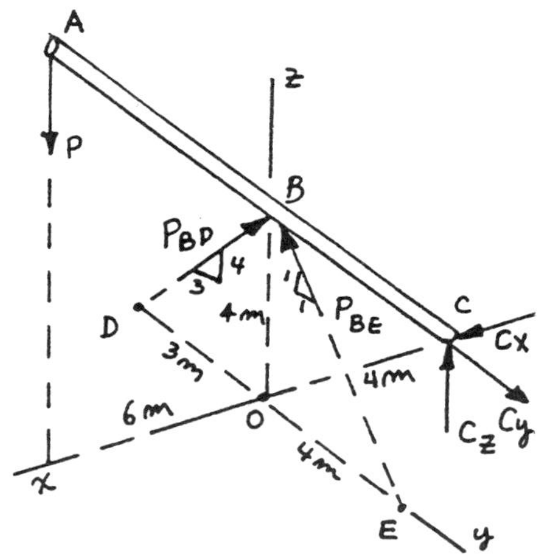

5.45

FBD of entire winch (not shown here) $\Sigma M_y = 0$: $360(200) = P(320)$ $\therefore\ P = 225$ N ◆

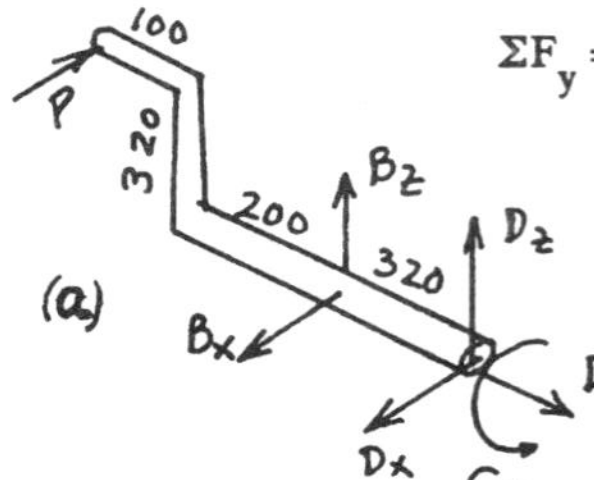

FBD (a)

$\Sigma F_y = 0$: $D_y = 0$ $\quad \Sigma M_{D_x} = 0$: $B_z = 0$ $\quad \Sigma F_z = 0$: $D_z = 0$

$\Sigma M_{D_z} = 0$: $225(620) = B_x(320)$ gives $B_x = 435.9$ N

$$\therefore\ B = \sqrt{B_x^2 + B_z^2} = 436 \text{ N} \blacklozenge$$

$\Sigma F_x = 0$: $D_x = 225 - B_x$

$\therefore\ D_x = 225 - 436 = -211$ N

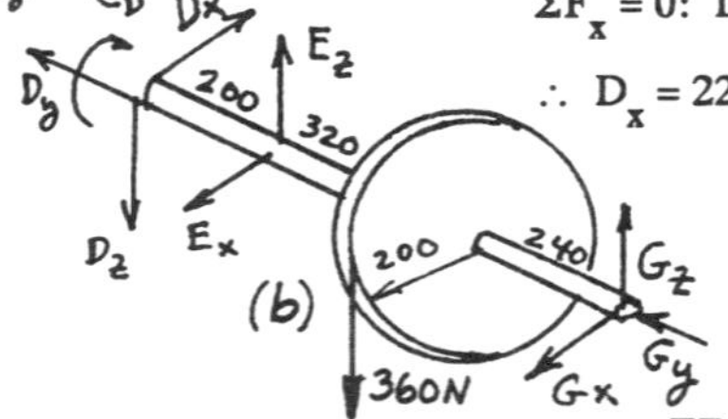

FBD (b)

$\Sigma M_{G_x} = 0$:

$360(240) = E_z(560)$ $\therefore\ E_z = 154.3$ N

$\Sigma M_{G_z} = 0$:

$E_x(560) = D_x(760)$

$\therefore\ E_x = (76/56)(-210.9) = -286.2$ N

$$E = \sqrt{154.3^2 + (-286.2)^2} = 325 \text{ N} \blacklozenge$$

$\Sigma F_y = 0$: $G_y = 0$

$\Sigma F_z = 0$: $G_z = 360 - E_z$

$\therefore\ G_z = 360 - 154.3 = 205.7$ N

$\Sigma F_x = 0$: $G_x = D_x - E_x$

$= -210.9 + 286.2$

$= 75.3$ N

$$G = \sqrt{75.3^2 + 205.7^2} = 219 \text{ N} \blacklozenge$$

5.46

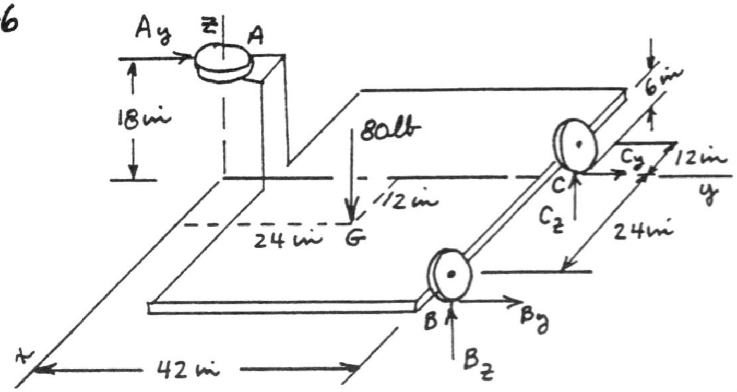

(continued)

$\Sigma M_{BC} = 0$: $A_y(18 + 6) - 80(42 - 24) = 0$ $\therefore A_y = 60$ lb

$\Sigma M_{B_z} = 0$: $-C_y(24 + 12) - A_y(24) = 0$ $\therefore C_y = -40$ lb

$\Sigma M_{B_y} = 0$: $C_z(24 + 12) - 80(24 - 12) = 0$ $\therefore C_z = 26.67$ lb

$\Sigma F_y = 0$: $B_y = -C_y - A_y = 40 - 60 = -20$ lb

$\Sigma F_z = 0$: $B_z = 80 - C_z = 80 - 26.67 = 53.33$ lb

Therefore, the magnitudes of the reactions at the rollers are:

$A = 60$ lb; $B = \sqrt{(-20)^2 + 53.33^2} = 57.0$ lb; $C = \sqrt{(-40)^2 + 26.67^2} = 48.1$ lb ◆

5.47

$\Sigma M_{AE} = 0$ gives $T = 240$ lb

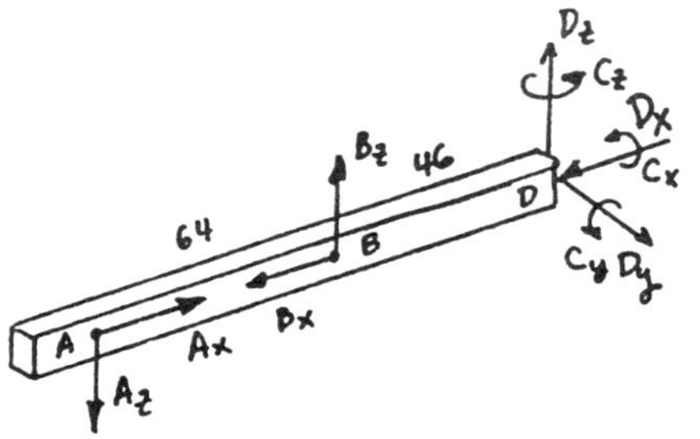

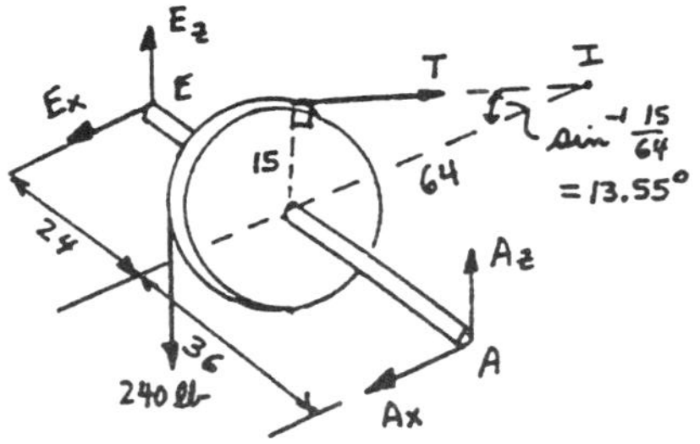

$\Sigma M_{E_z} = 0$:

$T \cos 13.55°(24) - A_x(60) = 0$
$\therefore A_x = 93.33$ lb

$\Sigma M_{E_x} = 0$:
$-(240 + T \sin 13.55°)(24) + A_z(60) = 0$
$\therefore A_z = 118.5$ lb

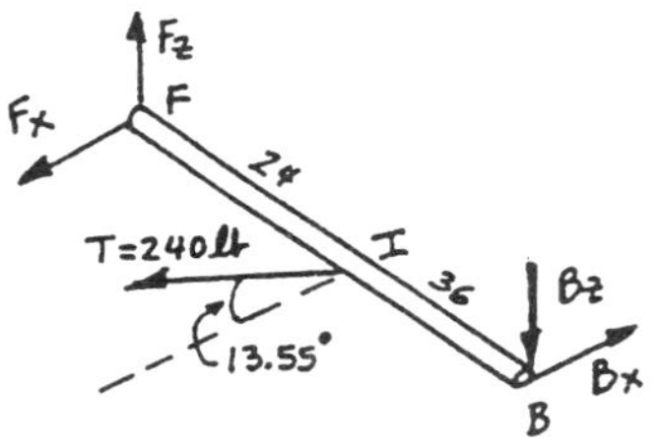

$\Sigma M_{F_z} = 0$:
$-240 \cos 13.55°(24) + B_x(60) = 0$
$\therefore B_x = 93.33$ lb

$\Sigma M_{F_x} = 0$:
$240 \sin 13.55°(24) - B_z(60) = 0$
$\therefore B_z = 22.49$ lb

dimensions in inches

$\Sigma M_x = 0$: $C_x = 0$

$\Sigma M_{D_z} = 0$: $C_z = 0$

$\Sigma F_x = 0$: $D_x = A_x - B_x = 0$

$\Sigma F_y = 0$: $D_y = 0$

$\Sigma F_z = 0$: $D_z = A_z - B_z$

$\Sigma M_{D_y} = 0$ $C_y = B_z(46) - A_z(110) = 22.49(46) - 118.5(110) = -12\,000$ lb·in

$= 118.5 - 22.49 = 96.0$ lb

The reactions at D acting on ABD are: $\mathbf{D} = 96.0\,\mathbf{k}$ lb and $\mathbf{C} = -1000\,\mathbf{j}$ lb·ft ◆

5.48

BE and CF are two-force bodies

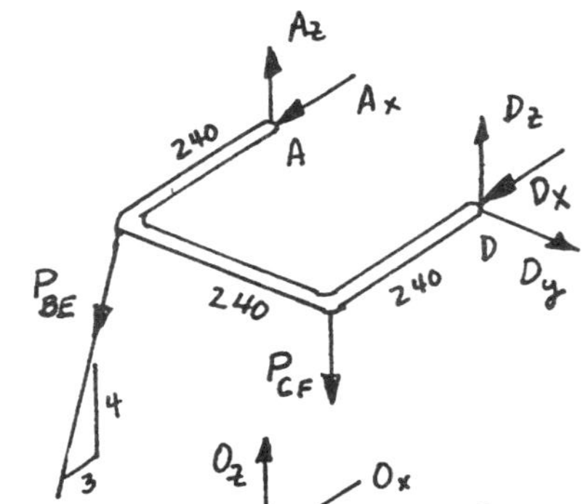

$\Sigma M_{AD} = 0$:
$240(P_{CF} + 0.8P_{BE}) = 0$
$\therefore P_{CF} = -0.8P_{BE}$ (1)

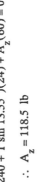

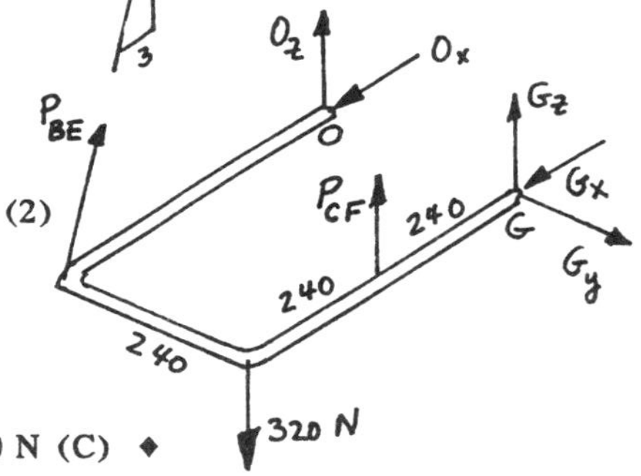

$\Sigma M_{OG} = 0$:
$(320 - 0.8P_{BE})(480) - P_{CF}(240) = 0$ (2)

Solving (1) and (2) gives:
$P_{BE} = 800$ N; $P_{CF} = -640$ N

Therefore, $P_{BE} = 800$ N (T); $P_{CF} = 640$ N (C) ◆

(continued)

5.49

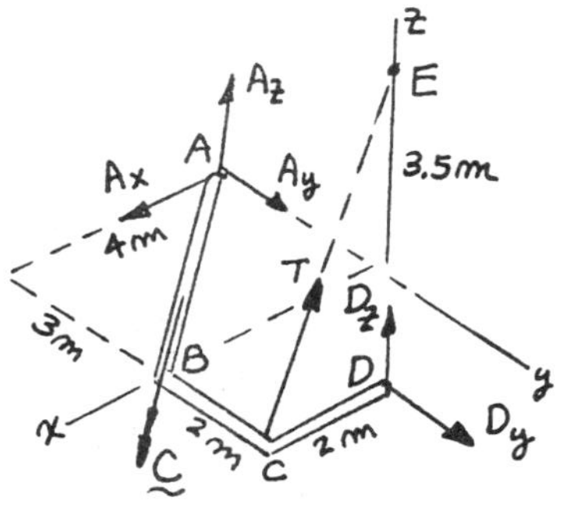

$$\mathbf{T} = T\left(\frac{-4\mathbf{i} - 2\mathbf{j} + 3.5\mathbf{k}}{\sqrt{32.25}}\right)$$

$$= T(-0.7044\mathbf{i} - 0.3522\mathbf{j} + 0.6163\mathbf{k})$$

$$\mathbf{C} = 40\left(\frac{4\mathbf{i} + 3\mathbf{j}}{5}\right) = 32\mathbf{i} + 24\mathbf{j} \text{ kN}\cdot\text{m}$$

$$\mathbf{r}_{AE} = 3\mathbf{j} + 3.5\mathbf{k} \text{ m}$$

$$\vec{\lambda}_{AD} = \frac{2\mathbf{i} + 5\mathbf{j}}{\sqrt{29}} = 0.3714\mathbf{i} + 0.9285\mathbf{j}$$

$$\Sigma M_{AD} = \mathbf{C} \cdot \vec{\lambda}_{AD} + \mathbf{r}_{AE} \times \mathbf{T} \cdot \vec{\lambda}_{AD} = 0$$

$$\therefore \ \Sigma M_{AD} = (32\mathbf{i} + 24\mathbf{j}) \cdot (0.3714\mathbf{i} + 0.9285\mathbf{j}) + T\begin{vmatrix} 0 & 3 & 3.5 \\ -0.7044 & -0.3522 & 0.6163 \\ 0.3714 & 0.9285 & 0 \end{vmatrix} = 0$$

Evaluating the dot product and the determinant gives:

$$34.17 - 1.1445T = 0 \qquad \therefore \ T = 29.9 \text{ kN} \ \blacklozenge$$

5.50

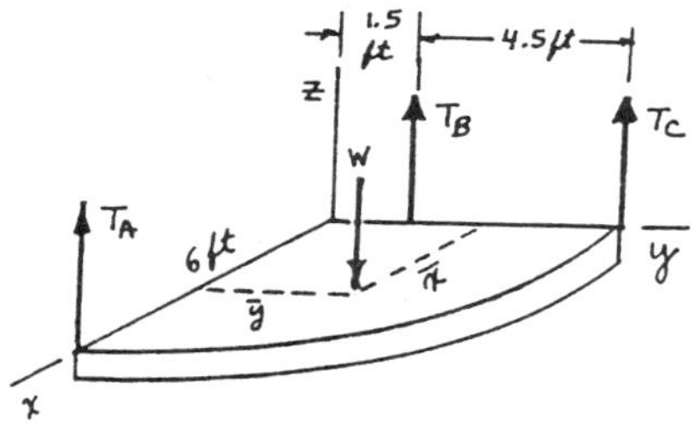

$$\bar{x} = \bar{y} = \frac{4R}{3\pi} = \frac{4(6)}{3\pi} = 2.546 \text{ ft}$$

$\Sigma M_y = 0$:

$$-T_A(6) + W(2.546) = 0 \qquad (1)$$

$\Sigma M_x = 0$:

$$T_B(1.5) + T_C(6) - W(2.546) = 0 \qquad (2)$$

$\Sigma F_z = 0$:

$$T_A + T_B + T_C - W = 0 \qquad (3)$$

From (1)-(3) we obtain $T_A = 0.4243\,W$; $T_B = 0.2018\,W$; $T_C = 0.3739\,W$

Therefore, the limiting condition is $T_A = 0.4243\,W = 500$ lb, which gives $W = 1178$ lb ◆

5.51

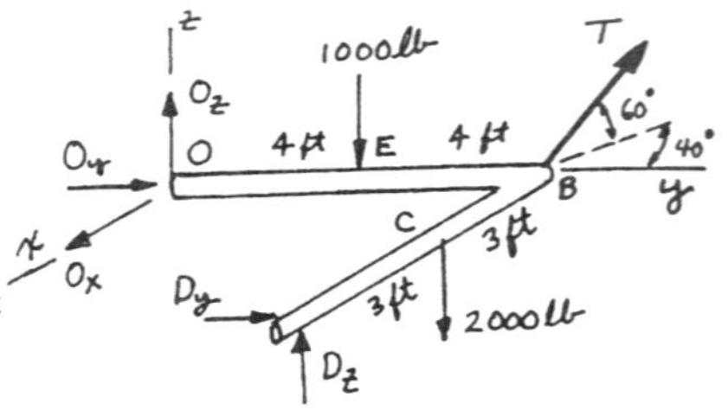

$$\Sigma \mathbf{M}_O = \left[\mathbf{r}_{OE} \times (-1000\,\mathbf{k})\right] + \left[\mathbf{r}_{OC} \times (-2000\,\mathbf{k})\right] + (\mathbf{r}_{OD} \times \mathbf{D}) + (\mathbf{r}_{OB} \times \mathbf{T}) = \mathbf{0}$$

$\mathbf{r}_{OE} = 4\,\mathbf{j}$ ft $\quad \mathbf{r}_{OC} = 3\,\mathbf{i} + 8\,\mathbf{j}$ ft $\quad \mathbf{r}_{OB} = 8\,\mathbf{j}$ ft

$\mathbf{r}_{OD} = 6\,\mathbf{i} + 8\,\mathbf{j}$ ft $\quad \mathbf{D} = D_y\,\mathbf{j} + D_z\,\mathbf{k}$

$$\mathbf{T} = T(-\cos 60^\circ \sin 40^\circ\,\mathbf{i} + \cos 60^\circ \cos 40^\circ\,\mathbf{j} + \sin 60^\circ\,\mathbf{k})$$

$$= T(-0.3214\,\mathbf{i} + 0.3830\,\mathbf{j} + 0.8660\,\mathbf{k})$$

$$\Sigma \mathbf{M}_O = \begin{vmatrix} \mathbf{i} & \mathbf{j} & \mathbf{k} \\ 0 & 4 & 0 \\ 0 & 0 & -1000 \end{vmatrix} + \begin{vmatrix} \mathbf{i} & \mathbf{j} & \mathbf{k} \\ 3 & 8 & 0 \\ 0 & 0 & -2000 \end{vmatrix} + \begin{vmatrix} \mathbf{i} & \mathbf{j} & \mathbf{k} \\ 6 & 8 & 0 \\ 0 & D_y & D_z \end{vmatrix}$$

$$+ T\begin{vmatrix} \mathbf{i} & \mathbf{j} & \mathbf{k} \\ 0 & 8 & 0 \\ -0.3214 & 0.3830 & 0.8660 \end{vmatrix} = \mathbf{0}$$

Expanding the determinants, the components of the moment equation are:

(**i** component) $\quad -4000 - 16\,000 + 8\,D_z + 6.9280\,T = 0 \qquad (1)$

(**j** component) $\quad 6\,D_z - 6000 = 0 \qquad (2)$

(**k** component) $\quad 6\,D_y + 2.571\,T = 0 \qquad (3)$

Solving (1)-(3) gives: $T = 1732$ lb ◆ $\quad D_y = -742.2$ lb $\quad D_z = 1000$ lb

$$D = \sqrt{(-742.2)^2 + 1000^2} = 1245 \text{ lb} \ \blacklozenge$$

5.52

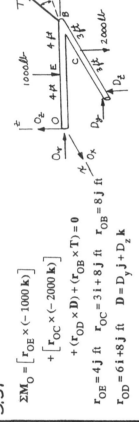

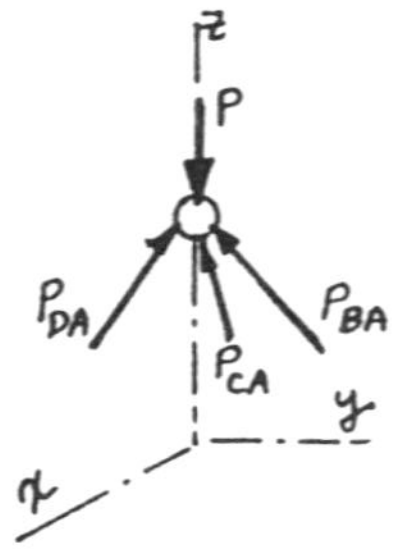

$$\mathbf{P}_{BA} = P_{BA}(-0.6000\,\mathbf{j} + 0.8000\,\mathbf{k})$$

$$\mathbf{P}_{CA} = P_{CA}\left(\frac{6\,\mathbf{i} + 3\,\mathbf{j} + 8\,\mathbf{k}}{10.440}\right)$$

$$= P_{CA}(0.5747\,\mathbf{i} + 0.2874\,\mathbf{j} + 0.7663\,\mathbf{k})$$

$$\mathbf{P}_{DA} = P_{DA}\left(\frac{-6\,\mathbf{i} + 3\,\mathbf{j} + 8\,\mathbf{k}}{10.440}\right)$$

$$= P_{DA}(-0.5747\,\mathbf{i} + 0.2874\,\mathbf{j} + 0.7663\,\mathbf{k})$$

$$\mathbf{P} = -P\,\mathbf{k}$$

(continued)

$\Sigma F_x = 0$: $\quad 0.5747\,P_{CA} - 0.5747\,P_{DA} = 0 \quad (1)$

$\Sigma F_y = 0$: $\quad -0.6000\,P_{BA} + 0.2874\,P_{CA} + 0.2874\,P_{DA} = 0 \quad (2)$

$\Sigma F_z = 0$: $\quad 0.8000\,P_{BA} + 0.7663\,P_{CA} + 0.7663\,P_{DA} - P = 0 \quad (3)$

Solving (1)-(3) gives: $P_{CA} = P_{DA} = 0.4350\,P$; $P_{BA} = 0.4167\,P$

Therefore, the limiting condition is: $0.4350\,P = 2000$ lb, which gives $P = 4600$ lb ◆

5.53

$$\Sigma \mathbf{M}_O = (\mathbf{r}_{OA} \times \mathbf{T}_{AB}) + (\mathbf{r}_{OA} \times \mathbf{T}_{AC}) + (\mathbf{r}_{OD} \times \mathbf{P}) = \mathbf{0}$$

$\mathbf{r}_{OA} = 8\mathbf{k}$ m $\quad \mathbf{r}_{OD} = 4\mathbf{k}$ m $\quad \mathbf{P} = 20\mathbf{j}$ kN

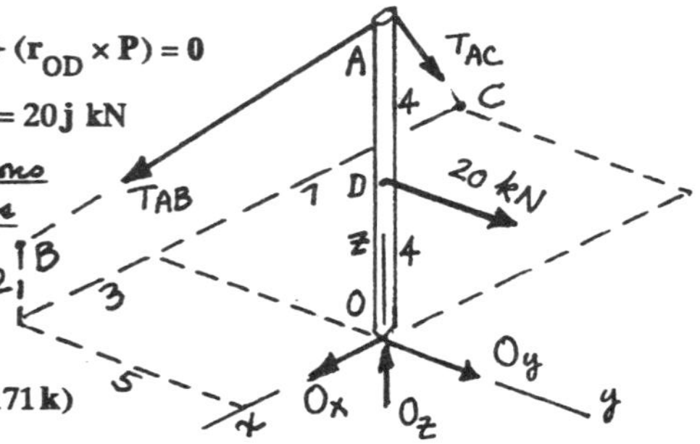

$$\mathbf{T}_{AB} = T_{AB}\left(\frac{3\mathbf{i} - 5\mathbf{j} - 6\mathbf{k}}{\sqrt{70}}\right)$$

$$= T_{AB}(0.3586\mathbf{i} - 0.5976\mathbf{j} - 0.7171\mathbf{k})$$

$$\mathbf{T}_{AC} = T_{AC}\left(\frac{-7\mathbf{i} - 5\mathbf{j} - 8\mathbf{k}}{\sqrt{138}}\right) = T_{AC}(-0.5959\mathbf{i} - 0.4256\mathbf{j} - 0.6810\mathbf{k})$$

$$\Sigma \mathbf{M}_O = T_{AB}\begin{vmatrix} \mathbf{i} & \mathbf{j} & \mathbf{k} \\ 0 & 0 & 8 \\ 0.3586 & -0.5976 & -0.7171 \end{vmatrix} + T_{AC}\begin{vmatrix} \mathbf{i} & \mathbf{j} & \mathbf{k} \\ 0 & 0 & 8 \\ -0.5959 & -0.4256 & -0.6810 \end{vmatrix} + \begin{vmatrix} \mathbf{i} & \mathbf{j} & \mathbf{k} \\ 0 & 0 & 4 \\ 0 & 20 & 0 \end{vmatrix} = \mathbf{0}$$

Expanding the determinants, and equating like components gives:

(i-component) $\quad 4.781\,T_{AB} + 3.405\,T_{AC} - 80 = 0 \quad (1)$

(j-component) $\quad 2.869\,T_{AB} - 4.767\,T_{AC} = 0 \quad (2)$

Solving (1) and (2) yields: $T_{AB} = 11.71$ kN and $T_{AC} = 7.05$ kN ◆

5.54

$$\Sigma \mathbf{M}_A = \left[\mathbf{r}_{AB} \times (\mathbf{N} + \mathbf{T})\right] + (\mathbf{r}_{AG} \times \mathbf{W}) = \mathbf{0}$$

$\mathbf{r}_{AB} = -4\mathbf{i} - 6\mathbf{j} + 5\mathbf{k}$ ft

$\mathbf{r}_{AG} = -2\mathbf{i} - 3\mathbf{j} + 2.5\mathbf{k}$ ft

$\mathbf{N} = N\mathbf{j}$

$\mathbf{W} = -80\mathbf{k}$ lb

$\mathbf{T} = T(\cos 30^\circ\mathbf{i} + \sin 30^\circ\mathbf{k})$

$\quad = T(0.8660\mathbf{i} + 0.5000\mathbf{k})$

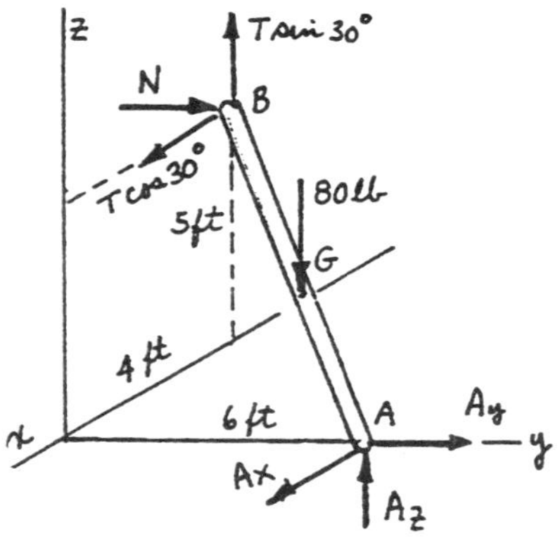

$$\Sigma \mathbf{M}_A = \begin{vmatrix} \mathbf{i} & \mathbf{j} & \mathbf{k} \\ -4 & -6 & 5 \\ 0.8660T & N & 0.5000T \end{vmatrix} + \begin{vmatrix} \mathbf{i} & \mathbf{j} & \mathbf{k} \\ -2 & -3 & 2.5 \\ 0 & 0 & -80 \end{vmatrix} = \mathbf{0}$$

Expanding the determinants, and equating like components gives:

(j-component) $\quad 6.330T - 160 = 0 \quad (1)$

(k-component) $\quad -4N + 5.196T = 0 \quad (2)$

Solving (1) and (2) yields: $T = 25.28$ lb ◆ and $N = 32.84$ lb

$\Sigma F_x = 0$: $\quad A_x = -T\cos 30^\circ = -25.28\cos 30^\circ = -21.89$ lb

$\Sigma F_y = 0$: $\quad A_y = -N = -32.84$ lb

$\Sigma F_z = 0$: $\quad A_z = 80 - T\sin 30^\circ = 80 - 25.28\sin 30^\circ = 67.36$ lb

$$\therefore\ A = \sqrt{(-21.89)^2 + (-32.84)^2 + 67.36^2} = 78.1 \text{ lb} \;◆$$

5.55

$\Sigma M_{BC} = \left(\mathbf{r}_{BA} \times \mathbf{T}_{AD} \bullet \vec{\lambda}_{BC}\right) + \left(\mathbf{r}_{BO} \times \mathbf{W} \bullet \vec{\lambda}_{BC}\right) = 0 \qquad (\text{gives } T_{AD})$

$\mathbf{r}_{BA} = 10\,\mathbf{i} - 2\,\mathbf{j}$ m; $\mathbf{r}_{BO} = 4\,\mathbf{i} + 2\,\mathbf{j}$ m

$\mathbf{W} = -500(9.81)\,\mathbf{k} = -4905\,\mathbf{k}$ N

$\vec{\lambda}_{BC} = \dfrac{4\,\mathbf{i} + 10\,\mathbf{j}}{10.77}$

$\mathbf{T}_{AD} = T_{AD}\left(\dfrac{6\,\mathbf{i} - 4\,\mathbf{j} + 10\,\mathbf{k}}{12.33}\right)$

$= T_{AD}(0.4866\,\mathbf{i} - 0.3244\,\mathbf{j} + 0.8110\,\mathbf{k})$

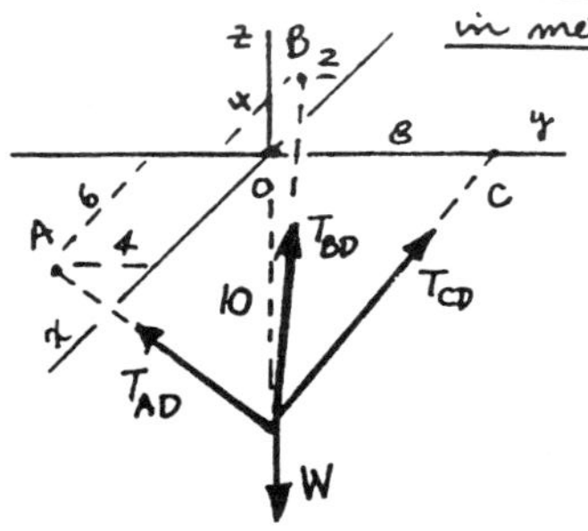

$$\therefore\ \Sigma M_{BC} = \frac{T_{AD}}{10.77}\begin{vmatrix} 10 & -2 & 0 \\ 0.4866 & -0.3244 & 0.8110 \\ 4 & 10 & 0 \end{vmatrix} + \frac{1}{10.77}\begin{vmatrix} 4 & 2 & 0 \\ 0 & 0 & -4905 \\ 4 & 10 & 0 \end{vmatrix} = 0$$

Cancelling 10.77, and expanding the determinants: $-87.59\,T_{AD} + 4905(32) = 0$

which gives $T_{AD} = 1792$ N ◆

5.56

$\mathbf{T} = T\vec{\lambda}_{DE} = T\left(\dfrac{6.325\mathbf{i} - 3\mathbf{j} + 4\mathbf{k}}{\sqrt{65}}\right) = T(0.7845\mathbf{i} - 0.3721\mathbf{j} + 0.4961\mathbf{k})$

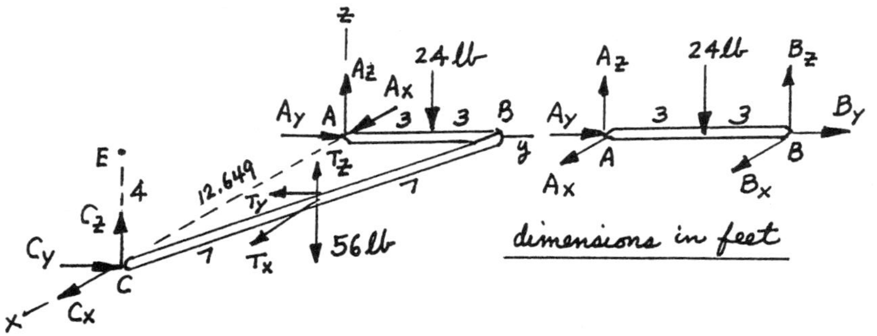

Using FBD of entire assembly

$\Sigma M_x = 0$: $(56 + 24)(3) - T_z(3) = 80(3) - (0.4961\,T)(3) = 0 \qquad \therefore\ T = 161.26$ lb ◆

(continued)

For the directions shown on the FBD:

$T_x = 0.7845(161.26) = 126.51$ lb; $T_y = 0.3721(161.26) = 60.00$ lb; $T_z = 80.00$ lb

$\Sigma M_y = 0$: $(56 - T_z)(6.325) - C_z(12.649) = 0 \qquad \therefore\ C_z = \dfrac{(56 - 80)(6.325)}{12.649} = -12$ lb

$\Sigma M_z = 0$: $C_y(12.649) - T_y(6.325) - T_x(3) = 0 \qquad \therefore\ C_y = \dfrac{60(6.325) + 126.51(3)}{12.649} = 60$ lb ◆

$\Sigma M_{CE} = 0$: $\therefore\ A_y = 0$

$\Sigma F_z = 0$: $A_z + C_z + T_z - 24 - 56 = 0 \quad \therefore\ A_z = 80 - C_z - T_z = 80 - (-12) - 80 = 12$ lb

Using FBD of bar AB

$\Sigma M_{A_x} = 0$: $B_z(6) = 24(3) \quad \therefore\ B_z = 12.00$ lb

$\Sigma F_y = 0$: $B_y = -A_y = 0 \qquad \Sigma M_{A_z} = 0$: $B_x = 0 \qquad \Sigma F_x = 0$: $A_x = -B_x = 0$

Using FBD of entire assembly

$\Sigma F_x = 0$: $A_x + C_x + T_x = 0 \quad \therefore\ C_x = -A_x - T_x = 0 - 126.51 = -126.51$ lb

Using the above results, the magnitudes of the reactions are:

$A = B = 12.00$ lb ◆ $\qquad C = \sqrt{(-126.51)^2 + 60^2 + (-12)^2} = 140.5$ lb ◆

5.57

$\Sigma \mathbf{M}_O = (\mathbf{r}_{OA} \times \mathbf{T}_{AD}) + (\mathbf{r}_{OB} \times \mathbf{T}_{BF}) + (\mathbf{r}_{OC} \times \mathbf{T}_{CE}) = 0$

$\mathbf{r}_{OA} = 2\,\mathbf{j}$ ft $\quad \mathbf{r}_{OB} = 4\,\mathbf{j}$ ft $\quad \mathbf{r}_{OC} = 6\,\mathbf{j}$ ft

$\mathbf{T}_{AD} = 1200\left(\dfrac{-2\,\mathbf{j} + 3\,\mathbf{k}}{\sqrt{13}}\right)$

$\mathbf{T}_{BF} = T_{BF}\left(\dfrac{4\,\mathbf{i} - 4\,\mathbf{j} - 4\,\mathbf{k}}{\sqrt{48}}\right)$

$\mathbf{T}_{CE} = T_{CE}\left(\dfrac{-6\,\mathbf{i} - 6\,\mathbf{j} + 3\,\mathbf{k}}{9}\right)$

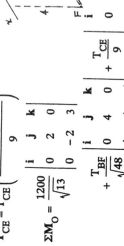

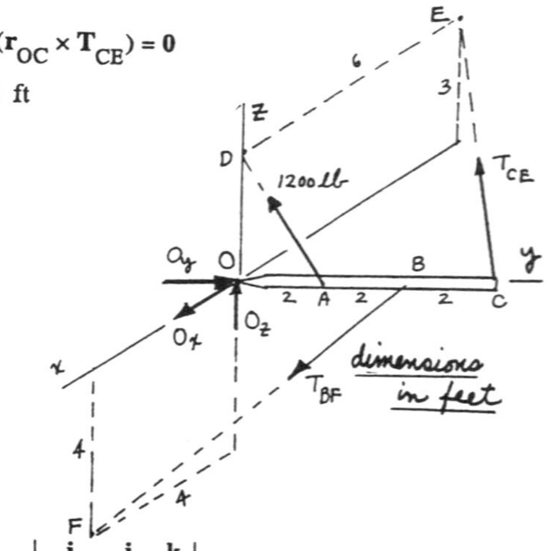

$$\Sigma \mathbf{M}_O = \frac{1200}{\sqrt{13}}\begin{vmatrix} \mathbf{i} & \mathbf{j} & \mathbf{k} \\ 0 & 2 & 0 \\ 0 & -2 & 3 \end{vmatrix} + \frac{T_{BF}}{\sqrt{48}}\begin{vmatrix} \mathbf{i} & \mathbf{j} & \mathbf{k} \\ 0 & 4 & 0 \\ 4 & -4 & -4 \end{vmatrix} + \frac{T_{CE}}{9}\begin{vmatrix} \mathbf{i} & \mathbf{j} & \mathbf{k} \\ 0 & 6 & 0 \\ -6 & -6 & 3 \end{vmatrix} = \mathbf{0}$$

(continued)

Expanding the determinants, and equating like components gives:

(i-component) $1997 - 2.309\,T_{BF} + 2.000\,T_{CE} = 0$ (1)

(k-component) $-2.309\,T_{BF} + 4.000\,T_{CE} = 0$ (2)

Solving (1) and (2) yields: $T_{CE} = 999$ lb and $T_{BF} = 1730$ lb ◆

5.58

$\Sigma M_{FE} = (\mathbf{r}_{FO} \times \mathbf{O}_y \cdot \vec{\lambda}_{FE}) + (\mathbf{r}_{FD} \times \mathbf{T}_{AD} \cdot \vec{\lambda}_{FE}) = 0$ (gives T_{AD})

$\mathbf{r}_{FO} = -4\mathbf{i} + 4\mathbf{k}$ ft $\quad \mathbf{r}_{FD} = -4\mathbf{i} + 7\mathbf{k}$ ft

$\mathbf{T}_{AD} = T_{AD}\left(\dfrac{-2\mathbf{j} + 3\mathbf{k}}{\sqrt{13}}\right)$

$\mathbf{O}_y = 600\,\mathbf{j}$ lb

$\vec{\lambda}_{FE} = \dfrac{-10\mathbf{i} + 7\mathbf{k}}{\sqrt{149}}$

dimensions in feet

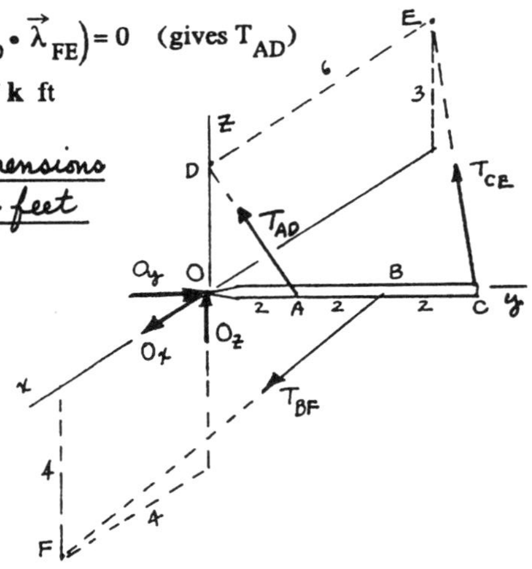

$$\therefore\ \Sigma M_{FE} = \frac{1}{\sqrt{149}}\begin{vmatrix} -4 & 0 & 4 \\ 0 & 600 & 0 \\ -10 & 0 & 7 \end{vmatrix} + \frac{T_{AD}}{\sqrt{13}\sqrt{149}}\begin{vmatrix} -4 & 0 & 7 \\ 0 & -2 & 3 \\ -10 & 0 & 7 \end{vmatrix} = 0$$

Cancelling $\sqrt{149}$ and expanding the determinants:

$$7200 + \frac{T_{AD}}{\sqrt{13}}(-84) = 0 \quad \text{which gives} \quad T_{AD} = 309 \text{ lb} ◆$$

5.59

$\Sigma M_x = 0$: $\quad P_C(2) - \frac{3}{5}(20) = 0$

$\therefore\ P_C = 6.00$ kN (T) ◆

$\Sigma M_y = 0$: $\quad -P_A(3) + \frac{4}{5}(20) = 0$

$\therefore\ P_A = 5.33$ kN (T) ◆

$\Sigma F_z = 0$: $\quad P_A + P_B + P_C = 0$

$\therefore\ P_B = -P_A - P_C = -5.33 - 6.00 = -11.33 = 11.33$ kN (C) ◆

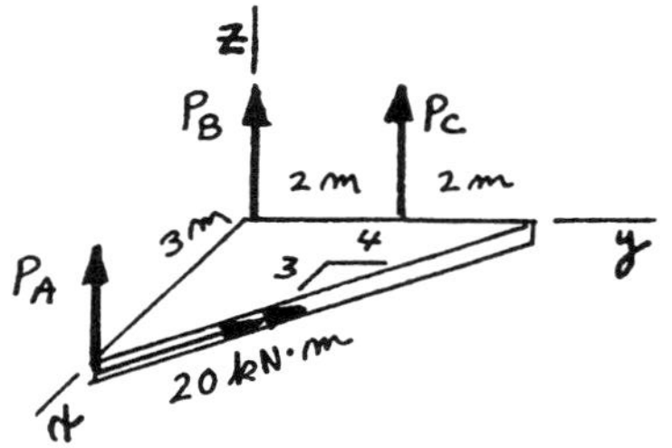

5.60

Note that AB is a two-force body.

<u>Using FBD for BC</u>:

$\mathbf{T} = T\left(\dfrac{-1.0\mathbf{i} - 2.0\mathbf{j} + 0.8\mathbf{k}}{\sqrt{5.64}}\right)$

$= T(-0.4211\mathbf{i} - 0.8422\mathbf{j} + 0.3369\mathbf{k})$

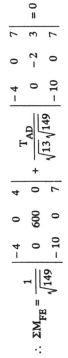

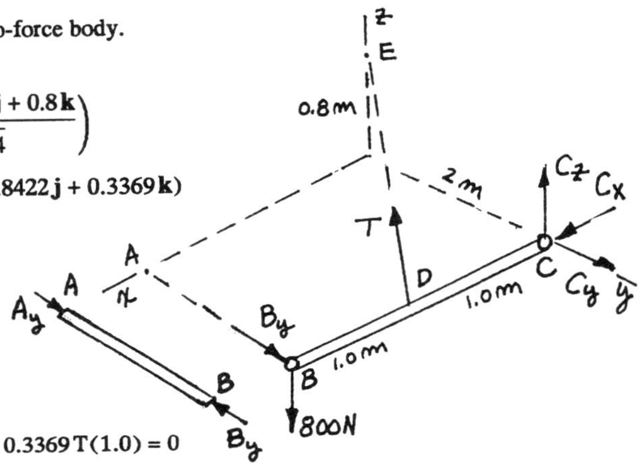

$\Sigma(M_C)_y = 800(2) - 0.3369\,T(1.0) = 0$

$\therefore\ T = 4749$ N

$\Sigma(M_C)_z = 2.0\,B_y - 0.8422\,T(1.0) = 0$

$\therefore\ B_y = 0.8422(4749)/2.0 = 2000$ N

<u>Using FBD for AB</u>: $\Sigma F_y = 0$: $\quad A_y = B_y = 2000$ N

Therefore the answers are: T = 4750 N; **A** = 2000**j** N ◆

5.61

$\Sigma \mathbf{M}_B = (\mathbf{r}_{BG} \times \mathbf{W}) + (\mathbf{r}_{BA} \times \mathbf{T}_{AC}) + (\mathbf{r}_{BA} \times \mathbf{T}_{AD}) = \mathbf{0}$

$\mathbf{W} = -150(9.81)\mathbf{k} = -1471.5\mathbf{k}$ N

$\mathbf{r}_{BG} = 1.5\mathbf{i}$ m

$\mathbf{r}_{BA} = 6\mathbf{i}$ m

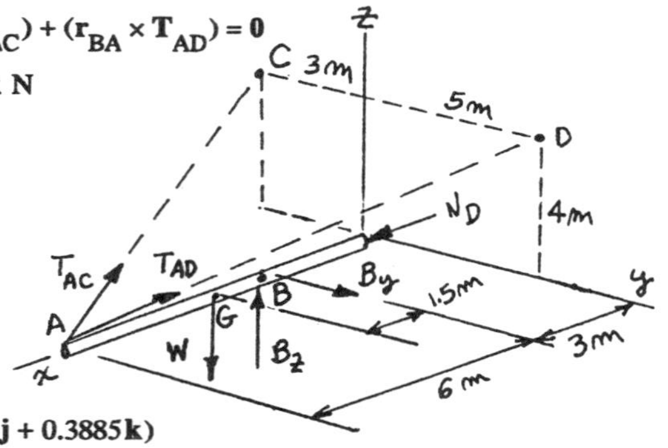

$$\mathbf{T}_{AC} = T_{AC}\left(\frac{-9\mathbf{i} - 3\mathbf{j} + 4\mathbf{k}}{\sqrt{106}}\right)$$

$$= T_{AC}(-0.8742\mathbf{i} - 0.2914\mathbf{j} + 0.3885\mathbf{k})$$

$$\mathbf{T}_{AD} = T_{AD}\left(\frac{-9\mathbf{i} + 5\mathbf{j} + 4\mathbf{k}}{\sqrt{122}}\right) = T_{AD}(-0.8148\mathbf{i} + 0.4527\mathbf{j} + 0.3621\mathbf{k})$$

$$\Sigma \mathbf{M}_B = \begin{vmatrix} \mathbf{i} & \mathbf{j} & \mathbf{k} \\ 1.5 & 0 & 0 \\ 0 & 0 & -1471.5 \end{vmatrix} + T_{AC}\begin{vmatrix} \mathbf{i} & \mathbf{j} & \mathbf{k} \\ 6 & 0 & 0 \\ -0.8742 & -0.2914 & 0.3885 \end{vmatrix} + T_{AD}\begin{vmatrix} \mathbf{i} & \mathbf{j} & \mathbf{k} \\ 6 & 0 & 0 \\ -0.8148 & 0.4527 & 0.3621 \end{vmatrix} = \mathbf{0}$$

Expanding the determinants, and equating like components gives:

(j-component) $\quad -2.331\,T_{AC} - 2.173\,T_{AD} + 2207 = 0 \quad$ (1)

(k-component) $\quad -1.7484\,T_{AC} + 2.716\,T_{AD} = 0 \quad$ (2)

Solving (1) and (2) yields: $T_{AC} = 591.7$ N; $T_{AD} = 380.9$ N ◆

$\Sigma F_x = 0$: $\quad (\mathbf{T}_{AC})_x + (\mathbf{T}_{AD})_x + N_D = 0$

$(591.7)(-0.8742) + (380.9)(-0.8148) + N_D = 0$ which gives $N_D = 827.6$ N ◆

5.62

$\Sigma \mathbf{M}_A = (\mathbf{r}_{AB} \times \mathbf{B}) + (\mathbf{r}_{AC} \times \mathbf{D}) + (\mathbf{r}_{AC} \times \mathbf{P}) = \mathbf{0}$

$\mathbf{r}_{AB} = 5\mathbf{k}$ ft

$\mathbf{r}_{AC} = 6\mathbf{j} + 7\mathbf{k}$ ft

$\mathbf{B} = B_x\mathbf{i} + B_y\mathbf{j}$

$\mathbf{D} = D\mathbf{i}$

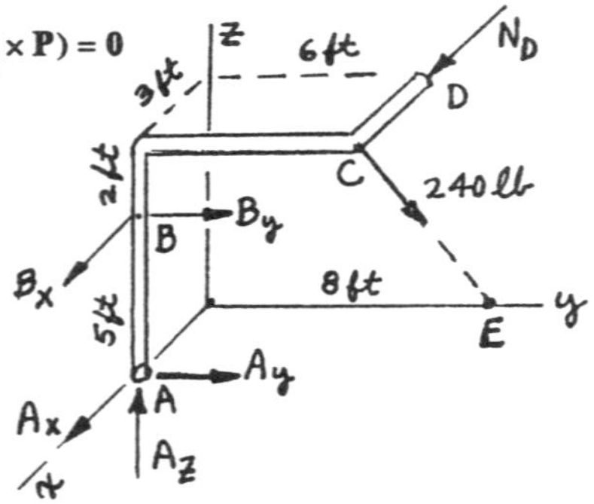

$$\mathbf{P} = 240\left(\frac{-3\mathbf{i} + 2\mathbf{j} - 7\mathbf{k}}{\sqrt{62}}\right)$$

$$= -91.44\mathbf{i} + 60.96\mathbf{j} - 213.4\mathbf{k} \text{ lb}$$

$$\Sigma \mathbf{M}_A = \begin{vmatrix} \mathbf{i} & \mathbf{j} & \mathbf{k} \\ 0 & 0 & 5 \\ B_x & B_y & 0 \end{vmatrix} + \begin{vmatrix} \mathbf{i} & \mathbf{j} & \mathbf{k} \\ 0 & 6 & 7 \\ D & 0 & 0 \end{vmatrix} + \begin{vmatrix} \mathbf{i} & \mathbf{j} & \mathbf{k} \\ 0 & 6 & 7 \\ -91.44 & 60.96 & -213.4 \end{vmatrix} = \mathbf{0}$$

Expanding the determinants, and equating like components gives:

(i-component) $\quad -5B_y - 1707.1 = 0 \quad$ (1)

(j-component) $\quad 5B_x + 7D - 640.1 = 0 \quad$ (2)

(k-component) $\quad -6D + 548.6 = 0 \quad$ (3)

Solving (1), (2), and (3) gives: $B_x = 0$; $B_y = -341.4$ lb; and $D = 91.44$ lb

Therefore the answers are $\mathbf{B} = -341\mathbf{j}$ lb; $\mathbf{D} = 91.4\mathbf{i}$ lb ◆

6.1

FBD of entire beam

$\Sigma M_B = 0: \quad N_A(6) = 3000(4)$

$\therefore \quad N_A = 2000 \text{ lb}$

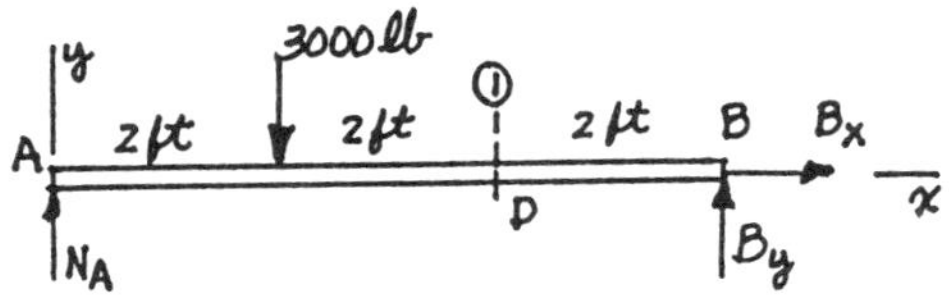

$\Sigma F_y = 0: \quad B_y = 3000 - 2000 = 1000 \text{ lb}$

$\Sigma F_x = 0: \quad B_x = 0$

FBD of segment AD

$\Sigma F_x = 0: \quad P_1 = 0$ ◆

$\Sigma F_y = 0: \quad V_1 = 3000 - 2000$

$\therefore \quad V_1 = 1000 \text{ lb}$ ◆

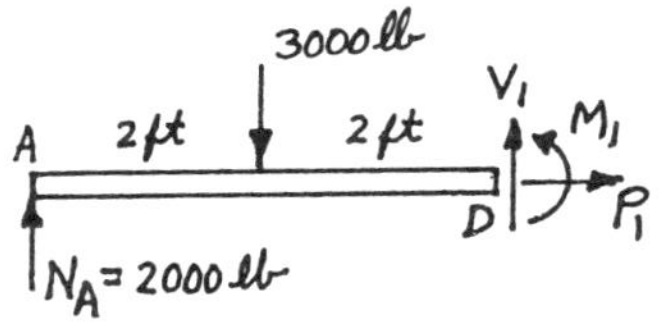

$\Sigma M_D = 0: \quad (+)\ 3000(2) - 2000(4) + M_1 = 0$

$\therefore \quad M_1 = 2000 \text{ lb}\cdot\text{ft}$ ◆

FBD of segment DB

$\Sigma F_x = 0: \quad P_1 = B_x = 0$ ◆

$\Sigma F_y = 0: \quad V_1 = B_y = 1000 \text{ lb}$ ◆

$\Sigma M_D = 0: \quad M_1 = B_y(2) = 2000 \text{ lb}\cdot\text{ft}$ ◆

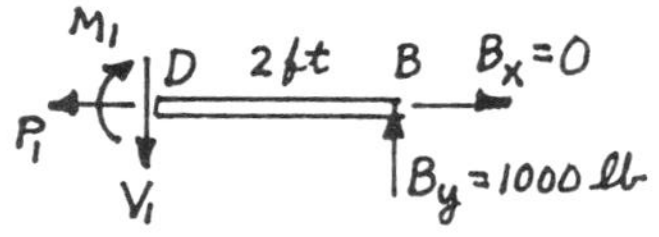

6.2

FBD of entire beam

$\Sigma M_A = 0: \quad B_y(4.5) = 180 \text{ kN}\cdot\text{m}$

$\therefore \quad B_y = 40 \text{ kN}$

$\Sigma F_y = 0: \quad N_A = B_y = 40 \text{ kN}$

$\Sigma F_x = 0: \quad B_x = 0$

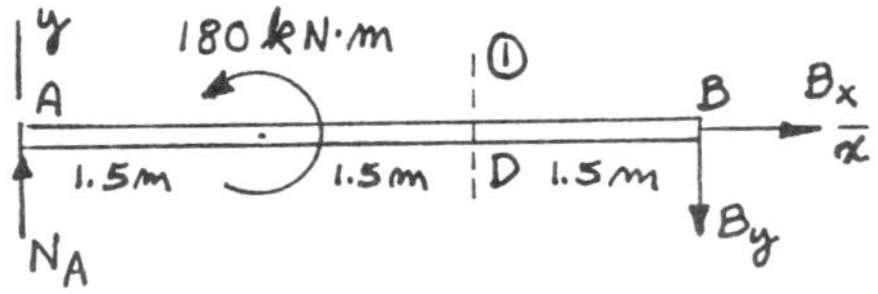

FBD of segment AD

$\Sigma F_x = 0: \quad P_1 = 0$ ◆

$\Sigma F_y = 0: \quad V_1 = N_A = 40 \text{ kN}$ ◆

$\Sigma M_D = 0: \quad (+)\ 180 - N_A(3) - M_1 = 0$

$\therefore \quad M_1 = 180 - 40(3) = 60 \text{ kN}\cdot\text{m}$ ◆

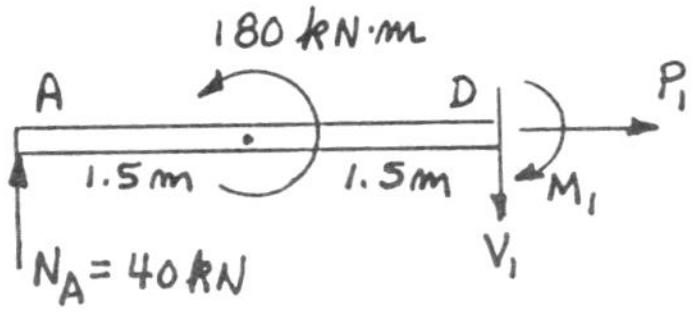

(continued)

FBD of segment DB

$\Sigma F_x = 0: \quad P_1 = B_x = 0$ ◆

$\Sigma F_y = 0: \quad V_1 = B_y = 40 \text{ kN}$ ◆

$\Sigma M_D = 0: \quad M_1 = B_y(1.5) = 40(1.5) = 60 \text{ kN}\cdot\text{m}$ ◆

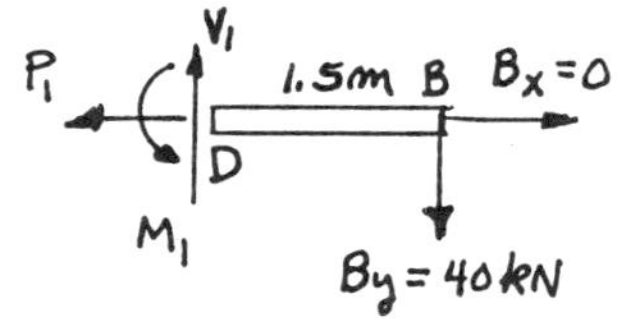

6.3

FBD of entire beam

By symmetry:

$N_A = B_y = 1800 \text{ lb}$

$\Sigma F_x = 0: \quad B_x = 0$

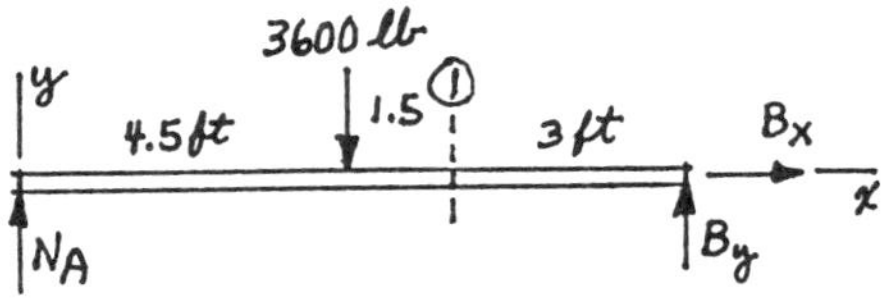

FBD of segment AD

$\Sigma F_x = 0: \quad P_1 = 0$ ◆

$\Sigma F_y = 0: \quad V_1 = 2400 - N_A$

$\therefore \quad V_1 = 2400 - 1800 = 600 \text{ lb}$ ◆

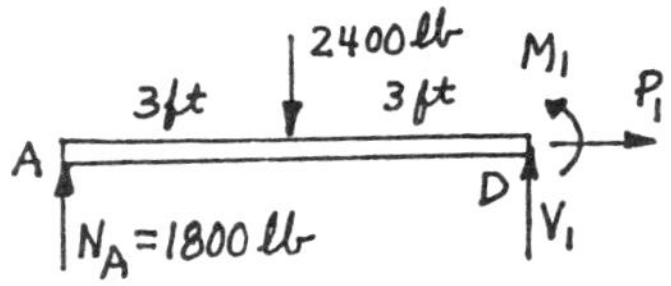

$\Sigma M_D = 0: \quad (+)\ -N_A(6) + 2400(3) + M_1 = 0$

$\therefore \quad M_1 = 1800(6) - 7200 = 3600 \text{ lb}\cdot\text{ft}$ ◆

FBD of segment DB

$\Sigma F_x = 0: \quad P_1 = B_x = 0$ ◆

$\Sigma F_y = 0: \quad V_1 = B_y - 1200$

$\therefore \quad V_1 = 1800 - 1200 = 600 \text{ lb}$ ◆

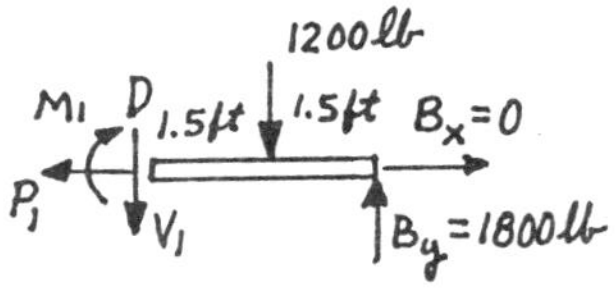

$\Sigma M_D = 0: \quad (+)\ B_y(3) - 1200(1.5) - M_1 = 0$

$\therefore \quad M_1 = 1800(3) - 1800 = 3600 \text{ lb}\cdot\text{ft}$ ◆

6.4

FBD of entire beam

$\Sigma M_A = 0: \quad N_B = 240 \text{ lb}$

$\Sigma F_y = 0: \quad A_y = 0$

$\Sigma F_x = 0: \quad A_x = 0$

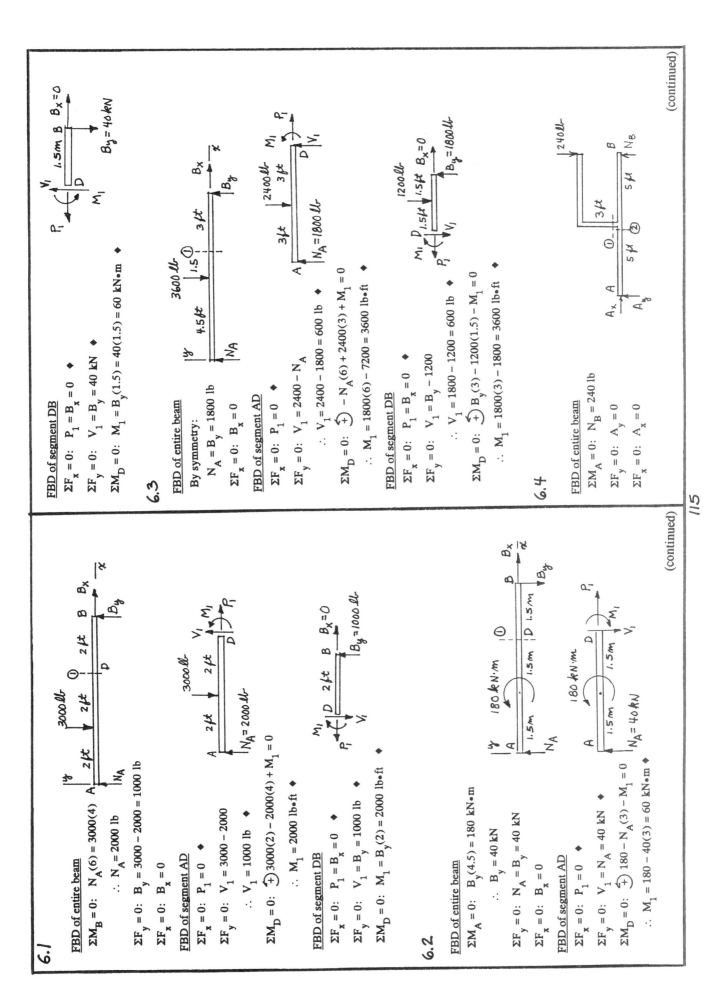

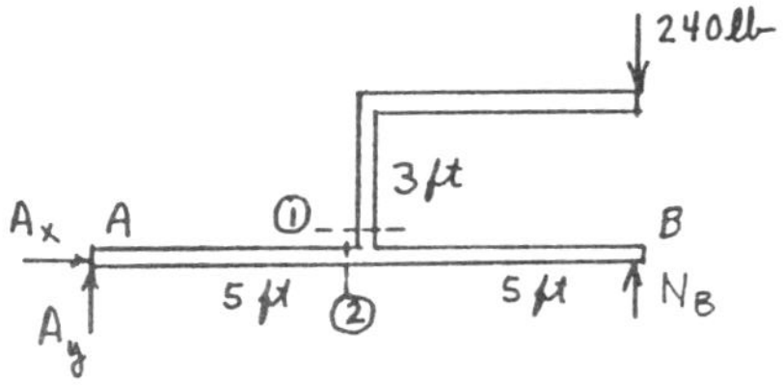

(continued)

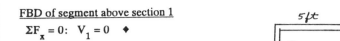

FBD of segment above section 1

$\Sigma F_x = 0$: $V_1 = 0$ ◆

$\Sigma F_y = 0$: $P_1 = 240$ lb (compression) ◆

$\Sigma M_C = 0$: $M_1 = 240(5) = 1200$ lb•ft ◆

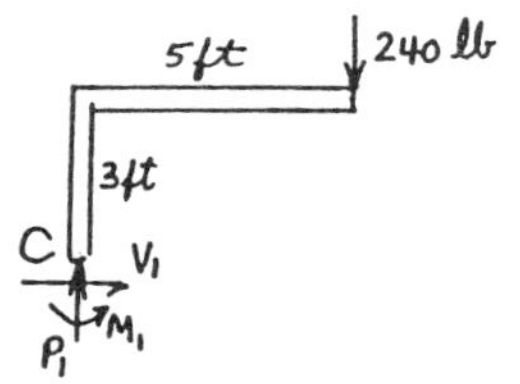

FBD of segment to the left of section 2

$\Sigma F_x = 0$: $P_2 = 0$ ◆

$\Sigma F_y = 0$: $V_2 = 0$ ◆

$\Sigma M_C = 0$: $M_2 = 0$ ◆

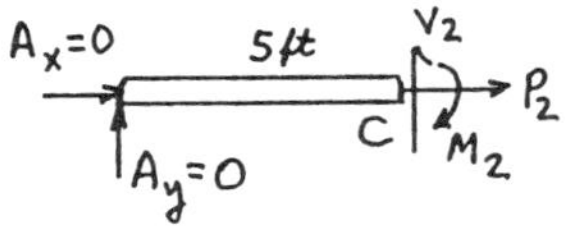

6.5

FBD of entire beam

$\Sigma M_A = 0$: $N_B(10) = 240(3)$

$\therefore N_B = 72$ lb

$\Sigma F_y = 0$: $A_y = N_B = 72$ lb

$\Sigma F_x = 0$: $A_x = 240$ lb

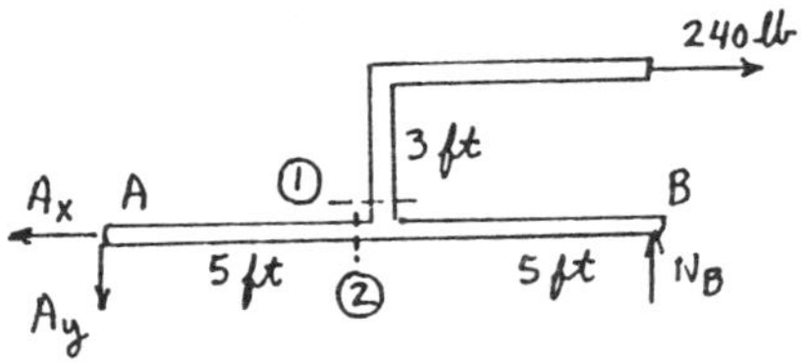

FBD of segment above section 1

$\Sigma F_x = 0$: $V_1 = 240$ lb ◆

$\Sigma F_y = 0$: $P_1 = 0$ ◆

$\Sigma M_C = 0$: $M_1 = 240(3) = 720$ lb•ft ◆

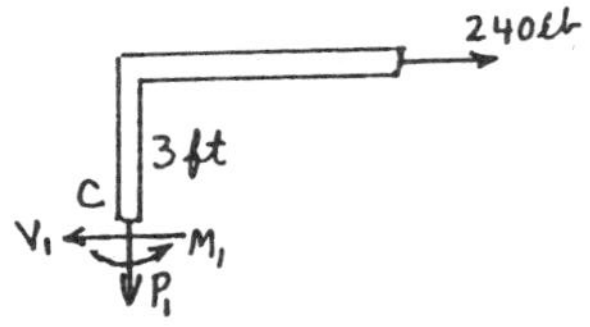

FBD of segment to the left of section 2

$\Sigma F_x = 0$: $P_2 = 240$ lb (tension) ◆

$\Sigma F_y = 0$: $V_2 = A_y = 72$ lb ◆

$\Sigma M_C = 0$: $M_2 = 72(5) = 360$ lb•ft ◆

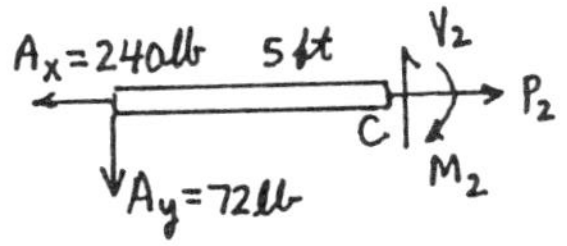

6.6

FBD of entire beam

$\Sigma M_A = 0$: $N_B(10) = 720$ lb•ft

$\therefore N_B = 72$ lb

$\Sigma F_y = 0$: $A_y = N_B = 72$ lb

$\Sigma F_x = 0$: $A_x = 0$

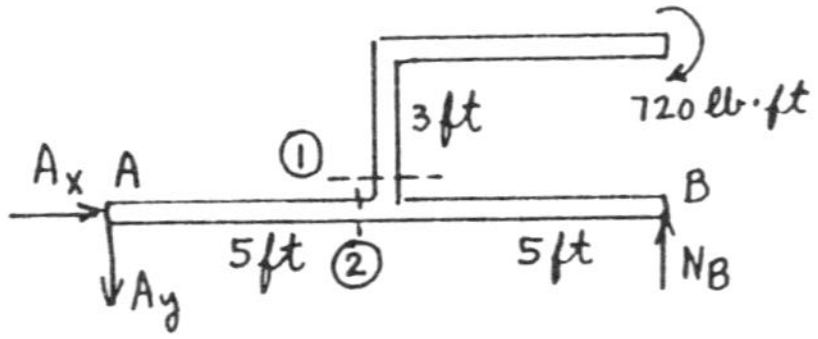

FBD of segment above section 1

$\Sigma F_x = 0$: $V_1 = 0$ ◆

$\Sigma F_y = 0$: $P_1 = 0$ ◆

$\Sigma M_C = 0$: $M_1 = 720$ lb•ft ◆

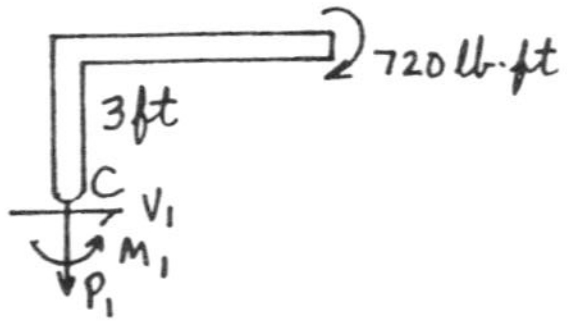

FBD of segment to the left of section 2

$\Sigma F_x = 0$: $P_2 = 0$ ◆

$\Sigma F_y = 0$: $V_2 = A_y = 72$ lb ◆

$\Sigma M_C = 0$: $M_2 = 72(5) = 360$ lb•ft ◆

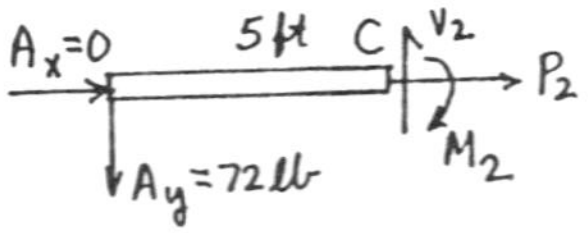

6.7

In each case, the maximum bending moment occurs at the support.

Case (a)

$\Sigma M_A = 0$:

$M_1 = P_1 L = 360\,L = M_{max}$

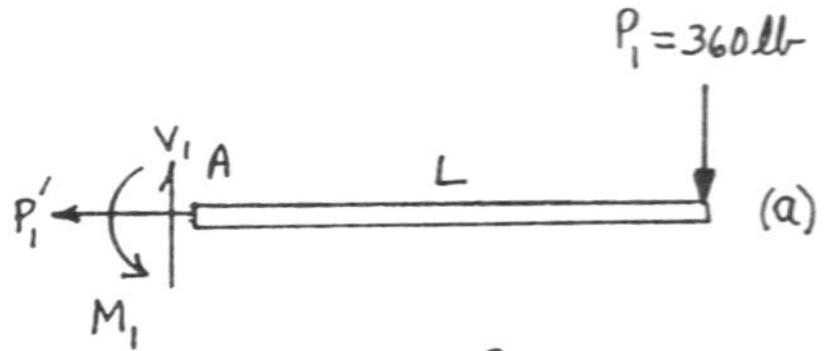

Case (b)

$\Sigma M_A = 0$:

$M_2 = P_2(L/2) = M_{max} = 360\,L$

$\therefore P_2 = 720$ lb ◆

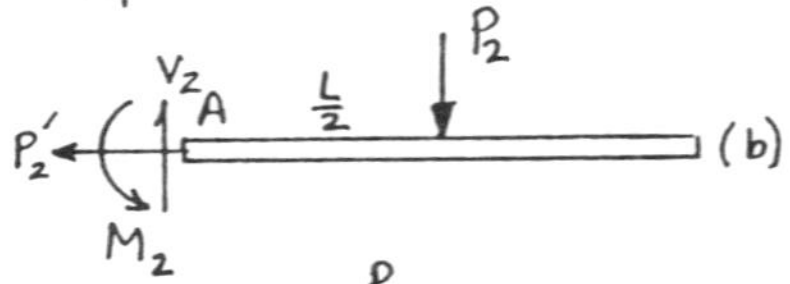

Case (c)

$\Sigma M_A = 0$:

$M_3 = P_3(L/3) = M_{max} = 360\,L$

$\therefore P_3 = 1080$ lb ◆

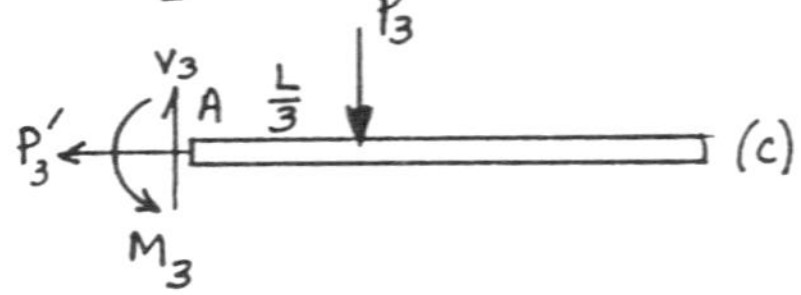

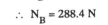

6.8

FBD of segment to the right of section 1

$\Sigma F_x = 0$: $P_1 = 28$ lb (tension) ◆

$\Sigma F_y = 0$: $V_1 = 0$ ◆

$\Sigma M_A = 0$: $M_1 = 28(3/4) = 21$ lb•in. ◆

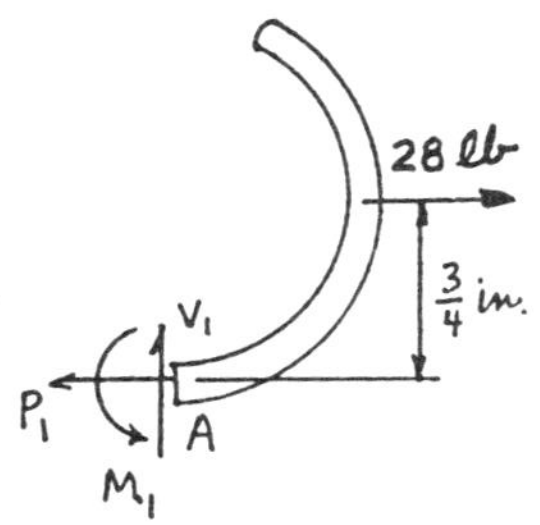

FBD of segment below section 2

$\Sigma F_x = 0$: $\overset{+}{\rightarrow}$ $28 - 40\sin 30^\circ - V_2 = 0$

$\therefore V_2 = 8$ lb ◆

$\Sigma F_y = 0$: $P_2 = 40\cos 30^\circ = 34.6$ lb ◆

$\Sigma M_B = 0$: ↺+ $28(1.25) - 40\sin 30^\circ(1.25) - M_2 = 0$

$\therefore M_2 = 10$ lb•in. ◆

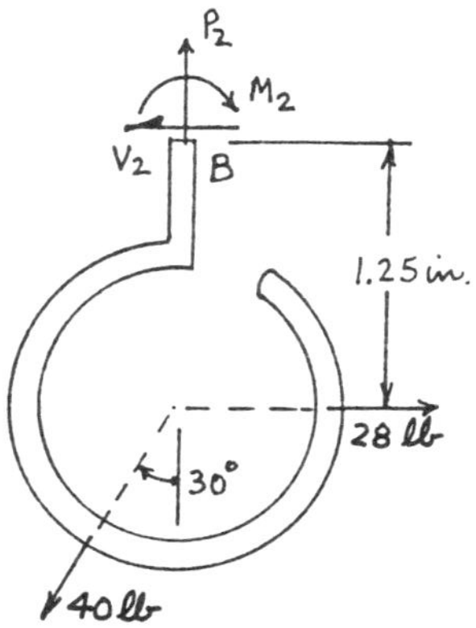

6.9

FBD of entire bar

Weight = 24.5(9.81) = 240.3 N

$\sin\theta = 5/13$ $\cos\theta = 12/13$

$\Sigma M_A = 0$: $0.5\,N_B = 240.3(0.6)$

$\therefore N_B = 288.4$ N

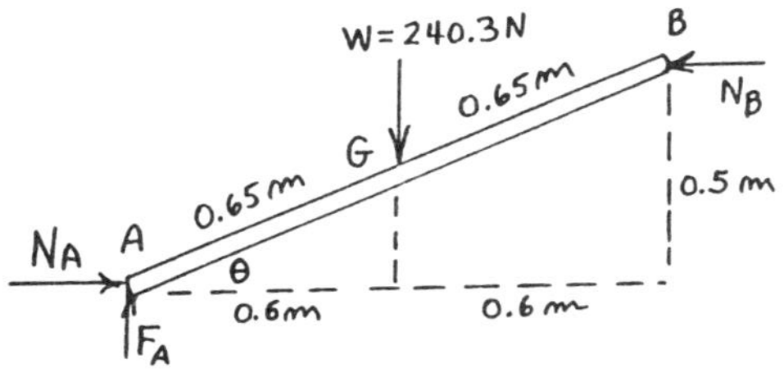

(continued)

FBD of upper half of bar

$\Sigma M_G = 0$: ↺+ $288.4(0.25) - 120.2(0.3) - M = 0$

$\therefore M = 36$ N•m ◆

$\Sigma F_{x'} = 0$:

$P - 120.2\sin\theta - 288.4\cos\theta = 0$

$\therefore P = 120.2(5/13) + 288.4(12/13)$

$= 312$ N ◆

$\Sigma F_{y'} = 0$:

$V - 120.2\cos\theta + 288.4\sin\theta = 0$

$\therefore V = 120.2(12/13) - 288.4(5/13) = 0$ ◆

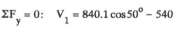

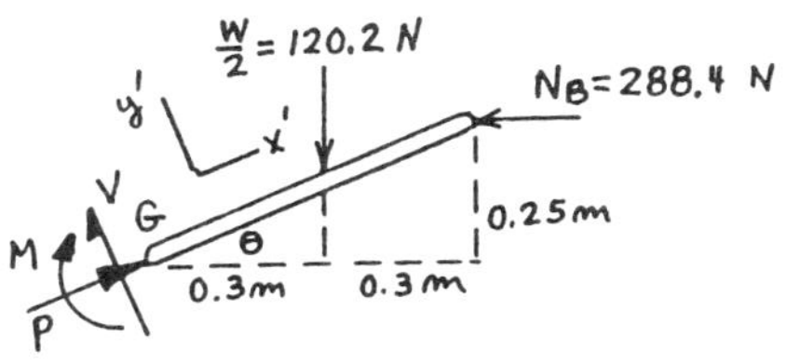

6.10

FBD of segment AB

$\Sigma M_B = 0$:

$N_A\cos 50^\circ(1.2) = 1080(0.6)$

$N_A = 840.1$ N

Dimensions in meters

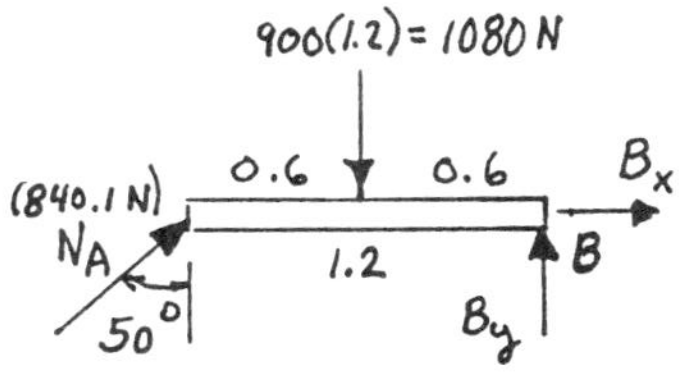

FBD of segment to left of section 1

$\Sigma F_x = 0$: $P_1 = 840.1\sin 50^\circ$

$= 644$ N (C) ◆

$\Sigma F_y = 0$: $V_1 = 840.1\cos 50^\circ - 540$

$= 0$ ◆

$\Sigma M_D = 0$: $M_1 = 840.1\cos 50^\circ(0.6) - 540(0.3)$

$= 162$ N•m ◆

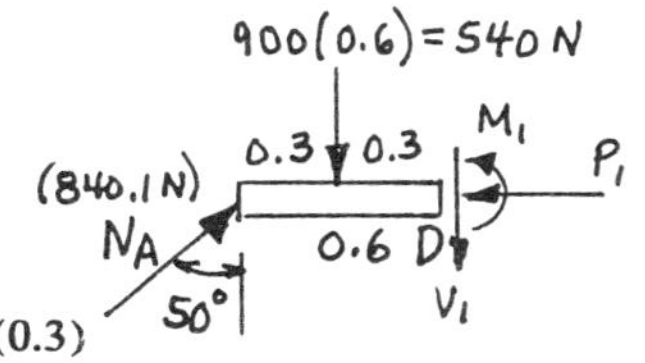

FBD of segment to left of section 2

$\Sigma F_x = 0$: $P_2 = 840.1\sin 50^\circ =$

$= 644$ N (C) ◆

$\Sigma F_y = 0$: $V_2 = 840.1\cos 50^\circ - 1080$

$= -540$ N ◆

$\Sigma M_E = 0$: $M_2 = 840.1\cos 50^\circ(1.8) - 1080(1.2)$

$= -324$ N•m ◆

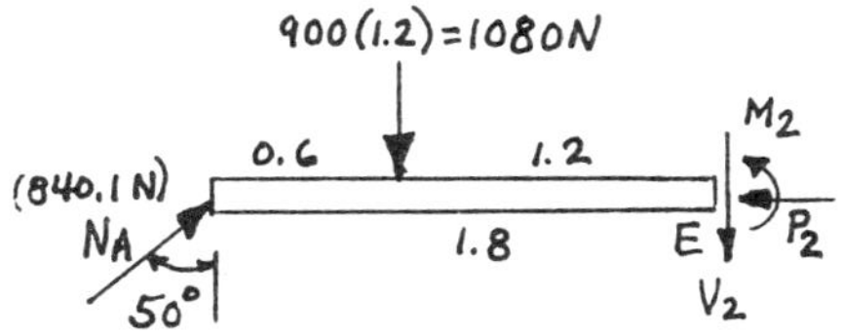

6.11

FBD of bar BCD (recognizing that AC is a two-force body)

$\Sigma M_D = 0$: $800(2.25) = 0.8P_{AC}(1.5)$

$\therefore\ P_{AC} = 1500$ N

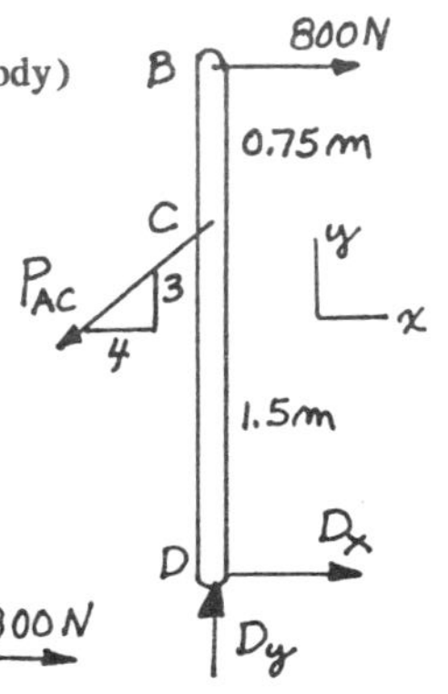

FBD of segment of bar BCD above section 1

$\Sigma F_x = 0$: $V_1 = 800$ N ◆

$\Sigma F_y = 0$: $P_1 = 0$ ◆

$\Sigma M_C = 0$: $M_1 = 800(0.75) = 600$ N•m ◆

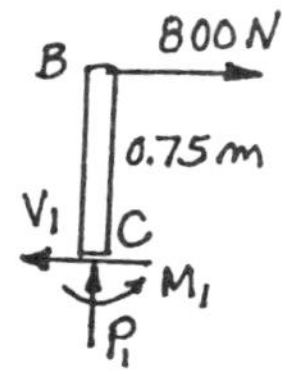

FBD of segment of bar BCD above section 2

$\Sigma F_x = 0$: $V_2 = 1200 - 800 = 400$ N ◆

$\Sigma F_y = 0$: $P_2 = 900$ N ◆

$\Sigma M_C = 0$: $M_1 = 800(0.75) = 600$ N•m ◆

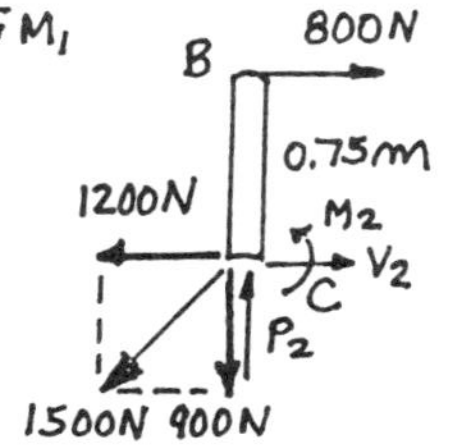

6.12

FBD of bar BCD (recognizing that AC is a two-force body)

$\Sigma M_D = 0$: $800(2.25) = 0.8P_{AC}(1.5)$

$\therefore\ P_{AC} = 1500$ N

$\Sigma F_x = 0$: $D_x = 0.8P_{AC} - 800$

$= 0.8(1500) - 800 = 400$ N

$\Sigma F_y = 0$: $D_y = 0.6P_{AC} = 0.6(1500) = 900$ N

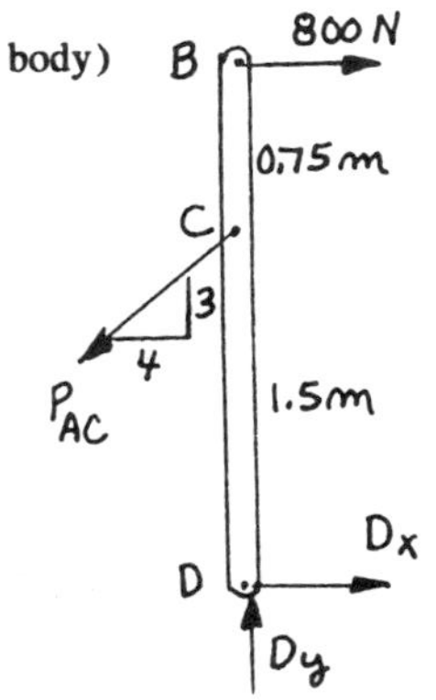

(continued)

FBD of segment of bar BCD below section 3

$\Sigma F_x = 0$: $V_3 = D_x = 400$ N ◆

$\Sigma F_y = 0$: $P_3 = D_y = 900$ N (C) ◆

$\Sigma M_E = 0$: $M_3 = D_x(0.75)$

$= 400(0.75) = 300$ N•m ◆

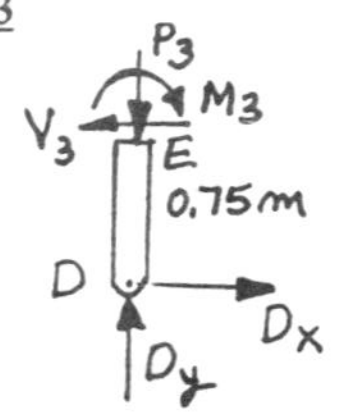

FBD of segment of bar AC below section 4

(recognizing that AC is a two-force body)

$\Sigma F_x = 0$: $V_4 = 1200$ N ◆

$\Sigma F_y = 0$: $P_4 = 900$ N (T) ◆

$\Sigma M_F = 0$: $M_4 = 1200(1.5) = 1800$ N•m ◆

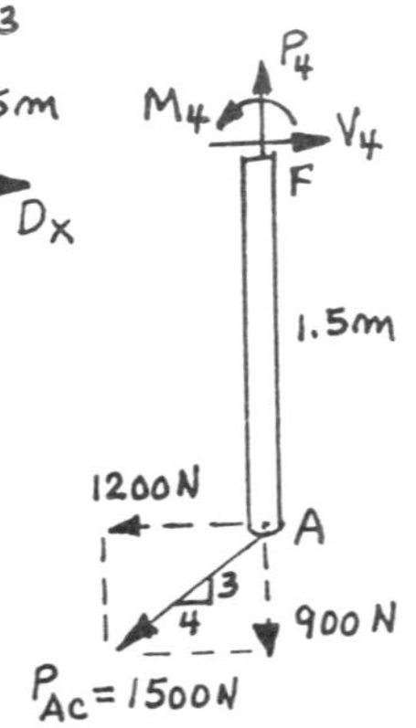

6.13

FBD of entire frame (recognizing that BC is a two-force body)

$\Sigma M_A = 0$:

(+) $BC \cos 45^o(0.4) - 240(0.7) + 240(0.4) = 0$

$\therefore\ BC = 254.6$ N

which gives: $BC_x = 254.6 \cos 45^o = 180$ N

$BC_y = 254.6 \sin 45^o = 180$ N

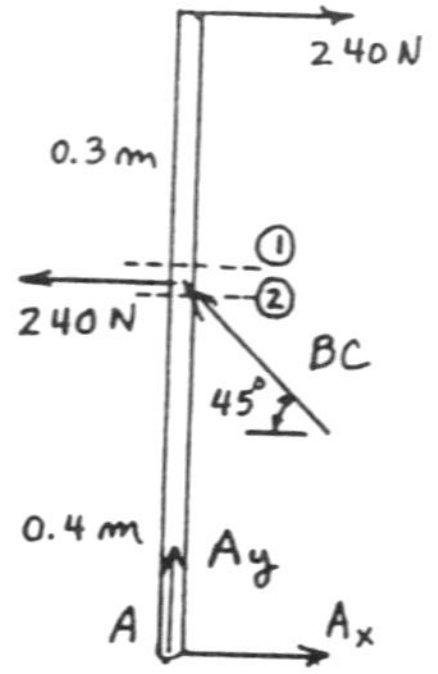

FBD of segment above section 1

$\Sigma F_x = 0$: $V_1 = 240$ N ◆

$\Sigma F_y = 0$: $P_1 = 0$ ◆

$\Sigma M_C = 0$: $M_1 = 240(0.3) = 72$ N•m ◆

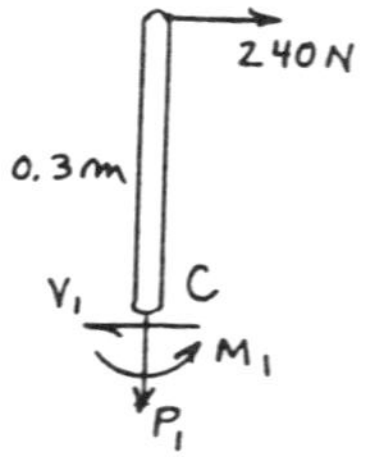

FBD of segment above section 2

$\Sigma F_x = 0$: $V_2 = 240 - 240 + 180 = 180$ N ◆

$\Sigma F_y = 0$: $P_2 = 180$ N (tension) ◆

$\Sigma M_C = 0$: $M_2 = 240(0.3) = 72$ N•m ◆

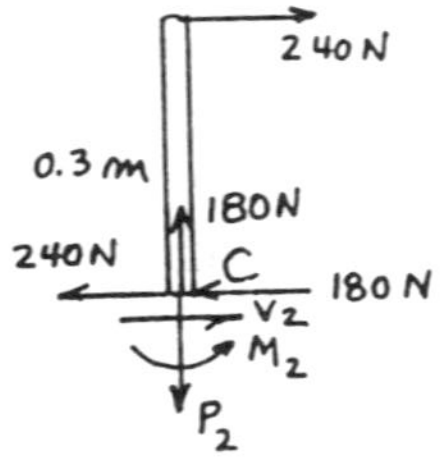

6.14

FBD of entire frame (recognizing that BC is a two-force body)

$\Sigma M_A = 0$:

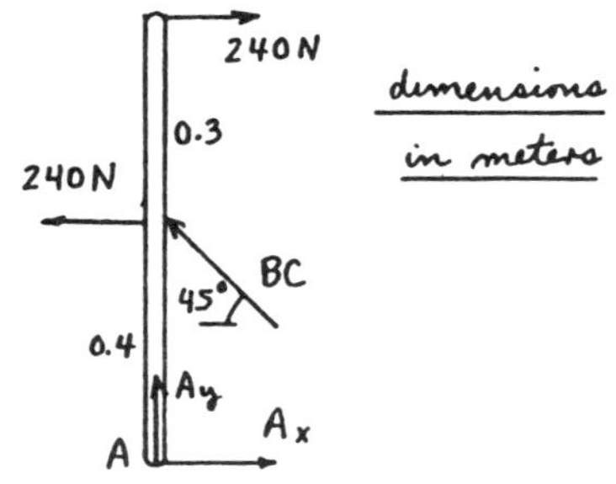

(+) $BC \cos 45^o(0.4) - 240(0.7) + 240(0.4) = 0$

$\therefore\ BC = 254.6\ N$

which gives: $BC_x = 254.6 \cos 45^o = 180\ N$

$BC_y = 254.6 \sin 45^o = 180\ N$

FBD of segment of BC that lies to the left of section 3

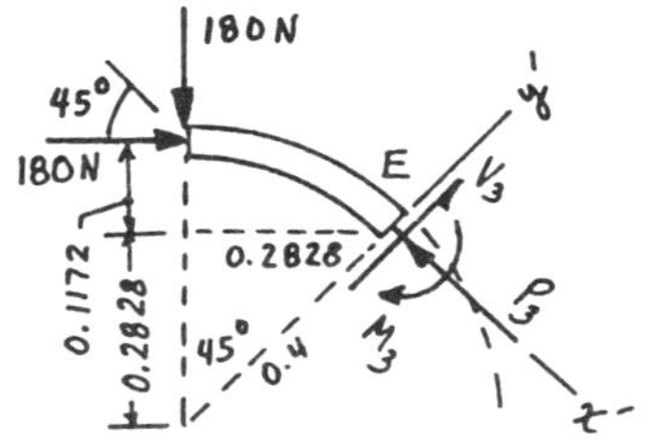

$\Sigma F_{x'} = 0$:

$P_3 = 180 \cos 45^o + 180 \cos 45^o = 255\ N$ (C) ◆

$\Sigma F_{y'} = 0$: $V_3 = 180 \sin 45^o - 180 \sin 45^o = 0$ ◆

$\Sigma M_E = 0$:

$M_3 = 180(0.2828) - 180(0.1172) = 29.8\ N \cdot m$ ◆

6.15

FBD of entire system

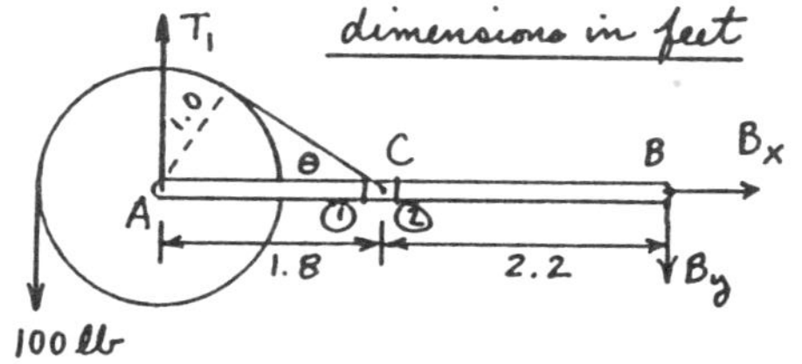

$\Sigma F_x = 0$: $B_x = 0$

$\Sigma M_A = 0$: $B_y(2.2 + 1.8) = 100(1.0)$

$\therefore\ B_y = 25\ lb$

Note that $\sin\theta = 1.0/1.8 = 0.5556$

and $\cos\theta = \sqrt{1.8^2 - 1.0^2}/1.8 = 0.8315$

FBD of segment to right of section 1

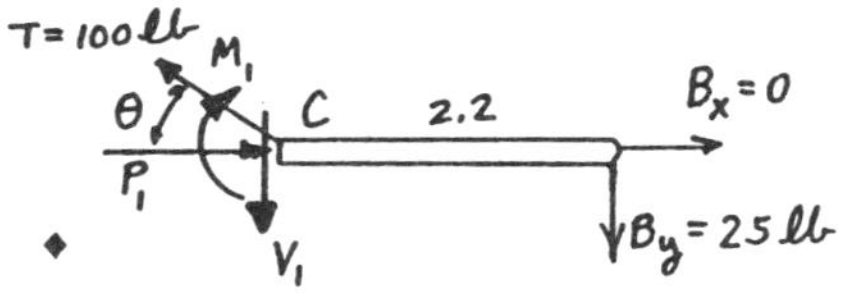

$\Sigma F_x = 0$: $P_1 = 100 \cos\theta = 100(0.8315)$

$= 83.2$ lb (compression) ◆

$\Sigma F_y = 0$: $V_1 = 100 \sin\theta - 25$

$= 100(0.5556) - 25 = 30.6$ lb ◆

$\Sigma M_C = 0$: $M_1 = 25(2.2) = 55.0\ lb \cdot ft$ ◆

(continued)

FBD of segment to right of section 2

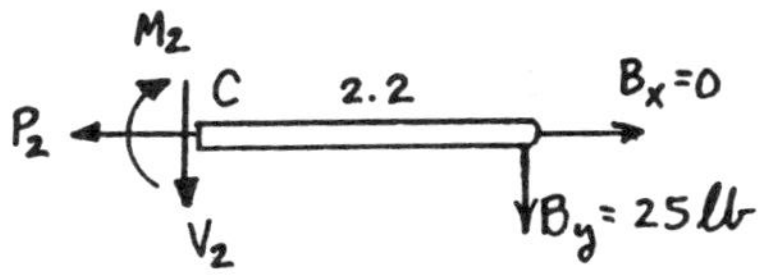

$\Sigma F_x = 0$: $P_2 = 0$ ◆

$\Sigma F_y = 0$: $V_2 = 25$ lb ◆

$\Sigma M_C = 0$: $M_2 = 25(2.2) = 55.0\ lb \cdot ft$ ◆

6.16

From the FBD of the entire frame, the horizontal and vertical components of the external reactions at A and F are $N_A = 50$ lb ↑, $F_y = 50$ ↓ and $F_x = 0$.

FBD of bar DEF (recognizing that CD and BE are two-force bodies)

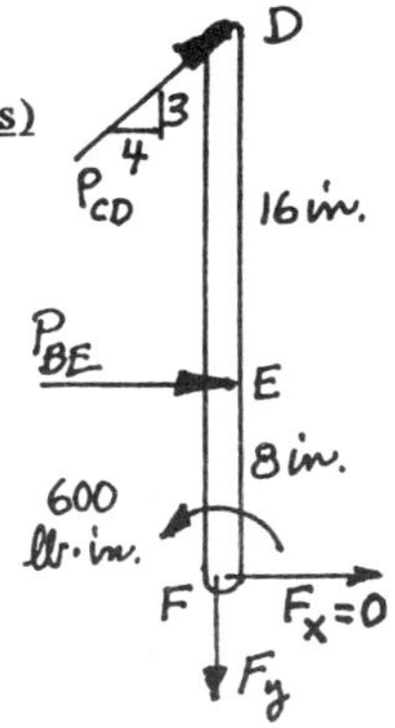

$\Sigma M_D = 0$: $16P_{BE} = 600$

$P_{BE} = 37.5$ lb

FBD of segment of DEF below section 1

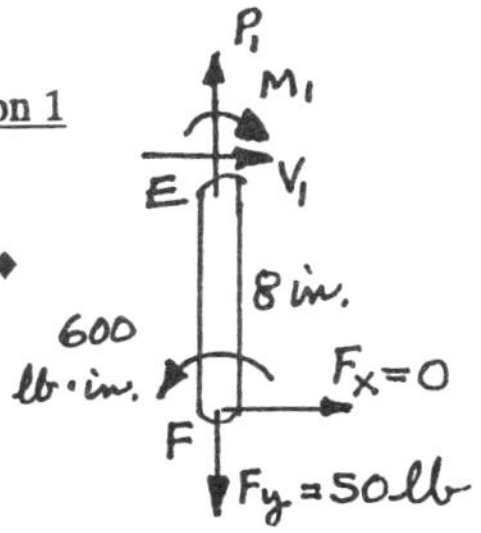

$\Sigma F_x = 0$: $V_1 = F_x = 0$ ◆

$\Sigma F_y = 0$: $P_1 = F_y = 50$ lb (T) ◆

$\Sigma M_E = 0$: $M_1 = 600\ lb \cdot in.$ ◆

FBD of segment of ABC below section 2

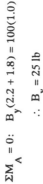

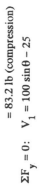

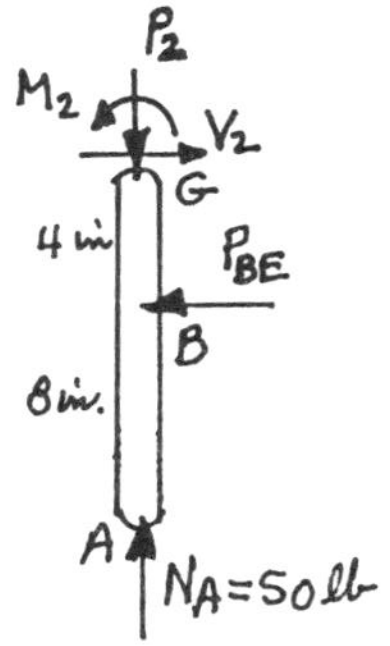

$\Sigma F_x = 0$: $V_2 = P_{BE} = 37.5$ lb ◆

$\Sigma F_y = 0$: $P_2 = N_A = 50$ lb (C) ◆

$\Sigma M_G = 0$: $M_2 = P_{BE}(4)$

$= 37.5(4) = 150\ lb \cdot in.$ ◆

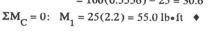

6.17

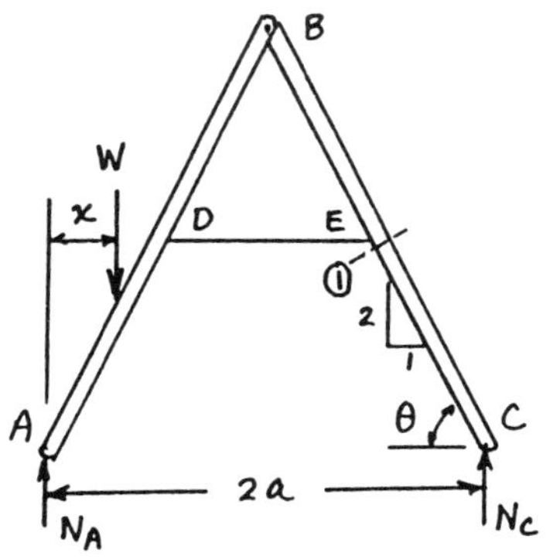

FBD of entire frame

$\Sigma M_A = 0$: $Wx = N_C(2a)$

$\therefore N_C = \dfrac{Wx}{2a}$

Note: $\sin\theta = \dfrac{2}{\sqrt{5}}$ and $\cos\theta = \dfrac{1}{\sqrt{5}}$

FBD of segment of BC that is below section 1

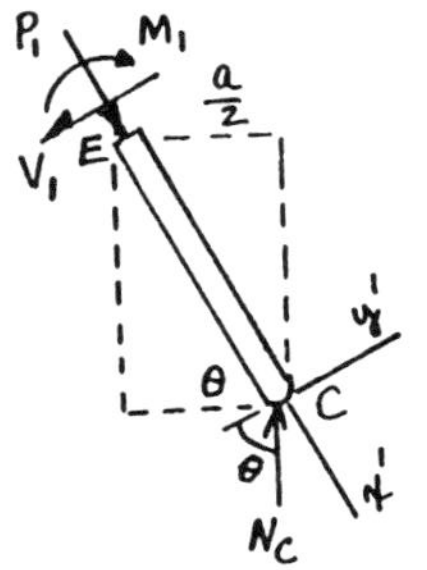

$\Sigma F_{x'} = 0$: $P_1 = N_C \sin\theta = \dfrac{Wx}{2a}\dfrac{2}{\sqrt{5}} = \dfrac{Wx}{a\sqrt{5}}$ ◆

$\Sigma F_{y'} = 0$: $V_1 = N_C \cos\theta = \dfrac{Wx}{2a}\dfrac{1}{\sqrt{5}} = \dfrac{Wx}{2a\sqrt{5}}$ ◆

$\Sigma M_E = 0$: $M_1 = N_C\left(\dfrac{a}{2}\right) = \dfrac{Wx}{2a}\left(\dfrac{a}{2}\right) = \dfrac{Wx}{4}$ ◆

6.18

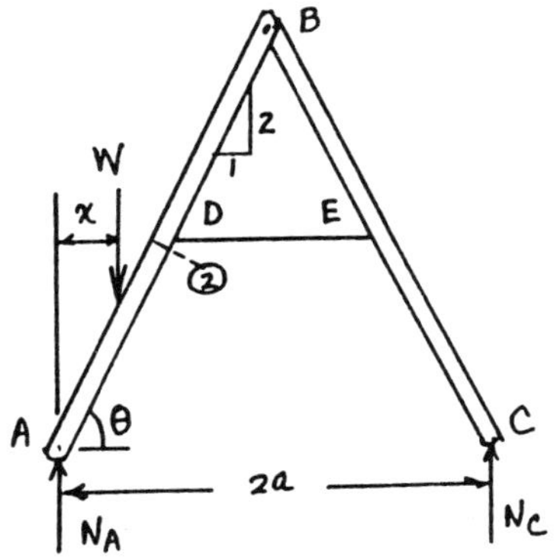

FBD of entire frame

$\Sigma M_C = 0$: $W(2a - x) = N_A(2a)$

$\therefore N_A = \dfrac{W(2a - x)}{2a} = W - \dfrac{Wx}{2a}$

Note: $\sin\theta = \dfrac{2}{\sqrt{5}}$ and $\cos\theta = \dfrac{1}{\sqrt{5}}$

(continued)

FBD of segment of AB that is below section 2

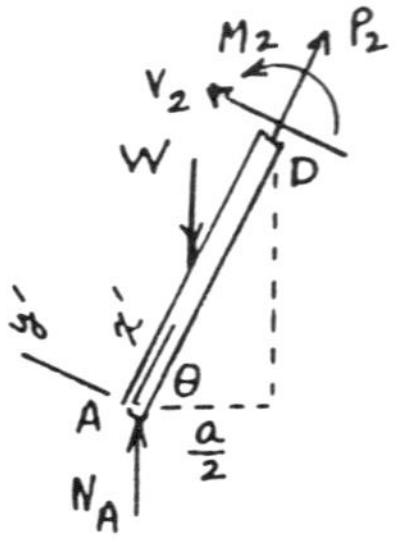

$\Sigma F_{x'} = 0$:

$$P_2 = W\sin\theta - N_A \sin\theta = \frac{2}{\sqrt{5}}\left[W - \left(W - \frac{Wx}{2a}\right)\right]$$

$\therefore P_2 = \dfrac{Wx}{a\sqrt{5}}$ (tension) ◆

$\Sigma F_{y'} = 0$:

$$V_2 = W\cos\theta - N_A \cos\theta = \frac{1}{\sqrt{5}}\left[W - \left(W - \frac{Wx}{2a}\right)\right] = \frac{Wx}{2a\sqrt{5}}$$ ◆

$\Sigma M_D = 0$:

$$M_2 = N_A\left(\frac{a}{2}\right) - W\left(\frac{a}{2} - x\right) = \frac{a}{2}\left[W - \frac{Wx}{2a}\right] - W\left(\frac{a}{2} - x\right) = \frac{3Wx}{4}$$ ◆

6.19

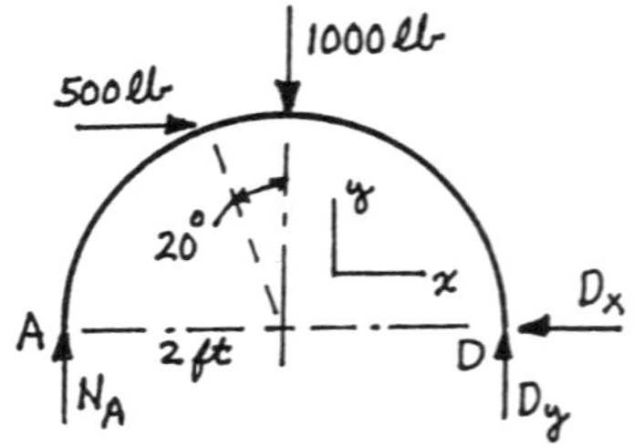

FBD of entire arch

$\Sigma F_x = 0$: $D_x = 500$ lb

$\Sigma M_A = 0$:

$\circlearrowleft{+}$ $D_y(4) - 1000(2) - 500(2\cos 20^\circ) = 0$

$\therefore D_y = 734.9$ lb

FBD of segment of arch below section 1

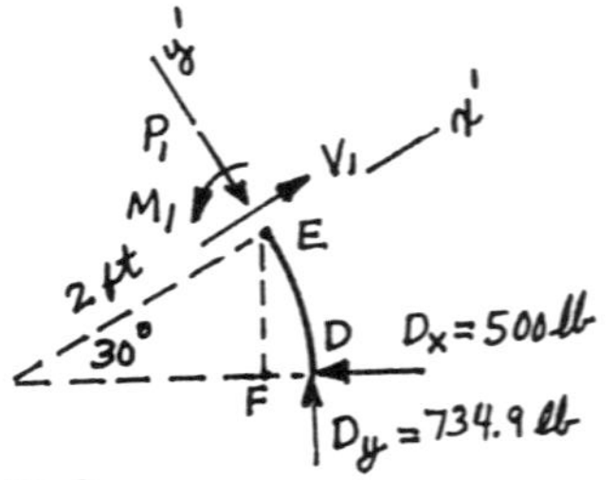

$\Sigma F_{x'} = 0$: $V_1 = 500\cos 30^\circ - 734.9\cos 60^\circ$

$V_1 = 65.56$ lb ◆

$\Sigma F_{y'} = 0$: $P_1 = 500\sin 30^\circ + 734.9\sin 60^\circ$

$P_1 = 886.4$ lb ◆

$\overline{EF} = 2\sin 30^\circ = 1.0$ ft; $\overline{FD} = 2 - 2\cos 30^\circ = 0.2680$ ft

$\Sigma M_E = 0$: $M_1 = D_x(\overline{EF}) - D_y(\overline{FD}) = 500(1.0) - 734.9(0.2680) = 303$ lb•ft

*6.20

From FBD of entire parabolic arch (not shown here), $A_y = 1000$ lb ↑ .

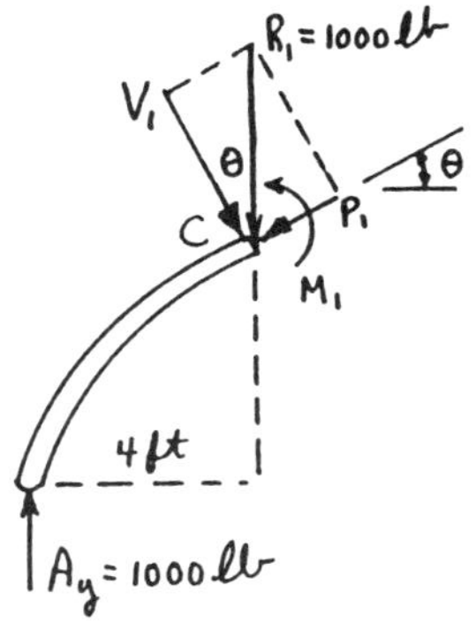

FBD of arch segment below section 1

$\Sigma M_C = 0$: $M_1 = 1000(4) = 4000$ lb•ft ◆

$\Sigma F_y = 0$: $R_1 = A_y = 1000$ lb

Note that P_1 and V_1 are components of R_1.

We must find θ, the slope of the arch at section 1 (i.e., at x = − 2 ft).

$$\frac{dy}{dx} = \frac{d}{dx}\left(\frac{36 - x^2}{6}\right) = -\frac{x}{3}$$

At x = − 2 ft, $\frac{dy}{dx} = \frac{2}{3}$, which gives $\theta = 33.69^o$.

Therefore, $P_1 = 1000 \sin\theta = 1000 \sin 33.69^o = 555$ lb ◆

$V_1 = 1000 \cos\theta = 1000 \cos 33.69^o = 832$ lb ◆

6.21

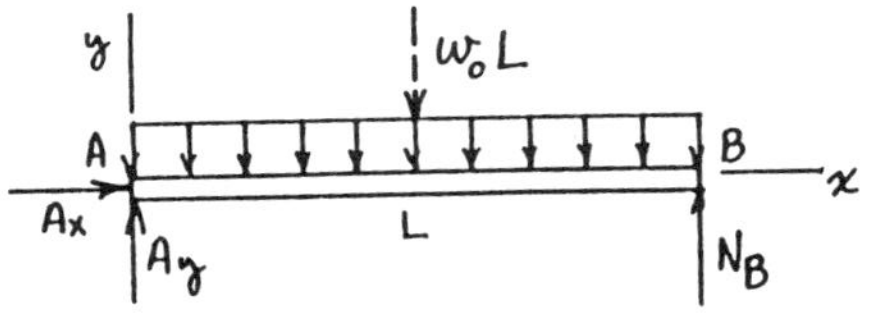

Reactions

By symmetry: $A_y = N_B = \frac{w_0 L}{2}$

$\Sigma F_x = 0$: $A_x = 0$

For 0 < x < L

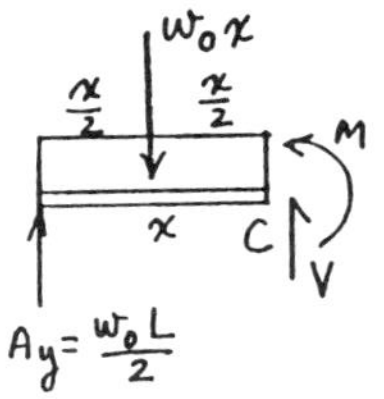

$\Sigma F_y = 0$: $V = w_0 x - \frac{w_0 L}{2} = w_0\left(x - \frac{L}{2}\right)$ ◆

$\Sigma M_C = 0$: $M = \frac{w_0 L}{2}(x) - w_0 x\left(\frac{x}{2}\right) = \frac{w_0 x}{2}(L - x)$ ◆

(continued)

V- and M-diagrams

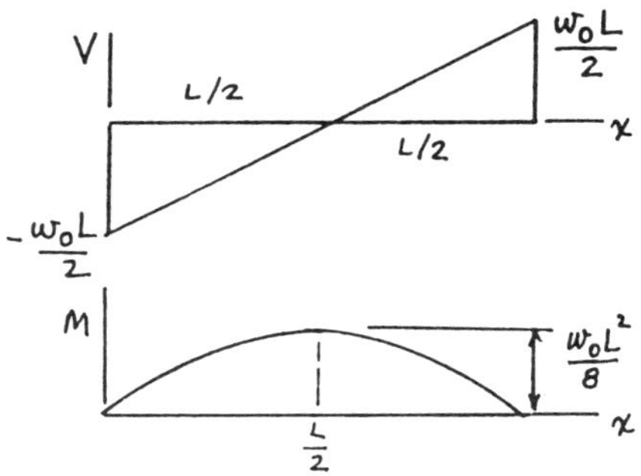

6.22

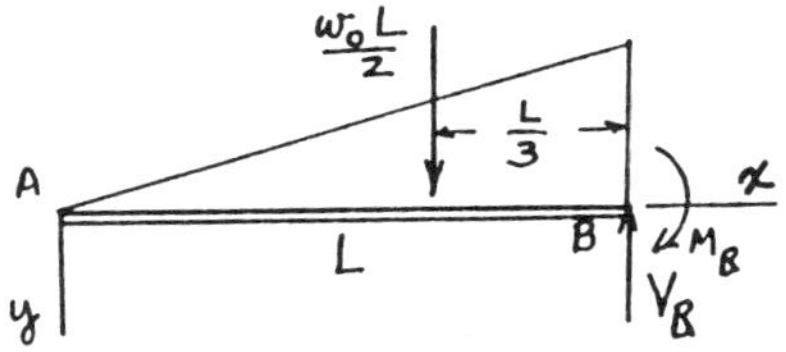

Reactions

$\Sigma F_y = 0$: $V_B = \frac{w_0 L}{2}$

$\Sigma M_B = 0$: $M_B = \frac{w_0 L}{2}\left(\frac{L}{3}\right) = \frac{w_0 L^2}{6}$

For 0 < x < L

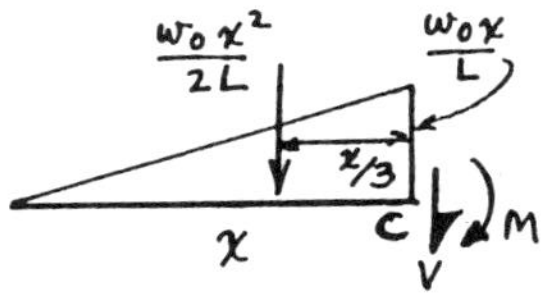

$\Sigma F_y = 0$: $V = -\frac{w_0 x^2}{2L}$ ◆

$\Sigma M_C = 0$: $M = \frac{w_0 x^2}{2L}\left(\frac{x}{3}\right) = \frac{w_0 x^3}{6L}$ ◆

V- and M-diagrams

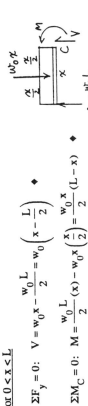

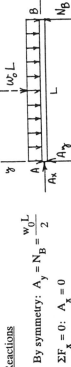

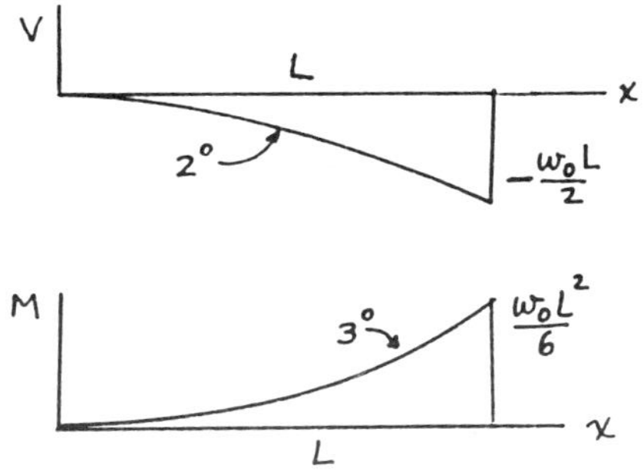

6.23

Reactions

The total applied load is $(1/2)w_0L$. Using the FBD of the entire beam (not shown here), symmetry gives $A_y = N_B = w_0L/4$, and $\Sigma F_x = 0$ gives $A_x = 0$.

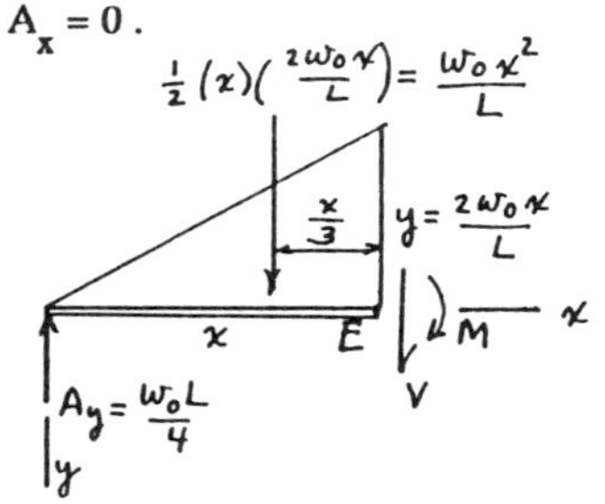

For $0 < x < L/2$

$\Sigma F_y = 0$:

$$V = \frac{w_0L}{4} - \frac{w_0x^2}{L} = \frac{w_0L}{4}\left(1 - \frac{4x^2}{L^2}\right) \quad \blacklozenge$$

$\Sigma M_E = 0$:

$$M = \frac{w_0x^2}{L}\left(\frac{x}{3}\right) - \frac{w_0L}{4}(x) = \frac{w_0Lx}{12}\left(\frac{4x^2}{L^2} - 3\right) \quad \blacklozenge$$

For $L/2 < x < L$

By inspection, V is skew-symmetric and M is symmetric about $x = L/2$, and the equations for this segment can be obtained by replacing x in the above equations by $(L - x)$. Therefore, we obtain

$$V = -\frac{w_0L}{4}\left[1 - \frac{4(L-x)^2}{L^2}\right] \quad \blacklozenge \qquad M = \frac{w_0L(L-x)}{12}\left[\frac{4(L-x)^2}{L^2} - 3\right] \quad \blacklozenge$$

V- and M-diagrams

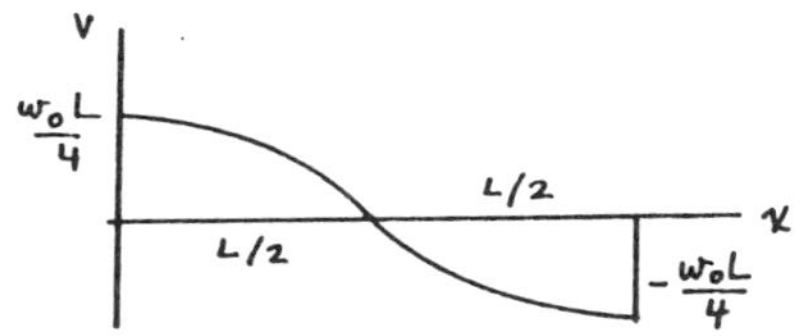

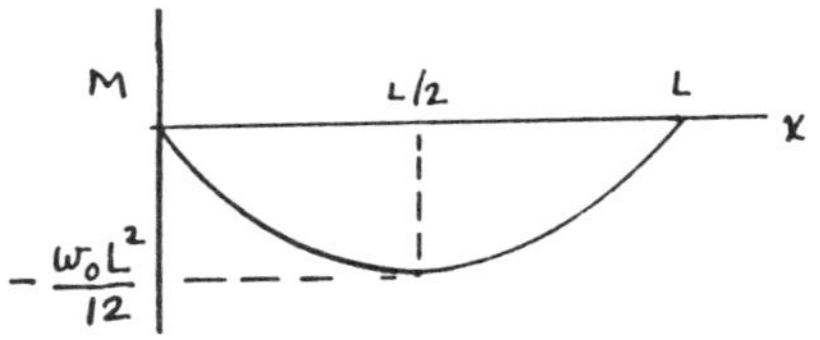

6.24

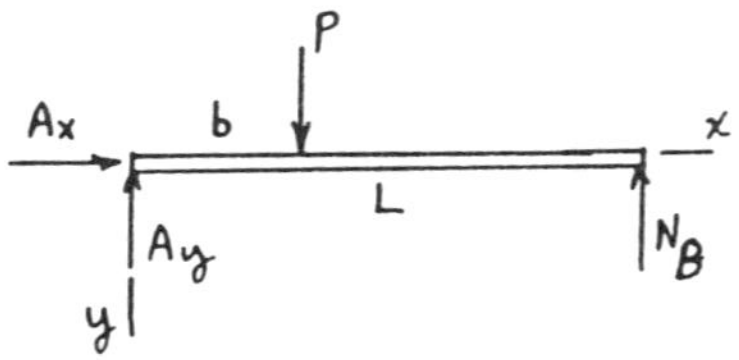

Reactions $\Sigma F_x = 0$: $A_x = 0$

$$\Sigma M_A = 0: \quad N_B = \frac{Pb}{L}$$

$$\Sigma F_y = 0: \quad A_y = \frac{P(L-b)}{L}$$

For $0 < x < b$

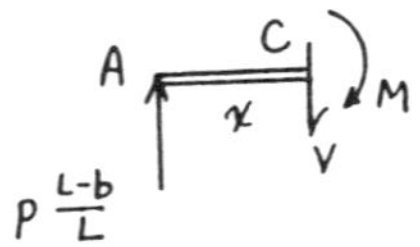

$$\Sigma F_y = 0: \quad V = \frac{P(L-b)}{L} \quad \blacklozenge$$

$$\Sigma M_C = 0: \quad M = -\frac{P(L-b)}{L}(x) \quad \blacklozenge$$

For $b < x < L$

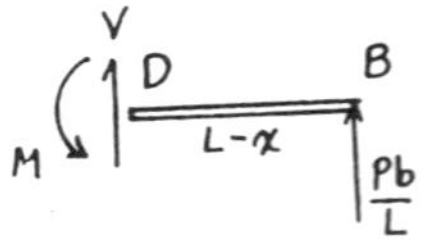

$$\Sigma F_y = 0: \quad V = -\frac{Pb}{L} \quad \blacklozenge$$

$$\Sigma M_D = 0: \quad M = -\frac{Pb}{L}(L - x) \quad \blacklozenge$$

V- and M-diagrams

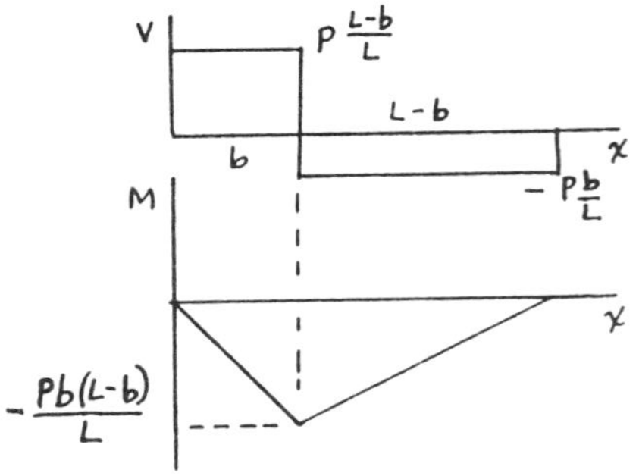

6.25

(a) <u>Reactions</u> $\Sigma F_x = 0$: $A_x = 0$

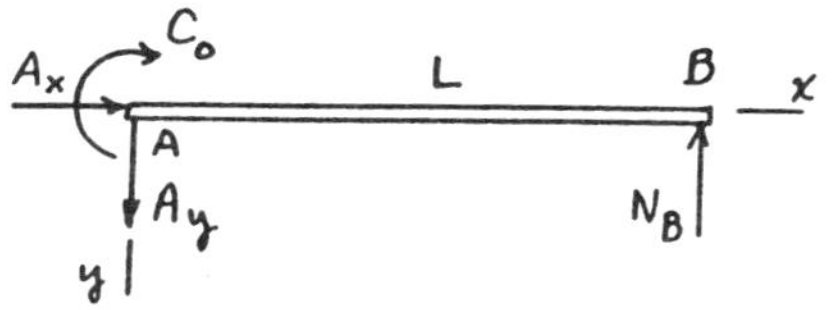

$\Sigma M_A = 0$: $N_B = C_0/L$

$\Sigma F_y = 0$: $A_y = C_0/L$

<u>For $0 < x < L$</u>

$\Sigma F_y = 0$: $V = -C_0/L$ ◆

$\Sigma M_E = 0$: $M = \dfrac{C_0}{L}(x) - C_0 = -C_0\left(1 - \dfrac{x}{L}\right)$ ◆

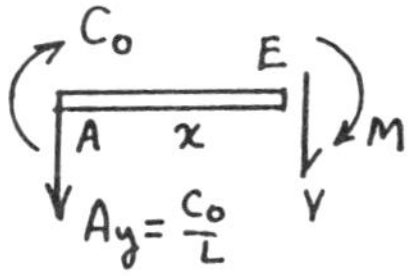

<u>V- and M-diagrams</u>

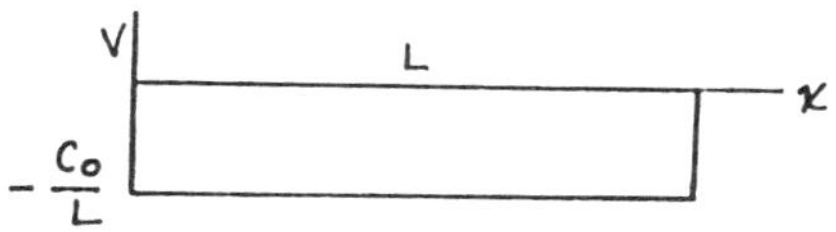

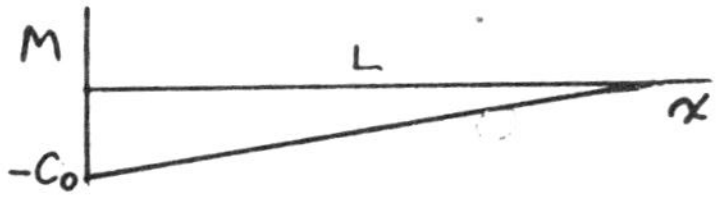

(b) <u>Reactions</u> Same as in Part (a)

<u>For $0 < x < L/2$</u>

$\Sigma F_y = 0$: $V = -C_0/L$ ◆

$\Sigma M_E = 0$: $M = (C_0/L)(x)$ ◆

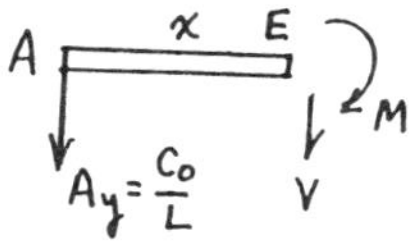

<u>For $L/2 < x < L$</u>

$\Sigma F_y = 0$: $V = -C_0/L$ ◆

$\Sigma M_F = 0$: $M = -(C_0/L)(L - x)$ ◆

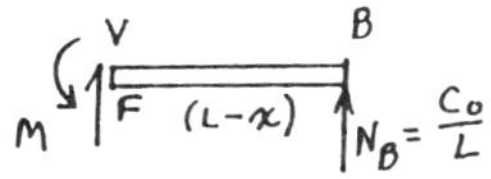

<u>V- and M-diagrams</u>

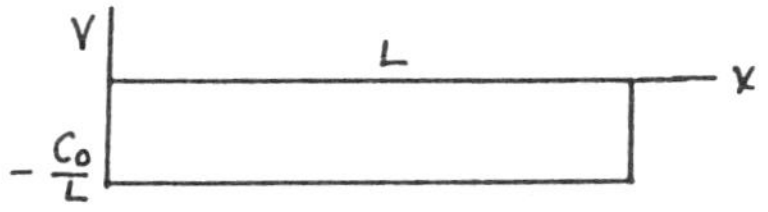

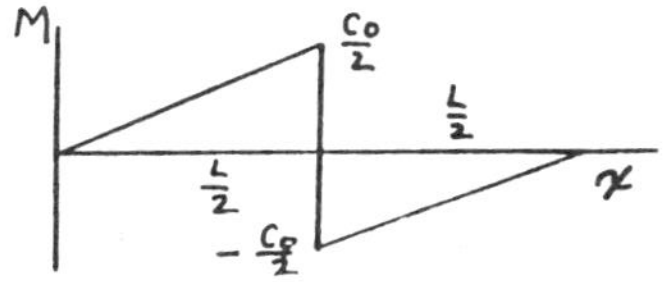

6.26

<u>FBD of entire beam</u>

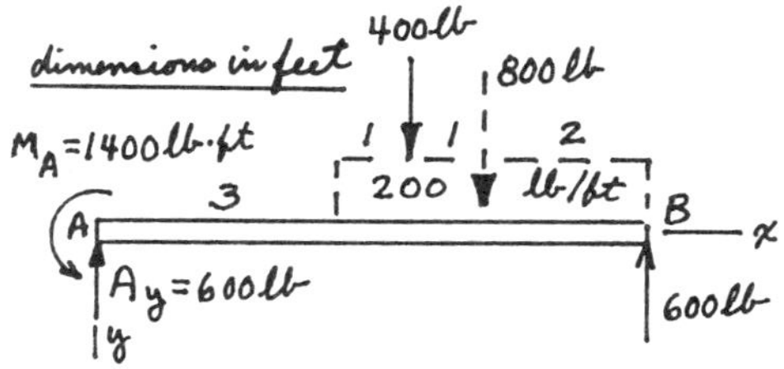

$\Sigma F_y = 0$:

$A_y = 400 + 800 - 600 = 600$ lb

$\Sigma M_A = 0$:

$M_A = 400(4) + 800(5) - 600(7)$

$= 1400$ lb•ft

<u>For $0 < x < 3$ ft</u>

$\Sigma F_y = 0$: $V = 600$ lb ◆

$\Sigma M_E = 0$: $M = 1400 - 600x$ lb•ft ◆

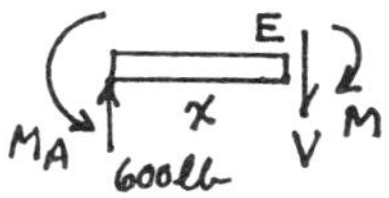

<u>For 3 ft $< x < 4$ ft</u>

$\Sigma F_y = 0$: $V = 600 - 200(x - 3)$

$= 1200 - 200x$ lb ◆

$\Sigma M_F = 0$: $M = 1400 - 600x + \dfrac{200(x-3)^2}{2}$

$= 2300 - 1200x + 100x^2$ lb•ft ◆

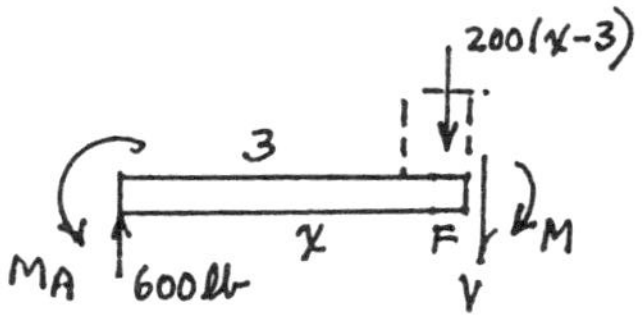

<u>For 4 ft $< x < 7$ ft</u>

$\Sigma F_y = 0$: $V = 600 - 200(x - 3) - 400$

$= 800 - 200x$ lb ◆

$\Sigma M_G = 0$: $M = 1400 - 600x + \dfrac{200(x-3)^2}{2}$

$+ 400(x - 4)$

$= 700 - 800x + 100x^2$ lb•ft ◆

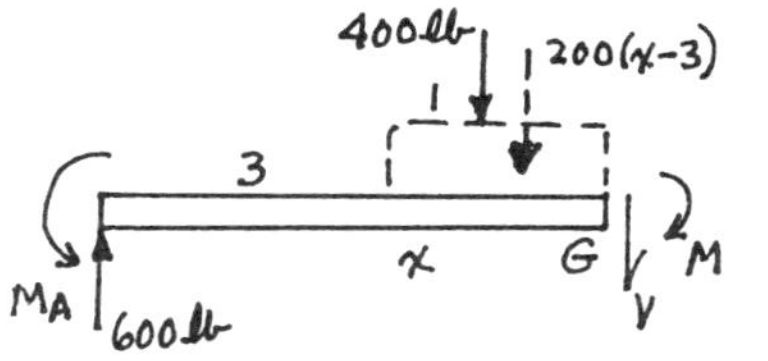

<u>V- and M- diagrams</u>

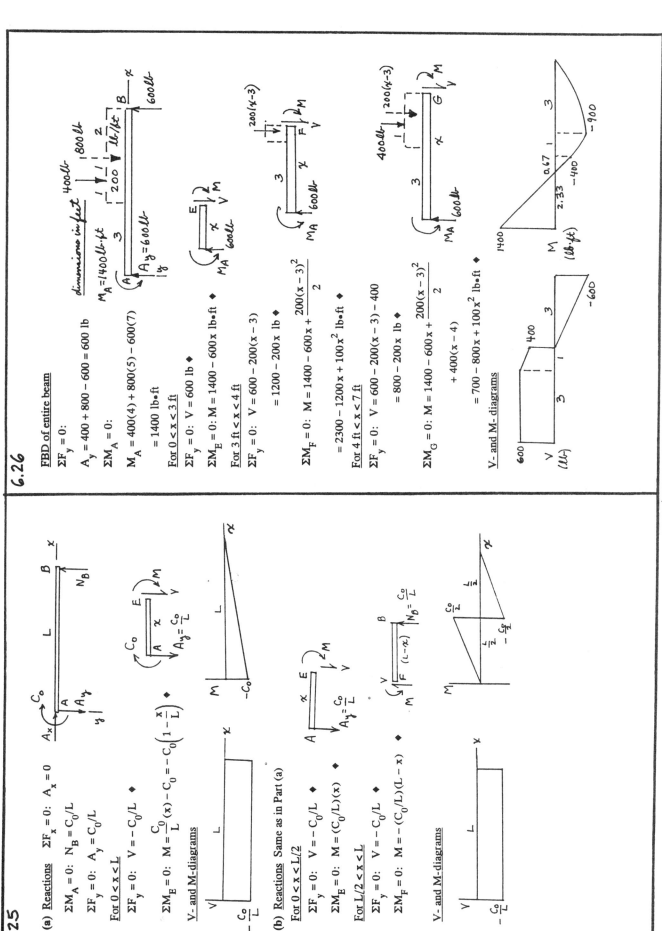

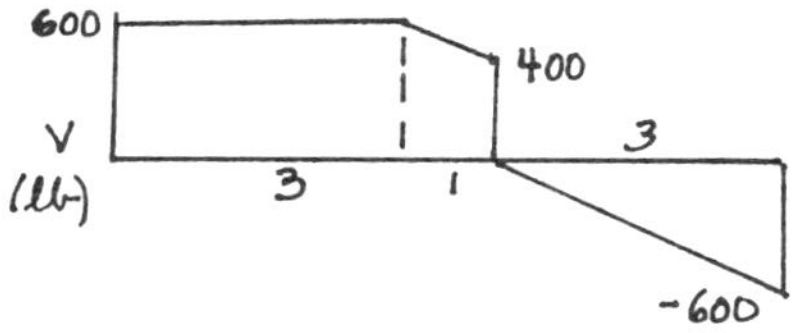

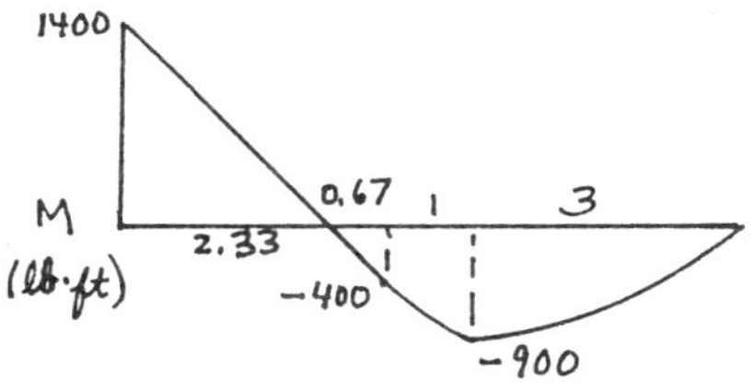

6.27

<u>FBD of entire beam</u> $\Sigma F_x = 0: \quad A_x = 0$

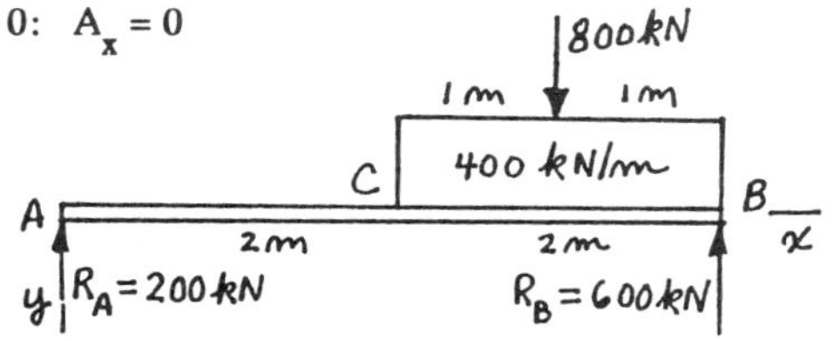

$\Sigma M_B = 0: \; R_A(4) = 800(1)$

$R_A = 200 \text{ kN}$

$\Sigma F_y = 0: \; R_B = 800 - 200$

$R_B = 600 \text{ kN}$

<u>For $0 < x < 2$ m</u>

$\Sigma F_y = 0: \quad V = 200 \text{ kN}$ ◆

$\Sigma M_D = 0: \quad M = -200x \text{ kN•m}$ ◆

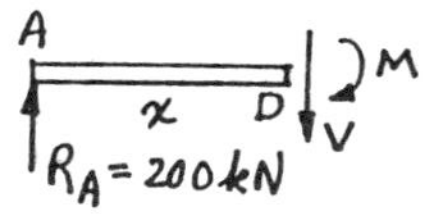

<u>For $2 \text{ m} < x < 4$ m</u>

$\Sigma F_y = 0: \quad V = 200 - 400(x-2) = 1000 - 400x \text{ kN}$ ◆

(Note: $V = 0$ at $x = 2.5$ m)

$\Sigma M_E = 0: \; M = -200x + \dfrac{400(x-2)^2}{2}$

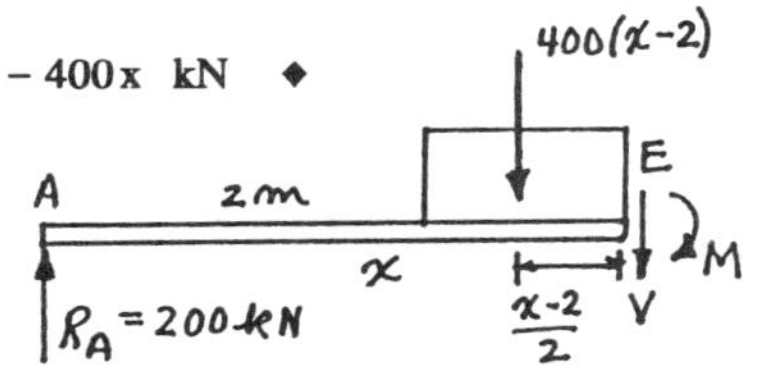

$\therefore \; M = 200x^2 - 1000x + 800 \text{ kN•m}$ ◆

(Note: at $x = 2.5$ m, $M = -450$ kN•m)

<u>V- and M-diagrams</u>

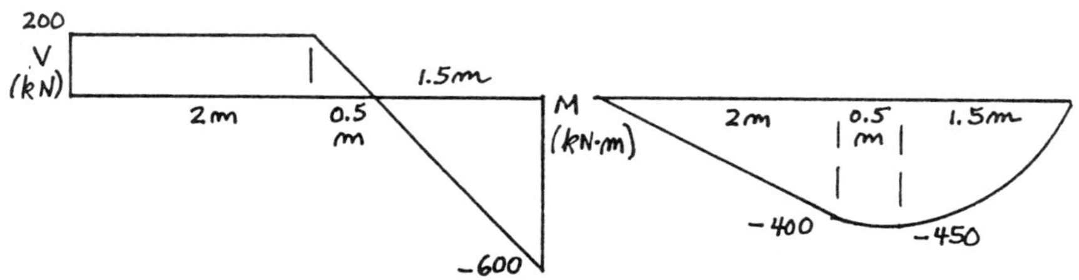

6.28

<u>FBD of entire beam</u>

$\Sigma M_B = 0:$

$R_A(7) = 3.6(5) + 5(2)$

$R_A = 4.0 \text{ kN}$

$\Sigma F_y = 0:$

$R_B = 5 + 3.6 - 4.0 = 4.6 \text{ kN}$

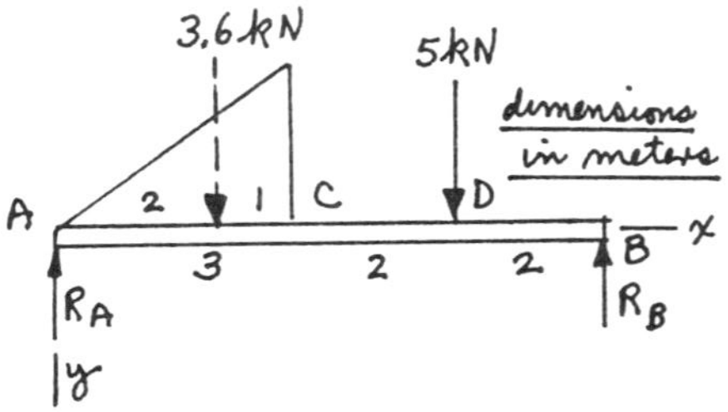

<u>For $0 < x < 3$ m</u>

$\Sigma F_y = 0: \; V = 4 - 0.4x^2 \text{ kN}$ ◆

$\Sigma M_E = 0: M = -4x + 0.4x^2(x/3)$

$= -4x + 0.1333x^3 \text{ kN•m}$ ◆

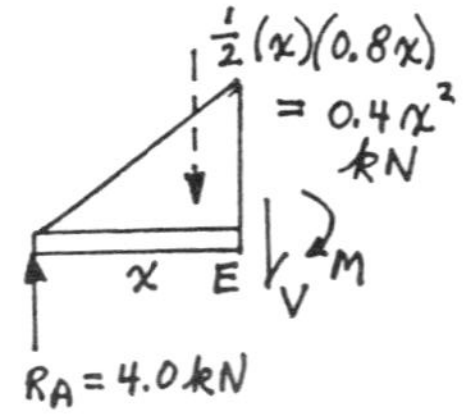

(At C: $M_C = -4(3) + 0.1333(3)^3 = -8.40$ kN•m)

<u>For $3 \text{ m} < x < 5$ m</u>

$\Sigma F_y = 0: \; V = 4 - 3.6 = 0.4 \text{ kN}$ ◆

$\Sigma M_F = 0: M = -4x + 3.6(x-2)$

$= -0.4x - 7.2 \text{ kN•m}$ ◆

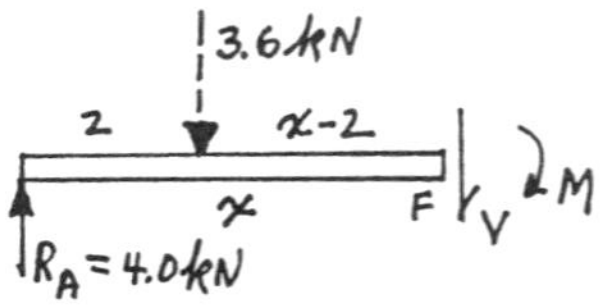

(At D: $M_D = -0.4(5) - 7.2 = -9.2$ kN•m)

<u>For $5 \text{ m} < x < 7$ m</u>

$\Sigma F_y = 0: \; V = 4 - 3.6 - 5 = -4.6 \text{ kN}$ ◆

$\Sigma M_G = 0: M = -4x + 3.6(x-2) + 5(x-5)$

$= 4.6x - 32.2 \text{ kN•m}$ ◆

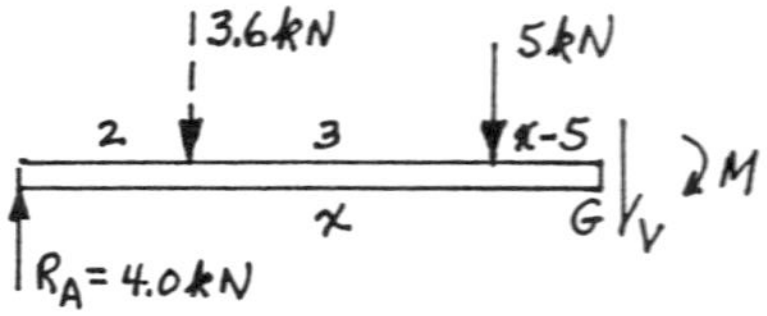

<u>V- and M- diagrams</u>

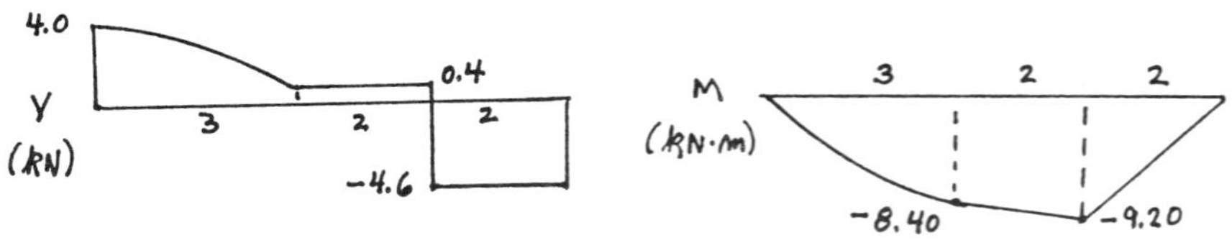

6.29

Reactions:

By inspection of the FBD of the entire beam, there are no external reactions at A.

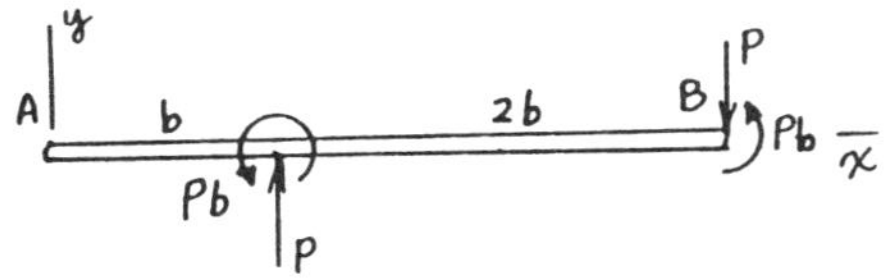

For $0 < x < b$

$\Sigma F_y = 0$: $V = 0$ ◆

$\Sigma M_A = 0$: $M = 0$ ◆

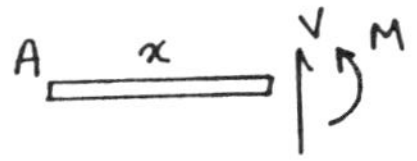

For $b < x < 3b$

$\Sigma F_y = 0$: $V = -P$ ◆

$\Sigma M_E = 0$: $M = Pb - P(3b - x) = P(x - 2b)$ ◆

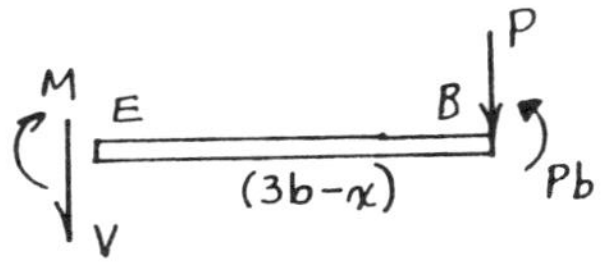

V- and M-diagrams

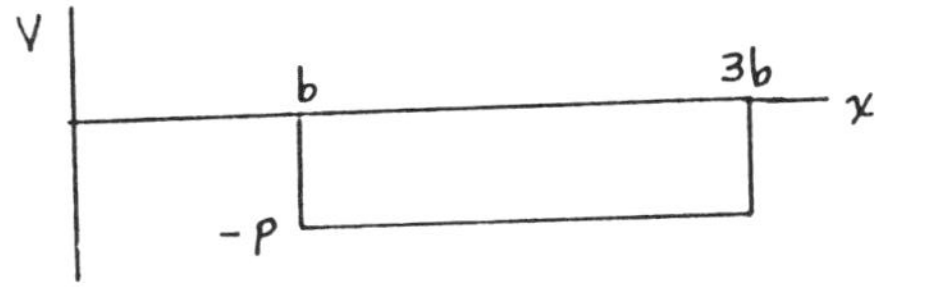

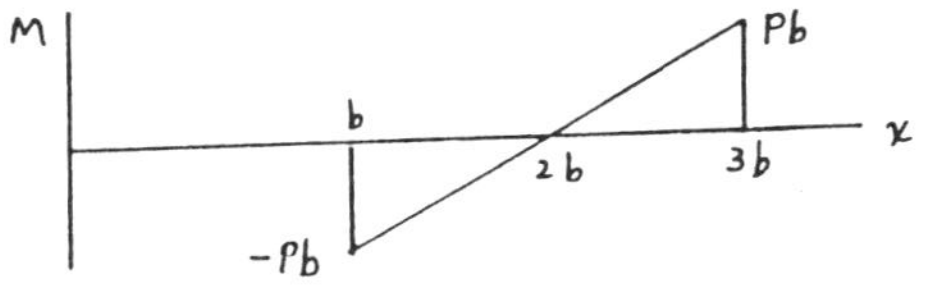

6.30

FBD of entire beam

$\Sigma M_B = 0$:

$R_C(5) = 40(2.5) - 20(2)$

$R_C = 12$ kN

$\Sigma F_y = 0$:

$R_B = 40 + 20 - 12 = 48$ kN

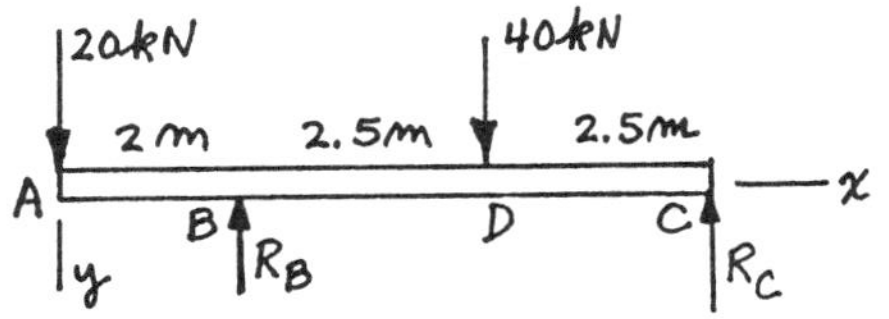

For $0 < x < 2$ m

$\Sigma F_y = 0$: $V = -20$ kN ◆

$\Sigma M_E = 0$: $M = 20x$ kN•m ◆

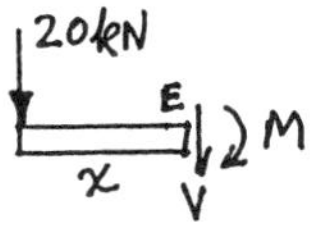

For $2 \text{ m} < x < 4.5$ m

$\Sigma F_y = 0$: $V = -20 + 48 = 28$ kN ◆

$\Sigma M_F = 0$: $M = 20x - 48(x - 2)$

$= -28x + 96$ kN•m◆

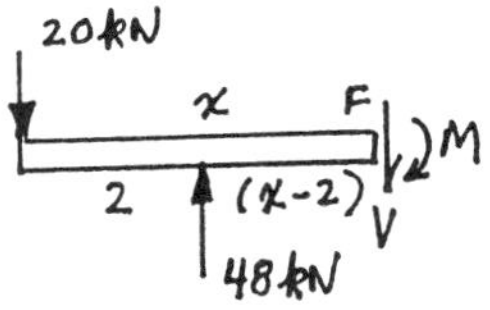

For $4.5 \text{ m} < x < 7$ m

$\Sigma F_y = 0$: $V = -20 + 48 - 40 = -12$ kN ◆

$\Sigma M_G = 0$: $M = 20x - 48(x - 2) + 40(x - 4.5)$

$= 12x - 84$ kN•m ◆

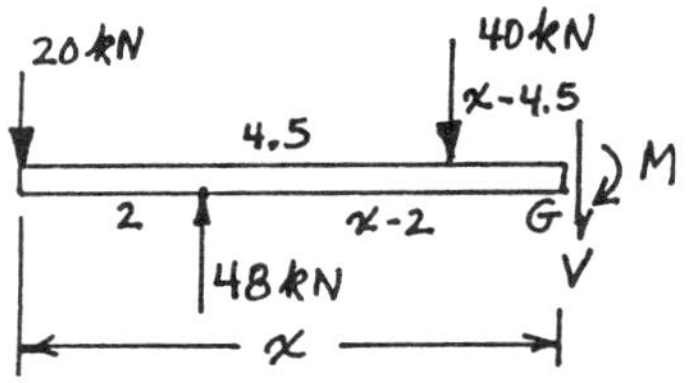

V- and M- diagrams

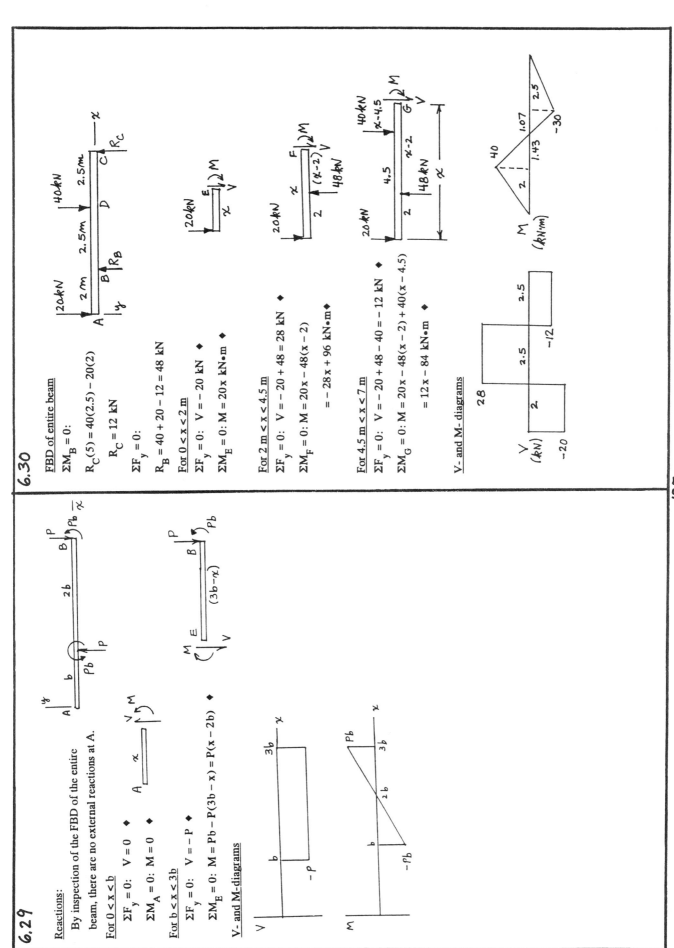

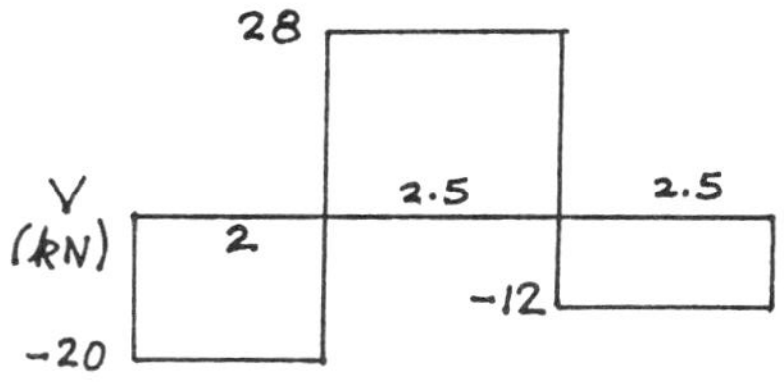

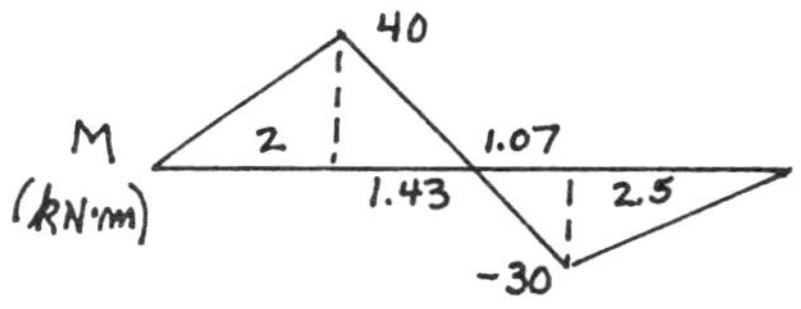

6.31

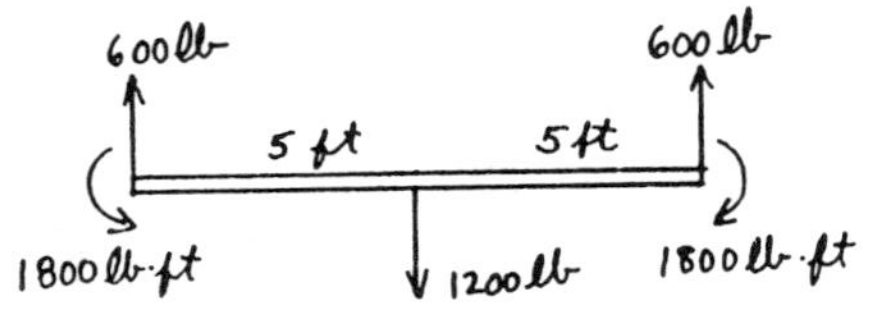

For 0 < x < 5 ft

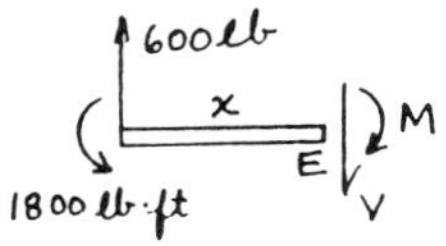

$\Sigma F_y = 0$: $V = 600$ lb ◆

$\Sigma M_E = 0$: $M = 1800 - 600x$ lb•ft ◆

For 5 ft < x < 10 ft

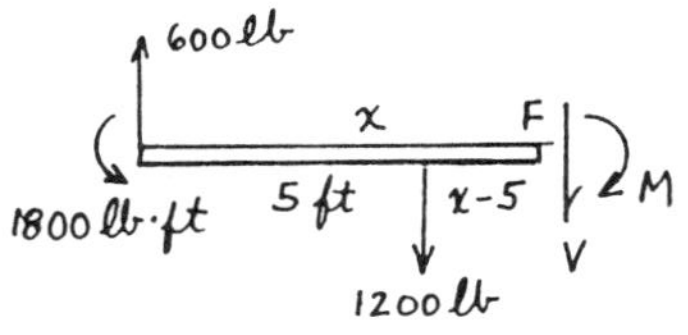

$\Sigma F_y = 0$: $V = 600 - 1200 = -600$ lb ◆

$\Sigma M_F = 0$: $M = 1800 - 600x + 1200(x - 5)$

$= -4200 + 600x$ lb•ft ◆

V- and M-diagrams

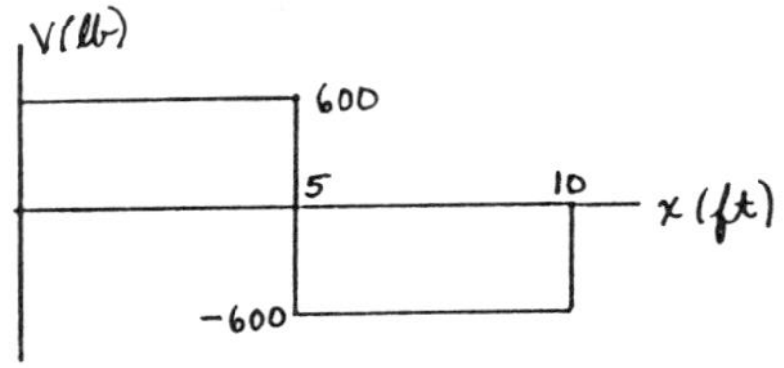

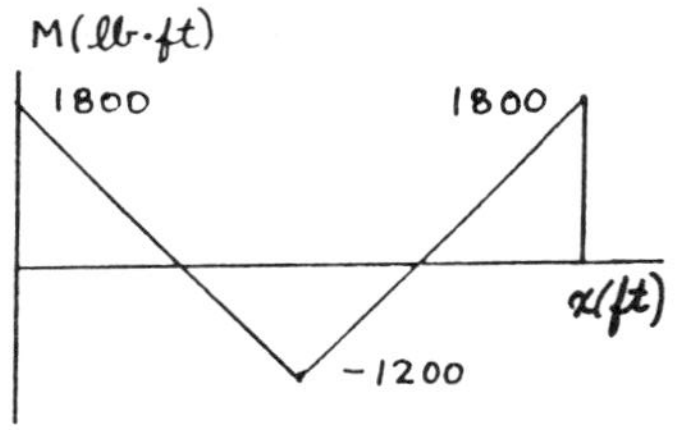

6.32

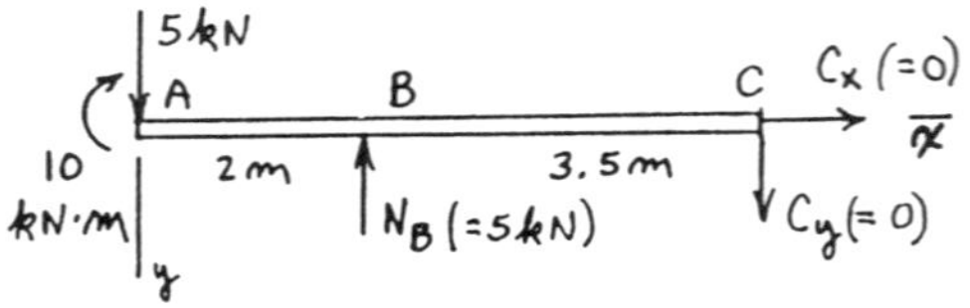

Reactions $\Sigma F_x = 0$: $C_x = 0$

$\Sigma M_C = 0$:

(+) $5(5.5) - 10 - N_B(3.5) = 0$

$\therefore N_B = 5$ kN

$\Sigma F_y = 0$: $C_y = N_B - 5 = 0$

For 0 < x < 2 m

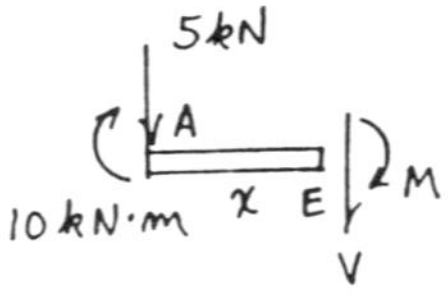

$\Sigma F_y = 0$: $V = -5$ kN ◆

$\Sigma M_E = 0$: $M = 5x - 10$ kN•m ◆

For 2 m < x < 5.5 m

By inspection, $V = 0$ ◆ and $M = 0$ ◆

V- and M-diagrams

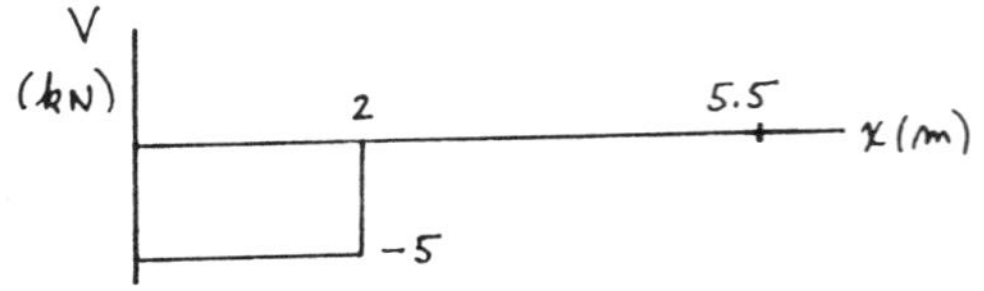

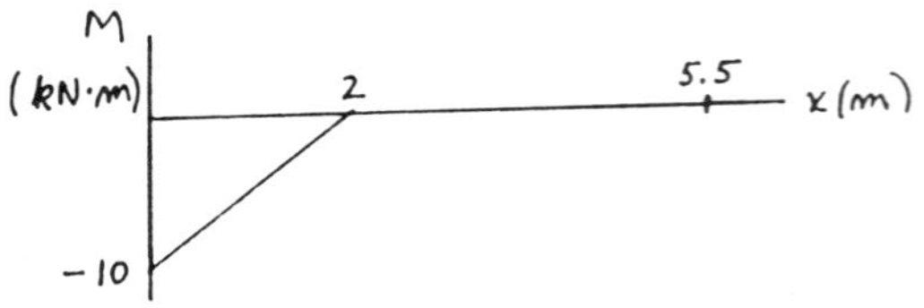

6.33

(a) Reactions $\Sigma F_x = 0$: $B_x = 0$

$\Sigma F_y = 0$: $B_y = 126$ lb

$\Sigma M_B = 0$: $M_B = 126(4.5) = 567$ lb•ft

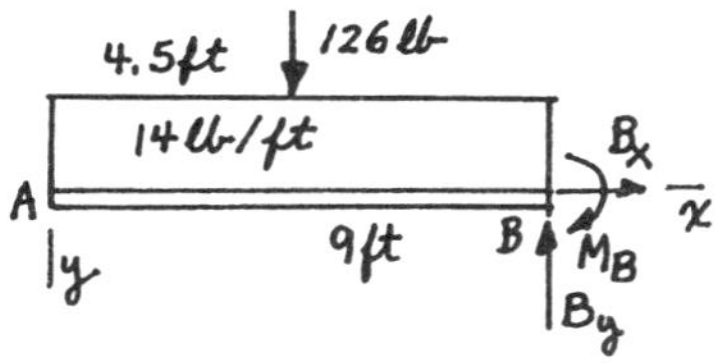

For $0 < x < 9$ ft

$\Sigma F_y = 0$: $V = -14x$ lb ◆

$\Sigma M_E = 0$: $M = 14x\left(\frac{x}{2}\right) = 7x^2$ lb•ft ◆

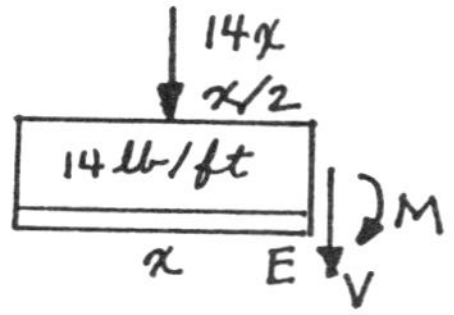

V- and M-diagrams

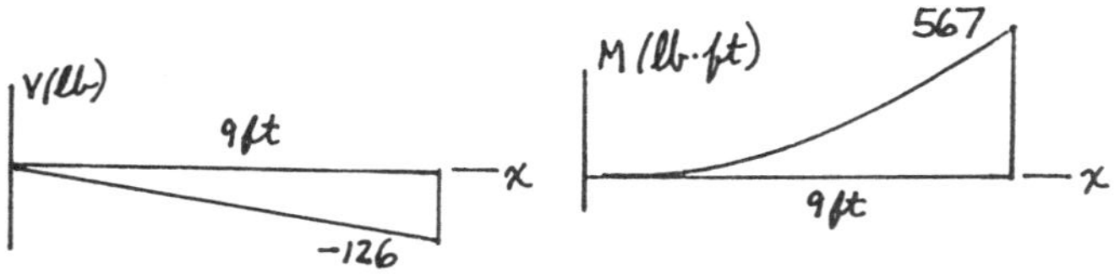

(b) Reactions $\Sigma F_x = 0$: $B_x = 0$

$\Sigma F_y = 0$: $B_y = 126$ lb

$\Sigma M_B = 0$: $M_B = 126(4.5) - 220 = 347$ lb•ft

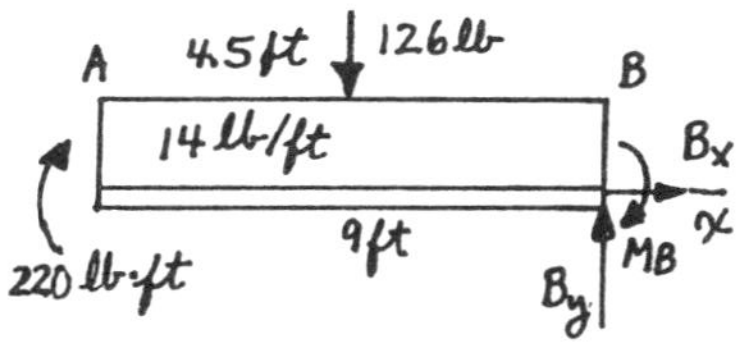

For $0 < x < 9$ ft

$\Sigma F_y = 0$: $V = -14x$ lb ◆

$\Sigma M_F = 0$: $M = 14x\left(\frac{x}{2}\right) - 220 = 7x^2 - 220$ lb•ft ◆

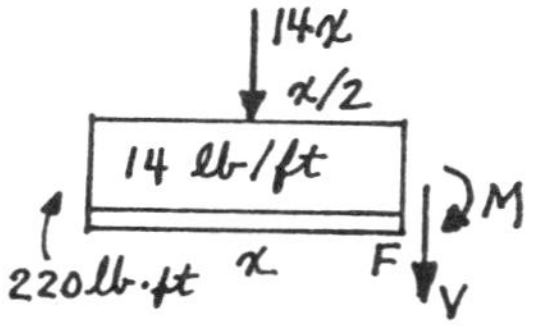

V- and M-diagrams

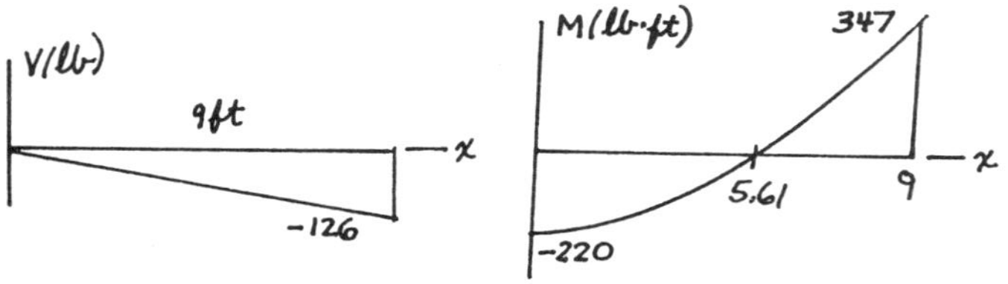

6.34

FBD of entire beam

$\Sigma M_A = 0$:

$R_B(6) = 2.4(3) + 1.8$

$R_B = 1.50$ kN

$\Sigma F_y = 0$:

$R_A = 2.4 - 1.5 = 0.9$ kN

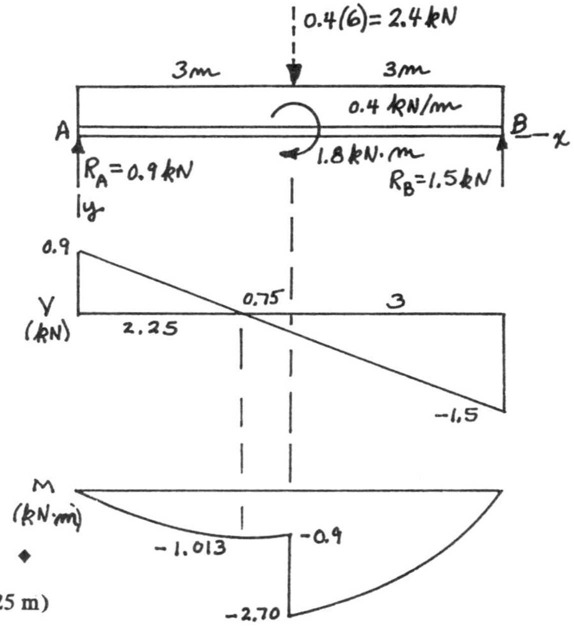

For $0 < x < 3$ m

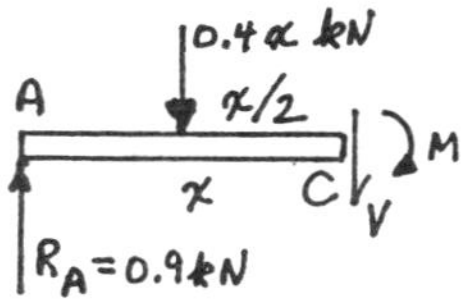

$\Sigma F_y = 0$: $V = 0.9 - 0.4x$ kN ◆

(V= 0, when $x = 0.9/0.4 = 2.25$ m)

$\Sigma M_C = 0$: $M = 0.4x(x/2) - 0.9x$

$= 0.2x^2 - 0.9x$ kN•m ◆

($x = 2.25$ m, $M = -1.013$ kN•m)

($x = 3$ m, $M = -0.9$ kN•m)

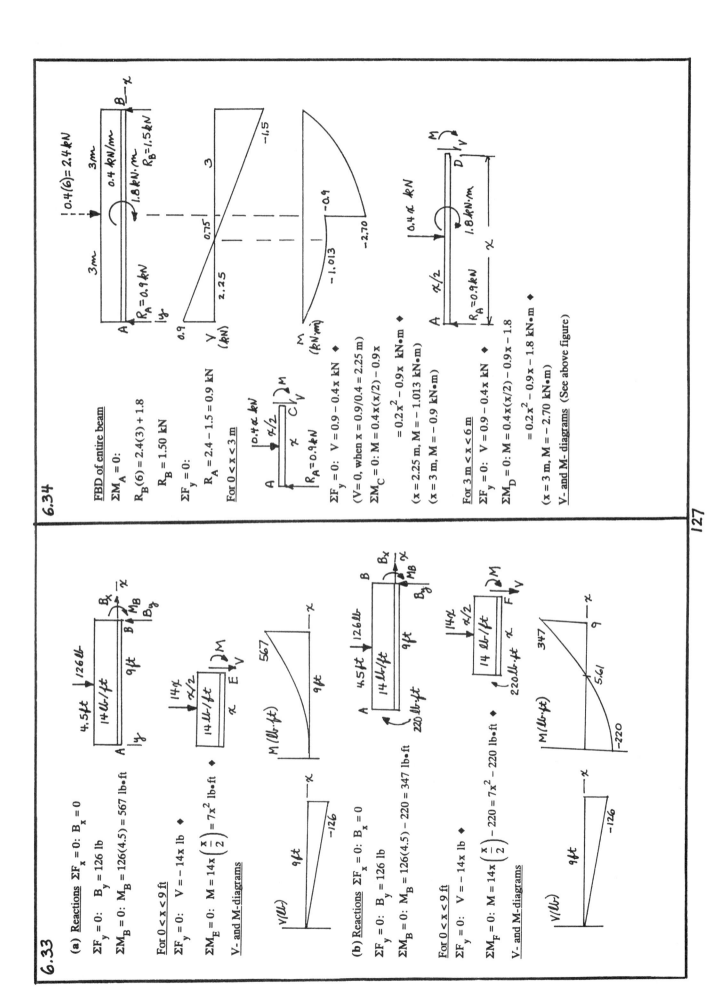

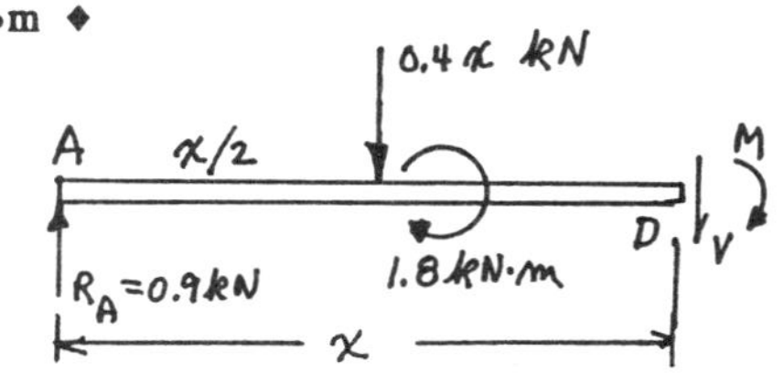

For $3\text{ m} < x < 6$ m

$\Sigma F_y = 0$: $V = 0.9 - 0.4x$ kN ◆

$\Sigma M_D = 0$: $M = 0.4x(x/2) - 0.9x - 1.8$

$= 0.2x^2 - 0.9x - 1.8$ kN•m ◆

($x = 3$ m, $M = -2.70$ kN•m)

V- and M- diagrams (See above figure)

6.35

Reactions $\Sigma F_x = 0$: $A_x = 0$

By symmetry, $A_y = N_B = 960$ lb

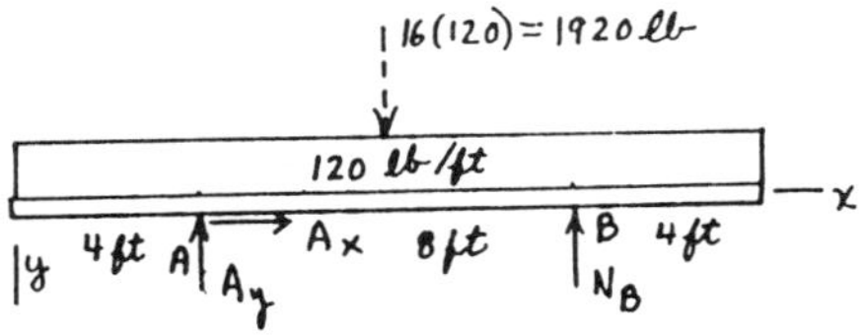

For 0 < x < 4 ft

$\Sigma F_y = 0$: $V = -120x$ lb ◆

$\Sigma M_E = 0$: $M = 120x\left(\frac{x}{2}\right) = 60x^2$ lb•ft ◆

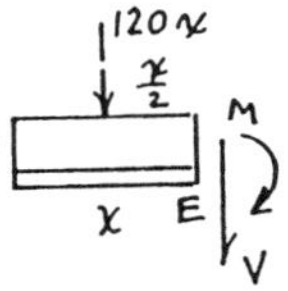

For 4 ft < x < 12 ft

$\Sigma F_y = 0$: $V = 960 - 120x$ lb ◆

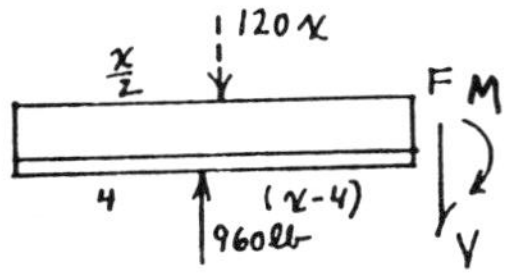

$\Sigma M_F = 0$: $M = 120x\left(\frac{x}{2}\right) - 960(x-4) = 60x^2 - 960x + 3840$ lb•ft ◆

For 12 ft < x < 16 ft

$\Sigma F_y = 0$: $V = 120(16 - x) = 1920 - 120x$ lb ◆

$\Sigma M_G = 0$: $M = 120(16 - x)\dfrac{(16 - x)}{2} = 60(16 - x)^2$ lb•ft ◆

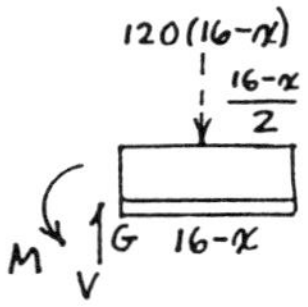

V- and M-diagrams

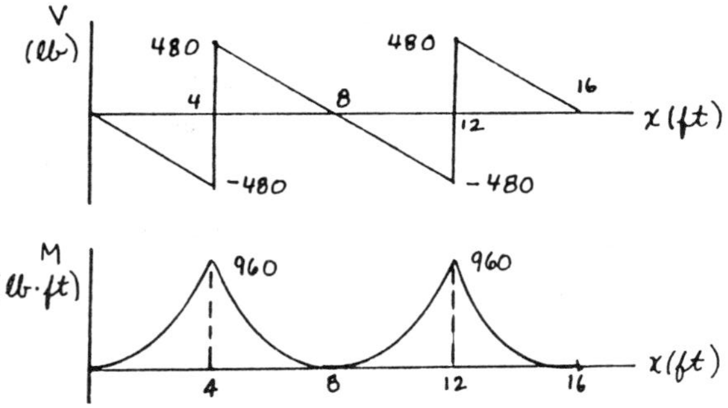

6.36

Reactions are the same as calculated in the solution to Prob. 6.35: $A_x = 0$; $A_y = N_B = 960$ lb.

(a) FBD of segment to left of A

$\Sigma M_A = 0$:

$M_A = 120b(b/2) = 60b^2$ lb•ft ◆

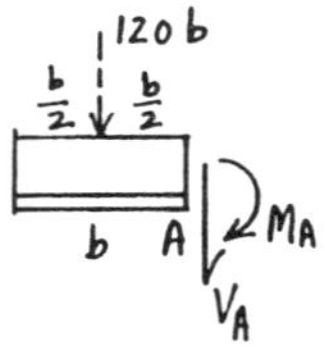

FBD of segment to left of C

$\Sigma M_C = 0$:

$M_C = 960(4) - 960(8 - b) = 960(b - 4)$ lb•ft ◆

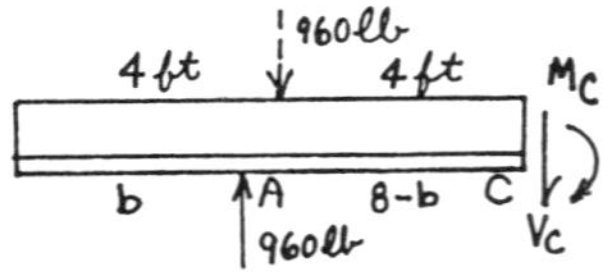

Plots of M_A and M_C as functions of b are shown below.

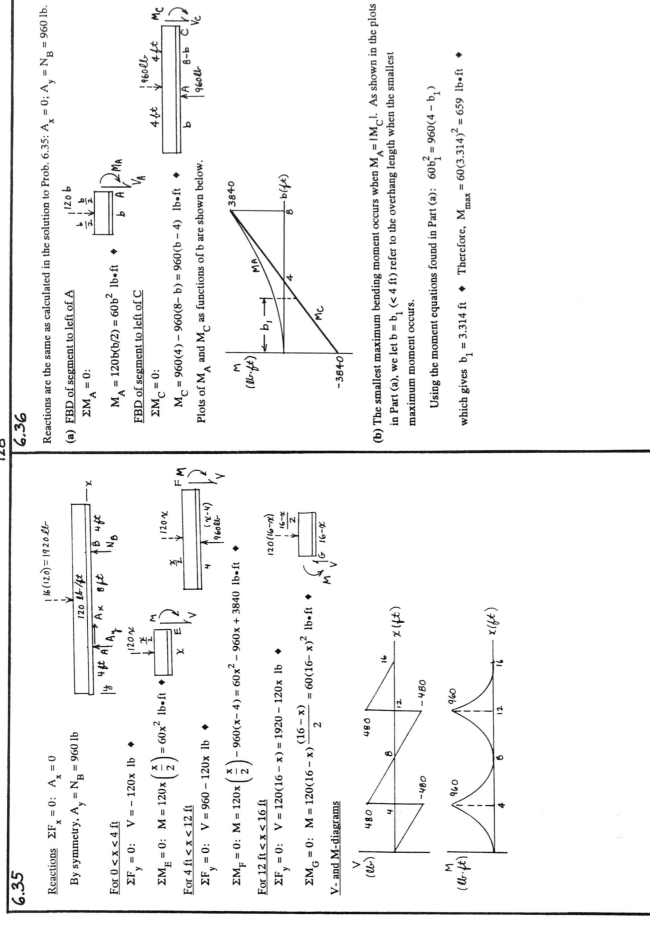

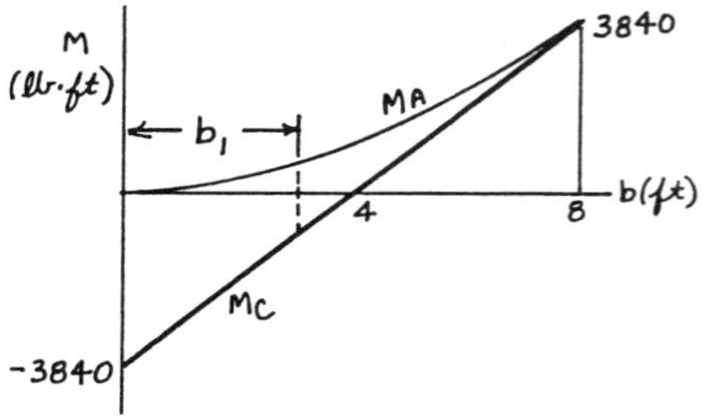

(b) The smallest maximum bending moment occurs when $M_A = |M_C|$. As shown in the plots in Part (a), we let $b = b_1$ (< 4 ft) refer to the overhang length when the smallest maximum moment occurs.

Using the moment equations found in Part (a): $60b_1^2 = 960(4 - b_1)$

which gives $b_1 = 3.314$ ft ◆ Therefore, $M_{max} = 60(3.314)^2 = 659$ lb•ft ◆

6.37

<u>Reactions</u> By symmetry, $R_A = R_B = 3$ kN

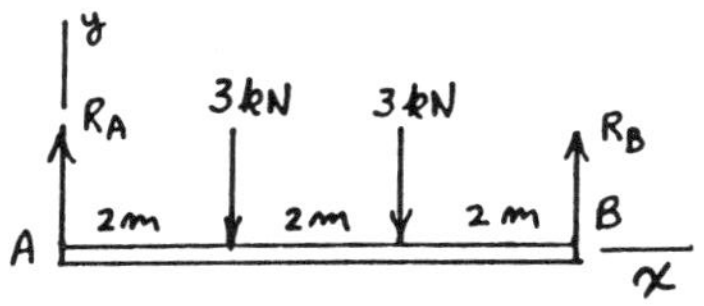

<u>For 0 < x < 2 m</u>

$\Sigma F_y = 0$: $V = -3$ kN ◆

$\Sigma M_E = 0$: $M = 3x$ kN•m ◆

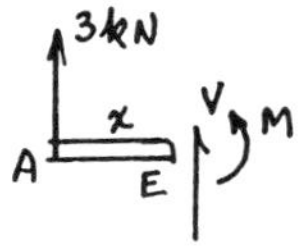

<u>For 2 m < x < 4 m</u>

$\Sigma F_y = 0$: $V = 0$ ◆

$\Sigma M_F = 0$: $M = 6$ kN•m ◆

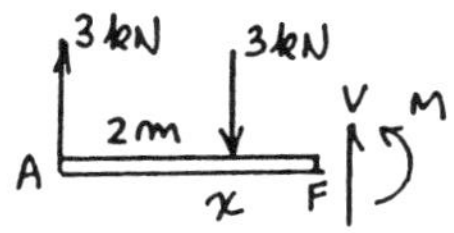

<u>For 4 m < x < 6 m</u>

$\Sigma F_y = 0$: $V = 3$ kN ◆

$\Sigma M_G = 0$: $M = 3(6 - x)$ kN•m ◆

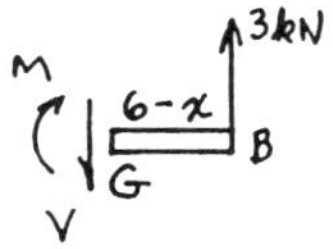

<u>V- and M-diagrams</u>

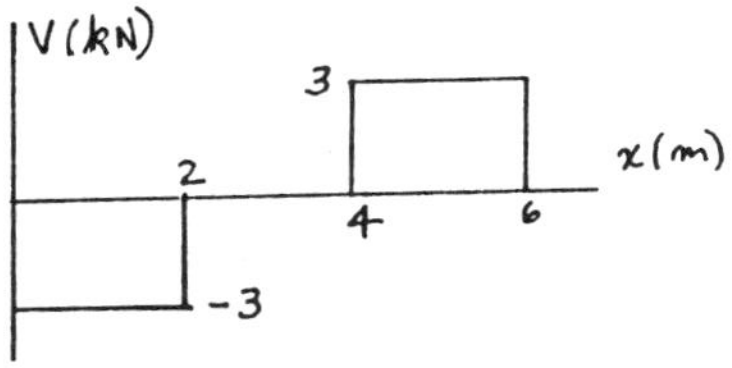

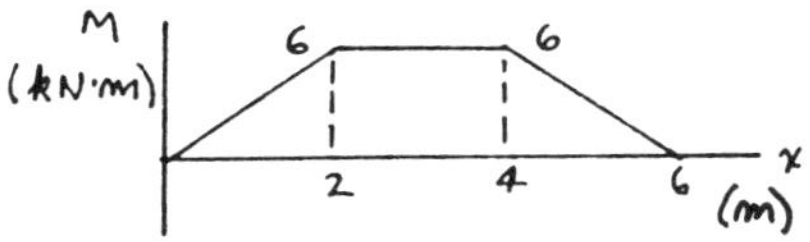

6.38

(a) <u>Reaction at A</u>

$\Sigma M_B = 0$: $R_A(6) = 3(6 - b) + 3(4 - b)$

$\therefore\ R_A = (5 - b)$ kN

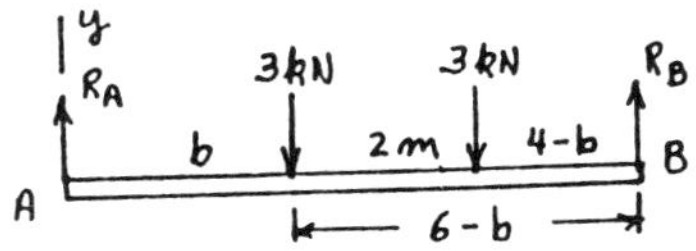

The moment at C is $M_C = R_A(b) = (5 - b)(b) = 5b - b^2$ kN•m

To maximize M_C: $dM_C/db = 5 - 2b = 0$ which gives $b = 2.5$ m ◆

(b) When $b = 2.5$ m, $R_A = 5 - 2.5 = 2.5$ kN and $R_B = 6 - R_A = 3.5$ kN

<u>For 0 < x < 2.5 m</u>

$\Sigma F_y = 0$: $V = -2.5$ kN ◆ $\Sigma M_E = 0$: $M = 2.5x$ kN•m ◆

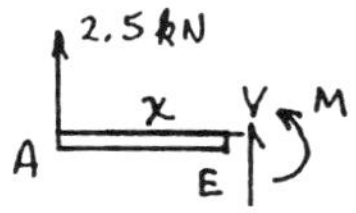

<u>For 2.5 m < x < 4.5 m</u>

$\Sigma F_y = 0$: $V = 3 - 2.5 = 0.5$ kN ◆

$\Sigma M_F = 0$: $M = 2.5x - 3(x - 2.5) = 7.5 - 0.5x$ kN•m ◆

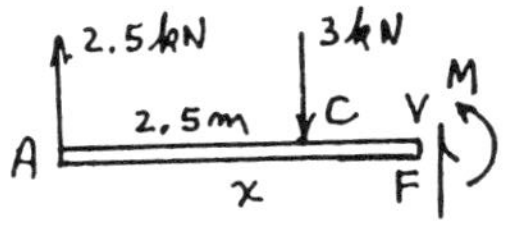

<u>For 4.5 m < x < 6 m</u>

$\Sigma F_y = 0$: $V = 3.5$ kN ◆ $\Sigma M_G = 0$: $M = 3.5(6 - x)$ kN•m ◆

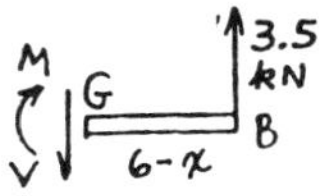

<u>V- and M-diagrams</u>

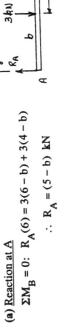

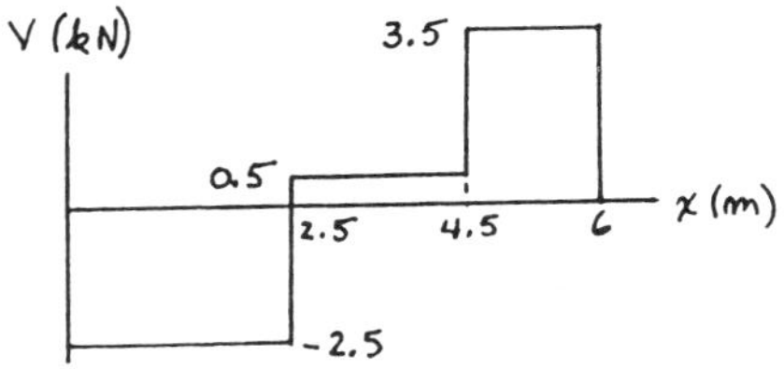

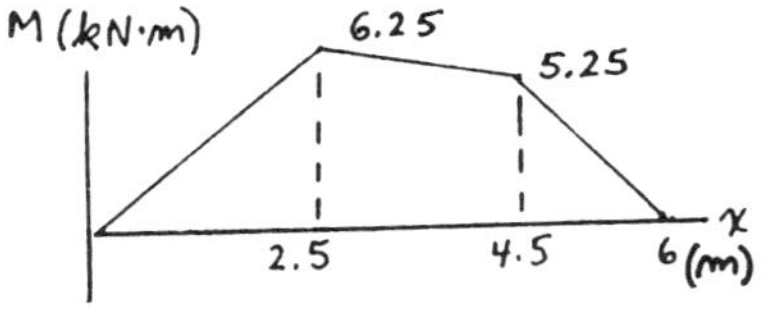

6.39

Reactions $\Sigma F_x = 0$: $A_x = 0$

$\Sigma M_B = 0$: $16\,A_y = 24 w_0(4)$

$\therefore\ A_y = 6w_0$

$\Sigma F_y = 0$: $N_B = 24w_0 - A_y = 18w_0$

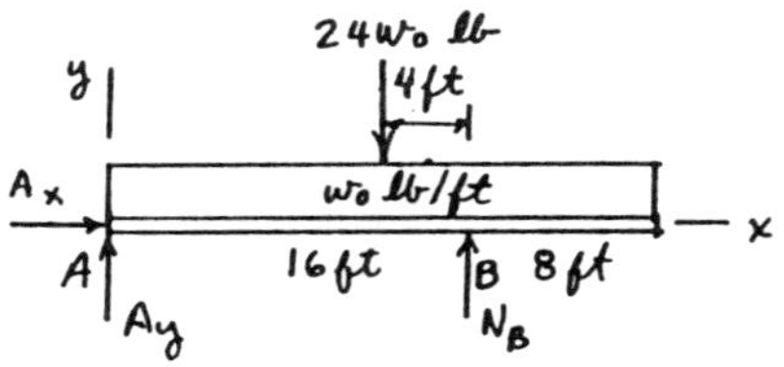

Moment at D

$\Sigma M_D = 0$:

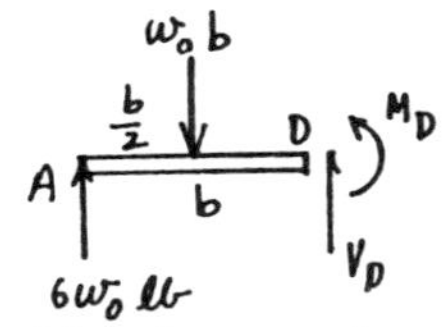

$$M_D = 6w_0(b) - w_0 b\left(\frac{b}{2}\right) = \frac{w_0 b}{2}(12 - b)$$

Note that $M_D = 0$ when b = 12 ft. Therefore, this is the most advantageous position for the joint D. ◆

6.40

Case 1

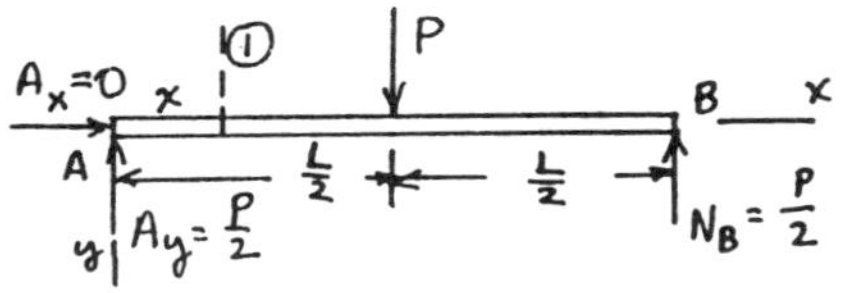

For $0 < x < L/2$

$\Sigma F_y = 0$: $V = -\dfrac{P}{2}$ ◆

$\Sigma M_E = 0$: $M = \dfrac{Px}{2}$ ◆

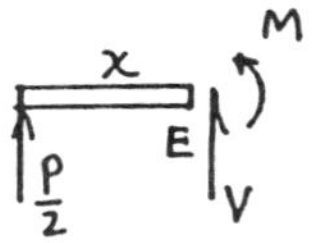

For $L/2 < x < L$

$\Sigma F_y = 0$: $V = \dfrac{P}{2}$ ◆

$\Sigma M_F = 0$: $M = \dfrac{P(L-x)}{2}$ ◆

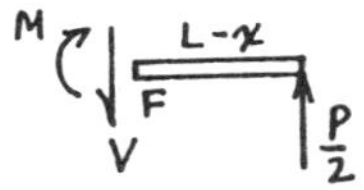

V- and M-diagrams

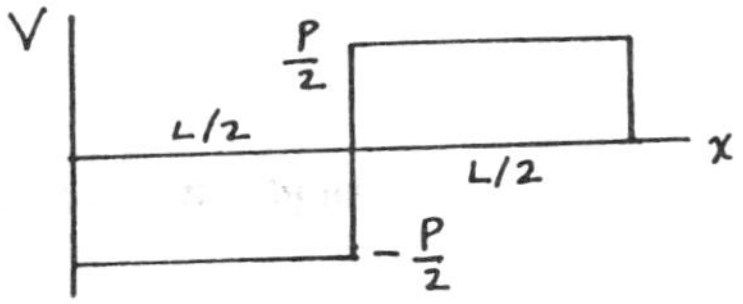

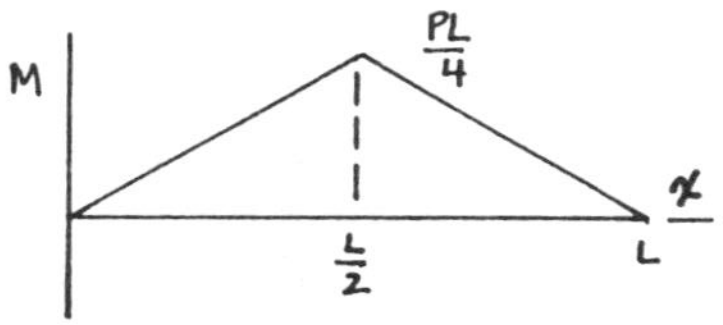

(continued)

Case 2

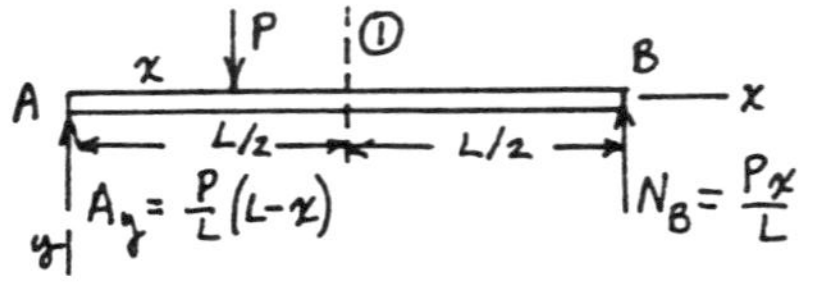

For $0 < x < L/2$

$\Sigma F_y = 0$: $V = \dfrac{Px}{L}$ ◆

$\Sigma M_G = 0$: $M = \dfrac{Px}{L}\left(\dfrac{L}{2}\right) = \dfrac{Px}{2}$ ◆

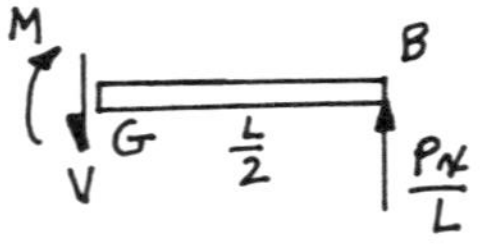

For $L/2 < x < L$

$\Sigma F_y = 0$: $V = -\dfrac{P(L-x)}{L}$ ◆

$\Sigma M_H = 0$: $M = \dfrac{P(L-x)}{L}\left(\dfrac{L}{2}\right) = \dfrac{P(L-x)}{2}$ ◆

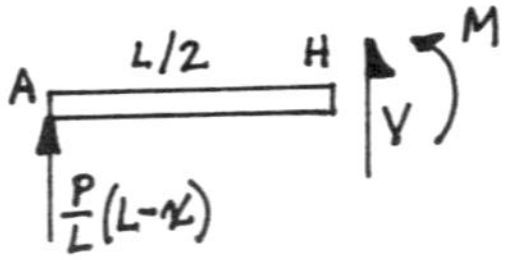

V- and M-diagrams

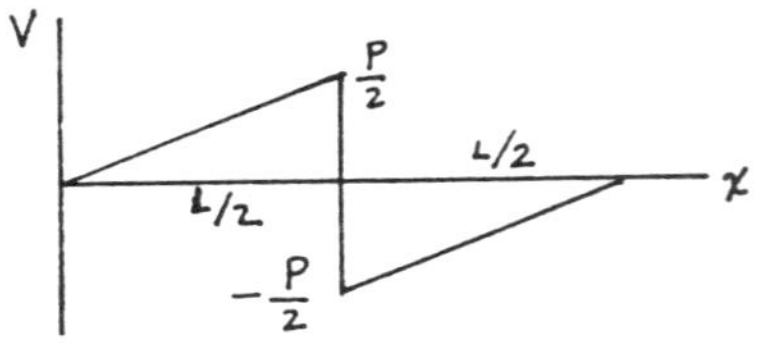

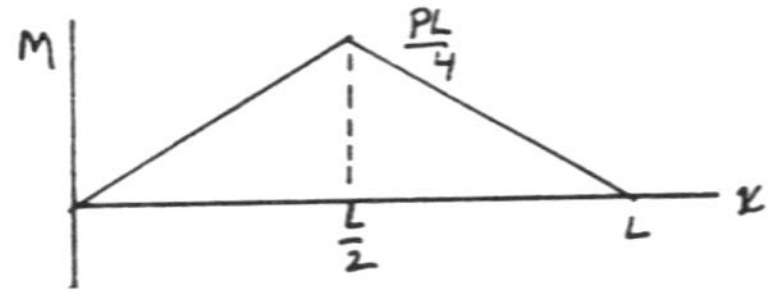

6.41

Reactions

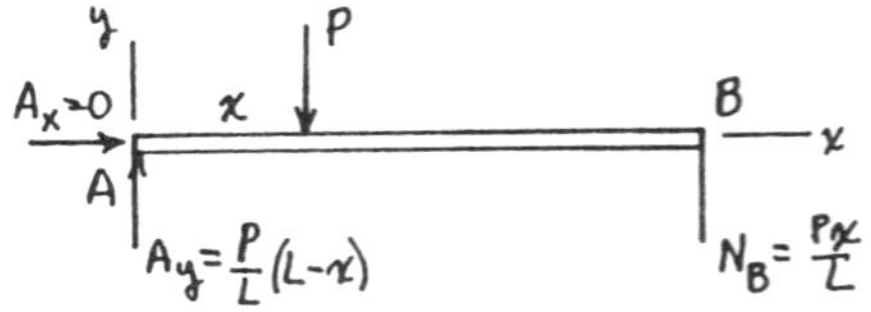

Maximum bending moment (occurs at point of application of P)

$\Sigma M_E = 0$: $M_{max} = \dfrac{Px}{L}(L - x)$ ◆

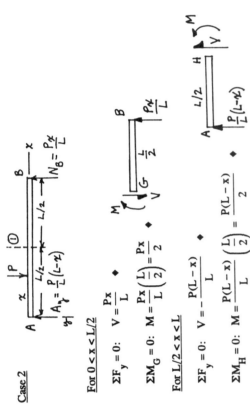

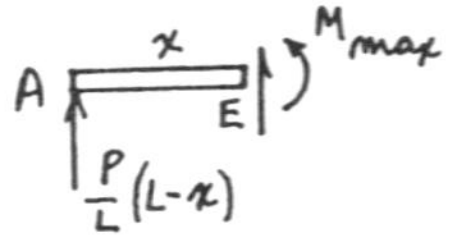

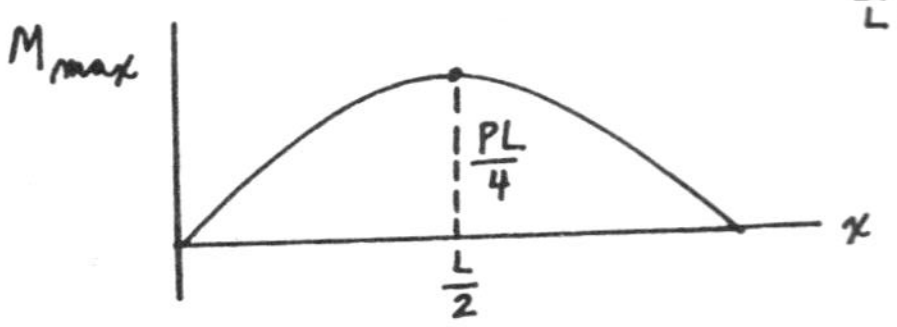

6.42

FBD of entire piling

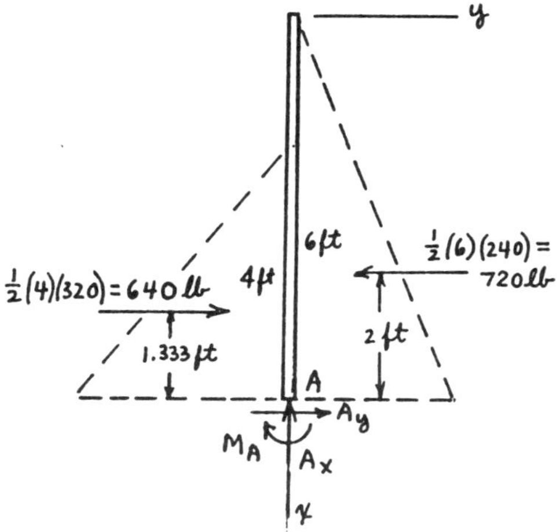

$\Sigma F_x = 0$:

$A_x = 0$

$\Sigma F_y = 0$:

$A_y = 720 - 640 = 80$ lb

$\Sigma M_A = 0$:

$M_A = 720(2) - 640(1.333)$

$= 587$ lb•ft

For 0 < x < 2 ft

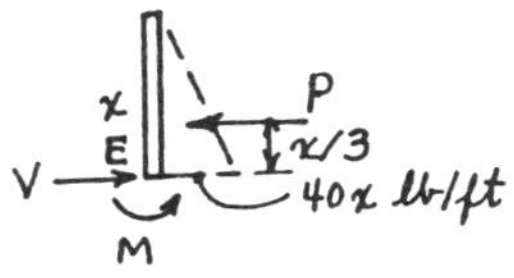

$P = \frac{1}{2}(x)(40x) = 20x^2$ lb

$\Sigma F_y = 0$: $V = P = 20x^2$ lb ◆

$\Sigma M_E = 0$: $M = -20x^2\left(\frac{x}{3}\right) = -\frac{20x^3}{3}$ lb•ft ◆

(continued)

For 2 ft < x < 6 ft

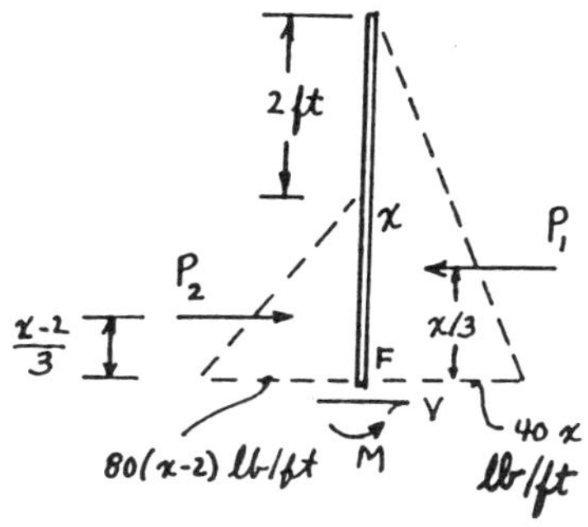

$P_1 = \frac{1}{2}(x)(40x) = 20x^2$ lb

$P_2 = \frac{1}{2}(x-2)(80)(x-2) = 40(x-2)^2$ lb

$\Sigma F_y = 0$:

$V = P_1 - P_2 = 20x^2 - 40(x-2)^2$ lb ◆

(note: $dV/dx = 0$ at $x = 4$ ft, which gives $V_{max} = V|_{x=4\text{ ft}} = 160$ lb)

$\Sigma M_F = 0$:

$$M = P_2\left(\frac{x-2}{3}\right) - P_1\left(\frac{x}{3}\right) = 40(x-2)^2\left(\frac{x-2}{3}\right) - 20x^2\left(\frac{x}{3}\right)$$

$$= \frac{40(x-2)^3}{3} - \frac{20x^3}{3} \text{ lb•ft}$$ ◆

V- and M-diagrams

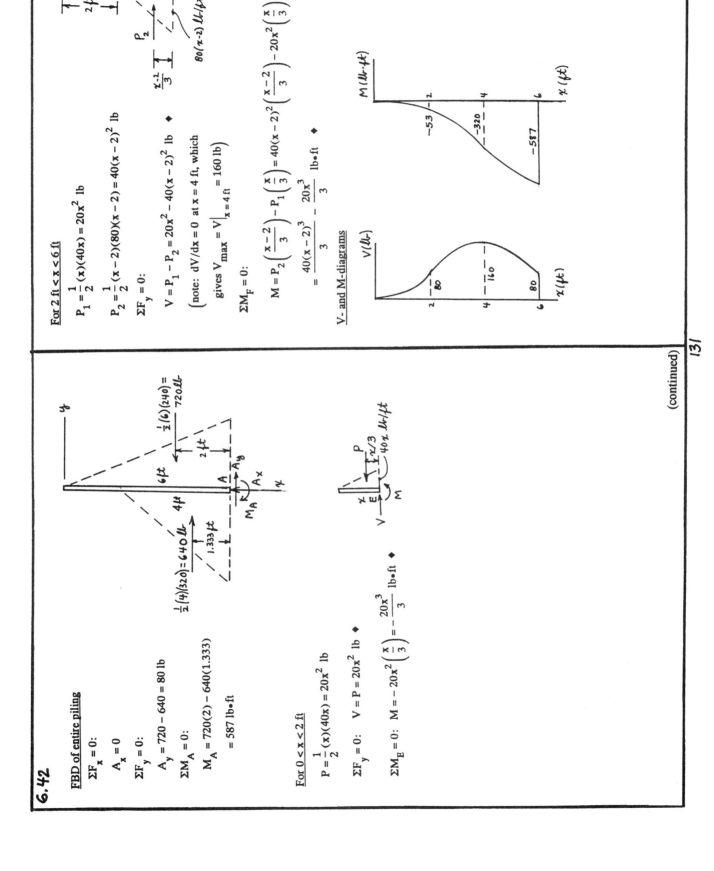

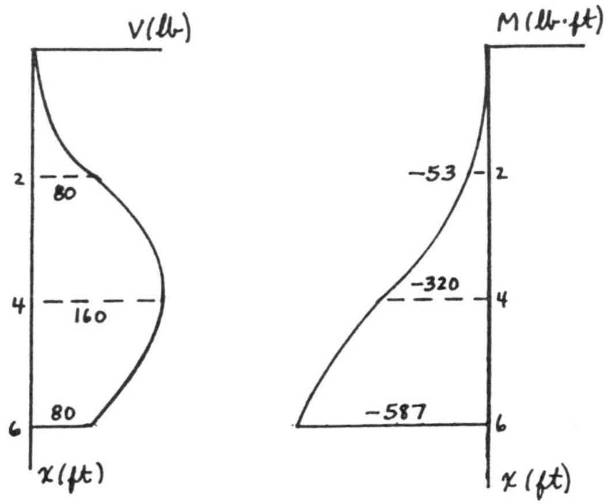

6.43

(a) $V_A^- = 0$

$V_A^+ = V_A^- - R_A = 0 - \frac{P}{2} = -\frac{P}{2}$

$V_B^- = V_A^+ - \text{area } w\Big]_A^B = -\frac{P}{2} - (-P) = \frac{P}{2}$

$V_B^+ = V_B^- - R_B = \frac{P}{2} - \frac{P}{2} = 0$ <u>checks!</u>

$M_A = 0$

$M_E = M_A - \text{area } V\Big]_A^E = 0 - \left(-\frac{PL}{8}\right) = \frac{PL}{8}$

$M_B = M_E - \text{area } V\Big]_E^B = \frac{PL}{8} - \frac{PL}{8} = 0$ <u>checks!</u>

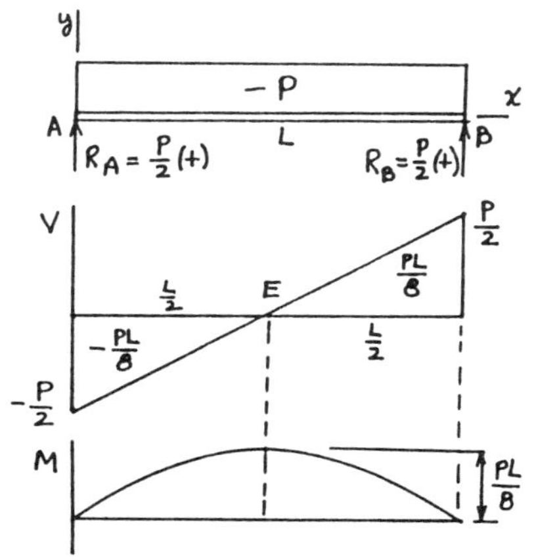

(b) $V_A^- = 0$

$V_A^+ = V_A^- - R_A = 0 - \frac{P}{2} = -\frac{P}{2} = V_C^-$

$V_C^+ = V_C^- - P_C = -\frac{P}{2} - \left(-\frac{P}{4}\right) = -\frac{P}{4} = V_D^-$

$V_D^+ = V_D^- - P_D = -\frac{P}{4} - \left(-\frac{P}{4}\right) = 0 = V_E^-$

$V_E^+ = V_E^- - P_E = 0 - \left(-\frac{P}{4}\right) = \frac{P}{4} = V_F^-$

$V_F^+ = V_F^- - P_F = \frac{P}{4} - \left(-\frac{P}{4}\right) = \frac{P}{2} = V_B^-$

$V_B^+ = V_B^- - R_B = \frac{P}{2} - \frac{P}{2} = 0$ <u>checks!</u>

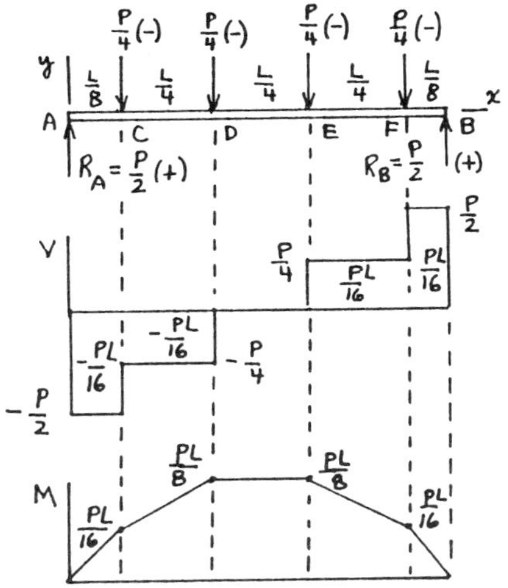

$M_A = 0$

$M_C = M_A - \text{area } V\Big]_A^C = 0 - \left(-\frac{PL}{16}\right) = \frac{PL}{16}$

$M_D = M_C - \text{area } V\Big]_C^D = \frac{PL}{16} - \left(-\frac{PL}{16}\right) = \frac{PL}{8}$

$M_E = M_D - \text{area } V\Big]_D^E = \frac{PL}{8} - 0 = \frac{PL}{8}$

$M_F = M_E - \text{area } V\Big]_E^F = \frac{PL}{8} - \frac{PL}{16} = \frac{PL}{16}$

$M_B = M_F - \text{area } V\Big]_F^B = \frac{PL}{16} - \frac{PL}{16} = 0$ <u>checks!</u>

<u>Comparison</u>: V_{max} and M_{max} are the same for both cases.

6.44

(a)

$V_A^- = 0$

$V_A^+ = V_A^- - R_A = 0 - \frac{Pd}{L} = -\frac{Pd}{L}$

$V_B^- = V_A^+ - \text{area } w\Big]_A^B$

$= -\frac{Pd}{L} - 0 = -\frac{Pd}{L}$

$V_B^+ = V_B^- - R_B$

$= -\frac{Pd}{L} - \left(-\frac{Pd}{L}\right) = 0$ <u>checks!</u>

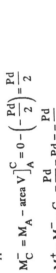

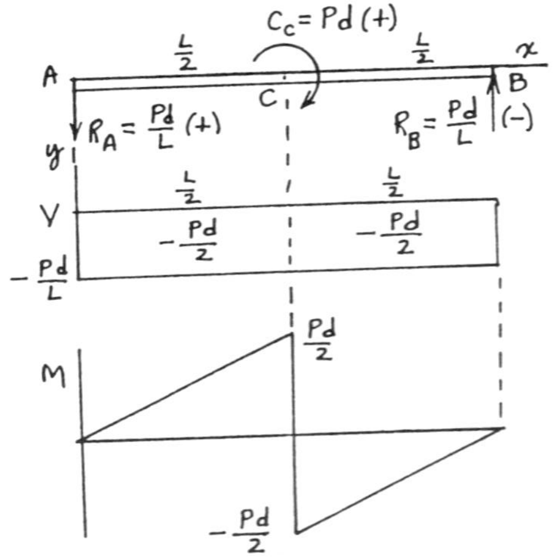

$M_A = 0$

$M_C^- = M_A - \text{area } V\Big]_A^C = 0 - \left(-\frac{Pd}{2}\right) = \frac{Pd}{2}$

$M_C^+ = M_C^- - C_C = \frac{Pd}{2} - Pd = -\frac{Pd}{2}$

$M_B = M_C^+ - \text{area } V\Big]_B^C = -\frac{Pd}{2} - \left(-\frac{Pd}{2}\right) = 0$ <u>checks!</u>

(continued)

(b) $V_A^- = 0$

$V_A^+ = V_A^- - R_A$

$= 0 - \frac{Pd}{L} = -\frac{Pd}{L} = V_C^-$

$V_C^+ = V_C^- - P_C$

$= -\frac{Pd}{L} - (-P)$

$= P\left(1 - \frac{d}{L}\right) = V_D^-$

$V_D^+ = V_D^- - P_D$

$= P\left(1 - \frac{d}{L}\right) - P$

$= -\frac{Pd}{L} = V_B^-$

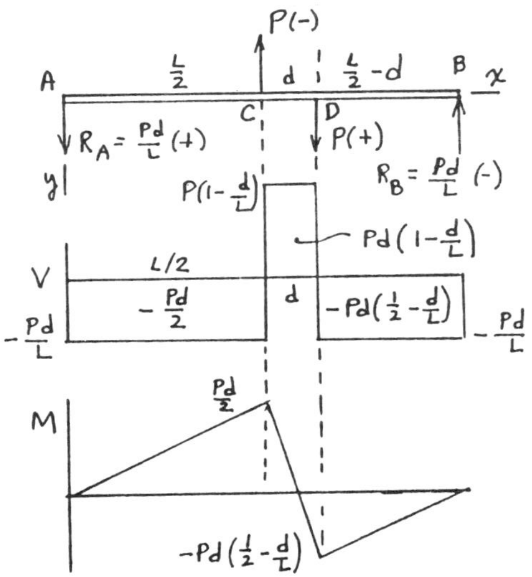

$V_B^+ = V_B^- - R_B = -\frac{Pd}{L} - \left(-\frac{Pd}{L}\right) = 0$ checks!

$M_A = 0$

$M_C = M_A - \text{area } V\Big]_A^C = 0 - \left(-\frac{Pd}{2}\right) = \frac{Pd}{2}$

$M_D = M_C - \text{area } V\Big]_C^D = \frac{Pd}{2} - Pd\left(1 - \frac{d}{L}\right) = -Pd\left(\frac{1}{2} - \frac{d}{L}\right)$

$M_B = M_D - \text{area } V\Big]_D^B = -Pd\left(\frac{1}{2} - \frac{d}{L}\right) - \left[-Pd\left(\frac{1}{2} - \frac{d}{L}\right)\right] = 0$ checks!

Comparison: When $\frac{d}{L} \to 0$, the shear force diagram for part (b) becomes

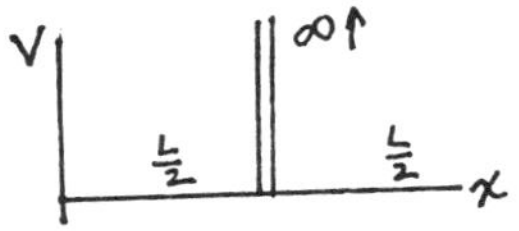

The bending moment diagrams for parts (a) and (b) become identical.

6.45

See solution of Prob. 6.26 for reactions.

$V_A^- = 0$

$V_A^+ = V_A^- - R_A = 0 - (-600) = 600$ lb

$V_C = V_A^+ - \text{area } w\Big]_A^C$

$= 600 - 0 = 600$ lb

$V_D^- = V_C - \text{area } w\Big]_C^D$

$= 600 - 200 = 400$ lb

$V_D^+ = V_D^- - P_D = 400 - 400 = 0$

$V_B^- = V_D^+ - \text{area } w\Big]_D^B$

$= 0 - 600 = -600$ lb

$V_B^+ = V_B^- - P_B$

$= -600 - (-600) = 0$ checks!

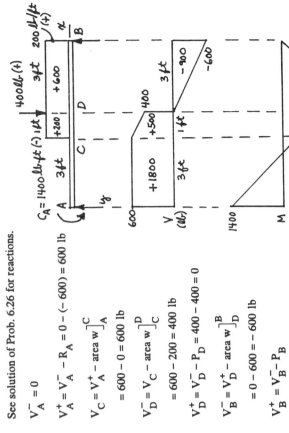

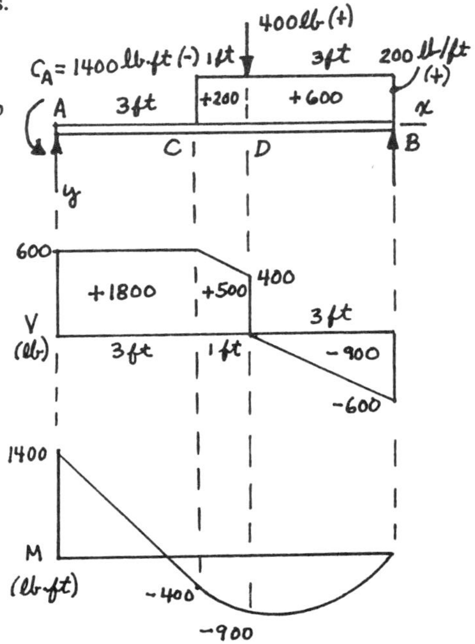

$M_A^- = 0$

$M_A^+ = M_A^- - C_A = 0 - (-1400) = 1400$ lb•ft

$M_C = M_A^+ - \text{area } V\Big]_A^C = 1400 - (+1800) = -400$ lb•ft

$M_D = M_C - \text{area } V\Big]_C^D = -400 - 500 = -900$ lb•ft

$M_B = M_D - \text{area } V\Big]_D^B = -900 - (-900) = 0$ checks!

6.46

<u>FBD of entire beam</u>

$\Sigma M_B = 0$: $R_A(4) = 800(1)$ gives $R_A = 200$ kN; $\Sigma F_y = 0$: $R_B = 800 - 200 = 600$ kN

$V_A^- = 0$

$V_A^+ = V_A^- - R_A = 0 - (-200) = 200$ kN

$V_C = V_A^+ - \text{area } w\Big]_A^C = 200 - 0 = 200$ kN

$V_B^- = V_C - \text{area } w\Big]_C^B$

$= 200 - 800 = -600$ kN

Let D be the point where the V-diagram crosses the axis.

By similar triangles: $\dfrac{200}{d} = \dfrac{600}{2-d}$

which gives $d = 0.5$ m

$V_B^+ = V_B^- - R_B$

$= -600 - (-600) = 0$ <u>checks!</u>

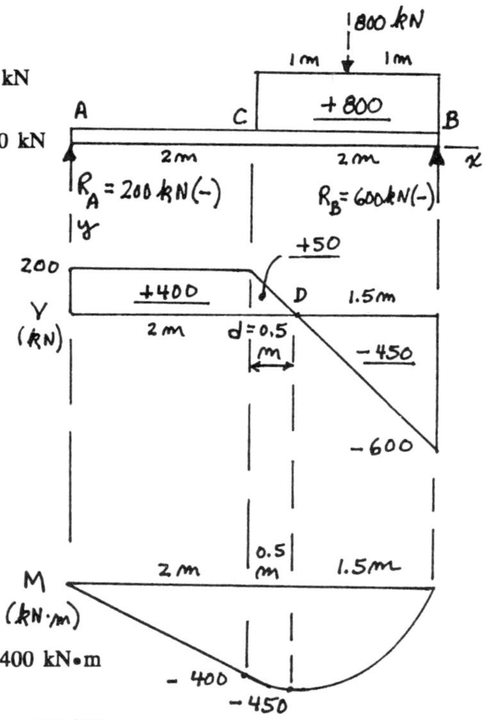

$M_A = 0$

$M_C = M_A - \text{area } V\Big]_A^C = 0 - 400 = -400$ kN•m

$M_D = M_C - \text{area } V\Big]_C^D = -400 - 50 = -450$ kN•m

$M_B = M_D - \text{area } V\Big]_D^B = -450 - (-450) = 0$ <u>checks!</u>

6.47

See solution of Prob. 6.28 for reactions.

$V_A^- = 0$

$V_A^+ = V_A^- - R_A = 0 - (-4) = 4$ kN

$V_C = V_A^+ - \text{area } w\Big]_A^C = 4 - 3.6 = 0.4$ kN

$V_D^- = V_C - \text{area } w\Big]_C^D = 0.4 - 0 = 0.4$ kN

$V_D^+ = V_D^- - P_D = 0.4 - 5 = -4.6$ kN

$V_B^- = V_D^+ - \text{area } w\Big]_D^B$

$= -4.6 - 0 = -4.6$ kN

$V_B^+ = V_B^- - R_B$

$= -4.6 - (-4.6) = 0$ <u>checks!</u>

$M_A = 0$

$M_C = M_A - \text{area } V\Big]_A^C$

$= 0 - [3(4) - (1/3)(3)(3.6)]$

$= -8.4$ kN•m

$M_D = M_C - \text{area } V\Big]_C^D$

$= -8.4 - 0.8 = -9.2$ kN•m

$M_B = M_D - \text{area } V\Big]_D^B = -9.2 - (-9.2) = 0$ <u>checks!</u>

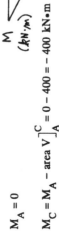

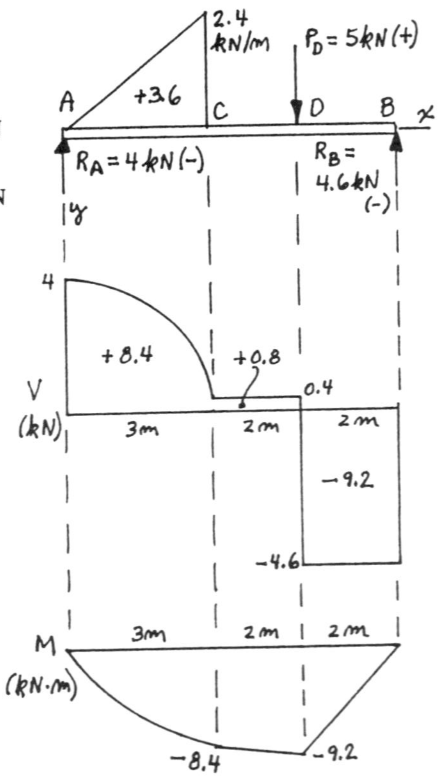

6.48

FBD of entire beam

$\Sigma M_B = 0$: $R_C(5) = 40(2.5) - 20(2)$ gives: $R_C = 12$ kN; $\Sigma F_y = 0$: $R_B = 60 - 12 = 48$ kN

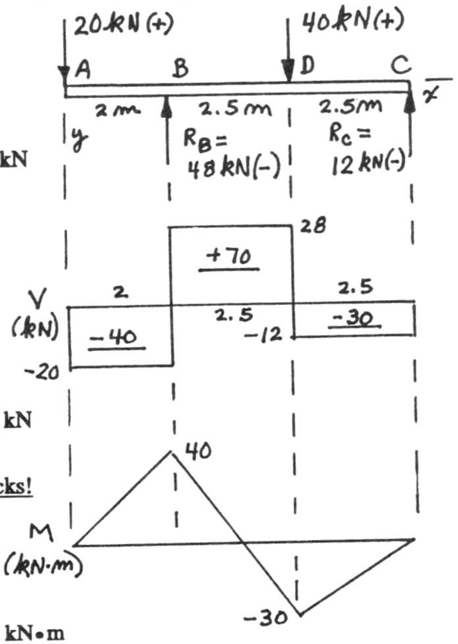

$V_A^- = 0$

$V_A^+ = V_A^- - P_A = 0 - (20) = -20$ kN

$V_B^- = V_A^+ - \text{area } w\Big]_A^B = -20 - 0 = -20$ kN

$V_B^+ = V_B^- - R_B = -20 - (-48) = 28$ kN

$V_D^- = V_B^+ - \text{area } w\Big]_B^D = 28 - 0 = 28$ kN

$V_D^+ = V_D^- - P_D = 28 - 40 = -12$ kN

$V_C^- = V_D^+ - \text{area } w\Big]_D^C = -12 - 0 = -12$ kN

$V_C^+ = V_C^- - P_C = -12 - (-12) = 0$ <u>checks!</u>

$M_A = 0$

$M_B = M_A - \text{area } V\Big]_A^B = 0 - (-40) = 40$ kN•m

$M_D = M_B - \text{area } V\Big]_B^D = 40 - 70 = -30$ kN•m

$M_C = M_D - \text{area } V\Big]_D^C = -30 - (-30) = 0$ <u>checks!</u>

6.49

See solution of Prob. 6.34 for weights and reactions.

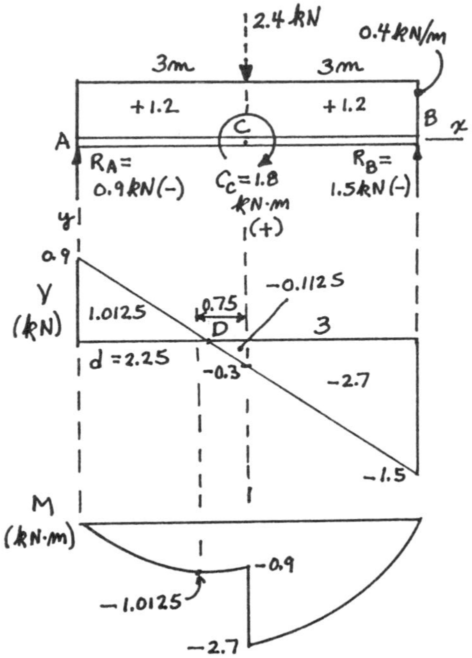

$V_A^- = 0$

$V_A^+ = V_A^- - R_A$

$= 0 - (-0.9) = 0.9$ kN

$V_C = V_A^+ - \text{area } w\Big]_A^C$

$= 0.9 - 1.2 = -0.3$ kN

$V_B^- = V_C - \text{area } w\Big]_C^B$

$= -0.3 - 1.2 = -1.5$ kN

$V_B^+ = V_B^- - R_B$

$= -1.5 - (-1.5) = 0$ <u>checks!</u>

Let D be the point where the V-diagram crosses the axis.

By similar triangles: $\dfrac{2.4}{6} = \dfrac{0.9}{d}$

which gives $d = 2.25$ m

$M_A = 0$

$M_D = M_A - \text{area } V\Big]_A^D = 0 - 1.0125 = -1.0125$ kN•m

$M_C^- = M_D - \text{area } V\Big]_D^C = -1.0125 - (-0.1125) = -0.9$ kN•m

$M_C^+ = M_C^- - C_C = -0.9 - 1.8 = -2.7$ kN•m

$M_B = M_C^+ - \text{area } V\Big]_C^B = -2.7 - (-2.7) = 0$ <u>checks!</u>

6.50

By symmetry, $R_A = R_B = 960$ lb.

$V_D = 0 \quad V_A^- = V_D - \text{area } w\Big]_D^A$

$= 0 - 480 = -480$ lb

$V_A^+ = V_A^- - R_A$

$= -480 - (-960) = 480$ lb

$V_B^- = V_A^+ - \text{area } w\Big]_A^B$

$= 480 - 960 = -480$ lb

$V_B^+ = V_B^- - R_B$

$= -480 - (-960) = 480$ lb <u>checks!</u>

$V_E = V_B^+ - \text{area } w\Big]_B^E$

$= 480 - 480 = 0$ <u>checks!</u>

$M_D = 0$

$M_A = M_D - \text{area } V\Big]_D^A$

$= 0 - (-960) = 960$ lb•ft

$M_C = M_A - \text{area } V\Big]_A^C = 960 - 960 = 0$

$M_B = M_C - \text{area } V\Big]_C^B = 0 - (-960) = 960$ lb•ft

$M_E = M_B - \text{area } V\Big]_B^E = 960 - 960 = 0$ <u>checks!</u>

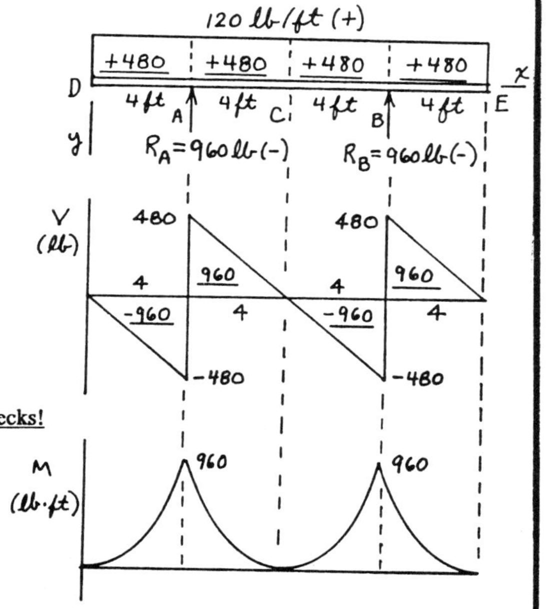

6.51

<u>Reactions</u> $\Sigma F_y = 0$: $R_A = 500$ lb

$\Sigma M_A = 0$: $C_A = 500(9) - 1500 = 3000$ lb•ft

$V_A^- = 0$

$V_A^+ = V_A^- - R_A$

$= 0 - 500 = -500$ lb

$V_C^- = V_A^+ - \text{area } w\Big]_A^C$

$= -500 - 0 = -500$ lb

$V_C^+ = V_C^- - P_C$

$= -500 - (-500) = 0$ <u>checks!</u>

$M_A^- = 0$

$M_A^+ = M_A^- - C_A$

$= 0 - 3000 = -3000$ lb•ft

$M_B^- = M_A^+ - \text{area } V\Big]_A^B = -3000 - (-2000) = -1000$ lb•ft

$M_B^+ = M_B^- - C_B = -1000 - 1500 = -2500$ lb•ft

$M_C = M_B^+ - \text{area } V\Big]_B^C = -2500 - (-2500) = 0$ <u>checks!</u>

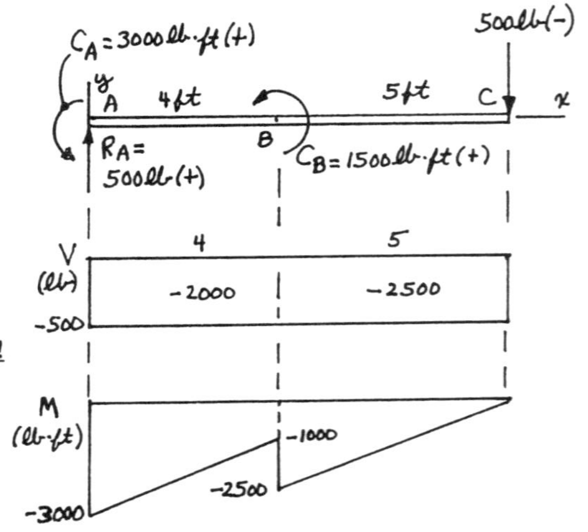

6.52

FBD of entire beam $\Sigma M_A = 0$: $C_A = 500(9) + 720(4.5) - 1500 = 6240$ lb•ft

$\Sigma F_y = 0$: $R_A = 500 + 720 = 1220$ lb

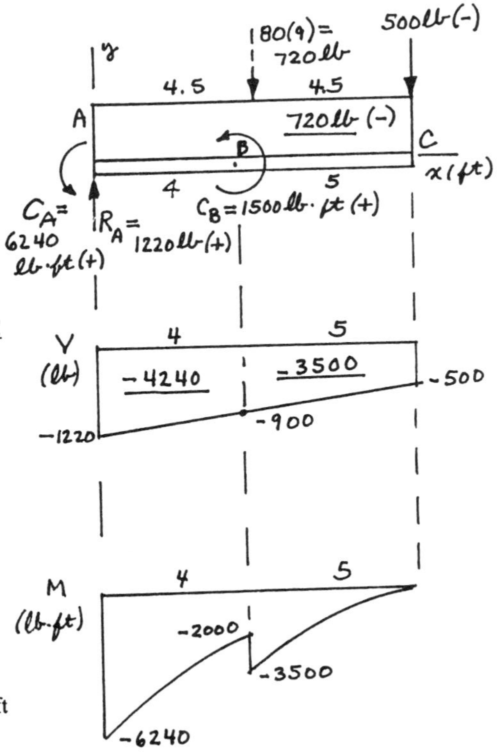

$V_A^- = 0$

$V_A^+ = V_A^- - R_A$

$= 0 - 1220 = -1220$ lb

$V_C^- = V_A^+ - \text{area } w\Big]_A^C$

$= -1220 - (-720) = -500$ lb

$V_C^+ = V_C^- - P_C$

$= -500 - (-500) = 0$ <u>checks!</u>

$M_A^- = 0$

$M_A^+ = M_A^- - C_A$

$= 0 - 6240 = -6240$ lb•ft

$M_B^- = M_A^+ - \text{area } V\Big]_A^B$

$= -6240 - (-4240)$

$= -2000$ lb•ft

$M_B^+ = M_B^- - C_B$

$= -2000 - 1500 = -3500$ lb•ft

$M_C = M_B^+ - \text{area } V\Big]_B^C$

$= -3500 - (-3500) = 0$ <u>checks!</u>

6.53

Reactions $\Sigma M_A = 0$: $R_D(18) = 480(6 + 14)$ $\therefore$ $R_D = 533.3$ lb

$\Sigma F_y = 0$: $R_A = 480 + 480 - 533.3 = 426.7$ lb

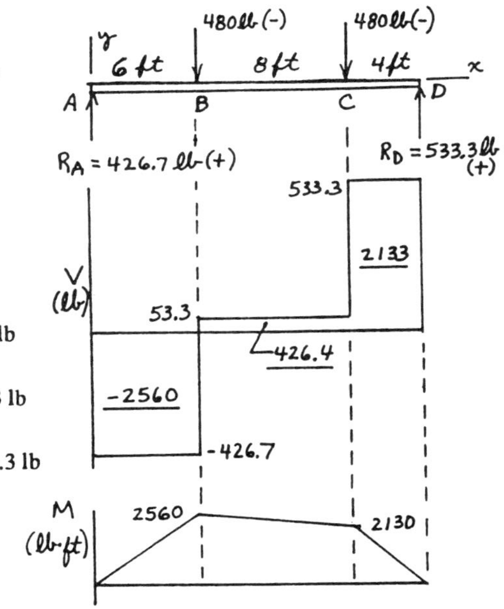

$V_A^- = 0$

$V_A^+ = V_A^- - R_A = 0 - 426.7 = -426.7$ lb

$V_B^- = V_A^+ - \text{area } w\Big]_A^B$

$= -426.7 - 0 = -426.7$ lb

$V_B^+ = V_B^- - P_B$

$= -426.7 - (-480) = 53.3$ lb

$V_C^- = V_B^+ - \text{area } w\Big]_B^C = 53.3 - 0 = 53.3$ lb

$V_C^+ = V_C^- - P_C = 53.3 - (-480) = 533.3$ lb

$V_D^- = V_C^+ - \text{area } w\Big]_C^D = 533.3 - 0 = 533.3$ lb

$V_D^+ = V_D^- - R_D$

$= 533.3 - 533.3 = 0$ <u>checks!</u>

$M_A = 0$

$M_B = M_A - \text{area } V\Big]_A^B = 0 - (-2560) = 2560$ lb•ft

$M_C = M_B - \text{area } V\Big]_B^C = 2560 - 426.4 = 2134$ lb•ft

$M_D = M_C - \text{area } V\Big]_C^D = 2134 - 2133 \approx 0$ <u>checks!</u>

6.54

<u>Reactions</u> $\Sigma M_A = 0$: $R_D(18) = 480(6 + 14) + 648(9)$ $\therefore$ $R_D = 857.3$ lb

$\Sigma F_y = 0$: $R_A = 480 + 480 + 648 - 857.3 = 750.7$ lb

$V_A^- = 0$ $V_A^+ = V_A^- - R_A = 0 - 750.7 = -750.7$ lb

$V_B^- = V_A^+ - \text{area } w\Big]_A^B = -750.7 - (-216) = -534.7$ lb

$V_B^+ = V_B^- - P_B = -534.7 - (-480) = -54.7$ lb

$V_C^- = V_B^+ - \text{area } w\Big]_B^C = -54.7 - (-288) = 233.3$ lb

Let E be point where V-diagram crosses the axis.

Similar triangles: $\dfrac{54.7}{b} = \dfrac{233.3}{8 - b}$ gives $b = 1.519$ ft.

$V_C^+ = V_C^- - P_C = 233.3 - (-480) = 713.3$ lb

$V_D^- = V_C^+ - \text{area } w\Big]_C^D = 713.3 - (-144) = 857.3$ lb

$V_D^+ = V_D^- - R_D = 857.3 - 857.3 = 0$ <u>checks!</u>

$M_A = 0$

$M_B = M_A - \text{area } V\Big]_A^B = 0 - (-3856) = 3856$ lb•ft

$M_E = M_B - \text{area } V\Big]_B^E = 3856 - (-41.5) = 3898$ lb•ft

$M_C = M_E - \text{area } V\Big]_E^C = 3898 - 756 = 3142$ lb•ft

$M_D = M_C - \text{area } V\Big]_C^D = 3142 - 3141 \approx 0$ <u>checks!</u>

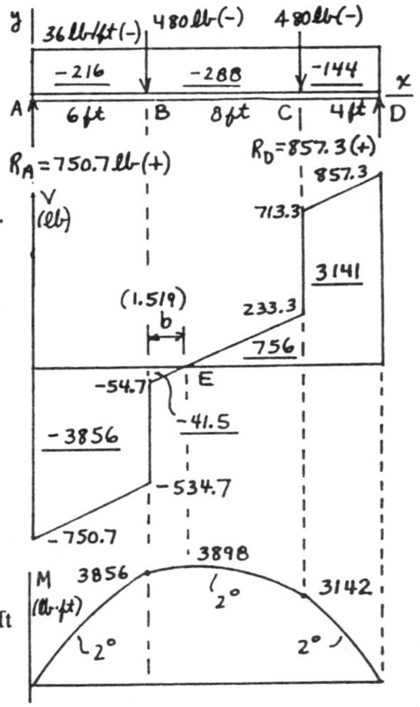

6.55

<u>Reactions</u> $\Sigma M_A = 0$: $R_B(6) = 600(8) + 2400(3)$ $\therefore$ $R_B = 2000$ lb

$\Sigma F_y = 0$: $R_A = 2400 + 600 - 2000 = 1000$ lb

$V_A^- = 0$

$V_A^+ = V_A^- - R_A$

$= 0 - (-1000) = 1000$ lb

$V_B^- = V_A^+ - \text{area } w\Big]_A^B$

$= 1000 - 2400 = -1400$ lb

$V_B^+ = V_B^- - R_B$

$= -1400 - (-2000) = 600$ lb

$V_C^- = V_B^+ - \text{area } w\Big]_B^C$

$= 600 - 0 = 600$ lb

$V_C^+ = V_C^- - P_C$

$= 600 - 600 = 0$ <u>checks!</u>

Let D be the point where the V-diagram crosses the axis.

By similar triangles: $\dfrac{2400}{6} = \dfrac{1000}{d}$

which gives $d = 2.5$ ft

$M_A = 0$

$M_D = M_A - \text{area } V\Big]_A^D = 0 - 1250 = -1250$ lb•ft

$M_B = M_D - \text{area } V\Big]_D^B = -1250 - (-2450) = 1200$ lb•ft

$M_C = M_B - \text{area } V\Big]_B^C = 1200 - 1200 = 0$ <u>checks!</u>

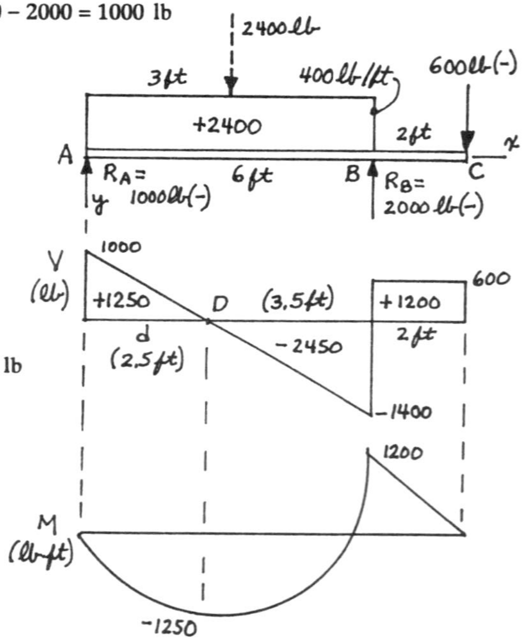

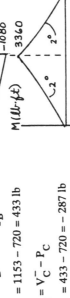

6.56

<u>Reactions</u> $\Sigma M_A = 0$: $R_D(8) = 6 + 0.8(5)(2.5)$ $\therefore$ $R_D = 2$ kN

$\Sigma F_y = 0$: $R_A = 0.8(5) - 2 = 2$ kN

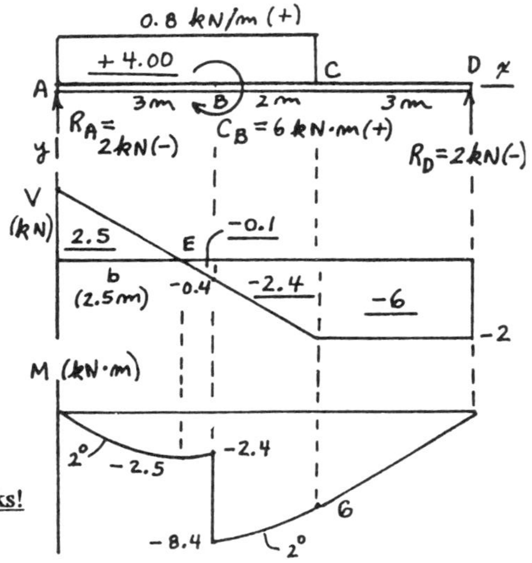

$V_A^- = 0$

$V_A^+ = V_A^- - R_A = 0 - (-2) = 2$ kN

$V_C = V_A^+ - \text{area } w\Big]_A^C = 2 - 4 = -2$ kN

Let E be point where V-diagram crosses the axis. Similar triangles:

$\dfrac{2}{b} = \dfrac{2}{5-b}$ gives b = 2.5 m.

$V_D^- = V_C - \text{area } w\Big]_C^D = -2 - 0 = -2$ kN

$V_D^+ = V_D^- - R_D = -2 - (-2) = 0$ <u>checks!</u>

$M_A = 0$

$M_E = M_A - \text{area } V\Big]_A^E = 0 - 2.5 = -2.5$ kN•m

$M_B^- = M_E - \text{area } V\Big]_E^B = -2.5 - (-0.1) = -2.4$ kN•m

$M_B^+ = M_B^- - C_B = -2.4 - 6 = -8.4$ kN•m

$M_C = M_B^+ - \text{area } V\Big]_B^C = -8.4 - (-2.4) = -6$ kN•m

$M_D = M_C - \text{area } V\Big]_C^D = -6 - (-6) = 0$ <u>checks!</u>

6.57

<u>Reactions</u> $\Sigma M_D = 0$: $R_B(9) = 600(13) + 720(3) + 120(13)(6.5)$ $\therefore$ $R_B = 2233$ lb

$\Sigma F_y = 0$: $R_D = 600 + 720 + 120(13) - 2233 = 647$ lb

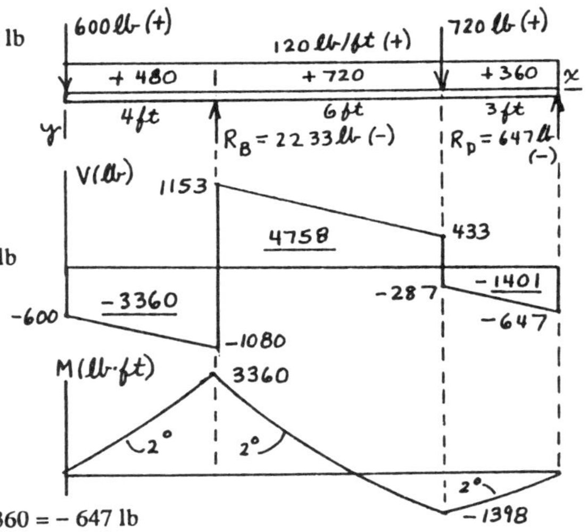

$V_A^- = 0$

$V_A^+ = V_A^- - P_A = 0 - 600 = -600$ lb

$V_B^- = V_A^+ - \text{area } w\Big]_A^B$

$= -600 - 480 = -1080$ lb

$V_B^+ = V_B^- - R_B$

$= -1080 - (-2233) = 1153$ lb

$V_C^- = V_B^+ - \text{area } w\Big]_B^C$

$= 1153 - 720 = 433$ lb

$V_C^+ = V_C^- - P_C$

$= 433 - 720 = -287$ lb

$V_D^- = V_C^+ - \text{area } w\Big]_C^D = -287 - 360 = -647$ lb

$V_D^+ = V_D^- - R_D = -647 - (-647) = 0$ <u>checks!</u>

$M_A = 0$ $\qquad M_B = M_A - \text{area } V\Big]_A^B = 0 - (-3360) = 3360$ lb•ft

$M_C = M_B - \text{area } V\Big]_B^C = 3360 - 4758 = -1398$ lb•ft

$M_D = M_C - \text{area } V\Big]_C^D = -1398 - (-1401) \approx 0$ <u>checks!</u>

6.58

Reactions $\Sigma M_A = 0$: $R_C(7.2) = 8(3.6) + 8(10.8) + 11.52(1.8 + 9)$ $\therefore$ $R_C = 33.28$ kN

$\Sigma F_y = 0$: $R_A = 2(11.52) + 2(8) - 33.28 = 5.76$ kN $\qquad V_A^- = 0$

$V_A^+ = V_A^- - R_A = 0 - (-5.76) = 5.76$ kN

$V_B^- = V_A^+ - \text{area } w\big]_A^B$

$= 5.76 - 11.52 = -5.76$ kN

$V_B^+ = V_B^- - P_B$

$= -5.76 - 8 = -13.76$ kN

$V_C^- = V_B^+ - \text{area } w\big]_B^C$

$= -13.76 - 0 = -13.76$ kN

$V_C^+ = V_C^- - R_C$

$= -13.76 - (-33.28) = 19.52$ kN

$V_D^- = V_C^+ - \text{area } w\big]_C^D = 19.52 - 11.52$

$= 8.00$ kN $\qquad V_D^+ = V_D^- - R_D = 8.00 - 8.00 = 0$ checks!

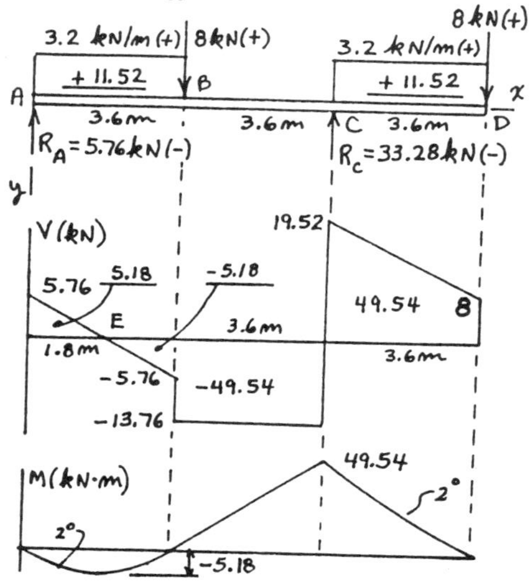

$M_A = 0$; $M_E = M_A - \text{area } V\big]_A^E = 0 - 5.18 = -5.18$ kN•m (E is midway between A and B)

$M_B = M_E - \text{area } V\big]_E^B = -5.18 - (-5.18) = 0$

$M_C = M_B - \text{area } V\big]_B^C = 0 - (-49.54) = 49.54$ kN•m

$M_D = M_C - \text{area } V\big]_C^D = 49.54 - 49.54 = 0$ checks!

6.59

Reactions $\Sigma F_y = 0$: $R_B = (0.5)(12)(96) = 576$ lb

$\Sigma M_B = 0$: $C_B = (0.5)(12)(96)(6) = 3456$ lb•ft

$V_A = 0$ $\qquad M_A = 0$

$V_C = V_A - \text{area } w\big]_A^C$ $\qquad M_C = M_A - \text{area } V\big]_A^C = 0 - 576 = -576$ lb•ft

$= 0 - (-288) = 288$ lb $\qquad M_B^- = M_C - \text{area } V\big]_C^B = -576 - 2880 = -3456$ lb•ft

$V_B^- = V_C - \text{area } w\big]_C^B$

$= 288 - (-288) = 576$ lb $\qquad M_B^+ = M_B^- - C_B = -3456 - (-3456) = 0$ checks!

$V_B^+ = V_B^- - R_B$

$= 576 - 576 = 0$ checks!

Area $A_1 = (1/3)(6)(288) = 576$ lb•ft

Area $A_2 = 6(576) - (1/3)(6)(288)$

$= 2880$ lb•ft

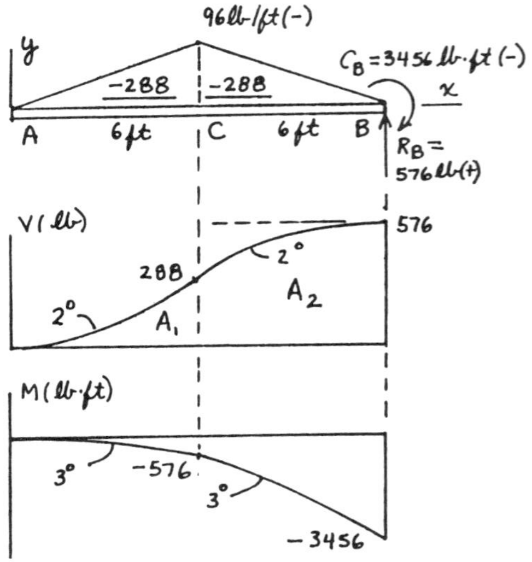

6.60

Reactions $\Sigma M_A = 0$: $C_A = 600(12) - (0.5)(12)(80)(8) = 3360$ lb•ft

$\Sigma F_y = 0$:

$R_A = 600 - (0.5)(12)(80) = 120$ lb

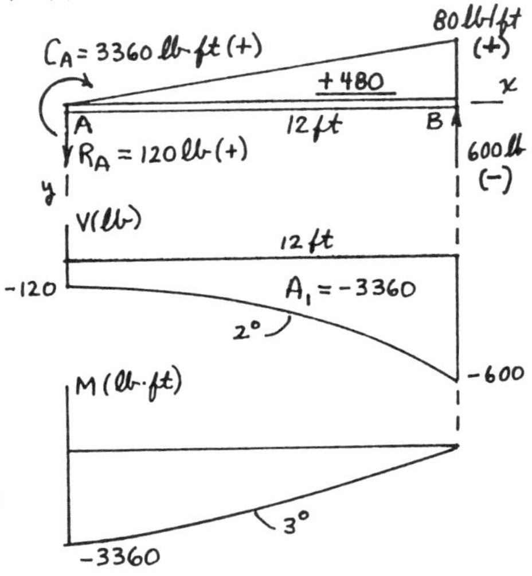

$V_A^- = 0$

$V_A^+ = V_A^- - R_A = 0 - 120 = -120$ lb

$V_B^- = V_A^+ - \text{area } w\big]_A^B$

$= -120 - 480 = -600$ lb

$V_B^+ = V_B^- - P_B$

$= -600 - (-600) = 0$ <u>checks!</u>

Area $A_1 = -600(12) + (2/3)(12)(480)$

$= -3360$ lb · ft

$M_A^- = 0$ $M_A^+ = M_A^- - C_A = 0 - 3360 = -3360$ lb•ft

$M_B = M_A^+ - \text{area } V\big]_A^B = -3360 - (-3360) = 0$ <u>checks!</u>

6.61

Reactions $\Sigma M_A = 0$: $C_A = (0.5)(12)(200)(8) - 600(12) = 2400$ lb•ft

$\Sigma F_y = 0$:

$R_A = (0.5)(12)(200) - 600 = 600$ lb

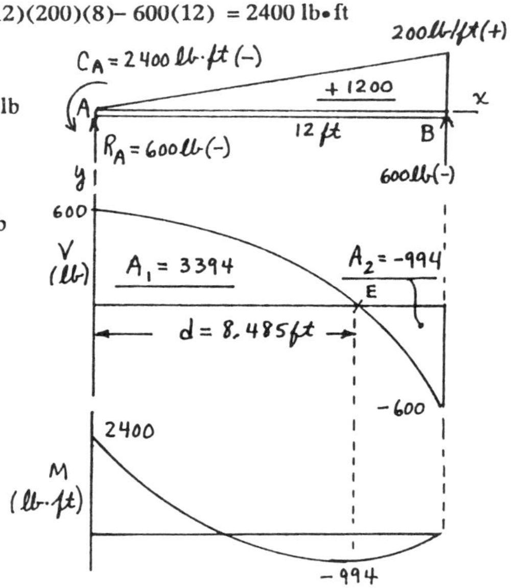

$V_A^- = 0$

$V_A^+ = V_A^- - R_A = 0 - (-600) = 600$ lb

$V_B^- = V_A^+ - \text{area } w\big]_A^B$

$= 600 - 1200 = -600$ lb

$V_B^+ = V_B^- - P_B$

$= -600 - (-600) = 0$ <u>checks!</u>

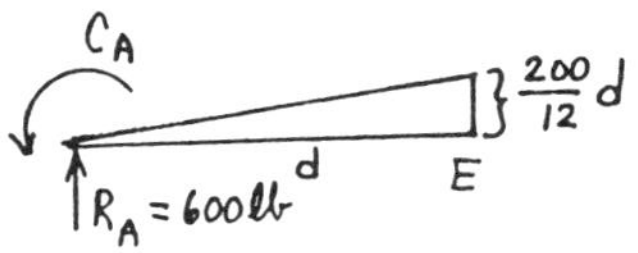

To find point E, area under load diagram equals 600 lb: $(0.5)(d)[(200/12)d] = 600$ lb which gives $d = 8.485$ ft. Area $A_1 = (2/3)(600)(8.485) = 3394$ lb · ft

Area $A_2 = -\left[(1/3)(12)(1200) - (1/3)(8.485)(600) - 600(12 - 8.485)\right] = -994$ lb · ft

$M_A^- = 0$ $M_A^+ = M_A^- - C_A = 0 - (-2400) = 2400$ lb•ft

$M_E = M_A^+ - \text{area } V\big]_A^E = 2400 - 3394 = -994$ lb•ft

$M_B = M_E - \text{area } V\big]_E^B = -994 - (-994) = 0$ <u>checks!</u>

6.62

From the FBD

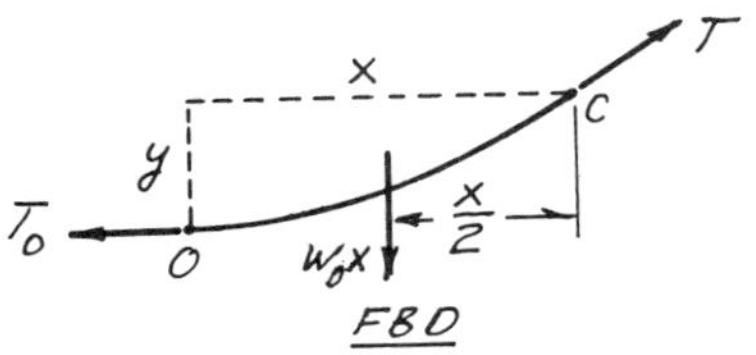

$$\Sigma M_C = 0: \circlearrowleft\!+ \quad (w_0x)\frac{x}{2} - T_0 y = 0$$

$$\therefore T_0 = \frac{w_0 x^2}{2y}$$

Equation (6.9) is

$$T = \sqrt{T_0^2 + (w_0x)^2} = \sqrt{\left(\frac{w_0x^2}{2y}\right)^2 + (w_0x)^2} = w_0 x\sqrt{\left(\frac{x}{2y}\right)^2 + 1} \quad \text{Q.E.D.}$$

6.63

The shape of the cable is parabolic.

From Eq. (6.10): $H = y\big|_{x=L/2} = \dfrac{w_0(L/2)^2}{2T_0}$ $\quad \therefore T_0 = \dfrac{L^2}{8H}w_0$ . . . . (a)

From Eq. (6.9): $T_{max} = T\big|_{x=L/2} = \sqrt{T_0^2 + \left[w_0(L/2)\right]^2}$ $\quad \therefore T_{max}^2 = T_0^2 + \left(\dfrac{L}{2}\right)^2 w_0^2$.

Substitute for T_0 from Eq. (a): $T_{max}^2 = \left(\dfrac{L^2}{8H}\right)^2 w_0^2 + \left(\dfrac{L}{2}\right)^2 w_0^2 = \left(\dfrac{L}{2}\right)^2 w_0^2\left[\left(\dfrac{L}{4H}\right)^2 + 1\right]$

$\therefore (36\,000)^2 = \left(\dfrac{60}{2}\right)^2 w_0^2\left[\left(\dfrac{60}{4\times 10}\right)^2 + 1\right]$ $\quad \therefore (36\,000)^2 = 2925 w_0^2$ $\quad \therefore w_0 = 666$ N/m ◆

6.64

From Eq. (6.10): $H = y\big|_{x=L/2} = \dfrac{w_0(L/2)^2}{2T_0} = \dfrac{(80)(210/2)^2}{2(30\,000)} = 14.70$ ft ◆

From Eq. (6.9): $\theta\big|_{x=L/2} = \tan^{-1}\dfrac{w_0(L/2)}{T_0} = \tan^{-1}\dfrac{(80)(210/2)}{30\,000} = 15.64°$ ◆

6.65

The shape of the cable is a parabola.

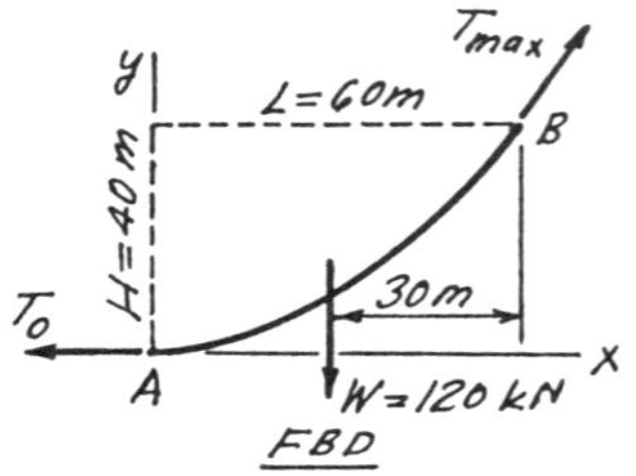

(a) The total load carried by cable is

$$W = w_0 L = (2)(60) = 120 \text{ kN}$$

From the FBD

$$\Sigma M_B = 0: \circlearrowleft\!+ \quad (120)(30) - 40T_0 = 0$$

$$\therefore T_0 = 90 \text{ kN}$$

Equation (6.8): $T_{max} = \sqrt{T_0^2 + W^2} = \sqrt{90^2 + 120^2} = 150$ kN ◆

(b) Eq. (6.12): $s(x) = \dfrac{x}{2}\sqrt{1 + (w_0x/T_0)^2} + \dfrac{1}{2}(T_0/w_0)\ln\left[(w_0x/T_0) + \sqrt{1 + (w_0x/T_0)^2}\right]$

Substituting $x = L = 60$ m, we have $\dfrac{w_0x}{T_0} = \dfrac{w_0L}{T_0} = \dfrac{(2)(60)}{90} = \dfrac{4}{3}$

$\therefore s_{AB} = s(L) = \dfrac{60}{2}\sqrt{1 + (4/3)^2} + \dfrac{1}{2}\dfrac{90}{2}\ln\left[4/3 + \sqrt{1 + (4/3)^2}\right] = 74.7$ m ◆

6.66

The cable is parabolic, the distributed loading being

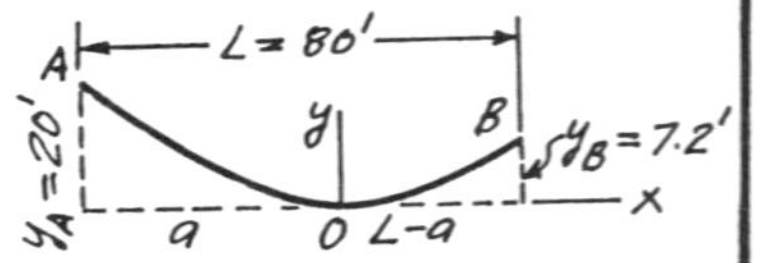

$$w_0 = \frac{W}{L} = \frac{960}{80} = 12 \text{ lb/ft}$$

Location of point O can be found from Eq. (6.10):

$y = \dfrac{w_0x^2}{2T_0}$ $\quad \therefore \dfrac{y_A}{y_B} = \dfrac{y\big|_{x=-a}}{y\big|_{x=L-a}} = \dfrac{a^2}{(L-a)^2}$ $\quad \therefore \dfrac{20}{7.2} = \dfrac{a^2}{(80-a)^2}$ $\quad \therefore a = 50$ ft

At point A, Eq. (6.10) becomes $y_A = \dfrac{w_0a^2}{2T_0}$ $\quad \therefore T_0 = \dfrac{w_0a^2}{2y_A} = \dfrac{(12)(50^2)}{2(20)} = 750$ lb

(continued)

6.66 continued

Equation (6.12): $s(x) = \frac{x}{2}\sqrt{1 + (w_0x/T_0)^2} + \frac{1}{2}(T_0/w_0)\ln\left[(w_0x/T_0) + \sqrt{1 + (w_0x/T_0)^2}\right]$

With x = 50 ft: $\frac{w_0x}{T_0} = \frac{(12)(50)}{750} = 0.8$

$\therefore s_{OA} = s(50\text{ ft}) = \frac{50}{2}\sqrt{1 + 0.8^2} + \frac{1}{2}\frac{750}{12}\ln\left[0.8 + \sqrt{1 + 0.8^2}\right] = 54.9\text{ ft}$

With x = 30 ft: $\frac{w_0x}{T_0} = \frac{(12)(30)}{750} = 0.48$

$\therefore s_{OB} = s(30\text{ ft}) = \frac{30}{2}\sqrt{1 + 0.48^2} + \frac{1}{2}\frac{750}{12}\ln\left[0.48 + \sqrt{1 + 0.48^2}\right] = 31.1\text{ ft}$

Total length of the cable is: $s = s_{OA} + s_{OB} = 54.9 + 31.1 = 86.0$ ft ◆

The maximum value of T occurs at A. Substituting x = 50 ft in Eq. (6.9), we get

$T_{max} = \sqrt{T_0^2 + (w_0a)^2} = \sqrt{750^2 + (12 \times 50)^2} = 960\text{ lb}$ ◆

6.67

From the FBD

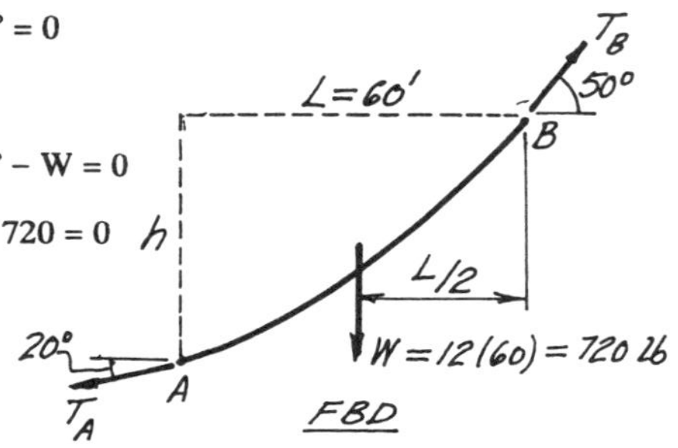

$\Sigma F_x = 0$: $\overset{+}{\rightarrow}$ $-T_A\cos 20° + T_B\cos 50° = 0$

$\therefore T_A = 0.6840\,T_B$

$\Sigma F_y = 0$: $+\uparrow$ $-T_A\sin 20° + T_B\sin 50° - W = 0$

$\therefore T_B(-0.6840\sin 20° + \sin 50°) - 720 = 0$

$\therefore T_B = 1353.1$ lb

$\therefore T_A = 0.6840(1353.1) = 925.5$ lb

$\therefore T_{max} = T_B = 1353$ lb ◆

$\Sigma M_A = 0$: (+) $(T_B\sin 50°)L - (T_B\cos 50°)h - W\frac{L}{2} = 0$

$\therefore h = \frac{(T_B\sin 50° - W/2)L}{T_B\cos 50°} = \frac{(1353.1\sin 50° - 720/2)60}{1353.1\cos 50°} = 46.7\text{ ft}$ ◆

6.68

The shape of the string is <u>catenary</u>.

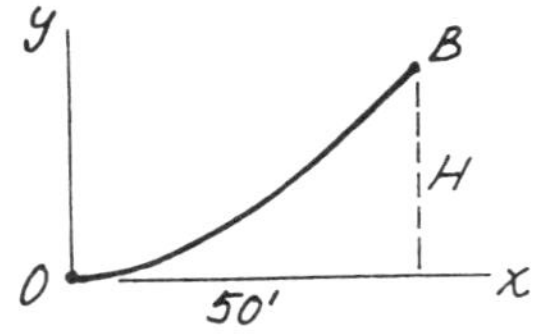

Equation (6.16): $H = \frac{T_0}{w_0}\left(\cosh\frac{w_0x_B}{T_0} - 1\right)$

Substitute $w_0 = \frac{0.4}{16} = 0.025$ lb/ft, $T_0 = 2.5$ lb,

$x_B = 50$ ft

$\therefore H = \frac{2.5}{0.025}\left[\cosh\frac{(0.025)(50)}{2.5} - 1\right] = 12.76\text{ ft}$ ◆

Equation (6.9): $T_B = \sqrt{T_0^2 + (w_0x_B)^2} = \sqrt{(2.5)^2 + (0.025 \times 50)^2} = 2.80\text{ lb}$ ◆

6.69

Equation (6.17): $T = T_0\cosh\frac{w_0x}{T_0}$ $\therefore \cosh\frac{w_0x}{T_0} = \frac{T}{T_0}$

Equation (6.16): $y = \frac{T_0}{w_0}\left(\cosh\frac{w_0x}{T_0} - 1\right) = \frac{T_0}{w_0}\left(\frac{T}{T_0} - 1\right)$ $\therefore T = T_0 + w_0y$ Q.E.D.

6.70

This is a <u>catenary</u> cable.

(a) From Prob. 6.69: $T = T_0 + w_0y$

At point B $T_0 = T_B - w_0y_B = 500 - (15)(8) = 380$ N

At point A $T_A = T_0 + w_0y_A = 380 + (15)(4) = 440$ N ◆

(b) Equation (6.17): $T = T_0\cosh\frac{w_0x}{T_0}$ $\therefore x = \frac{T_0}{w_0}\cosh^{-1}\frac{T}{T_0}$

$L = x_A + x_B = \frac{T_0}{w_0}\left(\cosh^{-1}\frac{T_A}{T_0} + \cosh^{-1}\frac{T_B}{T_0}\right) = \frac{380}{15}\left(\cosh^{-1}\frac{440}{380} + \cosh^{-1}\frac{500}{380}\right) = 33.7\text{ m}$ ◆

6.71

(a) Equation (6.16): $y = \frac{T_0}{w_0}\left(\cosh\frac{w_0 x}{T_0} - 1\right)$

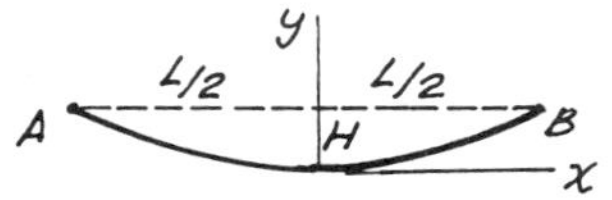

At point B: $H = \frac{T_0}{w_0}\left(\cosh\frac{w_0 L}{2T_0} - 1\right)$

$\therefore\ 10 = \frac{T_0}{50}\left[\cosh\frac{(50)(100)}{2T_0} - 1\right]$

$\therefore\ T_0\left(\cosh\frac{2500}{T_0} - 1\right) - 500 = 0$ The numerical solution is $T_0 = 6332$ N

Equation (6.17): $T = T_0\cosh\frac{w_0 x}{T_0}$ T_{max} occurs at A and B, i.e. at $x = \pm\frac{L}{2}$

$\therefore\ T_{max} = T_0\cosh\frac{w_0 L}{2T_0} = 6332\cosh\frac{(50)(100)}{2(6332)} = 6832$ N ◆

(b) $W = w_0\frac{L}{2} = 50\frac{100}{2} = 2500$ N

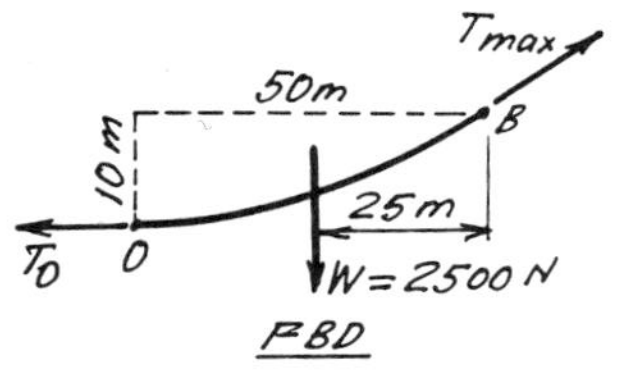

From FBD

$\Sigma M_B = 0$: (+) $(2500)(25) - 10T_0 = 0$

$\therefore\ T_0 = 6250$ N

Equation (6.8): $T_{max} = \sqrt{T_0^2 + W^2} = \sqrt{6250^2 + 2500^2} = 6731$ N ◆

(c) % error $= \frac{6731 - 6832}{6832} \times 100\% = -1.478\%$ ◆

6.72

Equation (6.17): $T = T_0\cosh\frac{w_0 x}{T_0}$ $\therefore\ T_{max} = T\big|_{x=L/2} = T_0\cosh\frac{w_0 L}{2T_0}$

$\therefore\ \frac{dT_{max}}{dT_0} = \cosh\frac{w_0 L}{2T_0} - \frac{w_0 L}{2T_0}\sinh\frac{w_0 L}{2T_0} = \cosh\xi - \xi\sinh\xi$ where $\xi = \frac{w_0 L}{2T_0}$

$\therefore\ \frac{dT_{max}}{dT_0} = 0$: $\cosh\xi - \xi\sinh\xi = 0$ The numerical solution is $\xi = 1.1997$

Equation (6.16): $y = \frac{T_0}{w_0}\left(\cosh\frac{w_0 x}{T_0} - 1\right)$

But $y\big|_{x=L/2} = H$ $\therefore\ H = \frac{T_0}{w_0}\left(\cosh\frac{w_0 L}{2T_0} - 1\right)$

$\therefore\ \frac{H}{L} = \frac{T_0}{w_0 L}\left(\cosh\frac{w_0 L}{2T_0} - 1\right) = \frac{\cosh\xi - 1}{2\xi} = \frac{\cosh 1.1997 - 1}{2(1.1997)} = 0.338$ ◆

6.73

Use the equations of the catenary.

$w_0 = (1.5)(9.81) = 14.715$ N/m

Equation (6.17): $T = T_0\cosh\frac{w_0 x}{T_0}$ $\therefore\ T_{max} = T\big|_{x=L/2} = T_0\cosh\frac{w_0 L}{2T_0}$

$\therefore\ (35)(9.81) = T_0\cosh\frac{(14.715)(18)}{2T_0}$ $\therefore\ T_0\cosh\frac{132.44}{T_0} - 343.4 = 0$

Numerical solution yields two roots: $T_0 = 51.07$ N and 315.2 N

Equation (6.16): $y = \frac{T_0}{w_0}\left(\cosh\frac{w_0 x}{T_0} - 1\right)$ $\therefore\ H = y\big|_{x=L/2} = \frac{T_0}{w_0}\left(\cosh\frac{w_0 L}{2T_0} - 1\right)$

$\therefore\ H_1 = \frac{51.07}{14.715}\left[\cosh\frac{(14.715)(18)}{2(51.07)} - 1\right] = 19.86$ m ◆

$\therefore\ H_2 = \frac{315.2}{14.715}\left[\cosh\frac{(14.715)(18)}{2(315.2)} - 1\right] = 1.919$ m ◆

6.74

$w_0 = (1.5)(9.81) = 14.715$ N/m $\quad \therefore\ W = w_0 \dfrac{L}{2} = 14.715 \dfrac{18}{2} = 132.44$ N

From the FBD

$\Sigma M_B = 0$: $(132.44)(4.5) - 1.8T_0 = 0$

$\therefore\ T_0 = 331.1$ N

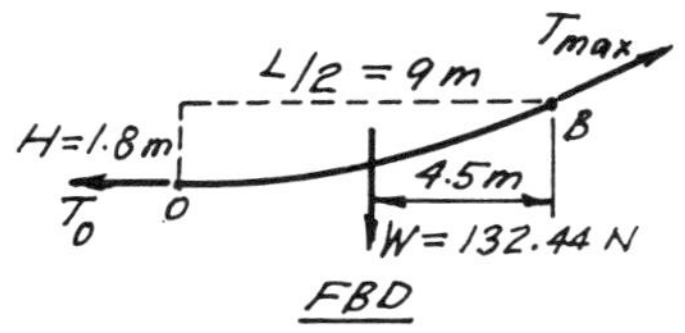

Equation (6.8): $T_{max} = \sqrt{T_0^2 + W^2}$

$= \sqrt{331.1^2 + 132.44^2} = 356.6$ N $\quad \therefore\ M = \dfrac{356.6}{9.81} = 36.4$ kg ◆

6.75

Equation (6.16): $y = \dfrac{T_0}{w_0}\left(\cosh \dfrac{w_0 x}{T_0} - 1\right) \quad \therefore\ H = y\Big|_{x=L/2} = \dfrac{T_0}{w_0}\left(\cosh \dfrac{w_0 L}{2T_0} - 1\right)$

$\therefore\ \dfrac{H}{L} = \dfrac{\cosh \xi - 1}{2\xi}$ where $\xi = \dfrac{w_0 L}{2T_0} \quad \therefore\ \dfrac{1.8}{18} = \dfrac{\cosh \xi - 1}{2\xi} \quad \therefore\ \cosh \xi - \dfrac{1}{5}\xi - 1 = 0$

Numerical solution: $\xi = 0.3948 \quad \therefore\ T_0 = \dfrac{w_0 L}{2\xi} = \dfrac{(14.715)(18)}{2(0.3948)} = 335.4$ N

Equation (6.17): $T_B = T\Big|_{x=L/2} = T_0 \cosh \dfrac{w_0 L}{2T_0} = 335.4 \cosh 0.3948 = 361.9$ N

$\therefore\ M = \dfrac{361.9}{9.81} = 36.9$ kg ◆

6.76

The tape is a catenary. $\quad w_0 = \dfrac{W}{L} = \dfrac{2.4}{50} = 0.048$ lb/ft

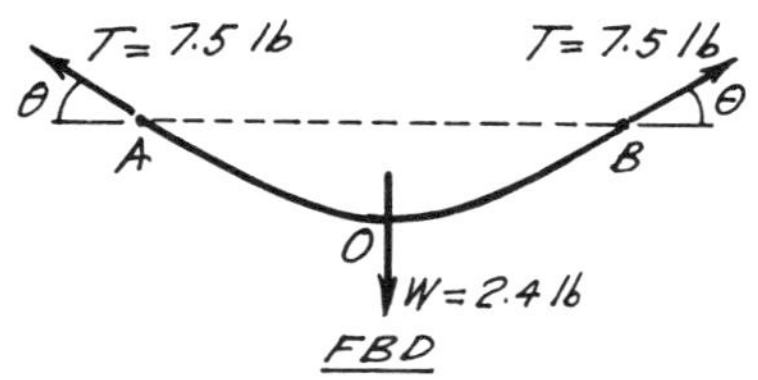

From the FBD

$\Sigma F_y = 0$: $+\uparrow\ 2(7.5)\sin\theta - 2.4 = 0$

$\therefore\ \theta = \sin^{-1} \dfrac{2.4}{2(7.5)} = 9.207°$

(continued)

6.76 continued

$T_0 = T\cos\theta = 7.5 \cos 9.207° = 7.403$ lb

Equation (6.15): $s = \dfrac{T_0}{w_0} \sinh \dfrac{w_0 x}{T_0} \quad \therefore\ x = \dfrac{T_0}{w_0} \sinh^{-1} \dfrac{w_0 s}{T_0}$

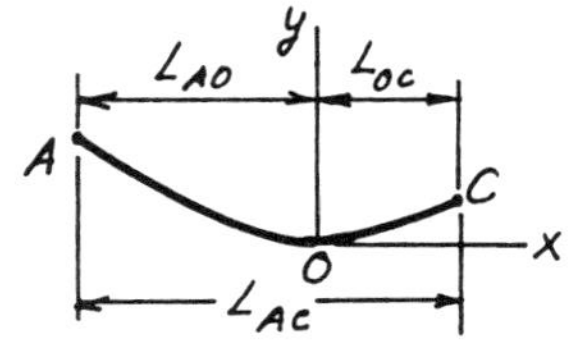

$L_{AC} = L_{AO} + L_{OC} = \dfrac{T_0}{w_0}\left(\sinh^{-1} \dfrac{w_0 s_A}{T_0} + \sinh^{-1} \dfrac{w_0 s_C}{T_0}\right)$

$= \dfrac{7.403}{0.048}\left[\sinh^{-1} \dfrac{(0.048)(25)}{7.403} + \sinh^{-1} \dfrac{(0.048)(11)}{7.403}\right]$

$= 24.89 + 10.99 = 35.88$ ft ◆

6.77

From FBD $\Sigma F_x = 0$: $\overset{+}{\rightarrow}\ -T_0 + 30 = 0$

$\therefore\ T_0 = 30$ N

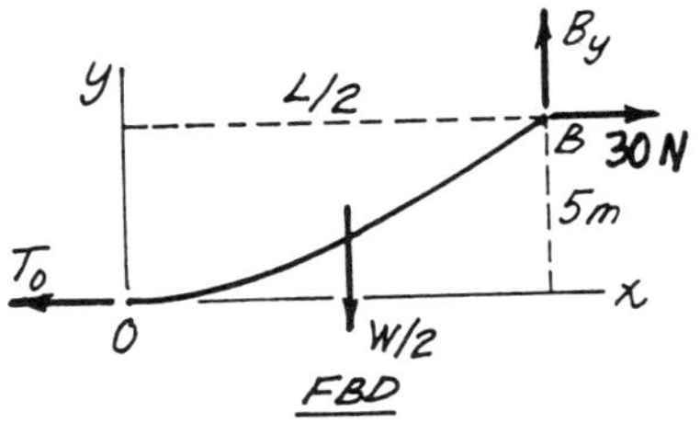

Equation (6.16): $y = \dfrac{T_0}{w_0}\left(\cosh \dfrac{w_0 x}{T_0} - 1\right)$

At point B: $5 = \dfrac{30}{4}\left[\cosh \dfrac{4(L/2)}{30} - 1\right]$

$\therefore\ L = 15 \cosh^{-1} \dfrac{5}{3} = 16.48$ m ◆

6.78

<u>Find x_A first</u>

From FBD

$\Sigma F_x = 0$: $\overset{+}{\rightarrow}\ 800 \cos 45° - T_0 = 0$

$\therefore\ T_0 = 565.7$ lb

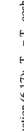

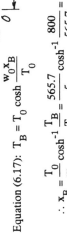

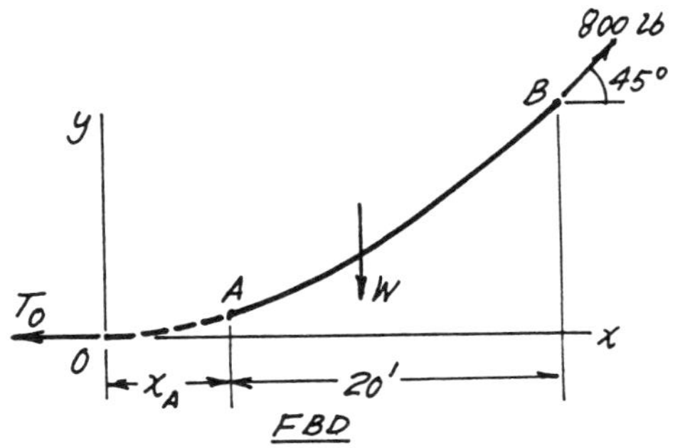

Equation (6.17): $T_B = T_0 \cosh \dfrac{w_0 x_B}{T_0}$

$\therefore\ x_B = \dfrac{T_0}{w_0} \cosh^{-1} \dfrac{T_B}{T_0} = \dfrac{565.7}{5} \cosh^{-1} \dfrac{800}{565.7} = 99.71$ ft

(continued)

6.78 continued

$x_A = x_B - 20 = 99.71 - 20 = 79.71$ ft

Equation (6.15): $s_A = \frac{T_0}{w_0}\sinh\frac{w_0 x_A}{T_0} = \frac{565.7}{5}\sinh\frac{(5)(79.71)}{565.7} = 86.47$ ft

$s_B = \frac{T_0}{w_0}\sinh\frac{w_0 x_B}{T_0} = \frac{565.7}{5}\sinh\frac{(5)(99.71)}{565.7} = 113.13$ ft

$s_{AB} = s_B - s_A = 113.13 - 86.47 = 26.7$ ft ◆

6.79

Each cable is a catenary.

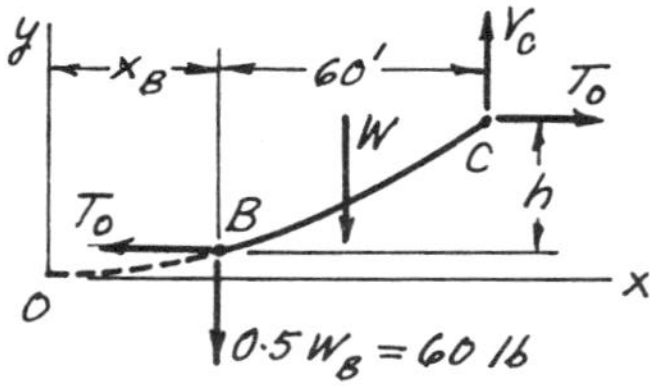

$T_B = \sqrt{T_0^2 + (0.5W_B)^2} = \sqrt{180^2 + 60^2} = 189.74$ lb

Equation (6.17): $T_B = T_0 \cosh\frac{w_0 x_B}{T_0}$

$\therefore x_B = \frac{T_0}{w_0}\cosh^{-1}\frac{T_B}{T_0} = \frac{180}{0.75}\cosh^{-1}\frac{189.74}{180} = 78.60$ ft

Equation (6.15): $s = \frac{T_0}{w_0}\sinh\frac{w_0 x}{T_0}$ $\quad\therefore s_{BC} = s_C - s_B = \frac{T_0}{w_0}\left(\sinh\frac{w_0 x_C}{T_0} - \sinh\frac{w_0 x_B}{T_0}\right)$

$\therefore s_{BC} = \frac{180}{0.75}\left[\sinh\frac{(0.75)(138.60)}{180} - \sinh\frac{(0.75)(78.60)}{180}\right] = 66.4$ ft ◆

Equation (6.16): $y = \frac{T_0}{w_0}\left(\cosh\frac{w_0 x}{T_0} - 1\right)$ $\quad\therefore h = y_C - y_B = \frac{T_0}{w_0}\left(\cosh\frac{w_0 x_C}{T_0} - \cosh\frac{w_0 x_B}{T_0}\right)$

$\therefore h = \frac{180}{0.75}\left[\cosh\frac{(0.75)(138.60)}{180} - \cosh\frac{(0.75)(78.60)}{180}\right] = 28.2$ ft ◆

6.80

From FBD of joint B

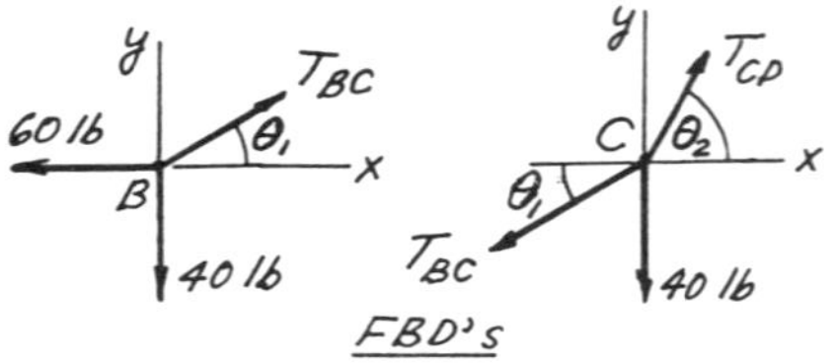

$\Sigma F_x = 0$: $\overset{+}{\rightarrow}$ $T_{BC}\cos\theta_1 - 60 = 0$

$\Sigma F_y = 0$: $+\uparrow$ $T_{BC}\sin\theta_1 - 40 = 0$

$\therefore \theta_1 = \tan^{-1}\frac{40}{60} = 33.69°$

$\therefore T_{BC} = \sqrt{60^2 + 40^2} = 72.1$ lb ◆

From FBD of joint C

$\Sigma F_x = 0$: $\overset{+}{\rightarrow}$ $T_{CD}\cos\theta_2 - T_{BC}\cos\theta_1 = 0$ $\quad\therefore T_{CD}\cos\theta_2 - 60.00 = 0$

$\Sigma F_y = 0$: $+\uparrow$ $T_{CD}\sin\theta_2 - T_{BC}\sin\theta_1 - 40 = 0$ $\quad\therefore T_{CD}\sin\theta_2 - 80.00 = 0$

$\therefore \theta_2 = \tan^{-1}\frac{80}{60} = 53.13°$ $\quad\therefore T_{CD} = \sqrt{60^2 + 80^2} = 100.0$ lb ◆

$\therefore h = s_{BC}\sin\theta_1 + s_{CD}\sin\theta_2 = 6(\sin 33.69° + \sin 53.13°) = 8.13$ ft ◆

6.81

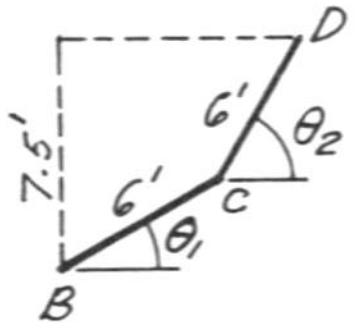

From geometry: $6\sin\theta_1 + 6\sin\theta_2 = 7.5$

$\therefore \sin\theta_1 + \sin\theta_2 = 1.25$ . . . . (a)

Applying Eq. (6.19) to joints B and C (note that $T_0 = P$):

$P(\tan\theta_1 - \tan 0) = 40$ $\quad P(\tan\theta_2 - \tan\theta_1) = 40$ . . . (b)

Equating the LHS's yields $2\tan\theta_1 = \tan\theta_2$ . . . . . (c)

We now reduce Eqs. (a) and (c) to a single equation in one unknown. We start with the trigonometric identity

$\sin\theta_2 = \frac{\tan\theta_2}{\sqrt{1+\tan^2\theta_2}}$ and then utilize Eq. (c), obtaining $\sin\theta_2 = \frac{2\tan\theta_1}{\sqrt{1+4\tan^2\theta_1}}$

Substitution in Eq. (a) yields $\sin\theta_1 + \frac{2\tan\theta_1}{\sqrt{1+4\tan^2\theta_1}} = 1.25$

The numerical solution is: $\theta_1 = 29.79°$

(continued)

6.81 continued

From Eq. (c): $\tan\theta_2 = 2\tan\theta_1 = 2\tan 29.79° = 1.1450 \qquad \therefore \theta_2 = 48.87°$

From the first of Eqs. (b): $P = \dfrac{40}{\tan\theta_1} = \dfrac{40}{\tan 29.79°} = 69.87 \text{ lb}$ ◆

Maximum tension is in segment CD. Applying Eq. (6.18) to joint C:

$$T_{CD}\cos\theta_2 = P \qquad \therefore T_{max} = T_{CD} = \frac{P}{\cos\theta_2} = \frac{69.87}{\cos 48.87°} = 106.2 \text{ lb} \ ◆$$

6.82

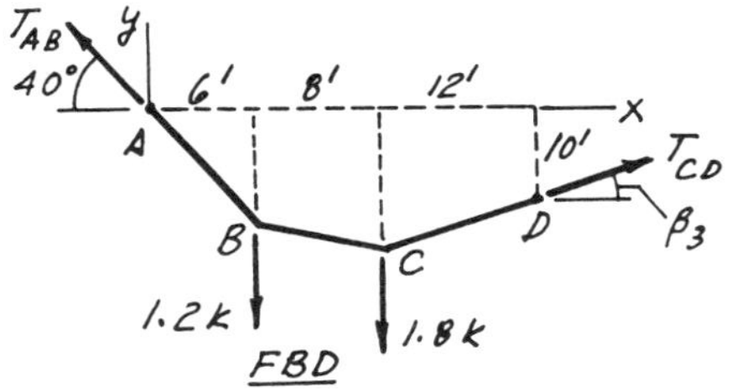

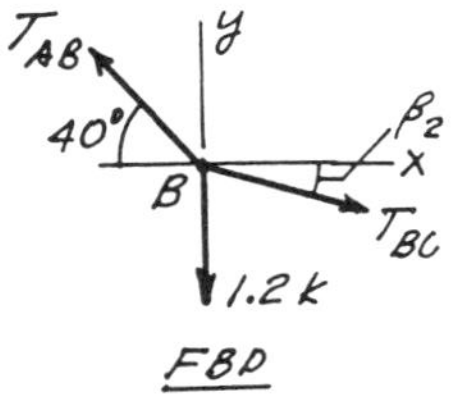

From the FBD of the cable

$$\Sigma M_D = 0: \circlearrowleft(+) \ (1.8)(12) + (1.2)(20) + T_{AB}(10\cos 40° - 26\sin 40°) = 0$$

$$\therefore T_{AB} = 5.0375 \text{ kips} \ ◆$$

$\Sigma F_x = 0: \ \overset{+}{\rightarrow} \ T_{CD}\cos\beta_3 - T_{AB}\cos 40° = 0 \qquad \therefore T_{CD}\cos\beta_3 = 3.859$

$\Sigma F_y = 0: \ +\uparrow \ T_{CD}\sin\beta_3 + T_{AB}\sin 40° - 1.2 - 1.8 = 0 \qquad \therefore T_{CD}\sin\beta_3 = -0.2380$

$\therefore \beta_3 = \tan^{-1}\dfrac{-0.2380}{3.859} = -3.53°$ ◆ $\qquad \therefore T_{CD} = \sqrt{3.859^2 + 0.2380^2} = 3.87 \text{ kips}$ ◆

From FBD of joint B

$\Sigma F_x = 0: \ \overset{+}{\rightarrow} \ T_{BC}\cos\beta_2 - T_{AB}\cos 40° = 0 \qquad \therefore T_{BC}\cos\beta_2 = 3.859$

$\Sigma F_y = 0: \ +\uparrow \ -T_{BC}\sin\beta_2 + T_{AB}\sin 40° - 1.2 = 0 \qquad \therefore T_{BC}\sin\beta_2 = 2.038$

$\therefore \beta_2 = \tan^{-1}\dfrac{2.038}{3.859} = 27.8°$ ◆ $\qquad \therefore T_{BC} = \sqrt{3.859^2 + 2.038^2} = 4.36 \text{ kips}$ ◆

6.83

From FBD of cable

$\Sigma M_E = 0: \circlearrowleft(+) \ 400(12 + 24 + 32) - 40A_y = 0$

$\Sigma F_y = 0: \ +\uparrow \ A_y + E_y - 3(400) = 0$

The solution is: $A_y = 680$ lb $\qquad E_y = 520$ lb

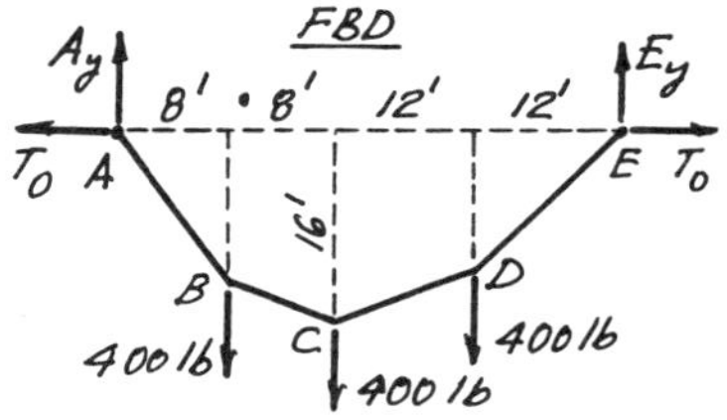

From FBD of portion AC

$\Sigma F_y = 0: \ +\uparrow \ V_{CD} + 680 - 2(400) = 0$

$\Sigma M_A = 0: \circlearrowleft(+) \ 16V_{CD} + 16T_0 - 400(8 + 16) = 0$

The solution is: $V_{CD} = 120$ lb $\qquad T_0 = 480$ lb

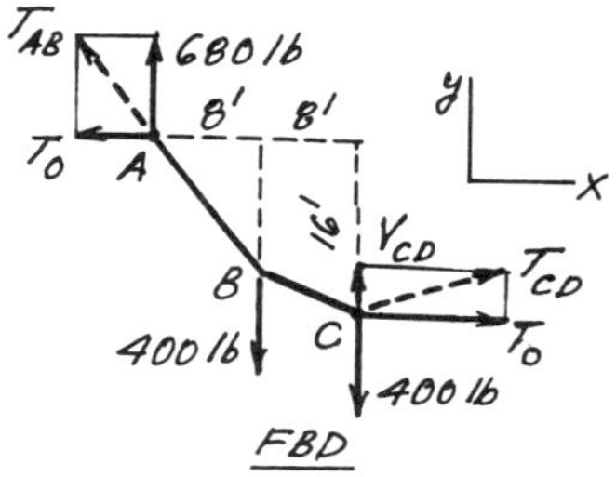

From FBD of portion CE

$\Sigma F_y = 0: \ +\uparrow \ V_{BC} + 520 - 2(400) = 0$

$\therefore V_{BC} = 280$ lb

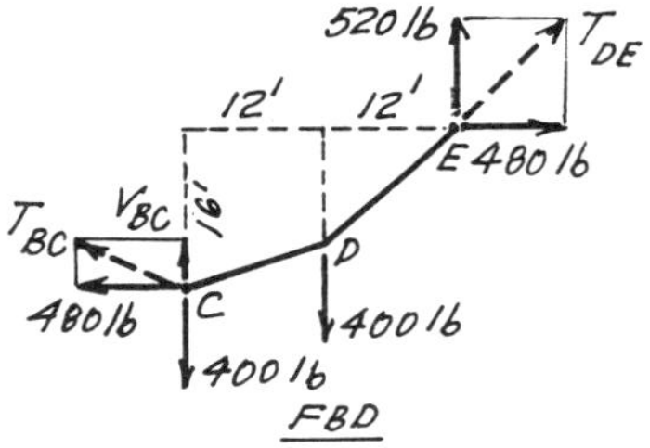

$\therefore T_{AB} = \sqrt{T_0^2 + A_y^2} = \sqrt{480^2 + 680^2} = 832 \text{ lb}$ ◆

$\therefore T_{BC} = \sqrt{T_0^2 + V_{BC}^2} = \sqrt{480^2 + 280^2} = 556 \text{ lb}$ ◆

$\therefore T_{CD} = \sqrt{T_0^2 + V_{CD}^2} = \sqrt{480^2 + 120^2} = 495 \text{ lb}$ ◆

$\therefore T_{DE} = \sqrt{T_0^2 + E_y^2} = \sqrt{480^2 + 520^2} = 708 \text{ lb}$ ◆

6.84

Assume maximum tension to occur in segment AB, i.e. assume $T_{AB} = 900$ lb

From the FBD of the cable

$\Sigma M_E = 0: \circlearrowleft(+) \ 400(12 + 24 + 32) - 40A_y = 0$

$\Sigma F_y = 0: \ +\uparrow \ A_y + E_y - 3(400) = 0$

The solution is: $A_y = 680$ lb $\qquad E_y = 520$ lb

$\therefore T_0 = \sqrt{T_{AB}^2 - A_y^2} = \sqrt{900^2 - 680^2} = 589.6 \text{ lb}$

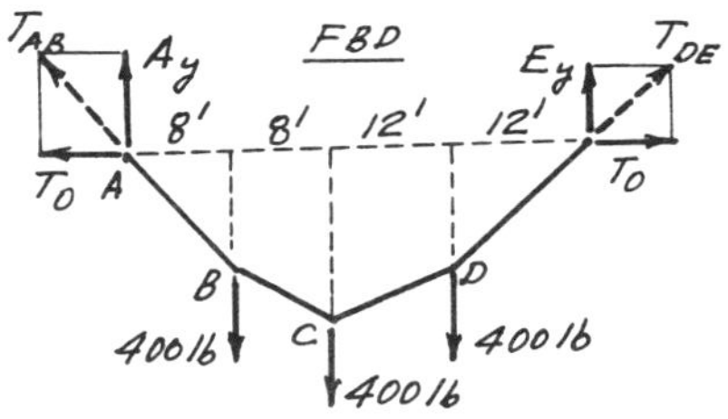

(continued)

6.84 continued

From FBD of portion ABC

$\Sigma M_C = 0$: $(+)$ $589.6h_C - (680)(16) + 400(8) = 0$

$\therefore h_C = 13.03$ ft ◆

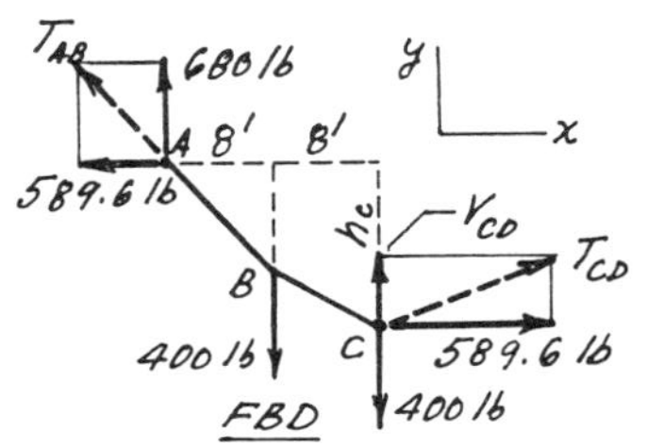

Check tension in DE

$T_{DE} = \sqrt{T_0^2 + E_y^2} = \sqrt{589.6^2 + 520^2} = 786 \text{ lb} < T_{AB}$ $\therefore$ Assumption was O.K.

6.85

(a) From geometry

$2\cos\beta_1 + 3\cos\beta_2 = 4 \ldots\ldots\ldots\ldots\ldots\ldots\ldots (a)$

$2\sin\beta_1 - 3\sin\beta_2 = 0 \qquad \therefore \sin\beta_2 = \frac{2}{3}\sin\beta_1 \ldots (b)$

Substituting Eq. (b) in the trigonometric identity

$\cos\beta_2 = \sqrt{1 - \sin^2\beta_2}$ we get

$$\cos\beta_2 = \sqrt{1 - \frac{4}{9}\sin^2\beta_1} = \sqrt{1 - \frac{4}{9}(1 - \cos^2\beta_1)} = \frac{1}{3}\sqrt{5 + 4\cos^2\beta_1}$$

Substitution in Eq. (a) yields

$2\cos\beta_1 + \sqrt{5 + 4\cos^2\beta_1} = 4 \qquad \therefore 5 + 4\cos^2\beta_1 = (4 - 2\cos\beta_1)^2$

$\therefore 16\cos\beta_1 = 11 \qquad \therefore \beta_1 = 46.57°$ ◆

From Eq. (b): $\sin\beta_2 = \frac{2}{3}\sin 46.57° \qquad \therefore \beta_2 = 28.96°$ ◆

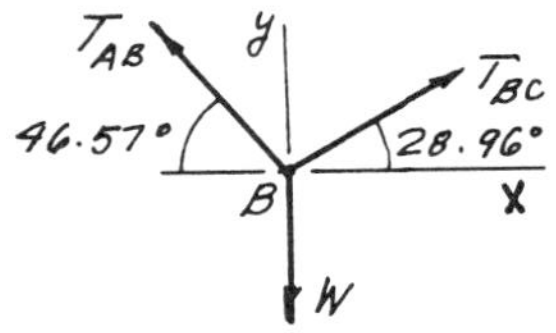

(b) From FBD of joint B

$\Sigma F_x = 0$: $\overset{+}{\rightarrow}$ $T_{BC}\cos 28.96° - T_{AB}\cos 46.57° = 0$

$\Sigma F_y = 0$: $+\uparrow$ $T_{BC}\sin 28.96° + T_{AB}\sin 46.57° - W = 0$

The solution is: $T_{AB} = 0.904\,W$ ◆ $T_{BC} = 0.621\,W$ ◆

6.86

From FBD of joint B

$\Sigma F_x = 0$: $\overset{+}{\rightarrow}$ $-\frac{3}{5}T_{AB} + \frac{4}{\sqrt{17}}T_{BC} = 0$

$\Sigma F_y = 0$: $+\uparrow$ $\frac{4}{5}T_{AB} - \frac{1}{\sqrt{17}}T_{BC} - 12 = 0$

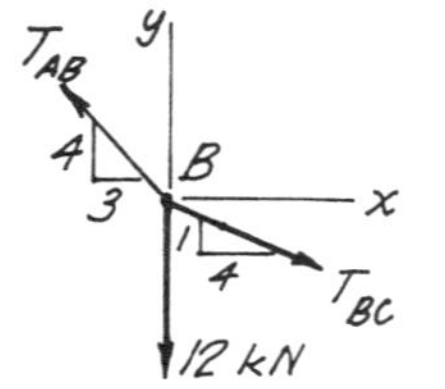

Solution is:

$T_{AB} = 18.462$ kN ◆ $T_{BC} = 11.418$ kN ◆

From FBD of joint C

$\Sigma F_x = 0$: $\overset{+}{\rightarrow}$ $-11.418\frac{4}{\sqrt{17}} + T_{CD}\frac{4}{\sqrt{41}} = 0$

$\Sigma F_y = 0$: $+\uparrow$ $11.418\frac{1}{\sqrt{17}} + T_{CD}\frac{5}{\sqrt{41}} - P = 0$

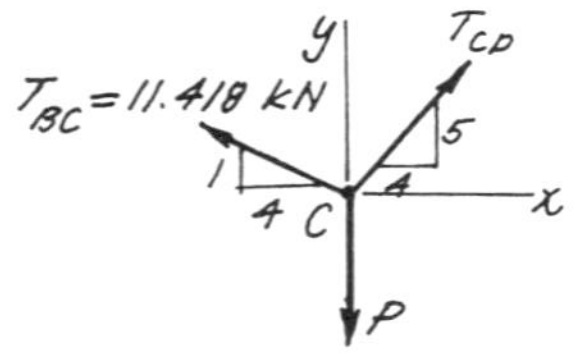

Solution is:

$T_{CD} = 17.73$ kN ◆ $P = 16.62$ kN ◆

6.87

$\Sigma M_A = 0$:

$(+)$ $150(3) - 80(4) - \frac{4}{5}T_{CD}(6) = 0$

$\therefore T_{CD} = 27.08$ lb ◆

$\Sigma M_B = 0$:

$(+)$ $\frac{4}{5}T_{CD}(3) + \frac{3}{5}T_{CD}(b) - 80(b - 4) = 0$

$\therefore \frac{27.08}{5}(12 + 3b) - 80(b - 4) = 0$

$\therefore 385.0 - 63.75b = 0 \qquad \therefore b = 6.04$ ft ◆

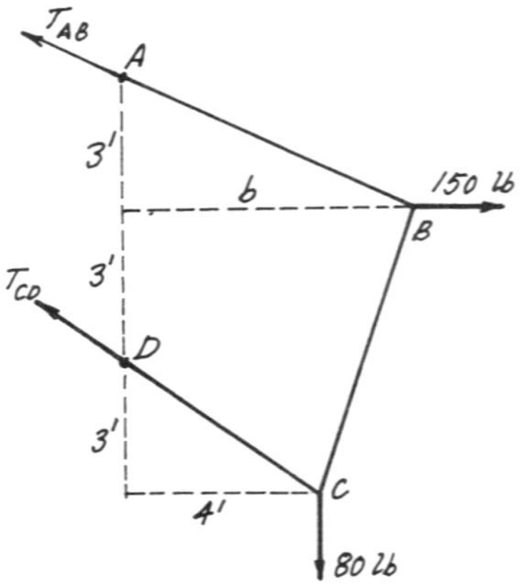

6.88

From geometry

$6\sin\beta_1 = 4\sin\beta_3 \quad \therefore \sin\beta_3 = 1.5\sin\beta_1 \; . . . \; (a)$

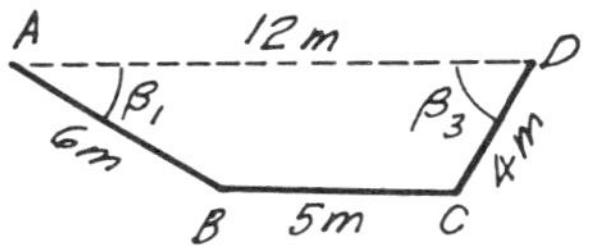

$6\cos\beta_1 + 5 + 4\cos\beta_3 = 12$

$\therefore 6\cos\beta_1 + 4\cos\beta_3 - 7 = 0 \; . . . . \; (b)$

Eliminate β_3 from the equations and solve for β_1

$$\cos\beta_3 = \sqrt{1 - \sin^2\beta_3} = \sqrt{1 - (1.5\sin\beta_1)^2} = \sqrt{1 - 1.5^2(1 - \cos^2\beta_1)}$$

$$= \sqrt{2.25\cos^2\beta_1 - 1.25}$$

Substitute in Eq. (b): $6\cos\beta_1 + 4\sqrt{2.25\cos^2\beta_1 - 1.25} - 7 = 0$

Numerical solution is (the equation could be turned into a quadratic equation in $\cos\beta_1$):

$\cos\beta_1 = 0.8214 \quad \therefore \beta_1 = 34.77°$

From Eq. (a): $\sin\beta_3 = 1.5\sin 34.77 \quad \therefore \beta_3 = 58.81°$

Apply Eq. (6.19) to joints B and C

$T_0(\tan\theta_2 - \tan\theta_1) = W_1 \quad \therefore T_0\left[\tan 0 - \tan(-\beta_1)\right] = W_1$

$T_0(\tan\theta_3 - \tan\theta_2) = W_2 \quad \therefore T_0(\tan\beta_3 - \tan 0) = W_2$

$$\therefore \frac{W_1}{W_2} = \frac{\tan\beta_1}{\tan\beta_3} = \frac{\tan 34.77°}{\tan 58.81°} = 0.420 \; ◆$$

6.89

(a) From geometry: $6\sin\beta_1 - 5\sin\beta_2 - 4\sin\beta_3 = 0 \; . . . . \; (a)$ ◆

$6\cos\beta_1 + 5\cos\beta_2 + 4\cos\beta_3 = 12 \; . . . . \; (b)$ ◆

Apply Eq. (6.19) to joints B and C:

$T_0(\tan\theta_2 - \tan\theta_1) = W \quad \therefore T_0\left[\tan\beta_2 - \tan(-\beta_1)\right] = W \; . . . . \; (c)$

$T_0(\tan\theta_3 - \tan\theta_2) = W \quad \therefore T_0(\tan\beta_3 - \tan\beta_2) = W$

Equating the LHS's yields: $\tan\beta_1 + 2\tan\beta_2 - \tan\beta_3 = 0 \; . . . . \; (d)$ ◆

Equations (a), (b) and (d) are the simultaneous equations for the β's

(continued)

6.89 continued

(b) Equation (a): $6\sin 41.0° - 5\sin 9.8° - 4\sin 50.5° = -0.001 \approx 0 \quad \therefore$ O.K.

Equation (b): $6\cos 41.0° + 5\cos 9.8° + 4\cos 50.5° = 12.00 \quad \therefore$ O.K.

Equation (d): $\tan 41.0° + 2\tan 9.8° - \tan 50.5° = 0.002 \approx 0 \quad \therefore$ O.K.

(c) From Eq. (c): $$T_0 = \frac{W}{\tan\beta_1 + \tan\beta_2} = \frac{W}{\tan 41.0° + \tan 9.8°} = 0.9597W$$

Applying Eq. (6.18) to joints B, C and D (note that $\theta_1 = -\beta_1$)

$$T_{AB} = \frac{T_0}{\cos(-\beta_1)} = \frac{0.9597W}{\cos(-41.0°)} = 1.272W \; ◆$$

$$T_{BC} = \frac{T_0}{\cos\beta_2} = \frac{0.9597W}{\cos 9.8°} = 0.974W \; ◆ \qquad T_{CD} = \frac{T_0}{\cos\beta_3} = \frac{0.9597W}{\cos 50.5°} = 1.509W \; ◆$$

6.90

s = 18 m: $\sqrt{4^2 + (H-2)^2} + \sqrt{12^2 + H^2} = 18$

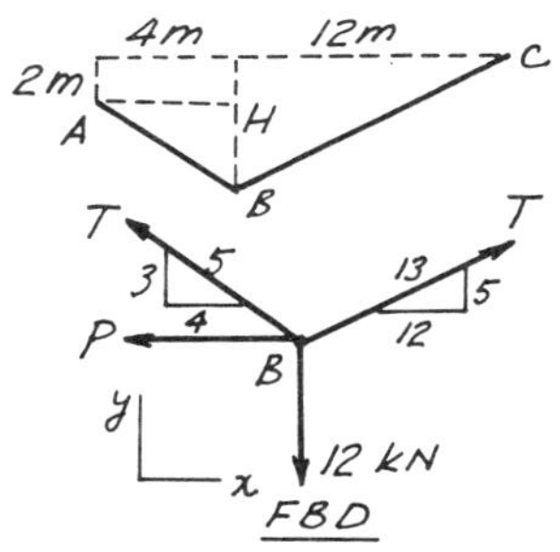

The solution is: H = 5 m

From the FBD of joint B:

$$\Sigma F_y = 0: \; +\uparrow \; T\left(\frac{3}{5} + \frac{5}{13}\right) - 12 = 0$$

$$\Sigma F_x = 0: \; \overset{+}{\rightarrow} \; T\left(\frac{12}{13} - \frac{4}{5}\right) - P = 0$$

The solution is: T = 12.19 kN P = 1.500 kN ◆

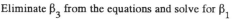

6.91

(a) From geometry:

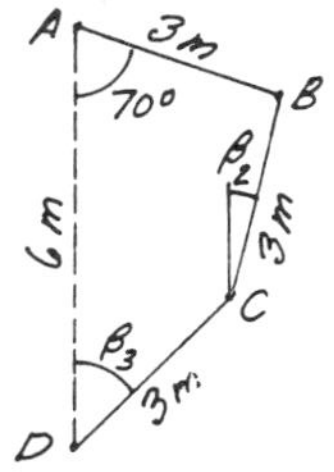

$$3\cos 70° + 3\cos\beta_2 + 3\cos\beta_3 = 6$$

$$3\sin 70° - 3\sin\beta_2 - 3\sin\beta_3 = 0$$

$$\therefore \cos\beta_2 + \cos\beta_3 = 2 - \cos 70°$$

$$\therefore \sin\beta_3 + \sin\beta_3 = \sin 70°$$

$$\therefore 2\cos\frac{\beta_3+\beta_2}{2}\cos\frac{\beta_3-\beta_2}{2} = 2 - \cos 70° \quad \text{(a)}$$

$$\therefore 2\sin\frac{\beta_3+\beta_2}{2}\cos\frac{\beta_3-\beta_2}{2} = \sin 70° \ldots\ldots \text{(b)}$$

Dividing Eq. (b) by Eq. (a):

$$\tan\frac{\beta_3+\beta_2}{2} = \frac{\sin 70°}{2-\cos 70°} = 0.566\,77 \qquad \therefore \frac{\beta_3+\beta_2}{2} = 29.543° \ldots\ldots \text{(c)}$$

Eq. (b): $2\sin 29.54°\cos\frac{\beta_3-\beta_2}{2} = \sin 70°$

$$\therefore \cos\frac{\beta_3-\beta_2}{2} = 0.952\,89 \qquad \therefore \frac{\beta_3-\beta_2}{2} = 17.657° \ldots\ldots\ldots\ldots\ldots \text{(d)}$$

$\therefore \beta_2 = 29.543° - 17.657° = 11.88°$ ◆ $\quad \beta_3 = 29.543° + 17.657° = 47.20°$ ◆

(b) From FBD of joint C

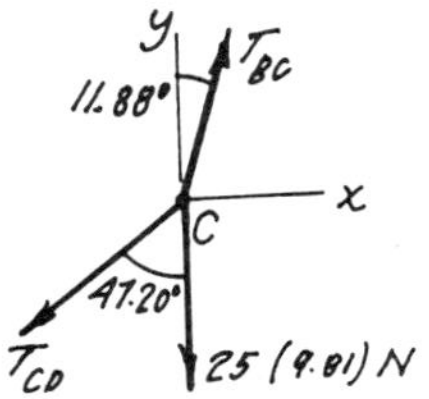

$\Sigma F_x = 0$:

$$\overset{+}{\rightarrow}\ T_{BC}\sin 11.88° - T_{CD}\sin 47.20° = 0$$

$$\therefore T_{BC} = 3.564T_{CD}$$

$\Sigma F_y = 0$: $+\uparrow$

$$T_{BC}\cos 11.88° - T_{CD}\cos 47.20° - 25(9.81) = 0$$

$$\therefore \left[3.564\cos 11.88° - \cos 47.20°\right]T_{CD} - 25\,(9.81) = 0$$

$\therefore T_{CD} = 87.3$ N ◆

7.1

Assume equilibrium.

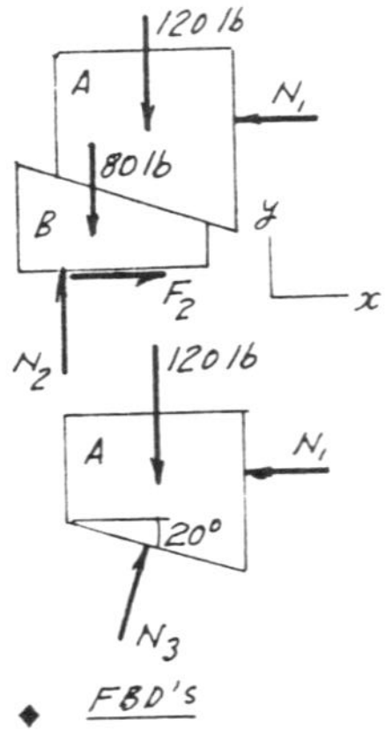

From FBD of system

$\Sigma F_x = 0$: $\overset{+}{\rightarrow}$ $-N_1 + F_2 = 0 \ldots\ldots\ldots\ldots$ (a)

$\Sigma F_y = 0$: $+\uparrow$ $N_2 - 120 - 80 = 0 \ldots\ldots\ldots$ (b)

From FBD of block A

$\Sigma F_x = 0$: $\overset{+}{\rightarrow}$ $N_3\sin 20° - N_1 = 0 \ldots\ldots$ (c)

$\Sigma F_y = 0$: $+\uparrow$ $N_3\cos 20° - 120 = 0 \ldots\ldots$ (d)

Solution of Eqs. (a)-(d) is

$N_1 = F_2 = 43.68$ lb $\quad N_2 = 200$ lb $\quad N_3 = 127.70$ lb

$\therefore \frac{F_2}{N_2} = \frac{43.68}{200} = 0.218 > \mu_s$ $\quad\therefore$ Equilibrium is not possible ◆

7.2

Assume impending motion of block B to the left.

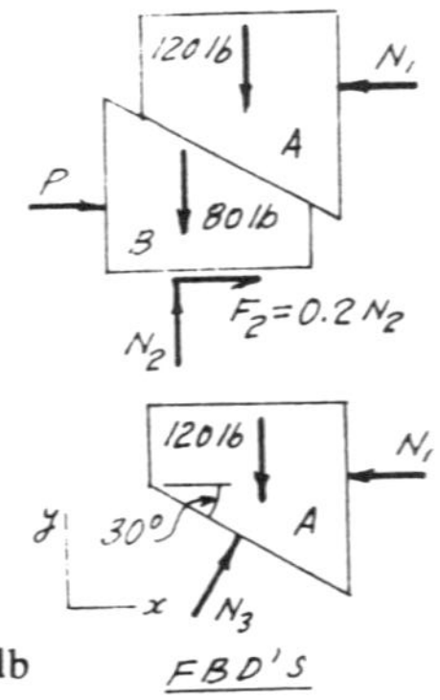

From FBD of the system

$\Sigma F_x = 0$: $\overset{+}{\rightarrow}$ $P + 0.2N_2 - N_1 = 0 \ldots\ldots$ (a)

$\Sigma F_y = 0$: $+\uparrow$ $N_2 - 120 - 80 = 0 \ldots\ldots$ (b)

From FBD of block A

$\Sigma F_x = 0$: $\overset{+}{\rightarrow}$ $N_3\sin 30° - N_1 = 0 \ldots\ldots$ (c)

$\Sigma F_y = 0$: $+\uparrow$ $N_3\cos 30° - 120 = 0 \ldots\ldots$ (d)

Solution of Eqs. (a)-(d) is

$P = 29.28$ lb $\quad N_1 = 69.28$ lb $\quad N_2 = 200$ lb $\quad N_3 = 138.56$ lb

Assume impending motion of block B to the right.

The sense of F_2 on the FBD of the system must be reversed. The above equations remain valid, with the exception of Eq. (a), which becomes

$\Sigma F_x = 0$: $\overset{+}{\rightarrow}$ $P - 0.2N_2 - N_1 = 0 \ldots\ldots$ (e)

The solution of Eqs. (b)-(e) is

$P = 109.28$ lb $\quad N_1 = 69.28$ lb $\quad N_2 = 200$ lb $\quad N_3 = 138.56$ lb

$\therefore$ The equilibrium range of P is $29.3 \text{ lb} \le P \le 109.3 \text{ lb}$ ◆

7.3

There are two possible modes of motion: sliding at A and B; and sliding at A and C.

<u>Assume impending sliding at A and C</u>

$\therefore F_A = 0.1N_A \quad F_C = 0.2N_C$

From FBD of the bar $\Sigma M_B = 0$:

$\circlearrowleft^{+}\ (30)(1.8) - 3N_C - 1.5(0.2N_C) = 0$

$\therefore N_C = 16.364$ lb

$\therefore F_C = 0.2(16.364) = 3.273$ lb

From FBD of the bar $\Sigma F_y = 0$:

$+\uparrow\ N_B + N_C - 30 = 0$

$\therefore N_B = 30 - N_C = 30 - 16.364 = 13.636$ lb

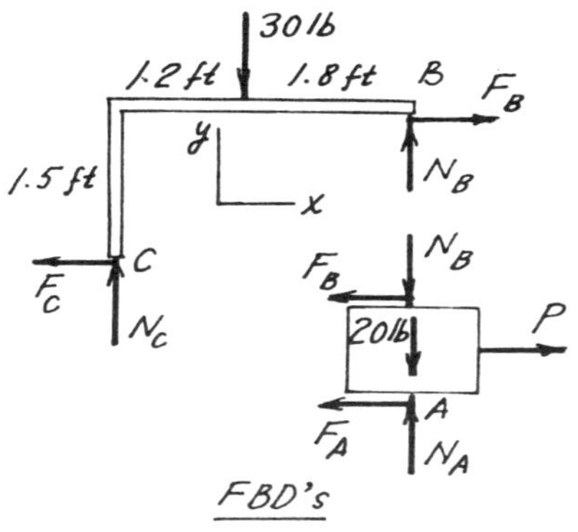

From FBD of the bar $\Sigma F_x = 0$: $\overset{+}{\rightarrow}\ F_B - F_C = 0 \quad \therefore F_B = F_C = 3.273$ lb

Check for sliding at B: $\dfrac{F_B}{N_B} = \dfrac{3.273}{13.636} = 0.2400 < \mu_B \quad \therefore$ The assumption was correct

From FBD of the block $\Sigma F_y = 0$: $+\uparrow\ N_A - N_B - 20 = 0$

$\therefore N_A = N_B + 20 = 13.636 + 20 = 33.64$ lb $\quad \therefore F_A = 0.1(33.64) = 3.364$ lb

From FBD of the block $\Sigma F_x = 0$: $\overset{+}{\rightarrow}\ P - F_A - F_B = 0$

$\therefore P = F_A + F_B = 3.364 + 3.273 = 6.64$ lb ◆

7.4

Slipping can occur at A, or at B.

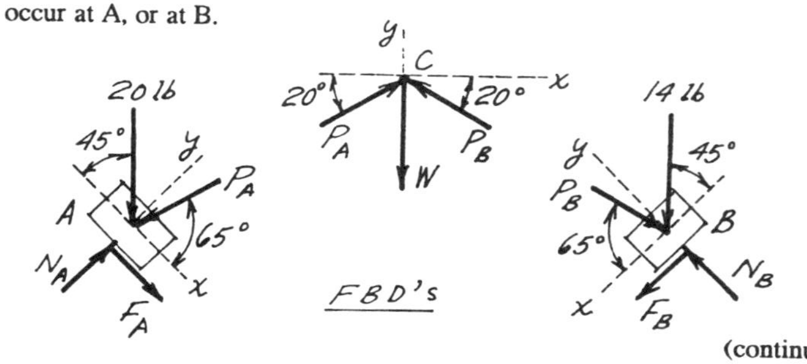

(continued)

7.4 continued

From FBD of pin C

$\Sigma F_x = 0$: $\overset{+}{\rightarrow}\ P_A \cos 20° - P_B \cos 20° = 0 \quad \therefore P_A = P_B$

$\Sigma F_y = 0$: $+\uparrow\ P_A \sin 20° + P_B \sin 20° - W = 0 \quad \therefore P_A = P_B = \dfrac{W}{2 \sin 20°} = 1.4619W$

From FBD of collar A

$\Sigma F_x = 0$: $\searrow^{+}\ F_A + 20 \cos 45° - P_A \cos 65° = 0$

$\therefore F_A = (1.4619W)\cos 65° - 20 \cos 45° = 0.6178W - 14.142$ lb

$\Sigma F_y = 0$: $+\nearrow\ N_A - 20 \sin 45° - P_A \sin 65° = 0$

$\therefore N_A = (1.4619W)\sin 65° + 20 \sin 45° = 1.3249W + 14.142$ lb

From FBD of collar B

$\Sigma F_x = 0$: $+\swarrow\ F_B + 14 \cos 45° - P_B \cos 65° = 0$

$\therefore F_B = (1.4619W)\cos 65° - 14 \cos 45° = 0.6178W - 9.899$ lb

$\Sigma F_y = 0$: $\nwarrow^{+}\ N_B - 14 \sin 45° - P_B \sin 65° = 0$

$\therefore N_B = (1.4619W)\sin 65° + 14 \sin 45° = 1.3249W + 9.899$ lb

<u>Assume impending sliding at A</u>

$\dfrac{F_A}{N_A} = 0.15$: $\dfrac{0.6178W - 14.142}{1.3249W + 14.142} = 0.15 \quad \therefore 0.6178W - 14.142 = 0.15(1.3249W + 14.142)$

$\therefore 0.4191W = 16.263 \quad \therefore W = 38.80$ lb

<u>Assume impending sliding at B</u>

$\dfrac{F_B}{N_B} = 0.2$: $\dfrac{0.6178W - 9.899}{1.3249W + 9.899} = 0.2 \quad \therefore 0.6178W - 9.899 = 0.2(1.3249W + 9.899)$

$\therefore 0.3528W = 11.879 \quad \therefore W = 33.67$ lb

$\therefore$ Largest weight that can be supported is $W = 33.7$ lb ◆

7.5

Assume equilibrium.

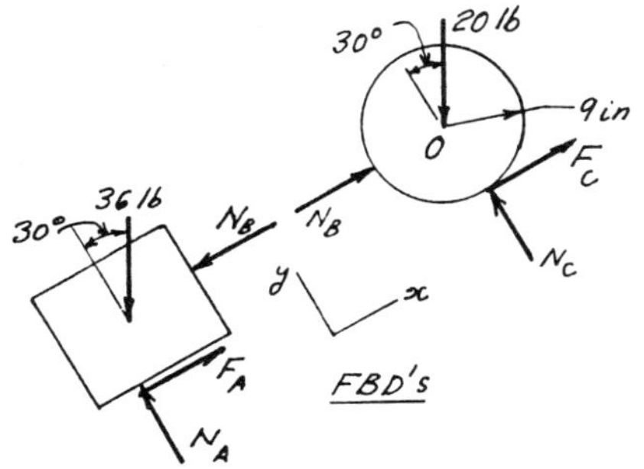

From FBD of cylinder

$\Sigma F_x = 0$: $+\nearrow$ $F_C + N_B - 20 \sin 30° = 0 \ldots$ (a)

$\Sigma M_O = 0$: $\circlearrowleft+$ $9F_C = 0 \ldots\ldots$ (b)

From FBD of block

$\Sigma F_x = 0$: $+\nearrow$ $F_A - N_B - 36 \sin 30° = 0 \ldots$ (c)

$\Sigma F_y = 0$: $\nwarrow+$ $N_A - 36 \cos 30° = 0 \ldots\ldots$ (d)

Solution of Eqs. (a)-(d) is

$N_A = 31.18$ lb $F_A = 28.0$ lb $N_B = 10.0$ lb $F_C = 0$

$\therefore \dfrac{F_A}{N_A} = \dfrac{28.0}{31.18} = 0.898 > \mu_s$ ∴ Block is <u>not in equilibrium</u> ◆

7.6

Geometry: $\bar{x} = 6 \cos\theta - 2 \sin\theta$

Assume impending sliding.

$\Sigma F_x = 0$: $\overset{+}{\rightarrow}$ $0.5N_A - N_B = 0$ $\therefore N_A = 2N_B$

$\Sigma F_y = 0$: $+\uparrow$ $N_A + 0.5N_B - W = 0$

$\therefore 2N_B + 0.5N_B - W = 0$ $\therefore N_B = 0.4W$

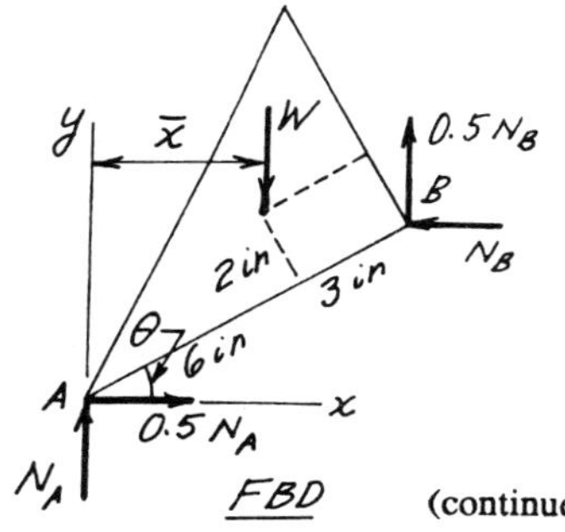

(continued)

7.6 continued

$\Sigma M_A = 0$:

$\circlearrowleft+$ $0.5N_B(9 \cos\theta) + N_B(9 \sin\theta) - W\bar{x} = 0$

$\therefore 0.5(0.4W)(9 \cos\theta) + (0.4W)(9 \sin\theta) - W(6 \cos\theta - 2 \sin\theta) = 0$

$\therefore 5.6 \sin\theta = 4.2 \cos\theta$ $\therefore \tan\theta = \dfrac{4.2}{5.6} = 0.75$ $\therefore \theta = 36.9°$ ◆

7.7

$W_C = 50(9.81) = 490.5$ N $W_B = 30(9.81) = 294.3$ N

From the FBD of the cylinder C

$\Sigma F_x = 0$: $\overset{+}{\rightarrow}$ $F_C - \dfrac{4}{5}P = 0 \ldots\ldots$ (a)

$\Sigma F_y = 0$: $+\uparrow$ $N_C + \dfrac{3}{5}P - 490.5 = 0 \ldots$ (b)

$\Sigma M_D = 0$: $\circlearrowleft+$ $\left(\dfrac{4}{5}P\right)(1.0) - C_0 = 0 \ldots$ (c)

From the FBD of the block B

$\Sigma F_x = 0$: $\overset{+}{\rightarrow}$ $\dfrac{4}{5}P - F_B = 0 \ldots\ldots$ (d)

$\Sigma F_y = 0$: $+\uparrow$ $N_B - \dfrac{3}{5}P - 294.3 = 0 \ldots$ (e)

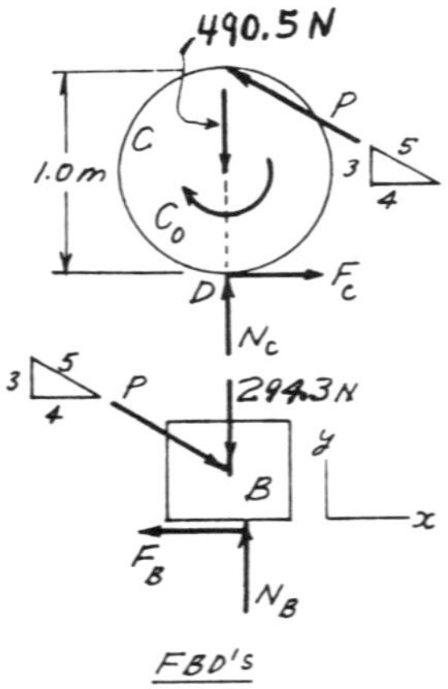

Solution of Eqs. (a)-(e) in terms of C_0 is:

$P = \dfrac{5}{4}C_0$ $F_C = C_0$ $N_C = 490.5 - \dfrac{3}{4}C_0$ $F_B = C_0$ $N_B = 294.3 + \dfrac{3}{4}C_0$

<u>Assume that the cylinder slips</u>

$F_C = 0.2N_C$: $C_0 = 0.2\left(490.5 - \dfrac{3}{4}C_0\right)$ $\therefore C_0 = 85.30$ N•m

<u>Assume that the block slips</u>

$F_B = 0.2N_B$: $C_0 = 0.2\left(294.3 + \dfrac{3}{4}C_0\right)$ $\therefore C_0 = 69.25$ N•m

∴ Largest couple that does not disturb equilibrium is $C_0 = 69.3$ N•m ◆

7.8

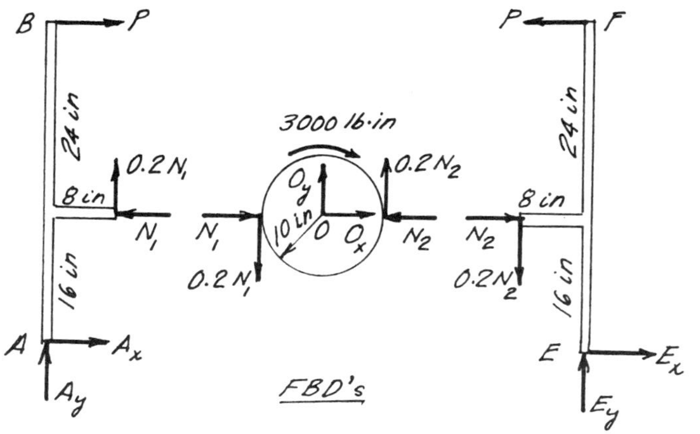

From FBD of EF

$\Sigma M_E = 0$: $(+)$ $P(40) - N_2(16) + (0.2N_2)(8) = 0 \quad \therefore N_2 = 2.778P$

From FBD of AB

$\Sigma M_A = 0$: $(+)$ $P(40) - N_1(16) - (0.2N_1)(8) = 0 \quad \therefore N_1 = 2.273P$

From FBD of cylinder

$\Sigma M_O = 0$: $(+)$ $(0.2N_1)(10) + (0.2N_2)(10) - 3000 = 0 \quad \therefore N_1 + N_2 = 1500$ lb

$\therefore 2.273P + 2.778P = 1500 \quad \therefore P = 297$ lb ◆

7.9

Assume equilibrium.

From FBD of cylinder A

$\Sigma F_y = 0$:

$+\uparrow \; 2(N_A \cos 30° + F_B \sin 30°) - W = 0$

$\therefore 1.7321N_A + F_B - W = 0$ . . . . (a)

From FBD of cylinder B

$\Sigma F_x = 0$:

$\overset{+}{\rightarrow} \; N_A \sin 30° - F_A \cos 30° - F_B = 0$

$\therefore 0.5N_A - 0.8660F_A - F_B = 0$ . . . . . . (b)

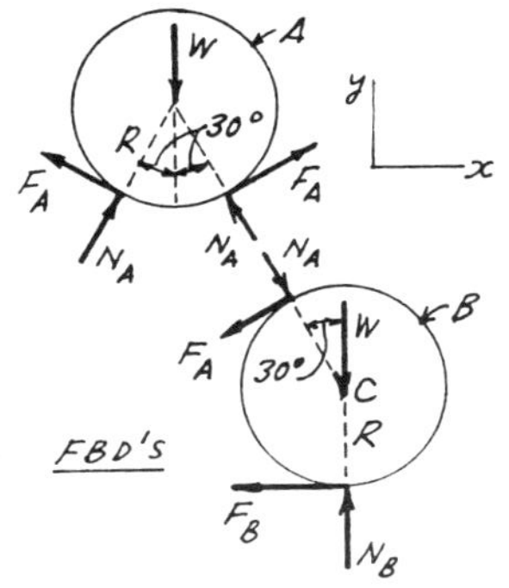

(continued)

7.9 continued

$\Sigma F_y = 0$:

$+\uparrow \; N_B - N_A \cos 30° - F_A \sin 30° - W = 0 \quad \therefore N_B - 0.8660N_A - 0.5F_A - W = 0$ (c)

$\Sigma M_C = 0$: $(+)$ $(F_A - F_B)R = 0 \quad \therefore F_A = F_B$ . . . . (d)

Solution of Eqs. (a)-(d) is

$F_A = F_B = 0.13397\,W \quad N_A = 0.5000\,W \quad N_B = 1.5000\,W$

$\therefore \dfrac{F_A}{N_A} = \dfrac{0.13397}{0.5000} = 0.268 < 0.3 \qquad \dfrac{F_B}{N_B} = \dfrac{0.13397}{1.5000} = 0.0893 < 0.1 \qquad \therefore$ Equilibrium O.K. ◆

7.10

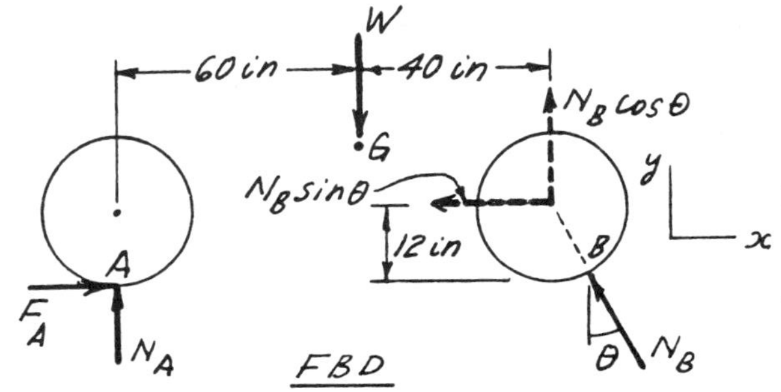

From the FBD of the truck (note that N_B was moved from B to the axle)

$\Sigma F_x = 0$: $\overset{+}{\rightarrow}$ $F_A - N_B \sin\theta = 0$ . . . . (a)

$\Sigma F_y = 0$: $+\uparrow$ $N_A + N_B \cos\theta - W = 0$ . . . . (b)

$\Sigma M_A = 0$: $(+)$ $(N_B \cos\theta)(100) + (N_B \sin\theta)(12) - 60W = 0$ . . . (c)

Solution of Eqs. (a)-(c) is

$N_B = \dfrac{15W}{25\cos\theta + 3\sin\theta} \qquad F_A = \dfrac{15W\sin\theta}{25\cos\theta + 3\sin\theta} \qquad N_A = \dfrac{(10\cos\theta + 3\sin\theta)W}{25\cos\theta + 3\sin\theta}$

Set $F_A = \mu N_A$: $15W\sin\theta = \mu(10\cos\theta + 3\sin\theta)W \quad \therefore \theta = \tan^{-1}\dfrac{10\mu}{15 - 3\mu}$

(a) With $\mu = \mu_k = 0.15$, we get $\theta = \tan^{-1}\dfrac{10(0.15)}{15 - 3(0.15)} = 5.89°$ ◆

(b) With $\mu = \mu_s = 0.18$, we get $\theta = \tan^{-1}\dfrac{10(0.18)}{15 - 3(0.18)} = 7.10°$ ◆

7.11

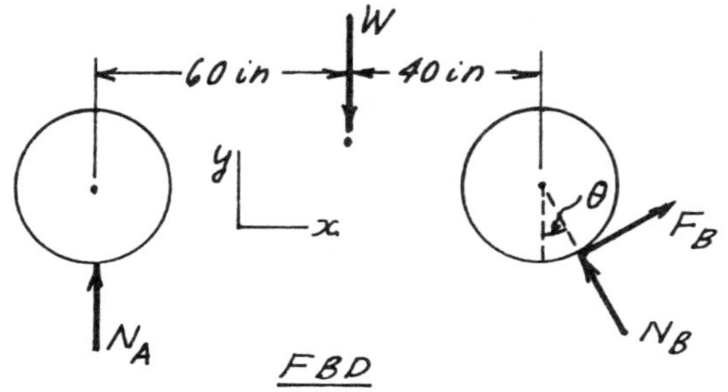

From the FBD of the truck

$\Sigma F_x = 0$: $\overset{+}{\rightarrow}$ $F_B \cos\theta - N_B \sin\theta = 0$

Set $F_B = \mu N_B$: $N_B(\mu \cos\theta - \sin\theta) = 0$ $\quad \therefore \theta = \tan^{-1}\mu$

(a) With $\mu = \mu_k = 0.15$ we get $\theta = \tan^{-1}(0.15) = 8.53°$ ◆

(b) With $\mu = \mu_s = 0.18$ we get $\theta = \tan^{-1}(0.18) = 10.20°$ ◆

7.12

$W_{bar} = 0.8(9.81) = 7.848$ N $\qquad W_{spool} = 1.6(9.81) = 15.696$ N

From FBD of bar

$\Sigma M_A = 0$: (+) $300N_B - (225)(7.848) = 0$

$\therefore N_B = 5.886$ N

From FBD of spool:

$\Sigma F_y = 0$: $+\uparrow$ $N_C - 15.696 - N_B = 0$

$\therefore N_C - 15.696 - 5.886 = 0 \quad \therefore N_C = 21.58$ N

$\Sigma M_B = 0$: (+) $200P - 250F_C = 0 \quad \therefore P = 1.25F_C$

$\Sigma M_C = 0$: (+) $50P - 250F_B = 0 \quad \therefore P = 5F_B$

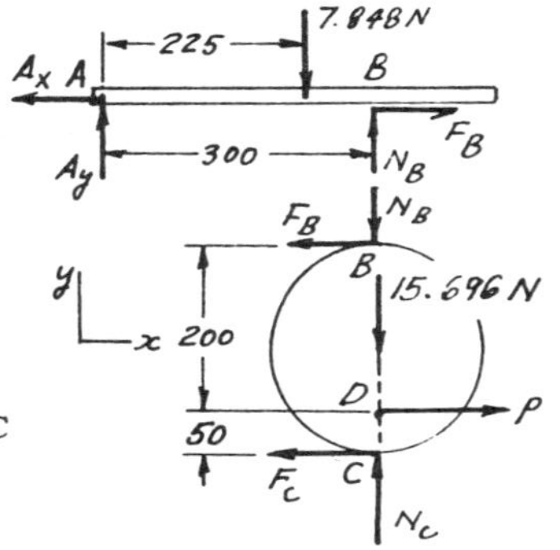

Assume impending sliding at B

$\therefore F_B = \mu_s N_B = 0.25(5.886) = 1.4715$ N $\qquad \therefore P = 5(1.4715) = 7.358$ N

Assume impending slipping at C

$\therefore F_C = \mu_s N_C = 0.25(21.58) = 5.395$ N $\qquad \therefore P = 1.25(5.395) = 6.744$ N

$\therefore$ Largest P that does not cause slipping is $P = 6.74$ N ◆

7.13

From solution of Prob. 7.12: $N_B = 5.886$ N $\quad N_C = 21.58$ N

From FBD of spool $\Sigma M_D = 0$: (+) $50F_C - 200F_B = 0 \quad \therefore 50(\mu_C N_C) - 200(\mu_B N_B) = 0$

$\therefore 50(21.58\mu_C) - 200(5.886\mu_B) = 0 \qquad \therefore \mu_C/\mu_B = 1.091$ ◆

7.14

$W = 24(9.81) = 235.4$ N

Geometry: $\frac{\theta}{2} = \tan^{-1}\frac{1}{3} \quad \therefore \theta = 36.87°$

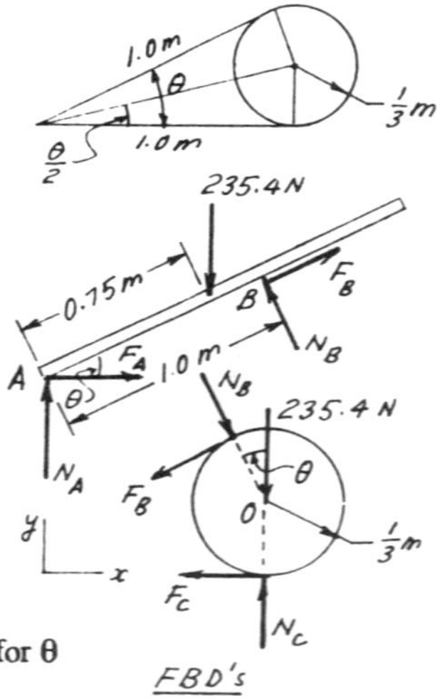

(a) From the FBD of the bar

$\Sigma F_x = 0$: $\overset{+}{\rightarrow}$ $F_A + F_B \cos\theta - N_B \sin\theta = 0$

$\Sigma F_y = 0$: $+\uparrow$ $N_A + N_B \cos\theta + F_B \sin\theta - 235.4 = 0$

$\Sigma M_A = 0$: (+) $N_B(1.0) - (235.4 \cos\theta)(0.75) = 0$

From the FBD of the cylinder

$\Sigma F_x = 0$: $\overset{+}{\rightarrow}$ $N_B \sin\theta - F_C - F_B\cos\theta = 0$

$\Sigma F_y = 0$: $+\uparrow$ $N_C - N_B \cos\theta - F_B \sin\theta - 235.4 = 0$

$\Sigma M_O = 0$: (+) $F_B - F_C = 0$

Solution of the above equations is, after substituting for θ

$F_A = F_B = F_C = 47.1$ N ◆

$N_A = 94.2$ N ◆ $\qquad N_B = 141.2$ N ◆ $\qquad N_C = 376.6$ N ◆

(b) The largest ratio $\frac{F}{N}$ occurs at A: $\frac{F_A}{N_A} = \frac{47.1}{94.2} = 0.500.$

$\therefore$ Smallest coefficient of friction required for equilibrium is $\mu_s = 0.500$ ◆

7.15

Assume equilibrium.

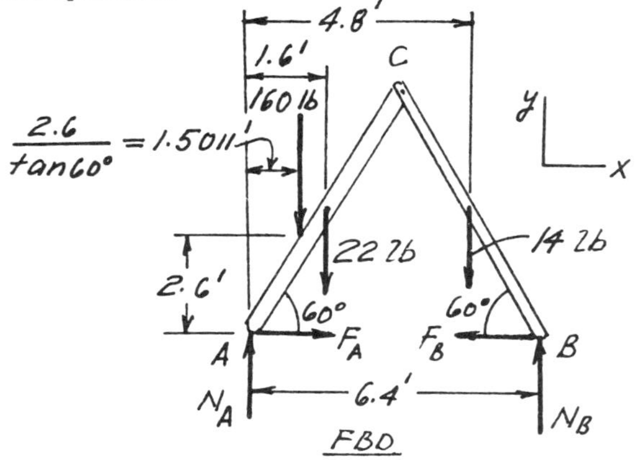

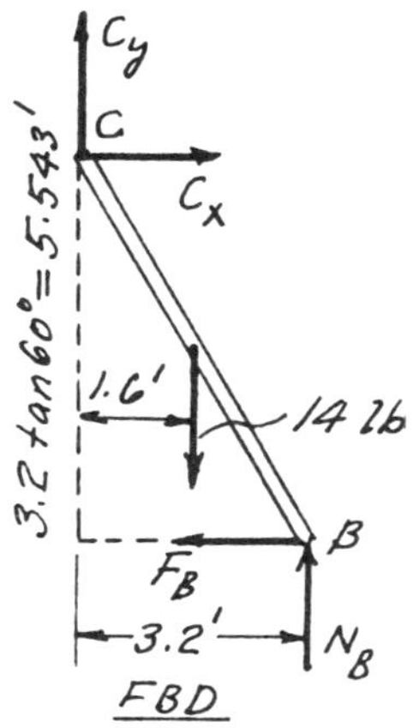

From FBD of ladder

$\Sigma M_A = 0$: (+) $6.4N_B - (14)(4.8) - (22)(1.6) - (160)(1.5011) = 0$

$\Sigma F_x = 0$: $\overset{+}{\rightarrow}$ $F_A - F_B = 0$

$\Sigma F_y = 0$: $+\uparrow$ $N_A + N_B - 14 - 22 - 160 = 0$

From FBD of BC

$\Sigma M_C = 0$: (+) $5.543F_B - 3.2N_B + (14)(1.6) = 0$

Solution is $N_A = 142.47$ lb $\quad N_B = 53.53$ lb $\quad F_A = F_B = 26.86$ lb

$\frac{F_A}{N_A} = \frac{26.86}{142.47} = 0.1885 < 0.48$ $\quad\therefore$ Ladder will not slide at A

$\frac{F_B}{N_B} = \frac{26.86}{53.53} = 0.502 > 0.48$ $\quad\therefore$ <u>Ladder will slide at B</u> ◆

7.16

Assume equilibrium.

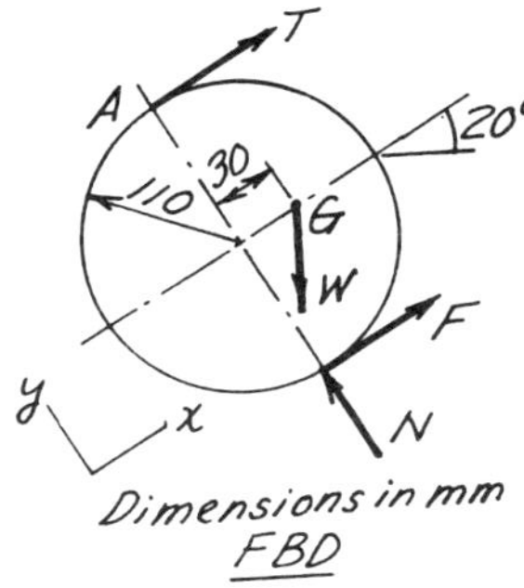

$\Sigma F_y = 0$:

$\nwarrow +$ $N - W\cos 20° = 0$ $\quad\therefore N = 0.9397W$

$\Sigma M_A = 0$:

(+) $F(220) - (W\sin 20°)(110) - (W\cos 20°)(30) = 0$

$\therefore F = 0.2992W$

$\frac{F}{N} = \frac{0.2992W}{0.9397W} = 0.318 > \mu_s$

$\therefore$ <u>Cylinder cannot be at rest</u> ◆

7.17

Resultant force of earth on piling is

$R = \frac{1}{2}(9000)(3) = 13\,500$ N

From the FBD of piling

$\Sigma M_C = 0$: (+) $1.5N_B - (13\,500)(1.0) = 0$ . . (a)

From the FBD of bar AB

$\Sigma F_x = 0$: $\overset{+}{\rightarrow}$ $N_A - N_B = 0$ . . . . (b)

$\Sigma F_y = 0$: $+\uparrow$ $F_A + F_B - P = 0$ . . . . (c)

$\Sigma M_A = 0$: (+) $0.8P - 2.8F_B = 0$ . . . . (d)

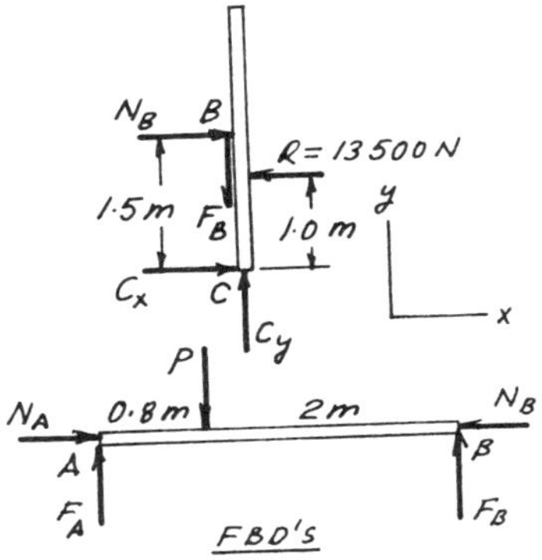

Solution of Eqs. (a)-(d) in terms of P is

$N_A = N_B = 9000$ N

$F_A = 0.7143P \quad F_B = 0.2857P$

<u>Assume slipping at A</u>: $F_A = 0.5N_A$ $\quad\therefore 0.7143P = 0.5(9000)$ $\quad\therefore P = 6300$ N

<u>Assume slipping at B</u>: $F_B = 0.25N_B$ $\quad\therefore 0.2857P = 0.25(9000)$ $\quad\therefore P = 7875$ N

$\therefore$ Smallest force required to move the bar is $P = 6300$ N ◆

7.18

Weight of the block is (40)(9.81) = 392.4 N

Due to symmetry about line OC:.

$T_{OA} = T_{OD} = T \quad N_B = N_E = N$

$F_B = F_E = F$

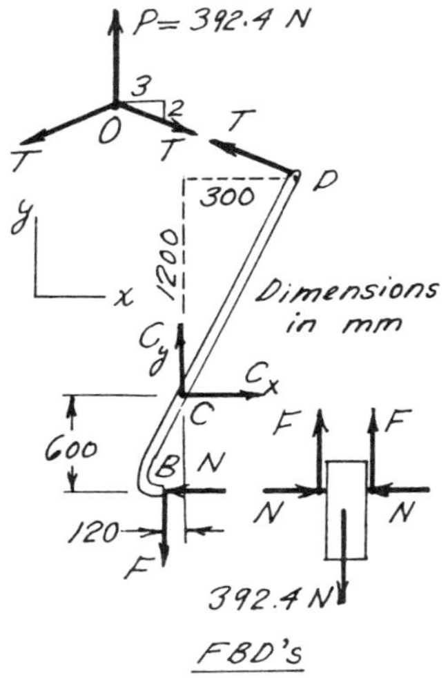

From FBD of assembly: $\Sigma F_y = 0$

$+\uparrow\ P - 392.4 = 0 \qquad \therefore\ P = 392.4\text{ N}$

From FBD of block: $\Sigma F_y = 0$

$+\uparrow\ 2F = 392.4 \qquad \therefore\ F = 196.2\text{ N}$

From FBD of joint O: $\Sigma F_y = 0$

$+\uparrow\ 392.4 - 2\left(T\dfrac{2}{\sqrt{13}}\right) = 0 \qquad \therefore\ T = 353.7\text{ N}$

From FBD of tong DCB: $\Sigma M_C = 0$

$$\circlearrowleft(+)\ \left(\frac{2}{\sqrt{13}}T\right)(300) + \left(\frac{3}{\sqrt{13}}T\right)(1200) + F(120) - N(600) = 0$$

$$\therefore\ \frac{4200}{\sqrt{13}}(353.7) + (196.2)(120) - 600N = 0 \qquad \therefore\ N = 725.9\text{ N}$$

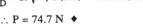

Smallest coefficient of friction that prevents slipping is $\mu_s = \dfrac{F}{N} = \dfrac{196.2}{725.9} = 0.270$ ◆

7.19

W = (80)(9.81) = 784.8 N

<u>Assume impending sliding at B</u> (rolling about A).

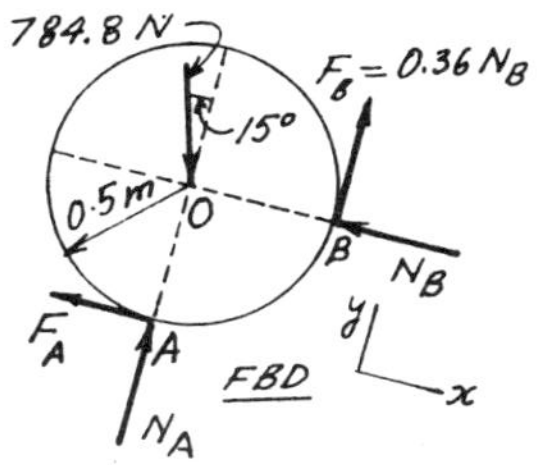

From the FBD of the spool

$\Sigma M_O = 0$: $\circlearrowleft(+)$ $0.5(0.36N_B) - 0.5F_A = 0$ . . . . (a)

$\Sigma F_x = 0$: $\overset{+}{\searrow}$ $784.8 \sin 15° - F_A - N_B = 0$ . . . . (b)

$\Sigma F_y = 0$: $+\nearrow$ $N_A + 0.36N_B - 784.8 \cos 15° = 0$ (c)

Solution of Eqs. (a)-(c) is $N_A = 704.34$ N $\quad F_A = 53.76$ N $\quad N_B = 149.34$ N

(continued)

7.19 continued

Check for sliding at A: $F_A/N_A = 53.76/704.34 = 0.0763 < 0.12$

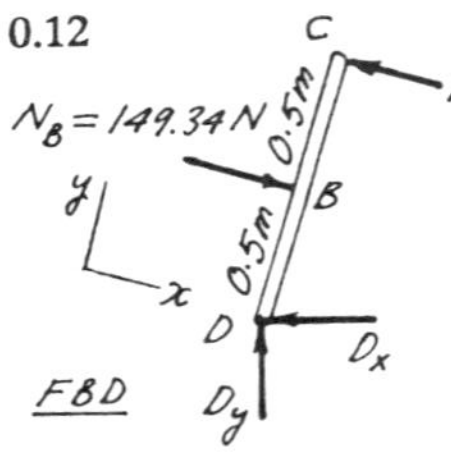

∴ No sliding at A; assumption was O.K.

From FBD of bar CD

$\Sigma M_D = 0$: $\circlearrowleft(+)$ $P(1.0) - 149.34(0.5) = 0$

$\therefore\ P = 74.7$ N ◆

7.20

W = (80)(9.81) = 784.8 N

<u>Assume impending sliding at B</u> (rolling about A).

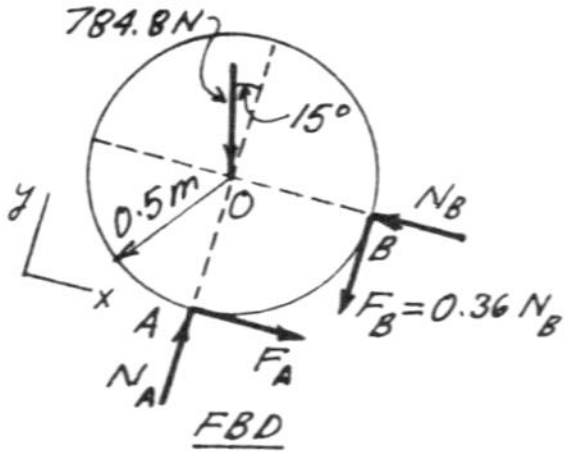

From the FBD of the spool

$\Sigma M_O = 0$: $\circlearrowleft(+)$ $0.5(0.36N_B) - 0.5F_A = 0$ . . . . (a)

$\Sigma F_x = 0$: $\overset{+}{\searrow}$ $784.8 \sin 15° + F_A - N_B = 0$ . . . . . (b)

$\Sigma F_y = 0$: $+\nearrow$ $N_A - 0.36N_B - 784.8 \cos 15° = 0$ (c)

Solution of Eqs. (a)-(c) is $N_A = 872.34$ N $\quad F_A = 114.24$ N

$N_B = 317.34$ N

Check for sliding at A: $F_A/N_A = 114.24/872.34 = 0.1310 > 0.12$

∴ Spool will slip at A; assumption was incorrect

<u>Assume impending sliding at A</u> (rolling about B)

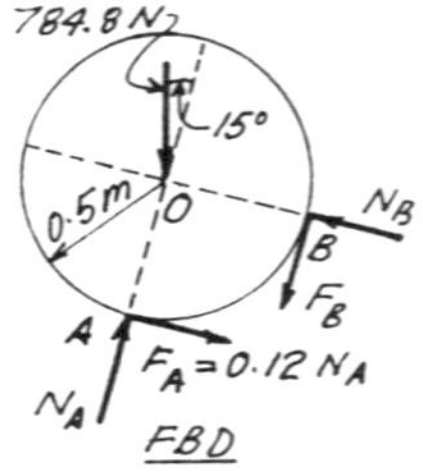

From FBD of the spool

$\Sigma M_O = 0$: $\circlearrowleft(+)$ $0.5F_B - 0.5(0.12N_A) = 0$ . . . . (d)

$\Sigma F_x = 0$: $\overset{+}{\searrow}$ $784.8 \sin 15° + 0.12N_A - N_B = 0$ . . (e)

$\Sigma F_y = 0$: $+\nearrow$ $N_A - F_B - 784.8 \cos 15° = 0$ . . . . . (f)

Solution of Eqs. (d)-(f) is $N_A = 861.48$ N $\quad N_B = 306.48$ N

$F_B = 103.38$ N

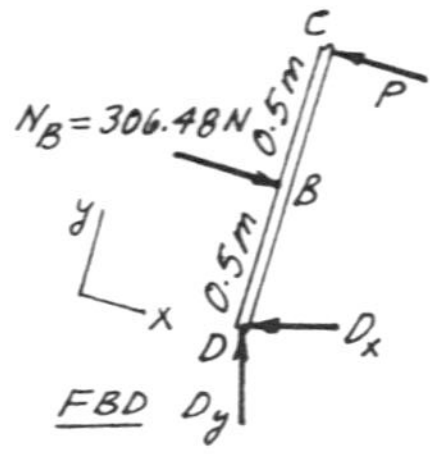

From FBD of bar CD

$\Sigma M_D = 0$: $\circlearrowleft(+)$ $P(1.0) - 306.48(0.5) = 0$

$\therefore\ P = 153.2$ N ◆

7.21

Assume impending sliding at B.

To find upper limit of P, assume that <u>motion of B impends downward</u>.

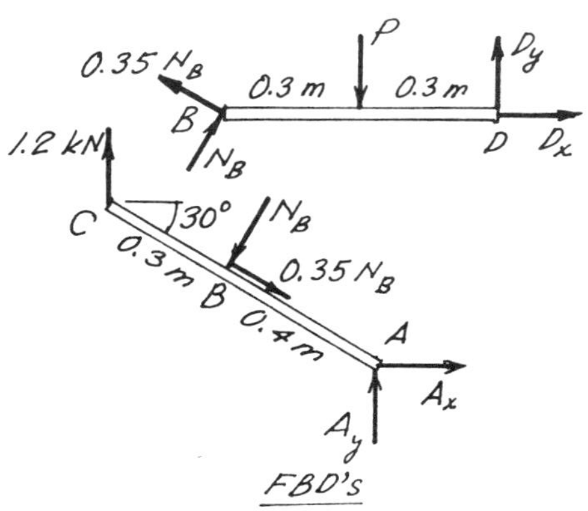

From FBD of bar AC $\Sigma M_A = 0$:

$(+)\ 1.2(0.7\cos 30°) - N_B(0.4) = 0$

$\therefore N_B = 1.8187 \text{ kN} \ldots\ldots\ldots \text{(a)}$

From FBD of bar BD $\Sigma M_D = 0$:

$(+)\ P(0.3) - (N_B \cos 30°)(0.6)$

$-\ (0.35N_B \sin 30°)(0.6) = 0 \ldots\ \text{(b)}$

$\therefore 0.3P - 0.6246N_B = 0 \quad \therefore 0.3P - 0.6246(1.8187) = 0 \quad \therefore P = 3.787 \text{ kN}$

To find the lower limit, assume that the <u>motion of B impends up</u>. Consequently, the direction of the friction force at B must be reversed on the FBD's. Equation (a) is unchanged, but the sign of the friction force in Eq. (b) must be reversed. Therefore, Eq. (b) becomes

$P(0.3) - (N_B \cos 30°)(0.6) + (0.35N_B \sin 30°)(0.6) = 0$

$\therefore 0.3P - 0.4146N_B = 0 \quad \therefore 0.3P - 0.4146(1.8187) = 0 \quad \therefore P = 2.513 \text{ kN}$

$\therefore$ The bars will be in equilibrium if $2.51 \text{ kN} < P < 3.79 \text{ kN}$ ◆

7.22

Let the x′ and y′ coordinate axes lie on the inclined plane, and let z′ be perpendicular to the plane. Assume equilibrium.

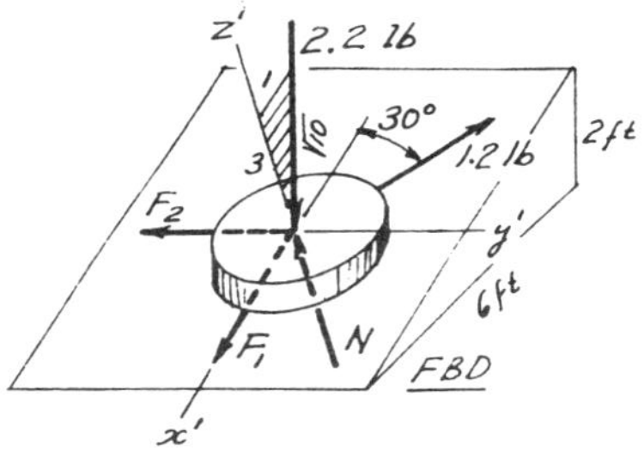

$\Sigma F_{x'} = 0: \quad F_1 + \dfrac{1}{\sqrt{10}}(2.2) - 1.2\cos 30° = 0$

$\therefore F_1 = 0.3435 \text{ lb}$

$\Sigma F_{y'} = 0: \quad -F_2 + 1.2\sin 30° = 0$

$\therefore F_2 = 0.600 \text{ lb}$

$\Sigma F_{z'} = 0: \quad N - \dfrac{3}{\sqrt{10}}(2.2) = 0 \quad \therefore N = 2.087 \text{ lb}$

$\dfrac{F}{N} = \dfrac{\sqrt{0.3435^2 + 0.600^2}}{2.087} = 0.331 < 0.4 \quad \therefore$ The disk is in equilibrium ◆

7.23

Let the x′ and y′ coordinate axes lie on the inclined plane, and let z′ be perpendicular to the plane.

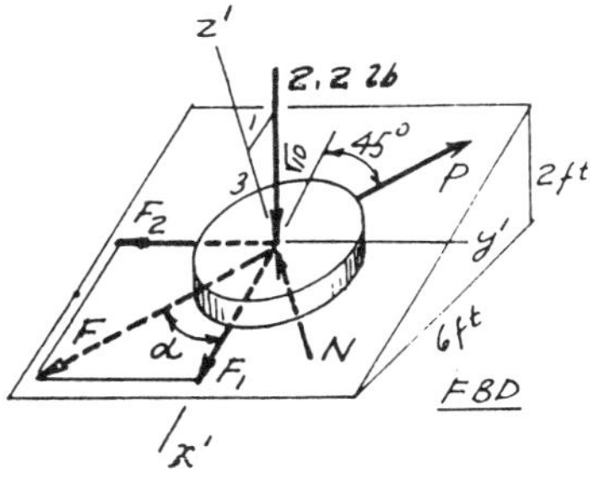

$\Sigma F_{x'} = 0: \quad F_1 + \dfrac{1}{\sqrt{10}}(2.2) - P\cos 45° = 0$

$\therefore F_1 = 0.7071P - 0.6957 \text{ lb}$

$\Sigma F_{y'} = 0: \quad -F_2 + P\sin 45° = 0$

$\therefore F_2 = 0.7071\,P$

$\Sigma F_{z'} = 0: \quad N - \dfrac{3}{\sqrt{10}}(2.2) = 0 \quad \therefore N = 2.087 \text{ lb}$

(a) Motion is impending if $F = \mu_s N$, i.e. $F_1^2 + F_2^2 = (\mu_s N)^2$

$\therefore (0.7071P - 0.6957)^2 + (0.7071P)^2 = \left[(0.4)(2.087)\right]^2$

$\therefore P^2 - 0.9839P - 0.2129 = 0 \qquad$ The positive root is $P = 1.166 \text{ lb}$ ◆

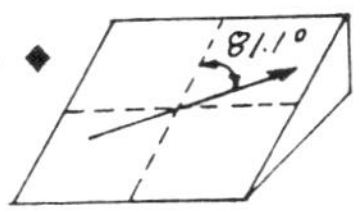

Direction of impend. sliding

(b) $\alpha = \tan^{-1}(F_2/F_1) = \tan^{-1}\dfrac{(0.7071)(1.166)}{(0.7071)(1.166) - 0.6957} = 81.1°$ ◆

7.24

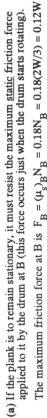

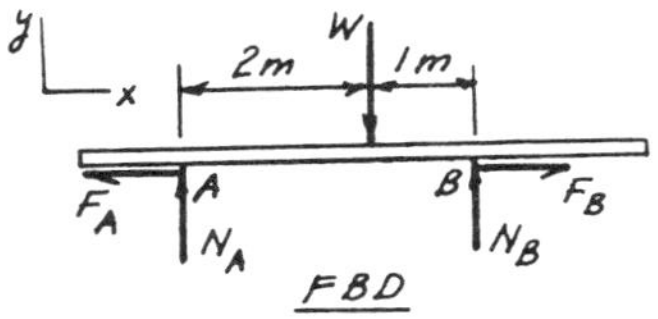

$\Sigma M_A = 0: \ (+)\ 3N_B - 2W = 0 \ldots\ldots \text{(a)}$

$\Sigma F_x = 0: \ \overset{+}{\rightarrow}\ F_B - F_A = 0 \ldots\ldots\ldots \text{(b)}$

$\Sigma F_y = 0: \ +\uparrow\ N_A + N_B - W = 0 \ldots \text{(c)}$

Solution of Eqs. (a)-(c) is

$N_A = \dfrac{W}{3} \qquad N_B = \dfrac{2W}{3} \qquad F_A = F_B$

(a) If the plank is to remain stationary, it must resist the maximum <u>static</u> friction force applied to it by the drum at B (this force occurs just when the drum starts rotating).

The maximum friction force at B is $F_B = (\mu_s)_B N_B = 0.18N_B = 0.18(2W/3) = 0.12W$

$\therefore F_A = 0.12W \quad \therefore \dfrac{F_A}{N_A} = \dfrac{0.12W}{W/3} = 0.36 > (\mu_s)_A \qquad \therefore$ Plank will slide at A ◆

(continued)

7.24 continued

(b) If the plank remains stationary, it must slip on the drum at B.

$\therefore\ F_B = (\mu_k)_B N_B = 0.15(2W/3) = 0.10W \quad \therefore\ F_A = 0.10W$

$\therefore\ \dfrac{F_A}{N_A} = \dfrac{0.10W}{W/3} = 0.30 < (\mu_s)_A \qquad \therefore$ The plank will not move ♦

7.25

Note that F_B on the FBD is drawn opposite to the direction of impending sliding.

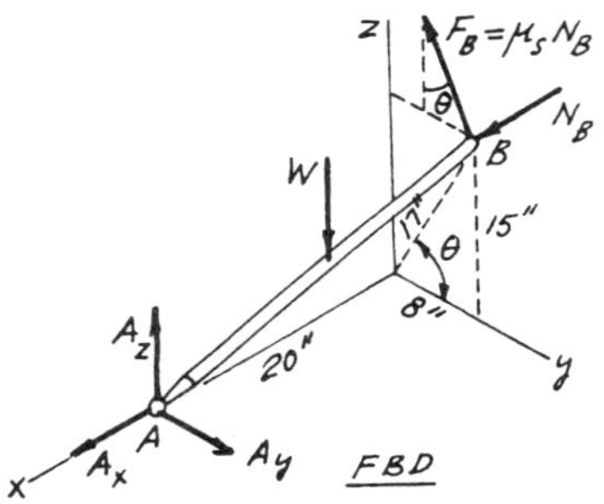

$\Sigma(M_A)_z = 0$:

$20(\mu_s N_B \sin\theta) - 8N_B = 0$

$\therefore\ 20\left(\mu_s N_B \dfrac{15}{17}\right) - 8N_B = 0$

$\therefore\ \mu_s = 0.453$ ♦

7.26

Assume that the plank comes to rest in the position shown below.

During the period of sliding $F_A = (\mu_k)_A N_A = 0.28N_A$ and $F_B = (\mu_s)_B N_B = 0.36N_B$

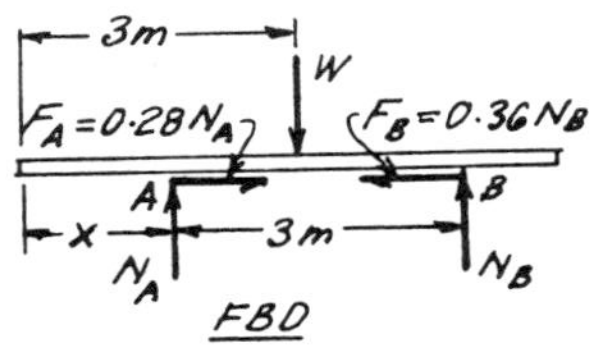

$\Sigma F_x = 0: \ \overset{+}{\rightarrow} \quad 0.28N_A - 0.36N_B = 0$

$\Sigma F_y = 0: \ +\uparrow \quad N_A + N_B - W = 0$

$\Sigma M_A = 0: \ \circlearrowleft(+) \quad 3N_B - (3 - x)W = 0$

Solution of the equations is: $N_A = 0.5625W$

$N_B = 0.4375W \quad x = 1.6875$ m ♦

7.27

The strut is a two-force member.

$\therefore\ \mathbf{F}_{AB} = F_{AB}\dfrac{-1.25\mathbf{i} + \mathbf{j} + 5\mathbf{k}}{\sqrt{1.25^2 + 1^2 + 5^2}}$

$= F_{AB}(-0.2381\mathbf{i} + 0.1905\mathbf{j} + 0.9524\mathbf{k})$

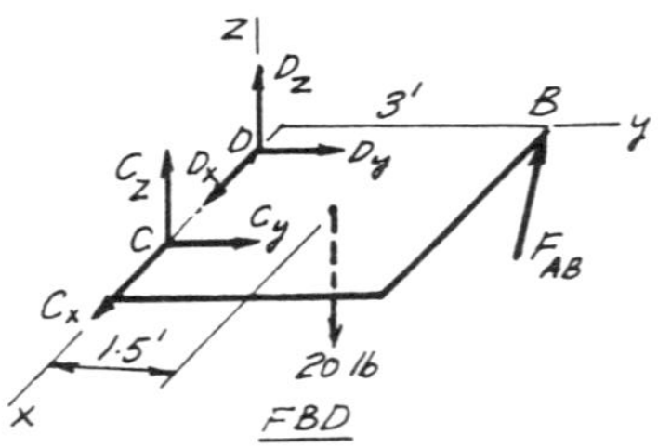

$\Sigma M_x = 0: \circlearrowleft(+) \ (0.9524F_{AB})(3) - (20)(1.5) = 0$

$\therefore\ F_{AB} = 10.5$ lb

$\therefore\ \mathbf{F}_{AB} = 10.5(-0.2381\mathbf{i} + 0.1905\mathbf{j} + 0.9524\mathbf{k}) = -2.5\mathbf{i} + 2.0\mathbf{j} + 10.0\mathbf{k}$ lb

$\therefore$ The friction and normal forces acting at end A of the strut are

$\mathbf{F} = -2.5\mathbf{i} + (2.0 + P)\mathbf{j}$ lb $\quad \mathbf{N} = 10.0\mathbf{k}$ lb

$\therefore\ F = \sqrt{2.5^2 + (2.0 + P)^2} = \sqrt{P^2 + 4P + 10.25}$

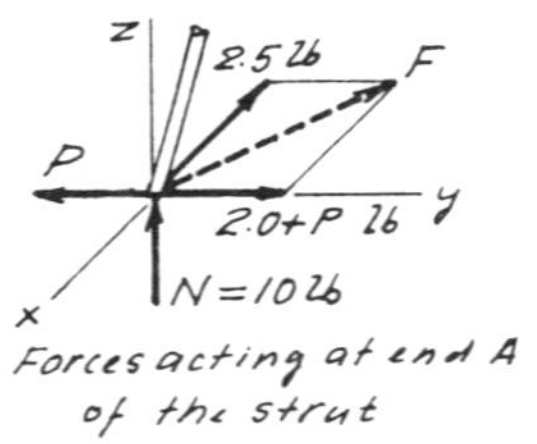

At impending sliding $F = \mu_s N$, i.e. $F^2 = (\mu_s N)^2$

$\therefore\ P^2 + 4P + 10.25 = (0.4 \times 10.0)^2$

$\therefore\ P^2 + 4P - 5.75 = 0$

The positive root is $P = 1.122$ lb ♦

7.28

Assume equilibrium.

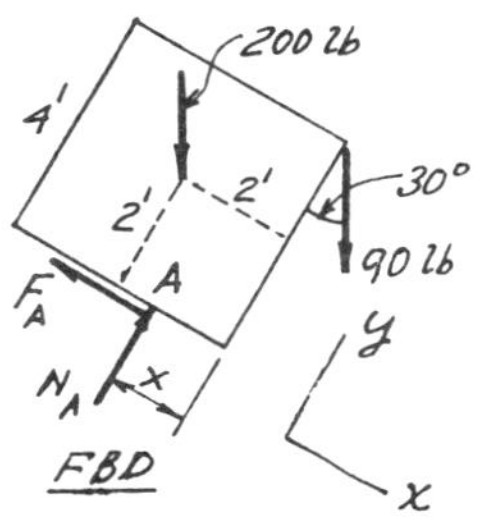

$\Sigma F_x = 0$: $\overset{+}{\searrow}$ $(200 + 90)\sin 30° - F_A = 0$

$\therefore F_A = 145.0$ lb

$\Sigma F_y = 0$: $+\nearrow$ $N_A - (200 + 90)\cos 30° = 0$

$\therefore N_A = 251.1$ lb

$\Sigma M_A = 0$: $(+)$ $(200 \cos 30°)(2 - x) - (200 \sin 30°)(2)$

$- (90 \cos 30°)(x) - (90 \sin 30°)(4) = 0$

$\therefore -251.1x - 33.59 = 0$ $\quad\therefore x = -0.1338$ ft

$\frac{F_A}{N_A} = \frac{145.0}{251.1} = 0.577 < 0.6$ $\quad\therefore$ The box will not slide

Because $x < 0$, the box will tip. $\therefore$ The box cannot be in equilibrium ◆

7.29

$W = (60)(9.81) = 588.6$ N

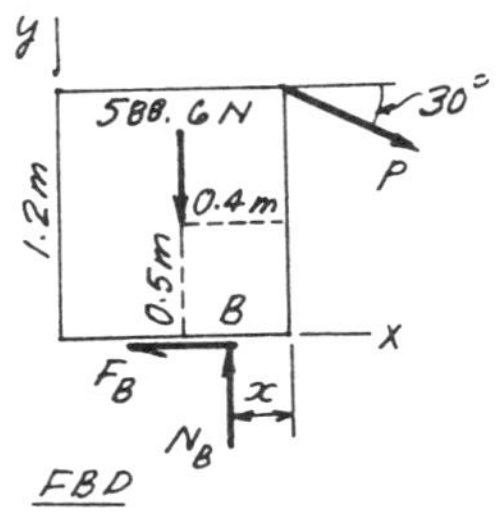

Assume impending sliding $(F_B = 0.3N_B)$

$\Sigma F_x = 0$: $\overset{+}{\rightarrow}$ $P \cos 30° - 0.3N_B = 0$

$\Sigma F_y = 0$: $+\uparrow$ $N_B - P \sin 30° - 588.6 = 0$

The solution is $N_B = 711.9$ N $\quad P = 246.6$ N

Assume impending tipping $(x = 0)$

$\Sigma M_B = 0$: $(+)$ $(P \cos 30°)(1.2) - (588.6)(0.4) = 0$

$\therefore P = 226.6$ N

$\therefore P = 227$ N, determined by tipping ◆

7.30

Assume impending sliding $(F_B = 0.3N_B)$

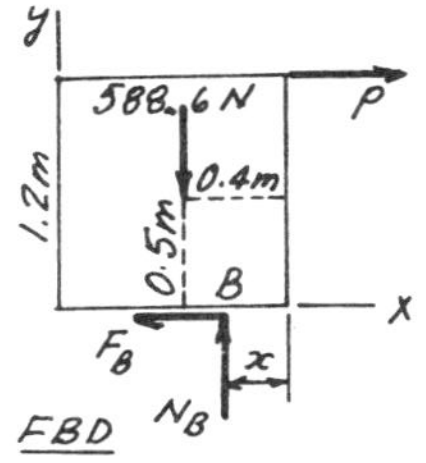

$\Sigma F_x = 0$: $\overset{+}{\rightarrow}$ $P - 0.3N_B = 0$

$\Sigma F_y = 0$: $+\uparrow$ $N_B - 588.6 = 0$

$\therefore N_B = 588.6$ N $\quad P = 176.58$ N

Assume impending tipping $(x = 0)$

$\Sigma M_B = 0$: $(+)$ $1.2P - (588.6)(0.4) = 0$

$\therefore P = 196.20$ N

$\therefore P = 176.6$ N determined by sliding ◆

7.31

Assume impending sliding $(F_A = 0.5N_A,\ F_B = 0.5\,N_B)$

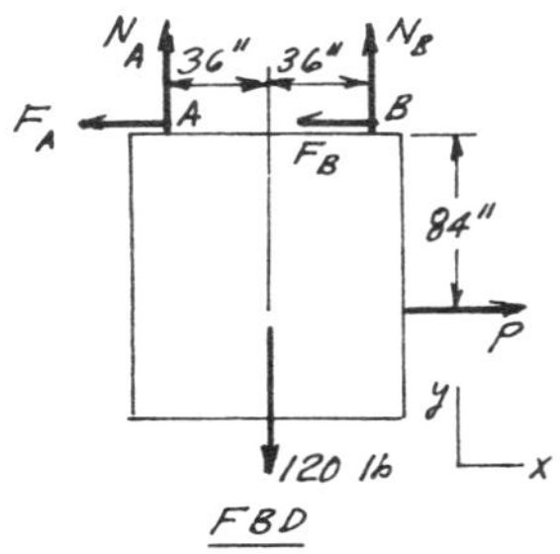

$\Sigma F_x = 0$: $\overset{+}{\rightarrow}$ $P - 0.5(N_A + N_B) = 0$

$\Sigma F_y = 0$: $+\uparrow$ $N_A + N_B - 120 = 0$

$\therefore P = 60.0$ lb

Assume impending tipping about A $(N_B = 0)$

$\Sigma M_A = 0$: $(+)$ $84P - (36)(120) = 0$

$\therefore P = 51.43$ lb

$\therefore P = 51.4$ lb determined by tipping ◆

7.32

$W = (18)(9.81) = 176.58$ N

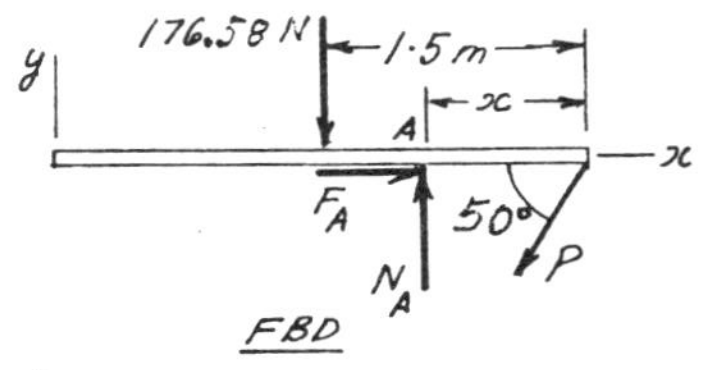

Assume impending sliding $(F_A = 0.2N_A)$

$\Sigma F_x = 0$: $\overset{+}{\rightarrow}$ $0.2N_A - P \cos 50° = 0$

$\Sigma F_y = 0$: $+\uparrow$ $N_A - P \sin 50° - 176.58 = 0$

Solution is $N_A = 231.9$ N $\quad P = 72.14$ N

Assume impending tipping about A $(x = 1.0$ m$)$

$\Sigma M_A = 0$: $(+)$ $176.58(1.5 - 1.0) - (P \sin 50°)(1.0) = 0$ $\quad\therefore P = 115.25$ N

$\therefore P = 115.3$ N determined by tipping ◆

7.33

$W = (60)(9.81) = 588.6$ N

Assume simultaneous impending sliding and tipping.

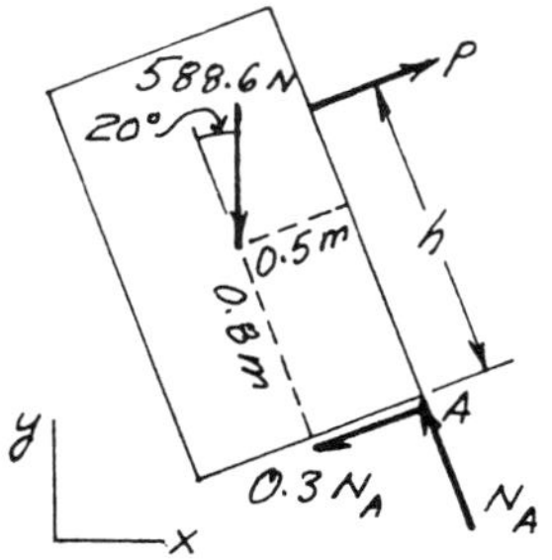

$\Sigma F_x = 0$: $P - 0.3N_A - 588.6 \sin 20° = 0$

$\Sigma F_y = 0$: $N_A - 588.6 \cos 20° = 0$

$\Sigma M_A = 0$: $(588.6 \sin 20°)(0.8) + (588.6 \cos 20°)(0.5) - Ph = 0$

The solution is

$N_A = 553$ N $\quad P = 367$ N ◆ $\quad h = 1.192$ m ◆

7.34

There are three possible modes of motion: (1) sliding of the block, (2) slipping of the spool, or (3) tipping of the block.

Assume impending sliding of the block.

From the FBD of the block

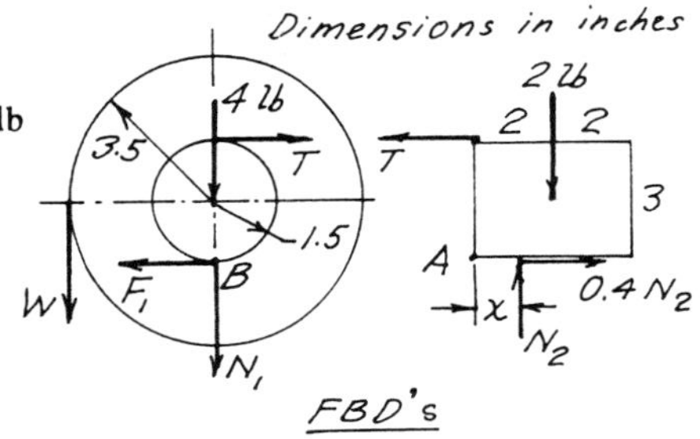

$\Sigma F_y = 0$: $+\uparrow$ $N_2 - 2 = 0 \quad \therefore N_2 = 2$ lb

$\Sigma F_x = 0$: $\overset{+}{\rightarrow}$ $0.4N_2 - T = 0$

$\therefore T = 0.4N_2 = 0.4(2) = 0.8$ lb

$\Sigma M_A = 0$ (+) $T(3) + N_2 x - 2(2) = 0$

$$\therefore x = \frac{4 - 3T}{N_2} = \frac{4 - 3(0.8)}{2} = 0.8 \text{ in}$$

Because $x > 0$, the block will not tip.

From FBD of the spool

$$\Sigma M_B = 0: (+)\ 3.5W - 2(1.5)T = 0 \quad \therefore W = \frac{3.0T}{3.5} = \frac{3.0(0.8)}{3.5} = 0.6857 \text{ lb}$$

$\Sigma F_x = 0$: $\overset{+}{\rightarrow}$ $T - F_1 = 0 \quad \therefore F_1 = T = 0.8$ lb

$\Sigma F_y = 0$: $+\uparrow$ $N_1 - 4 - W = 0 \quad \therefore N_1 = 4 + W = 4 + 0.6857 = 4.686$ lb

$$\frac{F_1}{N_1} = \frac{0.8}{4.686} = 0.1707 < \mu_s \quad \therefore \text{Spool will not slip}$$

$\therefore$ Largest weight that does not disturb equilibrium is $W = 0.686$ lb ◆

7.35

(a) Assume simultaneous impending tipping and sliding ($F = \mu_s N$).

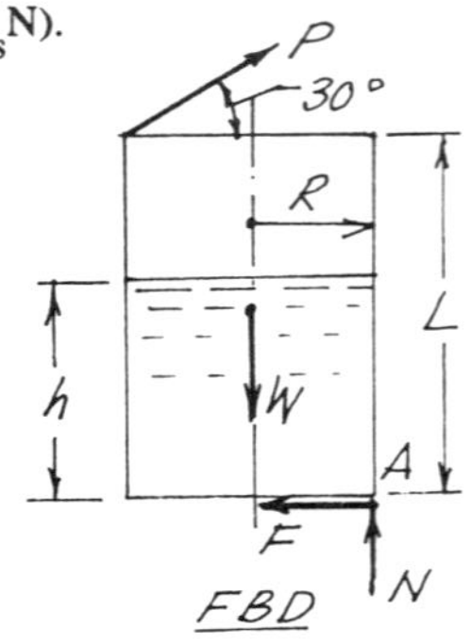

Full tank: $W = \gamma(\pi R^2 L) = 62.4\pi(1.4)^2(4) = 1536.9$ lb

$\Sigma M_A = 0$:

(+) $WR - (P \cos 30°)L - (P \sin 30°)(2R) = 0$

$$\therefore P = \frac{WR}{L \cos 30° + 2R \sin 30°} = \frac{(1536.9)(1.4)}{4 \cos 30° + 2.8 \sin 30°}$$

$= 442.4$ lb ◆

$\Sigma F_y = 0$: $+\uparrow$ $P \sin 30° + N - W = 0$

$\therefore N = W - P \sin 30° = 1536.9 - 442.4 \sin 30° = 1315.7$ lb

$\Sigma F_x = 0$: $\overset{+}{\rightarrow}$ $P \cos 30° - F = 0 \quad \therefore F = P \cos 30° = 442.4 \cos 30° = 383.1$ lb

$$\therefore \mu_s = \frac{F}{N} = \frac{383.1}{1315.7} = 0.291 \ ◆$$

(b) Assume impending tipping.

Partially filled tank: $W = \gamma(\pi R^2 h) = 62.4\pi(1.4)^2 h = 384.2h$

$\Sigma M_A = 0$: (+) $WR - (P \cos 30°)L - (P \sin 30°)(2R) = 0$

$\therefore (384.2h)(1.4) - 200 \cos 30° (4) - 200 \sin 30° (2.8) = 0 \quad \therefore h = 1.809$ ft ◆

7.36

Assume simultaneous impending sliding and tipping about A.

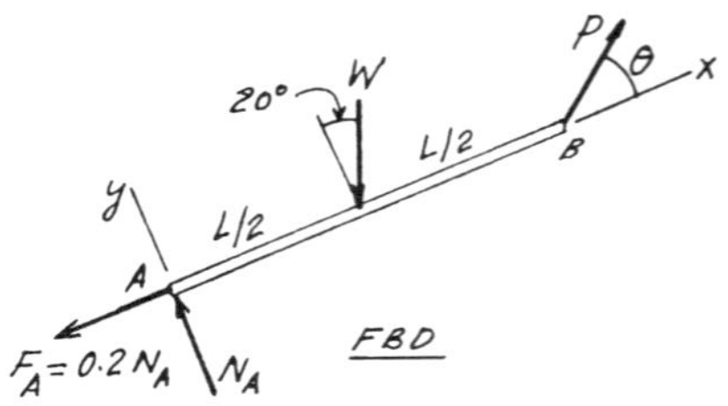

(continued)

7.36 continued

$\Sigma F_x = 0$: $+\nearrow$ $P\cos\theta - 0.2N_A - W\sin 20° = 0$ . . . . (a)

$\Sigma F_y = 0$: $+\nwarrow$ $N_A + P\sin\theta - W\cos 20° = 0$ . . . . . . (b)

$\Sigma M_A = 0$ (+) $(P\sin\theta)L - (W\cos 20°)(L/2) = 0$ . . . (c)

Eliminating $P\sin\theta$ from Eqs. (b)-(c) yields $N_A = \frac{W}{2}\cos 20°$ . . . (d)

Substituting Eq. (d) in Eq. (b), we get $P = \frac{W}{2}\frac{\cos 20°}{\sin\theta}$ . . . .(e)

Substitution of Eqs. (d) and (e) in Eq. (a) results in

$$\frac{W}{2}\frac{\cos 20°}{\tan\theta} - 0.2\left(\frac{W}{2}\cos 20°\right) - W\sin 20° = 0$$

$$\therefore \tan\theta = \frac{0.5\cos 20°}{0.1\cos 20° + \sin 20°} = 1.0777 \qquad \therefore \theta = 47.1° \ \blacklozenge$$

7.37

Assume equilibrium.

From the FBD of the ladder

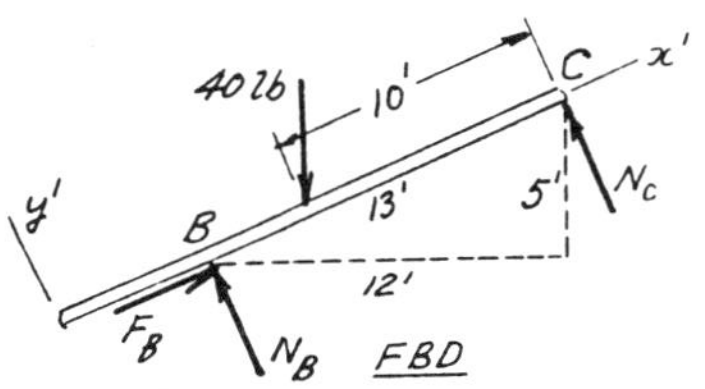

$\Sigma M_C = 0$: (+) $40\frac{12}{13}(10) - 13N_B = 0$

$\therefore N_B = 28.40$ lb

$\Sigma F_{x'} = 0$: $+\nearrow$ $F_B - 40\frac{5}{13} = 0$

$\therefore F_B = 15.385$ lb

$\frac{F_B}{N_B} = \frac{15.385}{28.40} = 0.542 < 0.6$ $\therefore$ Ladder does not slide on the block

(continued)

7.37 continued

From the FBD of the block

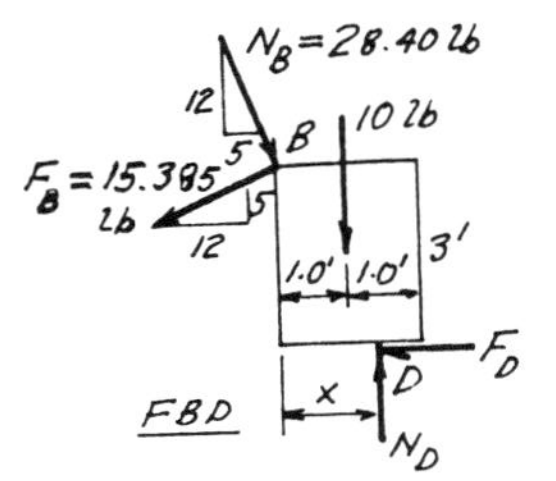

$\Sigma F_x = 0$: $\overset{+}{\rightarrow}$ $-15.385\frac{12}{13} + 28.40\frac{5}{13} - F_D = 0$

$\therefore F_D = -3.28$ lb

$\Sigma F_y = 0$: $+\uparrow$ $N_D - 15.385\frac{5}{13} - 28.40\frac{12}{13} - 10 = 0$

$\therefore N_D = 42.13$ lb

$\left|\frac{F_D}{N_D}\right| = \frac{3.28}{42.13} = 0.078 < 0.1$ $\therefore$ The block does not slide on the ground

$\Sigma M_D = 0$:

$$(+)\ \left(28.40\frac{12}{13}\right)x - \left(28.40\frac{5}{13}\right)(3) + \left(15.385\frac{12}{13}\right)(3) + \left(15.385\frac{5}{13}\right)x + 10(x - 1.0) = 0$$

$\therefore 42.13x - 0.1646 = 0$ $\therefore x = 0.0039$ ft > 0 $\therefore$ The block does not tip

$\therefore$ The system is in equilibrium (but the block is close to tipping) ◆

7.38

Assume equilibrium.

From FBD of upper block

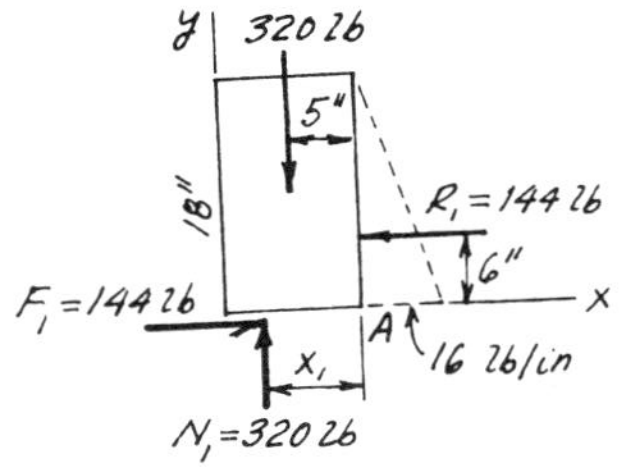

$R_1 = \frac{1}{2}(16)(18) = 144$ lb

$\Sigma F_x = 0$: $\overset{+}{\rightarrow}$ $F_1 - 144 = 0$ $\therefore F_1 = 144$ lb

$\Sigma F_y = 0$: $+\uparrow$ $N_1 - 320 = 0$ $\therefore N_1 = 320$ lb

$\frac{F_1}{N_1} = \frac{144}{320} = 0.450 < 0.5$ $\therefore$ Block does not slide

$\Sigma M_A = 0$: (+) $(320)(5) + (144)(6) - (320)x_1 = 0$

$\therefore x_1 = 7.70$ in < 10 in $\therefore$ Block does not tip

(continued)

7.38 continued

From FBD of both blocks

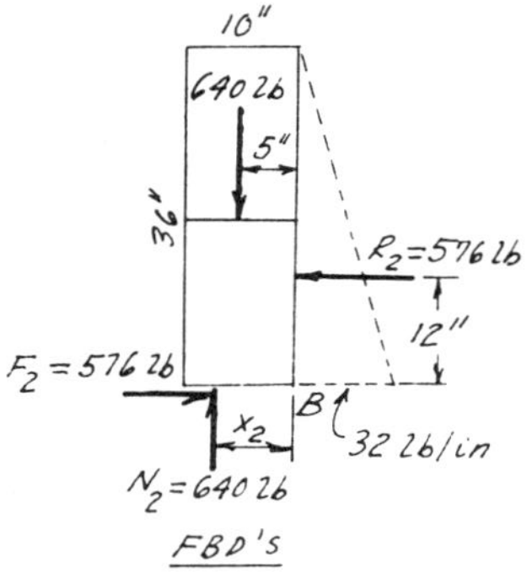

$$R_2 = \frac{1}{2}(32)(36) = 576 \text{ lb}$$

$\Sigma F_x = 0$: $\overset{+}{\rightarrow}$ $F_2 - 576 = 0$ $\quad \therefore F_2 = 576$ lb

$\Sigma F_y = 0$: $+\uparrow$ $N_2 - 640 = 0$ $\quad \therefore N_2 = 640$ lb

$\dfrac{F_2}{N_2} = \dfrac{576}{640} = 0.900 < 1.0$ $\quad \therefore$ Blocks do not slide

$\Sigma M_B = 0$: (+) $(640)(5) + (576)(12) - (640)x_2 = 0$

$\therefore x_2 = 15.8$ in > 10 in $\quad \therefore$ Blocks tip about corner B ◆

7.39

Assume impending sliding.

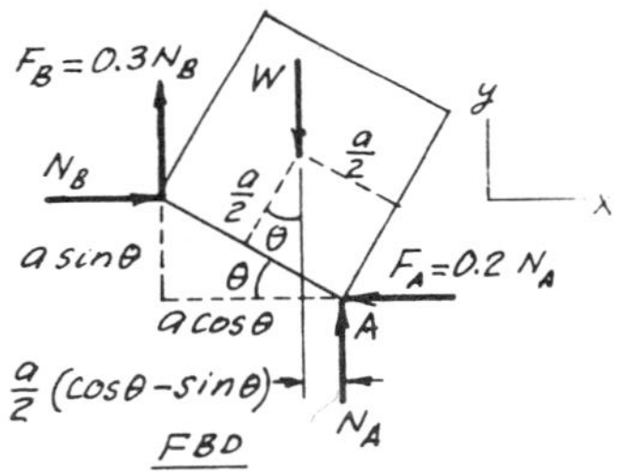

$\Sigma F_x = 0$: $\overset{+}{\rightarrow}$ $N_B - 0.2N_A = 0$

$\Sigma F_y = 0$: $+\uparrow$ $N_A + 0.3N_B - W = 0$

The solution is: $N_A = 0.9434W \quad N_B = 0.18868W$

$\Sigma M_A = 0$:

$$(+)\ (0.3N_B)(a\cos\theta) + N_B(a\sin\theta) - W\frac{a}{2}(\cos\theta - \sin\theta) = 0$$

$$\therefore \left[(0.3)(0.18868)\cos\theta + 0.18868\sin\theta - 0.5\cos\theta + 0.5\sin\theta\right]Wa = 0$$

$$\therefore -0.4434\cos\theta + 0.6887\sin\theta = 0 \qquad \therefore \theta = \tan^{-1}\frac{0.4434}{0.6887} = 32.8°$$

The above value of θ is the lower bound for equilibrium. The upper bound is $\theta = 45°$, determined by tipping about corner A.

$\therefore$ The block is in equilibrium if $32.8° \le \theta \le 45°$ ◆

7.40

The block may slide on the ground or tip. In either case, the pole slides on the block at B ($F_B = 0.2N_B$).

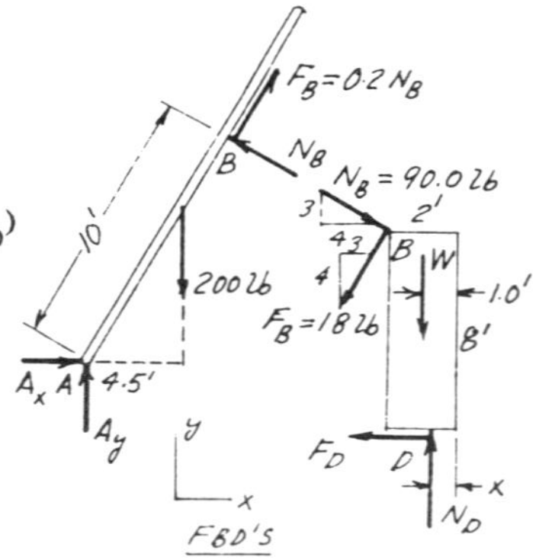

From FBD of the pole

$\Sigma M_A = 0$: (+) $10N_B - (200)(4.5) = 0$

$\therefore N_B = 90.0$ lb $\quad \therefore F_B = 0.2(90.0) = 18.0$ lb

Assume impending sliding of the block ($F_D = 0.2N_D$)

From FBD of the block

$\Sigma F_x = 0$: $\overset{+}{\rightarrow}$ $90.0\frac{4}{5} - 18.0\frac{3}{5} - 0.2N_D = 0$

$\Sigma F_y = 0$: $+\uparrow$ $N_D - 90.0\frac{3}{5} - 18.0\frac{4}{5} - W = 0$

The solution is $N_D = 306$ lb $\quad W = 238$ lb

Assume impending tipping of the block: $x = 0$

From FBD of the block

$$\Sigma M_D = 0: (+)\left(18.0\frac{3}{5}\right)(8) + \left(18.0\frac{4}{5}\right)(2) - \left(90.0\frac{4}{5}\right)(8) + \left(90.0\frac{3}{5}\right)(2) + W(1.0) = 0$$

$\therefore W = 353$ lb

$\therefore$ Smallest W required for equilibrium is $W = 353$ lb ◆

7.41

Geometry: $12(1 - \cos\theta) = 6 \qquad \therefore \theta = 60°$

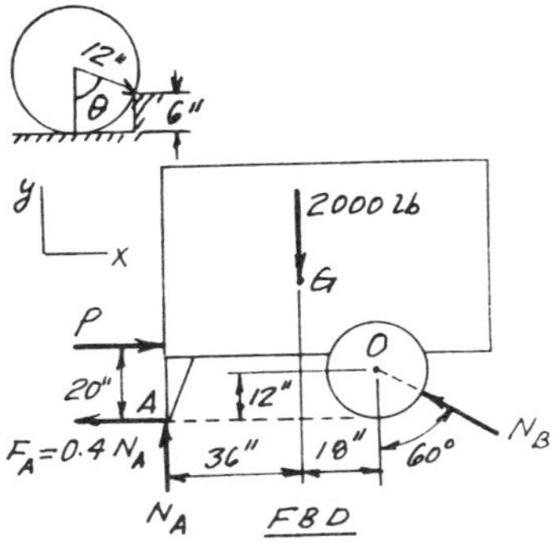

Assume impending sliding at A.

$\Sigma F_x = 0: \ \overset{+}{\rightarrow} \quad P - 0.4N_A - N_B \sin 60° = 0$

$\Sigma F_y = 0: \ +\uparrow \quad N_A + N_B \cos 60° - 2000 = 0$

$\Sigma M_O = 0:$ (+) $54N_A + 12(0.4N_A) + 8P$

$\qquad - (2000)(18) = 0$

The solution is:

$N_A = 172$ lb $\quad N_B = 3656$ lb $\quad P = 3235$ lb

Since $N_A > 0$, the trailer does not tip.

$\therefore$ Trailer can be pushed over the curb with P = 3235 lb ◆

7.42

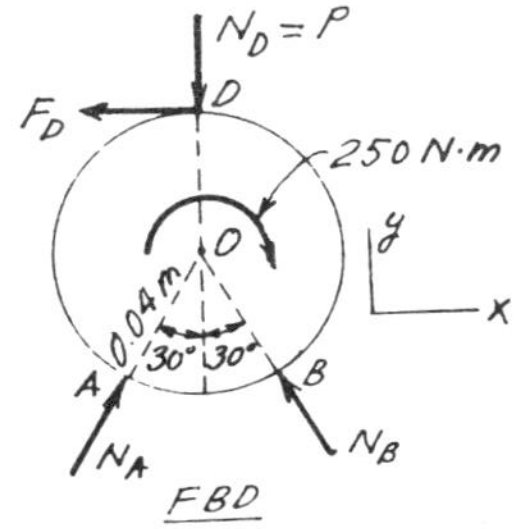

$\Sigma F_x = 0: \ \overset{+}{\rightarrow} \quad (N_A - N_B)\sin 30° - F_D = 0 \ldots$ (a)

$\Sigma F_y = 0: \ +\uparrow \quad (N_A + N_B)\cos 30° - P = 0 \ldots$ (b)

$\Sigma M_O = 0:$ (+) $0.04F_D - 250 = 0$

$\qquad \therefore F_D = 6250$ N $\ldots\ldots\ldots\ldots$ (c)

Assume impending slipping at D ($F_D = 1.6P$)

Equation (c) becomes $1.6P = 6250 \qquad \therefore P = 3910$ N

Assume impending rolling about D ($N_B = 0$)

From Eq. (a): $N_A \sin 30° - 6250 = 0 \qquad \therefore N_A = 12\,500$ N

From Eq. (b): $12\,500 \cos 30° - P = 0 \qquad \therefore P = 10\,830$ N

$\therefore$ The smallest force that prevents movement is P = 10.83 kN ◆

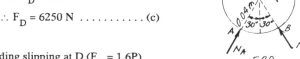

7.43

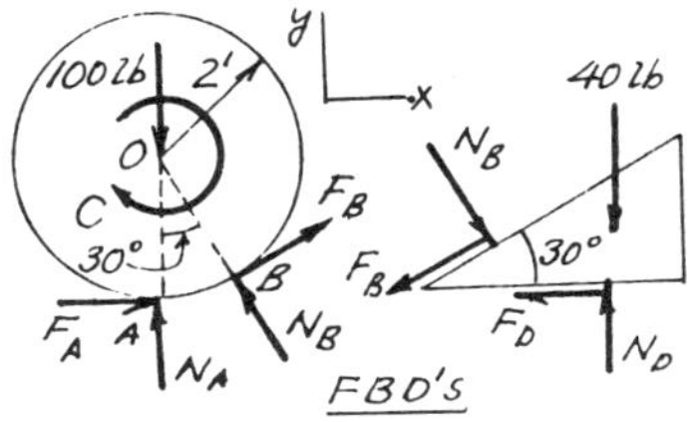

Assume cylinder rolls on wedge ($N_A = F_A = 0$)

From FBD of the cylinder

$\Sigma M_B = 0:$ (+) $(100)(2 \sin 30°) - C = 0$

$\therefore C = 100$ lb•ft

Assume cylinder rolls on surface & wedge slides

($F_B = 0.2N_B$, $F_D = 0.2N_D$)

From FBD of the wedge

$\Sigma F_x = 0: \ \overset{+}{\rightarrow} \quad N_B \sin 30° - 0.2N_B \cos 30° - 0.2N_D = 0 \ldots\ldots$ (a)

$\Sigma F_y = 0: \ +\uparrow \quad N_D - N_B \cos 30° - 0.2N_B \sin 30° - 40 = 0 \ldots$ (b)

From FBD of the cylinder

$\Sigma F_x = 0: \ \overset{+}{\rightarrow} \quad F_A - N_B \sin 30° + 0.2N_B \cos 30° = 0 \ldots\ldots\ldots$ (c)

$\Sigma M_O = 0$ (+) $(F_A + 0.2N_B)(2) - C = 0 \ldots\ldots\ldots\ldots\ldots\ldots$ (d)

The solution of Eqs. (a)-(d) is: $F_A = 19.57$ lb, $N_B = 59.88$ lb, $N_D = 97.84$ lb, C = 63.09 lb·ft

Assume cylinder slips & wedge remains stationary ($F_B = 0.2N_B \quad F_A = 0.2N_A$)

From FBD of cylinder

$\Sigma F_x = 0: \ \overset{+}{\rightarrow} \quad 0.2N_A + 0.2N_B \cos 30° - N_B \sin 30° = 0 \ldots\ldots$ (e)

$\Sigma F_y = 0: \ +\uparrow \quad N_A + N_B \cos 30° + 0.2N_B \sin 30° - 100 = 0 \ldots$ (f)

$\Sigma M_O = 0:$ (+) $(0.2N_A + 0.2N_B)(2) - C = 0 \ldots\ldots\ldots\ldots\ldots\ldots$ (g)

The solution of Eqs. (e)-(g) is: $N_A = 62.85$ lb $\quad N_B = 38.46$ lb $\quad C = 40.52$ lb·ft

The smallest couple that moves the cylinder is C = 40.5 lb•ft ◆

7.44

Assume impending slipping. Note that the bar is a 3-force body.

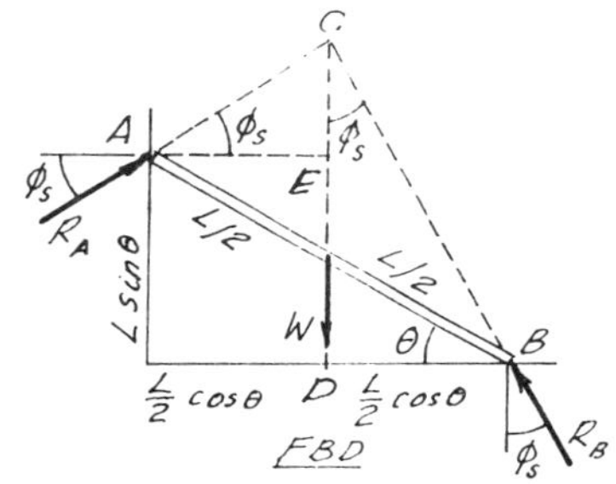

From geometry:

$$\overline{CD} = \overline{CE} + \overline{ED} = \frac{L}{2}\cos\theta\tan\phi_s + L\sin\theta \quad \text{(a)}$$

$$\overline{CD} = \frac{\overline{DB}}{\tan\phi_s} = \frac{L/2\cos\theta}{\tan\phi_s} \ldots\ldots\ldots\ldots\ldots \text{(b)}$$

Equating Eqs. (a) and (b):

$$\frac{1}{2}\cos\theta\tan\phi_s + \sin\theta = \frac{\cos\theta}{2\tan\phi_s} \qquad \therefore \sin\theta = \cos\theta\left(\frac{1}{2\tan\phi_s} - \frac{\tan\phi_s}{2}\right)$$

$$\therefore \tan\theta = \frac{1-\tan^2\phi_s}{2\tan\phi_s} = \frac{1-0.8^2}{2(0.8)} = 0.2250 \qquad \therefore \theta = 12.68° \ \blacklozenge$$

7.45

Assume impending slipping. Note that the bracket is a 3-force body with the forces intersecting at C.

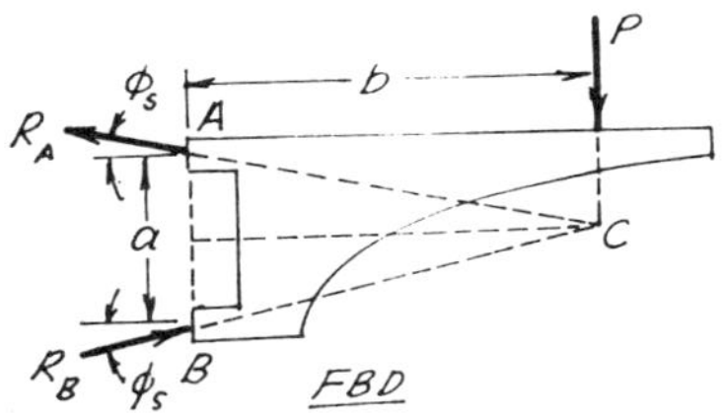

From geometry of triangle BAC:

$$\frac{a}{2} = b\tan\phi_s$$

$$\therefore \frac{b}{a} = \frac{1}{2\tan\phi_s} = \frac{1}{2(0.2)} = 2.5 \ \blacklozenge$$

7.46

Assume impending slipping. Note that the plank is a 3-force body with the forces intersecting at C.

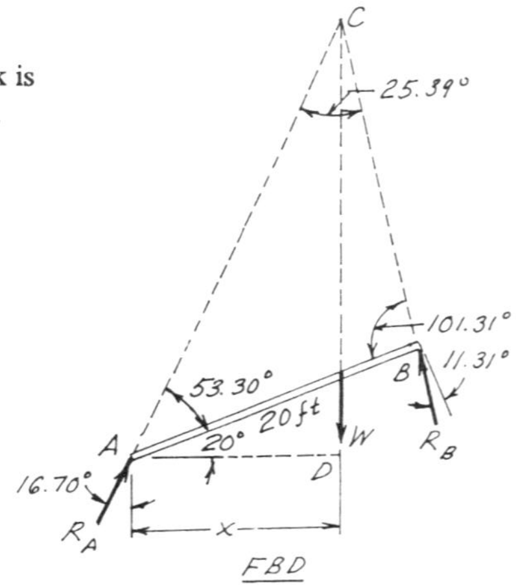

$$(\phi_s)_A = \tan^{-1} 0.3 = 16.70°$$

$$(\phi_s)_B = \tan^{-1} 0.2 = 11.31°$$

From triangle ACB: $\dfrac{20}{\sin 25.39°} = \dfrac{\overline{AC}}{\sin 101.31°}$

$\therefore \overline{AC} = 45.74$ ft

From triangle ACD: $x = \overline{AC}\cos 73.30°$

$\therefore x = 45.74\cos 73.30° = 13.14$ ft $\blacklozenge$

7.47

Assume impending slipping. Note that the vehicle is a 3-force body with the forces intersecting at C.

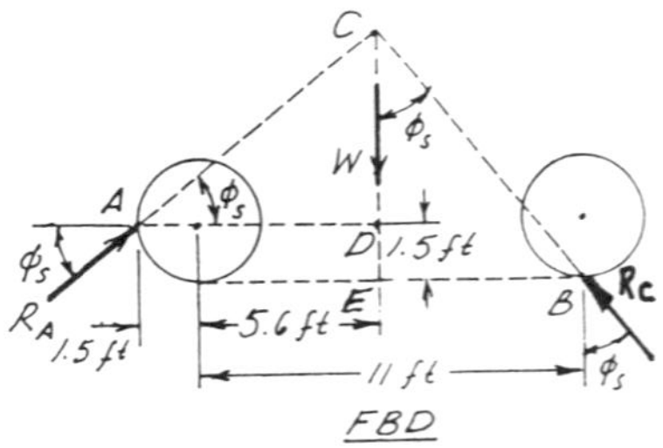

From triangle ACD:

$$\overline{CD} = (5.6 + 1.5)\tan\phi_s = 7.1\tan\phi_s \text{ ft}$$

From triangle CBE:

$$\tan\phi_s = \frac{\overline{EB}}{\overline{CD} + \overline{DE}} = \frac{11 - 5.6}{7.1\tan\phi_s + 1.5}$$

$$\therefore 7.1\tan^2\phi_s + 1.5\tan\phi_s - 5.4 = 0$$

The positive root is $\mu_s = \tan\phi_s = 0.773$ $\blacklozenge$

7.48

The hook is a three-force body, with the forces intersecting at C.

Assume impending sliding at A.

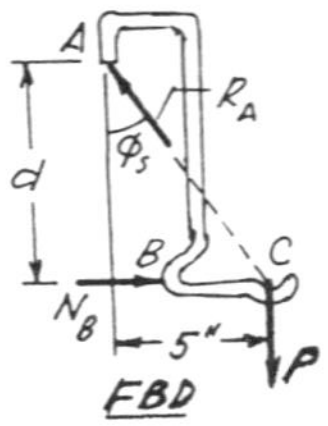

$$\tan\phi_s = \frac{5}{d}$$

$$\therefore d = \frac{5}{\tan\phi_s} = \frac{5}{0.6} = 8.33 \text{ in} \ \blacklozenge$$

7.49

The roller is a two-force body.

Assume impending sliding at B and C.

From geometry of the FBD:

$$\phi_s = \frac{\theta}{2}$$

$$\therefore\ \theta = 2\tan^{-1}\mu_s = 2\tan^{-1} 0.24 = 27.0° \ ♦$$

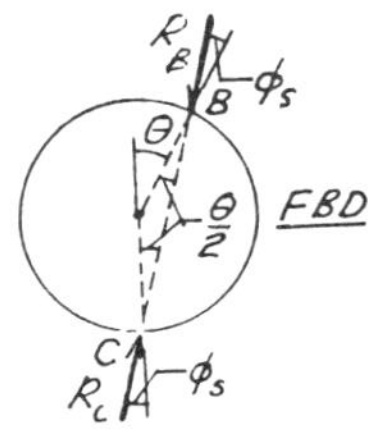

7.50

The wedge is a two-force body. Assuming impending sliding to the right, the geometry of the FBD yields

$$\theta = (\phi_s)_B + (\phi_s)_C = \tan^{-1} 0.12 + \tan^{-1} 0.2$$

$$= 6.84° + 11.31° = 18.15° \ ♦$$

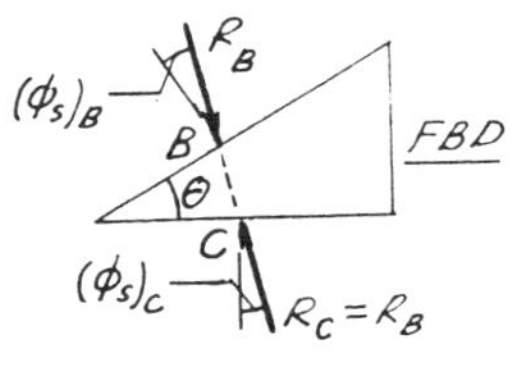

7.51

$$(\phi_s)_A = \tan^{-1} 0.12 = 6.84°$$

$$(\phi_s)_B = \tan^{-1} 0.2 = 11.31°$$

The wedge supports half the weight of the block. Thus the vertical component of R_B is

$$(2000)(9.81) = 19\,620 \text{ N}$$

(a) Assume impending sliding to the left.

From the force diagram

$$P = 19\,620(\tan 11.31° + \tan 21.84°)$$

$$= 11\,790 \text{ N} \leftarrow \ ♦$$

(b) Assume impending sliding to the right.

From the force diagram

$$P = 19\,620(\tan 11.31° - \tan 8.16°)$$

$$= 1110 \text{ N} \rightarrow \ ♦$$

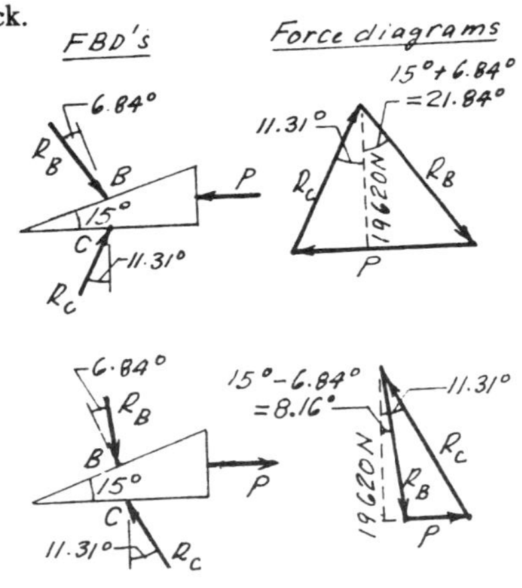

7.52

$$\phi_s = \tan^{-1} 0.3 = 16.70°$$

Assume impending slipping at A, the point of contact between the pulley and the shaft.

$\Sigma F_x = 0$: R must be vertical as shown

$\Sigma F_y = 0$: $+\uparrow$ $R - W - 10 = 0$

$\Sigma M_O = 0$: $+$ $4W - R(1.0 \sin 16.70°) = 0$

The solution is: $R = 10.774$ lb $W = 0.774$ lb ♦

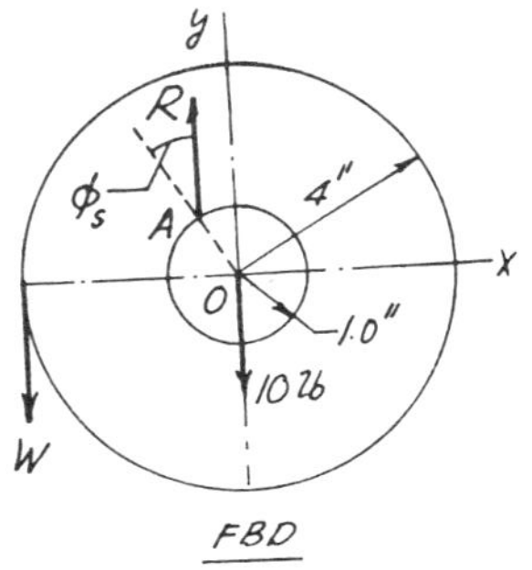

7.53

The collar is a three-force body, with the forces intersecting at C.

From the force diagram

$$\theta = \tan^{-1}\frac{150}{840} = 10.125°$$

From triangle ODC on the FBD

$$\frac{\sin(\pi - \phi_k)}{48} = \frac{\sin\theta}{10} \qquad \therefore\ \frac{\sin\phi_k}{48} = \frac{\sin 10.125°}{10}$$

$$\therefore\ \phi_k = 57.55° \qquad \therefore\ \mu_k = \tan 57.55° = 1.573 \ ♦$$

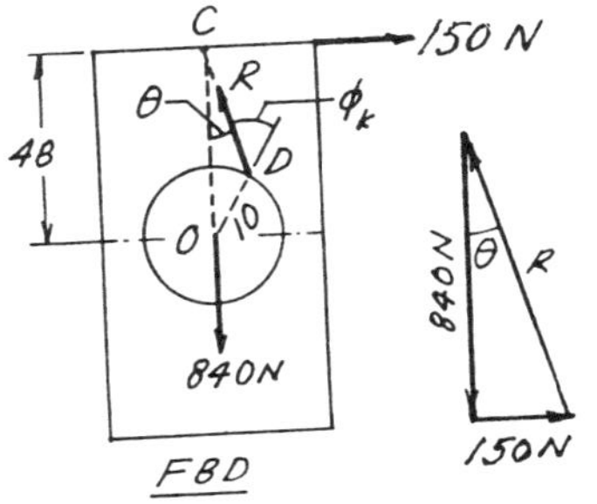

7.54

Assume impending sliding of end A up the incline.

From the FBD of the rod

$\Sigma M_z = 0$: $+$ $C_0 - \left[R_A \sin(\phi_s + \theta)\right]r = 0$

$\Sigma F_z = 0$: $+\uparrow$ $R_A \cos(\phi_s + \theta) - P = 0$

The solution is:

$$R_A = \frac{P}{\cos(\phi_s + \theta)} \qquad C_0 = Pr\tan(\phi_s + \theta) \ \text{Q.E.D.}$$

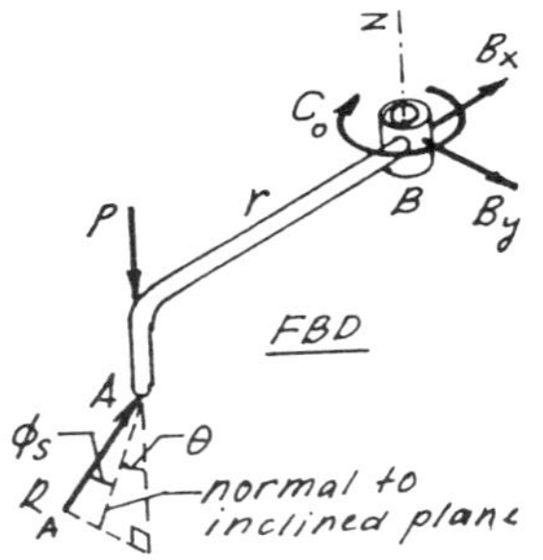

7.55

Assume impending advance:

Assume impending pullout:

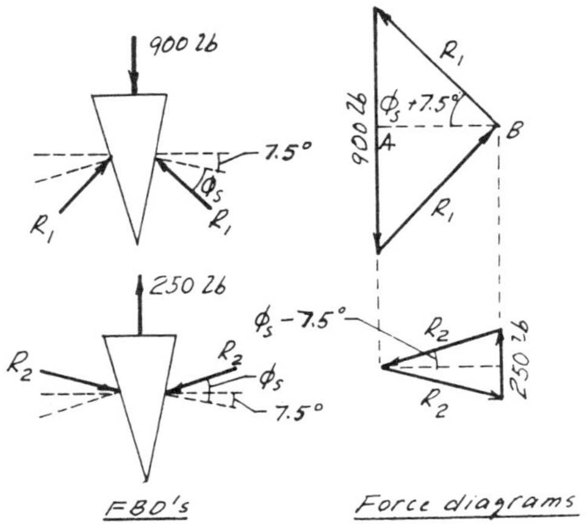

Since the horizontal component of R is the same in each case, we obtain from the force diagrams

$$\overline{AB} = \frac{900/2}{\tan(\phi_s + 7.5°)} = \frac{250/2}{\tan(\phi_s - 7.5°)} \qquad \therefore\ 3.6\tan(\phi_s - 7.5°) - \tan(\phi_s + 7.5°) = 0$$

Although the equation can be solved analytically, it is easiest to employ a numerical method (e.g. the secant method). There are two roots: $\phi_s = 0.2378$ and 1.3330 rad.

Choosing the smaller root: $\phi_s = 0.2378$ rad $\qquad \therefore\ \mu_s = \tan\phi_s = 0.242$ ◆

7.56

Given: $r = 0.0045$ m, $p = 0.0015$ m, $\mu_s = 0.2$

$\therefore$ The lead angle is $\theta = \tan^{-1}\dfrac{p}{2\pi r} = \tan^{-1}\dfrac{0.0015}{2\pi(0.0045)} = 3.037°$

$\therefore\ \phi_s = \tan^{-1}\mu_s = \tan^{-1}(0.2) = 11.310°$

(a) The clamping force F is found from $C = Fr\tan(\phi_s + \theta)$

$$\therefore\ F = \frac{C}{r\tan(\phi_s + \theta)} = \frac{1.25}{0.0045\tan(11.310° + 3.037°)} = 1086.0\text{ N} \ ◆$$

(b) The unclamping torque is

$$C' = FR\tan(\phi_s - \theta) = (1086.0)(0.0045)\tan(11.310° - 3.037°) = 0.711\text{ N·m} \ ◆$$

7.57

The lead angle is $\theta = \tan^{-1}\dfrac{p}{2\pi r} = \tan^{-1}\dfrac{10}{2\pi(18)} = 5.053°$

$\phi_k = \tan^{-1}\mu_k = \tan^{-1}0.06 = 3.434°$

The axial thrust W on the screw is found from $C_0 = Wr\tan(\phi_k + \theta)$. Note that the coefficient of <u>kinetic</u> friction is used, because sliding takes place.

$$\therefore\ W = \frac{C_0}{r\tan(\phi_k + \theta)} = \frac{10}{0.018\tan(3.434° + 5.053°)} = 3723\text{ N}$$

From FBD of the gear

$\Sigma M_O = 0$: (+↺) $(3723)(0.075) - C_1 = 0$

$\therefore\ C_1 = 279$ N·m ◆

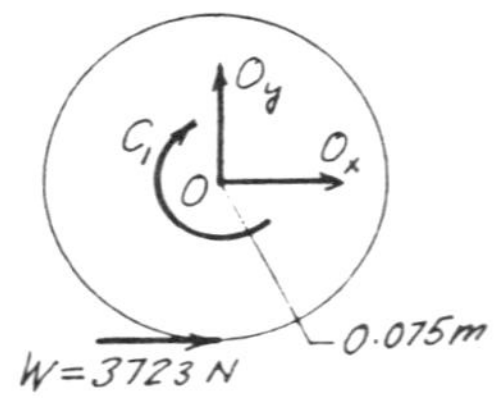

7.58

The lead angle is $\theta = \tan^{-1}\dfrac{p}{2\pi r} = \tan^{-1}\dfrac{0.1}{2\pi(0.175)} = 5.197°$

$\phi_s = \tan^{-1}\mu_s = \tan^{-1}0.08 = 4.574°$

(a) From the FBD of the strut AB (note that the strut is a two-force body, and that it supports half of the 1200 lb vertical load)

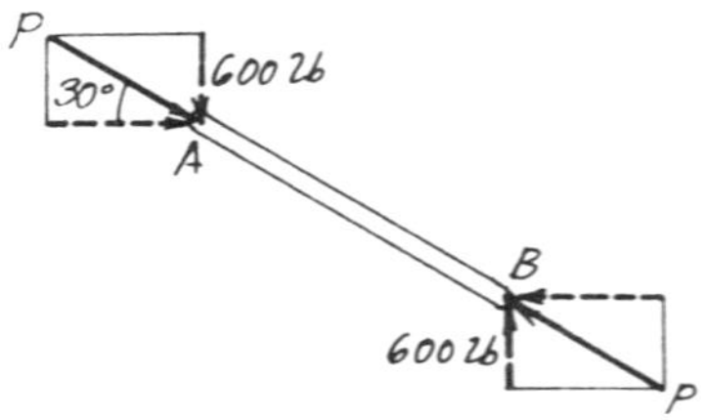

$$P = \frac{600}{\sin 30°} = 1200\text{ lb}$$

Due to symmetry, each strut carries the same axial force.

From the FBD of the collar

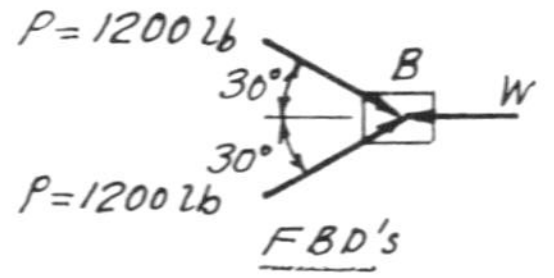

$\Sigma F_x = 0$ $\overset{+}{\rightarrow}$ $2(1200\cos 30°) - W = 0$

$\therefore\ W = 2078.5$ lb

Note that there are <u>two collars</u> that must be moved by C_0, so that

$$C_0 = 2Wr\tan(\phi_s + \theta) = 2(2078.5)(0.175)\tan(4.574° + 5.197°) = 125.3\text{ lb·in} \ ◆$$

(b) As $\theta > \phi_s$, the screw is not self-locking. Hence <u>no couple</u> is needed to lower the load ◆

7.59

$$\frac{T_2}{T_1} = e^{\mu_s \theta} \qquad \therefore \theta = \frac{1}{\mu_s} \ln \frac{T_2}{T_1} = \frac{1}{0.2} \ln \frac{9000}{60} = 25.05 \text{ rad}$$

$$\therefore n = \frac{\theta}{2\pi} = \frac{25.05}{2\pi} = 3.99 \text{ turns} \qquad \therefore \text{4 turns are required to hold the ship} \ \blacklozenge$$

7.60

Note that $T_2 > T_1$. $\therefore$ Use $T_2 = 3800$ lb

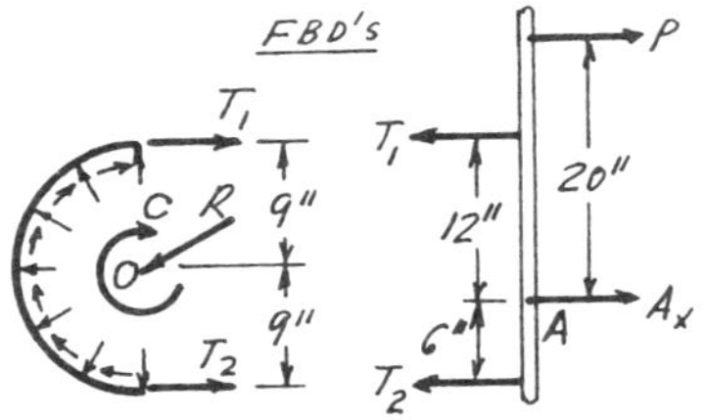

$$T_1 = T_2 e^{-\mu_s \theta} = 3800\, e^{-0.2\pi} = 2027 \text{ lb}$$

From FBD of the belt (R and C represent the resultant force-couple at O due to the distributed normal and friction forces):

$$\Sigma M_O = 0: (+) \ 9(T_2 - T_1) - C = 0$$

$$\therefore 9(3800 - 2027) - C = 0 \qquad \therefore C = 15\,960 \text{ lb·in} \ \blacklozenge$$

From FBD of the handle

$$\Sigma M_A = 0: (+) \ 12T_1 - 6T_2 - 20P = 0 \quad 12(2027) - 6(3800) - 20P = 0 \qquad \therefore P = 76.2 \text{ lb} \ \blacklozenge$$

7.61

Now $T_1 > T_2$. Therefore, use $T_1 = 3800$ lb.

Switching the roles of T_1 & T_2 results in $T_2 = T_1 e^{-\mu_s \theta} = 3800\, e^{-0.2\pi} = 2027$ lb

From FBD of the belt (see solution of Prob. 7.60):

$$\Sigma M_O = 0: (+) \ 9(T_2 - T_1) - C = 0 \quad \therefore 9(2027 - 3800) - C = 0 \quad \therefore C = -15\,960 \text{ lb·in} \ \blacklozenge$$

From FBD of the handle (see solution of Prob. 7.60):

$$\Sigma M_A = 0: (+) \ 12T_1 - 6T_2 - 20P = 0 \quad \therefore 12(3800) - 6(2027) - 20P = 0 \quad \therefore P = 1672 \text{ lb} \ \blacklozenge$$

7.62

Assume impending motion (block B down, block A up). $\therefore T_2 > T_1$

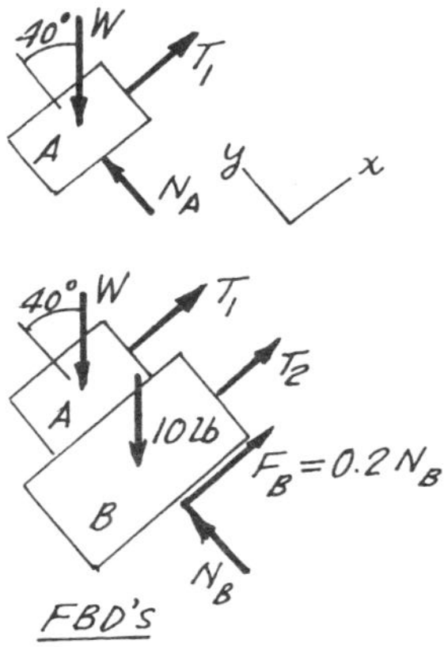

$$T_2 = T_1 e^{\mu\theta} = T_1 e^{0.2\pi} = 1.8745 T_1$$

From FBD of block A

$$\Sigma F_x = 0: \ + \ T_1 - W \sin 40° = 0$$

$$\therefore T_1 = 0.6428W$$

$$\therefore T_2 = 1.8745(0.6428W) = 1.2049W$$

From FBD of assembly

$$\Sigma F_y = 0: \ + \ N_B - (10 + W)\cos 40° = 0$$

$$\therefore N_B = 0.7660(10 + W) \text{ lb}$$

$$\therefore F_B = 0.2N_B = 0.15320(10 + W) \text{ lb}$$

$$\Sigma F_x = 0: \ + \ T_1 + T_2 + F_B - (10 + W)\sin 40° = 0$$

$$\therefore 0.6428W + 1.2049W + 0.15320(10 + W) - 0.6428(10 + W) = 0$$

$$\therefore 1.3581W - 4.896 = 0 \qquad \therefore W = 3.61 \text{ lb} \ \blacklozenge$$

7.63

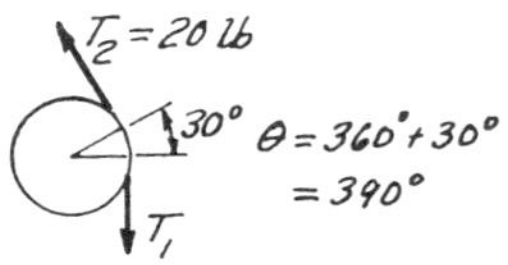

$$T_1 = T_2 e^{-\mu_s \theta} = 30\, e^{-(0.6)\frac{390\pi}{180}} = 0.5052 \text{ lb}$$

But T_1 is the weight of the free end of the rein.

$$\therefore T_1 = \frac{4}{16} L = 0.25L \text{ lb} \quad \therefore 0.5052 = 0.25L$$

$$\therefore L = 2.021 \text{ ft} = 24.2 \text{ in} \ \blacklozenge$$

7.64

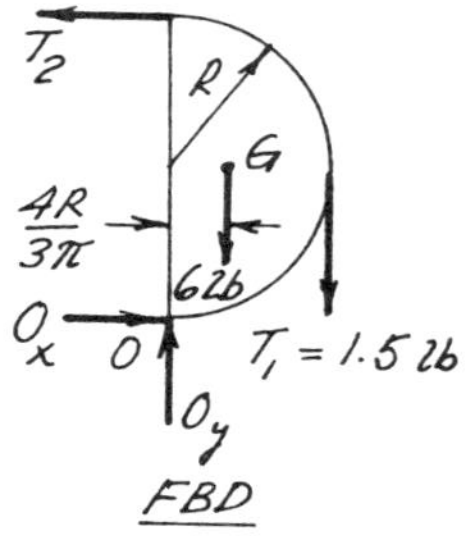

$$\Sigma M_O = 0: (+) \ T_2(2R) - 6\left(\frac{4R}{3\pi}\right) - 1.5R = 0$$

$$\therefore T_2 = 2.023 \text{ lb}$$

$$T_2 = T_1 e^{\mu_s \theta}$$

$$\therefore \mu_s = \frac{1}{\theta} \ln\left(\frac{T_2}{T_1}\right) = \frac{1}{\pi/2} \ln\left(\frac{2.023}{1.5}\right) = 0.190 \ \blacklozenge$$

7.65

$T_2 = T_1 e^{\mu_s \theta} = T_1 e^{0.5(\pi/2)} = 2.193 T_1$

$T_3 = T_2 e^{\mu_s \theta} = (2.193)^2 T_1 \quad \therefore T_1 = 0.2079 T_3$

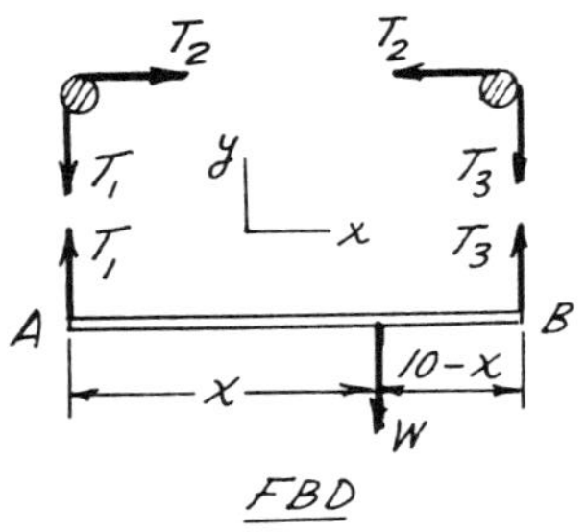

From FBD of rail

$\Sigma M_A = 0$: (+) $10T_3 - Wx = 0$

$\therefore T_3 = 0.1Wx \quad \therefore T_1 = 0.02079Wx$

$\Sigma F_y = 0$: $+\uparrow$ $T_1 + T_3 - W = 0$

$\therefore 0.02079Wx + 0.1Wx - W = 0$

$\therefore x = 8.28$ ft ◆

7.66

$T_2 = T_1 e^{\mu_s \theta} = T_1 e^{0.6\theta}$

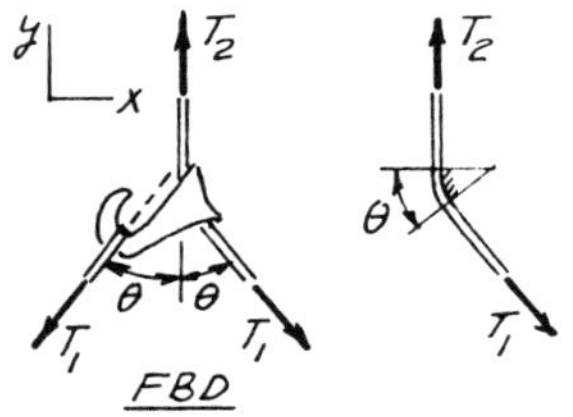

From the FBD

$\Sigma F_y = 0$: $+\uparrow$ $T_2 - 2T_1 \cos\theta = 0$

$\therefore T_1 e^{0.6\theta} - 2T_1 \cos\theta = 0$

$\therefore e^{0.6\theta} - 2\cos\theta = 0$

The solution, which must be obtained numerically, is:

$\theta = 0.7035$ rad $= 40.3°$ ◆

7.67

From the FBD (due to symmetry, the cable tensions are equal)

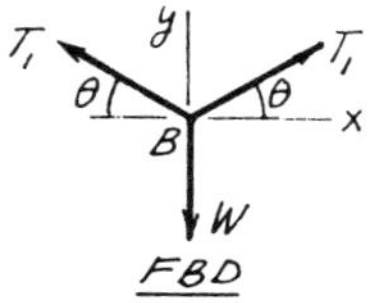

$\Sigma F_y = 0$: $+\uparrow$ $2T_1 \sin\theta = W \quad \therefore T_1 = \dfrac{W}{2\sin\theta}$

Assume impending motion of D down ($T_2 > T_1$).

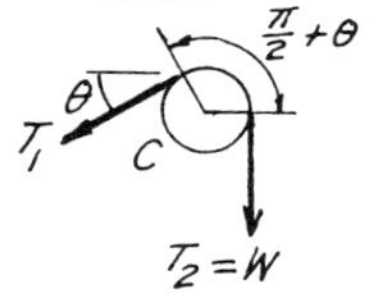

$\therefore T_2 = T_1 e^{\mu_s(\pi/2 + \theta)}$

$\therefore W = \dfrac{W}{2\sin\theta} e^{0.2(\pi/2+\theta)} \quad \therefore 1 - \dfrac{e^{0.2(\pi/2+\theta)}}{2\sin\theta} = 0$

This equation must be solved numerically.

(continued)

7.67 continued

The only positive root that is smaller than $\pi/2$ is

$\theta = 0.9858$ rad $= 56.5°$

Assume impending motion of D up ($T_1 > T_2$).

$\therefore T_1 = T_2 e^{\mu_s(\pi/2+\theta)} \quad \therefore \dfrac{W}{2\sin\theta} = We^{0.2(\pi/2+\theta)}$

$\therefore 1 - 2e^{0.2(\pi/2+\theta)} \sin\theta = 0$

Again, numerical analysis shows that the only positive root smaller than $\pi/2$ is

$\theta = 0.3476$ rad $= 19.9°$

$\therefore$ The equilibrium range of θ is: $19.9° \le \theta \le 56.5°$ ◆

7.68

(a) $\Sigma F_z = 0$: $+\uparrow$ $2N\sin(\beta/2) - P = 0$

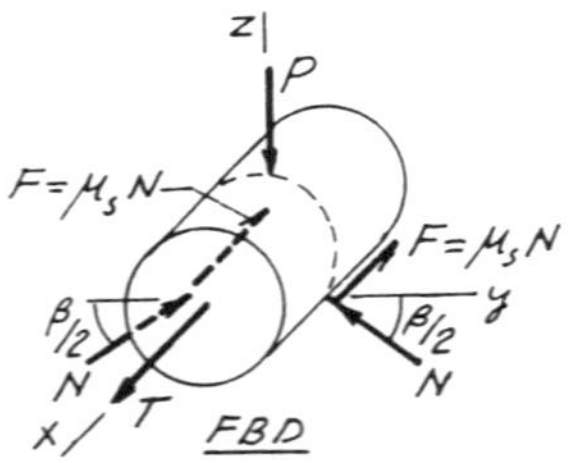

$\therefore N = \dfrac{P}{2\sin(\beta/2)}$

$\Sigma F_x = 0$: $T - 2\mu_s N = 0$

$\therefore T = 2\mu_s N = 2\mu_s \dfrac{P}{2\sin(\beta/2)} = \mu_s' P$

where $\mu_s' = \dfrac{\mu_s}{\sin(\beta/2)}$ ◆

(b) Refer to the derivation of Eq. (7.8) in the text. Instead of $dF = \mu_s\,dN$, substitute $dF = \mu_s' dN$ into Eq. (b). Since this step is the only place where μ_s entered the derivation of Eq. (7.8), all the equations arising in the derivation remain valid, provided that we replace μ_s by μ_s'. This also applies to Eq. (7.8), which now becomes

$T_2 = T_1 e^{\mu_s' \theta}$ Q.E.D. ◆

7.69

For uniform pressure (new surfaces), we have

$$C = \frac{2\mu_s P}{3}\left(\frac{R_o^3 - R_i^3}{R_o^2 - R_i^2}\right) = \frac{2(0.15)(400)}{3}\left(\frac{0.04^3 - 0.02^3}{0.04^2 - 0.02^2}\right) = 1.867 \text{ N·m}$$ ◆

7.70

The pressure distribution is linear: $p = A + Br$

$p = p_0$ at $r = 0$. $\therefore A = p_0$

$p = \frac{1}{2}p_0$ at $r = R$. $\therefore \frac{1}{2}p_0 = p_0 + BR$

$\therefore B = -\frac{p_0}{2R}$ $\therefore p = p_0\left(1 - \frac{r}{2R}\right)$

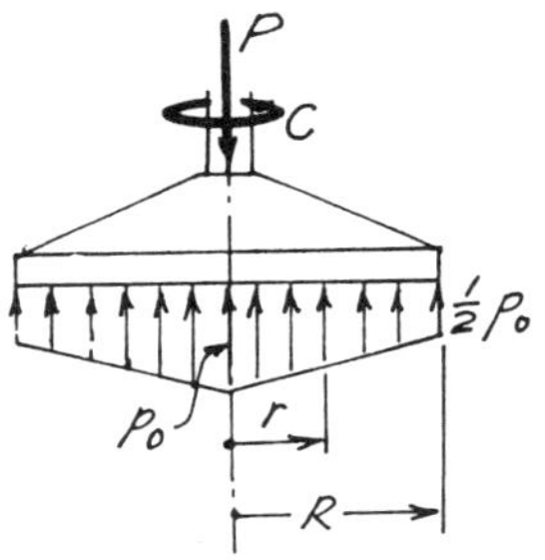

$$C = \mu_k \int_A pr\, dA = \mu_k p_0 \int_0^R \int_0^{2\pi} \left(1 - \frac{r}{2R}\right) r\, (r\, d\theta\, dr)$$

$$= 2\pi\, \mu_k p_0 \int_0^R \left(r^2 - \frac{r^3}{2R}\right) dr = 2\pi\, \mu_k p_0 \left(\frac{R^3}{3} - \frac{R^4}{8R}\right) = \frac{5\pi\, \mu_k p_0 R^3}{12}$$

$$P = \int_A p\, dA = p_0 \int_0^R \int_0^{2\pi} \left(1 - \frac{r}{2R}\right)(r\, d\theta\, dr) = 2\pi p_0 \int_0^R \left(r - \frac{r^2}{2R}\right) dr$$

$$= 2\pi p_0 \left(\frac{R^2}{2} - \frac{R^3}{6R}\right) = \frac{2\pi p_0 R^2}{3}$$

$$\therefore \frac{C}{P} = \frac{5}{8}\mu_k R \quad \therefore C = \frac{5}{8}\mu_k PR \ \blacklozenge$$

7.71

$\Sigma M_O = 0$: $(+)$ $C - (110)(1.4) = 0$

$\therefore C = 154.0$ lb·ft

Assuming unworn surfaces

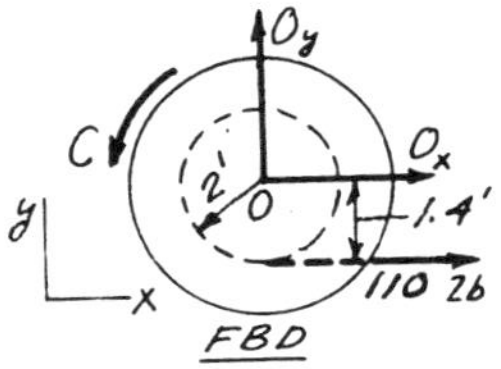

$$C = \frac{2}{3}\mu_s PR$$

$$\therefore \mu_s = \frac{3C}{2PR} = \frac{3(154.0)}{2(500)(1.4)} = 0.330 \ \blacklozenge$$

7.72

The equations for disk friction remain valid if the friction surface is a circular <u>sector</u> (the angle of the sector is irrelevant). Because there are two brake pads, the formula for the torque due to one pad must be doubled.

(a) New surfaces: $C = 2\frac{2\mu_k P}{3}\left(\frac{R_o^3 - R_i^3}{R_o^2 - R_i^2}\right) = 2\frac{2(0.9)(200)}{3}\left(\frac{0.02^3 - 0.012^3}{0.02^2 - 0.012^2}\right) = 6.01$ N·m $\blacklozenge$

(b) Worn surfaces: $C = 2\frac{\mu_k P}{2}(R_o + R_i) = 2\frac{(0.92)(200)}{2}(0.02 + 0.012) = 5.89$ N·m $\blacklozenge$

7.73

$$C = \mu_k \int_A pr\, dA = 0.86 \int_2^8 \int_0^{2\pi} \left(\frac{4}{3} + \frac{1}{6}r^2\right) r\, d\theta\, dr = 0.86(2\pi)\int_2^8 \left(\frac{4}{3}r + \frac{1}{6}r^3\right) dr$$

$$= 0.86(2\pi)\left[\frac{2}{3}r^2 + \frac{1}{24}r^4\right]_2^8 = 0.86(2\pi)(213.3 - 3.3) = 1135 \text{ lb•in} \ \blacklozenge$$

7.74

$$C = \mu_k \int_A pr\, dA = \mu_k \int_0^{0.05} \int_0^{2\pi} pr\, (r\, d\theta\, dr) = 2\pi\mu_k \int_0^{0.05} pr^2\, dr$$

Trapezoidal rule: $C \approx 2\pi\mu_k \frac{\Delta r}{2}\sum_i W_i p_i r_i^2 = 2\pi(0.2)\frac{0.01}{2}\sum_i W_i p_i r_i^2 = 0.006283 \sum_i W_i p_i r_i^2$

W	p (kN/m^2)	r (m)	Wpr^2
1	50	0.00	0.0000
2	51	0.01	0.0102
2	53	0.02	0.0424
2	60	0.03	0.1080
2	70	0.04	0.2240
1	86	0.05	0.2150
		Sum	0.5996

$\therefore C \approx 0.006283(0.5996) = 0.003767$ kN·m $\qquad \therefore C = 3.77$ N•m $\blacklozenge$

7.75

$$C = \frac{2}{3}\mu_s P \frac{R_o^3 - R_i^3}{R_o^2 - R_i^2} \qquad \therefore\ P = \frac{3C(R_o^2 - R_i^2)}{2\mu_s(R_o^3 - R_i^3)} = \frac{3(56 \times 12)(9^2 - 4^2)}{2(1.6)(9^3 - 4^3)} = 61.6\text{ lb} \ \blacklozenge$$

7.76

$$C = \frac{2}{3}\mu_s P \frac{R_o^3 - R_i^3}{R_o^2 - R_i^2} \qquad \therefore\ 120 \times 12 = \frac{2}{3}(1.6)(75)\frac{R_o^3 - 4^3}{R_o^2 - 4^2}$$

$$\therefore\ R_o^3 - 4^3 = \frac{3(120 \times 12)}{2(1.6)(75)}(R_o^2 - 4^2) \qquad \therefore\ R_o^3 - 4^3 = 18(R_o^2 - 4^2)$$

$$\therefore\ (R_o - 4)(R_o^2 + 4R_o + 4^2) = 18(R_o - 4)(R_o + 4)$$

After cancelling $(R_o - 4)$, we get $R_o^2 - 14R_o - 56 = 0$

The positive root is: $R_o = 17.25$ in ◆

7.77

Assume impending slipping.

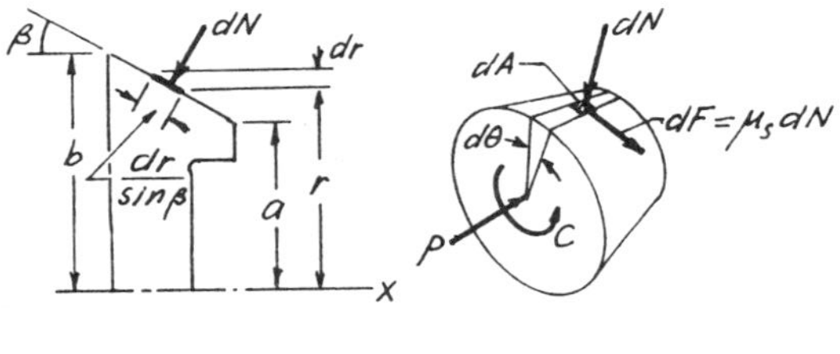

$$dN = p\,dA = p\frac{dr}{\sin\beta}(r\,d\theta)$$

$$\Sigma F_x = 0:\ P - \int_A \sin\beta\,dN = 0$$

$$\therefore\ P = \int_A \sin\beta\,dN$$

$$= p\int_a^b\int_0^{2\pi} r\,d\theta\,dr = 2\pi p\int_a^b r\,dr = \pi p(b^2 - a^2) \qquad \therefore\ p = \frac{P}{\pi(b^2 - a^2)} \ \ldots\ldots\ (a)$$

$$\Sigma M_x = 0:\ C - \int_A r(\mu_s dN) = 0$$

$$\therefore\ C = \mu_s\int_A r\,dN = \frac{\mu_s p}{\sin\beta}\int_a^b\int_0^{2\pi} r^2\,d\theta\,dr = \frac{2\pi\mu_s p}{\sin\beta}\int_a^b r^2\,dr = \frac{2\pi\mu_s p}{\sin\beta}\,\frac{b^3 - a^3}{3}$$

Substitute for p from Eq. (a): $C = \dfrac{2\mu_s P}{3\sin\beta}\,\dfrac{b^3 - a^3}{b^2 - a^2}$ ◆

7.78

Assume that the cylinder slides at B.

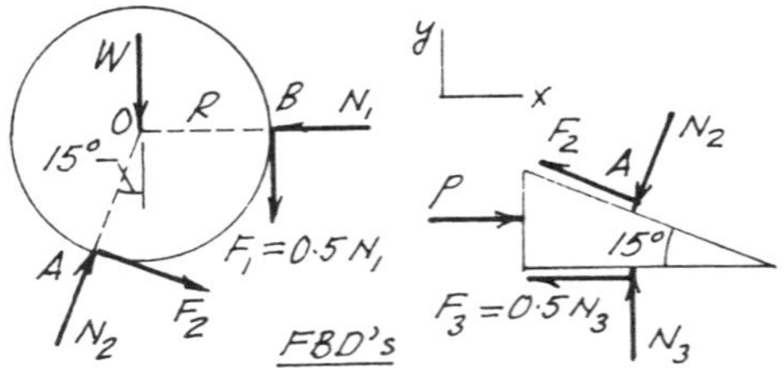

From FBD of the cylinder

$\Sigma M_A = 0$: (+) $N_1 R\cos 15° - 0.5N_1 R(1 + \sin 15°) - WR\sin 15° = 0 \qquad \therefore\ N_1 = 0.7691W$

$\Sigma M_O = 0$: (+) $F_2 R - 0.5N_1 R = 0 \qquad \therefore\ F_2 = 0.5N_1 = 0.5(0.7691W) = 0.3846W$

$\Sigma F_y = 0$: $+\uparrow$ $N_2\cos 15° - F_2\sin 15° - 0.5N_1 - W = 0$

$\therefore\ N_2\cos 15° - \left[0.3846\sin 15° + 0.5(0.7691) + 1\right]W = 0 \qquad \therefore\ N_2 = 1.5364W$

Check: $\dfrac{F_2}{N_2} = \dfrac{0.3846}{1.5364} = 0.250 < 0.5$ ∴ Cylinder will not slip at A

From FBD of the wedge

$\Sigma F_y = 0$: $+\uparrow$ $N_3 + F_2\sin 15° - N_2\cos 15° = 0$

$\therefore\ N_3 + (0.3846\sin 15° - 1.5364\cos 15°)W = 0 \qquad \therefore\ N_3 = 1.3845W$

$\Sigma F_x = 0$: $\overset{+}{\rightarrow}$ $P - 0.5N_3 - F_2\cos 15° - N_2\sin 15° = 0$

$\therefore\ P - \left[0.5(1.3845) + 0.3846\cos 15° + 1.5364\sin 15°\right]W = 0 \qquad \therefore\ P = 1.461W$ ◆

7.79

Assume impending sliding <u>up</u> the slope.

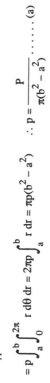

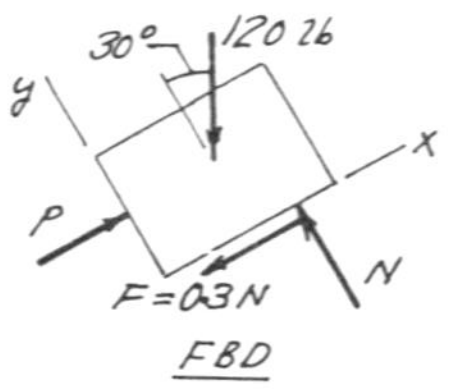

$\Sigma F_y = 0$: $\nwarrow +$ $N - 120\cos 30° = 0 \ldots\ldots\ldots$ (a)

$\therefore\ N = 103.92$ lb

$\Sigma F_x = 0$: $\nearrow +$ $P - 0.3N - 120\sin 30° = 0 \ldots$ (b)

$\therefore\ P - 0.3(103.92) - 120\sin 30° = 0$

$\therefore\ P = 91.18$ lb

(continued)

7.79 continued

Assume impending sliding <u>down</u> the slope.

Direction of F on the FBD must be reversed. Consequently, Eq. (a) is still valid, whereas Eq. (b) becomes

$\Sigma F_x = 0$: $+\nearrow$ $P + 0.3N - 120 \sin 30° = 0$

$\therefore P + 0.3(103.92) - 120 \sin 30° = 0 \qquad \therefore P = 28.82$ lb

$\therefore$ Block is in equilibrium if $28.8 \text{ lb} \le P \le 91.2 \text{ lb}$ ◆

7.80

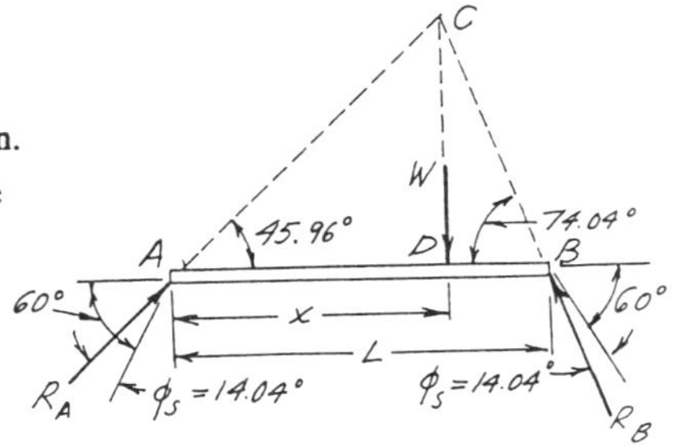

$\phi_s = \tan^{-1} 0.25 = 14.04°$

Assume that end A slides up and B slides down.

Note that the bar is a three-force body with the forces intersecting at C.

From triangle ACD: $\overline{CD} = x \tan 45.96°$

From triangle BCD: $\overline{CD} = (L - x)\tan 74.04°$

$\therefore x \tan 45.96° = (L - x)\tan 74.04°$

$\therefore \frac{x}{L} \tan 45.96° = \left(1 - \frac{x}{L}\right) \tan 74.04° \qquad \therefore \frac{x}{L} = \frac{\tan 74.04°}{\tan 45.96° + \tan 74.04°} = 0.772$ ◆

7.81

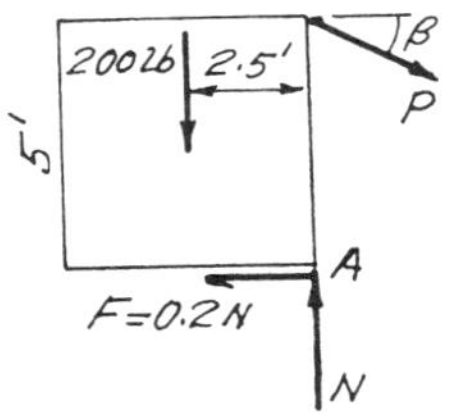

Assume simultaneous impending sliding and tipping.

$\Sigma M_A = 0$: $(+)$ $(200)(2.5) - 5(P \cos\beta) = 0$

$\therefore P \cos\beta = 100$ lb . . . . (a)

$\Sigma F_x = 0$: $\overset{+}{\rightarrow}$ $P \cos\beta - 0.2N = 0$

$\therefore 100 - 0.2N = 0 \qquad \therefore N = 500$ lb

$\Sigma F_y = 0$: $+\uparrow$ $N - P \sin\beta - 200 = 0$

Substitute $P = \frac{100}{\cos\beta}$ -- see Eq. (a)

$\therefore 500 - \frac{100}{\cos\beta} \sin\beta - 200 = 0 \qquad \therefore 300 - 100 \tan\beta = 0 \qquad \therefore \beta = 71.57°$ ◆

$\therefore P = \frac{100}{\cos 71.57°} = 316$ lb ◆

7.82

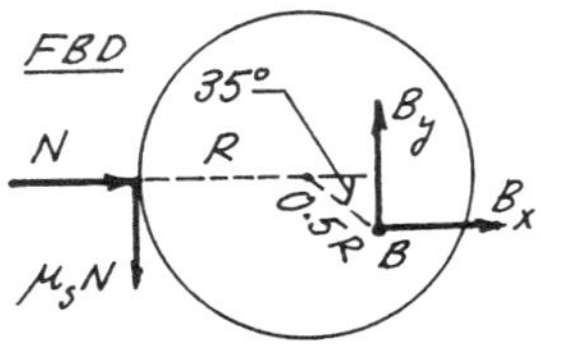

Assume impending slipping of the belt.

$\Sigma M_B = 0$:

$(+)$ $\mu_s N(R + 0.5R \cos 35°) - N(0.5R \sin 35°) = 0$

$\therefore \mu_s(1 + 0.5 \cos 35°) - 0.5 \sin 35° = 0$

$\therefore \mu_s = 0.203$ ◆

7.83

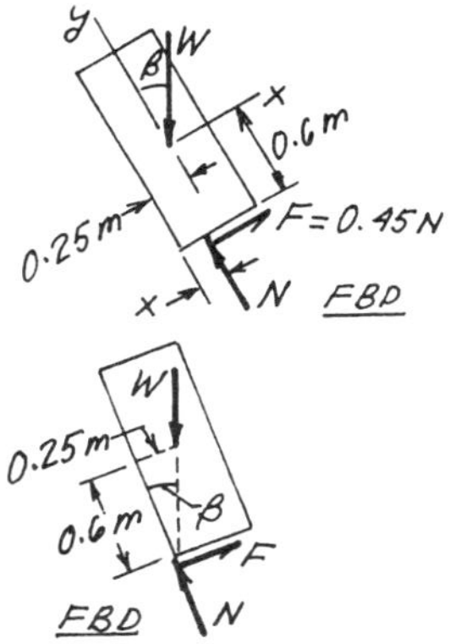

Assume impending sliding.

$\Sigma F_y = 0$: $+\nwarrow$ $N - W \cos\beta = 0 \qquad \therefore N = W \cos\beta$

$\Sigma F_x = 0$: $+\nearrow$ $0.45N - W \sin\beta = 0$

$\therefore 0.45W \cos\beta - W \sin\beta = 0 \qquad \therefore \beta = \tan^{-1} 0.45 = 24.22°$

Assume impending tipping.

$\beta = \tan^{-1} \frac{0.25}{0.6} = 22.62°$

$\therefore$ Largest possible angle for equilibrium is $\beta = 22.6°$ ◆

7.84

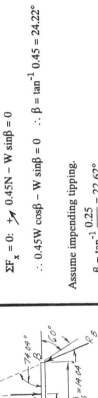

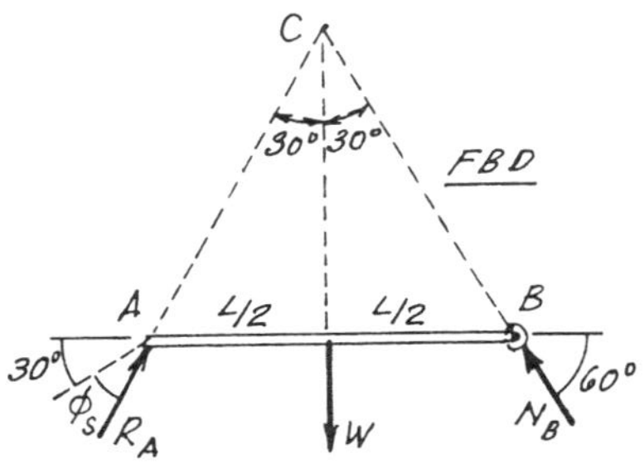

$\phi_s = \tan^{-1}\mu_s = \tan^{-1} 0.6 = 30.96°$

The bar is a three-force body, with the forces intersecting at C.

From geometry of the FBD: $\phi = 30°$

Since $\phi < \phi_s$ the bar is in equilibrium ◆

7.85

From FBD of the horizontal bar

$\Sigma M_C = 0$: (+) $(P_{AB}\cos 30°)L = P(2L)$

$\therefore P_{AB} = 2P/\cos 30°$

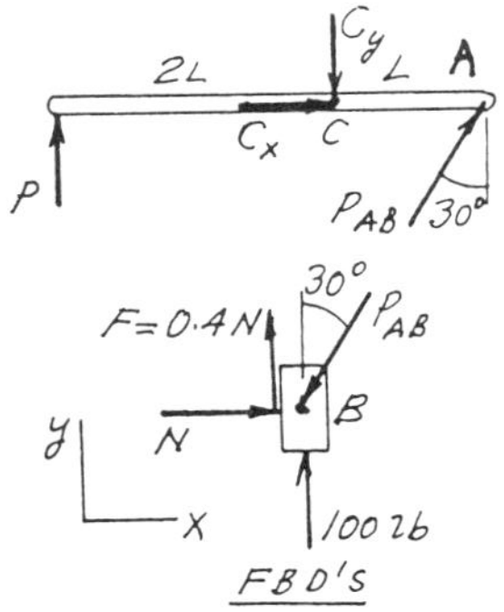

Assume impending motion of the slider <u>down</u>.

From the FBD of the slider

$\Sigma F_x = 0$: $\overset{+}{\rightarrow}$ $N - P_{AB}\sin 30° = 0$

$\therefore N = (2P/\cos 30°)\sin 30° = 2P\tan 30°$

$\Sigma F_y = 0$: $+\uparrow$ $100 + 0.4N - P_{AB}\cos 30° = 0$

$\therefore 100 + 0.4(2P\tan 30°) - 2P = 0 \quad \therefore P = 65.0\text{ lb}$ ◆

7.86

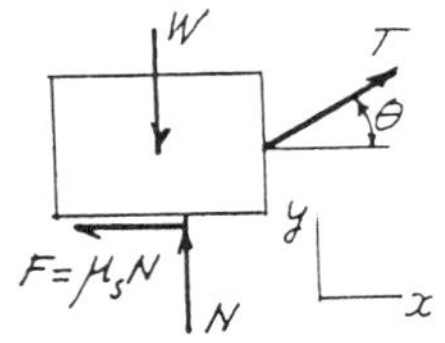

Assume impending sliding.

$\Sigma F_x = 0$: $\overset{+}{\rightarrow}$ $T\cos\theta - \mu_s N = 0$

$\Sigma F_y = 0$: $+\uparrow$ $T\sin\theta + N - W = 0$

The solution is: $N = \dfrac{W}{1 + \mu_s\tan\theta} \quad T = \dfrac{\mu_s W}{\cos\theta + \mu_s\sin\theta}$

T is minimized if $\cos\theta + \mu_s\sin\theta$ is maximized: $\dfrac{d}{d\theta}(\cos\theta + \mu_s\sin\theta) = 0$

$\therefore -\sin\theta + \mu_s\cos\theta = 0 \quad \therefore \theta = \tan^{-1}\mu_s$ ◆

$\therefore \sin\theta = \dfrac{\mu_s}{\sqrt{1+\mu_s^2}} \quad \therefore \cos\theta = \dfrac{1}{\sqrt{1+\mu_s^2}} \quad \therefore T = \dfrac{\mu_s W\sqrt{1+\mu_s^2}}{1+\mu_s^2} = \dfrac{\mu_s W}{\sqrt{1+\mu_s^2}}$ ◆

7.87

$p = 2\pi r\tan\theta$ (pitch of the screw) $\quad \therefore \theta = \tan^{-1}\dfrac{p}{2\pi r} = \tan^{-1}\dfrac{0.15}{2\pi(0.25)} = 5.455°$ (lead angle)

$\phi_s = \tan^{-1}\mu_s = \tan^{-1}(0.5) = 26.57°$

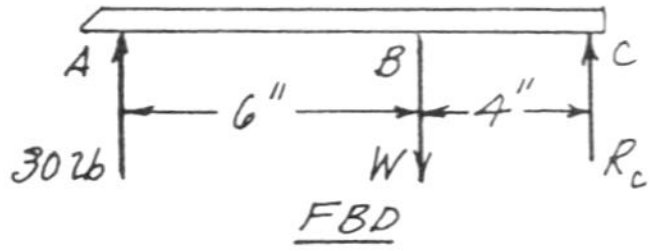

From FBD of member ABC

$\Sigma M_C = 0$: $+$ $4W - (30)(10) = 0$

$\therefore W = 75$ lb (axial thrust on the screw)

(a) $C_0 = Wr\tan(\phi_s + \theta) = (75)(0.25)\tan(26.57° + 5.45°) = 11.73\text{ lb}$ ◆

(b) $C_0 = Wr\tan(\phi_s - \theta) = (75)(0.25)\tan(26.57° - 5.45°) = 7.24\text{ lb}$ ◆

7.88

<u>Assume impending slipping at D and E</u> (cylinder rotates; block does not move)

From FBD of cylinder

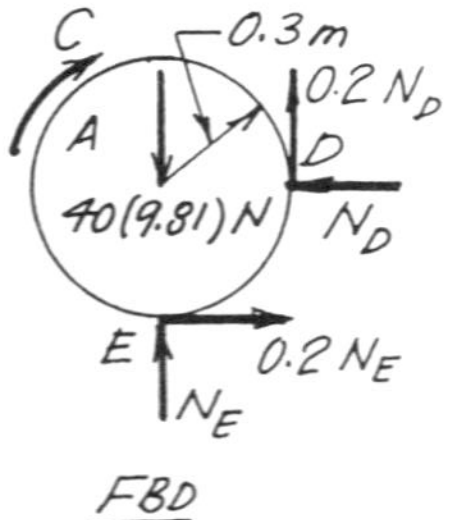

$\Sigma F_x = 0$: $\overset{+}{\rightarrow}$ $0.2N_E - N_D = 0$

$\Sigma F_y = 0$: $+\uparrow$ $N_E + 0.2N_D - (40)(9.81) = 0$

The solution is: $N_D = 75.46$ N, $N_E = 377.3$ N

$\Sigma M_D = 0$:

(+) $\left[0.2N_E - N_E + (40)(9.81)\right](0.3) - C = 0$

$\therefore C = 0.3\left[(40)(9.81) - 0.8N_E\right] = 0.3\left[392.4 - 0.8(377.3)\right] = 27.17\text{ N·m}$

<u>Check for slippage under the block</u>

From FBD of block

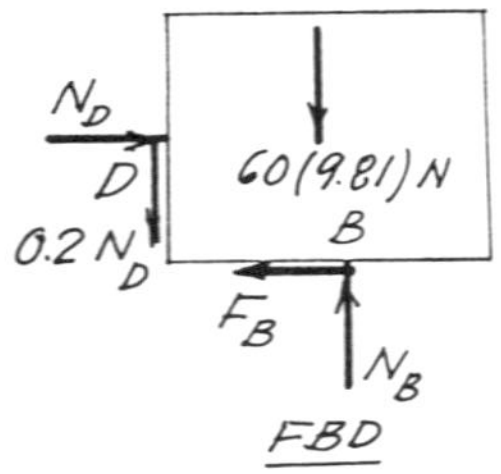

$\Sigma F_x = 0$: $\overset{+}{\rightarrow}$ $N_D - F_B = 0$

$\therefore F_B = N_D = 75.46$ N

$\Sigma F_y = 0$ $+\uparrow$ $N_B - 0.2N_D - (60)(9.81) = 0$

$\therefore N_B = 0.2N_D + (60)(9.81)$

$= 0.2(75.46) + (60)(9.81) = 603.7$ N

$\dfrac{F_B}{N_B} = \dfrac{75.46}{603.7} = 0.1250 < 0.2 \quad \therefore$ The block does not slip $\quad \therefore C = 27.2\text{ N·m}$ ◆

7.89

Assume impending sliding.

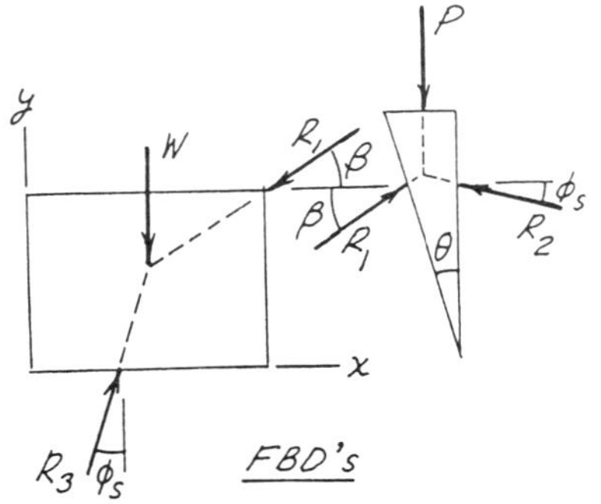

$\phi_s = \tan^{-1}\mu_s = \tan^{-1}(0.3) = 16.70°$

$\beta = \theta + \phi_s = 6° + 16.70° = 22.70°$

From FBD of the block

$\Sigma F_x = 0$: $\overset{+}{\rightarrow}$ $R_3 \sin\phi_s - R_1 \cos\beta = 0$

$\therefore R_3 \sin 16.70° - R_1 \cos 22.70° = 0$

$\Sigma F_y = 0$: $+\uparrow$ $R_3 \cos\phi_s - R_1 \sin\beta - W = 0$

$\therefore R_3 \cos 16.70° - R_1 \sin 22.70° - (200)(9.81) = 0$

The solution is: $R_1 = 729.6$ N, $R_3 = 2342$ N

From the FBD of the wedge

$\Sigma F_x = 0$: $\overset{+}{\rightarrow}$ $R_1 \cos\beta - R_2 \cos\phi_s = 0$ $\quad\therefore 729.6 \cos 22.70° - R_2 \cos 16.70° = 0$

$\Sigma F_y = 0$: $+\uparrow$ $R_1 \sin\beta + R_2 \sin\phi_s - P = 0$ $\quad\therefore 729.6 \sin 22.70° + R_2 \sin 16.70° - P = 0$

The solution is: $R_2 = 702.7$ N, $P = 483$ N ◆

7.90

Assume impending sliding downward.

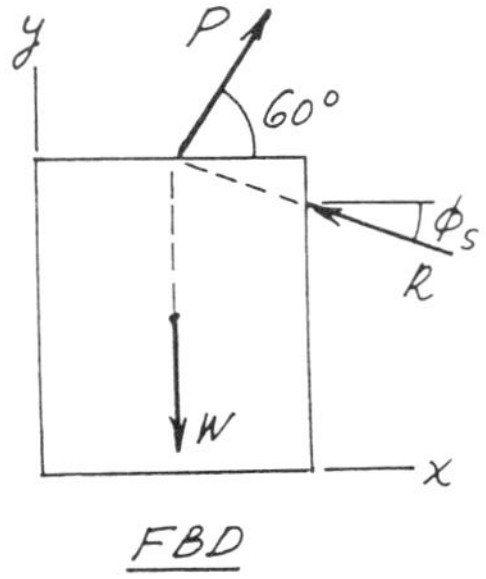

$\Sigma F_x = 0$: $\overset{+}{\rightarrow}$ $P \cos 60° - R \cos\phi_s = 0$

$$\therefore R = P \frac{\cos 60°}{\cos\phi_s}$$

$\Sigma F_y = 0$: $+\uparrow$ $P \sin 60° + R \sin\phi_s - W = 0$

$$\therefore P\left(\sin 60° + \frac{\cos 60°}{\cos\phi_s}\sin\phi_s\right) - W = 0$$

$$\therefore P = \frac{W}{\sin 60° + \mu_s \cos 60°} = \frac{12(9.81)}{\sin 60° + 0.24 \cos 60°} = 119.4 \text{ N} \;◆$$

8.1

We choose single integration

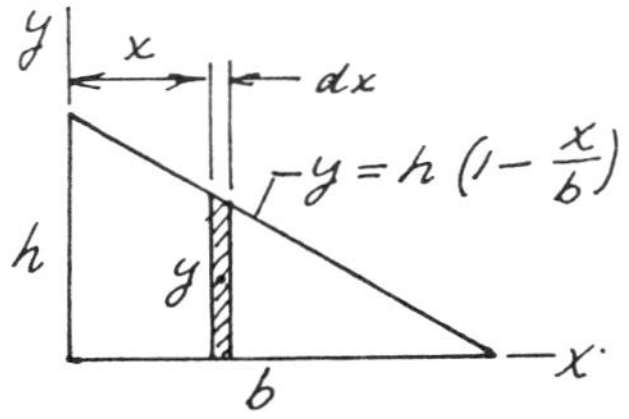

$$dA = y\,dx = h\left(1 - \frac{x}{b}\right)dx \qquad A = \frac{1}{2}bh$$

$$\bar{x}_{el} = x \qquad \bar{y}_{el} = \frac{y}{2} = \frac{h}{2}\left(1 - \frac{x}{b}\right)$$

$$Q_x = \int_A \bar{y}_{el}\,dA = \frac{h^2}{2}\int_0^b \left(1 - \frac{x}{b}\right)^2 dx$$

$$= \frac{h^2}{2}\left[x - \frac{x^2}{b} + \frac{x^3}{3b^2}\right]_0^b = \frac{bh^2}{6}$$

$$Q_y = \int_A \bar{x}_{el}\,dA = h\int_0^b x\left(1 - \frac{x}{b}\right)dx = h\left[\frac{x^2}{2} - \frac{x^3}{3b}\right]_0^b = \frac{b^2h}{6}$$

$$\therefore \bar{x} = \frac{Q_y}{A} = \frac{b^2h/6}{bh/2} = \frac{b}{3} \;◆ \qquad \therefore \bar{y} = \frac{Q_x}{A} = \frac{bh^2/6}{bh/2} = \frac{h}{3} \;◆$$

8.2

We choose single integration

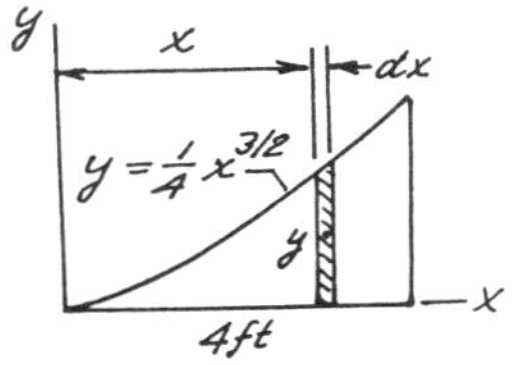

$$dA = y\,dx = \frac{1}{4}x^{3/2}dx \qquad \bar{x}_{el} = x \qquad \bar{y}_{el} = \frac{y}{2} = \frac{1}{8}x^{3/2}$$

$$A = \int_A dA = \frac{1}{4}\int_0^4 x^{3/2}dx = \frac{1}{4}\left[\frac{2}{5}x^{5/2}\right]_0^4 = \frac{16}{5}\text{ ft}^2$$

$$Q_x = \int_A \bar{y}_{el}\,dA = \frac{1}{32}\int_0^4 x^3 dx = \frac{1}{32}\left[\frac{x^4}{4}\right]_0^4 = 2\text{ ft}^3$$

$$Q_y = \int_A \bar{x}_{el}\,dA = \frac{1}{4}\int_0^4 x^{5/2}dx = \frac{1}{4}\left[\frac{2}{7}x^{7/2}\right]_0^4 = \frac{64}{7}\text{ ft}^3$$

$$\therefore \bar{x} = \frac{Q_y}{A} = \frac{64/7}{16/5} = \frac{20}{7} = 2.857\text{ ft} \;◆ \qquad \therefore \bar{y} = \frac{Q_x}{A} = \frac{2}{16/5} = \frac{5}{8} = 0.625\text{ ft} \;◆$$

8.3

We choose double integration

$dA = dx\,dy$

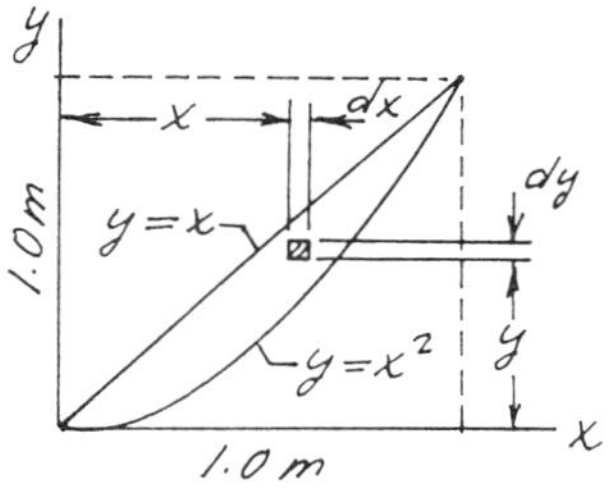

$$A = \int_A dA = \int_{x=0}^{1}\left(\int_{y=x^2}^{x} dy\right)dx = \int_0^1 \left[y\right]_{x^2}^{x} dx$$

$$= \int_0^1 (x - x^2)\,dx = \left[\frac{x^2}{2} - \frac{x^3}{3}\right]_0^1 = \frac{1}{6}\text{ m}^2$$

$$Q_x = \int_A y\,dA = \int_{x=0}^{1}\left(\int_{y=x^2}^{x} y\,dy\right)dx$$

$$= \int_0^1 \left[\frac{y^2}{2}\right]_{x^2}^{x} dx = \int_0^1 \frac{1}{2}(x^2 - x^4)\,dx = \frac{1}{2}\left[\frac{x^3}{3} - \frac{x^5}{5}\right]_0^1 = \frac{1}{15}\text{ m}^3$$

$$Q_y = \int_A x\,dA = \int_{x=0}^{1}\left(\int_{y=x^2}^{x} x\,dy\right)dx = \int_0^1 x\left[y\right]_{x^2}^{x} dx = \int_0^1 x(x - x^2)\,dx = \left[\frac{x^3}{3} - \frac{x^4}{4}\right]_0^1 = \frac{1}{12}\text{ m}^3$$

$\therefore\ \bar{x} = \dfrac{Q_y}{A} = \dfrac{1/12}{1/6} = 0.5\text{ m}$ ◆ $\qquad \therefore\ \bar{y} = \dfrac{Q_x}{A} = \dfrac{1/15}{1/6} = 0.4\text{ m}$ ◆

8.4

We choose double integration

$dA = dx\,dy$

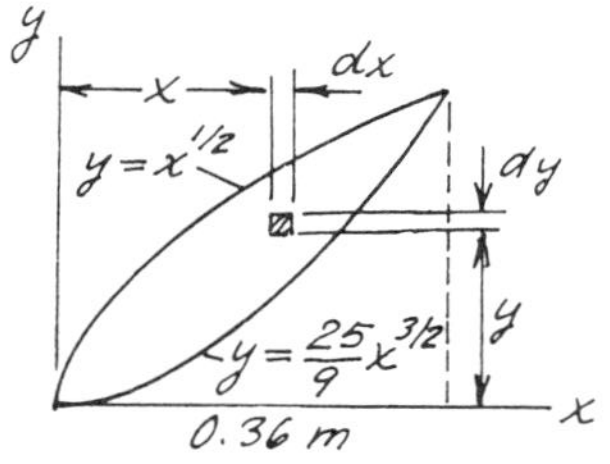

$$A = \int_A dA = \int_{x=0}^{0.36}\left(\int_{y=(25/9)x^{3/2}}^{x^{1/2}} dy\right)dx$$

$$= \int_0^{0.36} \left[y\right]_{(25/9)x^{3/2}}^{x^{1/2}} dx = \int_0^{0.36}\left(x^{1/2} - \frac{25}{9}x^{3/2}\right)dx$$

$$= \left[\frac{2}{3}x^{3/2} - \frac{25}{9}\frac{2}{5}x^{5/2}\right]_0^{0.36} = 0.05760\text{ m}^2$$

(continued)

8.4 continued

$$Q_x = \int_A y\,dA = \int_{x=0}^{0.36}\left(\int_{y=(25/9)x^{3/2}}^{x^{1/2}} y\,dy\right)dx = \int_0^{0.36}\left[\frac{y^2}{2}\right]_{(25/9)x^{3/2}}^{x^{1/2}} dx$$

$$= \int_0^{0.36} \frac{1}{2}\left[x - \left(\frac{25}{9}\right)^2 x^3\right]dx = \frac{1}{2}\left[\frac{x^2}{2} - \left(\frac{25}{9}\right)^2\frac{x^4}{4}\right]_0^{0.36} = 0.01620\text{ m}^3$$ ◆

$$Q_y = \int_A x\,dA = \int_{x=0}^{0.36}\left(\int_{y=(25/9)x^{3/2}}^{x^{1/2}} x\,dy\right)dx = \int_0^{0.36} x\left[y\right]_{(25/9)x^{3/2}}^{x^{1/2}} dx$$

$$= \int_0^{0.36}\left(x^{3/2} - \frac{25}{9}x^{5/2}\right)dx = \left[\frac{2}{5}x^{5/2} - \frac{25}{9}\frac{2}{7}x^{7/2}\right]_0^{0.36} = 0.008887\text{ m}^3$$

$\therefore\ \bar{x} = \dfrac{Q_y}{A} = \dfrac{0.008887}{0.05760} = 0.1543\text{ m}$ ◆ $\qquad \therefore\ \bar{y} = \dfrac{Q_x}{A} = \dfrac{0.01620}{0.05760} = 0.2813\text{ m}$ ◆

8.5

We choose single integration

$dA = x\,dy = y^{1/3}dy \qquad \bar{x}_{el} = \dfrac{x}{2} = \dfrac{1}{2}y^{1/3} \qquad \bar{y}_{el} = y$

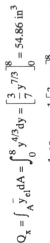

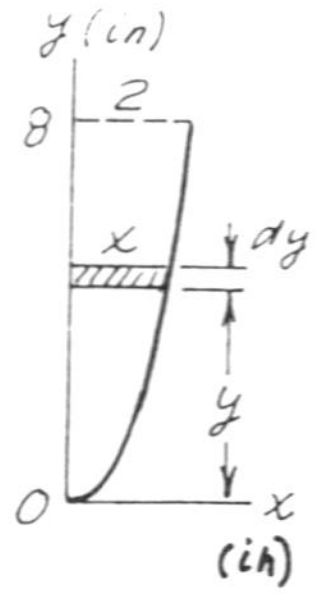

$$A = \int_A dA = \int_0^8 y^{1/3}dy = \left[\frac{3}{4}y^{4/3}\right]_0^8 = 12.0\text{ in}^2$$

$$Q_x = \int_A \bar{y}_{el}\,dA = \int_0^8 y^{4/3}dy = \left[\frac{3}{7}y^{7/3}\right]_0^8 = 54.86\text{ in}^3$$

$$Q_y = \int_A \bar{x}_{el}\,dA = \frac{1}{2}\int_0^8 y^{2/3} = \frac{1}{2}\left[\frac{3}{5}y^{5/3}\right]_0^8 = 9.60\text{ in}^3$$

$\therefore\ \bar{x} = \dfrac{Q_y}{A} = \dfrac{9.60}{12.0} = 0.80\text{ in}$ ◆ $\qquad \therefore\ \bar{y} = \dfrac{Q_x}{A} = \dfrac{54.86}{12.0} = 4.57\text{ in}$ ◆

8.6

We choose double integration

$dA = dx\,dy$

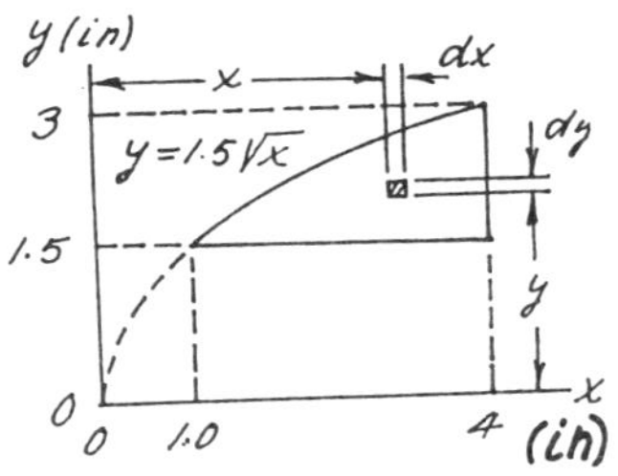

$$A = \int_A dA = \int_{x=1}^{4}\int_{y=1.5}^{1.5x^{1/2}} dx\,dy = \int_1^4 \Big[y\Big]_{1.5}^{1.5x^{1/2}} dx$$

$$= 1.5\int_1^4 (x^{1/2} - 1)dx = 1.5\left[\frac{2}{3}x^{3/2} - x\right]_1^4 = 2.50\text{ in}^2$$

$$Q_x = \int_A y\,dA = \int_{x=1}^{4}\int_{y=1.5}^{1.5x^{1/2}} y\,dx\,dy = \int_1^4 \left[\frac{1}{2}y^2\right]_{1.5}^{1.5x^{1/2}} dx$$

$$= \frac{1}{2}\int_1^4 (2.25x - 2.25)dx = \frac{1}{2}(2.25)\left[\frac{1}{2}x^2 - x\right]_1^4 = 5.0625\text{ in}^3$$

$$Q_y = \int_A x\,dA = \int_{x=1}^{4}\int_{y=1.5}^{1.5x^{1/2}} x\,dx\,dy = \int_1^4 x\Big[y\Big]_{1.5}^{1.5x^{1/2}} dx$$

$$= 1.5\int_1^4 (x^{3/2} - x)dx = 1.5\left[\frac{2}{5}x^{5/2} - \frac{1}{2}x^2\right]_1^4 = 7.35\text{ in}^3$$

$$\therefore\ \bar{x} = \frac{Q_y}{A} = \frac{7.35}{2.50} = 2.94\text{ in} \ \blacklozenge \qquad \therefore\ \bar{y} = \frac{Q_x}{A} = \frac{5.0625}{2.50} = 2.03\text{ in} \ \blacklozenge$$

8.7

(a) We choose single integration

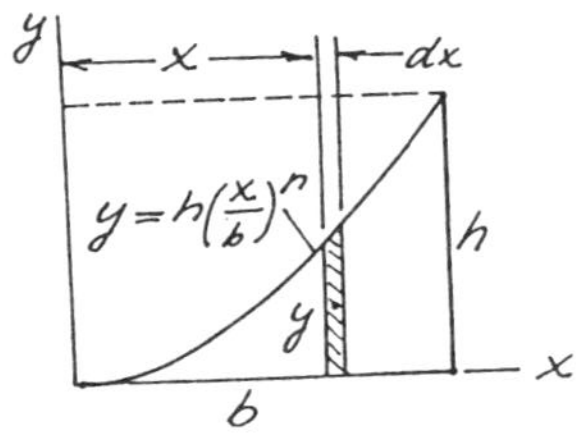

$$dA = y\,dx = h\left(\frac{x}{b}\right)^n dx$$

$$\bar{x}_{el} = x \qquad \bar{y}_{el} = \frac{y}{2} = \frac{h}{2}\left(\frac{x}{b}\right)^n$$

$$A = \int_A dA = \frac{h}{b^n}\int_0^b x^n\,dx = \frac{h}{b^n}\left[\frac{x^{n+1}}{n+1}\right]_0^b = \frac{bh}{n+1}$$

(continued)

8.7 continued

$$Q_x = \int_A \bar{y}_{el}\,dA = \frac{h^2}{2b^{2n}}\int_0^b x^{2n}\,dx = \frac{h^2}{2b^{2n}}\left[\frac{x^{2n+1}}{2n+1}\right]_0^b = \frac{bh^2}{2(2n+1)}$$

$$Q_y = \int_A \bar{x}_{el}\,dA = \frac{h}{b^n}\int_0^b x^{n+1}\,dx = \frac{h}{b^n}\left[\frac{x^{n+2}}{n+2}\right]_0^b = \frac{b^2h}{n+2}$$

$$\therefore\ \bar{x} = \frac{Q_y}{A} = \frac{b^2h/(n+2)}{bh/(n+1)} = \frac{n+1}{n+2}b \ \blacklozenge \qquad \therefore\ \bar{y} = \frac{Q_x}{A} = \frac{bh^2/[2(2n+1)]}{bh/(n+1)} = \frac{n+1}{2(2n+1)}h \ \blacklozenge$$

(b) When $n = 2$, the above formulas yield $\bar{x} = \frac{3}{4}b$, $\bar{y} = \frac{3}{10}h$, which agree with Table 8.1.

8.8

We choose single integration

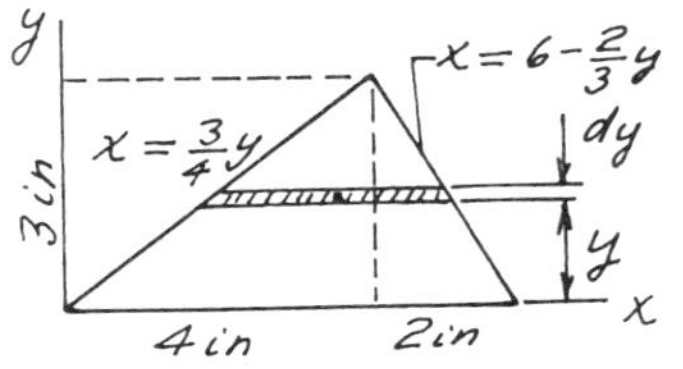

$$dA = \left[\left(6 - \frac{2}{3}y\right) - \frac{4}{3}y\right]dy = (6 - 2y)\,dy$$

$$\bar{x}_{el} = \frac{1}{2}\left[\left(6 - \frac{2}{3}y\right) + \frac{4}{3}y\right] = 3 + \frac{y}{3} \qquad \bar{y}_{el} = y$$

$$A = \frac{1}{2}(6)(3) = 9\text{ in}^2$$

$$Q_x = \int_A \bar{y}_{el}\,dA = \int_0^3 (6y - 2y^2)\,dy$$

$$= \left[6\frac{y^2}{2} - 2\frac{y^3}{3}\right]_0^3 = 9\text{ in}^3$$

$$Q_y = \int_A \bar{x}_{el}\,dA = \int_0^3 \left(3 + \frac{y}{3}\right)(6 - 2y)\,dy = \int_0^3 \left(18 - 4y - \frac{2}{3}y^2\right)dy$$

$$= \left[18y - 2y^2 - \frac{2}{9}y^3\right]_0^3 = 30\text{ in}^3$$

$$\therefore\ \bar{x} = \frac{Q_y}{A} = \frac{30}{9} = 3.33\text{ in} \ \blacklozenge \qquad \therefore\ \bar{y} = \frac{Q_x}{A} = \frac{9}{9} = 1.0\text{ in} \ \blacklozenge$$

<u>Check</u>: From Table 8.1 $\bar{x} = \frac{a+b}{3} = \frac{6+4}{3} = \frac{10}{3} = 3.33$ in $\quad \bar{y} = \frac{h}{3} = \frac{3}{3} = 1.0$ in O.K.

8.9

We choose single integration

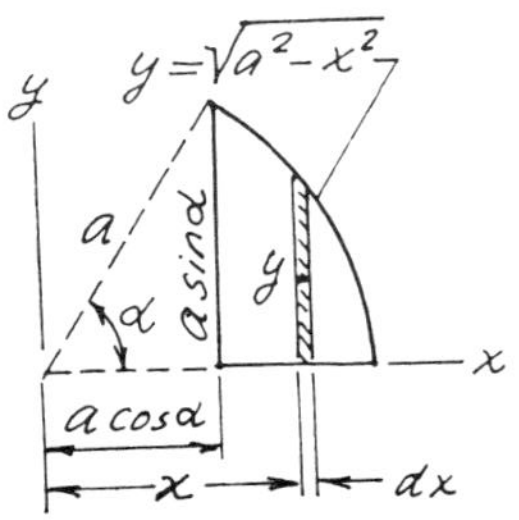

$dA = y\,dx = \sqrt{a^2 - x^2}\,dx$

$\bar{x}_{el} = x \qquad \bar{y}_{el} = \frac{y}{2} = \frac{1}{2}\sqrt{a^2 - x^2}$

$A = A_{sector} - A_{triangle} = \frac{\alpha a^2}{2} - \frac{(a\cos\alpha)(a\sin\alpha)}{2}$

$= \frac{a^2}{2}(\alpha - \sin\alpha\cos\alpha) = \frac{18^2}{2}\left(\frac{\pi}{4} - \sin 45° \cos 45°\right) = 46.23 \text{ in}^2$

$Q_x = \int_A \bar{y}_{el}\,dA = \frac{1}{2}\int_{a\cos\alpha}^{a}(a^2 - x^2)\,dx = \frac{1}{2}\left[a^2x - \frac{x^3}{3}\right]_{a\cos\alpha}^{a} = \frac{a^3}{2}\left[\left(1 - \frac{1}{3}\right) - \left(\cos\alpha - \frac{\cos^3\alpha}{3}\right)\right]$

$= \frac{a^3}{2}\left(\frac{2}{3} - \cos\alpha + \frac{\cos^3\alpha}{3}\right) = \frac{18^3}{2}\left(\frac{2}{3} - \cos 45° + \frac{\cos^3 45°}{3}\right) = 225.7 \text{ in}^3$

$\therefore \bar{y} = \frac{Q_x}{A} = \frac{225.7}{46.23} = 4.88 \text{ in}$ ◆

8.10

(a) We choose double integration

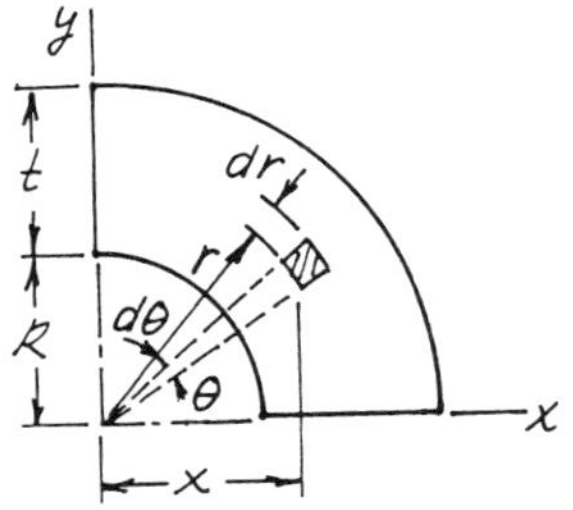

$dA = (dr)(r\,d\theta) \qquad x = r\cos\theta$

$A = \frac{\pi}{4}\left[(R + t)^2 - R^2\right] = \frac{\pi}{4}t(2R + t)$

$Q_y = \int_A x\,dA = \int_{r=R}^{R+t}\int_{\theta=0}^{\pi/2} r^2\cos\theta\,d\theta\,dr$

$= \int_R^{R+t} r^2\left[\sin\theta\right]_0^{\pi/2} dr = \left[\frac{r^3}{3}\right]_R^{R+t}$

$= \frac{1}{3}\left[(R + t)^3 - R^3\right] = \frac{t}{3}(3R^2 + 3Rt + t^2)$

$\therefore \bar{x} = \frac{Q_y}{A} = \frac{t(3R^2 + 3Rt + t^2)/3}{\pi t(2R + t)/4} = \frac{4}{3\pi}\frac{3R^2 + 3Rt + t^2}{2R + t}$ ◆ Due to symmetry $\bar{y} = \bar{x}$

(b) When $t \to 0$, then $\bar{x} \to \frac{2}{\pi}R$, which agrees with Table 8.2.

*8.11

We choose single integration.

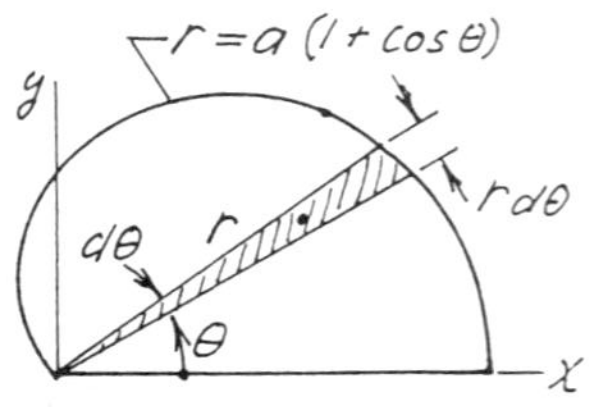

$dA = \frac{1}{2}r(r\,d\theta) = \frac{1}{2}a^2(1 + \cos\theta)^2\,d\theta$

$\bar{y}_{el} = \frac{2}{3}r\sin\theta = \frac{2}{3}a(1 + \cos\theta)\sin\theta$

$A = \int_A dA = \frac{1}{2}a^2\int_0^{\pi}(1 + \cos\theta)^2\,d\theta$

$= \frac{1}{2}a^2\int_0^{\pi}(1 + 2\cos\theta + \cos^2\theta)d\theta = \frac{1}{2}a^2\left(\pi + 0 + \frac{\pi}{2}\right) = \frac{3\pi}{4}a^2$

$Q_x = \int_A \bar{y}_{el}\,dA = \frac{1}{3}a^3\int_0^{\pi}(1 + \cos\theta)^3\sin\theta\,d\theta = \frac{1}{3}a^3\int_0^{\pi} d\left[-\frac{1}{4}(1 + \cos\theta)^4\right]$

$= -\frac{1}{12}a^3\left[(1 + \cos\theta)^4\right]_0^{\pi} = -\frac{1}{12}a^3(0 - 2^4) = \frac{4}{3}a^3$

$\therefore \bar{y} = \frac{Q_x}{A} = \frac{4a^3/3}{3\pi a^2/4} = \frac{16}{9\pi}a = 0.566\,a$ ◆

8.12

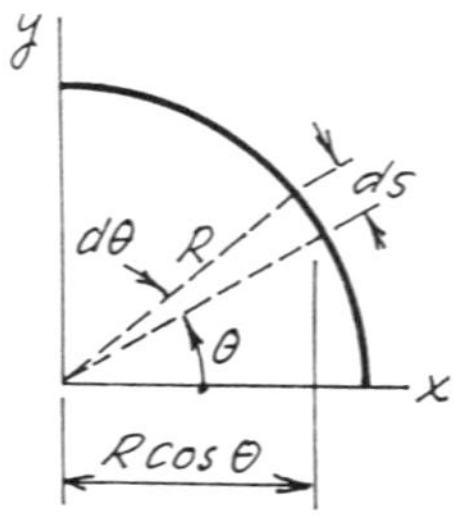

$ds = R\,d\theta \qquad L = \frac{\pi}{2}R \qquad x = R\cos\theta$

$Q_y = \int_L x\,ds = R^2\int_0^{\pi/2}\cos\theta\,d\theta = R^2\left[\sin\theta\right]_0^{\pi/2} = R^2$

$\therefore \bar{x} = \frac{Q_y}{L} = \frac{R^2}{\pi R/2} = \frac{2}{\pi}R$ ◆

Due to symmetry $\bar{y} = \bar{x}$

*8.13

$x = a(\theta - \sin\theta) \quad \therefore\ dx = a(1 - \cos\theta)d\theta$

$y = a(1 - \cos\theta) \quad \therefore\ dy = a \sin\theta\, d\theta$

$$ds = \sqrt{dx^2 + dy^2} = a\sqrt{(1-\cos\theta)^2 + \sin^2\theta}\, d\theta = a\sqrt{2(1-\cos\theta)}\, d\theta = 2a \sin\frac{\theta}{2}\, d\theta$$

$$L = \int_L ds = 2a\int_0^{2\pi} \sin\frac{\theta}{2}\, d\theta = 2a\left[-2\cos\frac{\theta}{2}\right]_0^{2\pi} = 8a$$

$$Q_x = \int_L y\, ds = 2a^2\int_0^{2\pi} (1-\cos\theta)\sin\frac{\theta}{2}\, d\theta = 2a^2\int_0^{2\pi}\left(2\sin^2\frac{\theta}{2}\right)\sin\frac{\theta}{2}\, d\theta = 4a^2\int_0^{2\pi}\sin^3\frac{\theta}{2}\, d\theta$$

Let $\varphi = \frac{\theta}{2} \quad \therefore\ d\theta = 2\, d\varphi$

$$\therefore\ Q_x = 8a^2\int_0^{\pi}\sin^3\varphi\, d\varphi = 8a^2\left(\frac{4}{3}\right) = \frac{32}{3}a^2$$

$\therefore\ \bar{y} = \frac{Q_x}{L} = \frac{32a^2/3}{8a} = \frac{4}{3}a$ ◆ By symmetry $\bar{x} = \pi a$ ◆

8.14

$A_1 = \frac{\pi R^2}{2} = \frac{\pi(5)^2}{2} = 39.27\ \text{in}^2$

$\bar{x}_1 = \frac{4R}{3\pi} = \frac{4(5)}{3\pi} = 2.122\ \text{in}$

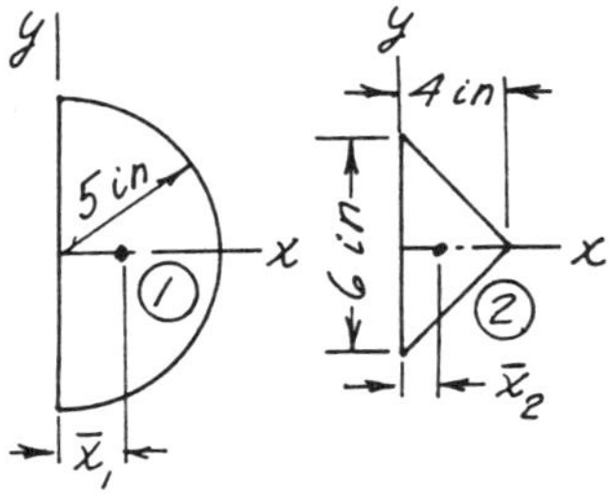

Part	A (in^2)	$\bar{x}$ (in)	$A\bar{x}$ (in^3)
1	39.27	2.122	83.33
2	−12.00	1.333	−16.00
Sum	27.27		67.33

$\therefore\ \bar{x} = \frac{67.33}{27.27} = 2.47\ \text{in}$ ◆ Due to symmetry $\bar{y} = 0$ ◆

8.15

$A_1 = (80)(50) = 4000\ \text{mm}^2 \quad A_2 = \frac{\pi(40)^2}{2} = 2513\ \text{mm}^2 \quad A_3 = -\pi(15)^2 = -707\ \text{mm}^2$

$\bar{y}_2 = 50 + \frac{4(40)}{3\pi} = 66.98\ \text{mm}$

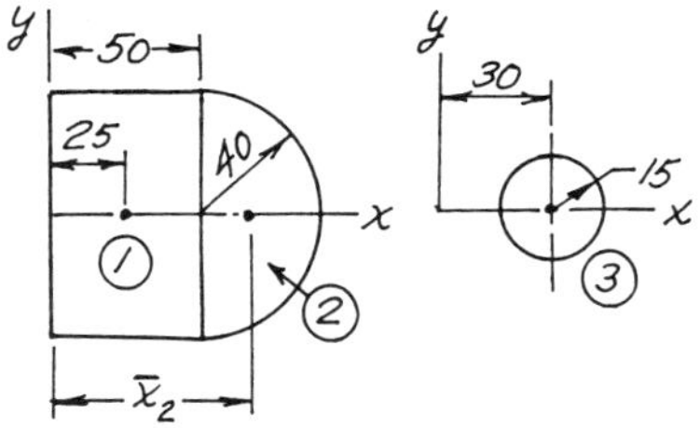

Part	A(mm^2)	$\bar{x}$ (mm)	$A\bar{x}$ (mm^3)
1	4000	25.00	100 000
2	2513	66.98	168 320
3	−707	30.00	−21 210
Sum	5806		247 110

$\therefore\ \bar{x} = \frac{247\,110}{5806} = 42.6\ \text{mm}$ ◆ Due to symmetry $\bar{y} = 0$ ◆

8.16

Consider the area as a composite of the circular sector 1 and the triangle 2.

$\alpha = \frac{\pi}{2} + \sin^{-1}\frac{3}{4.8} = 2.246\ \text{rad} = 128.68°$

$\bar{y}_1 = \frac{2(4.8)\sin 128.68°}{3(2.246)} = 1.1122\ \text{in} \qquad A_1 = (2.246)(4.8^2) = 51.75\ \text{in}^2$

$b = 2\sqrt{4.8^2 - 3^2} = 7.494\ \text{in} \qquad A_2 = \frac{1}{2}(7.494)(3) = 11.24\ \text{in}^2$

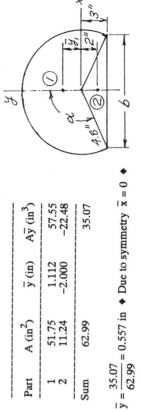

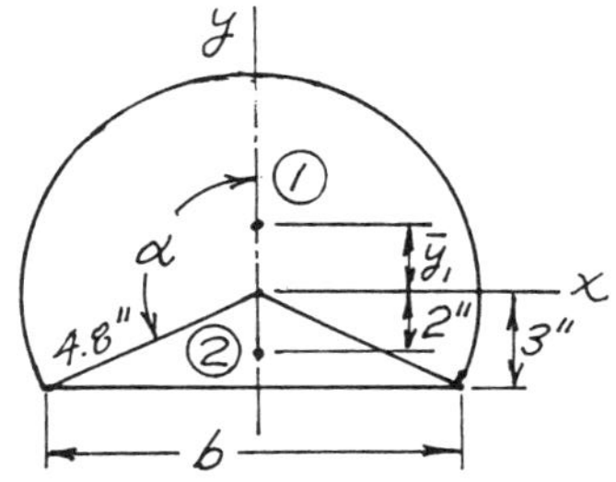

Part	A (in^2)	$\bar{y}$ (in)	$A\bar{y}$ (in^3)
1	51.75	1.112	57.55
2	11.24	−2.000	−22.48
Sum	62.99		35.07

$\bar{y} = \frac{35.07}{62.99} = 0.557\ \text{in}$ ◆ Due to symmetry $\bar{x} = 0$ ◆

8.17

Part	A (in^2)	$\bar{x}$ (in)	$A\bar{x}$ (in^3)	$\bar{y}$ (in)	$A\bar{y}$ (in^3)
1	18	4.5	81	11.0	198
2	16	8.0	128	6.0	96
3	20	5.0	100	1.0	20
Sum	54		309		314

$\bar{x} = \dfrac{309}{54} = 5.72$ in ◆

$\bar{y} = \dfrac{314}{54} = 5.81$ in ◆

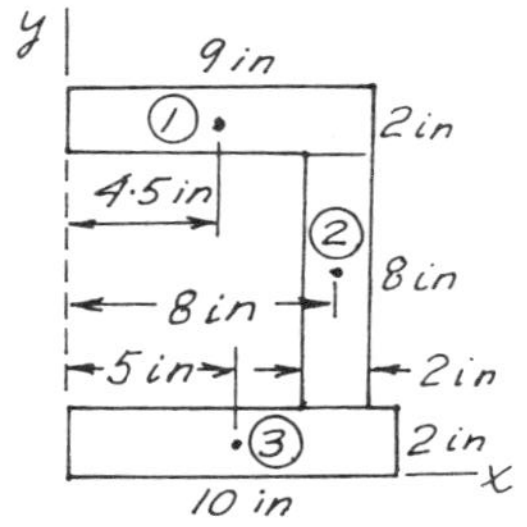

8.18

$A_4 = -\dfrac{\pi}{4}(20^2) = -314\ mm^2$

$\bar{x}_4 = 40 - \dfrac{4}{3\pi}(20) = 31.51$ mm

$\bar{y}_4 = 20 - \dfrac{4}{3\pi}(20) = 11.51$ mm

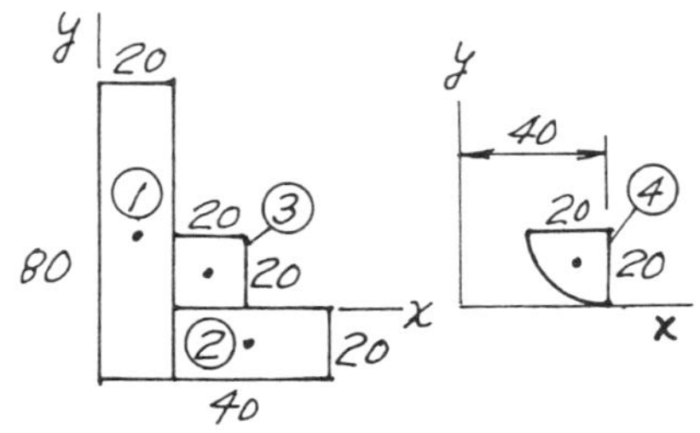

Part	A(mm^2)	$\bar{y}$ (mm)	$A\bar{y}$ (mm^3)	$\bar{x}$ (mm)	$A\bar{x}$ (mm^3)
1	1600	20.00	32 000	10.00	16 000
2	800	−10.00	−8 000	40.00	32 000
3	400	10.00	4 000	30.00	12 000
4	−314	11.51	−3 614	31.51	−9 894
Sum	2486		24 386		50 106

$\bar{x} = \dfrac{50\,106}{2486} = 20.16$ mm ◆ $\bar{y} = \dfrac{24\,386}{2486} = 9.81$ mm ◆

8.19

Part	A (mm^2)	$\bar{x}$ (mm)	$A\bar{x}$ (mm^3)	$\bar{y}$ (mm)	$A\bar{y}$ (mm^3)
1	1800	30.0	54 000	125.0	225 000
2	2250	12.5	28 125	65.0	146 250
3	1600	40.0	64 000	10.0	16 000
Sum	5650		146 125		387 250

$\bar{x} = \dfrac{146\,125}{5650} = 25.9$ mm ◆

$\bar{y} = \dfrac{387\,250}{5650} = 68.5$ mm ◆

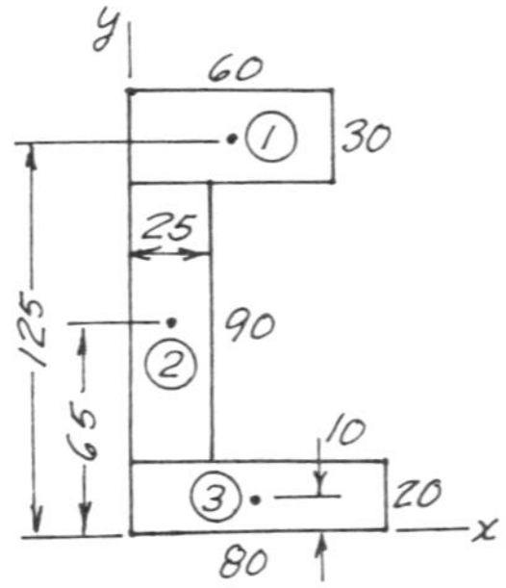

8.20

Part	A (in^2)	$\bar{x}$ (in)	$A\bar{x}$ (in^3)	$\bar{y}$ (in)	$A\bar{y}$ (in^3)
1	18	1.5	27.0	10.0	180.0
2	7	0.0	0.0	5.5	38.5
3	14	0.5	7.0	1.0	14.0
Sum	39		34.0		232.5

$\bar{x} = \dfrac{34.0}{39} = 0.872$ in ◆

$\bar{y} = \dfrac{232.5}{39} = 5.96$ in ◆

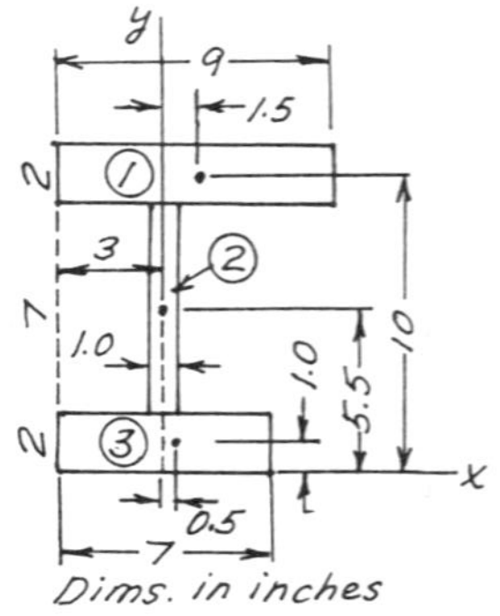

8.21

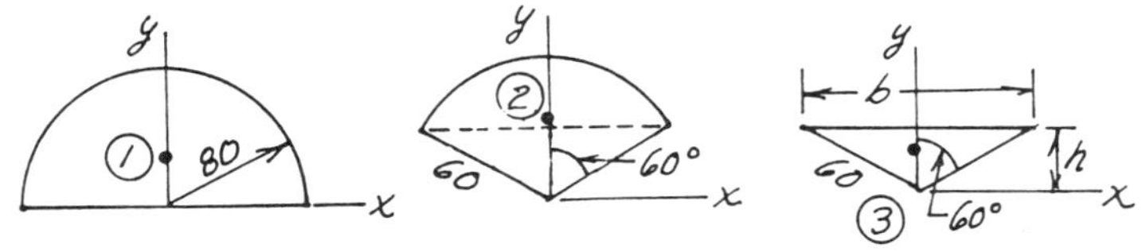

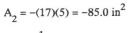

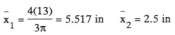

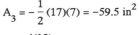

$h = 60 \cos 60° = 30$ mm $\quad b = 2(60 \sin 60°) = 103.92$ mm

$A_1 = \frac{1}{2}\pi(80)^2 = 10\,053$ mm^2 $\quad A_2 = -\frac{1}{3}\pi(60)^2 = -3770$ mm^2

$A_3 = \frac{1}{2}hb = \frac{1}{2}(30)(103.92) = 1558.8$ mm^2

$\bar{y}_1 = \frac{4(80)}{3\pi} = 33.95$ mm $\quad \bar{y}_2 = \frac{2(60)\sin 60°}{3(\pi/3)} = 33.08$ mm $\quad \bar{y}_3 = \frac{2h}{3} = \frac{2(30)}{3} = 20$ mm

Part	A(mm^2)	$\bar{y}$ (mm)	$A\bar{y}$ (mm^3)
1	10 053	33.95	341 299
2	−3 770	33.08	−124 712
3	1 559	20.00	31 180
Sum	7 842		247 767

$\bar{y} = \frac{247\,767}{7842} = 31.6$ mm ◆ $\quad$ Due to symmetry $\bar{x} = 0$ ◆

8.22

$A_1 = \frac{1}{2}\pi(13)^2 = 265.5$ in^2

$A_2 = -(17)(5) = -85.0$ in^2

$A_3 = -\frac{1}{2}(17)(7) = -59.5$ in^2

$\bar{x}_1 = \frac{4(13)}{3\pi} = 5.517$ in $\quad \bar{x}_2 = 2.5$ in

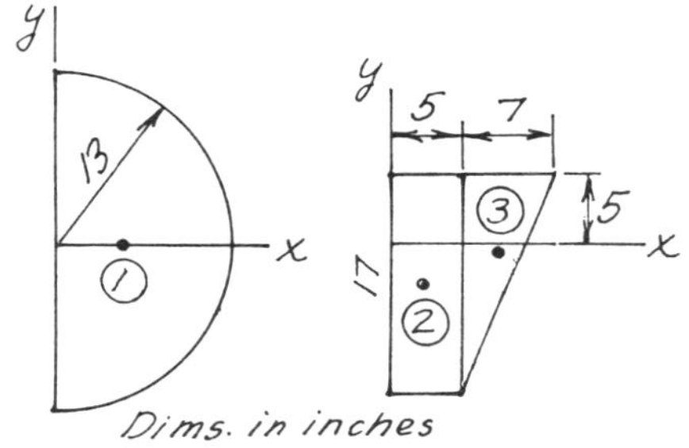

$\bar{x}_3 = 5 + \frac{1}{3}(7) = 7.333$ in $\quad \bar{y}_1 = 0 \quad \bar{y}_2 = \frac{17}{2} - 12 = -3.5$ in $\quad \bar{y}_3 = \frac{2}{3}(17) - 12 = -0.667$ in

(continued)

8.22 continued

Part	A(in^2)	$\bar{x}$ (in)	$A\bar{x}$ (in^3)	$\bar{y}$ (in)	$A\bar{y}$ (in^3)
1	265.5	5.517	1464.8	0.000	0.0
2	−85.0	2.500	−212.5	−3.500	297.5
3	−59.5	7.333	−436.3	−0.667	39.7
Sum	121.0		816.0		337.2

$\bar{x} = \frac{816.0}{121.0} = 6.74$ in ◆ $\quad \bar{y} = \frac{337.2}{121.0} = 2.79$ in ◆

8.23

$A_2 = \frac{1}{2}\pi(30)^2 = 1413.7$ mm^2

$A_4 = -\pi(15)^2 = -706.9$ mm^2

$\bar{x}_2 = -\frac{4(30)}{3\pi} = -12.732$ mm

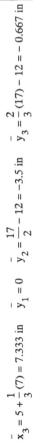

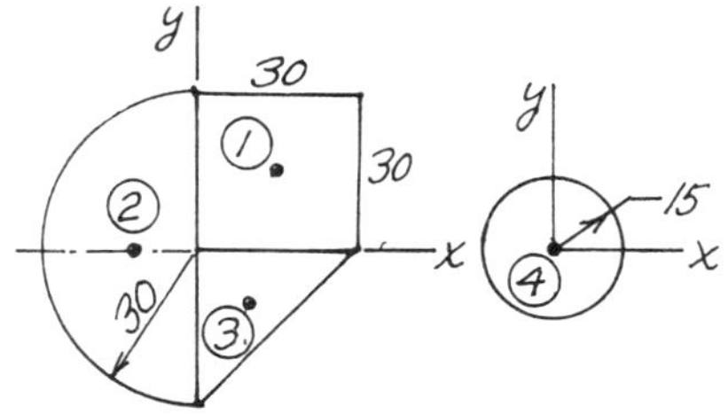

Part	A (mm^2)	$\bar{x}$ (mm)	$A\bar{x}$ (mm^3)	$\bar{y}$ (mm)	$A\bar{y}$ (mm^3)
1	900.0	15.000	13 500	15.000	13 500
2	1413.7	−12.732	−18 000	0.000	0
3	450.0	10.000	4 500	−10.000	−4 500
4	−706.9	0.000	0	0.000	0
Sum	2056.8		0		9 000

$\bar{x} = 0$ ◆ $\quad \bar{y} = \frac{9000}{2056.8} = 4.38$ mm ◆

8.24

$A_1 = (b - t)t \qquad A_2 = bt$

$\bar{x}_1 = \dfrac{b + t}{2} \qquad \bar{x}_2 = \dfrac{t}{2}$

$A_1\bar{x}_1 = \dfrac{t}{2}(b^2 - t^2) \qquad A_2\bar{x}_2 = \dfrac{1}{2}bt^2$

$$\therefore \bar{x} = \frac{\frac{t}{2}(b^2 - t^2) + \frac{1}{2}bt^2}{(b - t)t + bt} = \frac{b^2 + bt - t^2}{2(2b - t)} \blacklozenge$$

Due to symmetry $\bar{y} = \bar{x}$ ◆

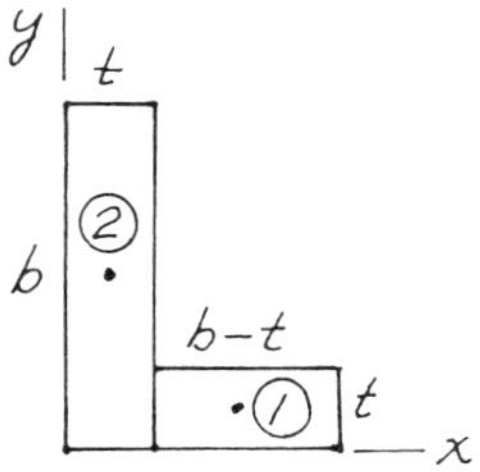

8.25

$A_1 = \alpha R^2 \qquad A_2 = -R^2 \sin\alpha \cos\alpha$

$\bar{x}_1 = \dfrac{2R \sin\alpha}{3\alpha} \qquad \bar{x}_2 = \dfrac{2}{3}R\cos\alpha$

$A_1\bar{x}_1 = \dfrac{2}{3}R^3 \sin\alpha$

$A_2\bar{x}_2 = -\dfrac{2}{3}R^3 \sin\alpha \cos^2\alpha$

$$\therefore \bar{x} = \frac{\frac{2}{3}R^3 \sin\alpha(1 - \cos^2\alpha)}{R^2(\alpha - \sin\alpha\cos\alpha)} = \frac{2R\sin^3\alpha}{3(\alpha - \sin\alpha\cos\alpha)} \blacklozenge$$

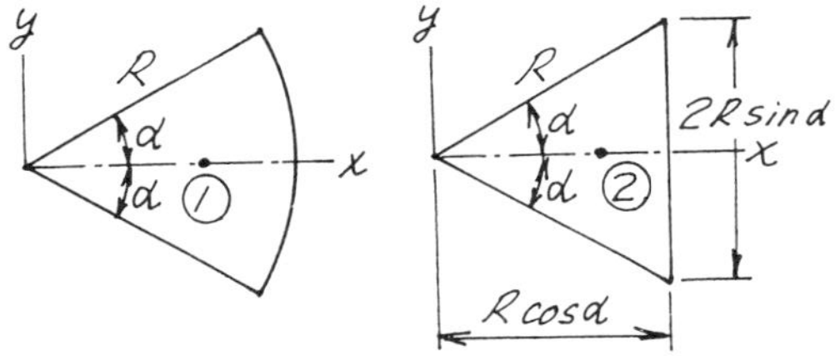

8.26

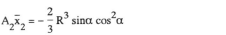

$A_1 = 16 \text{ ft}^2 \qquad A_2 = -2h$

$\bar{y}_1 = 2 \text{ ft} \qquad \bar{y}_2 = 0.5\,h$

$A_1\bar{y}_1 = 32 \text{ ft}^3 \qquad A_2\bar{y}_2 = -h^2$

$\therefore \bar{y} = \dfrac{32 - h^2}{16 - 2h}$ Setting $\bar{y} = h$ yields the quadratic equation $h^2 - 16h + 32 = 0$

The roots are h = 2.34 ft and 13.66 ft. Since we must have h < 4 ft, the second root is physically unacceptable.

$\therefore h = 2.34$ ft ◆

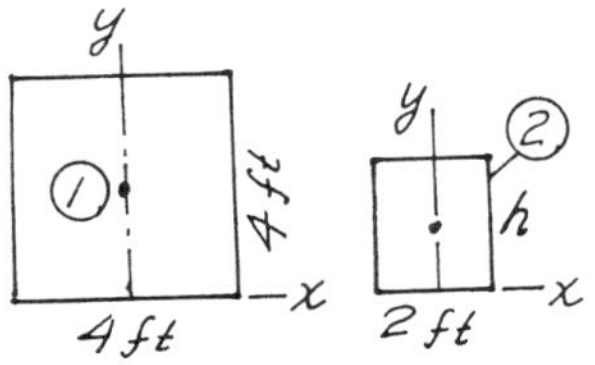

8.27

$A_1 = \dfrac{\pi}{2}(2^2) = 2\pi \text{ m}^2 \qquad A_2 = -\dfrac{\pi}{2}R^2$

$\bar{x}_1 = \dfrac{4}{3\pi}(2) = \dfrac{8}{3\pi}\text{ m} \qquad \bar{x}_2 = \dfrac{4}{3\pi}R$

$A_1\bar{x}_1 = \dfrac{16}{3}\text{ m}^3 \qquad A_2\bar{x}_2 = -\dfrac{2}{3}R^3$

$$\therefore \bar{x} = \frac{\frac{16}{3} - \frac{2}{3}R^3}{\pi\left(2 - \frac{1}{2}R^2\right)} = \frac{4(8 - R^3)}{3\pi(4 - R^2)}$$

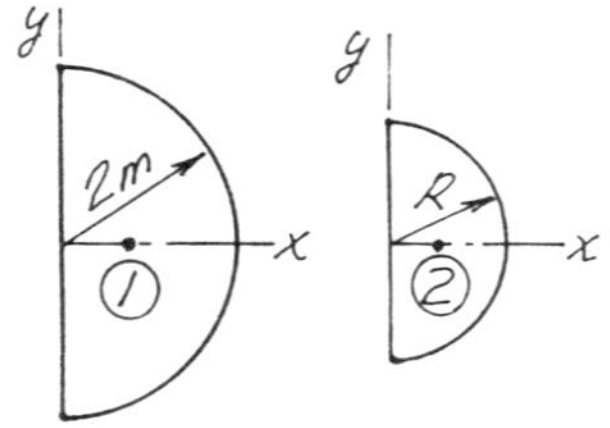

Setting $\bar{x} = R$ yields the cubic equation $3\pi R(4 - R^2) = 4(8 - R^3)$

$\therefore (3\pi - 4)R^3 - 12\pi R + 32 = 0 \qquad \therefore 5.425\,R^3 - 37.70\,R + 32 = 0$

Solving by a numerical method gives us $R = 0.987$ m ◆

8.28

$L_3 = \sqrt{60^2 + 30^2} = 67.08 \text{ mm} \qquad L_2 = \pi(30) = 94.25 \text{ mm} \qquad \bar{y}_2 = 60 + \dfrac{2(30)}{\pi} = 79.10 \text{ mm}$

Part	L (mm)	$\bar{x}$ (mm)	$L\bar{x}$ (mm²)	$\bar{y}$ (mm)	$L\bar{y}$ (mm²)
1	60.00	−30.00	−1800	30.00	1800
2	94.25	0.00	0	79.10	7455
3	67.08	15.00	1006	30.00	2012
Sum	221.33		−794		11 267

$\bar{x} = -\dfrac{794}{221.33} = -3.6 \text{ mm}$ ◆ $\qquad \bar{y} = \dfrac{11\,267}{221.33} = 50.9 \text{ mm}$ ◆

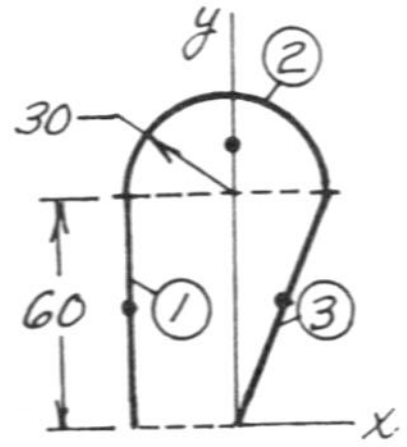

8.29

$L_1 = \frac{3}{4}(2\pi R) = \frac{6\pi(2)}{4} = 9.425$ in $\qquad r = \frac{R\sin\alpha}{\alpha} = \frac{2\sin 135°}{0.75\pi} = 0.6002$ in

$\bar{x}_1 = -r\sin 45° = 0.6002\sin 45° = -0.4244$ in

$\bar{y}_1 = 5.5 + r\cos 45° = 5.5 + 0.6002\cos 45° = 5.924$ in

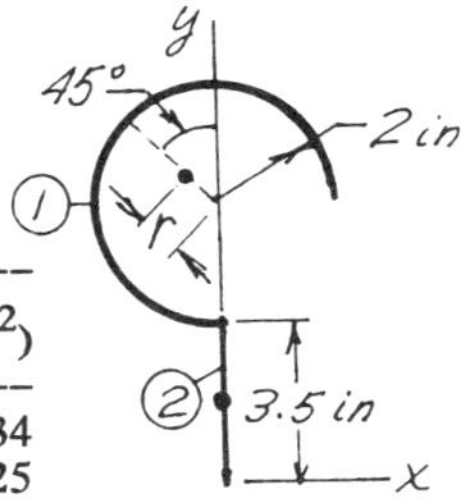

Part	L (in)	$\bar{x}$ (in)	$L\bar{x}$ (in^2)	$\bar{y}$ (in)	$L\bar{y}$ (in^2)
1	9.425	−0.4244	−4.000	5.924	55.834
2	3.500	0.0000	0.000	1.750	6.125
Sum	12.925		−4.000		61.959

$\bar{x} = -\frac{4.000}{12.925} = -0.31$ in ◆ $\qquad \bar{y} = \frac{61.959}{12.925} = 4.79$ in ◆

8.30

Part	L (ft)	$\bar{x}$ (ft)	$L\bar{x}$ (ft^2)	$\bar{y}$ (ft)	$L\bar{y}$ (ft^2)
1	3	1.5	4.5	0	0
2	5	1.5	7.5	2	10
3	4	0	0	2	8
Sum	12		12		18

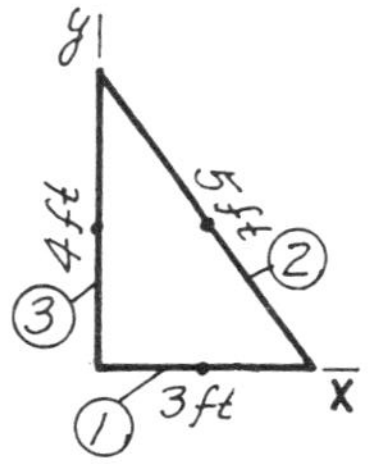

$\therefore \bar{x} = \frac{12}{12} = 1.0$ ft ◆ $\qquad \therefore \bar{y} = \frac{18}{12} = 1.5$ ft ◆

8.31

For the circular arc (part 1):

$\beta = \sin^{-1}\frac{10}{25} = 23.58° \quad \therefore \alpha = 180° - 23.58° = 156.42° = 2.730$ rad

$h = \sqrt{25^2 - 10^2} = 22.91$ mm $\qquad L_1 = 2\alpha R = 2(2.730)(25) = 136.50$ mm

$\bar{y}_1 = R\frac{\sin\alpha}{\alpha} = (25)\frac{\sin 156.42°}{2.730} = 3.663$ mm

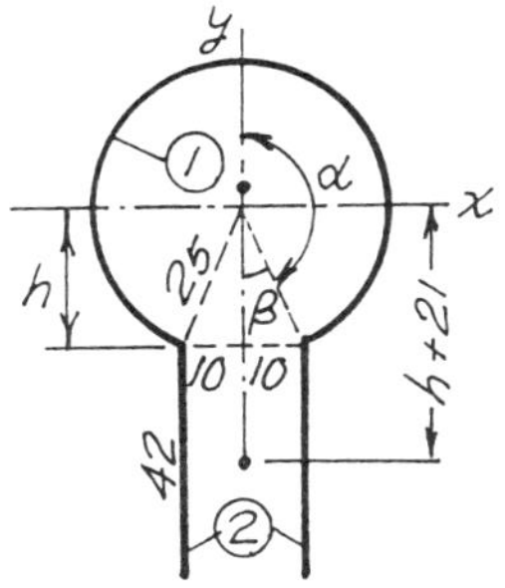

Part	L	$\bar{y}$	$L\bar{y}$
1	136.5	3.663	500
2	84.0	−43.91	−3688
Sum	220.5		−3188

$\therefore \bar{y} = \frac{-3188}{220.5} = -14.46$ mm ◆ $\qquad$ Due to symmetry $\bar{x} = 0$ ◆

8.32

$L_1 = \pi(200) = 628.3$ mm $\qquad \bar{y}_1 = 80 + \frac{2(200)}{\pi} = 207.3$ mm

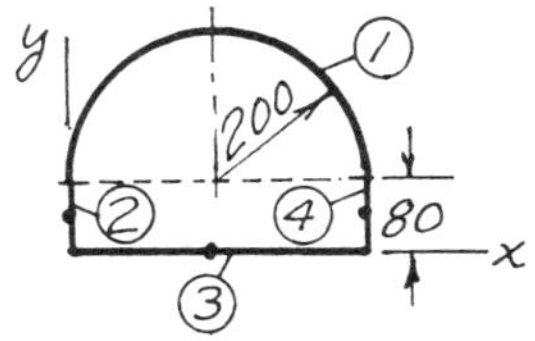

Part	L (mm)	$\bar{y}$ (mm)	$L\bar{y}$ (mm^2)
1	628.3	207.3	130 250
2	80.0	40.0	3 200
3	400.0	0.0	0
4	80.0	40.0	3 200
Sum	1188.3		136 650

$\therefore \bar{y} = \frac{136\,650}{1188.3} = 115.0$ mm ◆ $\qquad$ Due to symmetry $\bar{x} = 200$ mm ◆

8.33

$L_1 = \frac{\pi}{2}(5) = 7.854$ in $\quad \bar{x}_1 = \frac{2}{\pi}(5) = 3.183$ in $\quad \bar{y}_1 = -\bar{x} = -3.183$ in

Part	L (in)	$\bar{x}$ (in)	$L\bar{x}$ (in^2)	$\bar{y}$ (in)	$L\bar{y}$ (in^2)
1	7.854	3.183	25.0	−3.183	−25.0
2	2.000	4.000	8.0	0.000	0.0
3	4.000	3.000	12.0	2.000	8.0
4	3.000	1.500	4.5	4.000	12.0
5	9.000	0.000	0.0	−0.500	−4.5
Sum	25.854		49.5		−9.5

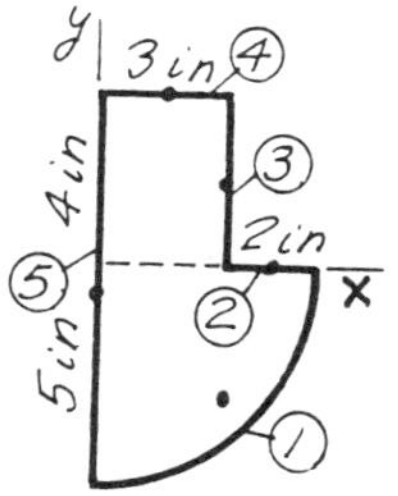

$\bar{x} = \frac{49.5}{25.854} = 1.915$ in ◆ $\quad \bar{y} = \frac{-9.5}{25.854} = -0.368$ in ◆

8.34

Part	L	$\bar{y}$	$L\bar{y}$
1	2a	0	0
2	2b	a	2ab
3	2a	0	0
4	$\sqrt{a^2+b^2}$	$-\frac{a}{2}$	$-\frac{a}{2}\sqrt{a^2+b^2}$
5	$\sqrt{a^2+b^2}$	$-\frac{a}{2}$	$-\frac{a}{2}\sqrt{a^2+b^2}$
Sum			$2ab - a\sqrt{a^2+b^2}$

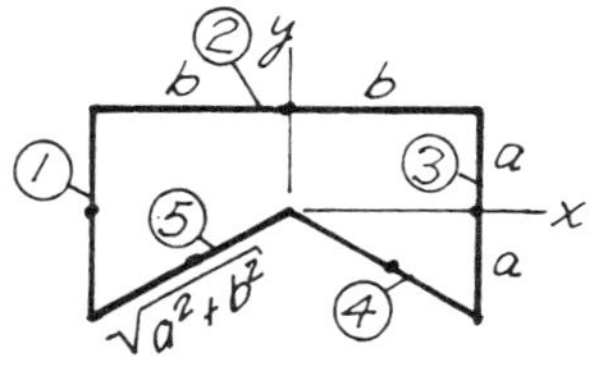

$\Sigma L\bar{y} = 0$ yields $2b - \sqrt{a^2+b^2} = 0 \quad \therefore (2b)^2 = a^2 + b^2 \quad \therefore 3b^2 = a^2 \quad \therefore \frac{a}{b} = \sqrt{3}$ ◆

8.35

Using single integration:

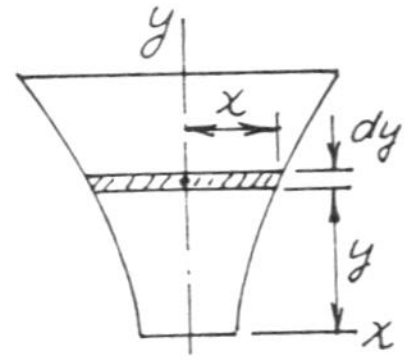

$dA = 2x\,dy \qquad \bar{y}_{el} = y$

$A = \int_A dA = 2\int_A x\,dy$

$Q_x = \int_A y_{el}\,dA = 2\int_A xy\,dA$

Computing the integrals with Simpson's rule:

$$A \approx 2\frac{\Delta y}{3}\sum_i W_i x_i = 2\frac{20}{3}\left[20 + 4(22) + 2(27) + 4(35) + 2(46) + 4(60) + 77\right] = 9480 \text{ mm}^2$$

$$Q_x \approx 2\frac{\Delta y}{3}\sum_i W_i x_i y_i$$

$$= 2\frac{20}{3}\left[(20)(0) + 4(22)(20) + 2(27)(40) + 4(35)(60) + 2(46)(80) + 4(60)(100) + 77(120)\right]$$

$$= 705\,600 \text{ mm}^3$$

$\bar{y} = \frac{Q_x}{A} = \frac{705\,600}{9480} = 74.4$ mm ◆ $\qquad$ Due to symmetry $\bar{x} = 0$ ◆

8.36

Using single integration:

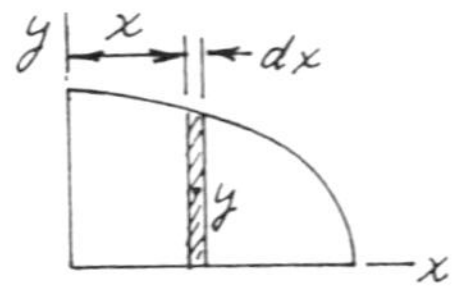

$dA = y\,dx \qquad \bar{x}_{el} = x \qquad \bar{y}_{el} = \frac{y}{2}$

$A = \int_A dA = \int_A y\,dx$

$Q_x = \int_A \bar{y}_{el}dA = \frac{1}{2}\int_A y^2\,dx$

$Q_y = \int_A \bar{x}_{el}dA = \int_A xy\,dx$

(continued)

8.36 continued

Evaluating the integrals with Simpson's Rule:

$$A \approx \frac{\Delta x}{3}\sum_i W_i y_i = \frac{4}{3}\left[10 + 4(9.68) + 2(8.66) + 4(6.61) + 0\right] = 123.3 \text{ in}^2$$

$$Q_x \approx \frac{1}{2}\frac{\Delta x}{3}\sum_i W_i y_i^2 = \frac{1}{2}\frac{4}{3}\left[10^2 + 4(9.68^2) + 2(8.66^2) + 4(6.61)^2 + 0^2\right] = 533.0 \text{ in}^3$$

$$Q_y \approx \frac{\Delta x}{3}\sum_i W_i x_i y_i = \frac{4}{3}\left[(0)(10) + 4(4)(9.68) + 2(8)(8.66) + 4(12)(6.61) + (16)(0)\right]$$

$$= 814.3 \text{ in}^3$$

$\bar{x} = \frac{Q_y}{A} = \frac{814.3}{123.3} = 6.60$ in ◆ $\quad \bar{y} = \frac{Q_x}{A} = \frac{533.0}{123.3} = 4.32$ in ◆

8.37

$\bar{y}_{el} = y = 40\left(1 - \frac{x^2}{3600}\right) \quad \therefore \frac{dy}{dx} = -\frac{x}{45}$

$\frac{ds}{dx} = \sqrt{1 + (dy/dx)^2} = \sqrt{1 + (x/45)^2}$

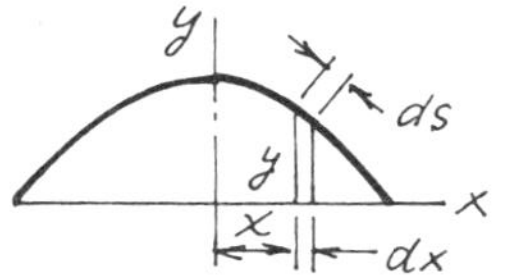

We evaluate the following integrals by Simpson's rule:

$$L = \int_L ds = \int_L \frac{ds}{dx}dx \approx \frac{\Delta x}{3}\sum_i W_i\left(\frac{ds}{dx}\right)_i$$

$$Q_x = \int_L \bar{y}_{el}\, ds = \int_L y\frac{ds}{dx}dx \approx \frac{\Delta x}{3}\sum_i W_i y_i\left(\frac{ds}{dx}\right)_i$$

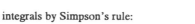

x (in)	y (in)	$\frac{dx}{dy}$	$\frac{ds}{dx}$	$y\frac{ds}{dx}$ (in)	W	$W\frac{ds}{dx}$	$Wy\frac{ds}{dx}$ (in)
0	40.0	0.0000	1.0000	40.00	1	1.0000	40.00
15	37.5	−0.3333	1.0541	39.53	4	4.2164	158.12
30	30.0	−0.6667	1.2019	36.06	2	2.4038	72.12
45	17.5	−1.0000	1.4142	24.75	4	5.6568	99.00
60	0.0	−1.3333	1.6667	0.00	1	1.6667	0.00
Sum						14.9437	369.24

$\bar{y} = \frac{Q_x}{L} = \frac{369.24}{14.9437} = 24.7$ in ◆ $\quad$ Due to symmetry $\bar{x} = 0$ ◆

8.38

$\bar{y}_{el} = y = 100\cosh\frac{x}{100} \quad \therefore \frac{dy}{dx} = \sinh\frac{x}{100}$

$\frac{ds}{dx} = \sqrt{1 + (dy/dx)^2} = \sqrt{1 + \sinh^2\frac{x}{100}}$

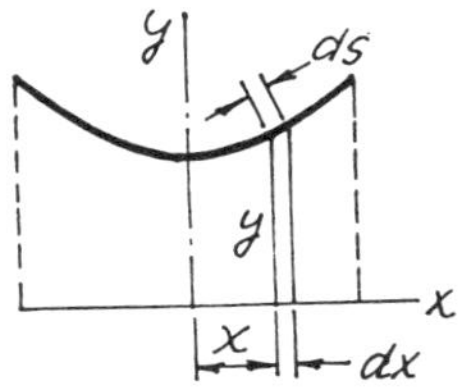

The following are integrated with Simpson's rule:

$$L = \int_L ds = \int_L \frac{ds}{dx}dx \approx \frac{\Delta x}{3}\sum_i W_i\left(\frac{ds}{dx}\right)_i$$

$$Q_x = \int_L \bar{y}_{el}\, ds = \int_L y\frac{ds}{dx}dx \approx \frac{\Delta x}{3}\sum_i W_i y_i\left(\frac{ds}{dx}\right)_i$$

x (ft)	y(ft)	$\frac{dy}{dx}$	$\frac{ds}{dx}$	$y\frac{ds}{dx}$ (ft)	W	$W\frac{ds}{dx}$	$Wy\frac{ds}{dx}$ (ft)
0	100.0	0.0000	1.0000	100.00	1	1.0000	100.00
25	103.1	0.2526	1.0314	106.38	4	4.1256	425.52
50	112.8	0.5211	1.1276	127.15	2	2.2552	254.30
75	129.5	0.8223	1.2947	167.62	4	5.1788	670.48
100	154.3	1.1752	1.5431	238.11	1	1.5431	238.11
Sum						14.1027	1688.41

$\bar{y} = \frac{Q_y}{A} = \frac{1688.41}{14.1027} = 119.7$ ft ◆

8.39

The volume element is the shaded thin disk.

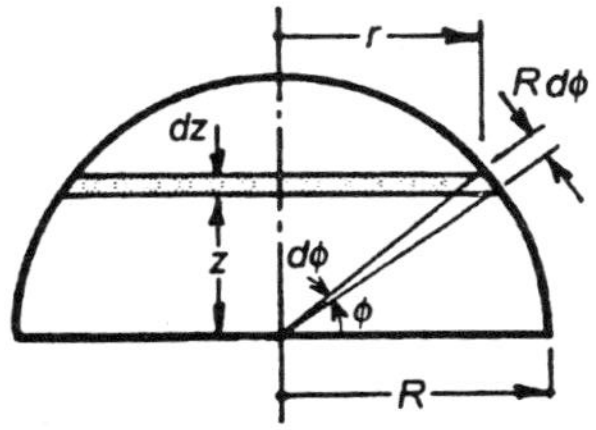

$r = R\cos\phi \qquad \bar{z}_{el} = z = R\sin\phi$

$\therefore\ dz = R\cos\phi\, d\phi \qquad dV = \pi r^2 dz = \pi R^3 \cos^3\phi\, d\phi$

$$V = \int_V dV = \pi R^3 \int_0^{\pi/2} \cos^3\phi\, d\phi = \frac{2\pi}{3} R^3$$

$$Q_{xy} = \int_V \bar{z}_{el}\, dV = \pi R^4 \int_0^{\pi/2} \sin\phi \cos^3\phi\, d\phi = \pi R^4 \int_0^{\pi/2} d\left(-\frac{1}{4}\cos^4\phi\right) = \frac{\pi}{4} R^4$$

$\therefore\ \bar{z} = \dfrac{Q_{xy}}{V} = \dfrac{\pi R^4/4}{2\pi R^3/3} = \dfrac{3}{8} R$ ◆ Due to symmetry $\bar{x} = \bar{y} = 0$ ◆ Agrees with Table 8.3

8.40

The surface element dA is the ring formed by rotating the arc R dφ about the z-axis (see figure in solution of Prob. 8.39).

$r = R\cos\phi \qquad \bar{z}_{el} = z = R\sin\phi \qquad dA = (2\pi r)(R\, d\phi) = 2\pi R^2 \cos\phi\, d\phi$

$$A = \int_A dA = 2\pi R^2 \int_0^{\pi/2} \cos\phi\, d\phi = 2\pi R^2$$

$$Q_{xy} = \int_A \bar{z}_{el}\, dA = 2\pi R^3 \int_0^{\pi/2} \sin\phi\cos\phi\, d\phi = \pi R^3 \int_0^{\pi/2} \sin 2\phi\, d\phi = \pi R^3$$

$\therefore\ \bar{z} = \dfrac{Q_{xy}}{A} = \dfrac{\pi R^3}{2\pi R^2} = \dfrac{1}{2} R$ ◆ Due to symmetry $\bar{x} = \bar{y} = 0$ ◆ Agrees with Table 8.4

8.41

The volume element is a thin disk obtained by rotating the shaded area about the x-axis.

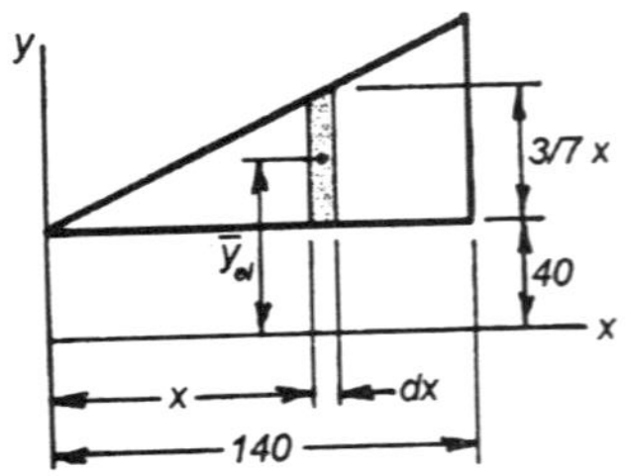

$\bar{x}_{el} = x$

$$dV = \pi\left[\left(\frac{3}{7}x + 2\right)^2 - 2^2\right]dx = \frac{3\pi}{7}\left(\frac{3}{7}x^2 + 4x\right)dx$$

$$V = \int_V dV = \frac{3\pi}{7}\int_0^7 \left(\frac{3}{7}x^2 + 4x\right)dx = 63\pi \text{ in}^3$$

$$Q_{yz} = \int_V \bar{x}_{el}\, dV = \frac{3\pi}{7}\int_0^7 \left(\frac{3}{7}x^3 + 4x^2\right)dx = \frac{1225}{4}\pi \text{ in}^4$$

$\therefore\ \bar{x} = \dfrac{Q_{yz}}{V} = \dfrac{1225\pi/4}{63\pi} = 4.86$ in ◆ Due to symmetry $\bar{y} = \bar{z} = 0$ ◆

8.42

The volume element is a thin cylinder formed by rotating the shaded area about the y-axis (see figure in the solution of Prob. 8.41).

$dV = 2\pi x\left(\dfrac{3}{7}x\right)dx = \dfrac{6\pi}{7}x^2\, dx \qquad \bar{y}_{el} = 2 + \dfrac{3}{14}x$

$V = \displaystyle\int_V dV = \frac{6\pi}{7}\int_0^7 x^2\, dx = 98\pi \text{ in}^3 \qquad Q_{zx} = \int_V \bar{y}_{el}\, dV = \frac{6\pi}{7}\int_0^7 \left(2x^2 + \frac{3}{14}x^3\right)dx = \frac{1225\pi}{4} \text{ in}^4$

$\therefore\ \bar{y} = \dfrac{Q_{zx}}{V} = \dfrac{1225\pi/4}{98\pi} = 3.125$ in ◆ Due to symmetry $\bar{x} = \bar{z} = 0$ ◆

8.43

The volume element is a thin disk obtained by rotating the shaded area about the x-axis.

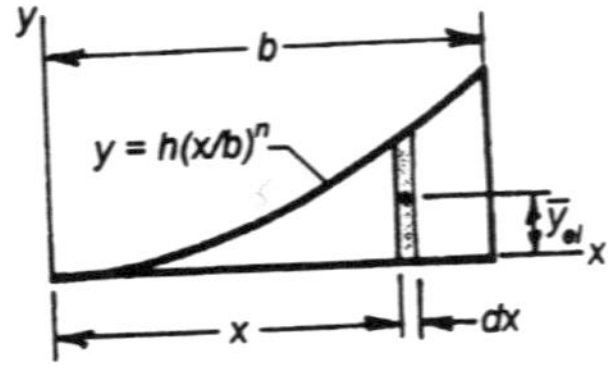

$dV = \pi y^2\, dx = \pi h^2 (x/b)^{2n}\, dx \qquad \bar{x}_{el} = x$

$$V = \int_V dV = \frac{\pi h^2}{b^{2n}}\int_0^b x^{2n}\, dx = \frac{\pi h^2 b}{2n+1}$$

$$Q_{yz} = \int_V \bar{x}_{el}\, dV = \frac{\pi h^2}{b^{2n}}\int_0^b x^{2n+1}\, dx = \frac{\pi h^2 b^2}{2n+2}$$

$\therefore\ \bar{x} = \dfrac{Q_{yz}}{V} = \dfrac{\pi h^2 b^2/(2n+2)}{\pi h^2 b/(2n+1)} = \dfrac{2n+1}{2n+2} b$ ◆ By symmetry $\bar{y} = \bar{z} = 0$ ◆

8.44

The volume element is a thin cylinder formed by rotating the shaded area about the y-axis (see figure in solution of Prob. 8.43)

$$dV = 2\pi xy\,dx = 2\pi \frac{h}{b^n} x^{n+1}\,dx \qquad \bar{y}_{el} = \frac{1}{2}y = \frac{1}{2}\frac{h}{b^n}x^n$$

$$V = \int_V dV = 2\pi \frac{h}{b^n}\int_0^b x^{n+1}\,dx = \frac{2\pi hb^2}{n+2} \qquad Q_{zx} = \int_V \bar{y}_{el}\,dV = \frac{\pi h^2}{b^{2n}}\int_0^b x^{2n+1}\,dx = \frac{\pi h^2 b^2}{2n+2}$$

$$\therefore \bar{y} = \frac{Q_{zx}}{V} = \frac{\pi h^2b^2/(2n+2)}{2\pi hb^2/(n+2)} = \frac{n+2}{2(2n+2)}h \ \blacklozenge \qquad \text{Due to symmetry } \bar{x} = \bar{z} = 0 \ \blacklozenge$$

8.45

The volume element is the thin rectangular plate shown.

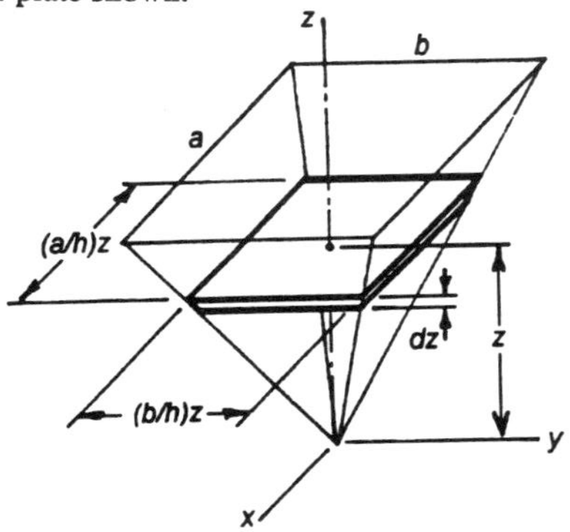

$$dV = \left(\frac{a}{h}z\right)\left(\frac{b}{h}z\right)dz = \frac{ab}{h^2}z^2\,dz \qquad \bar{z}_{el} = z$$

$$V = \int_V dV = \frac{ab}{h^2}\int_0^h z^2\,dz = \frac{abh}{3}$$

$$Q_{xy} = \int_V \bar{z}_{el}\,dV = \frac{ab}{h^2}\int_0^h z^3\,dz = \frac{abh^2}{4}$$

$$\therefore \bar{z} = \frac{Q_{xy}}{V} = \frac{abh^2/4}{abh/3} = \frac{3}{4}h \ \blacklozenge$$

Due to symmetry $\bar{x} = \bar{y} = 0$ ◆

8.46

The volume element is the thin "slice" shown.

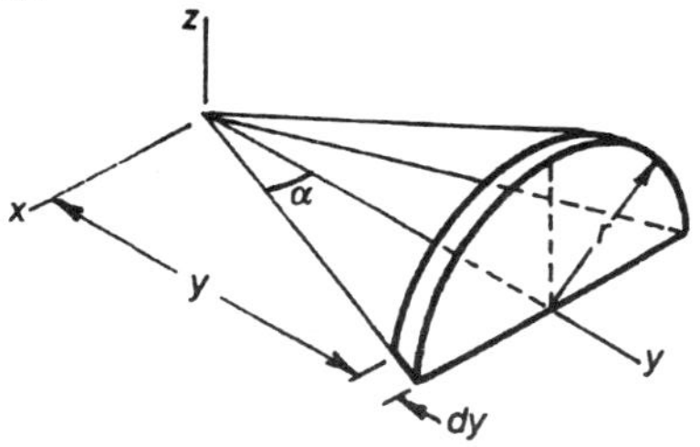

$$r = \frac{R}{h}y \qquad \bar{z}_{el} = \frac{4}{3\pi}r = \frac{4R}{3\pi h}y$$

$$dV = \frac{\pi}{2}r^2\,dy = \frac{\pi R^2}{2h^2}y^2\,dy$$

$$V = \int_V dV = \frac{\pi R^2}{2h^2}\int_0^h y^2\,dy = \frac{\pi R^2 h}{6}$$

$$Q_{xy} = \int_V \bar{z}_{el}\,dV = \frac{2R^3}{3h^3}\int_0^h y^3\,dy = \frac{R^3h}{6} \qquad \therefore \bar{z} = \frac{Q_{xy}}{V} = \frac{R^3h/6}{\pi R^2h/6} = \frac{R}{\pi} \ \blacklozenge$$

8.47

The area element is the shaded surface of the thin slice used in Prob. 8.46.

$$r = \frac{R}{h}y \qquad \bar{z}_{el} = \frac{2}{\pi}r = \frac{2R}{\pi h}y \qquad dA = \pi r\frac{dy}{\cos\alpha} = \frac{\pi R}{h\cos\alpha}y\,dy$$

$$A = \int_A dA = \frac{\pi R}{h\cos\alpha}\int_0^h y\,dy = \frac{\pi Rh}{2\cos\alpha} \qquad Q_{xy} = \int_A \bar{z}_{el}\,dA = \frac{2R^2}{h^2\cos\alpha}\int_0^h y^2\,dy = \frac{2R^2h}{3\cos\alpha}$$

$$\therefore \bar{z} = \frac{Q_{xy}}{A} = \frac{2R^2h/(3\cos\alpha)}{\pi Rh/(2\cos\alpha)} = \frac{4R}{3\pi} \ \blacklozenge$$

8.48

We use double integration.

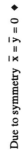

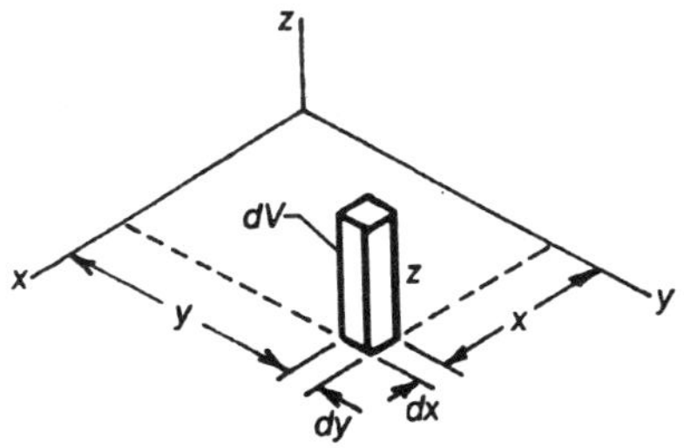

$$dV = z\,dx\,dy = \left[h_1 - (h_1 - h_2)\frac{xy}{ab}\right]dx\,dy$$

$$\bar{x}_{el} = x \qquad \bar{y}_{el} = y$$

$$V = \int_V dV = \int_0^b\int_0^a \left[h_1 - (h_1 - h_2)\frac{xy}{ab}\right]dx\,dy$$

$$= \int_0^b \left[h_1 a - (h_1 - h_2)\frac{ay}{2b}\right]dy$$

$$= h_1 ab - (h_1 - h_2)\frac{ab}{4} = (3h_1 + h_2)\frac{ab}{4}$$

$$Q_{yz} = \int_V \bar{x}_{el}\,dA = \int_0^b\int_0^a \left[h_1 x - (h_1 - h_2)\frac{x^2y}{ab}\right]dx\,dy = \int_0^b \left[h_1\frac{a^2}{2} - (h_1 - h_2)\frac{a^2y}{3b}\right]dy$$

$$= h_1\frac{a^2b}{2} - (h_1 - h_2)\frac{a^2b}{6} = (2h_1 + h_2)\frac{a^2b}{6}$$

$$\therefore \bar{x} = \frac{Q_{yz}}{V} = \frac{(2h_1 + h_2)a^2b/6}{(3h_1 + h_2)ab/4} = \frac{2(2h_1 + h_2)}{3(3h_1 + h_2)}a \ \blacklozenge \qquad \text{By analogy } \bar{y} = \frac{2(2h_1 + h_2)}{3(3h_1 + h_2)}b \ \blacklozenge$$

8.49

We choose double integration, using the same element as in Prob. 8.48.

$$dV = z\,dx\,dy = \frac{c}{a^2b^2}(a^2 - x^2)(b^2 - y^2)\,dx\,dy \qquad \bar{z}_{el} = \frac{1}{2}z = \frac{c}{2a^2b^2}(a^2 - x^2)(b^2 - y^2)$$

$$V = \int_V dV = \frac{c}{a^2b^2}\int_{-a}^{a}\int_{-b}^{b}(a^2 - x^2)(b^2 - y^2)\,dx\,dy = 4\frac{c}{a^2b^2}\int_0^a\int_0^b(a^2 - x^2)(b^2 - y^2)\,dx\,dy$$

$$= 4\frac{c}{a^2b^2}\left(\frac{2}{3}a^3\right)\left(\frac{2}{3}b^3\right) = \frac{16}{9}abc$$

$$Q_{xy} = \int_V \bar{z}_{el}\,dV = \frac{1}{2}\left(\frac{c}{a^2b^2}\right)^2\int_{-a}^{a}\int_{-b}^{b}(a^2 - x^2)^2(b^2 - y^2)^2\,dx\,dy$$

$$= 2\left(\frac{c}{a^2b^2}\right)^2\int_0^a\int_0^b(a^2 - x^2)^2(b^2 - y^2)^2\,dx\,dy = 2\left(\frac{c}{a^2b^2}\right)^2\left(\frac{8}{15}a^5\right)\left(\frac{8}{15}b^5\right) = \frac{128}{225}abc^2$$

$$\therefore \bar{z} = \frac{Q_{xy}}{V} = \frac{128\,abc^2/225}{16\,abc/9} = \frac{8}{25}c \;\blacklozenge \qquad \text{Due to symmetry } \bar{x} = \bar{y} = 0 \;\blacklozenge$$

8.50

$$dA = zR\,d\theta = \frac{hR}{\pi}\theta\,d\theta \qquad A = \frac{\pi}{2}hR$$

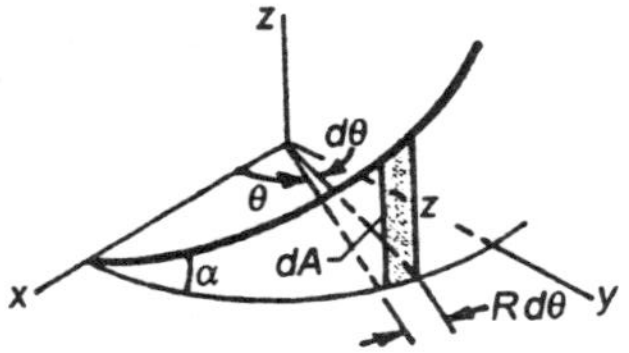

$$\bar{x}_{el} = R\cos\theta \qquad \bar{y}_{el} = R\sin\theta \qquad \bar{z}_{el} = \frac{z}{2} = \frac{h}{2\pi}\theta$$

$$Q_{xy} = \int_A \bar{z}_{el}\,dA = \frac{h^2R}{2\pi^2}\int_0^\pi \theta^2\,d\theta = \frac{\pi}{6}h^2R$$

$$Q_{yz} = \int_A \bar{x}_{el}\,dA = \frac{hR^2}{\pi}\int_0^\pi \theta\cos\theta\,d\theta = \frac{hR^2}{\pi}\Big[\cos\theta + \theta\sin\theta\Big]_0^\pi = -\frac{2}{\pi}hR^2$$

$$Q_{zx} = \int_A \bar{y}_{el}\,dA = \frac{hR^2}{\pi}\int_0^\pi \theta\sin\theta\,d\theta = \frac{hR^2}{\pi}\Big[\sin\theta - \theta\cos\theta\Big]_0^\pi = hR^2$$

$$\therefore \bar{x} = \frac{Q_{yz}}{A} = -\left(\frac{2}{\pi}\right)^2 R \;\blacklozenge \qquad \therefore \bar{y} = \frac{Q_{zx}}{A} = \frac{2}{\pi}R \;\blacklozenge \qquad \therefore \bar{z} = \frac{Q_{xy}}{A} = \frac{1}{3}h \;\blacklozenge$$

8.51

Refer to the figure in the solution of Prob. 8.50.

$$ds = \frac{R}{\cos\alpha}d\theta \qquad L = \frac{\pi R}{\cos\alpha} \qquad \bar{x}_{el} = R\cos\theta \qquad \bar{y}_{el} = R\sin\theta \qquad \bar{z}_{el} = z = \frac{h}{\pi}\theta$$

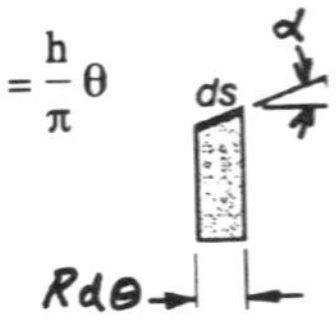

$$Q_{xy} = \int_L \bar{z}_{el}\,ds = \frac{Rh}{\pi\cos\alpha}\int_0^\pi \theta\,d\theta = \frac{\pi Rh}{2\cos\alpha}$$

$$Q_{yz} = \int_L \bar{x}_{el}\,ds = \frac{R^2}{\cos\alpha}\int_0^\pi \cos\theta\,d\theta = 0 \qquad Q_{zx} = \int_L \bar{y}_{el}\,ds = \frac{R^2}{\cos\alpha}\int_0^\pi \sin\theta\,d\theta = \frac{2R^2}{\cos\alpha}$$

$$\therefore \bar{x} = \frac{Q_{yz}}{L} = 0 \;\blacklozenge \qquad \therefore \bar{y} = \frac{Q_{zx}}{L} = \frac{2}{\pi}R \;\blacklozenge \qquad \therefore \bar{z} = \frac{Q_{xy}}{L} = \frac{1}{2}h \;\blacklozenge$$

8.52

Part	V (ft^3)	$\bar{x}$ (ft)	$V\bar{x}$ (ft^4)
1	128	4.000	512.0
2	−16	6.667	−106.7
Sum	112		405.3

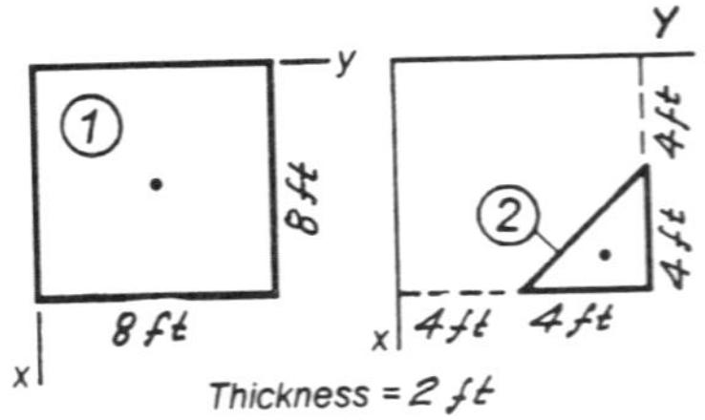

$$\therefore \bar{x} = \frac{405.3}{112} = 3.62 \text{ ft} \;\blacklozenge$$

Due to symmetry: $\bar{y} = \bar{x}$ ◆ $\bar{z} = 1.0$ ft ◆

8.53

$$V_1 = \pi\left(\frac{10}{2}\right)^2(19) = 1492.3 \text{ in}^3$$

$$V_2 = \pi\left(\frac{18}{2}\right)^2(13) = 3308.1^3$$

$$V_3 = \frac{\pi}{3}\left(\frac{18}{2}\right)^2(16) = 1357.2 \text{ in}^3$$

$$\bar{z}_3 = 19 + 13 + \frac{16}{4} = 36 \text{ in}$$

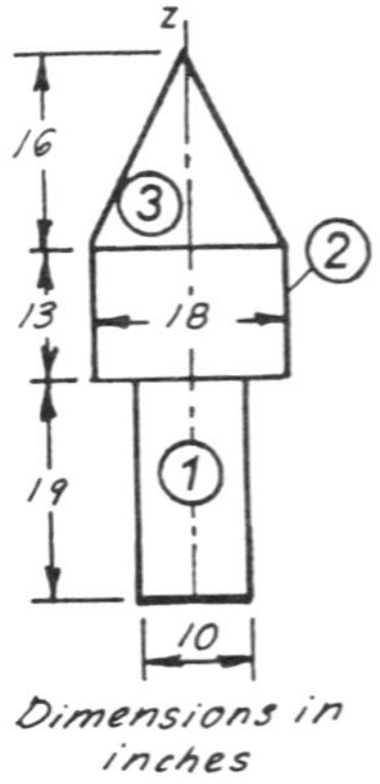

(continued)

8.53 continued

Part	V (in^3)	$\bar{z}$ (in)	$V\bar{z}$ (in^4)
1	1492.3	9.50	14 177
2	3308.1	25.50	84 357
3	1357.2	36.00	48 859
Sum	6157.6		147 393

$\therefore \bar{z} = \frac{147\,393}{6157.6} = 23.9$ in ◆ Due to symmetry: $\bar{x} = \bar{y} = 0$ ◆

8.54

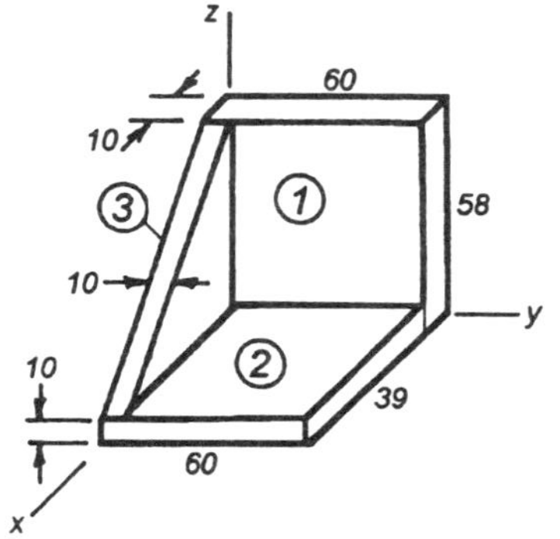

$V_1 = (60)(58)(10) = 34\,800$ mm^3

$V_2 = (60)(39)(10) = 23\,400$ mm^3

$V_3 = \frac{1}{2}(48)(39)(10) = 9\,360$ mm^3

$\bar{x}_3 = 10 + \frac{1}{3}(39) = 23$ mm

$\bar{z}_3 = 10 + \frac{1}{3}(48) = 26$ mm

Part	V (mm^3)	$\bar{x}$ (mm)	$V\bar{x}$ (mm^4)	$\bar{y}$ (mm)	$V\bar{y}$ (mm^4)	$\bar{z}$ (mm)	$V\bar{z}$ (mm^4)
1	34 800	5.0	174 000	30.0	1 044 000	29.0	1 009 200
2	23 400	29.5	690 300	30.0	702 000	5.0	117 000
3	9 360	23.0	215 280	5.0	46 800	26.0	243 360
Sum	67 560		1 079 580		1 792 800		1 369 560

$\therefore \bar{x} = \frac{1\,079\,580}{67\,560} = 15.98$ mm ◆ $\therefore \bar{y} = \frac{1\,792\,800}{67\,560} = 26.54$ mm ◆

$\therefore \bar{z} = \frac{1\,369\,560}{67\,560} = 20.27$ mm ◆

8.55

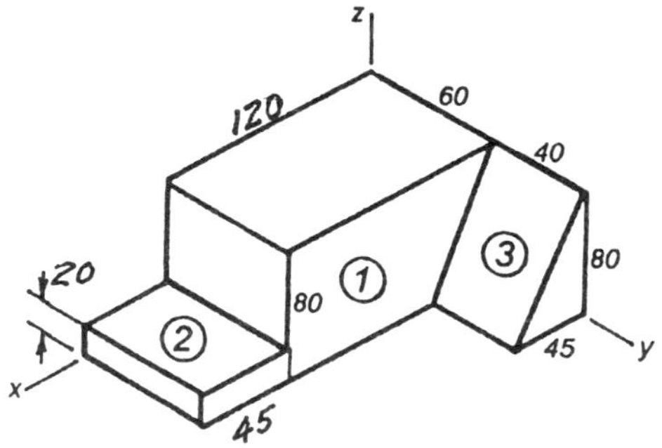

$V_1 = (120)(80)(60) = 576 \times 10^3$ mm^3

$V_2 = (45)(60)(20) = 54 \times 10^3$ mm^3

$V_3 = \frac{1}{2}(80)(45)(40) = 72 \times 10^3$ mm^3

$\bar{x}_3 = \frac{1}{3}(45) = 15$ mm

$\bar{z}_3 = \frac{1}{3}(80) = 26.67$ mm

Part	V 10^3 mm^3	$\bar{x}$ mm	$V\bar{x}$ 10^6 mm^4	$\bar{y}$ mm	$V\bar{y}$ 10^6 mm^4	$\bar{z}$ mm	$V\bar{z}$ 10^6 mm^4
1	576	60.0	34.56	30.0	17.28	40.00	23.04
2	54	142.5	7.70	30.0	1.62	10.00	0.54
3	72	15.0	1.08	80.0	5.76	26.67	1.92
Sum	702		43.34		24.66		25.50

$\therefore \bar{x} = \frac{43.34 \times 10^6}{702 \times 10^3} = 61.7$ mm ◆ $\therefore \bar{y} = \frac{24.66 \times 10^6}{702 \times 10^3} = 35.1$ mm ◆

$\therefore \bar{z} = \frac{25.50 \times 10^6}{702 \times 10^3} = 36.3$ mm ◆

8.56

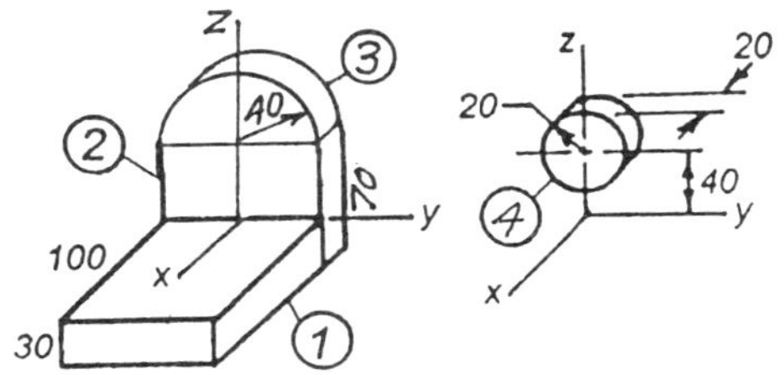

$V_1 = (100)(80)(30) = 240\,000$ mm^3

$V_2 = (70)(80)(20) = 112\,000$ mm^3

$V_3 = \frac{\pi}{2}(40)^2(20) = 50\,270$ mm^3

$V_4 = -\pi\,(20)^2(20) = -25\,130$ mm^3

$\bar{z}_3 = 40 + \frac{4}{3\pi}(40) = 56.98$ mm

(continued)

8.56 continued

Part	V 10^3 mm^3	$\bar{x}$ mm	$\bar{x}V$ 10^6 mm^4	$\bar{z}$ mm	$\bar{z}V$ 10^6 mm^4
1	240.00	50	12.000	−15.00	−3.600
2	112.00	−10	−1.120	5.00	0.560
3	50.27	−10	−0.503	56.98	2.864
4	−25.13	−10	0.251	40.00	−1.005
Sum	377.14		10.628		−1.181

$\therefore \bar{x} = \dfrac{10.628 \times 10^6}{377.14 \times 10^3} = 28.2$ mm ◆ $\therefore \bar{z} = \dfrac{-1.181 \times 10^6}{377.14 \times 10^6} = -3.1$ mm ◆ Symmetry: $\bar{y} = 0$ ◆

8.57

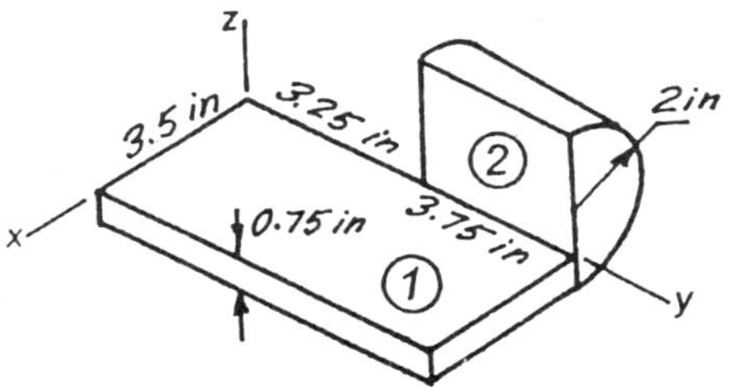

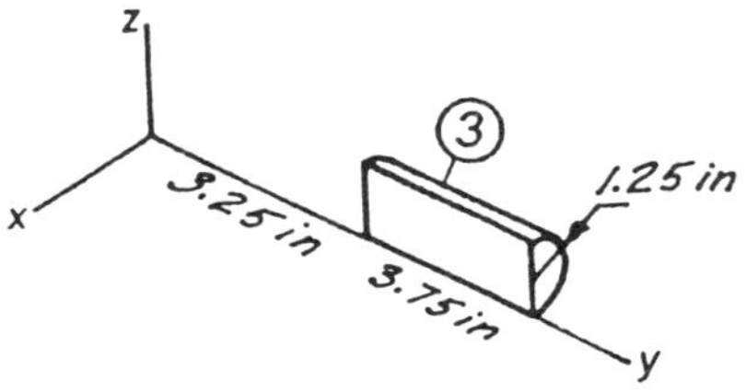

$V_1 = (7)(3.5)(0.75) = 18.375$ in^3

$V_2 = \dfrac{\pi}{2}(2^2)(3.75) = 23.562$ in^3

$\bar{x}_2 = -\dfrac{4(2)}{3\pi} = -0.8488$ in

$V_3 = -\dfrac{\pi}{2}(1.25^2)(3.75) = -9.204$ in^3

$\bar{x}_3 = -\dfrac{4(1.25)}{3\pi} = -0.5305$ in

Part	V (in^3)	$\bar{x}$ (in)	$V\bar{x}$ (in^4)	$\bar{y}$ (in)	$V\bar{y}$ (in^4)	$\bar{z}$ (in)	$V\bar{z}$ (in^4)
1	18.375	1.7500	32.156	3.5000	64.313	−0.3750	−6.891
2	23.562	−0.8488	−19.999	5.1250	120.755	1.2500	29.453
3	−9.204	−0.5305	4.883	5.1250	−47.171	1.2500	−11.505
Sum	32.733		17.040		137.897		11.057

$\therefore \bar{x} = \dfrac{17.040}{32.733} = 0.521$ in ◆ $\bar{y} = \dfrac{137.897}{32.733} = 4.213$ in ◆ $\bar{z} = \dfrac{11.057}{32.733} = 0.338$ in ◆

8.58

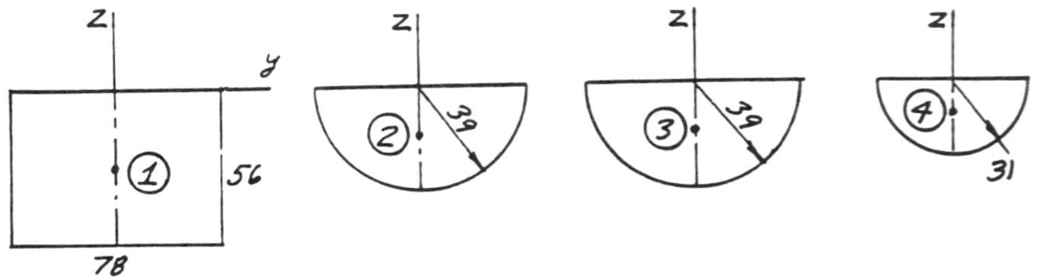

← 10 mm thick →   ← 40 mm thick →

$V_1 = (78)(56)(10) = 43\ 680$ mm^3

$\bar{z}_1 = -28$ mm

$V_2 = -\dfrac{\pi}{2}(39^2)(10) = -23\ 892$ mm^3

$\bar{z}_2 = -\dfrac{4(39)}{3\pi} = -16.552$ mm

$V_3 = \dfrac{\pi}{2}(39^2)(40) = 95\ 567$ mm^3

$\bar{z}_3 = -16.552$ mm

$V_4 = -\dfrac{\pi}{2}(31^2)(40) = -60\ 381$ mm^3

$\bar{z}_4 = -\dfrac{4(31)}{3\pi} = -13.157$ mm

$V = \Sigma V_i = 43\ 680 - 23\ 892 + 95\ 567 - 60\ 381 = 54\ 974$ mm^3

$Q_{xy} = \Sigma \bar{z}_i V_i = (43\ 680)(-28) + (-23\ 892)(-16.552) + (95\ 567)(-16.552)$
$+ (-60\ 381)(-13.157) = -1\ 614\ 972$ mm^4

$\therefore \bar{z} = \dfrac{Q_{xy}}{V} = -\dfrac{1\ 614\ 972}{54\ 974} = -29.4$ mm ◆

8.59

$V_1 = \pi(2^2)(6) = 24\pi$ in^3 $\bar{z}_1 = 3$ in

$V_2 = -\pi(1.5^2)h = -2.25\pi h$ in^3

$\bar{z}_2 = 6 - \dfrac{h}{2}$ in

$V = V_1 + V_2 = \pi(24 - 2.25h)$ in^3

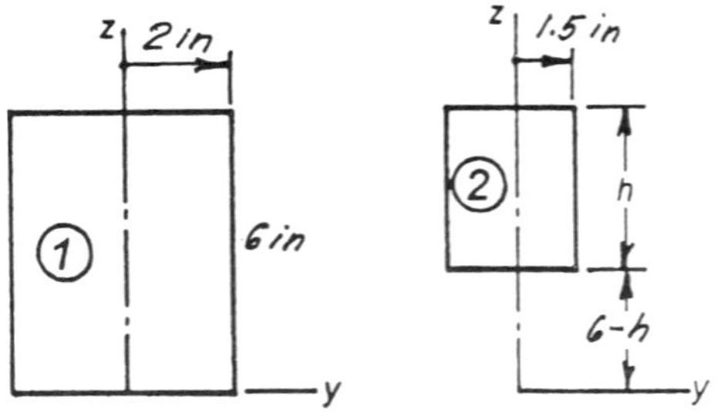

(continued)

8.59 continued

$$Q_{xy} = \bar{z}_1 V_1 + \bar{z}_2 V_2$$

$$= (3)(24\pi) + \left(6 - \frac{h}{2}\right)(-2.25\pi h) = \pi(72 - 13.5h + 1.125h^2)$$

$$\therefore\ \bar{z} = \frac{Q_{xy}}{V} = \frac{72 - 13.5h + 1.125h^2}{24 - 2.25h}$$

$$\therefore\ \frac{d\bar{z}}{dh} = \frac{(24 - 2.25h)(-13.5 + 2.25h) + (72 - 13.5h + 1.125h^2)(2.25)}{(24 - 2.25h)^2}$$

$$= \frac{-162 + 54h - 2.53125h^2}{(24 - 2.25h)^2}$$

$d\bar{z}/dh = 0$: $-162 + 54h - 2.53125h^2 = 0$ The positive root is $h = 3.61$ in ◆

8.60

$\bar{y}_1 = \bar{z}_1 = \frac{1}{3}(4) = 1.3333$ in

$A_2 = \frac{\pi}{4}(4)^2 = 12.566\ \text{in}^2$

$\bar{x}_2 = \bar{z}_2 = \frac{4}{3\pi}(4) = 1.6977$ in

$A_4 = -\pi(1.0)^2 = -3.142\ \text{in}^2$

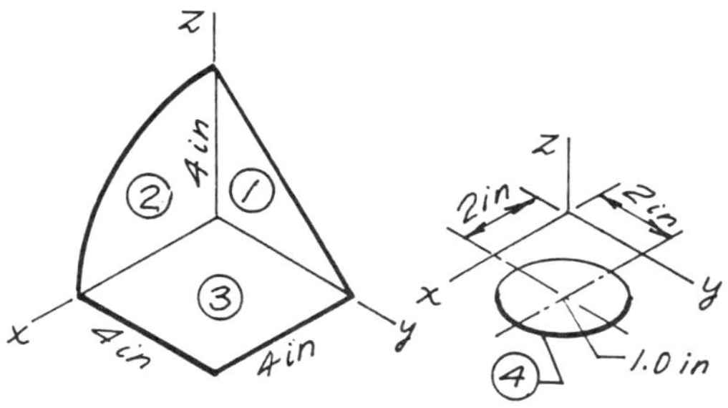

Part	A (in^2)	$\bar{x}$ (in)	$A\bar{x}$ (in^3)	$\bar{y}$ (in)	$A\bar{y}$ (in^3)	$\bar{z}$ (in)	$A\bar{z}$ (in^3)
1	8.000	0	0	1.3333	10.67	1.3333	10.67
2	12.566	1.6977	21.33	0	0	1.6977	21.33
3	16.000	2.0000	32.00	2.0000	32.00	0	0
4	−3.142	2.0000	−6.28	2.0000	−6.28	0	0
Sum	33.424		47.05		36.39		32.00

$\therefore\ \bar{x} = \frac{47.05}{33.424} = 1.408$ in ◆ $\therefore\ \bar{y} = \frac{36.39}{33.424} = 1.089$ in ◆ $\therefore\ \bar{z} = \frac{32.00}{33.424} = 0.957$ in ◆

8.61

$A_1 = A_4 = \frac{1}{2}\pi(1.5^2) = 3.534\ \text{in}^2$

$\bar{z}_1 = 3 + \frac{4}{3\pi}(1.5) = 3.637$ in

$\bar{y}_4 = 3.5 + \frac{4}{3\pi}(1.5) = 4.137$ in

$A_5 = -\pi(0.75^2) = -1.767\ \text{in}^2$

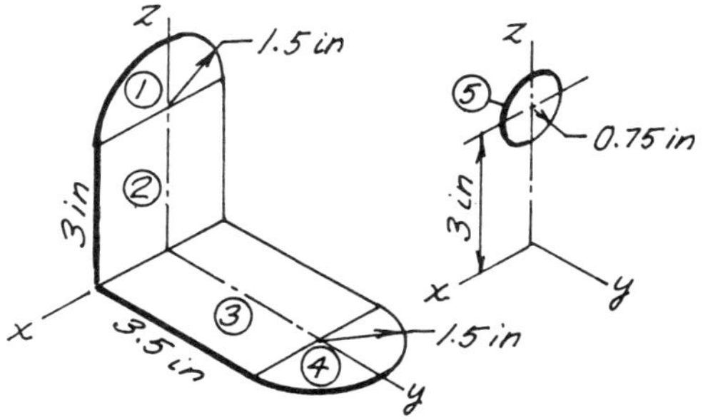

Part	A (in^2)	$\bar{y}$ (in)	$A\bar{y}$ (in^3)	$\bar{z}$ (in)	$A\bar{z}$ (in^3)
1	3.534	0	0	3.637	12.853
2	9.000	0	0	1.500	13.500
3	10.500	1.750	18.375	0	0
4	3.534	4.137	14.620	0	0
5	−1.767	0	0	3.000	−5.301
Sum	24.801		32.995		21.052

$\therefore\ \bar{y} = \frac{32.995}{24.801} = 1.330$ in ◆ $\therefore\ \bar{z} = \frac{21.052}{24.801} = 0.849$ in ◆ By symmetry $\bar{x} = 0$ ◆

8.62

Part	A (m^2)	$\bar{x}$ (m)	$A\bar{x}$ (m^3)	$\bar{y}$ (m)	$A\bar{y}$ (m^3)
1	0.08	0.10000	0.00800	0.10000	0.00800
2	0.04	0.06667	0.00267	0.26667	0.01067
3	0.04	0.20000	0.00800	0.10000	0.00400
4	0.08	0	0	0.20000	0.01600
Sum	0.24		0.01867		0.03867

$\therefore\ \bar{x} = \frac{0.01867}{0.24} = 0.0778\ \text{m} = 77.8\ \text{mm}$ ◆

$\therefore\ \bar{y} = \frac{0.03867}{0.24} = 0.1611\ \text{m} = 161.1\ \text{mm}$ ◆

Due to symmetry $\bar{z} = 100$ mm ◆

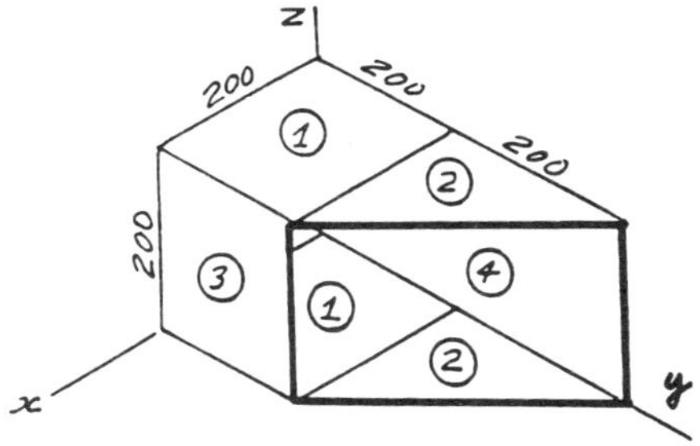

8.63

Part	A (m^2)	$\bar{y}$ (m)	$A\bar{y}$ (m^3)	$\bar{z}$ (m)	$A\bar{z}$ (m^3)
1	0.2773	0.450	0.1248	0.255	0.0707
2	0.1890	0.600	0.1134	0.220	0.0416
3	0.2700	0.450	0.1215	0.075	0.0203
4	0.1800	0.450	0.0810	0.000	0.0000
Sum	0.9163		0.4407		0.1326

$\therefore \bar{y} = \dfrac{0.4407}{0.9163} = 0.481$ m ◆

$\therefore \bar{z} = \dfrac{0.1326}{0.9163} = 0.145$ m ◆

Due to symmetry $\bar{x} = 0$ ◆

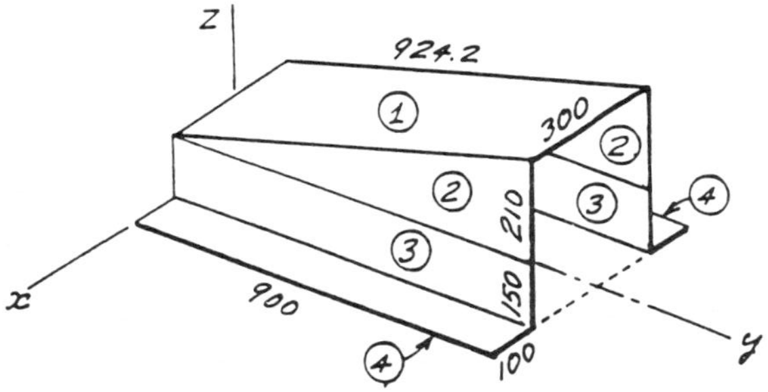

8.64

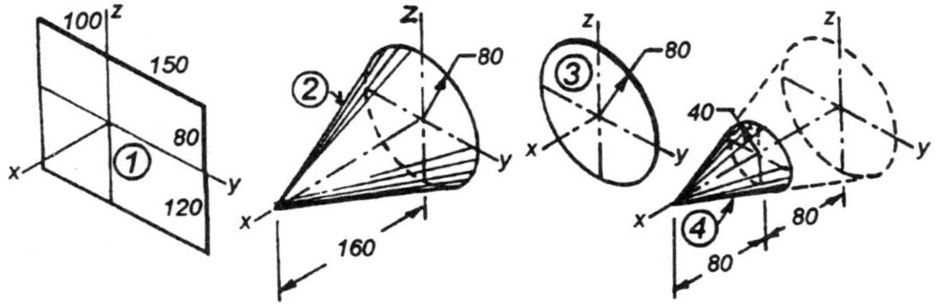

$A_1 = (250)(200) = 50\,000\ mm^2$ $\quad \bar{y}_1 = \dfrac{250}{2} - 100 = 25$ mm $\quad \bar{z}_1 = 80 - \dfrac{200}{2} = -20$ mm

$A_2 = \pi(80)\sqrt{80^2 + 160^2} = 44\,959\ mm^2$ $\quad \bar{x}_2 = \dfrac{1}{3}(160) = 53.333$ mm

$A_3 = -\pi(80^2) = -20\,106\ mm^2$

$A_4 = -\pi(40)\sqrt{40^2 + 80^2} = -11\,240\ mm^2$ $\quad \bar{x}_4 = 80 + \dfrac{1}{3}80 = 106.667$ mm

(continued)

8.64 continued

Part	A (mm^2)	$\bar{x}$ (mm)	$A\bar{x}$ (mm^3)	$\bar{y}$ (mm)	$A\bar{y}$ (mm^3)	$\bar{z}$ (mm)	$A\bar{z}$ (mm^3)
1	50 000	0.000	0	25.000	1 250 000	−20.000	−1 000 000
2	44 959	53.333	2 397 798	0.000	0	0.000	0
3	−20 106	0.000	0	0.000	0	0.000	0
4	−11 240	106.667	−1 198 937	0.000	0	0.000	0
Sum	63 613		1 198 861		1 250 000		−1 000 000

$\therefore \bar{x} = \dfrac{1\,198\,861}{63\,613} = 18.85$ mm, $\bar{y} = \dfrac{1\,250\,000}{63\,613} = 19.65$ mm, $\bar{z} = -\dfrac{1\,000\,000}{63\,613} = -15.72$ mm ◆

8.65

Part	A (in^2)	$\bar{y}$ (in)	$A\bar{y}$ (in^3)	$\bar{z}$ (in)	$A\bar{z}$ (in^3)
1	756	10.5	7 938	18.0	13 608
2	270	−5.0	−1 350	24.0	6 480
3	2106	−7.5	−15 795	18.0	37 908
4	270	−5.0	−1 350	24.0	6 480
5	756	10.5	7 938	18.0	13 608
Sum	4158		−2 619		78 084

$\therefore \bar{y} = -\dfrac{2619}{4158} = -0.63$ in ◆

$\therefore \bar{z} = \dfrac{78\,084}{4158} = 18.78$ in ◆

Due to symmetry $\bar{x} = 27.00$ in ◆

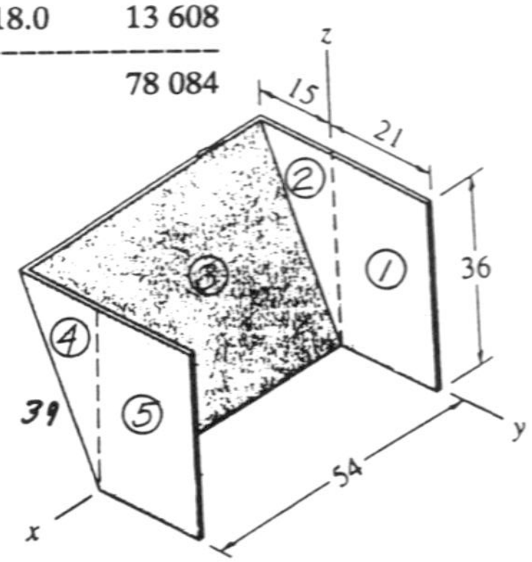

Dimensions in inches

8.66

$A_1 = (200)(250) = 50\,000\ \text{mm}^2 \qquad \bar{z}_1 = 125\ \text{mm}$

$A_2 = 75h\ \text{mm}^2 \qquad \bar{z}_2 = h/3$

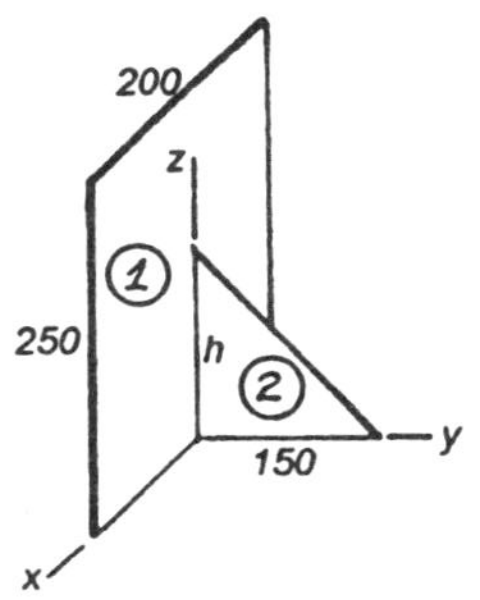

$A = \Sigma A_i = 50\,000 + 75h\ \ \text{mm}^2$

$\therefore Q_{xy} = \Sigma A_i \bar{z}_i = (50\,000)(125) + (75h)(h/3)$

$= 6\,250\,000 + 25h^2\ \ \text{mm}^3$

$$\therefore \bar{z} = \frac{6\,250\,000 + 25h^2}{50\,000 + 75\,h}$$

$$\therefore \frac{d\bar{z}}{dh} = \frac{(50\,000 + 75h)(50h) - (75)(6\,250\,000 + 25h^2)}{(50\,000 + 75h)^2} = \frac{1.875\,h^2 + 2500\,h - 468\,750}{(50\,000 + 75h)^2} \times 10^3$$

$\bar{z}$ is minimized when $d\bar{z}/dh = 0$

$\therefore 1.875\,h^2 + 2500\,h - 468\,750 = 0$ The positive root is $h = 166.7$ mm ◆

8.67

Part	L (mm)	$\bar{x}$ (mm)	$L\bar{x}$ (mm²)	$\bar{y}$ (mm)	$L\bar{y}$ (mm²)	$\bar{z}$ (mm)	$L\bar{z}$ (mm)
1	300	150	45 000	0	0	400	120 000
2	500	300	150 000	250	125 000	400	200 000
3	500	150	75 000	500	250 000	200	100 000
Sum	1300		270 000		375 000		420 000

$$\bar{x} = \frac{270\,000}{1300} = 208\ \text{mm}\ ◆$$

$$\bar{y} = \frac{375\,000}{1300} = 288\ \text{mm}\ ◆$$

$$\bar{z} = \frac{420\,000}{1300} = 323\ \text{mm}\ ◆$$

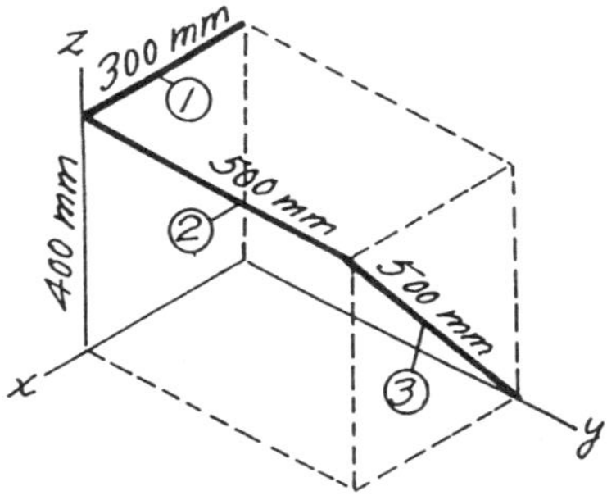

8.68

$L_4 = \pi(3) = 9.425\ \text{in} \qquad \bar{z}_4 = 7 + \frac{2}{\pi}(3) = 8.910\ \text{in}$

Part	L (in)	$\bar{y}$ (in)	$L\bar{y}$ (in²)	$\bar{z}$ (in)	$L\bar{z}$ (in²)
1	6.000	6.000	36.000	0.000	0.000
2	12.000	3.000	36.000	0.000	0.000
3	14.000	0.000	0.000	3.500	49.000
4	9.425	0.000	0.000	8.910	83.977
Sum	41.425		72.000		132.977

$$\bar{y} = \frac{72.000}{41.425} = 1.74\ \text{in}\ ◆$$

$$\bar{z} = \frac{132.977}{41.425} = 3.21\ \text{in}\ ◆$$

Due to symmetry $\bar{x} = 0$ ◆

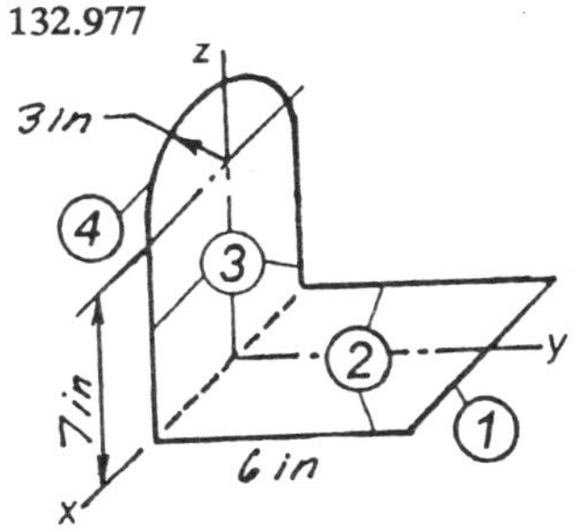

8.69

For part 1:

$$\alpha = \frac{3\pi}{4}\ \text{rad} = 135°$$

$$d = \frac{R \sin\alpha}{\alpha} = \frac{5 \sin 135°}{3\pi/4} = 1.5005\ \text{in}$$

$\bar{x} = \bar{y} = 1.5005 \sin 45° = 1.061$ in

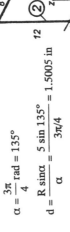

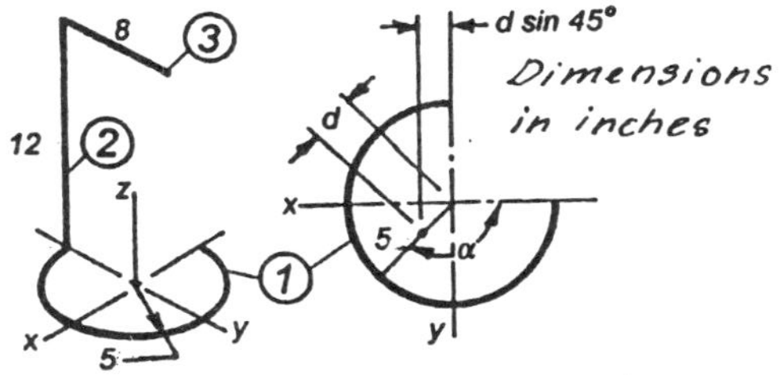

Part	L (in)	$\bar{x}$ (in)	$L\bar{x}$ (in²)	$\bar{y}$ (in)	$L\bar{y}$ (in²)	$\bar{z}$ (in)	$L\bar{z}$ (in²)
1	23.562	1.061	24.999	1.061	24.999	0.000	0.000
2	12.000	0.000	0.000	−5.000	−60.000	6.000	72.000
3	8.000	0.000	0.000	−1.000	−8.000	12.000	96.000
Sum	43.562		24.999		−43.001		168.000

$$\therefore \bar{x} = \frac{24.999}{43.562} = 0.574\ \text{in} \qquad \bar{y} = -\frac{43.001}{43.562} = -0.987\ \text{in} \qquad \bar{z} = \frac{168.000}{43.562} = 3.857\ \text{in}\ ◆$$

8.70

The volume element is the thin shell obtained by rotating the shaded area about the x-axis.

$dV = (2\pi y)(x')dy \qquad \bar{x}_{el} = 46.2 + x'/2$

$$V = \int_V dV = 2\pi \int_0^{80} yx'\,dy \qquad Q_{yz} = \int_V \bar{x}_{el}\,dV = \pi \int_0^{80} yx'(92.4 + x')\,dy$$

Evaluating the integrals with Simpson's rule:

y (mm)	x′ (mm)	W	Wyx′ (mm^2)	Wyx′(92.4 + x′)
0	46.2	1	0	0
20	44.0	4	3 520	480 128
40	37.1	2	2 968	384 356
60	24.0	4	5 760	670 464
80	0.0	1	0	0
			12 248	1 534 948

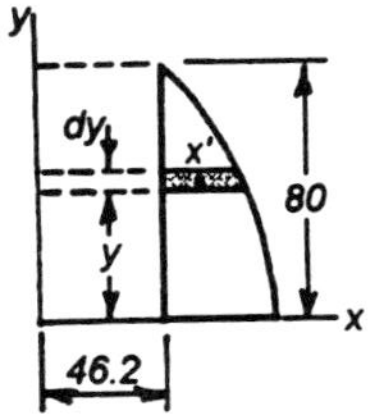

$$V \approx 2\pi \frac{\Delta y}{3} \sum_i W_i y_i x'_i = 2\pi \frac{20}{3}(12\,248) = 513.0 \times 10^3\ \text{mm}^3$$

$$Q_{yz} = \pi \frac{\Delta y}{3} \sum_i W_i y_i x'_i (92.4 + x'_i) = \pi \frac{20}{3}(1\,534\,948) = 32.15 \times 10^6\ \text{mm}^4$$

$$\therefore \bar{x} = \frac{32.15 \times 10^6}{513.0 \times 10^3} = 62.7\ \text{mm} \ \blacklozenge \qquad \text{Due to symmetry } \bar{y} = \bar{z} = 0 \ \blacklozenge$$

8.71

The volume element is the thin, annular plate obtained by rotating the shaded area about the y-axis.

$$dV = \pi\left[(46.2 + x')^2 - 46.2^2\right]dy = \pi(92.4 + x')x'\,dy \qquad \bar{y}_{el} = y$$

$$V = \int_V dV = \pi \int_0^{80} (92.4 + x')x'\,dy$$

$$Q_{zx} = \int_V \bar{y}_{el}\,dV = \pi \int_0^{80} (92.4 + x')yx'\,dy$$

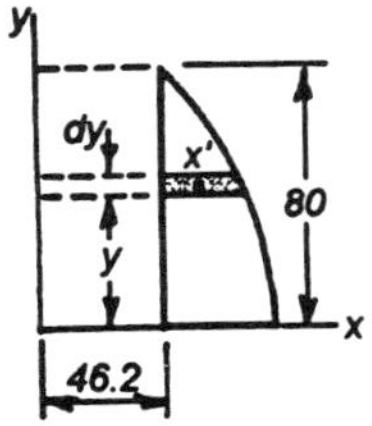

Evaluating the integrals by Simpson's rule:

(continued)

8.71 continued

y (in)	x′ (in)	W	W(92.4 + x′)x′	W(92.4 + x′)yx′
0	46.2	1	6 403	0
20	44.0	4	24 006	480 128
40	37.1	2	9 609	384 356
60	24.0	4	11 174	670 464
80	0.0	1	0	0
			51 192	1 534 948

$$V \approx \pi \frac{\Delta y}{3} \sum_i W_i(92.4 + x'_i)x'_i = \pi \frac{20}{3}(51\,192) = 1.0722 \times 10^6\ \text{mm}^3$$

$$Q_{zx} \approx \pi \frac{\Delta y}{3} \sum_i W_i(92.4 + x'_i)y_i x'_i = \pi \frac{20}{3}(1\,534\,948) = 32.15 \times 10^6\ \text{mm}^4$$

$$\therefore \bar{y} = \frac{32.15 \times 10^6}{1.0722 \times 10^6} = 30.0\ \text{mm} \ \blacklozenge \qquad \text{Due to symmetry } \bar{x} = \bar{z} = 0 \ \blacklozenge$$

8.72

The volume element is the thin cylindrical shell obtained by rotating the shaded area about the axis AB.

$dV = 2\pi(12 - x)y\,dx \qquad \bar{y}_{el} = y/2$

$$V = \int_V dV = 2\pi \int_0^{12} (12 - x)y\,dx \qquad Q_{zx} = \int_V \bar{y}_{el}\,dV = \pi \int_0^{12} (12 - x)y^2\,dx$$

Evaluating the integrals by Simpson's rule:

x (in)	y (in)	W	W(12 − x)y	W(12 − x)y^2
0	0.00	1	0.0	0
2	4.90	4	196.0	960
4	6.93	2	110.9	768
6	8.49	4	203.8	1730
8	9.80	2	78.4	768
10	10.95	4	87.6	959
12	12.00	1	0.00	0
			676.7	5185

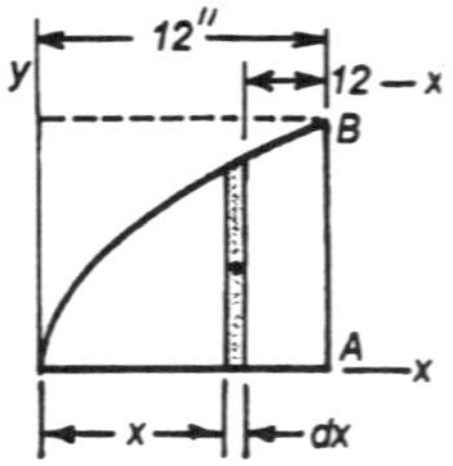

(continued)

8.72 continued

$$V \approx 2\pi \frac{\Delta x}{3} \sum_i W_i (12 - x_i) y_i = 2\pi \frac{2}{3}(676.7) = 2835 \text{ in}^3$$

$$Q_{zx} \approx \pi \frac{\Delta x}{3} \sum_i W_i (12 - x_i) y_i^2 = \pi \frac{2}{3}(5185) = 10\,859 \text{ in}^4$$

$\therefore \bar{y} = \dfrac{10\,859}{2835} = 3.83$ in ◆ Due to symmetry $\bar{x} = 12$ in ◆ $\bar{z} = 0$ ◆

8.73

The volume element is a thin disk obtained by rotating the shaded area about the x-axis.

$dV = \pi y^2\, dx \qquad \bar{x}_{el} = x$

$$V = \int_V dV = \pi \int_0^{12} y^2\, dx \qquad Q_{yz} = \int_V \bar{x}_{el}\, dV = \pi \int_0^{12} y^2 x\, dx$$

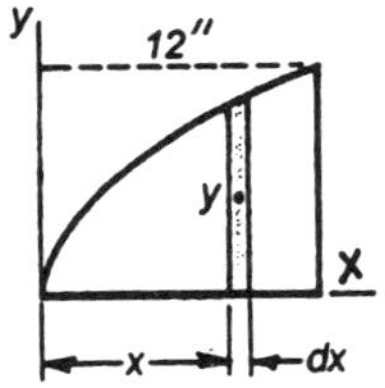

Evaluating the integrals by Simpson's rule:

x (in)	y (in)	W	Wy^2 (in^2)	Wy^2x (in^3)
0	0.00	1	0	0
2	4.90	4	96	192
4	6.93	2	96	384
6	8.49	4	288	1 730
8	9.80	2	192	1 537
10	10.95	4	480	4 796
12	12.00	1	144	1 728
			1 296	10 367

$$V \approx \pi \frac{\Delta x}{3} \sum_i W_i y_i^2 = \pi \frac{2}{3}(1296) = 2714 \text{ in}^3$$

$$Q_{yz} = \pi \frac{\Delta x}{3} \sum_i W_i y_i^2 x_i = \pi \frac{2}{3}(10\,367) = 21\,713 \text{ in}^4$$

$\therefore \bar{x} = \dfrac{21\,713}{2714} = 8.00$ in ◆ Due to symmetry $\bar{y} = \bar{z} = 0$ ◆

<u>Check</u>: for the paraboloid of revolution in Table 8.3

$V = \dfrac{\pi}{2} R^2 h = \dfrac{\pi}{2}(12^2)(12) = 2714 \text{ in}^3 \qquad \bar{x} = \dfrac{2}{3} h = \dfrac{2}{3}(12) = 8.00$ in Checks O.K.

8.74

The surface element is a ring obtained by rotating the line element of length ds about the y-axis.

$$y = \frac{3}{16}x^2 \qquad \therefore \frac{dy}{dx} = \frac{3}{8}x \qquad \therefore \frac{ds}{dx} = \sqrt{1 + (dy/dx)^2} = \sqrt{1 + (3x/8)^2}$$

$$dA = 2\pi x\, ds = 2\pi x \frac{ds}{dx} dx = 2\pi x \sqrt{1 + (3x/8)^2}\, dx \qquad \bar{y}_{el} = y$$

$$A = \int_A dA = 2\pi \int_0^4 x \sqrt{1 + (3x/8)^2}\, dx \qquad Q_{zx} = \int_A \bar{y}_{el}\, dA = 2\pi \int_0^4 xy \sqrt{1 + (3x/8)^2}\, dx$$

Evaluating the integrals with Simpson's rule:

x (m)	y (m)	W	$Wx\sqrt{1 + (3x/8)^2}$	$Wxy\sqrt{1 + (3x/8)^2}$
0	0.0000	1	0.000	0.000
1	0.1875	4	4.272	0.801
2	0.7500	2	5.000	3.750
3	1.6875	4	18.062	30.480
4	3.0000	1	7.211	21.633
			34.545	56.664

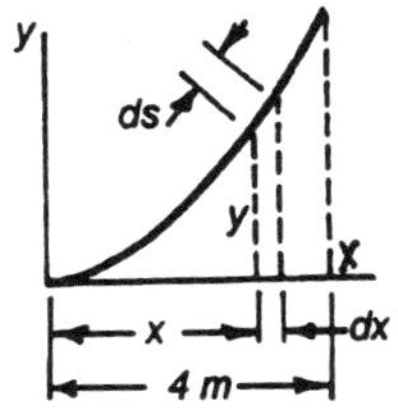

$$A \approx 2\pi \frac{\Delta x}{3} \sum_i W_i x_i \sqrt{1 + (3x_i/8)^2} = 2\pi \frac{1}{3}(34.545) = 72.35 \text{ m}^2$$

$$Q_{zx} = 2\pi \frac{\Delta x}{3} \sum_i W_i x_i y_i \sqrt{1 + (3x_i/8)^2} = 2\pi \frac{1}{3}(56.664) = 118.68 \text{ m}^3$$

$\therefore \bar{y} = \dfrac{118.68}{72.35} = 1.640$ m ◆ Due to symmetry $\bar{x} = \bar{z} = 0$ ◆

8.75

The surface element is a a ring obtained by rotating the line element of length ds about the x-axis.

$$y = \frac{3}{16}x^2 \qquad \therefore \frac{dy}{dx} = \frac{3}{8}x \qquad \therefore \frac{ds}{dx} = \sqrt{1 + (dy/dx)^2} = \sqrt{1 + (3x/8)^2}$$

$$dA = 2\pi y\, ds = 2\pi y \frac{ds}{dx} dx = 2\pi y \sqrt{1 + (3x/8)^2}\, dx \qquad \bar{x}_{el} = x$$

$$A = \int_A dA = 2\pi \int_0^4 y \sqrt{1 + (3x/8)^2}\, dx \qquad Q_{yz} = \int_A \bar{x}_{el}\, dA = 2\pi \int_0^4 xy \sqrt{1 + (3x/8)^2}\, dx$$

Evaluating the integral for A with Simpson's rule (the expression for Q_{yz} is the same as Q_{zx} in Prob. 8.74):

x (m)	y (m)	W	$Wy\sqrt{1 + (3x/8)^2}$
0	0.0000	1	0.000
1	0.1875	4	0.801
2	0.7500	2	1.875
3	1.6875	4	10.160
4	3.0000	1	5.408
			18.244

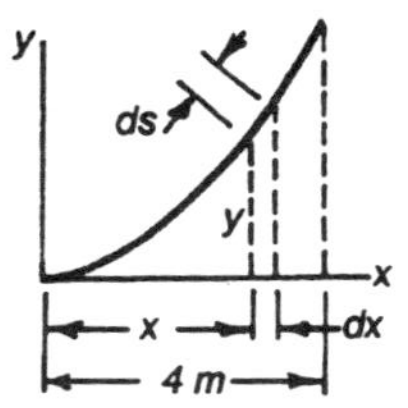

$$A \approx 2\pi \frac{\Delta x}{3} \sum_i W_i y_i \sqrt{1 + (3x_i/8)^2} = 2\pi \frac{1}{3}(18.244) = 38.21 \text{ m}^2$$

$Q_{yz} \approx 118.68 \text{ m}^3$ (from solution of Prob. 8.74)

$\therefore \bar{x} = \frac{118.68}{38.21} = 3.11$ m ◆ Due to symmetry $\bar{y} = \bar{z} = 0$ ◆

8.76

Volume

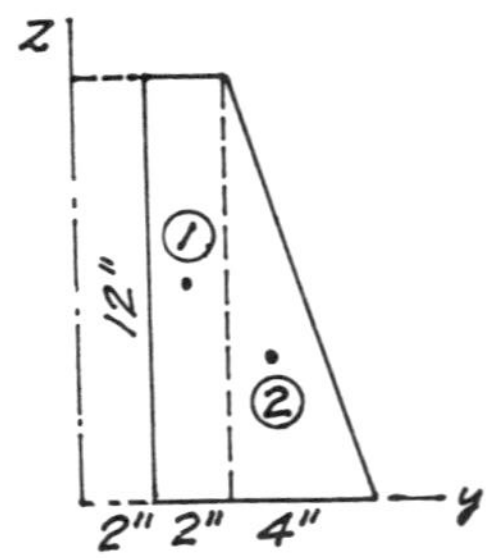

$$Q_z = A_1\bar{y}_1 + A_2\bar{y}_2 = (12 \times 2)(3) + \frac{12 \times 4}{2}\left(4 + \frac{4}{3}\right)$$

$$= 200.0 \text{ in}^3$$

$\therefore V = 2\pi Q_z = 2\pi(200.0) = 1257 \text{ in}^3$ ◆

Surface area

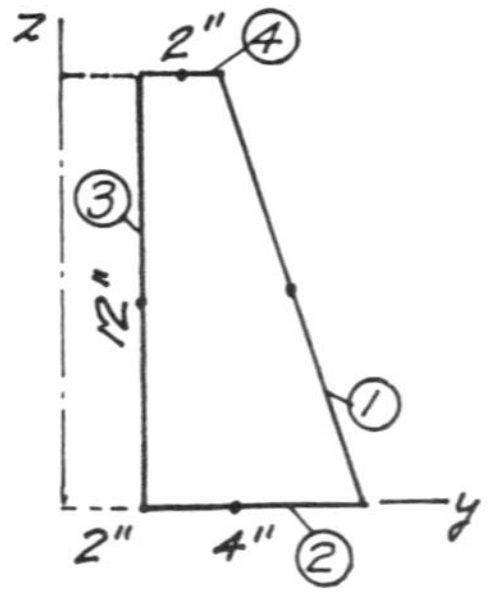

$$L_1 = \sqrt{12^2 + 4^2} = 12.649 \text{ in}$$

$$Q_z = \sum_{i=1}^{4} L_i\bar{y}_i = (12.649)(6) + (4)(4) + (12)(2) + (2)(3)$$

$$= 121.89 \text{ in}^2$$

$\therefore A = 2\pi Q_z = 2\pi(121.89) = 766 \text{ in}^2$ ◆

8.77

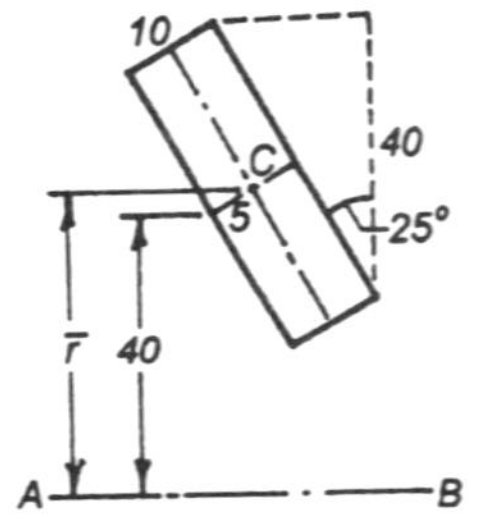

$$A = 10\frac{40}{\cos 25°} = 441.35 \text{ mm}^2$$

$$\bar{r} = 40 + 5 \sin 25° = 42.11 \text{ mm}$$

$$Q_{AB} = A\bar{r} = (441.35)(42.11) = 18\,585 \text{ mm}^3$$

$V = 2\pi Q_{AB} = 2\pi(18\,585) = 116.8 \times 10^3 \text{ mm}^3$ ◆

8.78

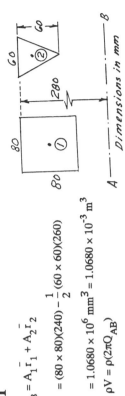

<u>Surface area</u>

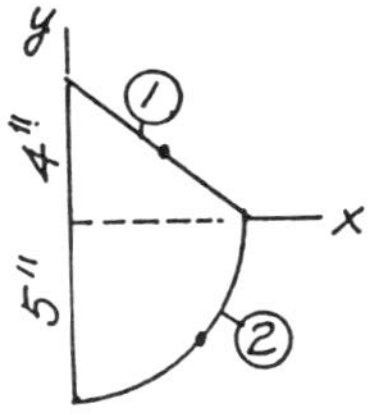

$L_1 = \sqrt{4^2 + 5^2} = 6.403$ in $\quad L_2 = \frac{\pi}{2}(5) = 7.854$ in

$\bar{x}_2 = \frac{2}{\pi}(5) = 3.183$ in

$Q_y = L_1\bar{x}_1 + L_2\bar{x}_2 = (6.403)(2.5) + (7.854)(3.183) = 41.01\ \text{in}^2$

$A = 2\pi Q_y = 2\pi(41.01) = 258\ \text{in}^2$ ◆

<u>Volume</u>

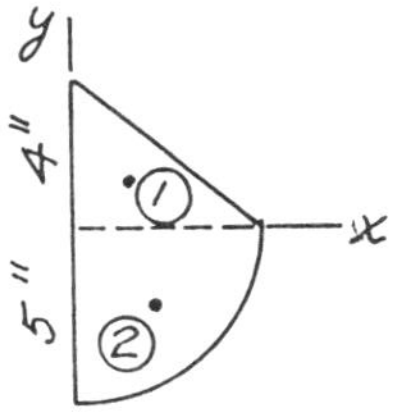

$A_2 = \frac{\pi}{4}(5)^2 = 19.635\ \text{in}^2 \quad \bar{x}_2 = \frac{4}{3\pi}(5) = 2.122$ in

$Q_y = A_1\bar{x}_1 + A_2\bar{x}_2 = (10)\left(\frac{5}{3}\right) + (19.635)(2.122) = 58.33\ \text{in}^3$

$V = 2\pi Q_y = 2\pi(58.33) = 366\ \text{in}^3$ ◆

8.79

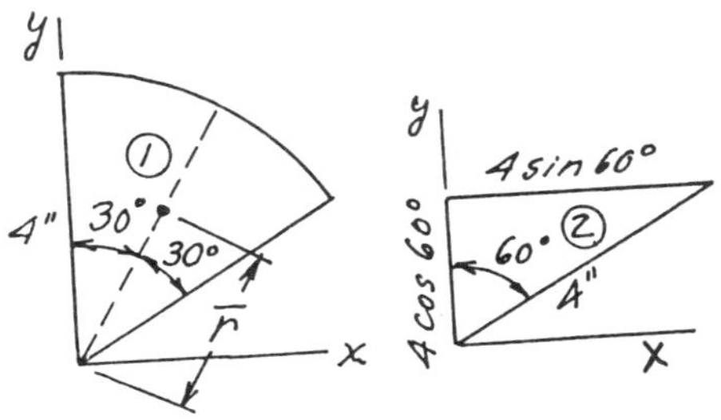

$A_1 = \frac{1}{2}R^2\theta = \frac{1}{2}(4)^2\left(\frac{\pi}{3}\right) = 8.378\ \text{in}^2$

$A_2 = -\frac{1}{2}(4\cos 60°)(4\sin 60°) = -3.464\ \text{in}^2$

$^{*}\ \bar{r} = \frac{2R\sin(\theta/2)}{3(\theta/2)} = \frac{2(4)\sin 30°}{3(\pi/6)} = 2.546$ in

$\bar{x}_1 = \bar{r}\sin 30° = 1.273$ in

$\bar{x}_2 = \frac{1}{3}(4\sin 60°) = 1.155$ in

$Q_y = A_1\bar{x}_1 + A_2\bar{x}_2 = (8.378)(1.273) - (3.464)(1.155) = 6.664\ \text{in}^3$

$V = 2\pi Q_y = 2\pi(6.664) = 41.9\ \text{in}^3$ ◆

8.80

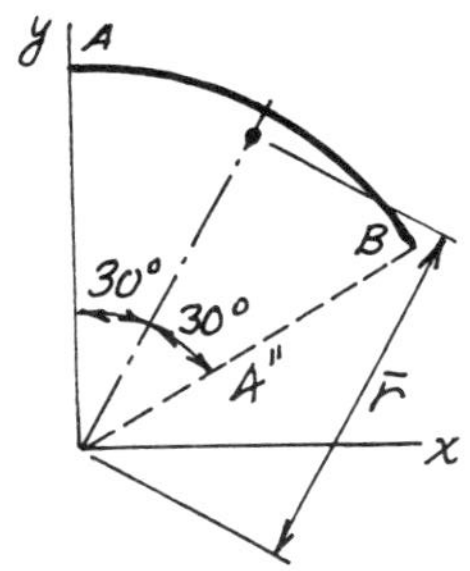

$L = R\theta = (4)\left(\frac{\pi}{3}\right) = 4.189$ in

$\bar{r} = \frac{R\sin(\theta/2)}{(\theta/2)} = \frac{(4)\sin 30°}{\pi/6} = 3.820$ in

$\bar{x} = \bar{r}\sin 30° = 3.820\sin 30° = 1.9099$ in

$Q_y = L\bar{x} = (4.189)(1.9099) = 8.001\ \text{in}^2$

$A = 2\pi Q_y = 2\pi(8.001) = 50.3\ \text{in}^2$ ◆

8.81

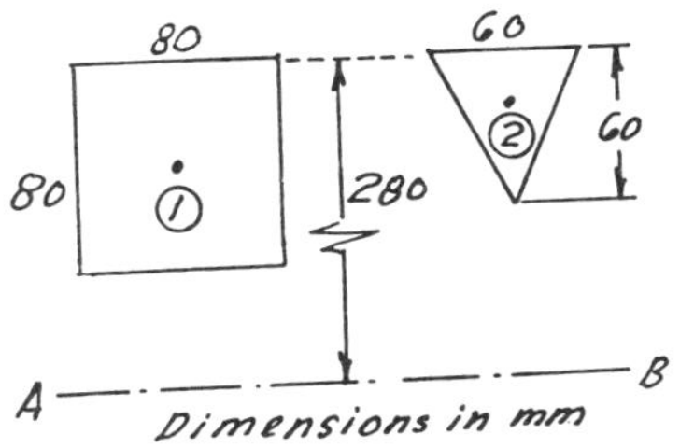

$Q_{AB} = A_1\bar{r}_1 + A_2\bar{r}_2$

$= (80 \times 80)(240) - \frac{1}{2}(60 \times 60)(260)$

$= 1.0680 \times 10^6\ \text{mm}^3 = 1.0680 \times 10^{-3}\ \text{m}^3$

$m = \rho V = \rho(2\pi Q_{AB})$

$= (7850)(2\pi)(1.0680 \times 10^3) = 52.7$ kg ◆

8.82

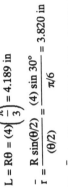

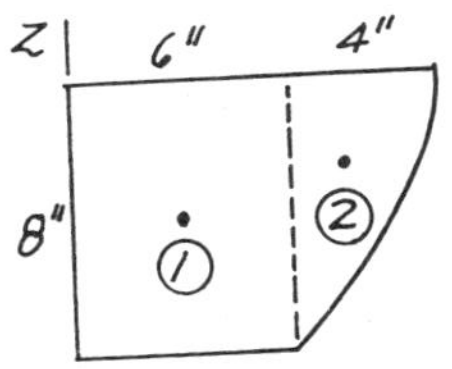

$A_1 = (6)(8) = 48\ \text{in}^2 \quad A_2 = \frac{2}{3}(4)(8) = \frac{64}{3}\ \text{in}^2$

$\bar{r}_1 = 3$ in $\quad \bar{r}_2 = 10 - \frac{3}{5}(4) = 7.6$ in

$Q_z = A_1\bar{r}_1 + A_2\bar{r}_2 = (48)(3) + \frac{64}{3}(7.6) = 306.1\ \text{in}^3$

$V = 2\pi Q_z = 2\pi(306.1) = 1923\ \text{in}^3$ ◆

8.83

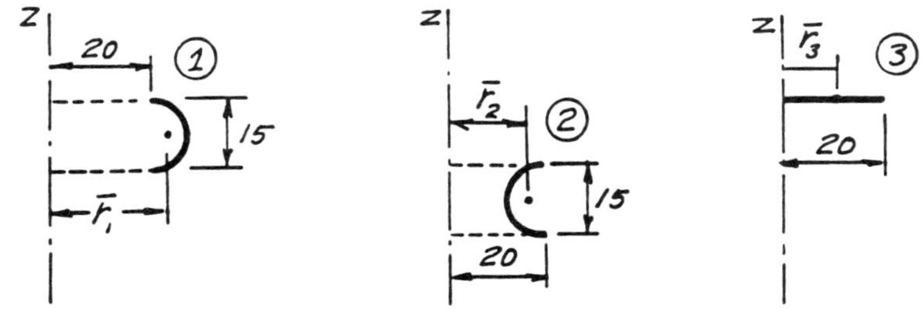

$L_1 = \pi(7.5)$ mm $L_2 = \pi(7.5)$ mm $L_3 = 20$ mm

$\bar{r}_1 = 20 + \frac{2}{\pi}(7.5)$ mm $\bar{r}_2 = 20 - \frac{2}{\pi}(7.5)$ mm $\bar{r}_3 = 10$ mm

$$Q_z = 3L_1\bar{r}_1 + 2L_2\bar{r}_2 + 2L_3\bar{r}_3$$

$$= 3\left[7.5(20\pi + 15)\right] + 2\left[7.5(20\pi - 15)\right] + 2(20)(10) = 2869 \text{ mm}^2$$

$$V = 2\pi Q_z = 2\pi(2869) = 18.02 \times 10^3 \text{ mm}^2 \ \blacklozenge$$

8.84

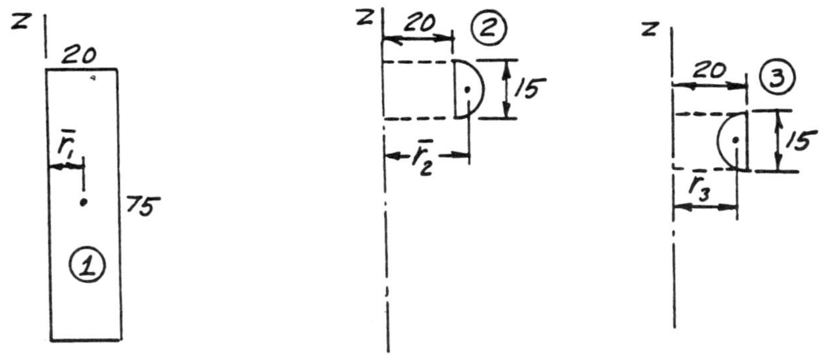

$A_1 = (20)(75) = 1500 \text{ mm}^2$ $A_2 = \frac{\pi}{2}(7.5^2) \text{ mm}^2$ $A_3 = \frac{\pi}{2}(7.5^2) \text{ mm}^2$

$\bar{r}_1 = 10$ mm $\bar{r}_2 = 20 + \frac{4}{3\pi}(7.5)$ mm $\bar{r}_3 = 20 - \frac{4}{3\pi}(7.5)$ mm

(continued)

8.84 continued

$$Q_z = A_1\bar{r}_1 + 3A_2\bar{r}_2 - 2A_3\bar{r}_3$$

$$= (1500)(10) + 3\left[(7.5^2)\left\{10\pi + \frac{2}{3}(7.5)\right\}\right] - 2\left[(7.5^2)\left\{10\pi - \frac{2}{3}(7.5)\right\}\right] = 18\,173 \text{ mm}^3$$

$$V = 2\pi Q_z = 2\pi(18\,173) = 114.2 \times 10^3 \text{ mm}^3 \ \blacklozenge$$

8.85

$L = 2(4) + 2(2) + 2\pi(2) = 24.57$ in

$\bar{r} = 9$ in

$Q_x = L\bar{r} = (24.57)(9) = 221.1 \text{ in}^2$

$A = \frac{1}{4}(2\pi Q_x) = \frac{1}{4}(2\pi)(221.1) = 347 \text{ in}^2 \ \blacklozenge$

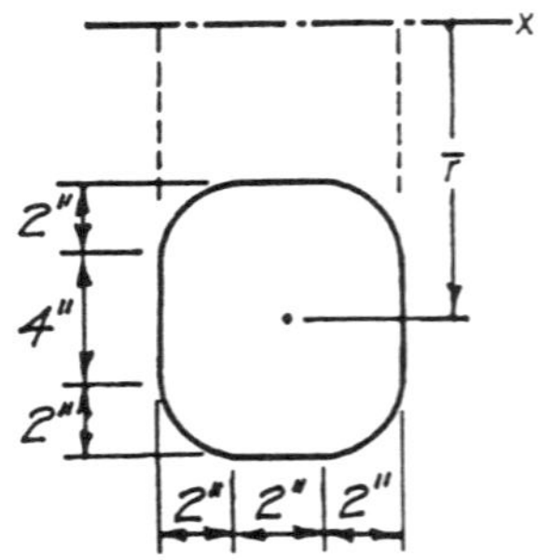

8.86

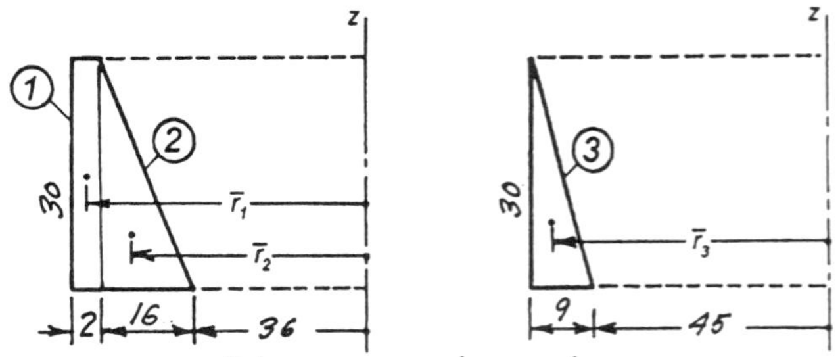

Dimensions in meters

$A_1 = (30)(2) = 60 \text{ m}^2$ $A_2 = \frac{1}{2}(30)(16) = 240 \text{ m}^2$ $A_3 = -\frac{1}{2}(30)(9) = -135 \text{ m}^2$

$\bar{r}_1 = 53$ m $\bar{r}_2 = 36 + \frac{2}{3}(16) = 46.67$ m $\bar{r}_3 = 45 + \frac{2}{3}(9) = 51$ m

$$Q_z = \Sigma A_i\bar{r}_i = (60)(53) + (240)(46.67) - (135)(51) = 7496 \text{ m}^3$$

$$V = \frac{60°}{360°}(2\pi Q_z) = \frac{1}{6}(2\pi)(7496) = 7850 \text{ m}^3 \ \blacklozenge$$

8.87

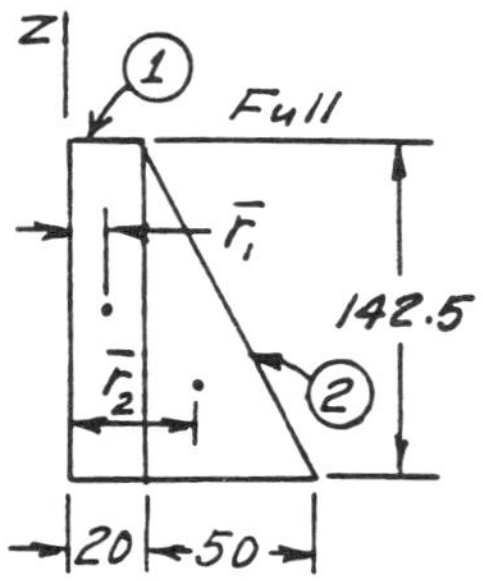

(a) $A_1 = (20)(142.5) = 2850\text{ mm}^2 \qquad \bar{r}_1 = 10\text{ mm}$

$A_2 = \frac{1}{2}(50)(142.5) = 3562\text{ mm}^2 \qquad \bar{r}_2 = 20 + \frac{50}{3} = 36.67\text{ mm}$

$Q_z = \Sigma A_i \bar{r}_i = (2850)(10) + (3562)(36.67) = 159.12 \times 10^3\text{ mm}^3$

$V = 2\pi Q_z = 2\pi(159.12 \times 10^3) = 1.000 \times 10^6\text{ mm}^3$ ◆

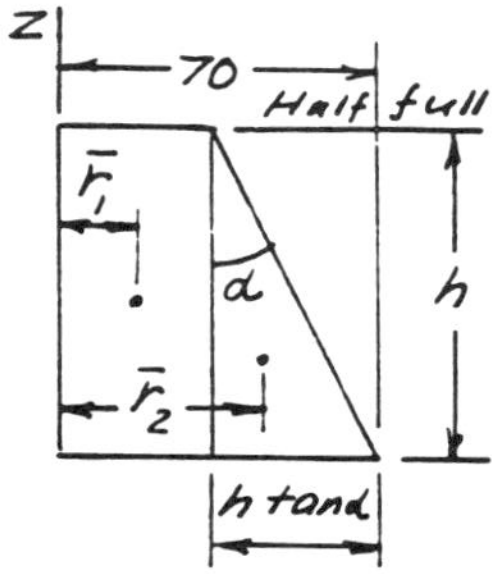

(b) $\tan\alpha = \frac{50}{142.5} = 0.3509$

$A_1 = (70 - h\tan\alpha)h \qquad A_2 = \frac{1}{2}(h\tan\alpha)h$

$\bar{r}_1 = \frac{1}{2}(70 - h\tan\alpha)$

$\bar{r}_2 = (70 - h\tan\alpha) + \frac{1}{3}h\tan\alpha = 70 - \frac{2}{3}h\tan\alpha$

$Q_z = \Sigma A_i \bar{r}_i = \frac{h}{2}(70 - h\tan\alpha)^2 + \frac{h^2}{2}\left(70 - \frac{2}{3}h\tan\alpha\right)\tan\alpha = \frac{h}{2}\left(70^2 - 70h\tan\alpha + \frac{h^2}{3}\tan^2\alpha\right)$

Given: $V = 2\pi Q_z = 0.5 \times 10^6\text{ mm}^3 \qquad \therefore \pi h\left(70^2 - 70h\tan\alpha + \frac{1}{3}h^2\tan^2\alpha\right) = 0.5 \times 10^6$

After substituting for $\tan\alpha$, we get: $0.12894\,h^3 - 77.17\,h^2 + 15\,394\,h - 500\,000 = 0$

The solution is (a numerical method must be used) $h = 39.9$ mm ◆

8.88

Excavation:

$A_1 = \frac{1}{2}a^2\tan\alpha \qquad \bar{r}_1 = \frac{a}{3}$

$V_1 = 2\pi A_1 \bar{r}_1 = \frac{\pi}{3}a^3\tan\alpha$

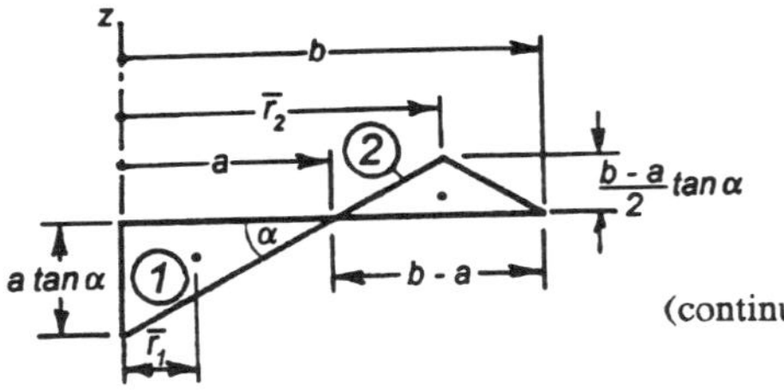

(continued)

8.88 continued

Fill:

$A_2 = \frac{1}{2}\frac{(b-a)^2}{2}\tan\alpha \qquad \bar{r}_2 = \frac{b+a}{2}$

$V_2 = 2\pi A_2 \bar{r}_2 = \frac{\pi}{4}(b-a)^2(b+a)\tan\alpha$

$V_1 = V_2$: $\frac{1}{3}a^3 = \frac{1}{4}(b-a)^2(b+a) \qquad \therefore 4a^3 = 3(b^3 - b^2a - ba^2 + a^3)$

$\therefore 3\left(\frac{b}{a}\right)^3 - 3\left(\frac{b}{a}\right)^2 - 3\left(\frac{b}{a}\right) - 1 = 0 \qquad$ The solution is $\frac{b}{a} = 1.702$ ◆

8.89

Due to symmetry: $\bar{x} = \bar{y} = 0$ ◆

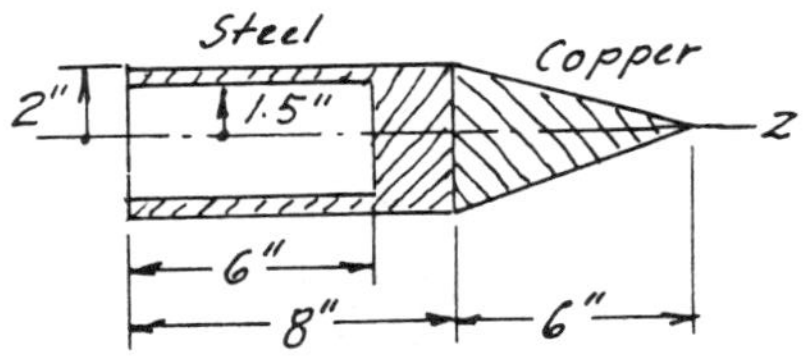

Copper: $\rho_c = \dfrac{556}{12^3} = 0.3218 \text{ lb/in}^3$

Steel: $\rho_s = \dfrac{489}{12^3} = 0.2830 \text{ lb/in}^3$

Steel cylinder without hole: $W_1 = \rho_s V_1 = 0.2830\left[\pi(2)^2(8)\right] = 28.45 \text{ lb}$ $\quad \bar{z}_1 = 4 \text{ in}$

Steel hole: $\quad W_2 = \rho_s V_2 = 0.2830\left[-\pi(1.5)^2(6)\right] = -12.00 \text{ lb}$ $\quad \bar{z}_2 = 3 \text{ in}$

Copper cone: $W_3 = \rho_c V_3 = 0.3218\left[\dfrac{\pi}{3}(2)^2(6)\right] = 8.09 \text{ lb}$ $\quad \bar{z}_3 = 8 + \dfrac{6}{4} = 9.5 \text{ in}$

Assembly: $\bar{z} = \dfrac{\Sigma W_i \bar{z}_i}{\Sigma W_i} = \dfrac{28.45(4) - 12.00(3) + 8.09(9.5)}{28.45 - 12.00 + 8.09} = 6.30 \text{ in}$ ◆

8.90

For one fin: $\bar{z} = \dfrac{1.8}{3} = 0.6 \text{ m}$ $\quad \bar{r} = 0.5 + \dfrac{0.36}{3} = 0.62 \text{ m}$

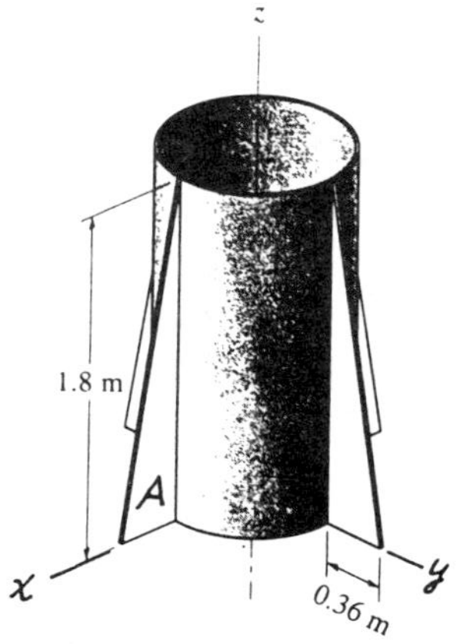

$$\bar{z} = \frac{\Sigma m_i \bar{z}_i}{\Sigma m_i} = \frac{120(0.9) + 3(15)(0.6)}{120 + 3(15)} = 0.818 \text{ m} \quad ◆$$

$$\bar{x} = \frac{\Sigma m_i \bar{x}_i}{\Sigma m_i} = \frac{15(-0.62)}{120 + 3(15)} = -0.056 \text{ m} \quad ◆$$

Due to symmetry: $\bar{y} = 0$ ◆

8.91

The center of gravity G must lie directly below A, i.e. $\bar{x} = -R$. Since the wire is uniform, its center of gravity and centroid coincide.

Part	L	$\bar{x}$	$L\bar{x}$
1	L	$-L/2$	$-L^2/2$
2	$\pi R/2$	$2R/\pi$	R^2
3	πR	0	0
Sum	$L + 3\pi R/2$		$-L^2/2 + R^2$

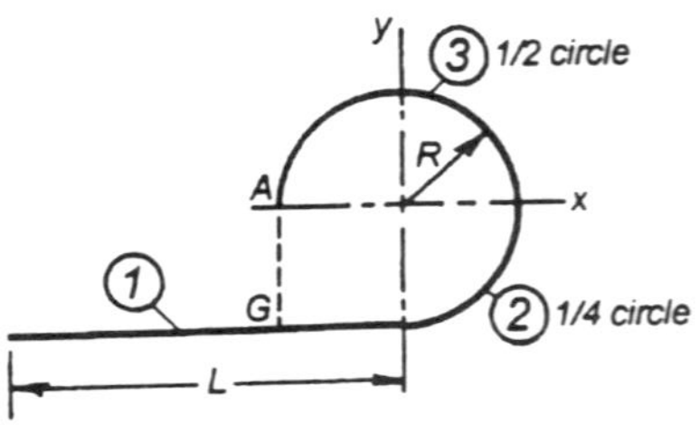

$\bar{x} = -R$: $\quad \dfrac{-L^2/2 + R^2}{L + 3\pi R/2} = -R$ $\qquad \therefore -R\left(L + \dfrac{3\pi}{2}R\right) + \dfrac{L^2}{2} - R^2 = 0$

$\therefore 0.5\left(\dfrac{L}{R}\right)^2 - \dfrac{L}{R} - 5.712 = 0$ $\qquad$ The positive root is $\dfrac{L}{R} = 4.52$ ◆

8.92

$W_1 = 0.283(4)(5)(1/20) = 0.2830 \text{ lb}$

$W_2 = 0.283(7)(5)(1/20) = 0.4953 \text{ lb}$

$W_3 = 0.283(2)(5)(1/20) = 0.1415 \text{ lb}$

$W_4 = 0.029(2)(2)(5) = 0.5800 \text{ lb}$

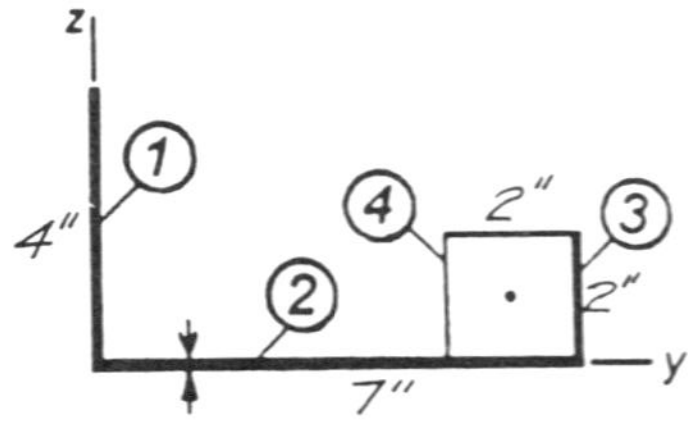

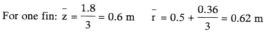

Part	W (lb)	$\bar{y}$ (in)	$W\bar{y}$	$\bar{z}$ (in)	$W\bar{z}$
1	0.2830	0.0	0.0000	2.0	0.5660
2	0.4953	3.5	1.7336	0.0	0.0000
3	0.1415	7.0	0.9905	1.0	0.1415
4	0.5800	6.0	3.4800	1.0	0.5800
Sum	1.4998		6.2041		1.2875

$\therefore \bar{y} = \dfrac{6.2041}{1.4998} = 4.137 \text{ in}$ ◆ $\qquad \therefore \bar{z} = \dfrac{1.2875}{1.4998} = 0.858 \text{ in}$ ◆

Due to symmetry $\bar{x} = 2.5 \text{ in}$ ◆

8.93

The partition does not tip if $\bar{y} > 0$, the limiting case being $\bar{y} = 0$.

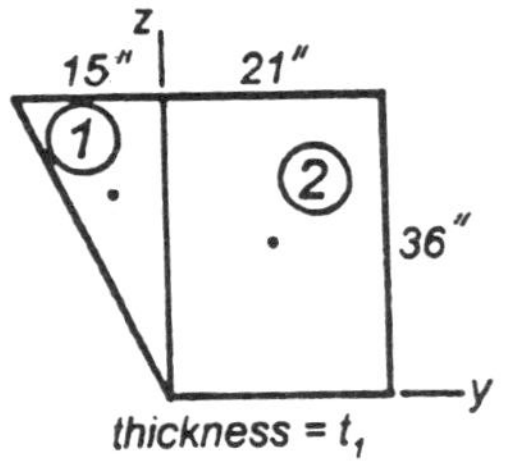

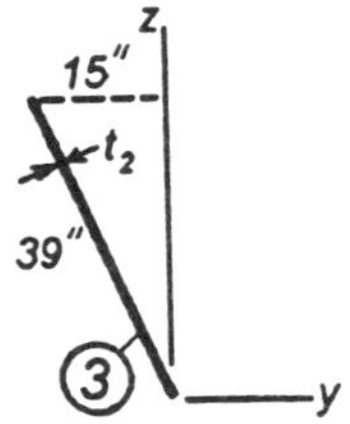

Part	V (in³)	$\bar{y}$ (in)	$V\bar{y}$ (in⁴)
1 (2 pcs)	$(15)(36)t_1 = 540\ t_1$	−5.0	$-2\,700\ t_1$
2 (2 pcs)	$2(21)(36)t_1 = 1512\ t_1$	10.5	$15\,876\ t_1$
3	$(39)(54)t_2 = 2106\ t_2$	−7.5	$-15\,795\ t_2$
Sum			$13\,176\ t_1 - 15\,795\ t_2$

If $\bar{y} = 0$, then $\Sigma V_i \bar{y}_i = 0$. $\quad \therefore 13\,176\ t_1 - 15\,795\ t_2 = 0 \quad \therefore t_2/t_1 = 0.834$ ◆

8.94

W_1 = weight of molten iron

W_2 = weight of crucible

$\Sigma M_O = 0$: (+) $F(0.28 \cos\alpha) - W_2\bar{x}_2 = 0$

$$\therefore F = \frac{W_2\bar{x}_2}{0.28 \cos\alpha}$$

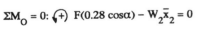

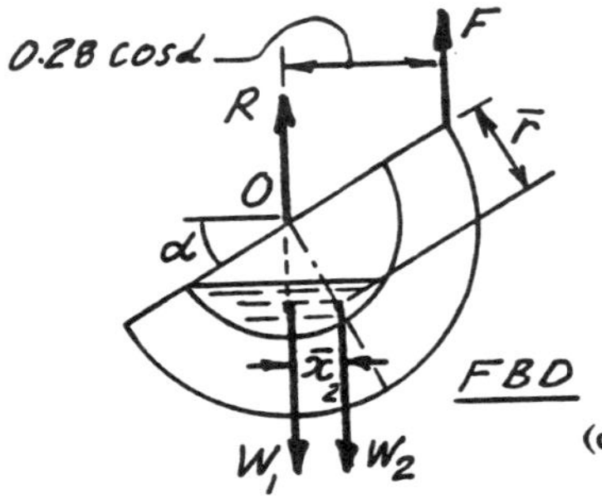

(continued)

8.94 continued

For the crucible:

$$W_2\bar{r} = (2000)(9.81)\left\{\left[\frac{2\pi}{3}(0.28)^3\right]\left[\frac{3}{8}(0.28)\right] - \left[\frac{2\pi}{3}(0.2)^3\right]\left[\frac{3}{8}(0.2)\right]\right\}$$

$$= (2000)(9.81)\frac{\pi}{4}(0.28^4 - 0.2^4) = 70.06\ \text{N}\cdot\text{m}^2$$

But $\bar{x}_2 = \bar{r}\sin\alpha$

$\therefore W_2\bar{x}_2 = 70.06 \sin\alpha\ \text{N}\cdot\text{m}^2$

$$\therefore F = \frac{70.06 \sin\alpha}{0.28 \cos\alpha} = 250 \tan\alpha\ \text{N}$$ ◆

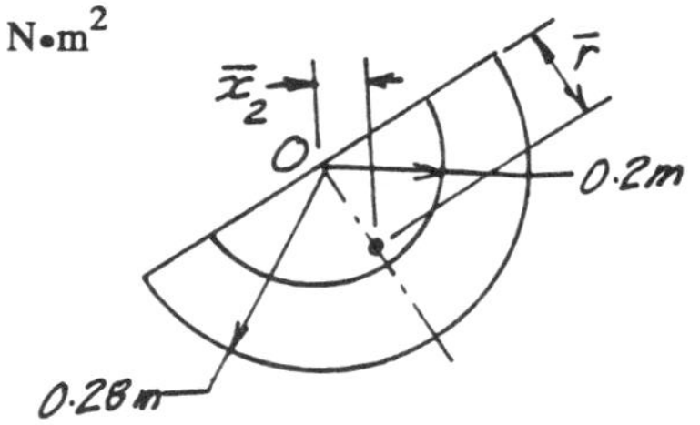

8.95

$$m_{AB} = 2700\left[\frac{\pi}{4}(0.006)^2(0.2)\right] = 0.01527\ \text{kg}$$

$$m_{CD} = 8910\left[\frac{\pi}{4}(0.008)^2(0.16)\right] = 0.07166\ \text{kg}$$

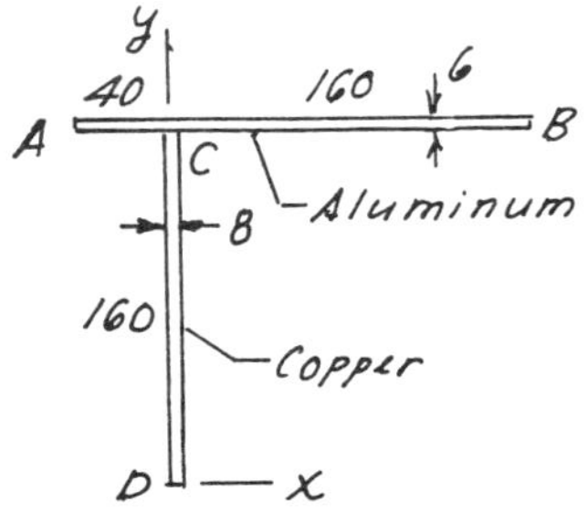

Part	m (kg)	$\bar{x}$ (m)	$m\bar{x}$ (kg·m)	$\bar{y}$ (m)	$m\bar{y}$ (kg·m)
AB	0.01527	0.06	0.009162	0.16	0.002443
CD	0.07166	0	0	0.08	0.005733
Sum	0.08693		0.009162		0.008176

$$\therefore \bar{x} = \frac{0.009162}{0.08693} = 0.1054\ \text{m} = 105.4\ \text{mm}$$ ◆ $$\therefore \bar{y} = \frac{0.008176}{0.08693} = 0.0941\ \text{m} = 94.1\ \text{mm}$$ ◆

8.96

$$W_1 = \frac{490}{12^3}\left[\frac{\pi}{2}(6)^2\left(\frac{1}{8}\right)\right] = 2.004 \text{ lb}$$

$$W_2 = \frac{166}{12^3}\left[\frac{1}{2}(9)(12)\right] = 5.188 \text{ lb}$$

$$\bar{z}_1 = \frac{4}{3\pi}(6) = 2.546 \text{ in}$$

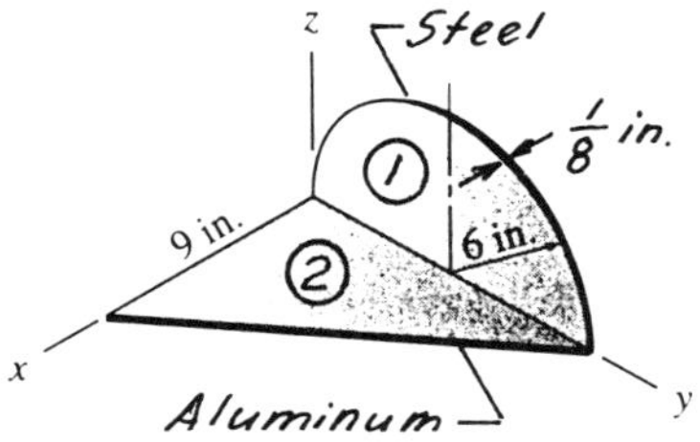

Part	W (lb)	$\bar{x}$ (in)	$W\bar{x}$ (lb·in)	$\bar{y}$ (in)	$W\bar{y}$ (lb·in)	$\bar{z}$ (in)	$W\bar{z}$ (lb·in)
1	2.004	0	0	6.000	12.024	2.546	5.102
2	5.188	3.000	15.564	4.000	20.752	0	0
Sum	7.192		15.564		32.776		5.102

$\therefore \bar{x} = \dfrac{15.564}{7.192} = 2.16 \text{ in}$ ◆ $\quad \bar{y} = \dfrac{32.776}{7.192} = 4.56 \text{ in}$ ◆ $\quad \bar{z} = \dfrac{5.102}{7.192} = 0.71 \text{ in}$ ◆

8.97

First find the center of mass centerof the reflector (it coincides with the centroid):

$$V_1 = \frac{\pi}{2}(60^2)(24) = 135\ 720 \text{ in}^3$$

$$V_2 = -\frac{\pi}{2}(48^2)(21) = -76\ 000 \text{ in}^3$$

$\bar{x}_1 = \dfrac{1}{3}(24) = 8 \text{ in} \qquad \bar{x}_2 = \dfrac{1}{3}(21) = 7 \text{ in}$

$$\therefore \bar{x} = \frac{(135\ 720)(8) - (76\ 000)(7)}{135\ 720 - 76\ 000} = 9.273 \text{ in}$$

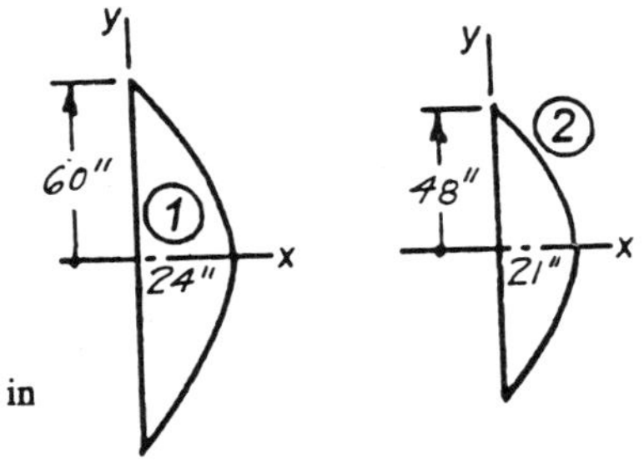

Part	W (lb)	$\bar{x}$ (in)	$W\bar{x}$ (lb•in)
Reflector	48	9.273	445.10
Boom	8	−7.500	−60.00
Receiver	16	−36.000	−576.00
Sum	72		−190.90

$\therefore \bar{x} = -\dfrac{190.90}{72} = -2.65 \text{ in}$ ◆ $\qquad$ Due to symmetry $\bar{y} = \bar{z} = 0$ ◆

8.98

First locate the center of gravity (it coincides with centroid) of the hammerhead:

$$V_1 = (90)(30)(40) = 108\ 000 \text{ mm}^3$$

$$V_2 = \frac{1}{2}(45)(30)(40) = 27\ 000 \text{ mm}^3$$

$$V_3 = -\pi(15)(12.5)(30) = -17\ 671 \text{ mm}^3$$

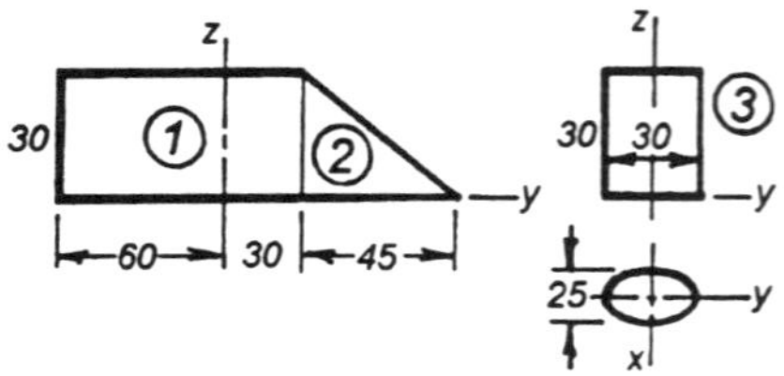

Part	V (mm³)	$\bar{y}$ (mm)	$V\bar{y}$ (mm⁴)	$\bar{z}$ (mm)	$V\bar{z}$ (mm⁴)
1	108 000	−15	−1 620 000	15	1 620 000
2	27 000	45	1 215 000	10	270 000
3	−17 670	0	0	15	−265 100
Sum	117 330		−405 000		1 624 900

$\therefore \bar{y} = -\dfrac{405\ 000}{117\ 330} = -3.452 \text{ mm} \qquad \therefore \bar{z} = \dfrac{1\ 624\ 900}{117\ 330} = 13.849 \text{ mm}$

For the handle: $\bar{y} = 0 \qquad \bar{z} = -75 \text{ mm}$

For the assembly:

$$\bar{y} = \frac{(0.919)(-3.452) + (0.0990)(0)}{0.919 + 0.0990} = -3.12 \text{ mm}$$ ◆

$$\bar{z} = \frac{(0.919)(13.849) + (0.0990)(-75)}{0.919 + 0.0990} = 5.21 \text{ mm}$$ ◆ Due to symmetry $\bar{x} = 0$ ◆

8.99

$(W\bar{x})_{assy} = (W\bar{x})_{wheel} + (W\bar{x})_{weights} = 0 \qquad \therefore \bar{x}_{wheel} = -\dfrac{(W\bar{x})_{weights}}{W_{wheel}}$

But $(W\bar{x})_{weights} = \dfrac{2}{16}(7 - 7 \sin 45°) = 0.2563 \text{ lb•in} \qquad W_{wheel} = 24 - \dfrac{2}{16}(2) = 23.75 \text{ lb}$

$$\therefore \bar{x}_{wheel} = -\frac{0.2563}{23.75} = -0.01079 \text{ in}$$ ◆

Similarly $\bar{y} = -\dfrac{(W\bar{y})_{weights}}{W_{wheel}} = -\dfrac{(2/16)(-7 \cos 45°)}{23.75} = 0.02605 \text{ in}$ ◆

8.100

$W_{tank} = 23\,000$ lb $W_{water} = (62.4)\left[\pi(12^2)h\right] = 28\,230\,h$ lb

$\bar{y}_{tank} = 9$ ft $\bar{y}_{water} = h/2$

$\bar{y} = h$: $\dfrac{W_{tank}\bar{y}_{tank} + W_{water}\bar{y}_{water}}{W_{tank} + W_{water}} = h$ $\therefore \dfrac{(23\,000)(9) + (28\,230\,h)(h/2)}{23\,000 + 28\,230\,h} = h$

$\therefore 14\,115\,h^2 + 23\,000\,h - 207\,000 = 0$ The positive root is $h = 3.10$ ft ◆

8.101

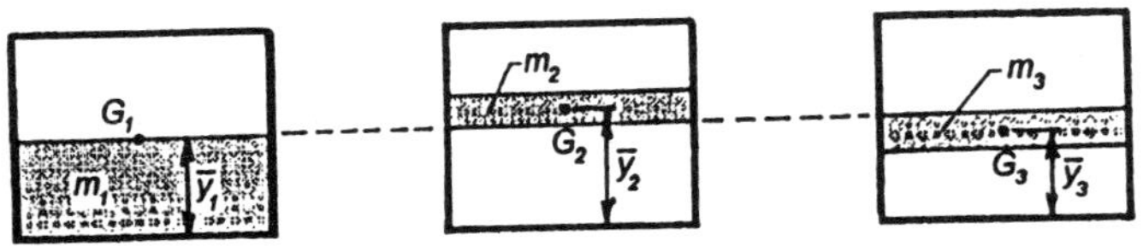

m_1 = mass of water + tank m_2 = mass of water added m_3 = mass of water removed

G_1 = COG of water G_2 = COG of added water G_3 = COG of removed water

Water added: COG moves to $\bar{y} = \dfrac{m_1\bar{y}_1 + m_2\bar{y}_2}{m_1 + m_2}$ $\therefore \Delta\bar{y} = \bar{y} - \bar{y}_1 = \dfrac{m_2(\bar{y}_2 - \bar{y}_1)}{m_1 + m_2} > 0$

Water removed: COG moves to $\bar{y} = \dfrac{m_1\bar{y}_1 - m_3\bar{y}_3}{m_1 - m_3}$ $\therefore \Delta\bar{y} = \bar{y} - \bar{y}_1 = \dfrac{m_3(\bar{y}_1 - \bar{y}_3)}{m_1 - m_3} > 0$

8.102

For COG to remain at O, the first moment of all removed areas about **x**-axis must be zero.

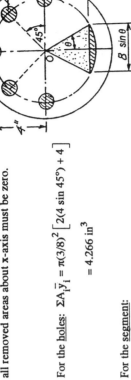

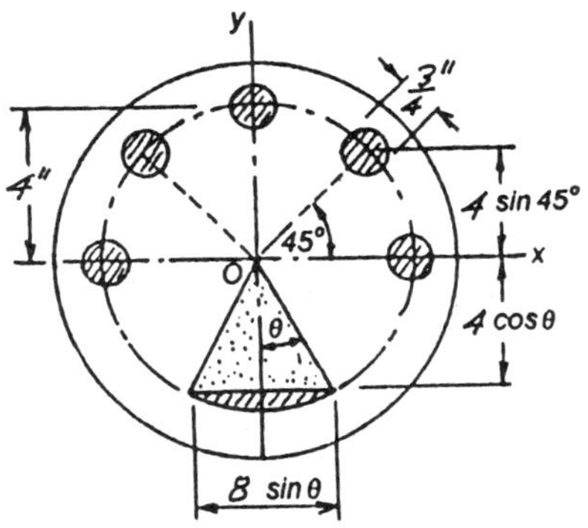

For the holes: $\Sigma A_i\bar{y}_i = \pi(3/8)^2\left[2(4\sin 45°) + 4\right]$

$= 4.266\ \text{in}^3$

For the segment:

Part	A (in²)	$\bar{y}$ (in)	$A\bar{y}$ (in³)
Sector	$\theta(4^2)$	$-\dfrac{2}{3}\dfrac{4\sin\theta}{\theta}$	$-\dfrac{128}{3}\sin\theta$
Triangle	$-\dfrac{1}{2}(4\cos\theta)(8\sin\theta)$	$-\dfrac{2}{3}(4\cos\theta)$	$\dfrac{128}{3}\cos^2\theta\sin\theta$
Segment			$-\dfrac{128}{3}\sin\theta(1 - \cos^2\theta)$

$(\Sigma A_i\bar{y}_i)_{holes} + (A\bar{y})_{segment} = 0$: $4.266 - \dfrac{128}{3}\sin\theta(1 - \cos^2\theta) = 0$

$\therefore 4.266 - \dfrac{128}{3}\sin^3\theta = 0$ $\therefore \sin^3\theta = 0.09998$ $\therefore \theta = 27.7°$ ◆

8.103

$dP = p\,dA = p(RL\,d\theta) = (p_0\cos\theta)(RL\,d\theta)$

$P_x = \int_A dP\cos\theta = p_0RL\int_0^{2\pi}\cos^2\theta\,d\theta = \pi p_0RL$

Due to symmetry: $P_y = 0$ $\quad\therefore P = \pi p_0RL \rightarrow$ ◆

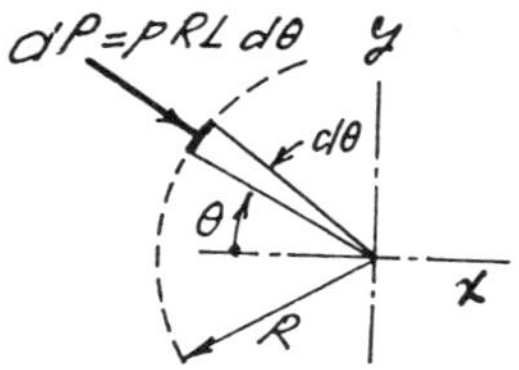

8.104

Use Simpon's rule of numerical integration. Note that $\Delta x = 2$ ft.

$R = \int_L w\,dx \approx \frac{2}{3}\left[0 + 4(122) + 2(221) + 4(253) + 2\,(332) + 4(330) + 248\right] = 2783$ lb

$R\bar{x} = \int_L wx\,dx = \frac{2}{3}\left[0 + 4(122)(2) + 2(221)(4) + 4(253)(6) + 2(332)(8) + 4(330)(10)\right.$
$\left. + (248)(12)\right] = 20\,200$ lb·ft

$\therefore R = 2780$ lb ◆ $\quad \bar{x} = \dfrac{20\,200}{2783} = 7.26$ ft ◆

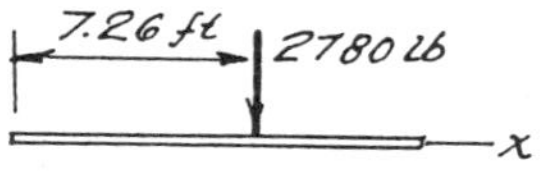

8.105

$R = \int_A p\,dA = \int_0^L\int_0^L p_0\left(2 - \frac{x}{L} - \frac{y}{L} + \frac{xy}{L^2}\right)dx\,dy$

$= \int_0^L p_0\left[2x - \frac{x^2}{2L} - \frac{xy}{L} + \frac{x^2y}{2L^2}\right]_{x=0}^{L} dy$

$= \int_0^L p_0\left(\frac{3}{2}L - \frac{1}{2}y\right)dy = p_0\left[\frac{3}{2}Ly - \frac{1}{4}y^2\right]_0^L = \frac{5}{4}p_0L^2$ ◆

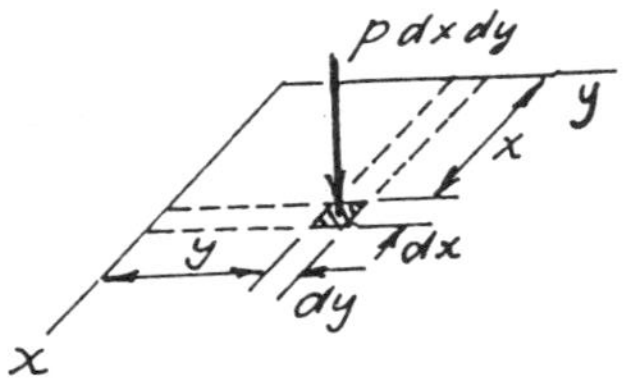

$R\bar{x} = \int_A px\,dA = \int_0^L\int_0^L p_0\left(2x - \frac{x^2}{L} - \frac{xy}{L} + \frac{x^2y}{L^2}\right)dx\,dy$

$= \int_0^L p_0\left[x^2 - \frac{x^3}{3L} - \frac{x^2y}{2L} + \frac{x^3y}{3L^2}\right]_{x=0}^{L} dy = \int_0^L p_0\left(\frac{2}{3}L^2 - \frac{1}{6}Ly\right)dy$

$= p_0\left[\frac{2}{3}L^2y - \frac{1}{12}Ly^2\right]_0^L = \frac{7}{12}p_0L^3 \qquad \therefore \bar{x} = \bar{y} = \dfrac{(7/12)p_0L^3}{(5/4)p_0L^2} = \dfrac{7}{15}L$ ◆

8.106

$R = \int_L wa\,d\theta = \int_0^{\pi}\left(w_0\frac{y}{a}\right)a\,d\theta = \int_0^{\pi} w_0y\,d\theta$

$= \int_0^{\pi} w_0a\sin\theta\,d\theta = 2w_0a$ ◆

$R\bar{y} = \int_L ywa\,d\theta = \int_0^{\pi} y\left(w_0\frac{y}{a}\right)a\,d\theta = \int_0^{\pi} w_0y^2\,d\theta$

$= \int_0^{\pi} w_0a^2\sin^2\theta\,d\theta = \frac{\pi}{2}w_0a^2 \qquad \therefore \bar{y} = \dfrac{(\pi/2)w_0a^2}{2w_0a} = \dfrac{\pi}{4}a$ ◆ $\quad$ By symmetry: $\bar{x} = 0$ ◆

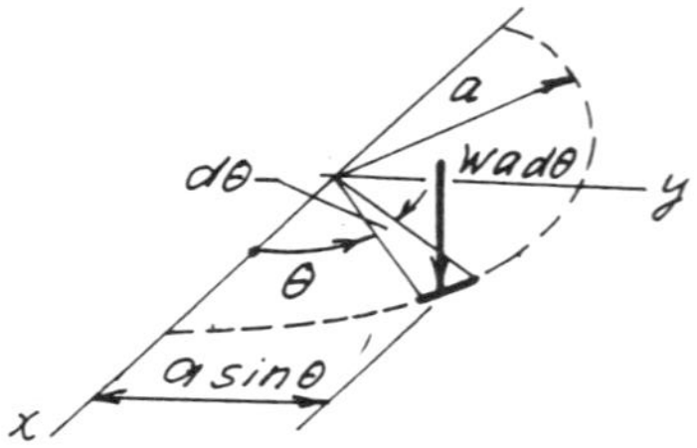

8.107

Due to symmetry: R is vertical and $\bar{x} = 0$.

$+\downarrow\ dR = (w_0\cos\theta)(a\,d\theta)\cos\theta = w_0a\cos^2\theta\,d\theta$

$\therefore R = \int_L dR = w_0a\int_{-\pi/2}^{\pi/2}\cos^2\theta\,d\theta = \frac{\pi}{2}w_0a \downarrow$ ◆

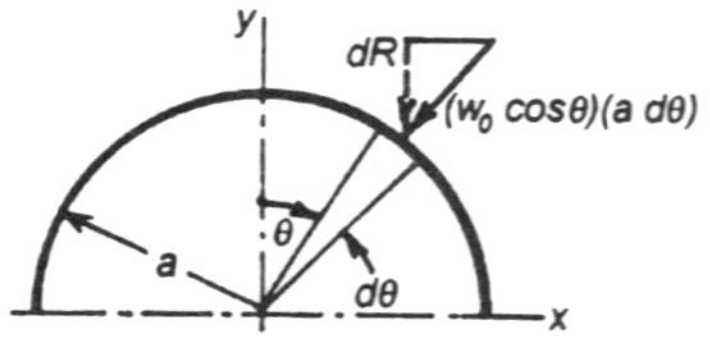

8.108

$+\downarrow\ R = \int_L w\,dx = \frac{1}{40}\int_0^{60}(40x - x^2)\,dx = \frac{1}{40}\left[20x^2 - \frac{1}{3}x^3\right]_0^{60} = 0$ ◆

$\circlearrowleft\!+\ C^R = \int_L wx\,dx = \frac{1}{40}\int_0^{60}(40x^2 - x^3)dx = \frac{1}{40}\left[\frac{40}{3}x^3 - \frac{1}{4}x^4\right]_0^{60} = -9000$ lb·in

$\therefore C^R = 9000$ lb·in $\curvearrowright$ ◆

8.109

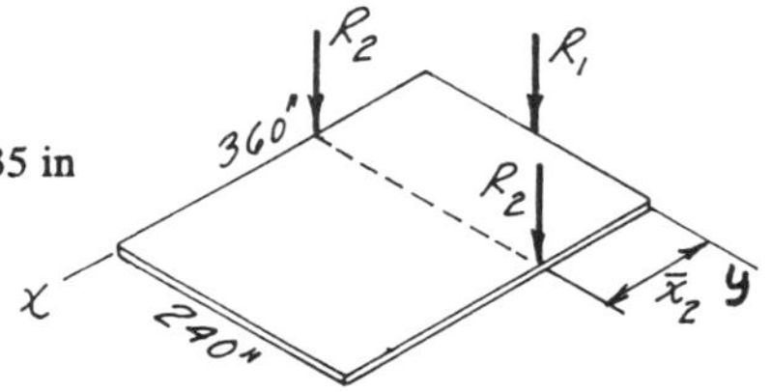

$R_1 = 240w_0 \quad \bar{x}_1 = 0$

$R_2 = \frac{2}{3}(360)w_0 = 240w_0 \quad \bar{x}_2 = \frac{3}{8}(360) = 135$ in

$R = R_1 + 2R_2 = \left[240 + 2(240)\right]w_0 = 720w_0$

$= 720(1.5) = 1080$ lb ◆

$R\bar{x} = R_1\bar{x}_1 + 2R_2\bar{x}_2 = \left[240(0) + 2(240)(135)\right]w_0 = 64\,800w_0$

$\therefore \bar{x} = \frac{64\,800w_0}{720w_0} = 90.0$ in ◆ By symmetry: $\bar{y} = 120$ in ◆

8.110

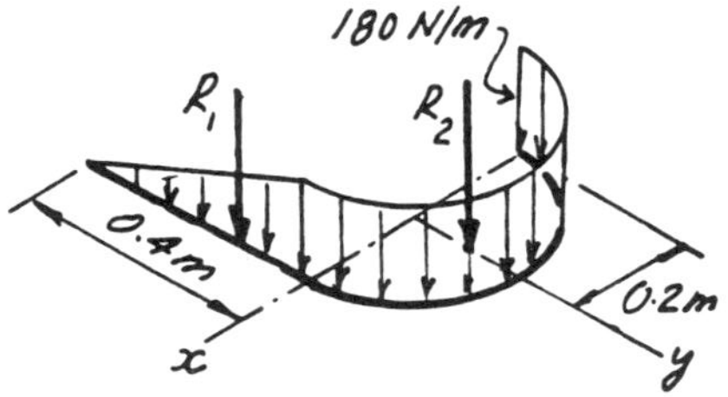

$R_1 = \frac{1}{2}(0.4)(180) = 36$ N

$R_2 = \pi(0.2)(180) = 113.10$ N

$\bar{y}_2 = \frac{2}{\pi}(0.2) = 0.12732$ m

Part	R (N)	$\bar{x}$ (m)	$R\bar{x}$ (N•m)	$\bar{y}$ (m)	$R\bar{y}$ (N•m)
1	36.00	0.200	7.200	−0.13333	−4.800
2	113.10	0.000	0.000	0.12732	14.400
Sum	149.10		7.200		9.600

$\therefore R = 149.1$ N ◆ $\bar{x} = \frac{7.200}{149.10} = 0.0483$ m ◆ $\bar{y} = \frac{9.600}{149.10} = 0.0644$ m ◆

8.111

(a) **R** = **0**

(b) $\mathbf{R} = -2aw_0\mathbf{j}$ passing through (0, 0)

(c) $\mathbf{R} = 2aw_0(-\mathbf{i} + \mathbf{j})$ passing through (−a, 0)

(d) $\mathbf{R} = -4aw_0\mathbf{j}$ passing through (a, 0)

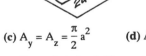

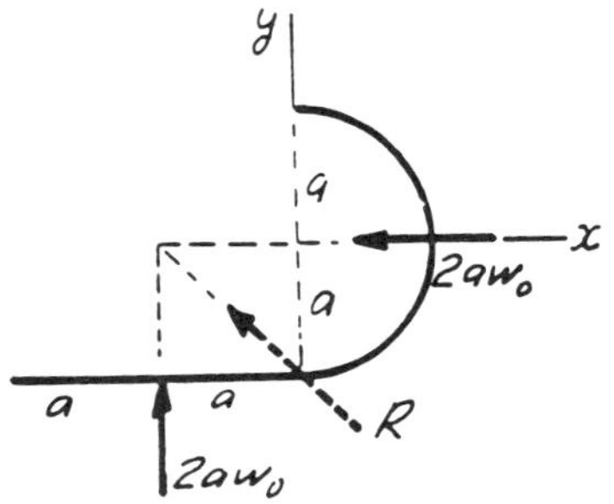

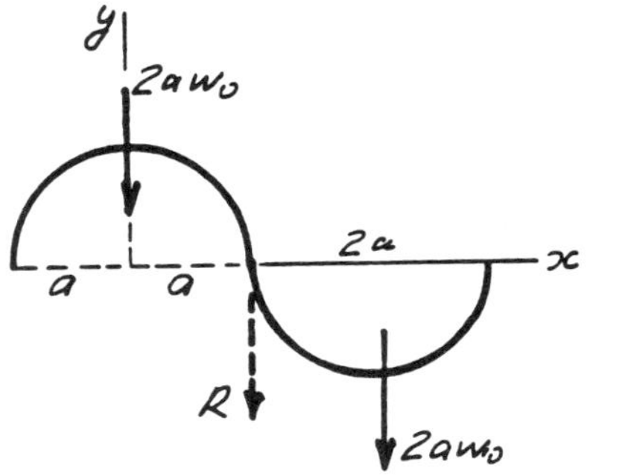

8.112

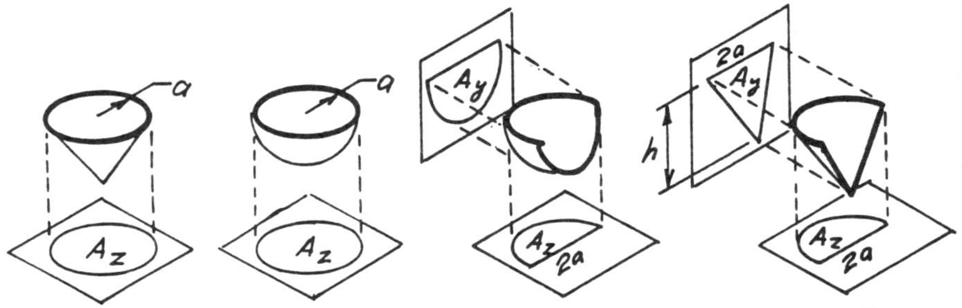

(a) $A_z = \pi a^2$

$\mathbf{R} = -p_0A_z\mathbf{k}$

$= -\pi a^2p_0\mathbf{k}$

$\therefore R = \pi a^2p_0$ ◆

(b) $A_z = \pi a^2$

$\mathbf{R} = -p_0A_z\mathbf{k}$

$= -\pi a^2p_0\mathbf{k}$

$\therefore R = \pi a^2p_0$ ◆

(c) $A_y = A_z = \frac{\pi}{2}a^2$

$\mathbf{R} = p_0(-A_y\mathbf{j} - A_z\mathbf{k})$

$= -\frac{\pi}{2}a^2p_0(\mathbf{j} + \mathbf{k})$

$\therefore R = 2.22a^2p_0$ ◆

(d) $A_y = ah \quad A_z = \frac{\pi}{2}a^2$

$\mathbf{R} = p_0(-A_y\mathbf{j} - A_z\mathbf{k})$

$= -\frac{ap_0}{2}(2h\mathbf{j} + \pi a\mathbf{k})$

$\therefore R = \frac{ap_0}{2}\sqrt{4h^2 + \pi^2a^2}$ ◆

8.113

At depth h − z the pressure is $p = \gamma(h - z)$.
The resultant of the pressure acting on the strip of width dz is
$dR = p\, dA_x = \gamma(h - z)(L\, dz)$.

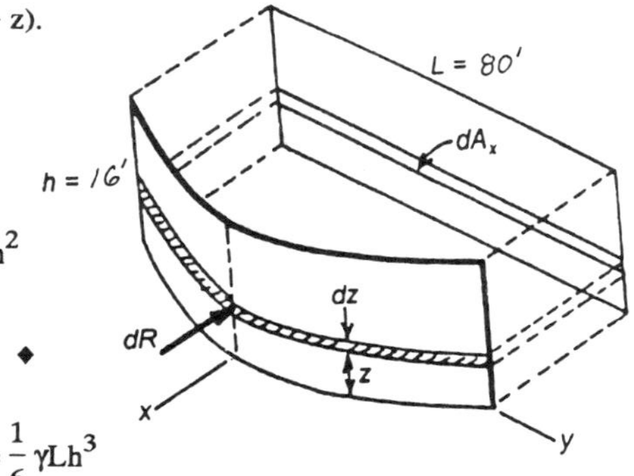

$$\therefore R = \int_A dR = \gamma L \int_0^h (h - z)\, dz = \frac{1}{2}\gamma L h^2$$

$$= \frac{1}{2}(62.4)(80)(16^2) = 639 \times 10^3 \text{ lb} \ \blacklozenge$$

$$\therefore M_y = \int_A z\, dR = \gamma L \int_0^h (hz - z^2)\, dz = \frac{1}{6}\gamma L h^3$$

$$\therefore \bar{z} = \frac{M_y}{R} = \frac{\gamma L h^3/6}{\gamma L h^2/2} = \frac{h}{3} = \frac{16}{3} = 5.33 \text{ ft} \ \blacklozenge$$

Due to symmetry $\bar{y} = 0$ ◆

8.114

The projected areas of the pressurized surfaces are

$$A_x = A_z = \frac{\pi}{4}d^2 \qquad A_y = 0$$

$$\therefore R_x = R_z = \frac{\pi}{4}p_0 d^2 \qquad R_y = 0$$

$$\therefore R = \sqrt{R_x^2 + R_z^2} = \sqrt{2}\,\frac{\pi}{4}p_0 d^2$$

$$= 1.111\, p_0 d^2 \ \blacklozenge$$

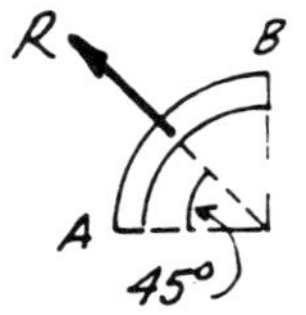

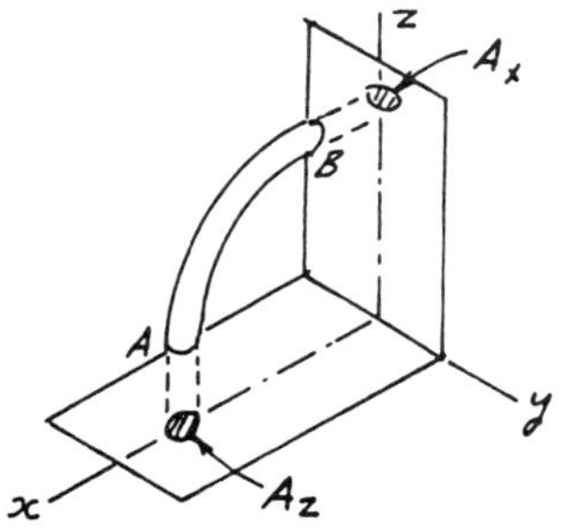

8.115

From FBD of floating body:

$$\Sigma F_z = 0 \quad +\uparrow \quad R - W_{body} = 0$$

$$\therefore R = W_{body}$$

But since R = W (weight of displaced water), we get

$W = W_{body}$ Q.E.D. ◆

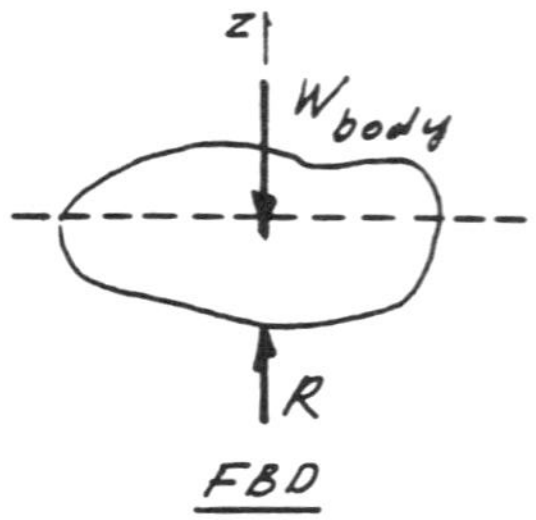

8.116

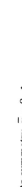

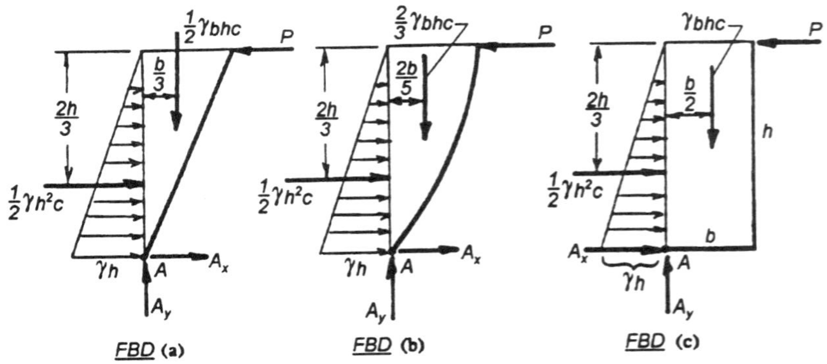

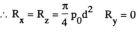

(a) $\Sigma M_A = 0$: $\circlearrowright +$ $\left(\frac{1}{2}\gamma h^2 c\right)\frac{h}{3} + \left(\frac{1}{2}\gamma bhc\right)\frac{b}{3} - Ph = 0$ $\qquad \therefore P = \gamma c\left(\frac{h^2}{6} + \frac{b^2}{6}\right)$ ◆

(b) $\Sigma M_A = 0$: $\circlearrowright +$ $\left(\frac{1}{2}\gamma h^2 c\right)\frac{h}{3} + \left(\frac{2}{3}\gamma bhc\right)\frac{2b}{5} - Ph = 0$ $\qquad \therefore P = \gamma c\left(\frac{h^2}{6} + \frac{4b^2}{15}\right)$ ◆

(c) $\Sigma M_A = 0$: $\circlearrowright +$ $\left(\frac{1}{2}\gamma h^2 c\right)\frac{h}{3} + (\gamma bhc)\frac{b}{2} - Ph = 0$ $\qquad \therefore P = \gamma c\left(\frac{h^2}{6} + \frac{b^2}{2}\right)$ ◆

8.117

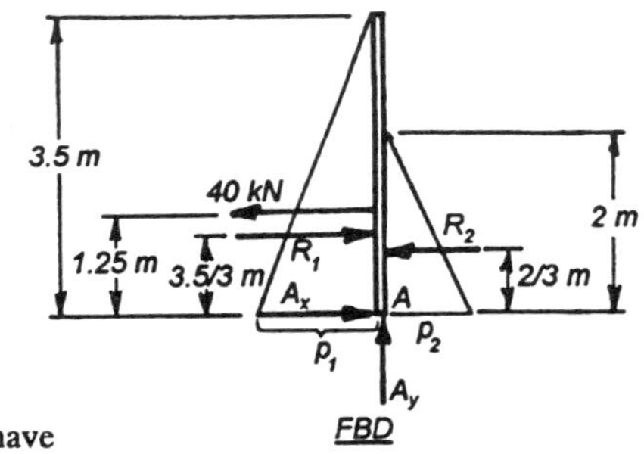

$p_1 = g\rho_1 h_1 = (9.81)(1.76 \times 10^3)(3.5)$

$= 60.43 \times 10^3$ N/m^2

$p_2 = g\rho_2 h_2 = (9.81)(1.0 \times 10^3)(2)$

$= 19.62 \times 10^3$ N/m^2

Let s be the spacing of the anchor bolts.
For length s of the wall (i.e. per bolt) we have

$$R_1 = \frac{1}{2}p_1h_1s = \frac{1}{2}(60.43 \times 10^3)(3.5)s = (105.75 \times 10^3)s \text{ N}$$

$$R_2 = \frac{1}{2}p_2h_2s = \frac{1}{2}(19.62 \times 10^3)(2)s = (19.62 \times 10^3)s \text{ N}$$

From FBD: $\Sigma M_A = 0$: (+↺) $\frac{3.5}{3}R_1 - \frac{2}{3}R_2 - (1.25)(40 \times 10^3) = 0$

$$\therefore \left[\frac{3.5}{3}(105.75 \times 10^3) - \frac{2}{3}(19.62 \times 10^3)\right]s - (1.25)(40 \times 10^3) = 0$$

$\therefore s = 0.453$ m ◆

8.118

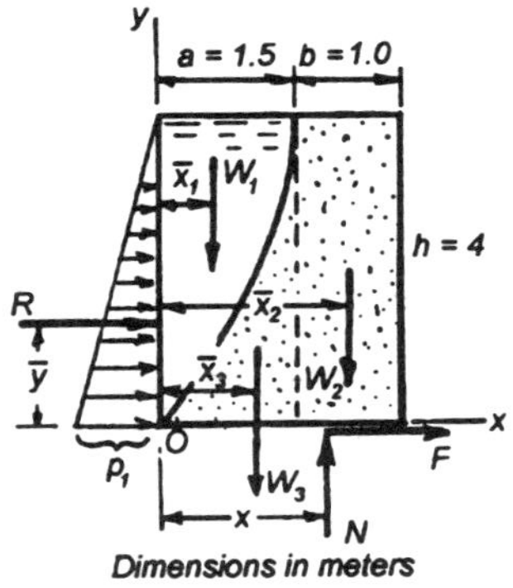

$p_1 = g\rho_w h = (9.81)(1030)(4) = 40.42 \times 10^3$ N/m^2

Work with <u>1m length</u> of dam from here on.

$$R = \frac{1}{2}p_1 h = \frac{1}{2}(40.42 \times 10^3)(4) = 80.83 \times 10^3 \text{ N}$$

$$\bar{y} = \frac{1}{3}h = \frac{4}{3} \text{ m}$$

$$W_1 = \frac{2}{3}g\rho_w ah = \frac{2}{3}(9.81)(1030)(1.5)(4) = 40.42 \times 10^3 \text{ N}$$

$$\bar{x}_1 = \frac{2}{5}a = \frac{2}{5}(1.5) = 0.6 \text{ m}$$

8.118 continued

$W_2 = g\rho_c bh = (9.81)(2400)(1.0)(4) = 94.18 \times 10^3$ N $\qquad \bar{x}_2 = a + \frac{b}{2} = 1.5 + 0.5 = 2.0$ m

$W_3 = \frac{1}{3}g\rho_c ah = \frac{1}{3}(9.81)(2400)(1.5)(4) = 47.09 \times 10^3$ N $\qquad \bar{x}_3 = \frac{7}{10}b = \frac{7}{10}(1.5) = 1.05$ m

From FBD: $\Sigma F_y = 0$: $+\uparrow$ $N - W_1 - W_2 - W_3 = 0$

$\therefore N = (40.42 + 94.18 + 47.09)10^3 = 181.69 \times 10^3$ N

$\Sigma M_O = 0$: (+↺) $Nx - R\bar{y} - W_1\bar{x}_1 - W_2\bar{x}_2 - W_3\bar{x}_3 = 0$

$$\therefore Nx = \left[(80.83)\frac{4}{3} + (40.42)(0.6) + (94.18)(2.0) + (47.09)(1.05)\right]10^3 = 369.8 \times 10^3 \text{ N·m}$$

$\therefore x = \frac{Nx}{N} = \frac{369.8 \times 10^3}{181.69 \times 10^3} = 2.04$ m $\quad$ Safe against tipping, since $x < a + b = 2.5$ m ◆

8.119

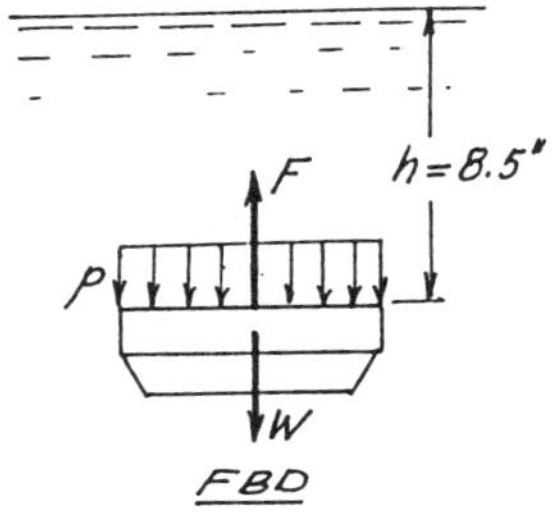

$p = \gamma h = 0.036(8.5) = 0.306$ lb/in^2

$\Sigma F = 0$: $+\uparrow$ $F - pA - W = 0$

$$\therefore F = pA + W = 0.306\pi + \frac{2.5}{16} = 1.118 \text{ lb} ◆$$

8.120

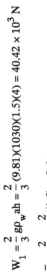

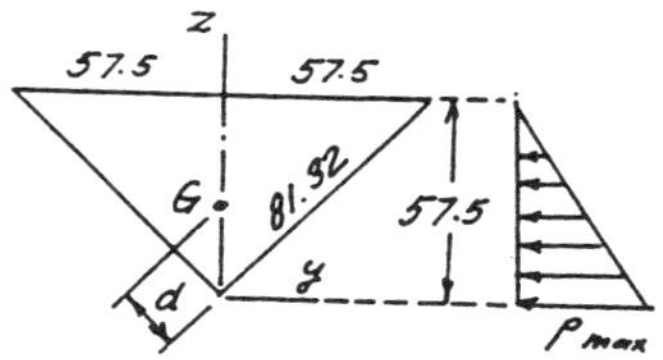

Maximum pressure acting on an end plate is

$$p_{max} = \rho gh = 1000(9.81)(57.5 \times 10^{-3}) = 564.1 \text{ N/m}^2$$

Resultant force acting on an end plate equals the volume under the load surface, which is a right tertahedron with the dimensions (see table in the back cover of text) a = b = 81.32 mm, c = 564.1 N/m.

$$\therefore R = \frac{1}{6}(564.1)(81.32 \times 10^{-3})^2 = 0.6217 \text{ N} ◆$$

$d = \frac{81.32}{4} = 20.33$ mm $\quad \therefore \bar{z} = \frac{d}{\cos 45°} = \frac{20.33}{\cos 45°} = 28.8$ mm ◆ $\quad$ By symmetry: $\bar{y} = 0$ ◆

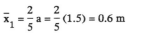

8.121

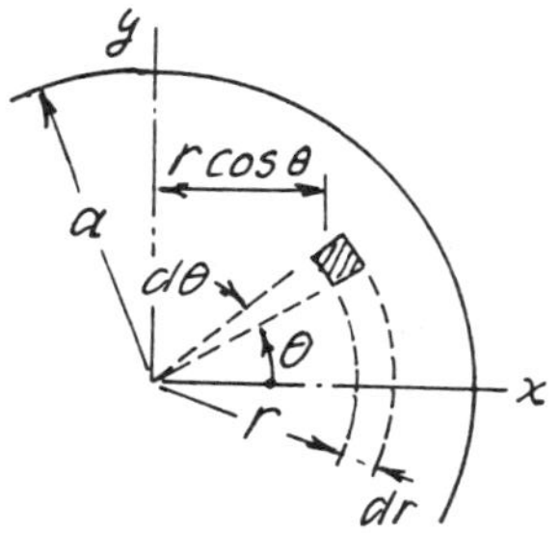

$$R = \int_A p\, dA = \int_0^{2\pi}\int_0^a p_0\left[1 + \frac{r}{a}\cos\theta\right] r\, dr\, d\theta$$

$$= \int_0^{2\pi}\int_0^a p_0\left[r + \frac{r^2}{a}\cos\theta\right] dr\, d\theta$$

$$= \int_0^{2\pi} p_0\left[\frac{a^2}{2} + \frac{a^3}{3a}\cos\theta\right] d\theta = \pi p_0 a^2 \ \blacklozenge$$

$$R\bar{x} = \int_A px\, dA = \int_0^{2\pi}\int_0^a p_0\left[1 + \frac{r}{a}\cos\theta\right](r\cos\theta)\, r\, dr\, d\theta$$

$$= \int_0^{2\pi}\int_0^a p_0\left[r^2\cos\theta + \frac{r^3}{a}\cos^2\theta\right] dr\, d\theta$$

$$= \int_0^{2\pi} p_0\left[\frac{a^3}{3}\cos\theta + \frac{a^4}{4a}\cos^2\theta\right] d\theta = \frac{\pi}{4} p_0 a^3$$

$\therefore \bar{x} = \dfrac{(\pi/4)p_0 a^3}{\pi p_0 a^2} = \dfrac{a}{4}$ ◆ Due to symmetry: $\bar{y} = 0$ ◆

8.122

Given:

$An = \mathbf{a} \times \mathbf{b}$ .... (a)

$\therefore An_z = (\mathbf{a} \times \mathbf{b})_z = a_x b_y - a_y b_x$ .... (b)

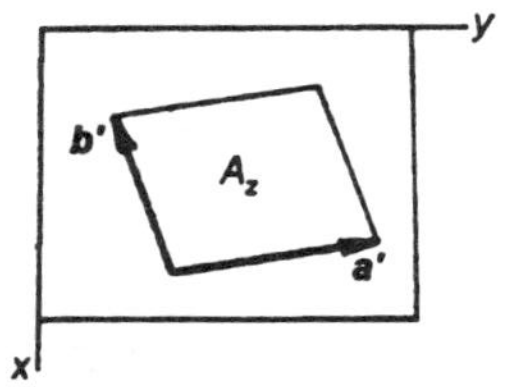

The projections of **a** and **b** on the xy plane are:

$\mathbf{a}' = a_x\mathbf{i} + a_y\mathbf{j}$ $\quad \mathbf{b}' = b_x\mathbf{i} + b_y\mathbf{j}$

The projected area A_z is obtained from Eq. (a):

$A_z\mathbf{k} = \mathbf{a}' \times \mathbf{b}'$

$\therefore A_z = (\mathbf{a}' \times \mathbf{b}')_z = a_x' b_y' - a_y' b_x' = a_x b_y - a_y b_x$

Comparison with Eq. (b) shows that $An_z = A_z$ Q.E.D.

8.123

Part	L (in)	$\bar{x}$ (in)	$L\bar{x}$ (in^2)	$\bar{y}$ (in)	$L\bar{y}$ (in^2)
1	15.708	0.0	0.00	6.5	102.10
2	4.000	0.0	0.00	2.0	8.00
3	3.000	1.5	4.50	0.0	0.00
Sum	22.708		4.50		110.10

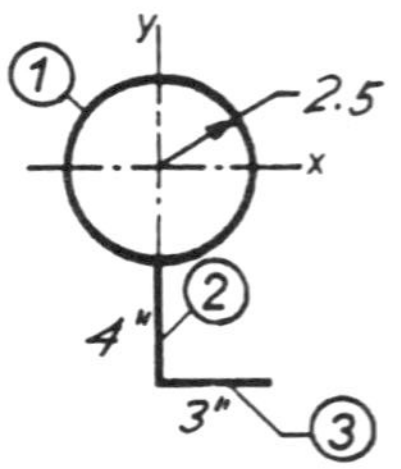

$\therefore \bar{x} = \dfrac{4.5}{22.708} = 0.198$ in ◆ $\quad \therefore \bar{y} = \dfrac{110.10}{22.708} = 4.849$ in ◆

8.124

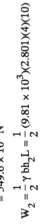

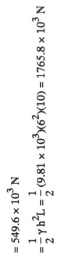

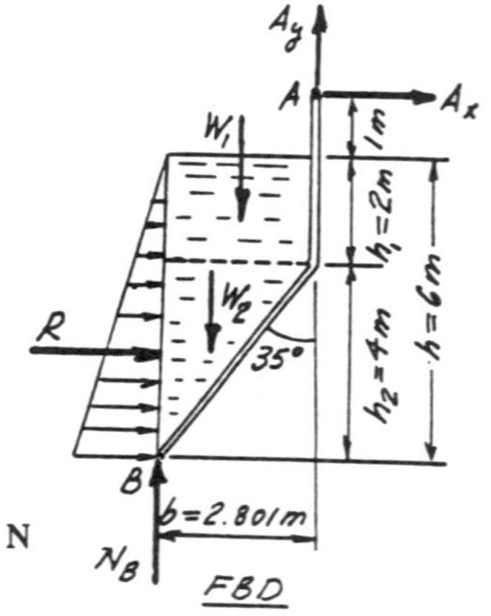

$\rho = 1000$ kg/m^3 $\quad \therefore \gamma = 9.81 \times 10^3$ N/m^3

$b = 4 \tan 35° = 2.801$ m

$W_1 = \gamma b h_1 L = (9.81 \times 10^3)(2.801)(2)(10)$

$= 549.6 \times 10^3$ N

$W_2 = \frac{1}{2}\gamma b h_2 L = \frac{1}{2}(9.81 \times 10^3)(2.801)(4)(10)$

$= 549.6 \times 10^3$ N

$= \frac{1}{2}\gamma h^2 L = \frac{1}{2}(9.81 \times 10^3)(6^2)(10) = 1765.8 \times 10^3$ N

From FBD

$$\Sigma M_A = 0: \circlearrowleft\!+ \quad \frac{b}{2}W_1 + \frac{2b}{3}W_2 + \left(1.0 + \frac{2h}{3}\right)R - bN_B = 0$$

$$\therefore \left\{\frac{1}{2}(2.801)(549.6) + \frac{2}{3}(2.801)(549.6) + \left[1 + \frac{2}{3}(6)\right](1765.8)\right\}10^3 - 2.801\, N_B = 0$$

$\therefore 10\,625 \times 10^3 - 2.801\, N_B = 0 \qquad \therefore N_B = 3.793 \times 10^6$ N ◆

$\Sigma F_x = 0$: $\overset{+}{\rightarrow}$ $R + A_x = 0 \qquad \therefore A_x = -R = -1.7658 \times 10^6$ N

$\Sigma F_y = 0$: $+\uparrow$ $N_B - W_1 - W_2 + A_y = 0$

$\therefore A_y = -N_B + W_1 + W_2 = (-3.793 + 0.5496 + 0.5496)10^6 = -2.694 \times 10^6$ N

$\therefore A = \sqrt{1.7658^2 + 2.694^2} \times 10^6 = 3.22 \times 10^6$ N ◆

8.125

$\Sigma M_O = 0$ (+) $C_O - \int_L wy\,dy = 0$

$\therefore C_O = \int_0^L w_0\left[y - y\exp(-5y/L)\right]dy$

$= w_0\left[\frac{y^2}{2} - \frac{\exp(-5y/L)}{(5/L)^2}\left(-\frac{5y}{L} - 1\right)\right]_0^L$

$= w_0\left\{\frac{L^2}{2} + \frac{L^2}{25}\left[6\exp(-5) - 1\right]\right\} = 0.462 w_0 L^2$ ◆

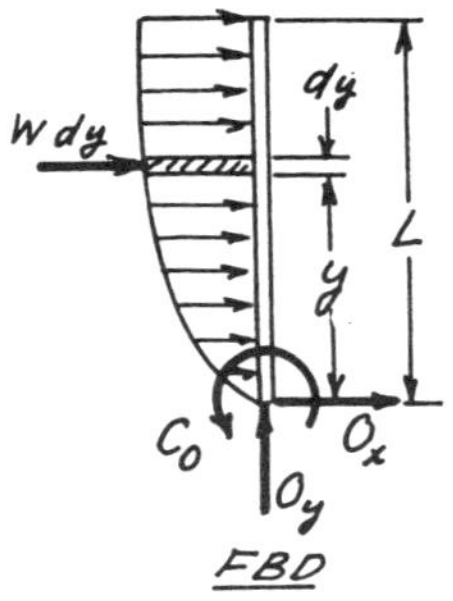

8.126

Since the thickness is uniform, the COG and centroid coincide.

Part	A (in^2)	$\bar{x}$ (in)	A$\bar{x}$ (in^3)	$\bar{z}$ (in)	A$\bar{z}$ (in^3)
1	3 000	0.000	0	30.000	90 000
2	3 142	15.915	50 000	20.000	62 840
3	982	10.610	10 420	0.000	0
Sum	7 124		60 420		152 840

$\bar{x} = \frac{60\,420}{7\,124} = 8.48$ in ◆ $\bar{z} = \frac{152\,840}{7\,124} = 21.45$ in ◆

Due to symmetry $\bar{y} = 0$ ◆

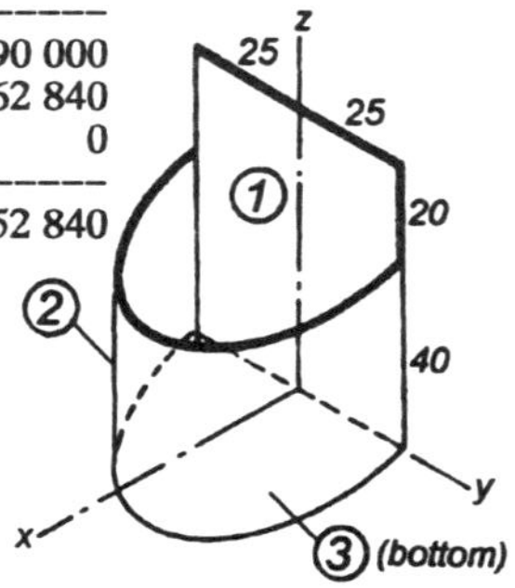

8.127

$A_2 = \frac{\pi}{4}(40^2) = 1256.6\text{ mm}^2$ $\bar{x}_2 = 30 + \frac{4}{3\pi}(40) = 46.98$ mm

Part	A (mm^2)	$\bar{x}$ (mm)	A$\bar{x}$ (mm^3)
1	400.0	40.00	16 000
2	1256.6	46.98	59 035
Sum			75 035

$\therefore V = 2\pi A\bar{x} = 2\pi(75\,035) = 471 \times 10^3\text{ mm}^3$ ◆

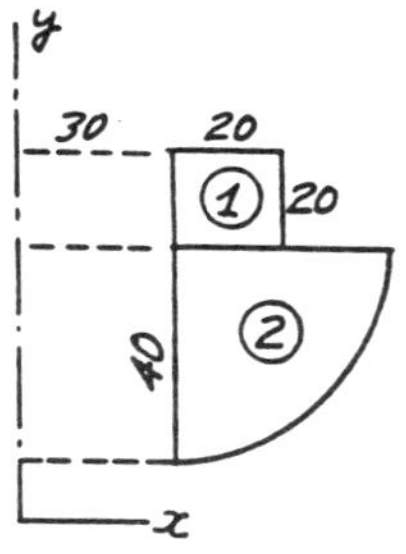

8.128

$L_4 = \frac{\pi}{2}(40) = 62.83$ mm $\bar{x}_4 = 30 + \frac{2}{\pi}(40) = 55.46$ mm

Part	L (mm)	$\bar{x}$ (mm)	L$\bar{x}$ (mm^2)
1	20.00	40.00	800
2	20.00	50.00	1000
3	20.00	60.00	1200
4	62.83	55.46	3485
5	60.00	30.00	1800
Sum			8285

$\therefore A = 2\pi L\bar{x} = 2\pi(8285) = 52.1 \times 10^3\text{ mm}^2$ ◆

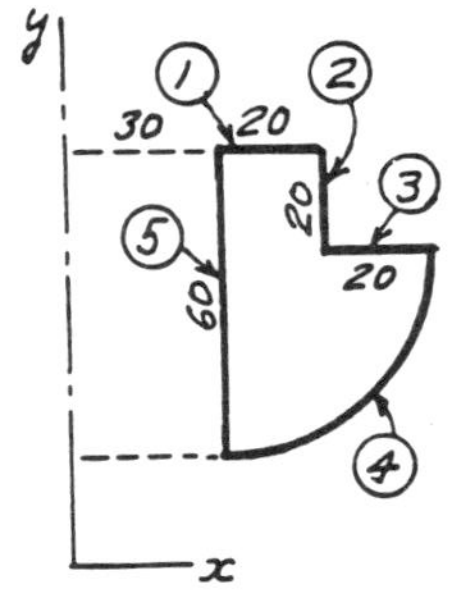

8.129

We choose single integration.

The volume element of the load diagram is

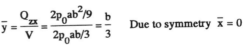

$dV = \frac{2}{3}p_0\left(1 - \frac{y}{b}\right)(2a)\,dy$ $\bar{y}_{el} = y$

$V = \int_V dV = \frac{4}{3}p_0 a\int_0^b\left(1 - \frac{y}{b}\right)dy = \frac{4}{3}p_0 a\frac{b}{2} = \frac{2}{3}p_0 ab$

$Q_{zx} = \int_V \bar{y}_{el}\,dV = \frac{4}{3}p_0 a\int_0^b\left(y - \frac{y^2}{b}\right)dy = \frac{2}{9}p_0 ab^2$

$\bar{y} = \frac{Q_{zx}}{V} = \frac{2p_0ab^2/9}{2p_0ab/3} = \frac{b}{3}$ Due to symmetry $\bar{x} = 0$

$\therefore R = V = \frac{2}{3}p_0 ab$ passing through (0, b/3) ◆

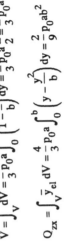

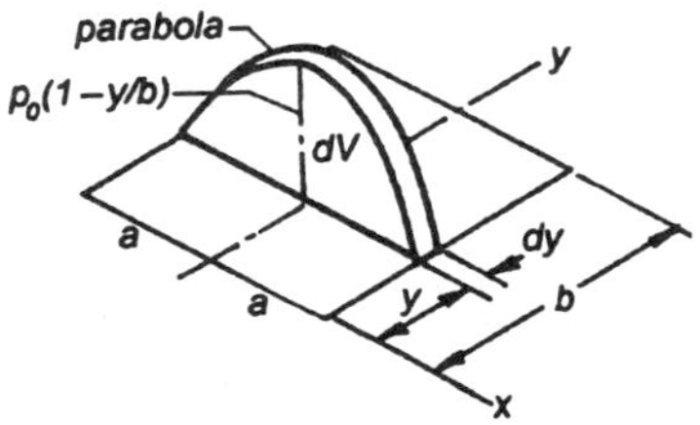

8.130

$W_1 = \gamma t b^2 = (0.284)(0.75)(20^2) = 85.20$ lb

$W_2 = -\gamma t \frac{\pi}{4} r^2 = -(0.284)(0.75)\frac{\pi}{4}(15^2) = -37.64$ lb

$\bar{x}_2 = b - \frac{4}{3\pi} r = 20 - \frac{4}{3\pi}(15) = 13.634$ in

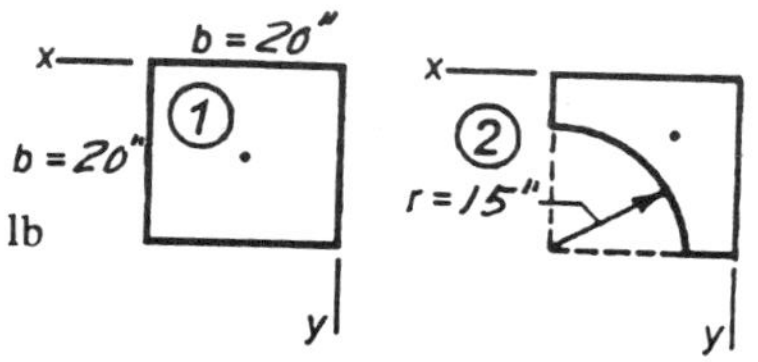

Part	W (lb)	$\bar{x}$ (in)	$W\bar{x}$ (lb•in)
1	85.20	10.000	852.0
2	−37.64	13.634	−513.2
Sum	47.56		338.8

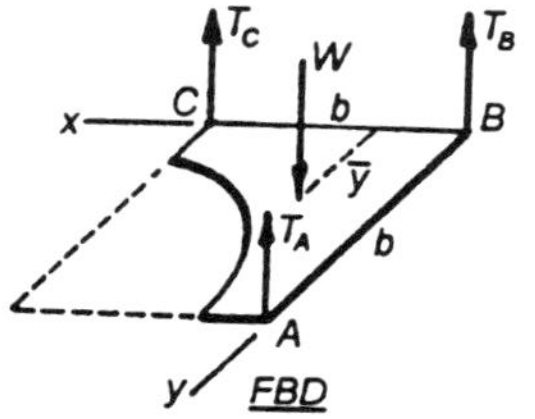

Due to symmetry $W\bar{y} = W\bar{x}$

From FBD

$\Sigma M_x = 0$: $W\bar{y} - T_A b = 0$ $\quad\therefore 338.8 - T_A(20) = 0$ $\quad\therefore T_A = 16.94$ lb ◆

Due to symmetry $T_C = T_A = 16.94$ lb ◆

$\Sigma F_z = 0$: $T_A + T_B + T_C - W = 0$

$\therefore T_B = W - 2T_A = 47.56 - 2(16.94) = 13.68$ lb ◆

8.131

$A = \frac{1}{3}(2b)h - \frac{1}{3} b \frac{h}{4} = \frac{7}{12} bh$

$A\bar{x} = \left[\frac{1}{3}(2b)h\right]\left[\frac{1}{4}(2b)\right] - \left(\frac{1}{3} b \frac{h}{4}\right)\left(b + \frac{b}{4}\right) = \frac{11}{48} b^2 h$

$A\bar{y} = \left[\frac{1}{3}(2b)h\right]\frac{3h}{10} - \left(\frac{1}{3} b \frac{h}{4}\right)\left(\frac{3}{10}\frac{h}{4}\right) = \frac{31}{160} bh^2$

$\therefore \bar{x} = \frac{11b^2h/48}{7bh/12} = \frac{11}{28} b$ ◆ $\quad \therefore \bar{y} = \frac{31bh^2/160}{7bh/12} = \frac{93}{280} h$ ◆

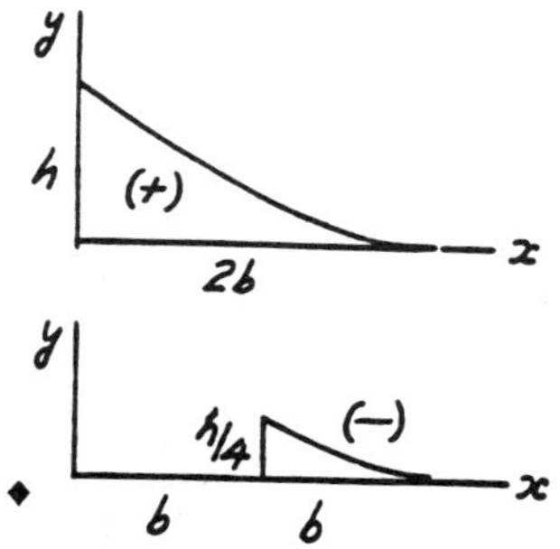

8.132

Equation of the parabola is obtained from the conditions y = h at x = 0, $y = \frac{dy}{dx} = 0$ at x = 2b:

$$y = \frac{h}{4b^2}(x - 2b)^2$$

We choose single integration.

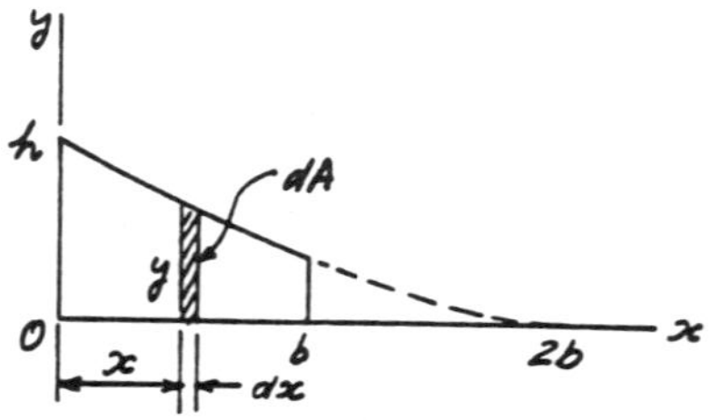

$dA = y\,dx = \frac{h}{4b^2}(x - 2b)^2\,dx$

$\bar{x}_{el} = x \qquad \bar{y}_{el} = \frac{y}{2} = \frac{h}{8b^2}(x - 2b)^2$

$A = \int_A dA = \frac{h}{4b^2}\int_0^b (x - 2b)^2\,dx = \frac{7}{12} bh$

$Q_x = \int_A \bar{y}_{el}\,dA = \frac{h^2}{32b^4}\int_0^b (x - 2b)^4\,dx = \frac{31}{160} bh^2$

$Q_y = \int_A \bar{x}_{el}\,dA = \frac{h}{4b^2}\int_0^b x(x - 2b)^2\,dx = \frac{11}{48} b^2 h$

$\bar{x} = \frac{Q_y}{A} = \frac{11b^2h/48}{7bh/12} = \frac{11}{28} b$ ◆ $\qquad \bar{y} = \frac{Q_x}{A} = \frac{31bh^2/160}{7bh/12} = \frac{93}{280} h$ ◆

8.133

$m_1 = (500)(0.2^2)(0.4) = 8.000$ kg

$m_2 = (7830)(0.3)(0.2)(0.02) = 9.396$ kg

$m_3 = (7830)(0.2^2)(0.02) = 6.264$ kg

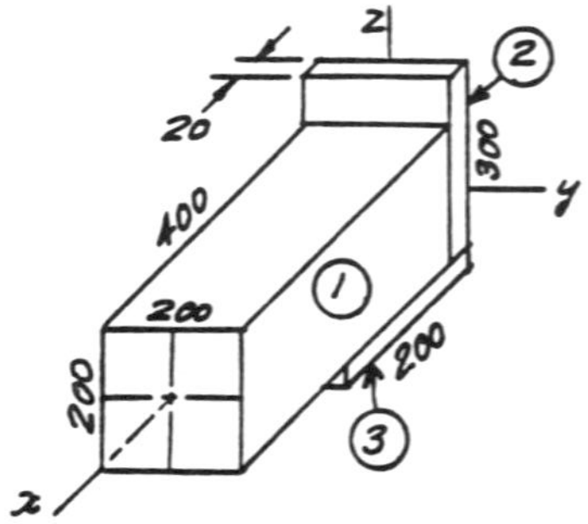

(continued)

8.133 continued

Part	m (kg)	$\bar{x}$ (m)	$m\bar{x}$ (kg•m)	$\bar{z}$ (m)	$m\bar{z}$ (kg•m)
1	8.000	0.22	1.7600	0.000	0.0000
2	9.396	0.01	0.0940	0.05	0.4698
3	6.264	0.10	0.6264	−0.11	−0.6890
Sum	23.660		2.4804		−0.2192

$\therefore \bar{x} = \dfrac{2.4804}{23.660} = 0.1048 \text{ m} = 104.8 \text{ mm}$ ◆ $\quad \therefore \bar{z} = -\dfrac{0.2192}{23.660} = -0.0093 \text{ m} = 9.3 \text{ mm}$ ◆

Due to symmetry $\bar{y} = 0$ ◆

8.134

Let the origin of the z-coordinate be at C.

Part	V (in^3)	$\bar{z}$ (in)	$V\bar{z}$ (in^4)
1	$\pi(20^2)(30) = 37\,700$	−15	−565 550
2	$\frac{\pi}{3}(20^2)(2h) = 837.75h$	$\frac{h}{2}$	$418.88h^2$
3	$-\frac{\pi}{3}(10^2)h = -104.72h$	$\frac{5h}{4}$	$-130.90h^2$
Sum			$-565\,550 + 287.98h^2$

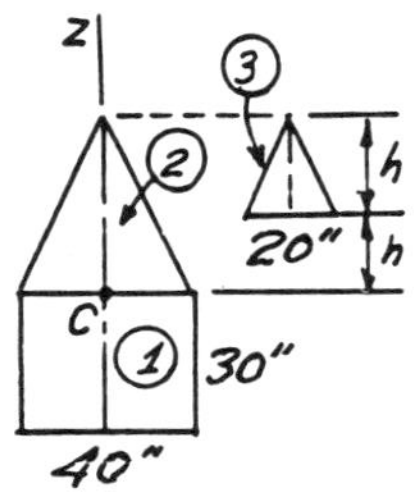

If the centroid is at C, then $\Sigma V_i \bar{z}_i = 0$:

$-565\,550 + 287.98h^2 = 0$

$\therefore h = 44.3$ in ◆

8.135

The resultant of pressure actin on a hemisphere is

$R = \pi p R^2 = \pi(300)(0.5)^2 = 235.6$ kN

The force in each bolt is

$T = \dfrac{R}{12} = \dfrac{235.6}{12} = 19.63$ kN ◆

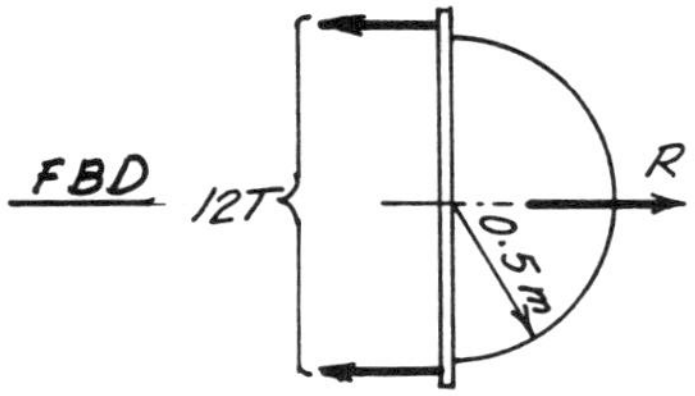

8.136

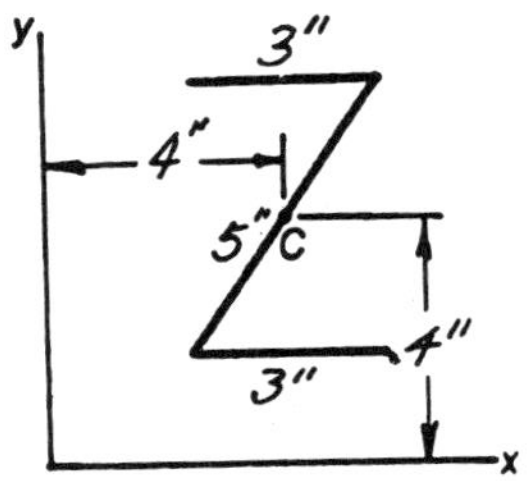

L = 3 + 5 + 3 = 11 in

Centroid C of the curve can be located by inspection.

$\bar{x} = \bar{y} = 4$ in

(a) $Q_x = L\bar{y} = (11)(4) = 44 \text{ in}^2$

$A = 2\pi Q_x = 2\pi(44) = 276 \text{ in}^2$ ◆

(b) Since $Q_x = Q_y$, we have from above

$A = 276 \text{ in}^2$ ◆

8.137

The resultant is the couple $\mathbf{C}^R = C^R\mathbf{j}$, where

$$C^R = \Sigma M_y = -2(w_0 a)a - 4\left(\frac{1}{2}w_0 a\right)\left(\frac{2a}{3}\right)$$

$$= -\frac{10}{3}w_0 a = -\frac{10}{3}(36)(3) = -360 \text{ lb·ft}$$

$\therefore \mathbf{C}^R = -360\mathbf{j}$ lb·ft ◆

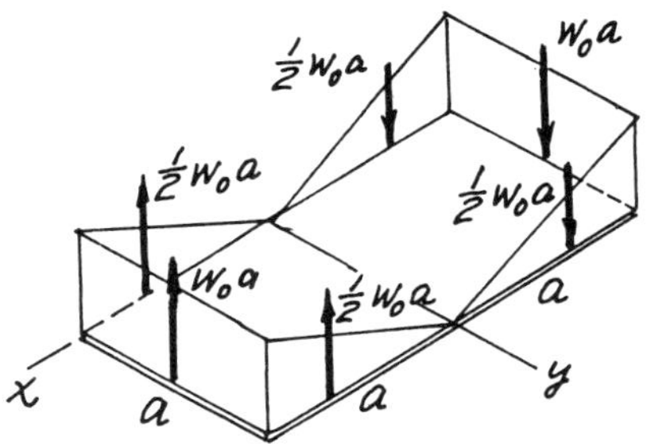

8.138

Part	A (in)^2	$\bar{y}$ (in)	$A\bar{y}$ (in^3)
1	18	10.0	180.0
2	7	5.5	38.5
3	10	1.0	10.0
Sum	35		228.5

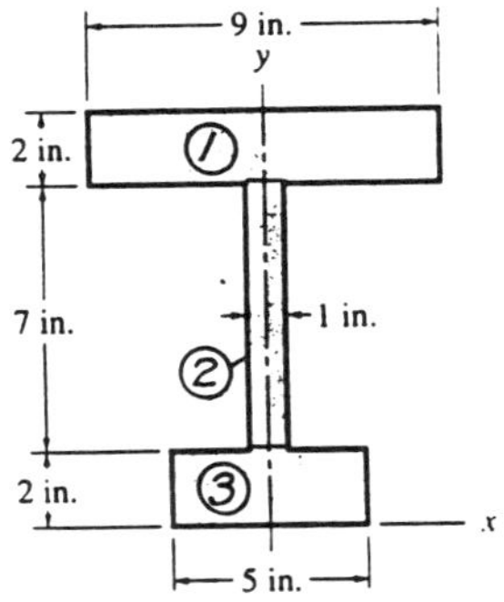

Due to symmetry: $\bar{x} = 0$

$\bar{y} = \dfrac{228.5}{35} = 6.53$ in ◆

8.139

$A_1 = (1.5\pi)(5) = 23.56 \text{ ft}^2$ $\quad \bar{z}_1 = -\frac{2}{\pi}(1.5) = -0.9549 \text{ ft}$

$A_2 = A_3 = \frac{1}{2}\pi(1.5)^2 = 3.534 \text{ ft}^2$ $\quad \bar{z}_2 = \bar{z}_3 = -\frac{4}{3\pi}(1.5) = -0.6366 \text{ ft}$

Part	A (ft^2)	$\bar{z}$ (ft)	$A\bar{z}$ (ft^3)
1	23.56	−0.9549	−22.50
2	3.53	−0.6366	−2.25
3	3.53	−0.6366	−2.25
Sum	30.62		−27.00

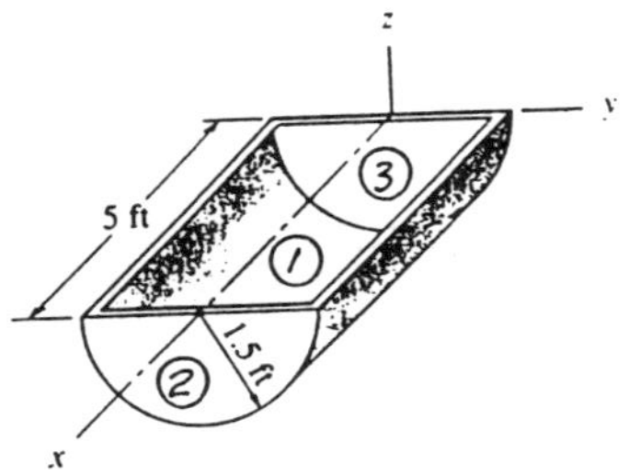

Due to symmetry: $\bar{x} = 2.5$ ft ◆ $\quad \bar{y} = 0$ ◆

$\bar{z} = -\frac{27.00}{30.62} = -0.882$ ft ◆

8.140

$W_1 = 0.2$ lb

$W_2 = V_2\gamma = \frac{2\pi}{3}(2.5)^2(0.036) = 0.471$ lb

$R = A\gamma h = \pi(3)^2(0.036)(8) = 8.143$ lb

$\Sigma F = 0 \quad +\downarrow \quad P - R + W_1 + W_2 = 0$

$\therefore P = R - W_1 - W_2$

$= 8.143 - 0.2 - 0.471 = 7.47$ lb ◆

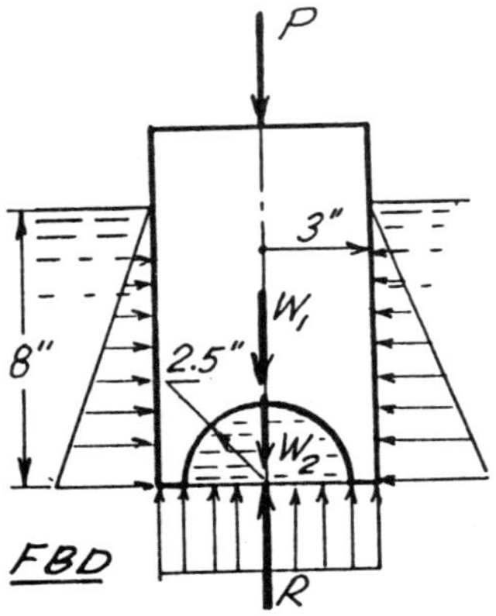

8.141

$A_1 = \frac{\pi}{2}(35)^2 = 1924 \text{ mm}^2$ $\quad A_2 = 70^2 = 4900 \text{ mm}^2$ $\quad A_3 = -\pi(14)^2 = -616 \text{ mm}^2$

$\bar{y}_1 = 70 + \frac{4}{3\pi}(35) = 84.85$ mm

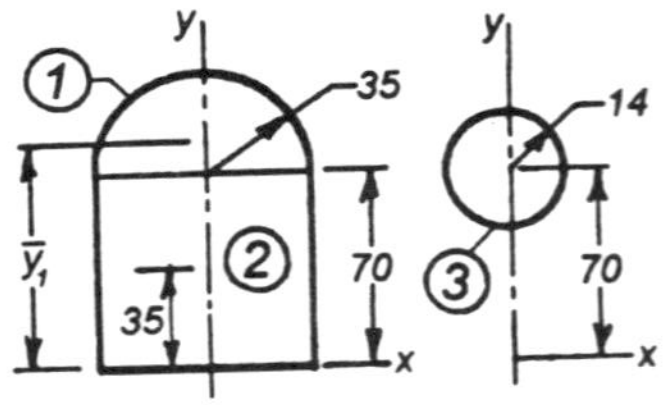

Part	A (mm^2)	$\bar{y}$ (mm)	$A\bar{y}$ (mm^3)
1	1924	84.85	163 300
2	4900	35.00	171 500
3	−616	70.00	−43 100
Sum	6208		291 700

Due to symmetry $\bar{x} = 0$ ◆

$\bar{y} = \frac{291\,700}{6208} = 47.0$ mm ◆

9.1

(a) $A = \frac{1}{2}bh = \frac{1}{2}(4)(3) = 6 \text{ in}^2$

$\bar{J}_C = \bar{I}_x + \bar{I}_y = \frac{bh^3}{36} + \frac{b^3h}{48} = \frac{(4)(3)^3}{36} + \frac{(4)^3(3)}{48} = 7 \text{ in}^4$

(b) $J_O = \bar{J}_C + Ad^2 = 7 + (6)(2)^2 = 31 \text{ in}^4$ ◆

(c) $k_O = \sqrt{J_O/A} = \sqrt{(31)/(6)} = 2.27 \text{ mm}$ ◆

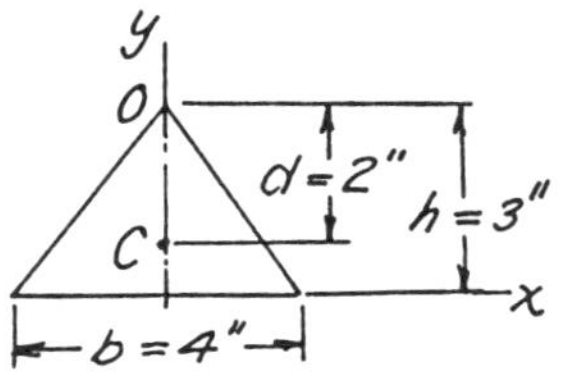

9.2

$J_O = \bar{J}_C + Ad^2 = I_x + I_y$

$\therefore A = \frac{I_x + I_y - \bar{J}_C}{d^2} = \frac{(600 + 350 - 50)(10^3)}{50^2} = 360 \text{ mm}^2$ ◆

$\bar{I}_x = I_x - A\bar{y}^2 = 600 \times 10^3 - (360)(40^2) = 24 \times 10^3 \text{ mm}^4$ ◆

$\bar{I}_y = I_y - A\bar{x}^2 = 350 \times 10^3 - (360)(30^2) = 26 \times 10^3 \text{ mm}^4$ ◆

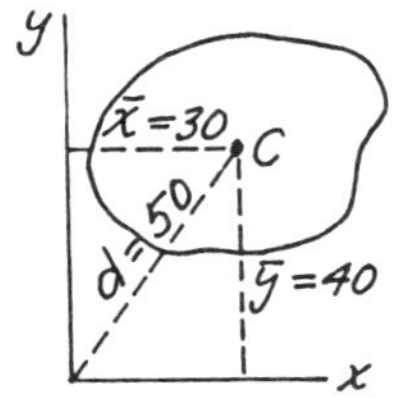

9.3

$\bar{I}_x = I_x - Ad^2 = I_u - A(h + d)^2$

$\therefore A = \frac{I_u - I_x}{(h + d)^2 - d^2} = \frac{(38 - 14)(10^9)}{(200 + 300)^2 - 300^2} = 150 \times 10^3 \text{ mm}^2$ ◆

$\therefore \bar{I}_x = 14 \times 10^9 - (150 \times 10^3)(300^2) = 500 \times 10^6 \text{ mm}^4$

$\bar{k}_x = \sqrt{\bar{I}_x/A} = \sqrt{(500 \times 10^6)/(150 \times 10^3)} = 57.7 \text{ mm}$ ◆

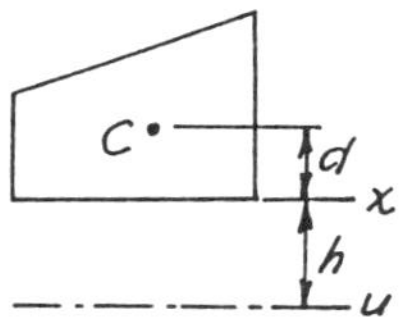

9.4

Refer to figure in solution of Prob. 9.3.

$\bar{I}_x = I_x - Ad^2 = 14 \times 10^9 - (90 \times 10^3)(300^2) = 5.90 \times 10^9 \text{ mm}^4$

$I_u = \bar{I}_x + A(h + d)^2 \quad \therefore h = \sqrt{\frac{I_u - \bar{I}_x}{A}} - d = \sqrt{\frac{(120 - 5.90)(10^9)}{90 \times 10^3}} - 300 = 826 \text{ mm}$ ◆

9.5

$I_x = \int_0^\pi y^2\, dA = \int_0^\pi (R \sin\theta)^2 (tR\, d\theta)$

$= tR^3 \int_0^\pi \sin^2\theta\, d\theta = \frac{\pi}{2} tR^3$

$A = \int_0^\pi dA = \int_0^\pi tR\, d\theta = tR \int_0^\pi d\theta = \pi tR$

$k_x = \sqrt{I_x/A} = \sqrt{(\pi tR^3/2) / (\pi tR)} = R/\sqrt{2}$ ◆

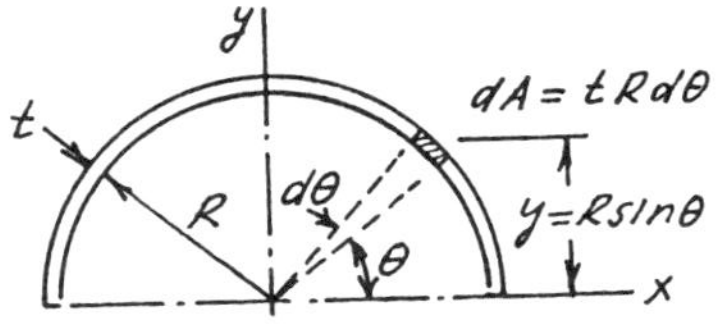

9.6

$I_x = \int_A y^2\, dA = \int_0^L (s \sin\alpha)^2 (t\, ds)$

$= t \sin^2\alpha \int_0^L s^2\, ds = \frac{1}{3} tL^3 \sin^2\alpha$ ◆

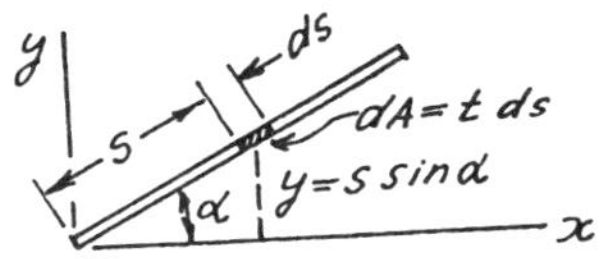

9.7

$dA = \left[(y + 4) - \frac{1}{2}y^2\right]dy$

$I_x = \int_A y^2\, dA = \int_0^4 \left(y^3 + 4y^2 - \frac{1}{2}y^4\right) dy$

$= \left[\frac{1}{4}y^4 + \frac{4}{3}y^3 - \frac{1}{10}y^5\right]_0^4 = 46.9 \text{ in}^4$ ◆

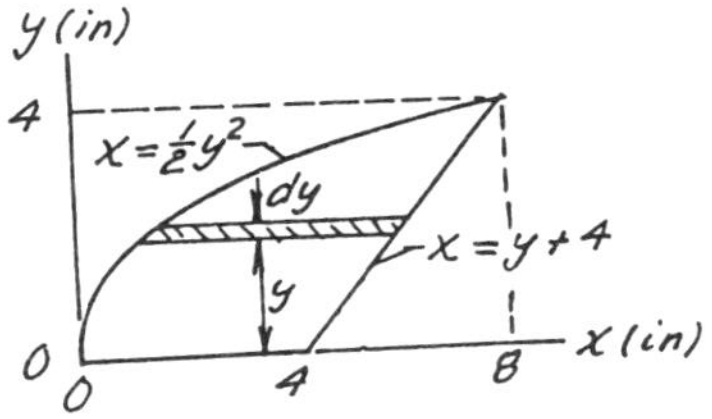

9.8

$$J_O = \int_A r^2\,dA = \int_{r=0}^{R}\int_{\theta=-\alpha}^{\alpha} r^2(r\,dr\,d\theta)$$

$$= 2\alpha\int_0^R r^3\,dr = 2\alpha\,\frac{R^4}{4} = \frac{1}{2}R^4\alpha \ \blacklozenge$$

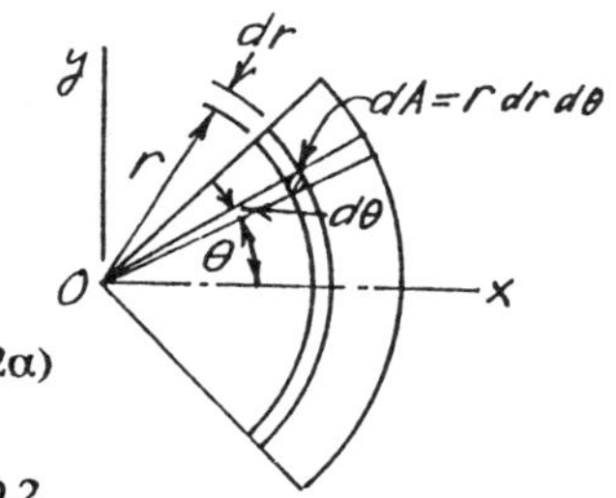

<u>Check</u>: $I_x = \frac{1}{8}R^4(2\alpha - \sin 2\alpha) \qquad I_y = \frac{1}{8}R^4(2\alpha + \sin 2\alpha)$

$\therefore J_O = I_x + I_y = \frac{1}{2}R^4\alpha$ Checks with Table 9.2

9.9

For the area element: $dI_x = \frac{1}{3}y^3\,dx = \frac{1}{3}h^3(x/b)^{3n}\,dx$

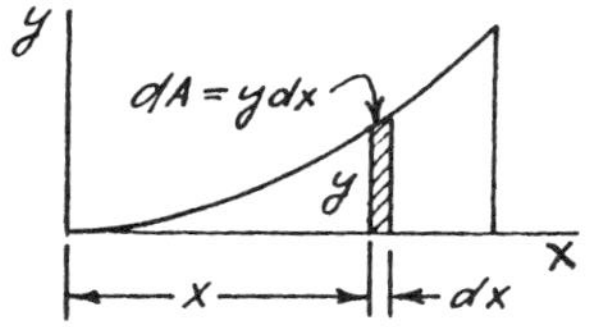

$$\therefore I_x = \int_A dI_x = \frac{1}{3}\frac{h^3}{b^{3n}}\int_0^b x^{3n}\,dx$$

$$= \frac{1}{3}\frac{h^3}{b^{3n}}\frac{b^{3n+1}}{3n+1} = \frac{bh^3}{3(3n+1)} \ \blacklozenge$$

$$I_y = \int_A x^2\,dA = \int_0^b x^2 h\left(\frac{x}{b}\right)^n dx = \frac{h}{b^n}\int_0^b x^{n+2}\,dx = \frac{h}{b^n}\frac{b^{n+3}}{n+3} = \frac{b^3h}{n+3} \ \blacklozenge$$

<u>Check</u>: With $n = 2$, we have $I_x = \frac{bh^3}{21}$ and $I_y = \frac{b^3h}{5}$ Checks with Table 9.2

9.10

$$I_x = \int_A y^2\,dA = \int_{x=0}^{1}\int_{y=x^2}^{x} y^2\,dx\,dy = \int_0^1\left[\frac{y^3}{3}\right]_{x^2}^{x} dx$$

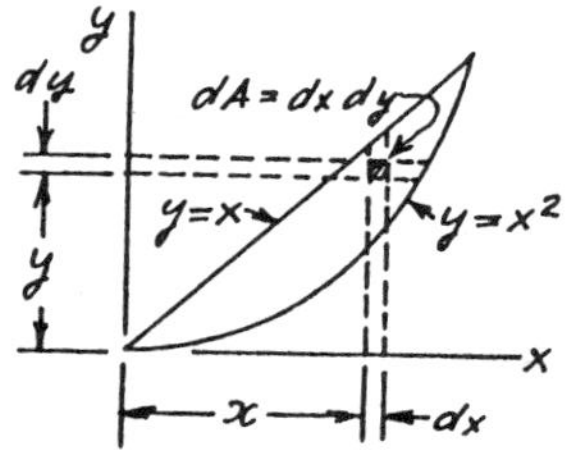

$$= \frac{1}{3}\int_0^1 (x^3 - x^6)\,dx = \frac{1}{3}\left(\frac{1}{4} - \frac{1}{7}\right) = \frac{1}{28}\ \text{m}^4 \ \blacklozenge$$

$$I_y = \int_A x^2\,dA = \int_{x=0}^{1}\int_{y=x^2}^{x} x^2\,dx\,dy = \int_0^1 x^2\big[y\big]_{x^2}^{x} dx$$

$$= \int_0^1 (x^3 - x^4)\,dx = \frac{1}{4} - \frac{1}{5} = \frac{1}{20}\ \text{m}^4 \ \blacklozenge$$

9.11

For the area element: $dI_x = \frac{1}{3}y^3\,dx$

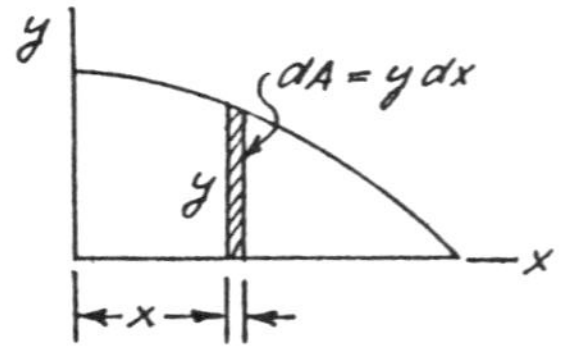

Utilizing symmetry: $I_x = \int_A dI_x = 2\int_0^{20}\frac{1}{3}y^3\,dx$

$$= 2\int_0^{20}\frac{1}{3}\left(12\cos\frac{\pi x}{40}\right)^3 dx$$

Let $\frac{\pi x}{40} = \xi \qquad \therefore dx = \frac{40}{\pi}d\xi \qquad \therefore I_x = \frac{2}{3}\frac{40}{\pi}(12^3)\int_0^{\pi/2}\cos^3\xi\,d\xi = \frac{2}{3}\frac{40}{\pi}(12^3)\frac{2}{3} = 9780\ \text{in}^4 \ \blacklozenge$

9.12

Utilizing symmetry: $I_y = \int_A x^2\,dA = 2\int_0^{20} x^2y\,dx = 2(12)\int_0^{20} x^2\cos\frac{\pi x}{40}\,dx$

From table of integrals: $\int x^2\cos ax\,dx = \frac{2x}{a}\cos ax - \frac{2}{a^3}\sin ax + \frac{x^2}{a}\sin ax$

$$\therefore I_y = 2(12)\left[2x\left(\frac{40}{\pi}\right)\cos\frac{\pi x}{40} - 2\left(\frac{40}{\pi}\right)^3\sin\frac{\pi x}{40} + x^2\left(\frac{40}{\pi}\right)\sin\frac{\pi x}{40}\right]_0^{20}$$

$$= 2(12)\left[-2\left(\frac{40}{\pi}\right)^3\sin\frac{\pi x}{40} + x^2\left(\frac{40}{\pi}\right)\sin\frac{\pi x}{40}\right]_{x=20} = 23\,150\ \text{in}^4 \ \blacklozenge$$

9.13

For the rectangle: $\bar{I}_x = \frac{bh^3}{12} \qquad \bar{I}_y = \frac{b^3h}{12}$

$\therefore \bar{I}_x\bar{I}_y = \frac{(bh)^4}{144} \qquad \therefore A = bh = \sqrt[4]{144\,\bar{I}_x\bar{I}_y} = \sqrt[4]{144(272)(88.6)} = 43.16\ \text{in}^2 \approx 43.2\ \text{in}^2 \ \blacklozenge$

$\bar{I}_x = \frac{(bh)h^2}{12} = \frac{Ah^2}{12} \qquad \therefore h = \sqrt{(12\,\bar{I}_x)/A} = \sqrt{\frac{12(272)}{43.16}} = 8.696\ \text{in} \approx 8.70\ \text{in} \ \blacklozenge$

$b = \frac{A}{h} = \frac{43.16}{8.696} = 4.96\ \text{in} \ \blacklozenge$

9.14

Column: $\bar{k}_x^2 = \bar{I}_x/A = \dfrac{272}{19.7} = 13.807\ \text{in}^2$ $\quad \bar{k}_y^2 = \bar{I}_y/A = \dfrac{88.6}{19.7} = 4.497\ \text{in}^2$

Rectangle: $\bar{k}_x^2 = \dfrac{bh^3}{12}\dfrac{1}{bh} = \dfrac{h^2}{12}$ $\quad \bar{k}_y^2 = \dfrac{b^3h}{12}\dfrac{1}{bh} = \dfrac{b^2}{12}$

Equating the radii of gyration:

$\therefore \dfrac{h^2}{12} = 13.807 \quad \therefore h = 12.87\ \text{in}$ ◆ $\qquad \dfrac{b^2}{12} = 4.497 \quad \therefore b = 7.35\ \text{in}$ ◆

9.15

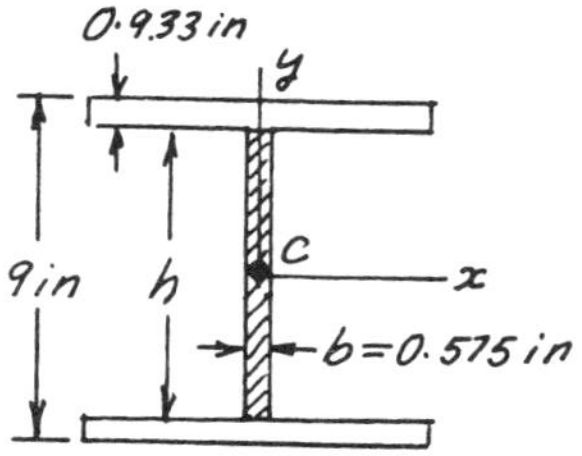

Web:

$h = 9 - 2(0.933) = 7.134\ \text{in}$

$I_x = \dfrac{bh^3}{12} = \dfrac{(0.575)(7.134^3)}{12} = 17.4\ \text{in}^4$

$I_y = \dfrac{b^3h}{12} = \dfrac{(0.575^3)(7.134)}{12} = 0.1\ \text{in}^4$

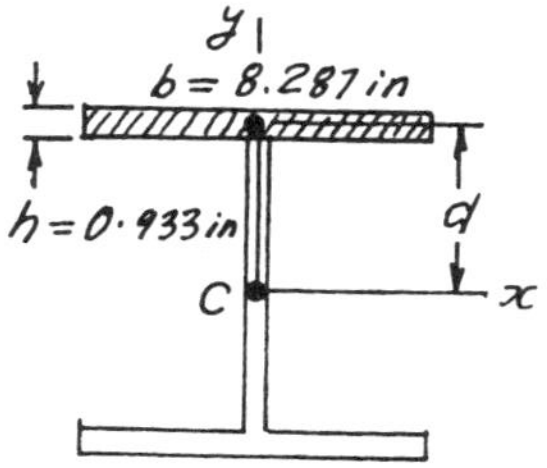

Flange:

$A = bh = (8.287)(0.933) = 7.732\ \text{in}^2$

$d = 4.5 - \dfrac{0.933}{2} = 4.0335\ \text{in}$

$I_x = \dfrac{bh^3}{12} + Ad^2 = \dfrac{(8.287)(0.933^3)}{12} + (7.732)(4.0335^2)$

$= 126.35\ \text{in}^4$

$I_y = \dfrac{b^3h}{12} = \dfrac{(8.287^3)(0.933)}{12} = 44.25\ \text{in}^4$

Entire cross section:

$\bar{I}_x = (I_x)_{web} + 2(I_x)_{flange} = 17.4 + 2(126.35) = 270.1\ \text{in}^4$ (272 in^4 in handbook) ◆

$\bar{I}_y = (I_y)_{web} + 2(I_y)_{flange} = 0.1 + 2(44.25) = 88.6\ \text{in}^4$ (88.6 in^4 in handbook) ◆

9.16

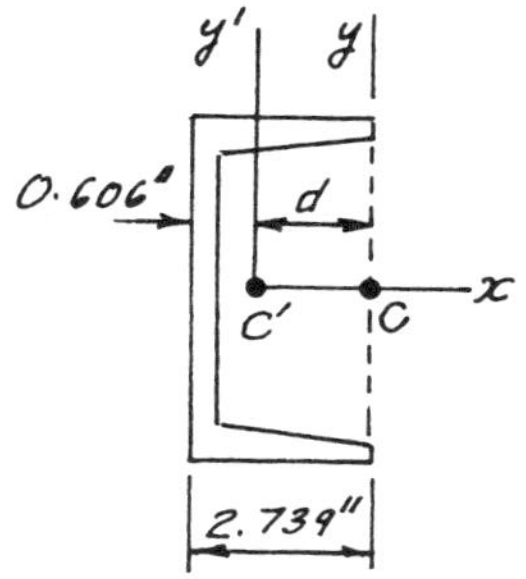

For one channel:

$I_x = 78.9\ \text{in}^4$

$I_y = I_{y'} + Ad^2$

$= 2.81 + (5.88)(2.739 - 0.606)^2 = 29.56\ \text{in}^4$

For the assembly:

$\bar{I}_x = 2I_x = 2(78.9) = 157.8\ \text{in}^4$ ◆

$\bar{I}_y = 2I_y = 2(29.56) = 59.1\ \text{in}^4$ ◆

9.17

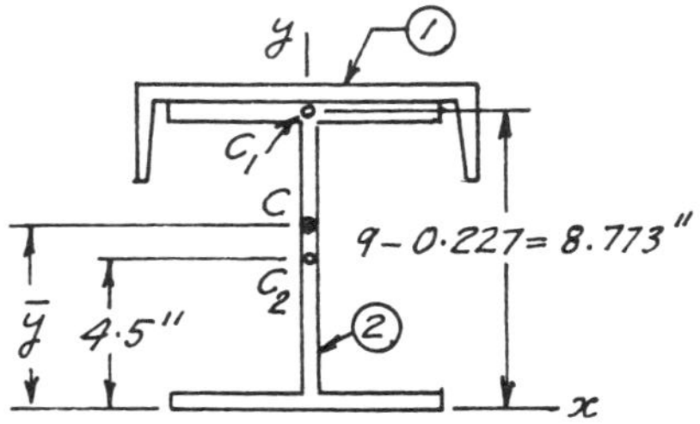

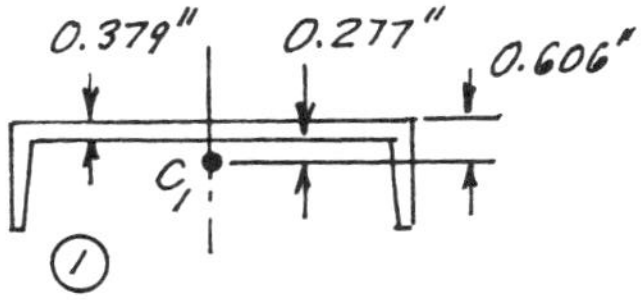

For the composite areas:

Part	$\bar{I}_x$ (in^4)	A (in^2)	$\bar{y}$ (in)	$A\bar{y}$ (in^3)	$\bar{I}_x + A\bar{y}^2$	I_y (in^4)
1	2.81	5.88	8.773	51.59	455.4	78.9
2	272	19.70	4.50	88.65	670.9	88.6
Sum		25.58		140.24	1126.3	167.5

For the assembly:

$\bar{y} = \dfrac{\Sigma A\bar{y}}{\Sigma A} = \dfrac{140.24}{25.58} = 5.482\ \text{in}$ $\quad I_x = \Sigma(\bar{I}_x - A\bar{y}^2) = 1126.3\ \text{in}^4$ $\quad I_y = \Sigma I_y = 167.5\ \text{in}^4$

$\bar{I}_x = I_x - A\bar{y}^2 = 1126.3 - (25.58)(5.482^2) = 358\ \text{in}^4$ ◆ $\qquad \bar{I}_y = I_y = 167.5\ \text{in}^4$ ◆

9.18

$$I_x = (I_1)_x + (I_2)_x - (I_3)_x$$

$$= \frac{(50)(80)^3}{12} + \frac{\pi(40)^4}{8} - \frac{\pi(15)^4}{4}$$

$$= 3.099 \times 10^6 \text{ mm}^4$$

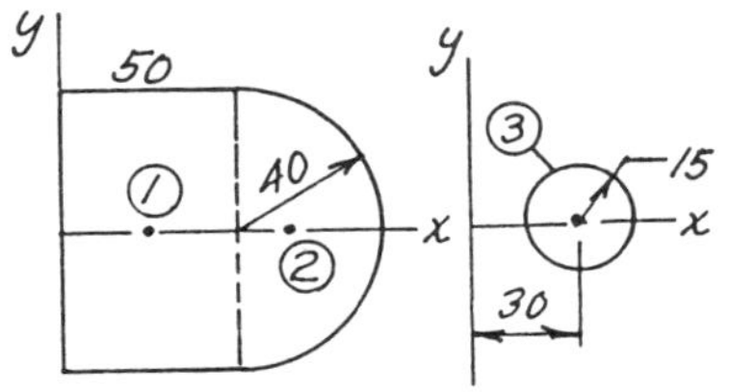

$$I_y = (I_1)_y + (I_2)_y - (I_3)_y$$

$$= \frac{(80)(50)^3}{3} + \left\{0.1098(40)^4 + \frac{\pi(40)^2}{2}\left[50 + \frac{4}{3\pi}(40)\right]^2\right\} - \left[\frac{\pi(15)^4}{4} + \pi(15)^2(30)^2\right]$$

$$= 14.212 \times 10^6 \text{ mm}^4$$

$$J_O = I_x + I_y = (3.099 + 14.212)10^6 = 17.31 \times 10^6 \text{ mm}^4 \ \blacklozenge$$

9.19

$$\bar{y} = \frac{A_1\bar{y}_1 + A_2\bar{y}_2 + A_3\bar{y}_3}{A_1 + A_2 + A_3}$$

$$= \frac{(18)(10) + (7)(5.5) + (10)(1)}{18 + 7 + 10} = 6.529 \text{ in}$$

$$\bar{I}_y = \underbrace{\frac{(2)(9)^3}{12}}_{\text{Part 1}} + \underbrace{\frac{(7)(1)^3}{12}}_{\text{Part 2}} + \underbrace{\frac{(2)(5)^3}{12}}_{\text{Part 3}} = 142.9 \text{ in}^4 \ \blacklozenge$$

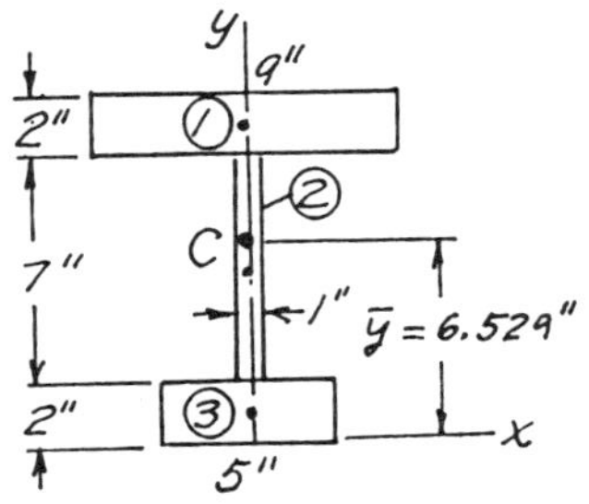

$$\bar{I}_x = \underbrace{\left[\frac{(9)(2)^3}{12} + 18(10 - 6.529)^2\right]}_{\text{Part 1}} + \underbrace{\left[\frac{(1)(7)^3}{12} + 7(5.5 - 6.529)^2\right]}_{\text{Part 2}} + \underbrace{\left[\frac{(5)(2)^3}{12} + 10(1 - 6.529)^2\right]}_{\text{Part 3}}$$

$$= 567.9 \text{ in}^4 \ \blacklozenge$$

9.20

$$\bar{I}_x = \frac{(60)(30)^3}{12} + 1800(125 - 68.54)^2 \quad \leftarrow \text{Part 1}$$

$$+ \frac{(25)(90)^3}{12} + 2250(65 - 68.54)^2 \quad \leftarrow \text{Part 2}$$

$$+ \frac{(80)(20)^3}{12} + 1600(10 - 68.54)^2 \quad \leftarrow \text{Part 3}$$

$$= 12.96 \times 10^6 \text{ mm}^4 \ \blacklozenge$$

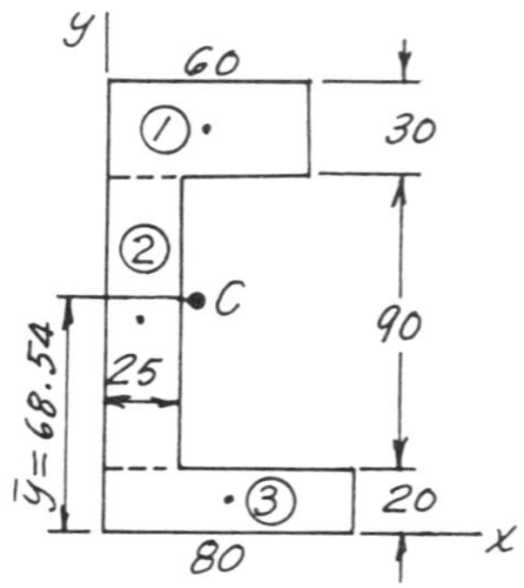

9.21

$$\bar{I}_y = \frac{(30)(60)^3}{12} + 1800(30 - 25.86)^2 \quad \leftarrow \text{Part 1}$$

$$+ \frac{(90)(25)^3}{12} + 2250(12.5 - 25.86)^2 \quad \leftarrow \text{Part 2}$$

$$+ \frac{(20)(80)^3}{12} + 1600(40 - 25.86)^2 \quad \leftarrow \text{Part 3}$$

$$= 2.26 \times 10^6 \text{ mm}^4 \ \blacklozenge$$

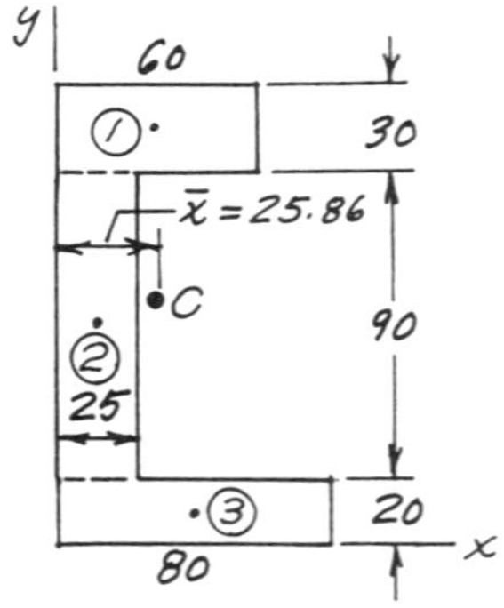

9.22

$$A_1 = \frac{\pi(5)^2}{2} = 39.27 \text{ in}^2 \qquad A_2 = \frac{(6)(4)}{2} = 12.0 \text{ in}^2$$

$$\bar{x}_1 = \frac{4}{3\pi}(5) = 2.122 \text{ in} \qquad \bar{x}_2 = \frac{4}{3} = 1.333 \text{ in}$$

$$\bar{x} = \frac{39.27(2.122) - 12.0(1.333)}{39.27 - 12.0} = 2.469 \text{ in}$$

$$\bar{I}_x = \frac{\pi R^4}{8} - \frac{b^3h}{48} = \frac{\pi(5)^4}{8} - \frac{(6)^3(4)}{48} = 227 \text{ in}^4 \ \blacklozenge$$

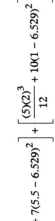

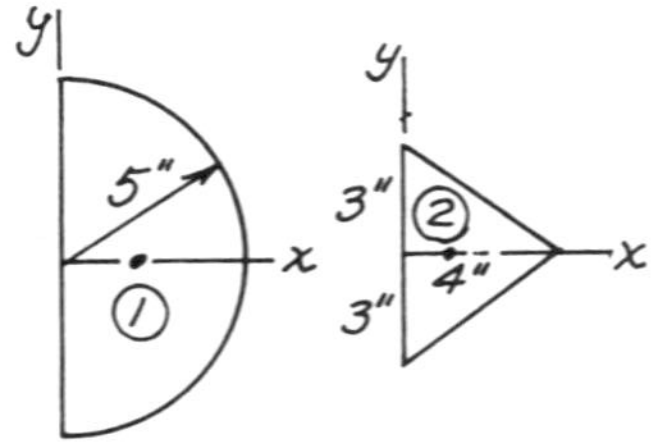

$$\bar{I}_y = \left[0.1098R^4 + A_1(\bar{x}_1 - \bar{x})^2\right] - \left[\frac{bh^3}{36} + A_2(\bar{x}_2 - \bar{x})^2\right]$$

$$= \left[0.1098(5)^4 + 39.27(2.122 - 2.469)^2\right] - \left[\frac{(6)(4)^3}{36} + 12.0(1.333 - 2.469)^2\right] = 47.2 \text{ in}^4 \ \blacklozenge$$

9.23

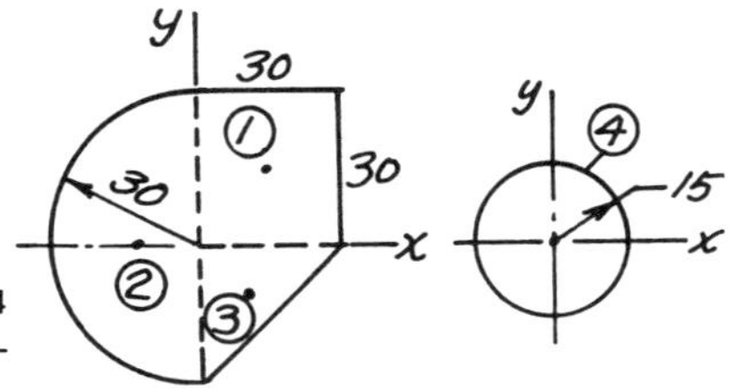

(a) $I_x = \underbrace{\frac{bh^3}{3}}_{1} + \underbrace{\frac{\pi R^4}{8}}_{2} + \underbrace{\frac{bh^3}{12}}_{3} - \underbrace{\frac{\pi r^4}{4}}_{4}$

$$= \frac{(30)(30)^3}{3} + \frac{\pi(30)^4}{8} + \frac{(30)(30)^3}{12} - \frac{\pi(15)^4}{4}$$

$$= 615.84 \times 10^3 \text{ mm}^4 \; ◆$$

(b) $A_2 = \frac{\pi(30)^2}{2} = 1413.7 \text{ mm}^2 \qquad A_4 = -\pi(15)^2 = -706.9 \text{ mm}^2$

Part	A (mm^2)	$\bar{y}$ (mm)	$A\bar{y}$ (mm^3)
1	900.0	15	13 500
2	1413.7	0	0
3	450.0	−10	−4 500
4	−706.9	0	0
Sum	2056.8		9 000

$\bar{y} = \frac{9000}{2056.8} = 4.376$ in $\qquad \bar{I}_x = I_x - A\bar{y}^2 = 615.84 \times 10^3 - 2056.8(4.376)^2 = 576 \times 10^3 \text{ mm}^4$ ◆

9.24

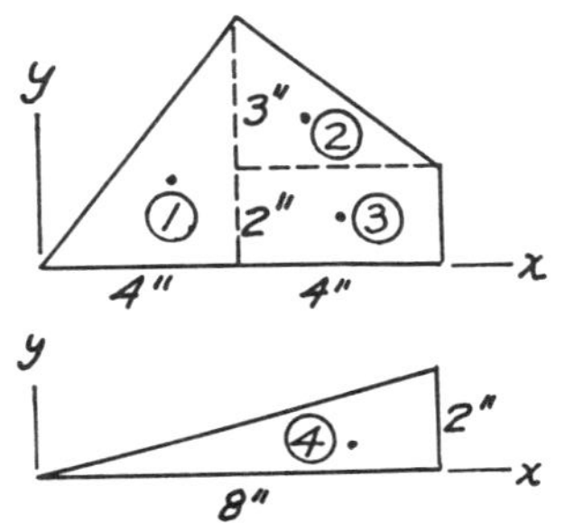

Part	A (in^2)	$\bar{y}$ (in)	$A\bar{y}$ (in^3)
1	10	5/3	50/3
2	6	3	18
3	8	1	8
4	−8	2/3	−16/3
Sum	16		112/3

$\bar{y} = \frac{112/3}{16} = 7/3$ in $\qquad I_x = \underbrace{\frac{(4)(5)^3}{12}}_{\text{Part 1}} + \underbrace{\left[\frac{4(3)^3}{36} + 6(3)^2\right]}_{\text{Part 2}} + \underbrace{\frac{(4)(2)^3}{3}}_{\text{Part 3}} - \underbrace{\frac{(8)(2)^3}{12}}_{\text{Part 4}} = 104.00 \text{ in}^4$

$\bar{I}_x = I_x - A\bar{y}^2 = 104.0 - (16)(7/3)^2 = 16.89 \text{ in}^4$ ◆

9.25

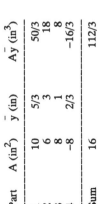

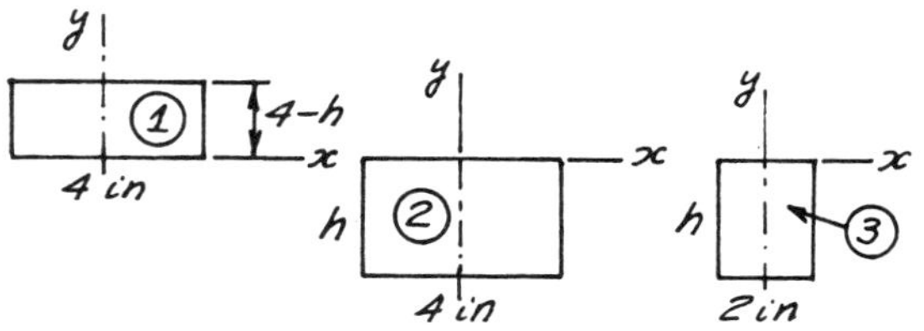

$$I_x = (I_x)_1 + (I_x)_2 - (I_x)_3 = \frac{4(4-h)^3}{3} + \frac{4h^3}{3} - \frac{2h^3}{3} = \frac{4(4-h)^3 + 2h^3}{3}$$

I_x is minimized with respect to h if $\frac{\partial I_x}{\partial h} = \frac{-(4)(3)(4-h)^2 + (2)(3)h^2}{3} = 0$

$\therefore h^2 - 16h + 32 = 0 \qquad \therefore h = \frac{16 \pm \sqrt{16^2 - 4(32)}}{2} = \frac{16 \pm 11.314}{2}$

The smaller root (h < 4 ft) is h = 2.34 ft ◆

9.26

For circle with hole:

$$I_x = (I_x)_{circle} - (I_x)_{hole} = \frac{\pi R^4}{4} - \left[\frac{\pi(R/2)^4}{4} + \pi(R/2)^2 d^2\right] = \frac{15\pi R^4}{64} - \frac{\pi R^2 d^2}{4}$$

$A = \pi R^2 - \pi\left(\frac{R}{2}\right)^2 = \frac{3\pi R^2}{4} \qquad \therefore k_x^2 = \frac{I_x}{A} = \frac{5R^2}{16} - \frac{d^2}{3}$ .... (a)

For solid circle:

$I_x = \frac{\pi R^4}{4} \qquad A = \pi R^2 \qquad \therefore k_x^2 = \frac{I_x}{A} = \frac{R^2}{4}$ .... (b)

Equating the right-hand sides of Eqs. (a) and (b):

$\frac{5R^2}{16} - \frac{d^2}{3} = \frac{R^2}{4} \qquad \therefore d = \sqrt{\frac{3}{16}}R = 0.433 R$ ◆

9.27

For the triangle shown: $A = \frac{1}{2}ab = \frac{1}{2}h\sqrt{a^2+b^2}$ $\quad \therefore h = ab/\sqrt{a^2+b^2}$

From Table 9.2 $I_u = \frac{1}{12}h^3\sqrt{a^2+b^2} = \frac{(ab)^3}{12(a^2+b^2)}$

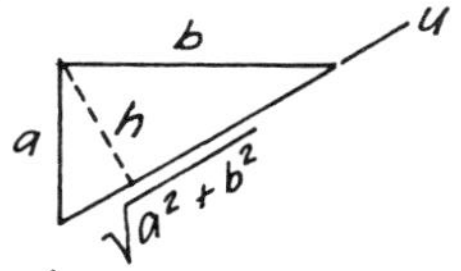

For the rectangle: $I_x = I_u$ gives $\frac{a^3b}{12} = 2\frac{(ab)^3}{12(a^2+b^2)}$ $\quad \therefore \frac{a}{b} = 1$ ◆

9.28

$\bar{I}_x = \frac{1}{36}bh^3 \qquad \bar{I}_y = \frac{1}{48}b^3h$

$\therefore \bar{I}_x = \bar{I}_y$ gives $\frac{1}{36}bh^3 = \frac{1}{48}b^3h$ $\quad \therefore h^2 = \frac{3}{4}b^2$

From geometry: $h^2 = a^2 - (b/2)^2$ $\quad \therefore a^2 - \frac{1}{4}b^2 = \frac{3}{4}b^2$ $\quad \therefore \frac{a}{b} = 1$ ◆

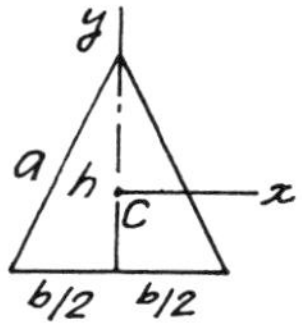

*9.29

Due to symmetry, consider only one quarter of the log.

Before sawing: $(I_x)_{before} = \frac{\pi R^4}{16}$

After sawing:

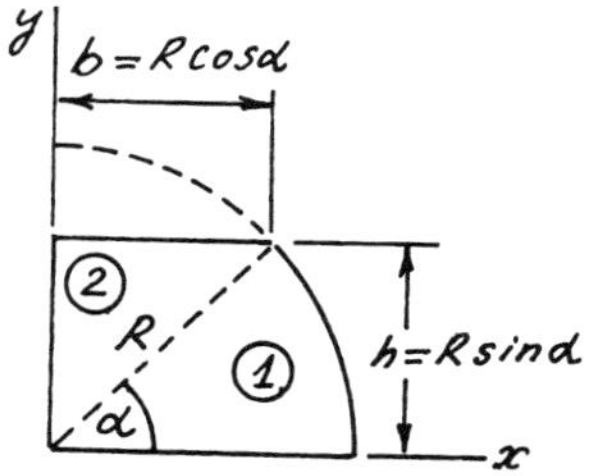

$(I_x)_1 = \frac{1}{2}\left[\frac{R^4}{8}(2\alpha - \sin 2\alpha)\right] = \frac{R^4}{16}(2\alpha - \sin 2\alpha)$

$(I_x)_2 = (\bar{I}_x)_2 + A_2d^2 = \frac{bh^3}{36} + \frac{1}{2}bh\left(\frac{2h}{3}\right)^2 = \frac{bh^3}{4}$

$= \frac{1}{4}(R\cos\alpha)(R\sin\alpha)^3 = \frac{1}{4}R^4\cos\alpha\sin^3\alpha$

$= \frac{1}{4}R^4(\sin\alpha\cos\alpha)(\sin^2\alpha) = \frac{1}{4}R^4\left(\frac{1}{2}\sin 2\alpha\right)\left[\frac{1}{2}(1-\cos 2\alpha)\right] = \frac{R^4}{16}\sin 2\alpha(1-\cos 2\alpha)$

(continued)

***9.29 continued**

$\therefore (I_x)_{after} = (I_x)_1 + (I_x)_2 = \frac{R^4}{16}\left[2\alpha - \sin 2\alpha + \sin 2\alpha(1-\cos 2\alpha)\right]$

$= \frac{R^4}{16}(2\alpha - \sin 2\alpha\cos 2\alpha)) = \frac{R^4}{32}(4\alpha - \sin 4\alpha)$

$\frac{1}{2}(I_x)_{before} = (I_x)_{after}$: $\frac{\pi R^4}{32} = \frac{R^4}{32}(4\alpha - \sin 4\alpha)$ $\quad \therefore \pi = 4\alpha - \sin 4\alpha$ $\quad \therefore \alpha = \frac{\pi}{4}$

$\therefore h = R\sin\alpha = R\sin\frac{\pi}{4} = 0.707\,R$ ◆

9.30

$A = \alpha R^2 \qquad \bar{x} = \frac{2R\sin\alpha}{3\alpha}$

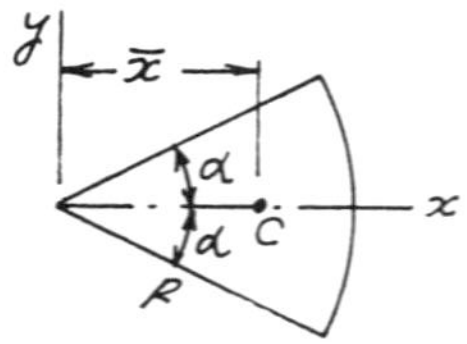

$I_x = \bar{I}_x = \frac{1}{8}R^4(2\alpha - \sin 2\alpha) = R^4\frac{\alpha - \sin\alpha\cos\alpha}{4}$

$I_y = \frac{1}{8}R^4(2\alpha + \sin 2\alpha)$

$\therefore \bar{I}_y = I_y - A\bar{x}^2 = \frac{1}{8}R^4(2\alpha + \sin 2\alpha) - \alpha R^2\left(\frac{2R\sin\alpha}{3\alpha}\right)^2 = R^4\left[\frac{\alpha + \sin\alpha\cos\alpha}{4} - \frac{4\sin^2\alpha}{9\alpha}\right]$

$\bar{I}_x = \bar{I}_y$: $\frac{\alpha - \sin\alpha\cos\alpha}{4} = \frac{\alpha + \sin\alpha\cos\alpha}{4} - \frac{4\sin^2\alpha}{9\alpha}$ $\quad \therefore \left(\frac{\cos\alpha}{2} - \frac{4\sin\alpha}{9\alpha}\right)\sin\alpha = 0$

Discarding the solution $\alpha = 0$, we have $9\alpha\cos\alpha - 8\sin\alpha = 0$

The solution, which must be obtained numerically, is $\alpha = 0.5710$ rad $= 32.7°$ ◆

9.31

Consider the <u>right half</u> of the region only. For the area element shown:

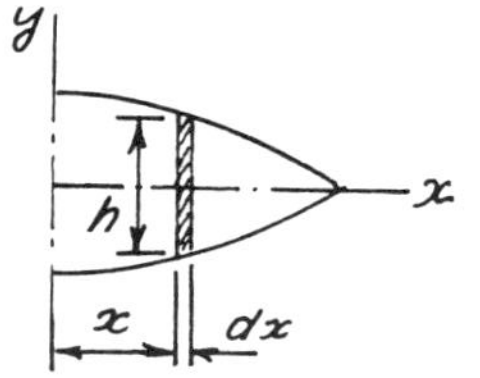

$dA = h\,dx \qquad dI_x = \frac{1}{12}h^3\,dx \qquad dI_y = x^2 dA = hx^2\,dx$

$I_x = \int_A dI_x = \int_0^{24\text{ in}} \frac{h^3}{12}\,dx \qquad I_y = \int_A dI_y = \int_0^{24\text{ in}} hx^2\,dx$

Using Simpson's rule to evaluate the integrals:

$$I_x \approx \frac{1}{12}\left(\sum_i W_i h_i^3\right)\frac{\Delta x}{3} = \frac{1}{12}\left[24^3 + 4(22.16^3) + 2(16.97^3) + 4(9.18^3) + 0\right]\frac{6}{3} = 11\ 703\text{ in}^4$$

$$I_y \approx \left(\sum_i W_i h_i x_i^2\right)\frac{\Delta x}{3} = \left[0 + 4(22.16)(6^2) + 2(16.97)((12^2) + 4(9.18)(18^2) + 0\right]\frac{6}{3}$$

$$= 39\ 951\text{ in}^4$$

<u>For the entire region</u>: $I_x = 2(11\ 703) = 23.4 \times 10^3\text{ in}^4$ ◆

$I_y = 2(39\ 951) = 79.9 \times 10^3\text{ in}^4$ ◆

9.32

For the area element shown: $dA = 2x\,dy$

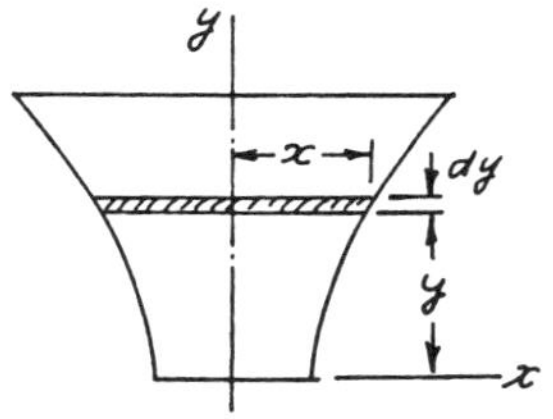

$dI_x = y^2\,dA = 2xy^2\,dy \qquad dI_y = \frac{1}{12}(2x)^3\,dx = \frac{2}{3}x^3\,dx$

$\therefore I_x = \int_A dI_x = 2\int_0^{120\text{ mm}} xy^2\,dy$

$\therefore I_y = \int_A dI_y = \frac{2}{3}\int_0^{120\text{ mm}} x^3\,dx$

Using Simpson's rule to evaluate the integrals:

$$I_x \approx 2\left(\sum_i W_i x_i y_i^2\right)\frac{\Delta y}{3} = 2\left[0 + 4(22)(20^2) + 2(27)(40^2) + 4(35)(60^2) + 2(46)(80^2)\right.$$

$$\left. + 4(60)(100^2) + (77)(120^2)\right]\frac{20}{3} = 62.98 \times 10^6\text{ mm}^4 \ ◆$$

$$I_y \approx \frac{2}{3}\left(\sum_i W_i x_i^3\right)\frac{\Delta y}{3} = \frac{2}{3}\left[20^3 + 4(22^3) + 2(27^3) + 4(35^3) + 2(46^3) + 4(60^3) + 77^3\right]\frac{20}{3}$$

$$= 7.90 \times 10^6\text{ mm}^4 \ ◆$$

9.33

For the area element shown: $dA = y\,dx \qquad dI_x = \frac{1}{3}y^3\,dx \qquad dI_y = x^2\,dA = x^2 y\,dx$

$\therefore I_x = \int_A dI_x = \int_0^{12\text{ in}} y^3/3\,dx \qquad I_y = \int_A dI_y = \int_0^{12\text{ in}} x^2 y\,dx$

x	y	$y^3/3$	x^2y
0	8.0000	170.67	0.00
2	7.8881	163.61	31.55
4	7.5425	143.03	120.68
6	6.9282	110.85	249.42
8	5.9628	70.67	381.62
10	4.4222	28.83	442.22
12	0.0000	0.00	0.00

Note that $y = 8\sqrt{1 - (x/12)^2}$ in.

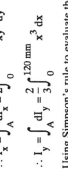

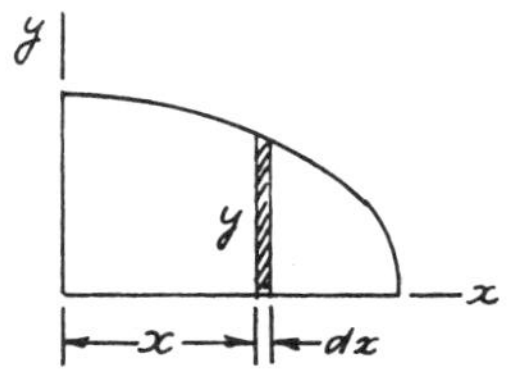

Utilizing Simpson's rule and the above table:

$$I_x \approx \left(\sum_i W_i y_i^3/3\right)\frac{\Delta x}{3} = \left[170.67 + 4(163.61) + 2(143.03) + 4(110.85) + 2(70.67)\right.$$

$$\left. + 4(28.83) + 0\right]\frac{2}{3} = 1207\text{ in}^4 \ ◆$$

$$I_y \approx \left(\sum_i W_i x_i^2 y_i\right)\frac{\Delta x}{3} = \left[0 + 4(31.55) + 2(120.68) + 4(249.42) + 2(381.62)\right.$$

$$\left. + 4(442.22) + 0\right]\frac{2}{3} = 2598\text{ in}^4 \ ◆$$

Table 9.2 gives $I_x = \frac{\pi(12)(8^3)}{16} = 1206\text{ in}^4 \qquad I_y = \frac{\pi(12^3)(8)}{16} = 2714\text{ in}^4$

9.34

Use double integration.

$$dI_{xy} = xy\,dx\,dy$$

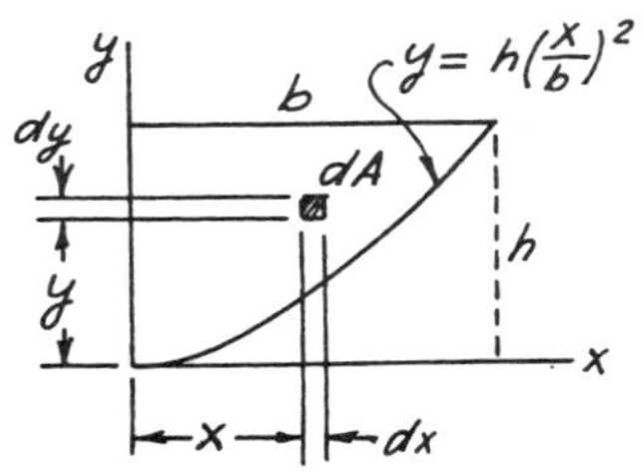

$$\therefore I_{xy} = \int_A dI_{xy} = \int_{x=0}^{b}\int_{y=h(x/b)^2}^{h} xy\,dx\,dy$$

$$= \int_0^b x\left[\frac{y^2}{2}\right]_{h(x/b)^2}^{h} dx = \int_0^b \frac{1}{2}x\left[h^2 - h^2\left(\frac{x}{b}\right)^4\right]dx$$

$$= \frac{h^2}{2}\left(\frac{b^2}{2} - \frac{b^2}{6}\right) = \frac{h^2b^2}{6} \quad \blacklozenge$$

9.35

(a) Use single integration.

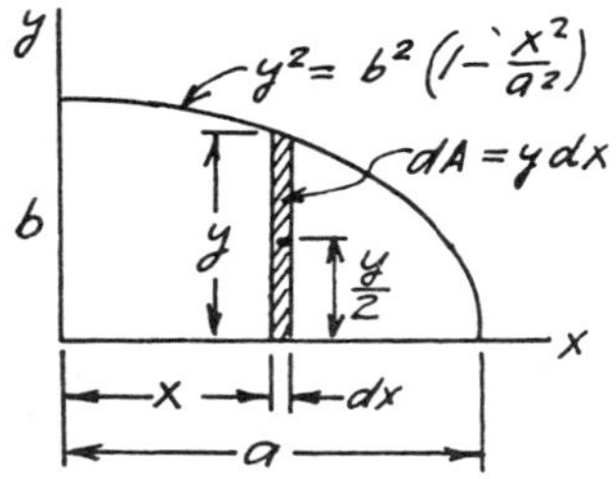

$$dI_{xy} = \bar{x}_{el}\bar{y}_{el}\,dA = x\frac{y}{2}(y\,dx) = \frac{1}{2}xy^2\,dx$$

$$= \frac{1}{2}x\left[b^2\left(1 - \frac{x^2}{a^2}\right)\right]dx$$

$$\therefore I_{xy} = \int_A dI_{xy} = \frac{b^2}{2}\int_0^a\left(x - \frac{x^3}{a^2}\right)dx = \frac{a^2b^2}{8} \quad \blacklozenge$$

(b) From Table 8.1: $A = \frac{\pi}{4}ab \qquad \bar{x} = \frac{4}{3\pi}a \qquad \bar{y} = \frac{4}{3\pi}b$

$$\therefore \bar{I}_{xy} = I_{xy} - A\bar{x}\bar{y} = \frac{a^2b^2}{8} - \left(\frac{\pi}{4}ab\right)\left(\frac{4}{3\pi}\right)^2 ab = a^2b^2\left(\frac{1}{8} - \frac{4}{9\pi}\right) = -0.01647\,a^2b^2 \quad \blacklozenge$$

9.36

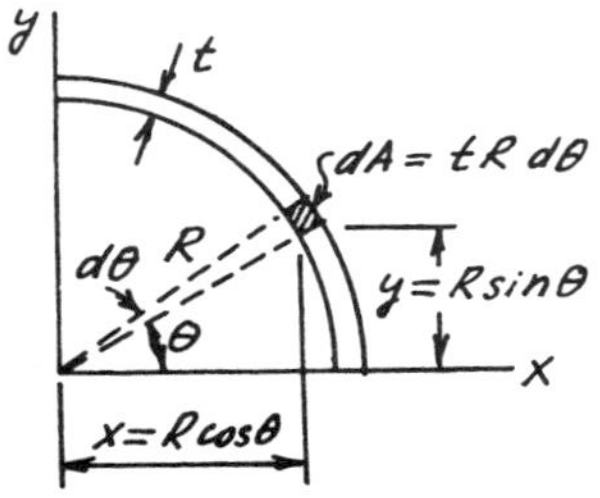

$$dI_{xy} = xy\,dA = (R\cos\theta)(R\sin\theta)(tR\,d\theta)$$

$$= tR^3\sin\theta\cos\theta\,d\theta = \frac{1}{2}tR^3\sin 2\theta\,d\theta$$

$$\therefore I_{xy} = \int_A dI_{xy} = \frac{1}{2}tR^3\int_0^{\pi/2}\sin 2\theta\,d\theta$$

$$= \frac{1}{2}tR^3\left[-\frac{1}{2}\cos 2\theta\right]_0^{\pi/2} = \frac{1}{2}tR^3 \quad \blacklozenge$$

9.37

Use double integration.

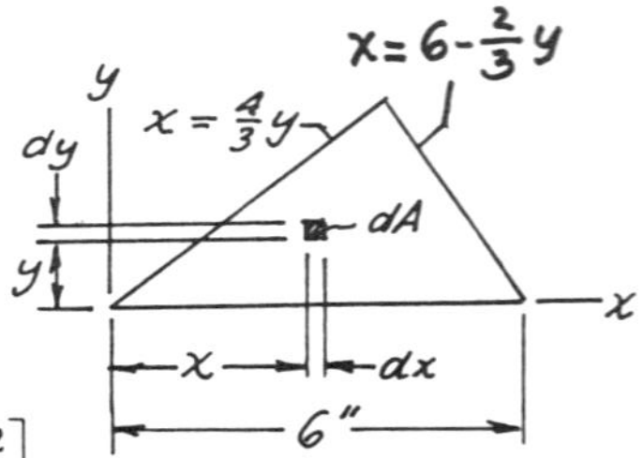

$$dI_{xy} = xy\,dA = xy\,dx\,dy$$

$$I_{xy} = \int_A dI_{xy} = \int_{y=0}^{3}\int_{x=4y/3}^{6-2y/3} xy\,dx\,dy$$

$$= \int_0^3 y\left[\frac{x^2}{2}\right]_{4y/3}^{6-2y/3} dy = \frac{1}{2}\int_0^3 y\left[\left(6 - \frac{2}{3}y\right)^2 - \left(\frac{4}{3}y\right)^2\right]dy$$

$$= \frac{1}{2}\int_0^3\left(36y - 8y^2 - \frac{4}{3}y^3\right)dy = \frac{1}{2}\left[18y^2 - \frac{8}{3}y^3 - \frac{1}{3}y^4\right]_0^3 = 31.5\text{ in}^4 \quad \blacklozenge$$

From Table 9.2: $I_{xy} = \frac{bh^2}{24}(2a + b) = \frac{(6)(3)^2}{24}\left[2(4) + 6\right] = 31.5\text{ in}^4$ Checks.

9.38

$$\bar{I}_{xy} = I_{xy} - A\bar{x}\bar{y} = 520\times 10^3 - (400)(30)(40) = 40\times 10^3\text{ mm}^4$$

$$I_{uv} = \bar{I}_{xy} + A\bar{u}\bar{v} = \bar{I}_{xy} + A(\bar{x} - d)\bar{v} = 40\times 10^3 + (400)(30 - 40)(40) = -120\times 10^3\text{ mm}^4 \quad \blacklozenge$$

9.39

$$\bar{I}_{xy} = I_{xy} - A\bar{x}\bar{y} = 320\times 10^3 - (400)\bar{x}(40) = (320 - 16\bar{x})\times 10^3 \;\ldots\ldots\; (a)$$

$$\bar{I}_{xy} = I_{uv} - A\bar{u}\bar{v} = 0 - (400)(\bar{x} - d)(40) = 16(d - \bar{x})\times 10^3 \;\ldots\ldots\; (b)$$

Equating the right-hand sides of Eqs. (a) and (b):

$$(320 - 16\bar{x}) = 16(d - \bar{x}) \qquad \therefore 320 = 16d \qquad \therefore d = 20.0\text{ mm} \quad \blacklozenge$$

9.40

$A_1 = (60)(120) = 7200 \text{ mm}^2 \qquad (\bar{I}_{xy})_1 = 0$

$A_2 = \frac{1}{2}(60)(120) = 3600 \text{ mm}^2$

$(\bar{I}_{xy})_2 = -\frac{b^2h^2}{72} = -\frac{(60)^2(120)^2}{72} = -0.720 \times 10^6 \text{ mm}^4$

$A_3 = -\frac{\pi}{2}(60)^2 = -5655 \text{ mm}^2 \qquad (\bar{I}_{xy})_3 = 0$

$\bar{x}_3 = \frac{4R}{3\pi} = \frac{4(60)}{3\pi} = 25.46 \text{ mm}$

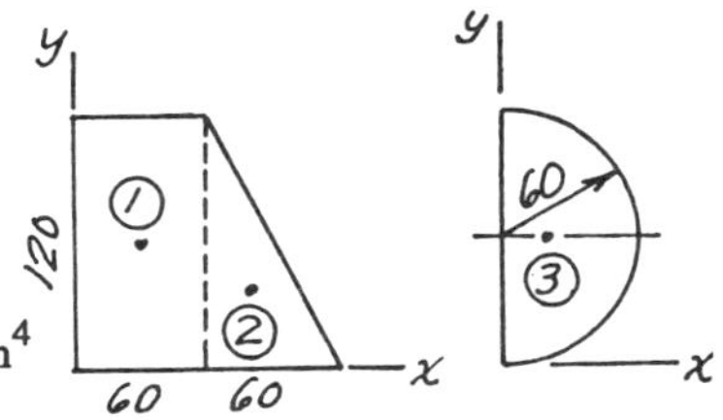

Part	A (mm²)	$\bar{x}$ (mm)	$\bar{y}$ (mm)	$A\bar{x}\bar{y}$ (10^6 mm⁴)	$\bar{I}_{xy}$ (10^6 mm⁴)	$I_{xy} = A\bar{x}\bar{y} + \bar{I}_{xy}$
1	7200	30.00	60.00	12.960	0	12.960
2	3600	80.00	40.00	11.520	−0.720	10.800
3	−5655	25.46	60.00	-8.635	0	-8.635
Sum						15.125

$\therefore I_{xy} = 15.125 \times 10^6 \text{ mm}^4$ ◆

9.41

<u>Part 1</u>: $I_{xy} = \bar{I}_{xy} + A\bar{x}\bar{y}$

$= 0 + \left(\frac{\pi}{2}R^2\right)(R)\left(R + \frac{4R}{3\pi}\right) = \left(\frac{\pi}{2} + \frac{2}{3}\right)R^4$

<u>Part 2</u>: $I_{xy} = \frac{b^2h^2}{4} = \frac{(2R)^2(R)^2}{4} = R^4$

<u>Part 3</u>: (to be subtracted) $I_{xy} = \frac{b^2h^2}{24} = \frac{(2R)^2(R)^2}{24} = \frac{R^4}{6}$

<u>Assembly</u>: $I_{xy} = \left(\frac{\pi}{2} + \frac{2}{3} + 1 - \frac{1}{6}\right)R^4 = 3.07R^4$ ◆

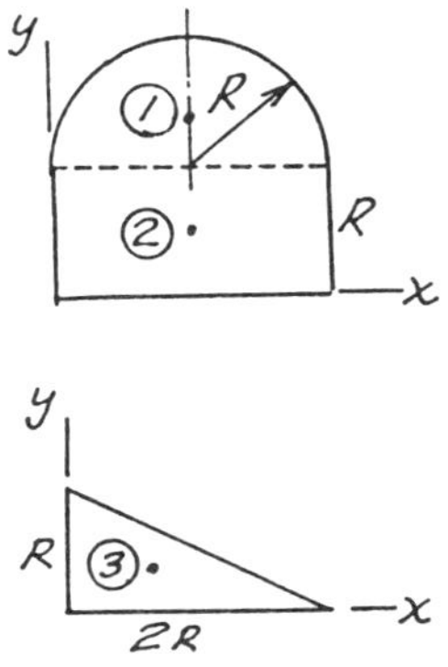

9.42

Centroid C can be found by inspection.

$\bar{I}_{xy} = \sum_i \left[(\bar{I}_{xy})_i + A_i\bar{x}_i\bar{y}_i\right] = 2(A\bar{x}\bar{y})_{\text{flange}}$

$= 2(160 \times 40)(-60)(80) = -61.4 \times 10^6 \text{ mm}^4$ ◆

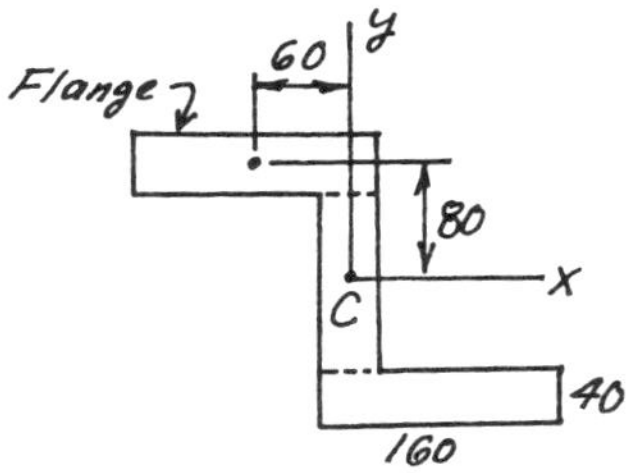

9.43

Centroid C can be found by inspection.

$\bar{I}_{xy}$ of the area is due to the parabolic cutouts only.

$\therefore \bar{I}_{xy} = -2\left[\bar{I}_{xy} + A\bar{x}'\bar{y}'\right]_{\text{parabola}}$

$= -2\left(\frac{b^2h^2}{120} + \frac{bh}{3}\bar{x}'\bar{y}'\right)$

$= -2\left[\frac{(9^2)(6^2)}{120} + \frac{(9)(6)}{3}(-5.75)(6.2)\right]$

$= 1235 \text{ in}^4$ ◆

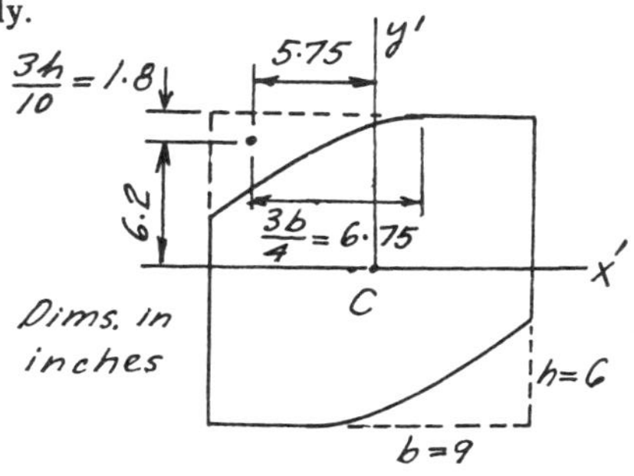

9.44

$\bar{I}_{xy} = \sum_i \left[(\bar{I}_{xy})_i + A_i\bar{x}_i\bar{y}_i\right] = 0 + \sum_i A_i\bar{x}_i\bar{y}_i$

Part	A (mm²)	$\bar{x}$ (mm)	$\bar{y}$ (mm)	$A\bar{x}\bar{y}$ (mm⁴)
1	800	−11.5	13.5	-124.2×10^3
2	500	18.5	−21.5	-198.9×10^3
Sum				-323.1×10^3

$\therefore I_{xy} = -323 \times 10^3 \text{ mm}^4$ ◆

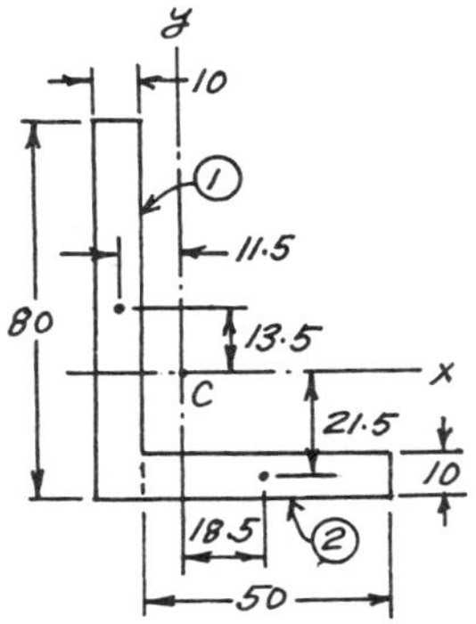

9.45

$$I_{xy} = \sum_i \left[(\bar{I}_{xy})_i + A_i \bar{x}_i \bar{y}_i \right] = 0 + \sum_i A_i \bar{x}_i \bar{y}_i$$

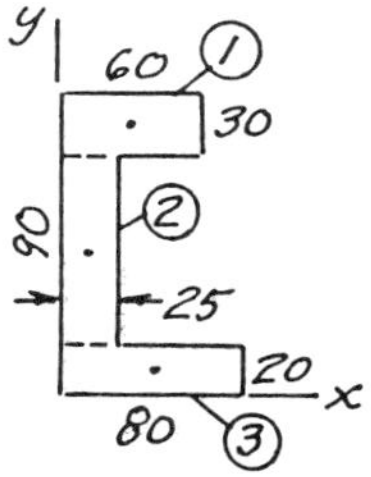

Part	$A(mm^2)$	$\bar{x}$ (mm)	$\bar{y}$ (mm)	$A\bar{x}\bar{y}$ (mm^4)
1	1800	30.0	125	6.750×10^6
2	2250	12.5	65	1.828×10^6
3	1600	40.0	10	0.640×10^6
Sum	5650			9.218×10^6

$\therefore \bar{I}_{xy} = I_{xy} - A\bar{x}\bar{y} = 9.218 \times 10^6 - (5650)(25.86)(68.54) = -0.796 \times 10^6 \text{ mm}^4$ ◆

9.46

Find the centroid first:

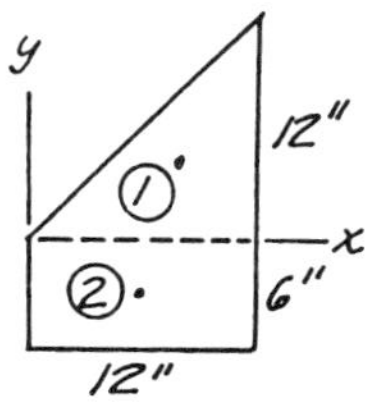

Part	$A(in^2)$	$\bar{x}$ (in)	$\bar{y}$ (in)	$A\bar{x}$ (in^3)	$A\bar{y}$ (in^3)
1	72	8	4	576	288
2	72	6	-3	432	-216
Sums	144			1008	72

$\bar{x} = \dfrac{\Sigma A\bar{x}}{\Sigma A} = \dfrac{1008}{144} = 7.00$ in $\qquad \bar{y} = \dfrac{\Sigma A\bar{y}}{\Sigma A} = \dfrac{72}{144} = 0.50$ in

$(I_{xy})_1 = \dfrac{b^2h^2}{8} = \dfrac{(12^2)(12^2)}{8} = 2592 \text{ in}^4$

$(I_{xy})_2 = -\dfrac{b^2h^2}{4} = -\dfrac{(12^2)(6^2)}{4} = -1296 \text{ in}^4$ (note that the area is in region of negative y)

For the composite area:

$\bar{I}_{xy} = I_{xy} - A\bar{x}\bar{y} = (2592 - 1296) - (144)(7.00)(0.50) = 792 \text{ in}^4$ ◆

9.47

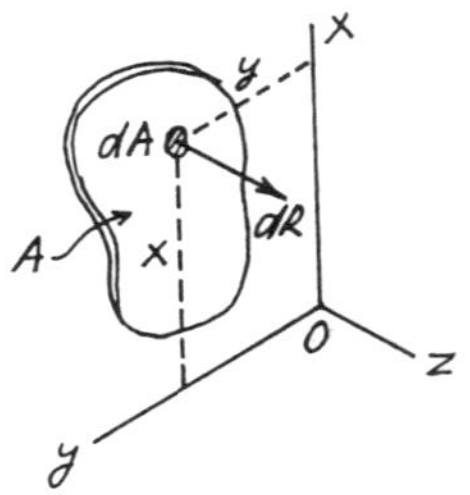

$dR = p\, dA = cy\, dA$

$R = \int_A dR = c\int_A y\, dA = cQ_x$

$\therefore \mathbf{R} = cQ_x\mathbf{i}$ Q.E.D

$C_x^R = \int_A y\, dR = c\int_A y^2\, dA = cI_x$

$C_y^R = \int_A (-x)\, dR = -c\int_A xy\, dA = -cI_{xy}$

$\therefore \mathbf{C}^R = c(I_x\mathbf{i} - I_{xy}\mathbf{j})$ Q.E.D

9.48

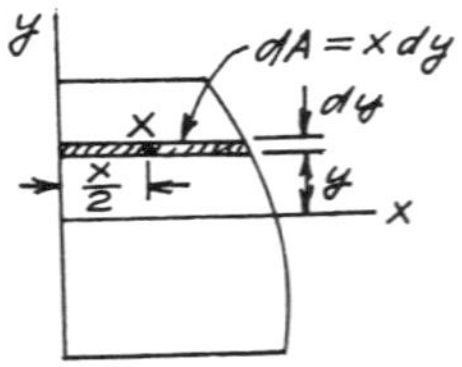

$dI_{xy} = \bar{x}_{el}\bar{y}_{el}\, dA = \dfrac{x}{2} y\,(x\, dy) = \dfrac{1}{2}x^2 y\, dy$

$I_{xy} = \int_A dI_{xy} = \dfrac{1}{2}\int_A x^2 y\, dy$

Using Simpson's rule:

$$I_{xy} \approx \frac{1}{2}\left(\frac{\Delta y}{3}\sum_{i=1}^{5} W_i x_i^2 y_i\right) = \frac{1}{2}\frac{185}{3}\sum_{i=1}^{5} W_i x_i^2 y_i$$

x_i (mm)	y_i (mm)	W_i	$W_i x_i^2 y_i$ (mm^3)
406	-370	1	-60.99×10^6
420	-185	4	-130.54×10^6
392	0	2	0.00×10^6
338	185	4	84.54×10^6
218	370	1	17.58×10^6
Sum			-89.41×10^6

$\therefore I_{xy} = \dfrac{1}{2}\dfrac{185}{3}(-89.41 \times 10^6) = -2.76 \times 10^9 \text{ mm}^4$ ◆

9.49

$dI_{xy} = \bar{x}_{el}\bar{y}_{el}\,dA = x\frac{y}{2}(y\,dx) = \frac{1}{2}xy^2\,dx$

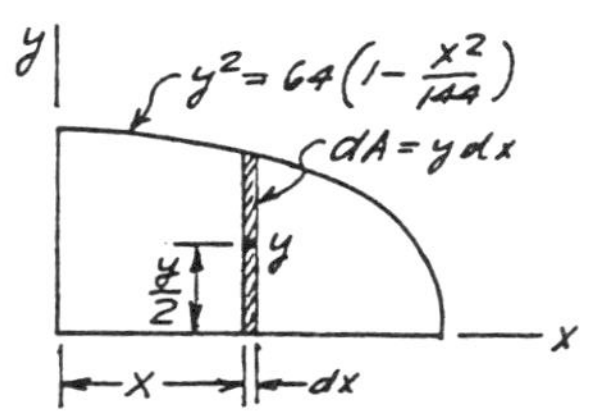

$\therefore I_{xy} = \int_A dI_{xy} = \frac{1}{2}\int_A xy^2\,dx$

Using Simpson's rule:

$$I_{xy} \approx \frac{1}{2}\left(\frac{\Delta x}{3}\sum_{i=1}^{7} W_i x_i y_i^2\right) = \frac{1}{2}\left(\frac{2}{3}\sum_{i=1}^{7} W_i x_i y_i^2\right)$$

where $y_i^2 = 64 - \frac{64}{144}x_i^2 = 64 - \frac{4}{9}x_i^2$

x_i (in)	y_i^2 (in^2)	W_i	$W_i x_i y_i^2$ (in^3)
0	64.00	1	0
2	62.22	4	498
4	56.89	2	455
6	48.00	4	1152
8	35.56	2	569
10	19.56	4	782
12	0.00	1	0
Sum			3456

$\therefore I_{xy} = \frac{1}{2}\frac{2}{3}(3456) = 1152\text{ in}^4$ ◆

Check: from Table 9.2: $I_{xy} = \frac{(ab)^2}{8} = \frac{(12 \times 8)^2}{8} = 1152\text{ in}^4$ O.K.

9.50

(a) Due to symmetry, the x and y-axes are the principal axes at C. ◆

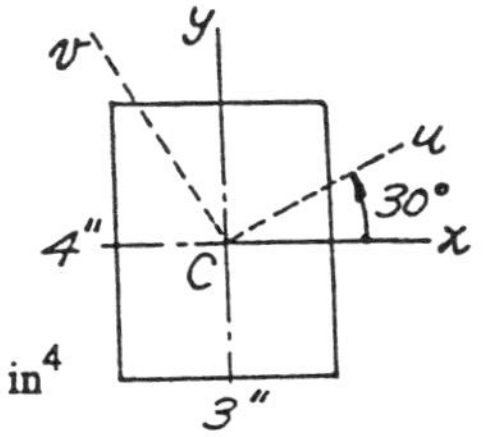

$I_1 = I_x = \frac{bh^3}{12} = \frac{(3)(4)^3}{12} = 16\text{ in}^4$ ◆

$I_2 = I_y = \frac{hb^3}{12} = \frac{(4)(3)^3}{12} = 9\text{ in}^4$ ◆

(b) $\frac{1}{2}(I_x + I_y) = \frac{16+9}{2} = 12.5\text{ in}^4$ $\quad \frac{1}{2}(I_x - I_y) = \frac{16-9}{2} = 3.5\text{ in}^4$

$I_u = \frac{1}{2}(I_x + I_y) + \frac{1}{2}(I_x - I_y)\cos 2\theta - I_{xy}\sin 2\theta = 12.5 + 3.5\cos 60° - 0 = 14.25\text{ in}^4$ ◆

$I_v = \frac{1}{2}(I_x + I_y) - \frac{1}{2}(I_x - I_y)\cos 2\theta + I_{xy}\sin 2\theta = 12.5 - 3.5\cos 60° + 0 = 10.75\text{ in}^4$ ◆

$I_{uv} = \frac{1}{2}(I_x - I_y)\sin 2\theta + I_{xy}\cos 2\theta = 3.5\sin 60° + 0 = 3.03\text{ in}^4$ ◆

9.51

(a) Due to symmetry, the x and y-axes are the principal axes at C. ◆

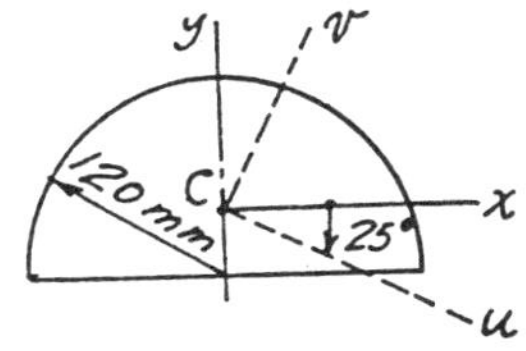

$I_1 = I_y = \frac{\pi}{8}R^4 = \frac{\pi}{8}(120)^4 = 81.43 \times 10^6\text{ mm}^4$ ◆

$I_2 = I_x = 0.1098R^4 = 0.1098(120)^4 = 22.77 \times 10^6\text{ mm}^4$ ◆

(b) $\frac{1}{2}(I_x + I_y) = \frac{1}{2}(22.77 + 81.43) \times 10^6 = 52.10 \times 10^6\text{ mm}^4$

$\frac{1}{2}(I_x - I_y) = \frac{1}{2}(22.77 - 81.43) \times 10^6 = -29.33 \times 10^6\text{ mm}^4$ $\quad \theta = -25°$

$I_u = \frac{1}{2}(I_x + I_y) + \frac{1}{2}(I_x - I_y)\cos 2\theta - I_{xy}\sin 2\theta = \left[52.10 - 29.33\cos(-50°) - 0\right] \times 10^6$

$= 33.2 \times 10^6\text{ mm}^4$ ◆

$I_v = \frac{1}{2}(I_x + I_y) - \frac{1}{2}(I_x - I_y)\cos 2\theta + I_{xy}\sin 2\theta = \left[52.10 + 29.33\cos(-50°) + 0\right] \times 10^6$

$= 71.0 \times 10^6\text{ mm}^4$ ◆

$I_{uv} = \frac{1}{2}(I_x - I_y)\sin 2\theta + I_{xy}\cos 2\theta = \left[-29.33\sin(-50°) + 0\right] \times 10^6 = 22.5 \times 10^6\text{ mm}^4$ ◆

9.52

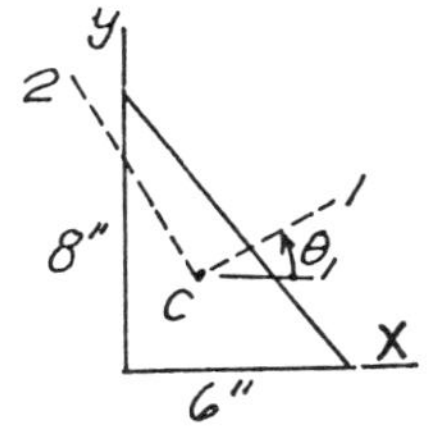

$$\bar{I}_x = \frac{bh^3}{36} = \frac{(6)(8)^3}{36} = 85.33 \text{ in}^4 \qquad \bar{I}_y = \frac{b^3h}{36} = \frac{(6)^3(8)}{36} = 48.0 \text{ in}^4$$

$$\bar{I}_{xy} = -\frac{b^2h^2}{72} = -\frac{(6)^2(8)^2}{72} = -32.0 \text{ in}^4$$

$$b = \frac{1}{2}(\bar{I}_x + \bar{I}_y) = \frac{1}{2}(85.33 + 48.0) = 66.67 \text{ in}^4$$

$$R = \sqrt{\left[(\bar{I}_x - \bar{I}_y)/2\right]^2 + \bar{I}_{xy}^2} = \sqrt{\left[(85.33 - 48.0)/2\right]^2 + (-32.0)^2} = 37.05 \text{ in}^4$$

$\bar{I}_1 = b + R = 66.67 + 37.05 = 103.7 \text{ in}^4$ ◆ $\quad \bar{I}_2 = b - R = 66.67 - 37.05 = 29.6 \text{ in}^4$ ◆

$$\sin 2\theta_1 = -\bar{I}_{xy}/R = -\frac{-32.0}{37.05} = 0.8637 \qquad \cos 2\theta_1 = (\bar{I}_x - \bar{I}_y)/(2R) = \frac{85.33 - 48.0}{2(37.05)} > 0$$

$\therefore 2\theta_1$ lies in the first quadrant. $\therefore 2\theta_1 = 59.73°$

$\therefore \theta_1 = 29.9°$ ◆ $\quad \theta_2 = \theta_1 + 90° = 119.9°$ ◆

9.53

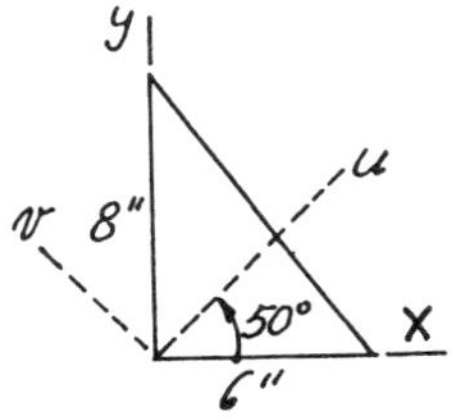

$$I_x = \frac{bh^3}{12} = \frac{(6)(8)^3}{12} = 256 \text{ in}^4 \qquad I_y = \frac{b^3h}{12} = \frac{(6)^3(8)}{12} = 144 \text{ in}^4$$

$$I_{xy} = \frac{b^2h^2}{24} = \frac{(6)^2(8)^2}{24} = 96 \text{ in}^4$$

$$\frac{I_x + I_y}{2} = \frac{256 + 144}{2} = 200 \text{ in}^4 \qquad \frac{I_x - I_y}{2} = \frac{256 - 144}{2} = 56 \text{ in}^4$$

$I_u = \frac{I_x + I_y}{2} + \frac{I_x - I_y}{2}\cos 2\theta - I_{xy}\sin 2\theta = 200 + 56\cos 100° - 96\sin 100° = 95.7 \text{ in}^4$ ◆

$I_v = \frac{I_x + I_y}{2} - \frac{I_x - I_y}{2}\cos 2\theta + I_{xy}\sin 2\theta = 200 - 56\cos 100° + 96\sin 100° = 304.3 \text{ in}^4$ ◆

$I_{uv} = \frac{I_x - I_y}{2}\sin 2\theta + I_{xy}\cos 2\theta = 56\sin 100° + 96\cos 100° = 38.5 \text{ in}^4$ ◆

9.54

$$\frac{I_x + I_y}{2} = \frac{4000 + 1000}{2} = 2500 \text{ in}^4 \qquad \frac{I_x - I_y}{2} = \frac{4000 - 1000}{2} = 1500 \text{ in}^4$$

$I_u = 2500 + 1500\cos 240° + 800\sin 240° = 1057 \text{ in}^4$ ◆

$I_v = 2500 - 1500\cos 240° - 800\sin 240° = 3943 \text{ in}^4$ ◆

$I_{uv} = 1500\sin 240° - 800\cos 240° = -899 \text{ in}^4$ ◆

9.55

$$\frac{I_x + I_y}{2} = \frac{10 + 20}{2} \times 10^6 = 15 \times 10^6 \text{ mm}^4 \qquad \frac{I_x - I_y}{2} = \frac{10 - 20}{2} \times 10^6 = -5 \times 10^6 \text{ mm}^4$$

$I_u = (15 - 5\cos 67.4° - 12\sin 67.4°) \times 10^6 = 2.00 \times 10^6 \text{ mm}^4$ ◆

$I_v = (15 + 5\cos 67.4° + 12\sin 67.4°) \times 10^6 = 28.00 \times 10^6 \text{ mm}^4$ ◆

$I_{uv} = (-5\sin 67.4° + 12\cos 67.4°) \times 10^6 = 0$ ◆

9.56

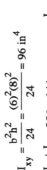

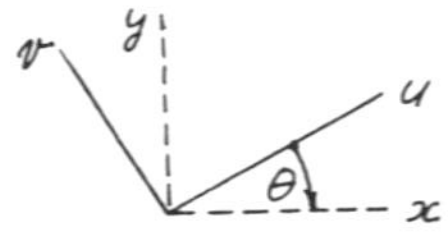

To transform the moments of inertia from (u, v) to (x, y) coordinates, we can use Eqs. (9.17)–(9.19), but we must interchange the roles of (x, y) and (u, v). In addition, the direction of θ must be reversed, so that it points from u-axis to the x-axis. Thus Eqs. (19.17)–(19.19) become

$I_x = \frac{I_u + I_v}{2} + \frac{I_u - I_v}{2}\cos 2\theta = \frac{7600 + 5000}{2} + \frac{7600 - 5000}{2}\cos 67.4° = 6800 \text{ in}^4$ ◆

$I_y = \frac{I_u + I_v}{2} - \frac{I_u - I_v}{2}\cos 2\theta = \frac{7600 + 5000}{2} - \frac{7600 - 5000}{2}\cos 67.4° = 5800 \text{ in}^4$ ◆

$I_{xy} = \frac{I_u - I_v}{2}\sin(-2\theta) = \frac{7600 - 5000}{2}\sin(-67.4°) = -1200 \text{ in}^4$ ◆

9.57

(a) $I_{uv} = \frac{I_x - I_y}{2}\sin 2\theta + I_{xy}\cos 2\theta = \frac{I_x - I_y}{2}\sin 2\theta + 0$

I_{uv} is maximized when $\sin 2\theta = 1$, i.e. when $\theta = 45°$ ◆

(b) $\frac{I_x + I_y}{2} = \frac{6+2}{2} \times 10^6 = 4 \times 10^6 \text{ mm}^4 \qquad \frac{I_x - I_y}{2} = \frac{6-2}{2} \times 10^6 = 2 \times 10^6 \text{ mm}^4$

$I_u = \frac{I_x + I_y}{2} + \frac{I_x - I_y}{2}\cos 2\theta - I_{xy}\sin 2\theta = (4 + 2\cos 90° - 0) \times 10^6 = 4 \times 10^6 \text{ mm}^4$ ◆

$I_v = \frac{I_x + I_y}{2} - \frac{I_x - I_y}{2}\cos 2\theta + I_{xy}\sin 2\theta = (4 - 2\cos 90° + 0) \times 10^6 = 4 \times 10^6 \text{ mm}^4$ ◆

$I_{uv} = \frac{I_x - I_y}{2}\sin 2\theta + I_{xy}\cos 2\theta = 2 \times 10^6 \sin 90° = 2 \times 10^6 \text{ mm}^4$ ◆

9.58

$\sin 2\theta_1 = -\frac{I_{xy}}{R} \qquad \therefore R = -\frac{I_{xy}}{\sin 2\theta_1} = -\frac{(-30 \times 10^6)}{\sin 36.88°} = 50.0 \times 10^6 \text{ mm}^4$

$I_1 = I_u = \frac{I_x + I_y}{2} + R \qquad \therefore I_x + I_y = 2(I_u - R) = 2(160 - 50) \times 10^6 = 220 \times 10^6 \text{ mm}^4$

But $I_x + I_y = I_u + I_v \qquad \therefore I_v = (I_x + I_y) - I_u = (220 - 160) \times 10^6 = 60 \times 10^6 \text{ mm}^4$ ◆

9.59

Part 1:

$I_x = \frac{bh^3}{3} = \frac{(90)(120)^3}{3} = 51.84 \times 10^6 \text{ mm}^4$

$I_y = \frac{b^3h}{3} = \frac{(90)^3(120)}{3} = 29.16 \times 10^6 \text{ mm}^4$

$I_{xy} = \frac{b^2h^2}{4} = \frac{(90)^2(120)^2}{4} = 29.16 \times 10^6 \text{ mm}^4$

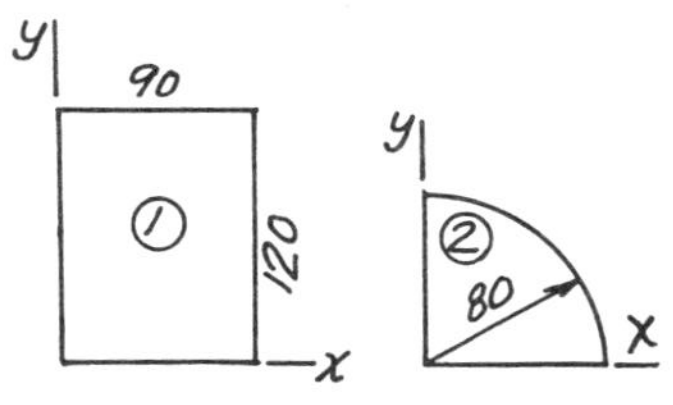

(continued)

9.59 continued

Part 2 (to be subtracted):

$I_x = I_y = \frac{\pi R^4}{16} = \frac{\pi(80)^4}{16} = 8.04 \times 10^6 \text{ mm}^4 \qquad I_{xy} = \frac{R^4}{8} = \frac{(80)^4}{8} = 5.12 \times 10^6 \text{ mm}^4$

Composite area:

$I_x = (51.84 - 8.04) \times 10^6 = 43.80 \times 10^6 \text{ mm}^4$

$I_y = (29.16 - 8.04) \times 10^6 = 21.12 \times 10^6 \text{ mm}^4$

$I_{xy} = (29.16 - 5.12) \times 10^6 = 24.04 \times 10^6 \text{ mm}^4$

$b = \frac{I_x + I_y}{2} = \frac{43.80 + 21.12}{2} \times 10^6 = 32.46 \times 10^6 \text{ mm}^4$

$R = \sqrt{\left[\frac{1}{2}(I_x - I_y)\right]^2 + I_{xy}^2} = \sqrt{\left[\frac{1}{2}(43.80 - 21.12)\right]^2 + (24.04)^2} \times 10^6 = 26.58 \times 10^6 \text{ mm}^4$

$I_1 = b + R = (33.96 + 26.58) \times 10^6 = 59.04 \times 10^6 \text{ mm}^4$ ◆

$I_2 = b - R = (33.96 - 26.58) \times 10^6 = 5.88 \times 10^6 \text{ mm}^4$ ◆

$\sin 2\theta_1 = -\frac{I_{xy}}{R} = -\frac{24.04}{26.58} = -0.9044 \qquad \cos 2\theta_1 = \frac{I_x - I_y}{2R} = \frac{43.80 - 21.12}{2(26.58)} > 0$

$\therefore 2\theta_1$ lies in the 4th quadrant. $\therefore 2\theta_1 = -64.74°$

$\therefore \theta_1 = -32.4°$ ◆ $\quad \theta_2 = \theta_1 + 90° = 57.6°$ ◆

9.60

(a) $I_x = \frac{bh^3}{3} = \frac{(80)(150)^3}{3} = 90 \times 10^6 \text{ mm}^4$

$I_y = \frac{b^3h}{3} = \frac{(80)^3(150)}{3} = 25.6 \times 10^6 \text{ mm}^4$

$I_{xy} = \frac{b^2h^2}{4} = \frac{(80)^2(150)^2}{4} = 36 \times 10^6 \text{ mm}^4$

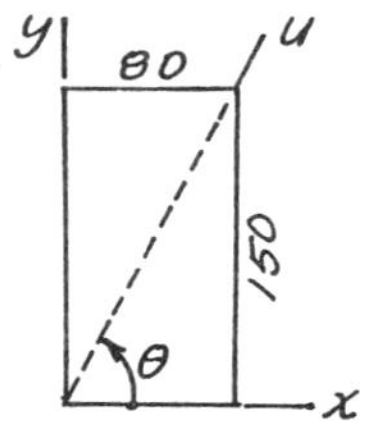

$\theta = \tan^{-1}\frac{150}{80} = 61.93° \qquad \therefore 2\theta = 123.86° \qquad \sin 2\theta = 0.8304 \qquad \cos 2\theta = -0.5572$

(continued)

9.60 continued

$$I_u = \frac{1}{2}(I_x + I_y) + \frac{1}{2}(I_x - I_y)\cos 2\theta - I_{xy}\sin 2\theta$$

$$= \left[\frac{90 + 25.6}{2} + \frac{90 - 25.6}{2}(-0.5572) - 36(0.8304)\right] \times 10^6 = 9.96 \times 10^6 \text{ mm}^4 \ ◆$$

(b) $\bar{I}_x = \frac{bh^3}{12} = \frac{(80)(150)^3}{12} = 22.5 \times 10^6 \text{ mm}^4$

$\bar{I}_y = \frac{b^3h}{12} = \frac{(80)^3(150)}{12} = 6.4\times 10^6 \text{ mm}^4 \qquad \bar{I}_{xy} = 0$

$$I_u = \left[\frac{22.5 + 6.4}{2} + \frac{22.5 - 6.4}{2}(-0.5572)\right] \times 10^6 = 9.96 \times 10^6 \text{ mm}^4 \ ◆$$

(c) For a triangle: $b = \sqrt{150^2 + 80^2} = 170$ mm

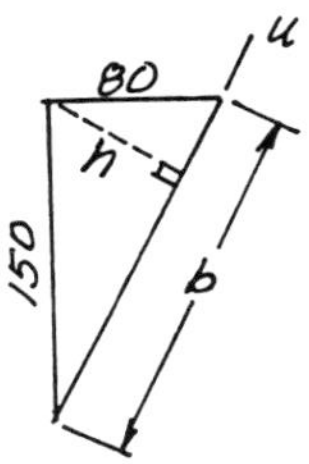

From similar triangles: $\frac{h}{150} = \frac{80}{b} \qquad \therefore\ h = \frac{(150)(80)}{170} = 70.59$ mm

$I_u = \frac{bh^3}{12} = \frac{(170)(70.59^3)}{12} = 4.983 \times 10^6 \text{ mm}^4$

For the rectangle: $I_u = 2(4.983 \times 10^6) = 9.97 \times 10^6 \text{ mm}^4$ ◆

9.61

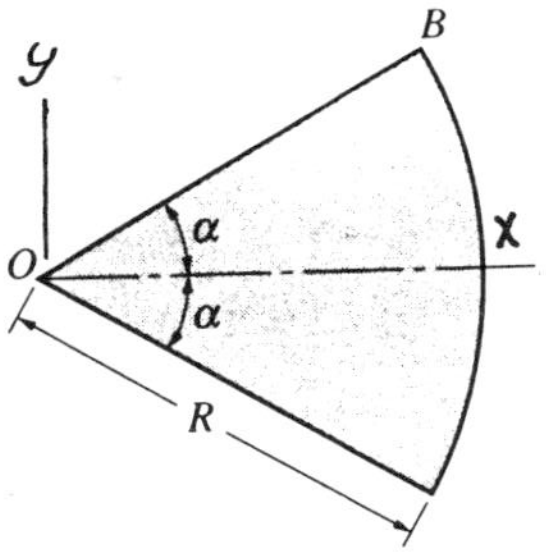

$I_x = \frac{R^4}{8}(2\alpha - \sin 2\alpha) \qquad I_y = \frac{R^4}{8}(2\alpha + \sin 2\alpha) \qquad I_{xy} = 0$

$\frac{I_x + I_y}{2} = \frac{R^4}{8}(2\alpha) \qquad \frac{I_x - I_y}{2} = -\frac{R^4}{8}\sin 2\alpha$

$$I_{OB} = \frac{I_x + I_y}{2} + \frac{I_x - I_y}{2}\cos 2\alpha - I_{xy}\sin 2\alpha$$

$$= \frac{R^4}{8}(2\alpha) - \frac{R^4}{8}\sin 2\alpha \cos 2\alpha - 0 = \frac{R^4}{16}(4\alpha - \sin 4\alpha) \ ◆$$

When $\alpha = 45°$, i.e., $4\alpha = \pi$ rad:

$I_{OB} = \frac{\pi R^4}{16}$ which agrees with I_x of quarter circle in Table 9.2.

9.62

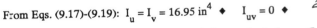

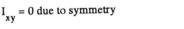

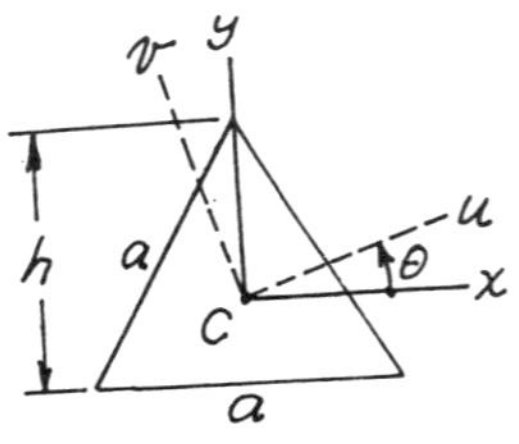

$h = \sqrt{a^2 - (a/2)^2} = (\sqrt{3}/2)a$

$\bar{I}_x = \frac{bh^3}{36} = \frac{(a)\left[(\sqrt{3}/2)a\right]^3}{36} = \frac{\sqrt{3}a^4}{96}$

$\bar{I}_y = \frac{b^3h}{48} = \frac{(a^3)(\sqrt{3}/2)a}{48} = \frac{\sqrt{3}a^4}{96} \qquad \bar{I}_{xy} = 0$

Since $\bar{I}_x = \bar{I}_y$ and $\bar{I}_{xy} = 0$, we conclude from Eqs. (9.17)–(9.19) that

$I_u = I_v = \frac{\sqrt{3}a^4}{96}$ and $I_{uv} = 0$ for all θ

$\therefore$ Every axis passing through C is a principal axis ($I_{uv} = 0$), with the moment of inertia $\frac{\sqrt{3}a^4}{96}$

9.63

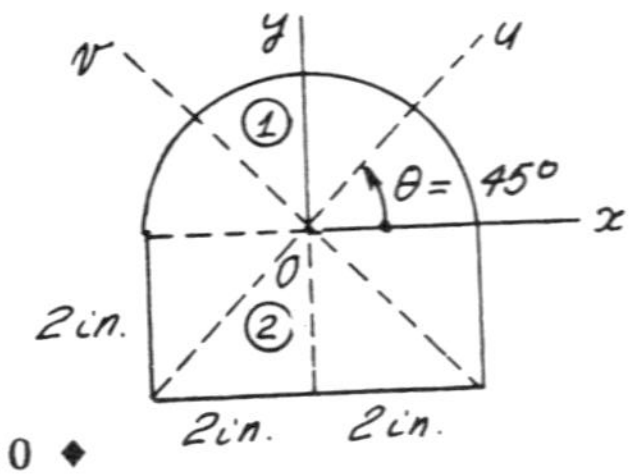

$I_x = (I_x)_1 + (I_x)_2 = \frac{\pi(2)^4}{8} + \frac{(4)(2)^3}{3} = 16.950 \text{ in}^4$

$I_y = (I_y)_1 + (I_y)_2 = \frac{\pi(2)^4}{8} + \frac{(4)^3(2)}{12} = 16.950 \text{ in}^4$

$I_{xy} = 0$ due to symmetry

From Eqs. (9.17)-(9.19): $I_u = I_v = 16.95 \text{ in}^4$ ◆ $\quad I_{uv} = 0$ ◆

Note: In this case, all axes passing through O are principal axes ($I_{uv} = 0$).

9.64

(a) $I_x + I_y = I_1 + I_2 = (0.808 + 0.388) \times 10^6 = 1.196 \times 10^6 \text{ mm}^4$

$\therefore\ I_1 = I_x + I_y - I_2 = (1.196 - 0.213) \times 10^6 = 0.983 \times 10^6 \text{ mm}^4$ ◆

(continued)

9.64 continued

(b) $I_1 = \frac{1}{2}(I_x + I_y) + R$

$\therefore R = I_1 - \frac{1}{2}(I_x + I_y) = \left(0.983 - \frac{1.196}{2}\right) \times 10^6 = 0.385 \times 10^6 \text{ mm}^4$

$\cos 2\theta_1 = \frac{I_x - I_y}{2R} = \frac{0.808 - 0.388}{2(0.385)} = 0.5455 \qquad \therefore 2\theta_1 = \pm 56.94°$

$\sin 2\theta_1 = -\frac{I_{xy}}{R} > 0$ (it was stated that $I_{xy} < 0$) $\qquad \therefore 2\theta_1 = 56.94°$

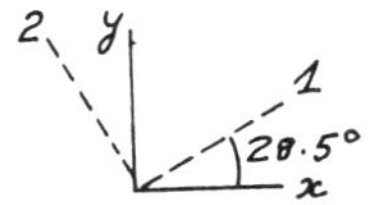

$\therefore \theta_1 = 28.5°$ ◆ $\qquad \therefore \theta_2 = 28.5° + 90° = 118.5°$ ◆

9.65

(a) $\bar{I}_x = \frac{37\,bh^3}{2100} = \frac{37(80)(60)^3}{2100} = 304.5 \times 10^3 \text{ mm}^4$

$\bar{I}_y = \frac{b^3h}{80} = \frac{(80)^3(60)}{80} = 384.0 \times 10^3 \text{ mm}^4$

$\bar{I}_{xy} = \frac{b^2h^2}{120} = \frac{(80)^2(60)^2}{120} = 192.0 \times 10^3 \text{ mm}^4$

$R = \sqrt{\left[\frac{1}{2}(\bar{I}_x - \bar{I}_y)\right]^2 + \bar{I}_{xy}^2} = 10^3\sqrt{\left(\frac{304.5 - 384.0}{2}\right)^2 + (192.0)^2} = 196.1 \times 10^3 \text{ mm}^4$

$b = \frac{1}{2}(\bar{I}_x + \bar{I}_y) = \frac{304.5 + 384.0}{2} \times 10^3 = 344.3 \text{ mm}^4$

$I_1 = b + R = (344.3 + 196.1) \times 10^3 = 540 \times 10^3 \text{ mm}^4$ ◆

$I_2 = b - R = (344.3 - 196.1) \times 10^3 = 148 \times 10^3 \text{ mm}^4$ ◆

(b) Eq. (9.21): $\sin 2\theta_1 = -\frac{\bar{I}_{xy}}{R} = -\frac{192.0}{196.1} = -0.9791 \qquad \therefore 2\theta_1 = -78.26°$ or $258.26°$

$\cos 2\theta_1 = \frac{\bar{I}_x - \bar{I}_y}{2R} = \frac{304.5 - 384.0}{2(196.1)} < 0 \qquad \therefore 2\theta_1 = 258.26°$

$\therefore \theta_1 = 129.1°$ ◆

$\therefore \theta_2 = 129.1° + 90° = 219.1°$ ◆

9.66

$I_x = \frac{bh^3}{21} = \frac{(21)(20)^3}{21} = 8000 \text{ in}^4 \qquad I_y = \frac{b^3h}{5} = \frac{(21)^3(20)}{5} = 37\,044 \text{ in}^4$

$I_{xy} = \frac{b^2h^2}{12} = \frac{(21)^2(20)^2}{12} = 14\,700 \text{ in}^4$

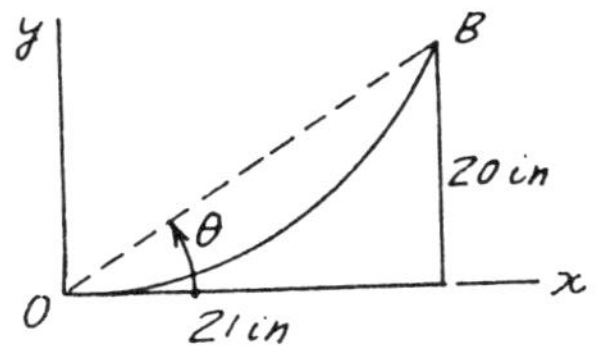

Geometry: $\theta = \tan^{-1}\frac{20}{21} = 43.60° \qquad \therefore 2\theta = 87.20°$

$I_{OB} = \frac{1}{2}(I_x + I_y) + \frac{1}{2}(I_x - I_y)\cos 2\theta - I_{xy}\sin 2\theta$

$= \frac{1}{2}(8000 + 37\,044) + \frac{1}{2}(8000 - 37\,044)\cos 87.20° - 14\,700 \sin 87.20° = 7130 \text{ in}^4$ ◆

9.67

The region may be viewed as a square with parabolic cutouts. Centroid C of the region is found by inspection.

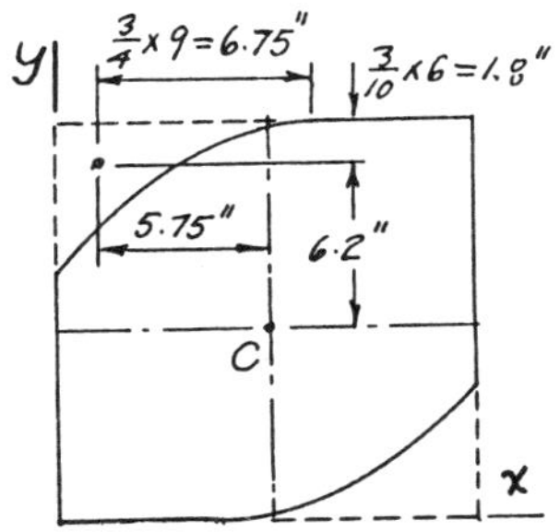

<u>Properties of one parabolic cutout</u> about centroidal axes:

$\bar{I}_x = \frac{37\,bh^3}{2100} + A\bar{y}^2 = \frac{37(9)(6)^3}{2100} + (18)(6.2)^2 = 726.2 \text{ in}^4$

$\bar{I}_y = \frac{b^3h}{80} + A\bar{x}^2 = \frac{(9)^3(6)}{80} + (18)(-5.75)^2 = 649.8 \text{ in}^4$

$\bar{I}_{xy} = \frac{b^2h^2}{120} + A\bar{x}\bar{y} = \frac{(9)^2(6)^2}{120} + (18)(-5.75)(6.2) = -617.4 \text{ in}^4$

<u>Properties of the region</u> ($\bar{I} = \bar{I}_{square} - 2\bar{I}_{parabola}$):

$\bar{I}_x = \frac{16^4}{12} - 2(726.2) = 4009 \text{ in}^4 \qquad \bar{I}_y = \frac{16^4}{12} - 2(649.9) = 4162 \text{ in}^4$

$\bar{I}_{xy} = 0 - 2(-617.4) = 1235 \text{ in}^4$

(continued)

9.67 continued

$$R = \sqrt{\left(\frac{4009 - 4162}{2}\right)^2 + (1235)^2} = 1237 \text{ in}^4 \qquad b = \frac{\bar{I}_x + \bar{I}_y}{2} = \frac{4009 + 4162}{2} = 4086 \text{ in}^4$$

$I_1 = b + R = 4086 + 1237 = 5320 \text{ in}^4$ ◆ $\qquad I_2 = b - R = 4086 - 1237 = 2850 \text{ in}^4$ ◆

$$\sin 2\theta_1 = -\frac{\bar{I}_{xy}}{R} = -\frac{1235}{1237} = -0.9984 \qquad \therefore 2\theta_1 = -86.74° \text{ or } 266.74°$$

$$\cos 2\theta_1 = \frac{\bar{I}_x - \bar{I}_y}{2R} = \frac{4009 - 4162}{2(1237)} < 0 \qquad \therefore 2\theta_1 = 266.74°$$

$\therefore \theta_1 = 133.4°$ ◆ $\qquad \therefore \theta_2 = 133.4° + 90° = 223.4°$ ◆

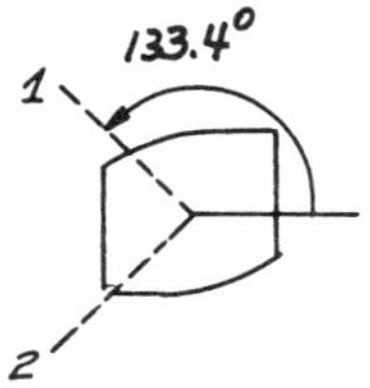

9.68

Part 1: $I_x = \frac{bh^3}{12} + A\bar{y}^2 = \frac{(160)(40)^3}{12} + (6400)(80)^2 = 41.81 \times 10^6 \text{mm}^4$

$$I_y = \frac{b^3h}{12} + A\bar{x}^2 = \frac{(160)^3(40)}{12} + (6400)(-60)^2 = 36.69 \times 10^6 \text{ mm}^4$$

$$I_{xy} = A\bar{x}\bar{y} = (6400)(-60)(80) = -30.72 \times 10^6 \text{ mm}^4$$

Part 2: $I_x = \frac{bh^3}{12} = \frac{(40)(120)^3}{12} = 5.76 \times 10^6 \text{ mm}^4$

$$I_y = \frac{b^3h}{12} = \frac{(40)^3(120)}{12} = 0.64 \times 10^6 \text{ mm}^4 \qquad I_{xy} = 0$$

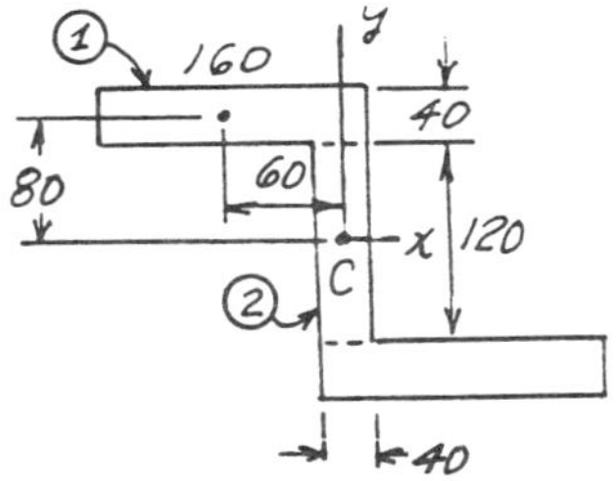

Composite area ($I = 2I_1 + I_2$):

$$I_x = \left[2(41.81) + 5.76\right] \times 10^6 = 89.38 \times 10^6 \text{ mm}^4$$

$$I_y = \left[2(36.69) + 0.64\right] \times 10^6 = 74.02 \times 10^6 \text{ mm}^4$$

$$I_{xy} = 2(-30.72) \times 10^6 + 0 = -61.44 \times 10^6 \text{ mm}^4$$

(continued)

9.68 continued

$$R = \sqrt{\left[\frac{1}{2}(I_x - I_y)\right]^2 + I_{xy}^2} = 10^6\sqrt{\left(\frac{89.39 - 74.03}{2}\right)^2 + (-61.44)^2} = 61.92 \times 10^6 \text{ mm}^4$$

$$b = \frac{1}{2}(\bar{I}_x + \bar{I}_y) = \frac{89.39 + 74.03}{2} \times 10^6 = 81.71 \times 10^6 \text{ mm}^4$$

$I_1 = b + R = (81.71 + 61.92) \times 10^6 = 143.6 \times 10^6 \text{ mm}^4$ ◆

$I_2 = b - R = (81.71 - 61.92) \times 10^6 = 19.8 \times 10^6 \text{ mm}^4$ ◆

$$\sin 2\theta_1 = -\frac{I_{xy}}{R} = -\frac{(-61.44)}{61.92} = 0.9922 \qquad \therefore 2\theta_1 = 82.86° \text{ or } 97.14°$$

$$\cos 2\theta_1 = \frac{I_x - I_y}{R} = \frac{89.39 - 74.03}{2(61.92)} > 0 \qquad \therefore 2\theta_1 = 82.86°$$

$\therefore \theta_1 = 41.4°$ ◆ $\qquad \therefore \theta_2 = 41.4° + 90° = 131.4°$ ◆

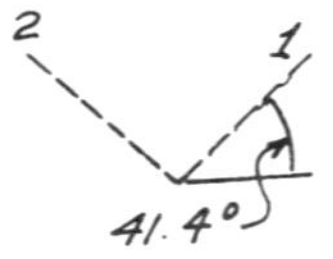

9.69

$$I_x = \frac{bh^3}{12} = \frac{(3)(4)^3}{12} = 16 \text{ in}^4$$

$$I_y = \frac{b^3h}{12} = \frac{(3)^3(4)}{12} = 9 \text{ in}^4 \qquad I_{xy} = 0$$

$$b = \frac{I_x + I_y}{2} = \frac{16 + 9}{2} = 12.5 \text{ in}^4$$

$$R = \frac{I_x - I_y}{2} = \frac{16 - 9}{2} = 3.5 \text{ in}^2$$

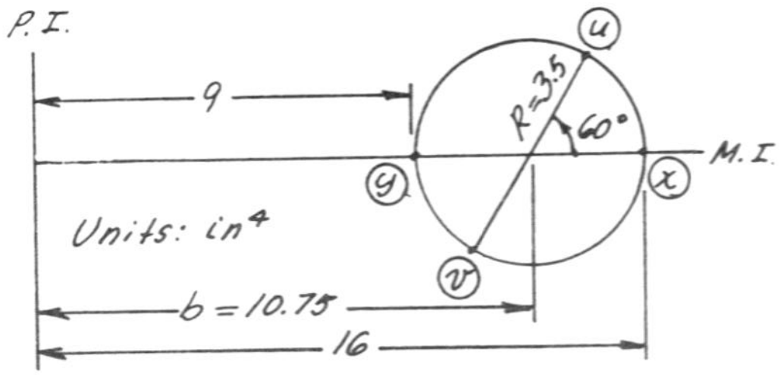

$I_u = 12.5 + 3.5 \cos 60° = 14.25 \text{ in}^4$ ◆ $\qquad I_v = 12.5 - 3.5 \cos 60° = 10.75 \text{ in}^4$ ◆

$I_{uv} = 3.5 \sin 60° = 3.03 \text{ in}^4$ ◆

9.70

$I_x = 0.1098R^4 = 0.1098(120)^4$

$= 22.77 \times 10^6 \text{ mm}^4$

$I_y = \dfrac{\pi R^4}{8} = \dfrac{\pi(120)^4}{8} = 81.43 \times 10^6 \text{ mm}^4$

$I_{xy} = 0$

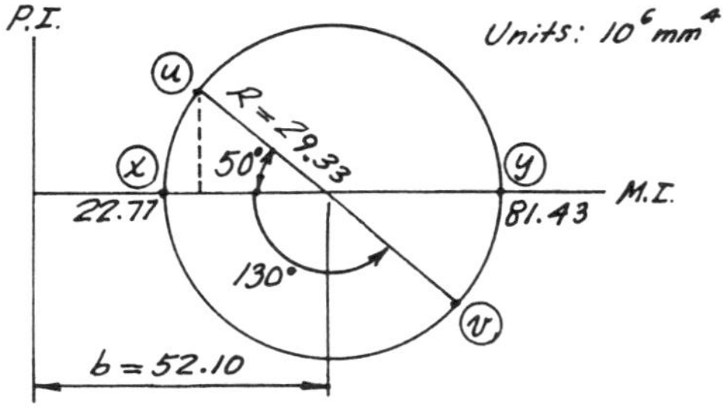

$b = \dfrac{22.77 + 81.43}{2} \times 10^6 = 52.10 \times 10^6 \text{ mm}^4 \quad R = \dfrac{81.43 - 22.77}{2} \times 10^6 = 29.33 \times 10^6 \text{ mm}^4$

$I_u = (52.10 - 29.33 \cos 50°) \times 10^6 = 33.3 \times 10^6 \text{ mm}^4$ ◆

$I_v = (52.10 + 29.33 \cos 50°) \times 10^6 = 71.0 \times 10^6 \text{ mm}^4$ ◆

$I_{uv} = 29.33 \times 10^6 \sin 50° = 22.5 \times 10^6 \text{ mm}^4$ ◆

9.71

$\bar{I}_x = \dfrac{bh^3}{36} = \dfrac{(6)(8)^3}{36} = 85.33 \text{ in}^4$

$\bar{I}_y = \dfrac{b^3h}{36} = \dfrac{(6)^3(8)}{36} \; 48.00 \text{ in}^4$

$\bar{I}_{xy} = -\dfrac{b^2h^2}{72} = -\dfrac{(6)^2(8)^2}{72} = -32.00 \text{ in}^4$

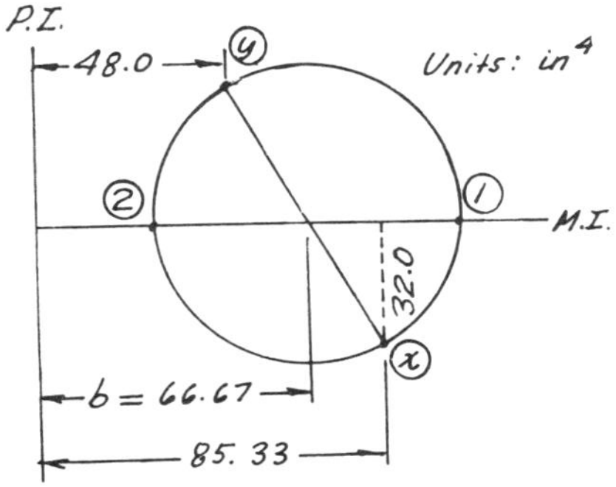

$b = \dfrac{85.33 + 48.00}{2} = 66.67 \text{ in}^4$

$R = \sqrt{\left(\dfrac{85.33 - 48.00}{2}\right)^2 + (32.00)^2} = 37.05 \text{ in}^4$

$I_1 = 66.67 + 37.05 = 103.7 \text{ in}^4$ ◆ $\quad I_2 = 66.67 - 37.05 = 29.6 \text{ in}^4$ ◆

$2\theta_1 = \sin^{-1}\dfrac{32.00}{37.05} = 59.73° \quad \therefore \theta_1 = 29.9°$ ◆

$\therefore \theta_2 = \theta_1 + 90° = 119.9°$ ◆

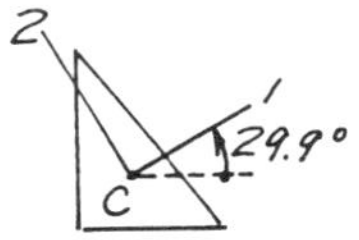

9.72

$I_x = \dfrac{bh^3}{12} = \dfrac{(6)(8)^3}{12} = 256 \text{ in}^4$

$I_y = \dfrac{b^3h}{12} = \dfrac{(6)^3(8)}{12} = 144 \text{ in}^4$

$I_{xy} = \dfrac{b^2h^2}{24} = \dfrac{(6)^2(8)^2}{24} = 96 \text{ in}^4$

$b = \dfrac{256 + 144}{2} = 200 \text{ in}^4$

$R = \sqrt{\left(\dfrac{256 - 144}{2}\right)^2 + (96)^2} = 111.14 \text{ in}^4$

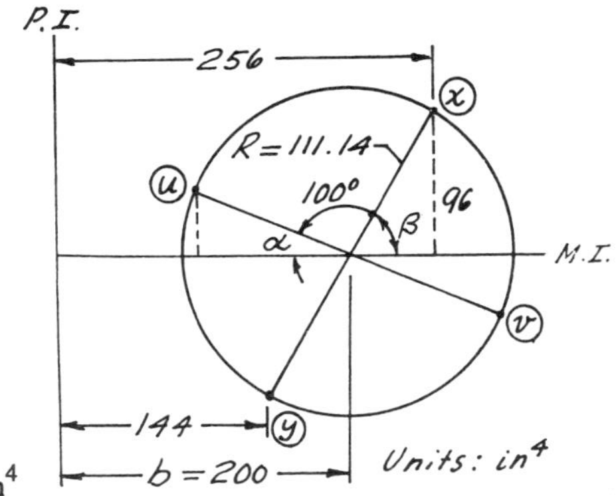

$\beta = \sin^{-1}\dfrac{96}{111.14} = 59.74° \quad \therefore \alpha = 180° - (100° + 59.74°) = 20.26°$

$I_u = b - R\cos\alpha = 200 - 111.14 \cos 20.26° = 95.7 \text{ in}^4$ ◆

$I_v = b + R\cos\alpha = 200 + 111.14 \cos 20.26° = 304.3 \text{ in}^4$ ◆

$I_{uv} = R\sin\alpha = 111.14 \sin 20.26° = 38.5 \text{ in}^4$ ◆

9.73

$b = \dfrac{4000 + 1000}{2} = 2500 \text{ in}^4$

$R = \sqrt{1500^2 + 800^2} = 1700 \text{ in}^4$

$\alpha = \tan^{-1}\dfrac{800}{1500} = 28.07°$

$\alpha + \beta + 180° = 240°$

$\therefore \beta = 240° - (\alpha + 180°)$

$= 240° - (28.07° + 180°) = 31.93°$

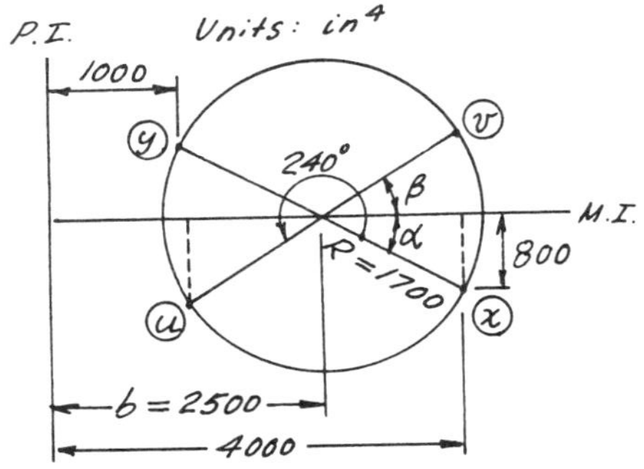

$I_u = b - R\cos\beta = 2500 - 1700 \cos 31.93° = 1057 \text{ in}^4$ ◆

$I_v = b + R\cos\beta = 2500 + 1700 \cos 31.93° = 3943 \text{ in}^4$ ◆

$I_{uv} = -R\sin\beta = -1700 \sin 31.93° = -899 \text{ in}^4$ ◆

9.74

$$b = \frac{20 + 10}{2} \times 10^6 = 15 \times 10^6 \text{ mm}^4$$

$$R = 10^6\sqrt{5^2 + 12^2} = 13 \times 10^6 \text{ mm}^4$$

$$\beta = \tan^{-1}\frac{12}{5} = 67.4°$$

$2\theta = 2(33.7°) = 67.4°$

Since $\beta = 2\theta$, the u and v-axes are the principal directions.

$I_u = b - R = (15 - 13) \times 10^6 = 2 \times 10^6 \text{ mm}^4$ ◆

$I_v = b + R = (15 + 13) \times 10^6 = 28 \times 10^6 \text{ mm}^4$ ◆

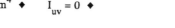

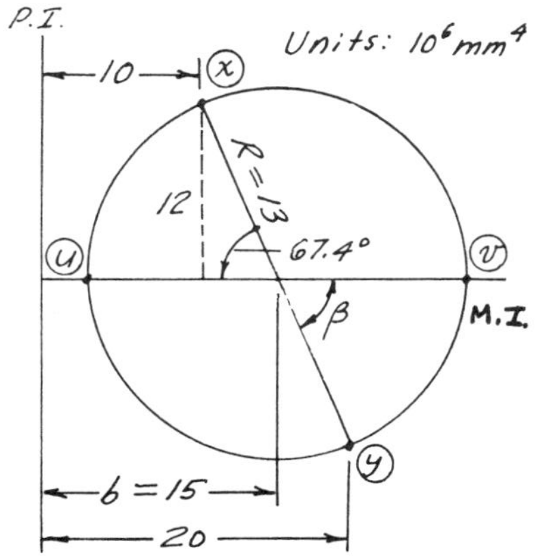

$I_{uv} = 0$ ◆

9.75

$$b = \frac{8400 + 5000}{2} = 6700 \text{ in}^4$$

$$R = \frac{8400 - 5000}{2} = 1700 \text{ in}^4$$

$I_x = 6700 + 1700 \cos 50° = 7790 \text{ in}^4$ ◆

$I_y = 6700 - 1700 \cos 50° = 5610 \text{ in}^4$ ◆

$I_{xy} = -1700 \sin 50° = -1302 \text{ in}^4$ ◆

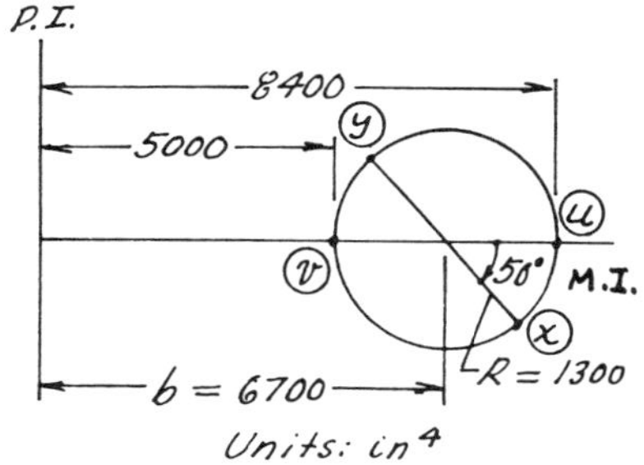

9.76

$$b = \frac{8 + 2}{2} \times 10^6 = 5 \times 10^6 \text{ mm}^4$$

$$R = \frac{8 - 2}{2} \times 10^6 = 3 \times 10^6 \text{ mm}^4$$

(a) I_{uv} is maximized at $2\theta = 90°$, or $\theta = 45°$ ◆

(b) $|I_{uv}| = 3 \times 10^6 \text{ mm}^4$ ◆

$I_u = I_v = 5 \times 10^6 \text{ mm}^4$ ◆

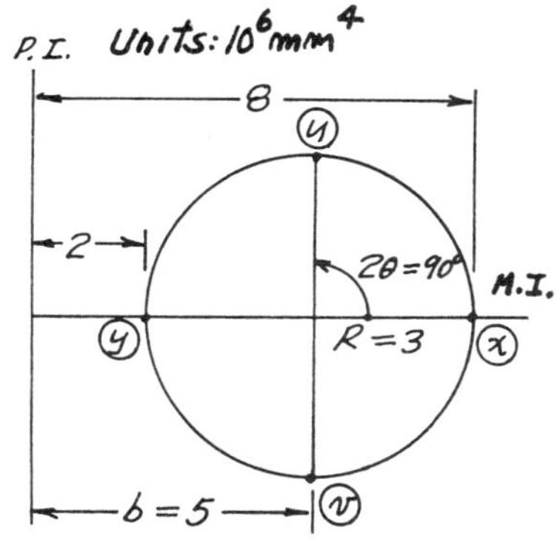

9.77

$$R = \frac{30 \times 10^6}{\sin 36°} = 51.04 \times 10^6 \text{ mm}^4$$

$I_v = I_u - 2R = \left[140 - 2\,(51.40)\right] \times 10^6$

$= 37.9 \times 10^6 \text{ mm}^4$ ◆

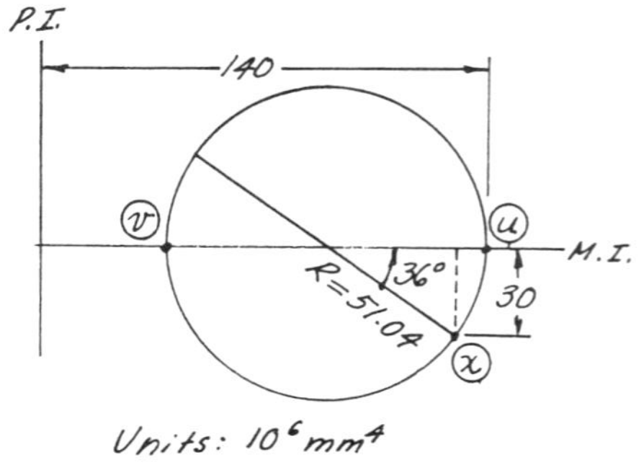

9.78

$$a = \frac{I_x - I_y}{2} = \frac{0.808 - 0.388}{2} \times 10^6$$

$= 0.210 \times 10^6 \text{ mm}^4$

$$b = \frac{I_x + I_y}{2} = \frac{0.808 + 0.388}{2} \times 10^6$$

$= 0.598 \times 10^6 \text{ mm}^4$

$R = b - I_2 = (0.598 - 0.213) \times 10^6$

$= 0.385 \times 10^6 \text{ mm}^4$

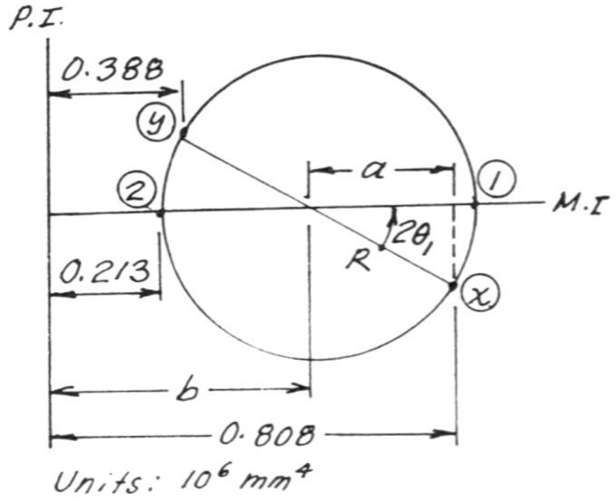

(a) $I_1 = b + R = (0.598 + 0.385) \times 10^6 = 0.983 \times 10^6 \text{ mm}^4$ ◆

(b) $2\theta_1 = \cos^{-1}\frac{a}{R} = \cos^{-1}\frac{0.210}{0.385} = 56.94°$ $\quad \therefore\ \theta_1 = 28.5°$ ◆ $\quad \theta_2 = 28.5° + 90° = 118.5°$ ◆

9.79

$$I_u = \frac{bh^3}{12} = \frac{(120)(80)^3}{12} = 5.12 \times 10^6 \text{ mm}^4 \qquad I_v = \frac{b^3h}{12} = \frac{(120)^3(80)}{12} = 11.52 \times 10^6 \text{ mm}^4$$

$I_{uv} = 0$

Since we have transformation from (u, v) to (x, y) coordinates, we must reverse the roles of (x, y) and (u, v) in Eqs. (9.17)–(9.19). With $2\theta = 2(-30°) = -60°$, these equations become

(continued)

9.79 continued

$$\bar{I}_x = \frac{1}{2}(I_u + I_v) + \frac{1}{2}(I_u - I_v)\cos 2\theta = \left[\frac{5.12 + 11.52}{2} + \frac{5.12 - 11.52}{2}\cos(-60°)\right] \times 10^6$$

$$= 6.72 \times 10^6\ \text{mm}^4\ ◆$$

$$\bar{I}_y = \frac{1}{2}(I_u + I_v) - \frac{1}{2}(I_u - I_v)\cos 2\theta = \left[\frac{5.12 + 11.52}{2} - \frac{5.12 - 11.52}{2}\cos(-60°)\right] \times 10^6$$

$$= 9.92 \times 10^6\ \text{mm}^4\ ◆$$

$$\bar{I}_{xy} = \frac{1}{2}(I_u - I_v)\sin 2\theta = \left[\frac{5.12 - 11.52}{2}\sin(-60°)\right] \times 10^6 = 2.77 \times 10^6\ \text{mm}^4\ ◆$$

9.80

(a) $I_1 = \frac{I_x + I_y}{2} + R \qquad I_2 = \frac{I_x + I_y}{2} - R$

$$\therefore R = \frac{I_1 - I_2}{2} = \frac{60 - 30}{2} \times 10^6 = 15 \times 10^6\ \text{mm}^4$$

$$\therefore \frac{I_x + I_y}{2} = \frac{I_1 + I_2}{2} = \frac{60 + 30}{2} \times 10^6 = 45 \times 10^6\ \text{mm}^4 \ldots\ldots\ldots\ldots\text{(a)}$$

$$R^2 = \left(\frac{I_x - I_y}{2}\right)^2 + I_{xy}^2$$

$$\therefore \frac{I_x - I_y}{2} = \sqrt{R^2 - I_{xy}^2} = 10^6\sqrt{15^2 - 10^2} = 11.18 \times 10^6\ \text{mm}^4 \ldots\ldots\text{(b)}$$

Solution of Eqs. (a) and (b) is $I_x = 56.2 \times 10^6\ \text{mm}^4$ ◆ $\quad I_y = 33.8 \times 10^6\ \text{mm}^4$ ◆

(b) $I_u = \frac{I_x + I_y}{2} + \frac{I_x - I_y}{2}\cos 2\theta - I_{xy}\sin 2\theta$

$$= (45 + 11.18\cos 100° - 10\sin 100°) \times 10^6 = 33.2 \times 10^6\ \text{mm}^4\ ◆$$

$$I_v = \frac{I_x + I_y}{2} - \frac{I_x - I_y}{2}\cos 2\theta + I_{xy}\sin 2\theta$$

$$= (45 - 11.18\cos 100° + 10\sin 100°) \times 10^6 = 56.8 \times 10^6\ \text{mm}^4\ ◆$$

9.81

$dA = dr(r\,d\theta) \qquad x = r\cos\theta \qquad y = r\sin\theta$

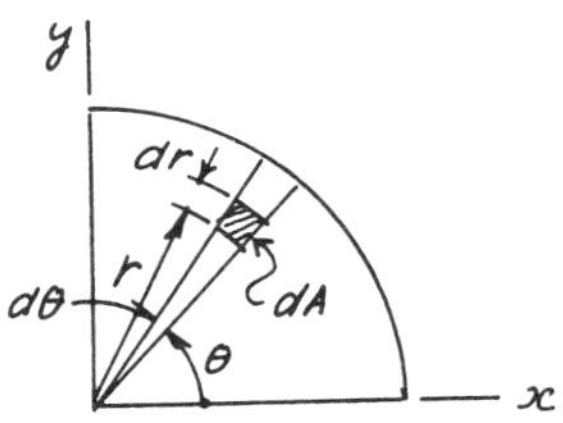

$$I_{xy} = \int_A xy\,dA = \int_0^{\pi/2}\int_0^R r^3 \sin\theta\cos\theta\,dr\,d\theta$$

$$= \frac{R^4}{4}\int_0^{\pi/2}\frac{1}{2}\sin 2\theta\,d\theta = \frac{R^4}{8}\left[-\frac{\cos 2\theta}{2}\right]_0^{\pi/2} = \frac{R^4}{8}\ ◆$$

9.82

For a semicircle:

$$A = \frac{\pi}{2}R^2 \qquad \bar{x} = \frac{4R}{3\pi} \qquad \therefore A\bar{x} = \frac{2}{3}R^3 \quad I_x = I_y = \frac{\pi}{8}R^4$$

For the annular region:

$$A = \Sigma A_i = \frac{\pi}{2}\left[(60)^2 - (40)^2\right] = 3.142 \times 10^3\ \text{mm}^2$$

$$\bar{x} = \frac{\Sigma A_i \bar{x}_i}{A} = \frac{(2/3)\left[(60)^3 - (40)^3\right]}{3.142 \times 10^3} = 32.25\ \text{mm}$$

$$I_x = I_y = \frac{\pi}{8}(60^4 - 40^4) = 4.084 \times 10^6\ \text{mm}^4 \qquad \bar{I}_x = I_x = 4.084 \times 10^6\ \text{mm}^4\ ◆$$

$$\bar{I}_y = I_y - A\bar{x}^2 = 4.084 \times 10^6 - (3.142 \times 10^3)(32.25)^2 = 0.816 \times 10^6\ \text{mm}^4\ ◆$$

9.83

Use single integration

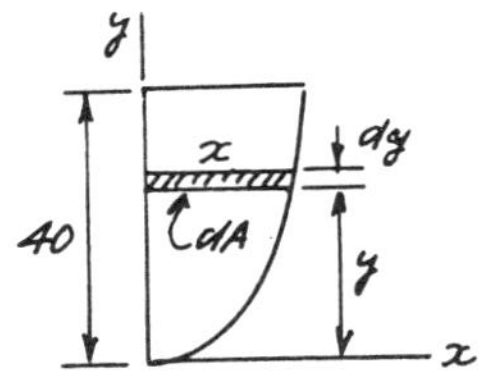

$$dA = x\,dy = \sqrt[3]{200\,y}\,dy$$

$$dI_x = y^2\,dA = \sqrt[3]{200}\,y^{7/3}\,dy$$

$$dI_y = \frac{1}{3}x^3\,dy = \frac{1}{3}(200\,y)\,dy$$

$$I_x = \sqrt[3]{200}\int_0^{40} y^{7/3}\,dy = \sqrt[3]{200}\,\frac{3}{10}\left[y^{10/3}\right]_0^{40} = 384.0 \times 10^3\ \text{mm}^4\ ◆$$

$$I_y = \frac{200}{3}\int_0^{40} y\,dy = \frac{200}{3}\left[\frac{y^2}{2}\right]_0^{40} = 53.3 \times 10^3\ \text{mm}^4\ ◆$$

9.84

$$R = \sqrt{\left(\frac{I_x - I_y}{2}\right)^2 + I_{xy}^2} = 10^6\sqrt{\left(\frac{200-300}{2}\right)^2 + (-120)^2} = 130 \times 10^6 \text{ mm}^4$$

$$b = \frac{I_x + I_y}{2} = \frac{200+300}{2} \times 10^6 = 250 \times 10^6 \text{ mm}^4$$

$I_1 = b + R = (250 + 130) \times 10^6 = 380 \times 10^6 \text{ mm}^4$ ◆

$I_2 = b - R = (250 - 130) \times 10^6 = 120 \times 10^6 \text{ mm}^4$ ◆

$\sin 2\theta_1 = -\frac{I_{xy}}{R} = -\frac{(-120)}{130} = 0.9231 \quad \therefore 2\theta_1 = 67.38° \text{ or } 112.62°$

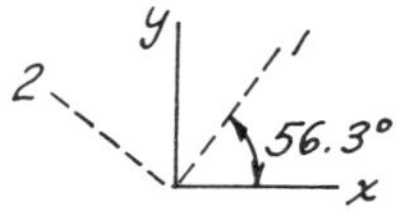

$\cos 2\theta_1 = \frac{I_x - I_y}{2R} = \frac{200-300}{2(130)} < 0 \quad \therefore 2\theta_1 = 112.62° \quad \therefore \theta_1 = 56.3°$ ◆

$\therefore \theta_2 = 56.3° + 90° = 146.3°$ ◆

9.85

Part	A (in²)	$\bar{y}$ (in.)	$A\bar{y}$ (in³)
1	6.0	7.5	45.0
2	6.0	4.0	24.0
3	3.0	0.5	1.5
Sum	15.0	12.0	70.5

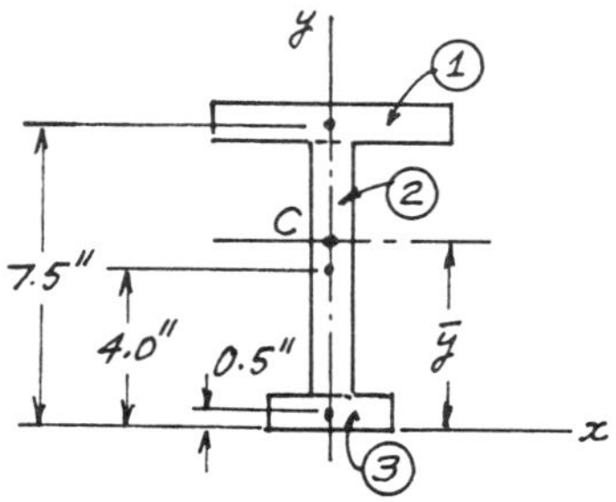

$\therefore \bar{y} = \frac{70.5}{15.0} = 4.70$ in.

$$I_x = \left[\frac{(6)(1)^3}{12} + (6)(7.5)^2\right] + \left[\frac{(1)(6)^3}{12} + (6)(4.0)^2\right] + \left[\frac{(3)(1)^3}{12} + (3)(0.5)^2\right] = 453.0 \text{ in}^4$$

$$I_y = \frac{(6)^3(1)}{12} + \frac{(1)^3(6)}{12} + \frac{(3)^3(1)}{12} = 20.75 \text{ in}^4$$

$\bar{I}_x = I_x - A\bar{y}^2 = 453.0 - (15.0)(4.70)^2 = 121.7 \text{ in}^4$ ◆

$\bar{I}_y = I_y = 20.8 \text{ in}^4$ ◆

9.86

Solid plate: $(J_O)_1 = \frac{\pi R^4}{2} = \frac{\pi (5)^4}{2} = 981.7 \text{ in}^4$

10 holes: $(J_O)_2 = 10\left[\frac{\pi (0.25)^4}{2} + \pi (0.25)^2(4)^2\right] = 31.48 \text{ in}^4$

% reduction $= (J_O)_2/(J_O)_1 = \frac{31.48}{981.7} \times 100\% = 3.21\%$ ◆

9.87

(a) $\bar{I}_2 = A\bar{k}_2^2 = (2400)(21.9)^2 = 1.151 \times 10^6 \text{ mm}^4$

$\bar{I}_1 + \bar{I}_2 = \bar{I}_x + \bar{I}_y$

$\therefore \bar{I}_1 = \bar{I}_x + \bar{I}_y - \bar{I}_2 = (5.58 + 2.03 - 1.151) \times 10^6 = 6.459 \times 10^6 \text{ mm}^4$ ◆

(b) $\bar{I}_1 = \frac{1}{2}(\bar{I}_x + \bar{I}_y) + R$

$$\therefore R = \bar{I}_1 - \frac{\bar{I}_x + \bar{I}_y}{2} = \left(6.459 - \frac{5.58 + 2.03}{2}\right) \times 10^6 = 2.654 \times 10^6 \text{ mm}^4$$

$\sin 2\theta_2 = \bar{I}_{xy}/R \quad \therefore \bar{I}_{xy} = R \sin 2\theta_2$

But $\theta_2 = \theta_1 + 90° = 24.0° + 90° = 114.0° \quad \therefore 2\theta_2 = 228.0°$

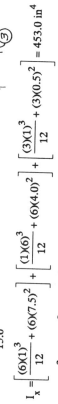

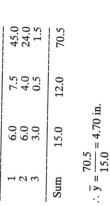

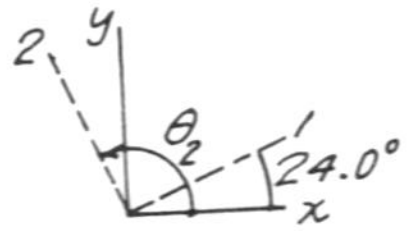

$\therefore \bar{I}_{xy} = (2.654 \times 10^6)\sin 228.0° = -1.972 \times 10^6 \text{ mm}^4$ ◆

9.88

(a) $\bar{I}_2 = A\bar{k}_2^2 = (11.0)(0.846)^2 = 7.87 \text{ in}^4$

$\bar{I}_1 + \bar{I}_2 = \bar{I}_x + \bar{I}_y \quad \therefore \bar{I}_1 = \bar{I}_x + \bar{I}_y - \bar{I}_2 = (69.6 + 11.6 - 7.87) = 73.33 \text{ in}^4$ ◆

(continued)

9.88 continued

(b) $\bar{I}_1 = \frac{1}{2}(\bar{I}_x + \bar{I}_y) + R \quad \therefore R = \bar{I}_1 - \frac{\bar{I}_x + \bar{I}_y}{2} = \left(73.33 - \frac{69.6 + 11.6}{2}\right) = 32.73 \text{ in}^4$

$\sin 2\theta_2 = \bar{I}_{xy}/R \quad \therefore \bar{I}_{xy} = R \sin 2\theta_2$

But $\theta_2 = 13.9° + 90° = 103.9° \quad \therefore 2\theta_2 = 207.8°$

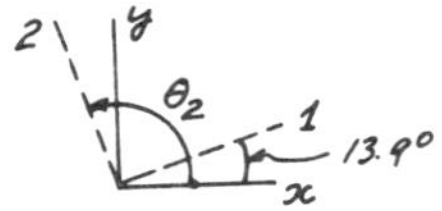

$\therefore \bar{I}_{xy} = (32.73)\sin 207.8° = -15.26 \text{ in}^4$ ◆

9.89

(a) $I_{xy} = \frac{bh^2}{24}(2a + b) = \frac{(90)(90)^2}{24}\left[2(60) + 90\right] = 6.379 \times 10^6 \text{ mm}^4$ ◆

(b) $\bar{I}_x = \frac{bh^3}{36} = \frac{(90)(90)^3)}{36} = 1.823 \times 10^6 \text{ mm}^4$ ◆

9.90

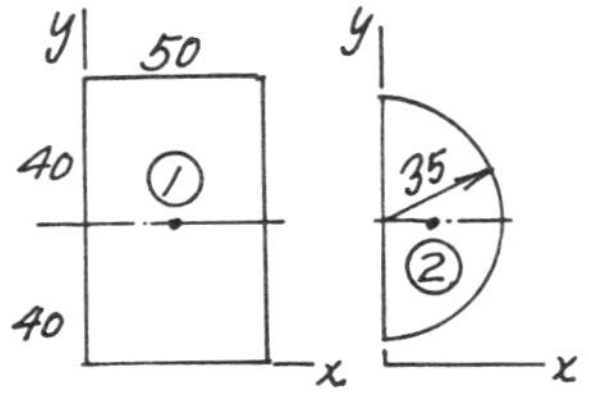

$A_1 = (50)(80) = 4000 \text{ mm}^2$

$A_2 = \frac{\pi}{2}(35)^2 = 1924 \text{ mm}^2$

$A = A_1 - A_2 = 4000 - 1924 = 2076 \text{ mm}^2$

$\bar{x}_1 = 25 \text{ mm} \quad \bar{x}_2 = \frac{4R}{3\pi} = \frac{4(35)}{3\pi} = 14.854 \text{ mm}$

$\bar{x} = \frac{A_1\bar{x}_1 - A_2\bar{x}_2}{A} = \frac{(4000)(25) - (1924.2)(14.854)}{2076} = 34.40 \text{ mm}$

$\bar{I}_x = \frac{bh^3}{12} - \frac{\pi R^4}{8} = \frac{(50)(80)^3}{12} - \frac{\pi(35)^4}{8} = 1.544 \times 10^6 \text{ mm}^4$ ◆

$I_y = \frac{b^3h}{3} - \frac{\pi R^4}{8} = \frac{(50)^3(80)}{3} - \frac{\pi(35)^4}{8} = 2.744 \times 10^6 \text{ mm}^4$

$\bar{I}_y = I_y - A\bar{x}^2 = 2.744 \times 10^6 - (2076)(34.40)^2 = 0.287 \times 10^6 \text{ mm}^4$ ◆

Due to symmetry $\bar{I}_{xy} = 0$ ◆

9.91

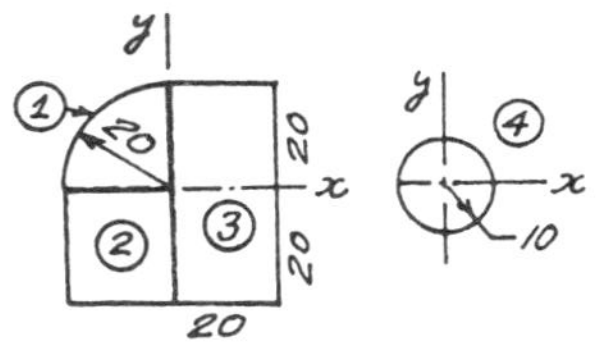

(a) $I_x = \Sigma(I_x)_i = \frac{\pi(20)^4}{16} + \frac{(20)(20)^3}{3} + \frac{(20)(40)^3}{12} - \frac{\pi(10)^4}{4}$

$= 183.57 \times 10^3 \text{ mm}^4$

Due to symmetry: $I_y = I_x = 183.57 \times 10^6 \text{ mm}^4$ ◆

(b)

Part	A (mm^2)	$\bar{y}$ (mm)	$A\bar{y}$ (mm^3)
1	$\pi(20)^2/4 = 314.2$	$4(20)/(3\pi) = 8.488$	2667
2	$(20)(20) = 400.0$	−10	−4000
3	$(20)(40) = 800.0$	0	0
4	$-\pi(10)^2 = -314.2$	0	0
Sum	1200.0		−1333

$\bar{y} = \frac{-1333}{1200} = -1.111 \text{ mm}$

$\bar{I}_x = \bar{I}_y = I_x - A\bar{x}^2 = 180.57 \times 10^3 - (1200)(1.111)^2 = 182.1 \times 10^3 \text{ mm}^4$ ◆

9.92

Use double integration.

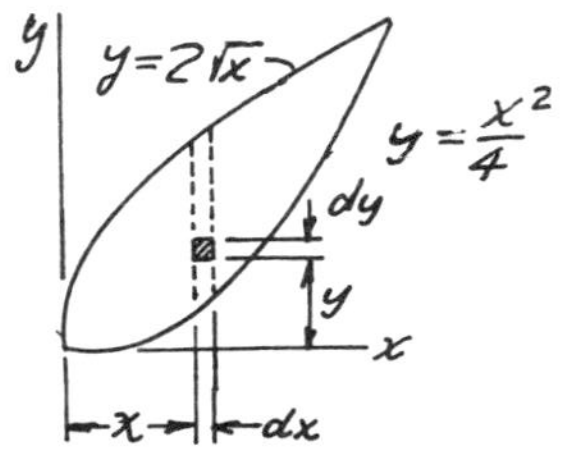

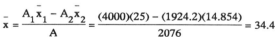

$I_x = \int_A y^2\, dA = \int_0^4 \int_{x^2/4}^{2\sqrt{x}} y^2\, dy\, dx = \int_0^4 \left[\frac{y^3}{3}\right]_{x^2/4}^{2\sqrt{x}} dx$

$= \frac{1}{3}\int_0^4 \left(8x^{3/2} - \frac{x^6}{64}\right) dx = \frac{1}{3}\left[\frac{16x^{5/2}}{5} - \frac{x^7}{448}\right]_0^4 = 21.9 \text{ in}^4$ ◆

$I_y = \int_A x^2\, dA = \int_0^4 \int_{x^2/4}^{2\sqrt{x}} x^2\, dy\, dx = \int_0^4 x^2 \left[y\right]_{x^2/4}^{2\sqrt{x}} dx$

$= \int_0^4 \left(2x^{5/2} - \frac{x^4}{4}\right) dx = \left[\frac{4}{7}x^{7/2} - \frac{x^5}{20}\right]_0^4 = 21.9 \text{ in}^4$ ◆

(continued)

9.92 continued

Note that $I_x = I_y$, which was expected due to symmetry.

$$I_{xy} = \int_A xy\,dA = \int_0^4 \int_{x^2/4}^{2\sqrt{x}} xy\,dy\,dx = \int_0^4 x\left[\frac{y^2}{2}\right]_{x^2/4}^{2\sqrt{x}} dx = \int_0^4 \left(2x^2 - \frac{x^5}{32}\right) dx$$

$$= \left[\frac{2}{3}x^3 - \frac{x^6}{192}\right]_0^4 = 21.3 \text{ in}^4 \quad ◆$$

9.93

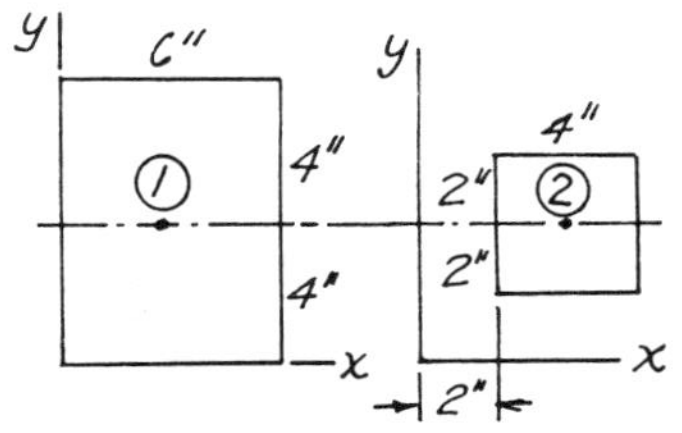

$$I_x = (I_x)_1 - \left[(\bar{I}_x)_2 + A_2\bar{y}_2^2\right]$$

$$= \frac{(6)(8)^3}{3} - \left[\frac{(4)(4)^3}{12} + (16)(4)^2\right] = 746.7 \text{ in}^4$$

$$I_y = (I_y)_1 - \left[(I_y)_2 + A_2\bar{x}_2^2\right]$$

$$= \frac{(6)^3(8)}{3} - \left[\frac{(4)^3(4)}{12} + (16)(4)^2\right] = 298.7 \text{ in}^4$$

$$I_{xy} = A_1\bar{x}_1\bar{y}_1 - A_2\bar{x}_2\bar{y}_2 = (48)(3)(4) - (16)(4)(4) = 320.0 \text{ in}^4$$

$$R = \sqrt{\left[\frac{1}{2}(I_x - I_y)\right]^2 + I_{xy}^2} = \sqrt{\left(\frac{746.7 - 298.7}{2}\right)^2 + (320.0)^2} = 390.6 \text{ in}^4$$

$$b = \frac{1}{2}(I_x + I_y) = \frac{746.7 + 298.7}{2} = 522.7 \text{ in}^4$$

$I_1 = b + R = 522.7 + 390.6 = 913.3 \text{ in}^4$ ◆ $\quad I_2 = b - R = 522.7 - 390.6 = 132.1 \text{ in}^4$ ◆

$$\sin 2\theta_1 = -\frac{I_{xy}}{R} = -\frac{320.0}{390.6} = -0.8193 \quad \therefore 2\theta_1 = -55.0° \text{ or } -125.0°$$

$$\cos 2\theta_1 = \frac{I_x - I_y}{2R} = \frac{746.7 - 298.7}{2(390.6)} > 0 \quad \therefore 2\theta_1 = -55.0°$$

$\therefore \theta_1 = -27.5°$ ◆ $\quad \theta_2 = \theta_1 + 90° = -27.5° + 90° = 62.5°$ ◆

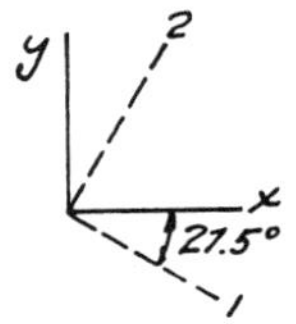

9.94

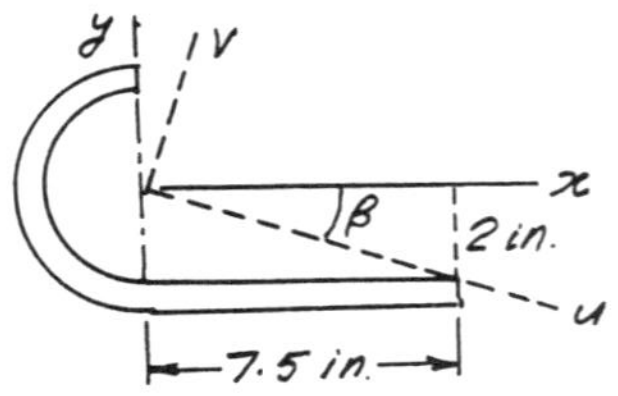

From geometry: $\beta = \tan^{-1}\dfrac{2}{7.5} = 14.93°$

Note that $\theta = -\beta \quad \therefore 2\theta = -29.86°$

$$\frac{1}{2}(I_x + I_y) = \frac{140 + 264}{2} = 202 \text{ in}^4$$

$$\frac{1}{2}(I_x - I_y) = \frac{140 - 264}{2} = -62 \text{ in}^4 \qquad I_{xy} = -116 \text{ in}^4$$

$$I_u = \frac{1}{2}(I_x + I_y) + \frac{1}{2}(I_x - I_y)\cos 2\theta - I_{xy}\sin 2\theta$$

$$= 202 + (-62)\cos(-29.86°) - (-116)\sin(-29.86°) = 90.5 \text{ in}^4 \quad ◆$$

$$I_v = \frac{1}{2}(I_x + I_y) - \frac{1}{2}(I_x - I_y)\cos 2\theta + I_{xy}\sin 2\theta$$

$$= 202 - (-62)\cos(-29.86°) + (-116)\sin(-29.86°) = 313.5 \text{ in}^4 \quad ◆$$

$$I_{uv} = \frac{1}{2}(I_x - I_y)\sin 2\theta + I_{xy}\cos 2\theta = -62\sin(-29.86°) + (-116)\cos(-29.86°) = -69.7 \text{ in}^4 \quad ◆$$

10.1

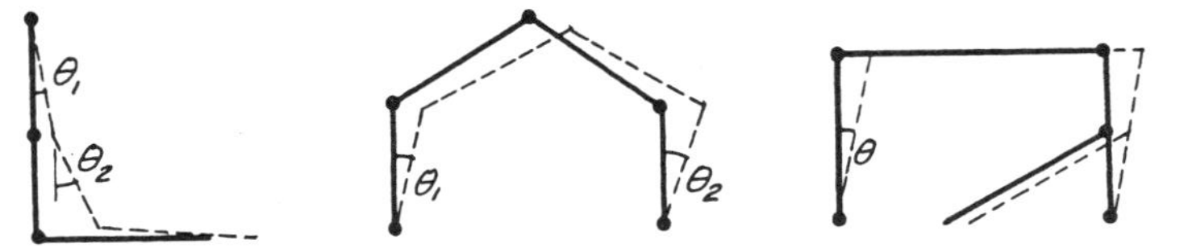

(a) Two DOF (b) Two DOF (c) One DOF

(d) One DOF (e) One DOF (f) Three DOF

10.2

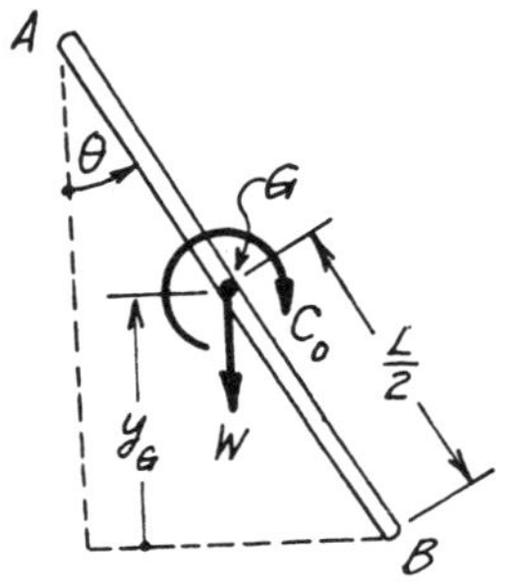

$y_G = \frac{L}{2}\cos\theta \quad \therefore\ \delta y_G = -\frac{L}{2}\sin\theta\ \delta\theta$

$\delta U = -C_0\delta\theta - W\delta y_G = \left[-C_0 - W\left(-\frac{L}{2}\sin\theta\right)\right]\delta\theta$

$\delta U = 0: \quad -C_0 + \frac{WL}{2}\sin\theta = 0$

$\therefore\ C_0 = \frac{WL}{2}\sin\theta$ ◆

10.3

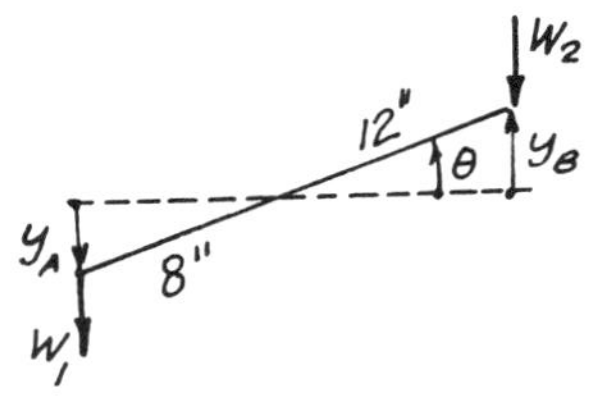

$y_A = 8\sin\theta$ in ↓ $\quad y_B = 12\sin\theta$ in ↑

$\therefore\ \delta y_A = 8\cos\theta\ \delta\theta$ in ↓ $\quad \therefore\ \delta y_B = 12\cos\theta\ \delta\theta$ in ↑

$\delta U = W_1\delta y_A - W_2\delta y_B = \left[W_1(8) - W_2(12)\right]\cos\theta\ \delta\theta$

$\delta U = 0: \quad W_1/W_2 = 12/8 = 1.5$ ◆

10.4

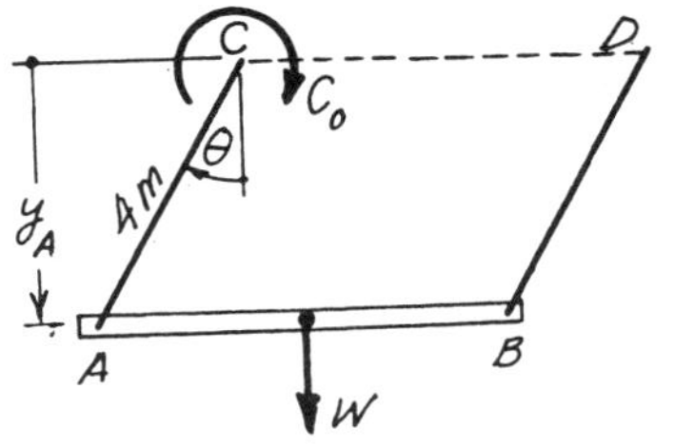

Note that AB remains horizontal.

$y_A = 4\cos\theta \quad \therefore\ \delta y_A = -4\sin\theta\ \delta\theta$

$\delta U = C_0\ \delta\theta + W\ \delta y_A = [C_0 + W(-4\sin\theta)]\delta\theta$

$\delta U = 0: \quad C_0 - 4W\sin\theta = 0$

$\therefore\ \sin\theta = \frac{C_0}{4W} = \frac{610}{4(25 \times 9.81)} = 0.6218$

$\therefore\ \theta = 38.5°$ ◆

10.5

The boat translates only. Thus all points on the boat have the same virtual displacement.

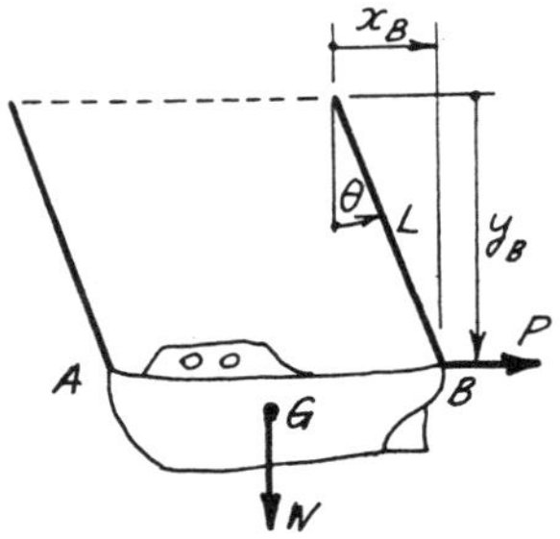

$x_B = L\sin\theta \quad \therefore\ \delta x_B = L\cos\theta\ \delta\theta$

$y_B = L\cos\theta \quad \therefore\ \delta y_B = \delta y_G = -L\sin\theta\ \delta\theta$

$\delta U = P\ \delta x_B + W\ \delta y_G = [PL\cos\theta + W(-L\sin\theta)]\delta\theta$

$\delta U = 0: \quad PL\cos\theta - WL\sin\theta = 0$

$\therefore\ P = W\tan\theta = 17.658\tan 20° = 6.43$ kN ◆

10.6

Note that BE remains vertical.

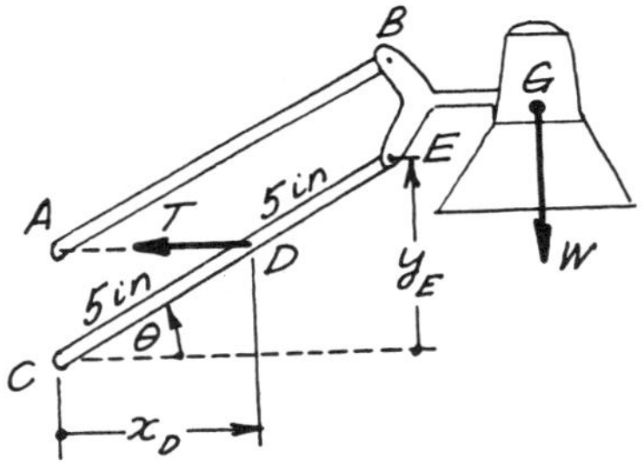

$x_D = 5\cos\theta \quad \therefore\ \delta x_D = -5\sin\theta\ \delta\theta$

$y_E = 10\sin\theta \quad \therefore\ \delta y_E = \delta y_G = 10\cos\theta\ \delta\theta$

$\delta U = -T\ \delta x_D - W\ \delta y_G$

$= [T(5\sin\theta) - (5)(10\cos\theta)]\delta\theta$

$\delta U = 0: \quad 5T\sin\theta - 50\cos\theta = 0$

$\therefore\ T = 10\cot\theta = 10\cot 30° = 17.32$ lb◆

10.7

The mechanism has a single DOF. Choose θ as the kinematically independent variable.

θ and α are related by the geometric constraint

$15\sin\theta + 8\sin\alpha = 15$

$\therefore \sin\alpha = \dfrac{15(1-\sin\theta)}{8} = \dfrac{15(1-\sin 40°)}{8} = 0.6698$

$\therefore \alpha = 42.05°$

The geometric constraint also yields

$15\cos\theta\,\delta\theta + 8\cos\alpha\,\delta\alpha = 0$

$\therefore \delta\alpha = -\dfrac{15\cos\theta}{8\cos\alpha}\delta\theta = -\dfrac{15\cos 40°}{8\cos 42.05°}\delta\theta = -1.9343\,\delta\theta$

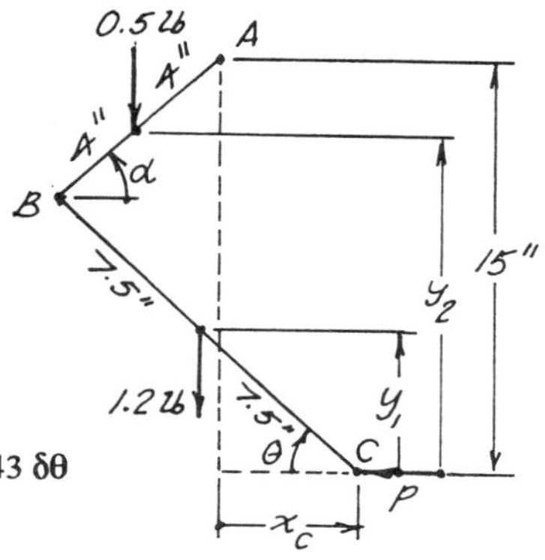

$x_C = 15\cos\theta - 8\cos\alpha$

$\therefore \delta x_C = -15\sin\theta\,\delta\theta + 8\sin\alpha\,\delta\alpha = -15\sin 40°\,\delta\theta + 8\sin 42.05°(-1.9343)\delta\theta = -20.01\,\delta\theta$

$y_1 = 7.5\sin\theta \quad \therefore \delta y_1 = 7.5\cos\theta\,\delta\theta = 7.5\cos 40°\,\delta\theta = 5.745\,\delta\theta$

$y_2 = 15\sin\theta + 4\sin\alpha$

$\therefore \delta y_2 = 15\cos\theta\,\delta\theta + 4\cos\alpha\,\delta\alpha = 15\cos 40°\,\delta\theta + 4\cos 42.05°(-1.9343\,\delta\theta) = 5.745\,\delta\theta$

$\delta U = -W_{BC}\delta y_1 - W_{AB}\delta y_2 - P\,\delta x_C = \left[-1.2(5.745) - 0.5(5.745) - P(-20.01)\right]\delta\theta$

$= (-9.767 + 20.01P)\delta\theta$

$\delta U = 0{:}\ -9.767 + 20.01P = 0 \qquad \therefore P = 0.488\text{ lb}$ ◆

10.8

Release horizontal constraint at B, so that B_x becomes an active force.

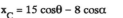

$x_B = L\sin\theta \quad \therefore \delta x_B = L\cos\theta\,\delta\theta$

$y_G = \dfrac{L}{2}\cos\theta \quad \therefore \delta y_G = -\dfrac{L}{2}\sin\theta\,\delta\theta$

$\delta U = -B_x\delta x_B - W\,\delta y_G = \left[-B_x L\cos\theta - W\left(-\dfrac{L}{2}\sin\theta\right)\right]\delta\theta$

$\delta U = 0{:}\ -B_x\cos\theta + \dfrac{1}{2}W\sin\theta = 0 \qquad \therefore B_x = \dfrac{W}{2}\tan\theta$ ◆

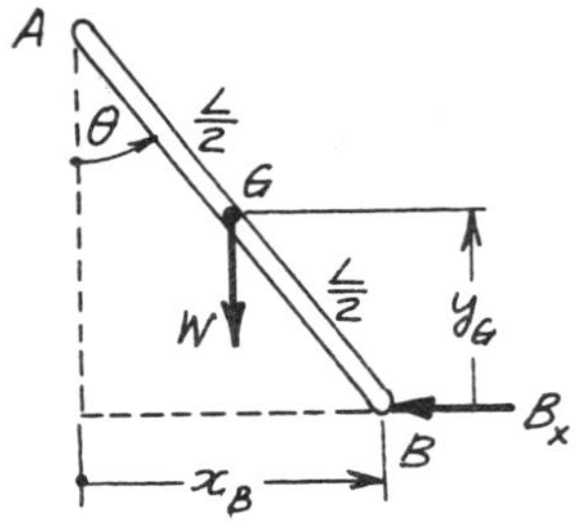

10.9

Release the rope, so that the tension T becomes an active force

From geometry:

$\theta = \tan^{-1}(0.7) = 34.99°$

From the figure of BC:

$x_B = L\cos\theta \quad \therefore \delta x_B = -L\sin\theta\,\delta\theta$

$y_C = L\sin\theta \quad \therefore \delta y_C = L\cos\theta\,\delta\theta$

$\delta U = -W\,\delta y_C - T\,\delta x_B$

$= \left[-W(L\cos\theta) - T(-L\sin\theta)\right]\delta\theta$

$\delta U = 0{:}\ -W\cos\theta + T\sin\theta = 0$

$\therefore T = W\cot\theta = (15\times 9.81)\cot 34.99° = 210\text{ N}$ ◆

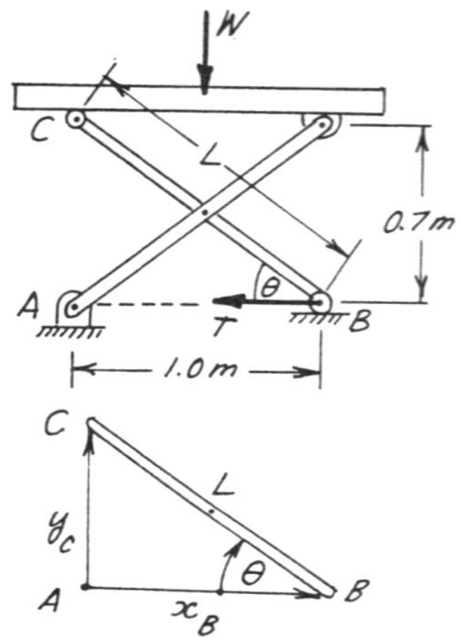

10.10

Release cable at A, so that cable tension T becomes an active force.

$y_G = 9\sin\theta$

$\therefore \delta y_G = 9\cos\theta\,\delta\theta = 9\cos 40°\,\delta\theta = 6.894\,\delta\theta$

$x_A = 18\cos\theta$

$\therefore \delta x_A = -18\sin\theta\,\delta\theta = -18\sin 40°\,\delta\theta = -11.570\,\delta\theta$

$\delta U = (-T\cos 55°)\,\delta x_A - W\,\delta y_G$

$= \left[(-T\cos 55°)(-11.570) - (320)(6.894)\right]\delta\theta = (6.636\,T - 2206)\delta\theta$

$\delta U = 0{:}\ 6.636T - 2206 = 0 \qquad \therefore T = \dfrac{2206}{6.636} = 332\text{ lb}$ ◆

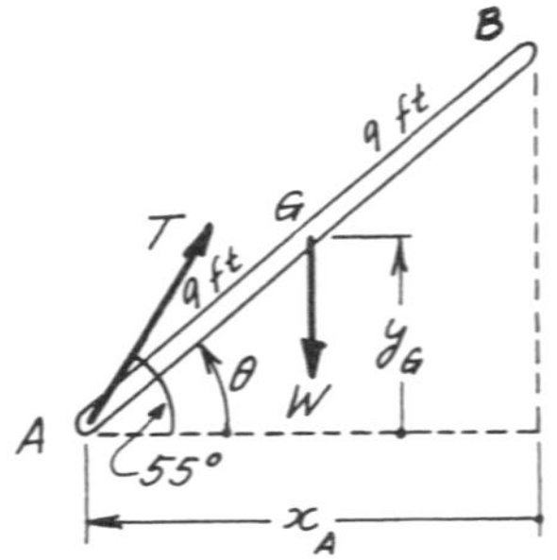

10.11

$y_Q = 2a\cos\theta \quad \therefore \delta y_Q = -2a\sin\theta\,\delta\theta$

$x_P = 5a\sin\theta \quad \therefore \delta x_P = 5a\cos\theta\,\delta\theta$

$\delta U = P\,\delta x_P + Q\,\delta y_Q = \left[P(5\cos\theta) + Q(-2\sin\theta)\right]a\,\delta\theta$

$\delta U = 0{:}\ P(5\cos\theta) - Q(2\sin\theta) = 0 \qquad \therefore \dfrac{P}{Q} = 0.4\tan\theta$ ◆

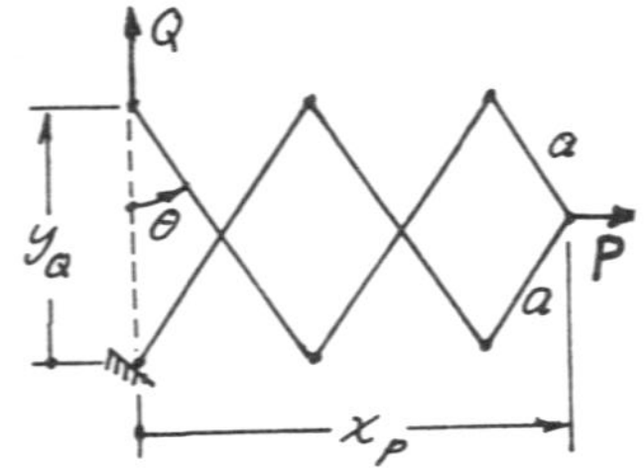

10.12

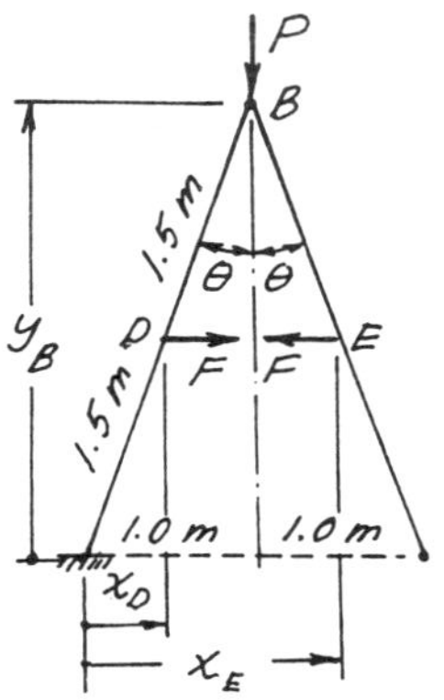

Release the spring, so that the spring force F becomes an active force.

$F = k(L - L_0) = 1.2(1.0 - 0.5) = 0.6$ kN

$y_B = 3\cos\theta$ m $\quad \therefore\ \delta y_B = -3\sin\theta\,\delta\theta$ m

$x_D = 1.5\sin\theta$ m $\quad \therefore\ \delta x_D = 1.5\cos\theta\,\delta\theta$ m

$x_E = 4.5\sin\theta$ m $\quad \therefore\ \delta x_E = 4.5\cos\theta\,\delta\theta$ m

$$\delta U = -P\,\delta y_B + F\,\delta x_D - F\,\delta x_E$$

$$= \left[-P(-3\sin\theta) + F(1.5 - 4.5)\cos\theta\right]\delta\theta$$

$\delta U = 0$: $P\sin\theta - F\cos\theta = 0 \quad \therefore\ P = \dfrac{F}{\tan\theta}$

From geometry: $\tan\theta = \dfrac{1.0}{\sqrt{3^2 - 1^2}} = 0.3536 \quad \therefore\ P = \dfrac{0.6}{0.3536} = 1.697$ kN ◆

10.13

Let φ be the kinematically independent coordinate, measured from the equilibrium position.

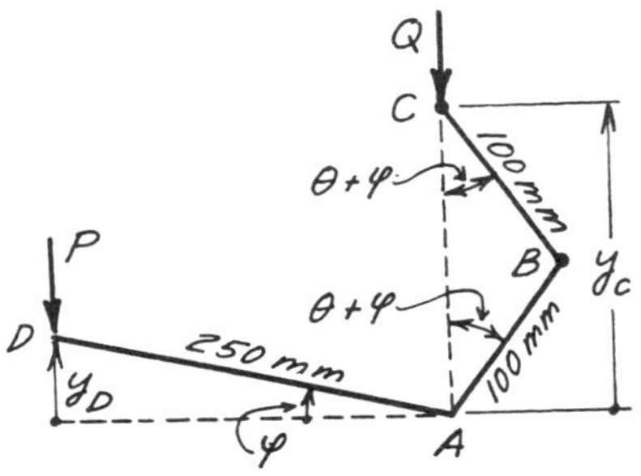

$y_C = 2[100\cos(\theta + \varphi)]$

$\therefore\ \delta y_C = -200\sin(\theta + \varphi)\,\delta\varphi$

$y_D = 250\sin\varphi \quad \therefore\ \delta y_D = 250\cos\varphi\,\delta\varphi$

When $\varphi = 0$:

$\delta y_C = -200\sin\theta\,\delta\varphi \quad \delta y_D = 250\,\delta\varphi$

$\delta U = -P\,\delta y_D - Q\,\delta y_C$

$= [-P(250) - Q(-200\sin\theta)]\delta\varphi$

$\delta U = 0$: $-250P + 200Q\sin\theta = 0$

$\therefore\ \sin\theta = \dfrac{250}{200}\dfrac{P}{Q} = \dfrac{250}{200}\dfrac{1}{4} = 0.3125 \quad \therefore\ \theta = 18.21°$ ◆

10.14

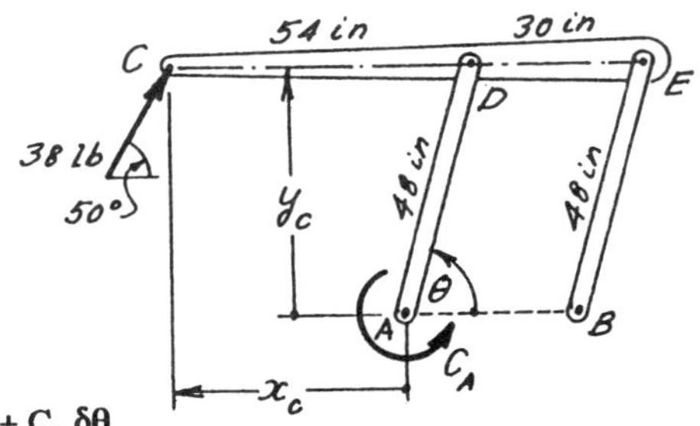

$x_C = 54 - 48\cos\theta \quad \therefore\ \delta x_C = 48\sin\theta\,\delta\theta$

$y_C = 48\sin\theta \quad \therefore\ \delta y_C = 48\cos\theta\,\delta\theta$

When $\theta = 70°$:

$\delta x_C = 48\sin 70°\,\delta\theta = 45.11\,\delta\theta$

$\delta y_C = 48\cos 70°\,\delta\theta = 16.42\,\delta\theta$

$\delta U = 38\sin 50°\,\delta y_C - 38\cos 50°\,\delta x_C + C_A\delta\theta$

$= [38\sin 50°(16.42) - 38\cos 50°(45.11) + C_A]\delta\theta$

$= (-623.9 + C_A)\delta\theta$

$\delta U = 0$: $C_A = 624$ lb•in ◆

10.15

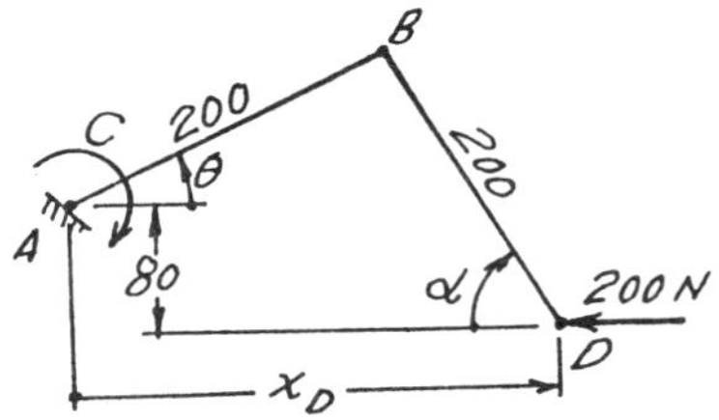

The mechanism has a single degree of freedom. Choose θ as the kinematically independent variable.

θ and α are related by the geometric constraint

$200\sin\alpha - 200\sin\theta = 80$

$\therefore\ \sin\alpha = 0.4 + \sin\theta = 0.4 + \sin 25° = 0.8226$

$\therefore\ \alpha = 55.35°$

The geometric constraint also yields

$200\cos\alpha\,\delta\alpha - 200\cos\theta\,\delta\theta = 0 \quad \therefore\ \delta\alpha = \dfrac{\cos\theta}{\cos\alpha}\delta\theta = \dfrac{\cos 25°}{\cos 55.35°}\delta\theta = 1.5940\,\delta\theta$

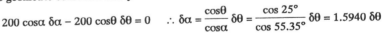

$x_D = 200\cos\theta + 200\cos\alpha$ mm

$\therefore\ \delta x_D = -200(\sin\theta\,\delta\theta + \sin\alpha\,\delta\alpha) = -200\left[\sin 25° + \sin 55.35°(1.5940)\right]\delta\theta = -346.8\,\delta\theta$ mm

$\delta U = -C\,\delta\theta - 200\,\delta x_D = -C\,\delta\theta - 200(-346.8)\delta\theta = (-C + 69\,360)\delta\theta$

$\delta U = 0$: $C = 69\,400$ N·mm $= 69.4$ N·m ◆

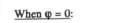

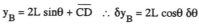

10.16

From geometry:

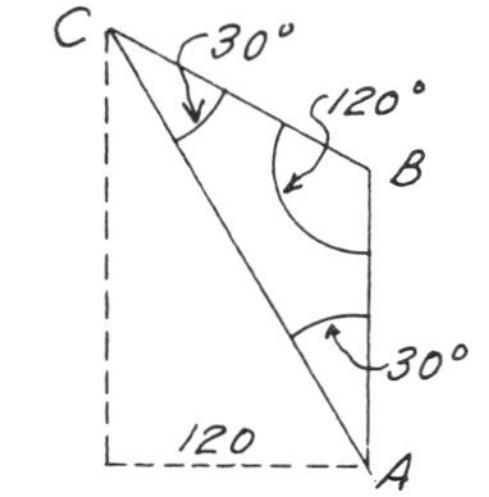

$$\overline{AC} = \frac{120}{\sin 30°} = 240 \text{ mm}$$

$$\frac{\overline{AB}}{\sin 30°} = \frac{\overline{AC}}{\sin 120°}$$

$$\therefore \overline{AB} = \overline{AC}\frac{\sin 30°}{\sin 120°} = 240\frac{\sin 30°}{\sin 120°} = 138.56 \text{ mm}$$

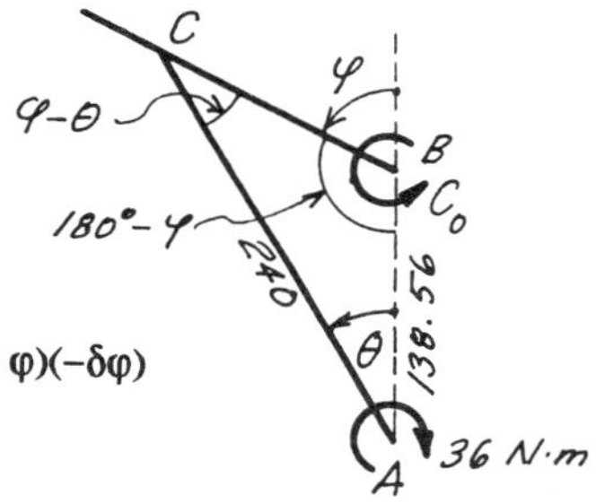

From the active force diagram:

$$\frac{240}{\sin(180° - \varphi)} = \frac{138.56}{\sin(\varphi - \theta)}$$

$\therefore$ $240 \sin(\varphi - \theta) = 138.56 \sin(180° - \varphi)$

$\therefore$ $240 \cos(\varphi - \theta)(\delta\varphi - \delta\theta) = 138.56 \cos(180° - \varphi)(-\delta\varphi)$

<u>When $\theta = 30°$ and $\varphi = 60°$</u>:

$240 \cos(60° - 30°)(\delta\varphi - \delta\theta) = -138.56 \cos(180° - 60°)\delta\varphi$ $\quad\therefore\ \delta\varphi = 1.500\ \delta\theta$

$\delta U = -36\ \delta\theta + C_0\ \delta\varphi = (-36 + 1.5\ C_0)\delta\theta$

$$\delta U = 0: \ C_0 = \frac{36}{1.5} = 24 \text{ N·m} \ ◆$$

10.17

Due to symmetry, it is sufficient to consider half of the mechanism.

From geometry:

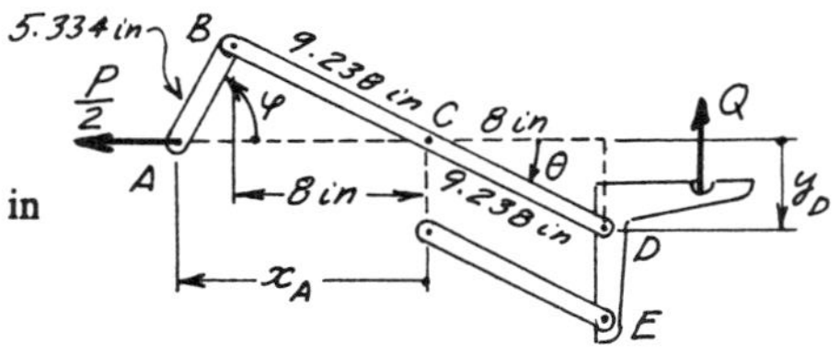

$$\overline{BC} = \overline{CD} = \frac{8}{\cos\theta} = \frac{8}{\cos 30°} = 9.238 \text{ in}$$

$\overline{AB} = \overline{BC} \tan\theta = 9.238 \tan 30° = 5.334$ in

$$\frac{\sin\theta}{5.334} = \frac{\sin\varphi}{9.238} \quad \therefore\ \sin\varphi = 1.7319 \sin\theta$$

$\therefore$ $\cos\varphi\ \delta\varphi = 1.7319 \cos\theta\ \delta\theta$

$$\therefore\ \delta\varphi = 1.7319\frac{\cos\theta}{\cos\varphi}\delta\theta = 1.7319\frac{\cos 30°}{\cos 60°}\delta\theta = 3.000\ \delta\theta$$

(continued)

10.17 continued

$x_A = 9.238 \cos\theta + 5.334 \cos\varphi$

$\therefore\ \delta x_A = -9.238 \sin\theta\ \delta\theta - 5.334 \sin\varphi\ \delta\varphi = [-9.238 \sin 30° - (5.334 \sin 60°)(3.000)]\delta\theta$

$= -18.477\ \delta\theta$

$y_D = 9.238 \sin\theta \quad \therefore\ \delta y_D = 9.238 \cos\theta\ \delta\theta = 9.238 \cos 30°\ \delta\theta = 8.000\ \delta\theta$

$$\delta U = \frac{P}{2}\delta x_A + Q\ \delta y_D = \left[\frac{P}{2}(-18.477) + Q(8.000)\right]\delta\theta$$

$$\delta U = 0: \ P = \frac{(8.000)(2)}{18.477} Q = 0.866Q \ ◆$$

10.18

Consider kinematics of half of the mechanism. If screw turned though 2π radians, D moves <u>to the left</u> by

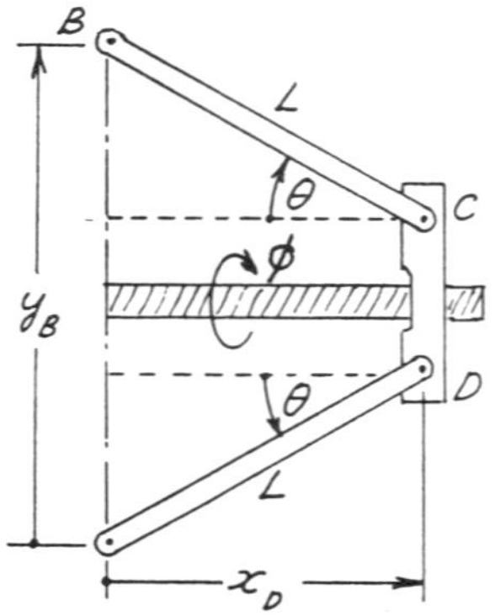

$$s = \frac{1}{2}(2.5) = 1.25 \text{ mm}$$

$$\therefore\ \delta x_D = -\frac{s}{2\pi}\delta\phi = -\frac{1.25}{2\pi}\delta\phi$$

$= -0.19894\ \delta\phi$ . . . . (a)

From geometry:

$x_D = L \cos\theta \quad \therefore\ \delta x_D = -L \sin\theta\ \delta\theta$ (b)

$y_B = 2L \sin\theta + \overline{CD} \quad \therefore\ \delta y_B = 2L \cos\theta\ \delta\theta$

$$\text{Equating (a) and (b): } \delta\theta = \frac{0.19894\ \delta\phi}{L \sin\theta}$$

$$\therefore\ \delta y_B = 2L \cos\theta \frac{0.19894\ \delta\phi}{L \sin\theta} = 0.3979 \cot\theta\ \delta\phi = 0.3979 \cot 30°\ \delta\phi = 0.6892\ \delta\phi$$

Consider the virtual work on the whole mechanism.

$\delta U = C_0\ \delta\phi - P\ \delta y_B = [C_0 - (3)(0.6892)]\delta\phi = (C_0 - 2.068)\delta\phi$

$\delta U = 0: \ C_0 - 2.068 = 0 \quad \therefore\ C_0 = 2.07$ kN·m ◆

10.19

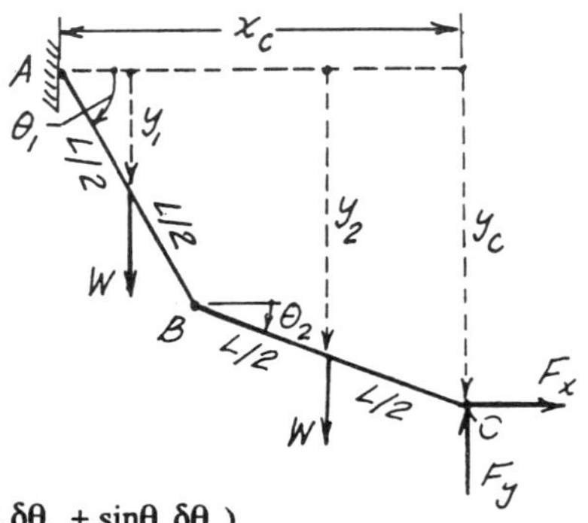

The linkage has two DOF.

$y_1 = \frac{L}{2}\sin\theta_1 \quad \therefore \delta y_1 = \frac{L}{2}\cos\theta_1\delta\theta_1$

$y_2 = L\sin\theta_1 + \frac{L}{2}\sin\theta_2$

$\therefore \delta y_2 = L\left(\cos\theta_1\delta\theta_1 + \frac{1}{2}\cos\theta_2\delta\theta_2\right)$

$y_C = L\sin\theta_1 + L\sin\theta_2$

$\therefore \delta y_C = L(\cos\theta_1\delta\theta_1 + \cos\theta_2\delta\theta_2)$

$x_C = L\cos\theta_1 + L\cos\theta_2 \quad \therefore \delta x_C = -L(\sin\theta_1\delta\theta_1 + \sin\theta_2\delta\theta_2)$

$\delta U = W(\delta y_1 + \delta y_2) + F_x\delta x_C - F_y\delta y_C$

$= WL\left(\frac{3}{2}\cos\theta_1\delta\theta_1 + \frac{1}{2}\cos\theta_2\delta\theta_2\right) - F_xL(\sin\theta_1\delta\theta_1 + \sin\theta_2\delta\theta_2)$

$- F_yL(\cos\theta_1\delta\theta_1 + \cos\theta_2\delta\theta_2)$

$= \left(\frac{3}{2}W\cos\theta_1 - F_x\sin\theta_1 - F_y\cos\theta_1\right)L\,\delta\theta_1 + \left(\frac{1}{2}W\cos\theta_2 - F_x\sin\theta_2 - F_y\cos\theta_2\right)L\,\delta\theta_2$

$\delta U = 0$: $\frac{3}{2}W\cos\theta_1 - F_x\sin\theta_1 - F_y\cos\theta_1 = 0$

$\frac{1}{2}W\cos\theta_2 - F_x\sin\theta_2 - F_y\cos\theta_2 = 0$

Substituting $\theta_1 = 60°$ and $\theta_2 = 15°$, we get

$$\left.\begin{aligned}0.8660F_x + 0.5F_y &= 0.75W\\ 0.2588F_x + 0.9659F_y &= 0.4830W\end{aligned}\right\}\text{Solution is: } F_x = 0.6830W \quad F_y = 0.3171W$$

$\therefore F = W\sqrt{0.6830^2 + 0.3171^2} = 0.753W$ ◆ $\quad \alpha = \tan^{-1}\frac{0.3171}{0.6830} = 24.9°$ ◆

10.20

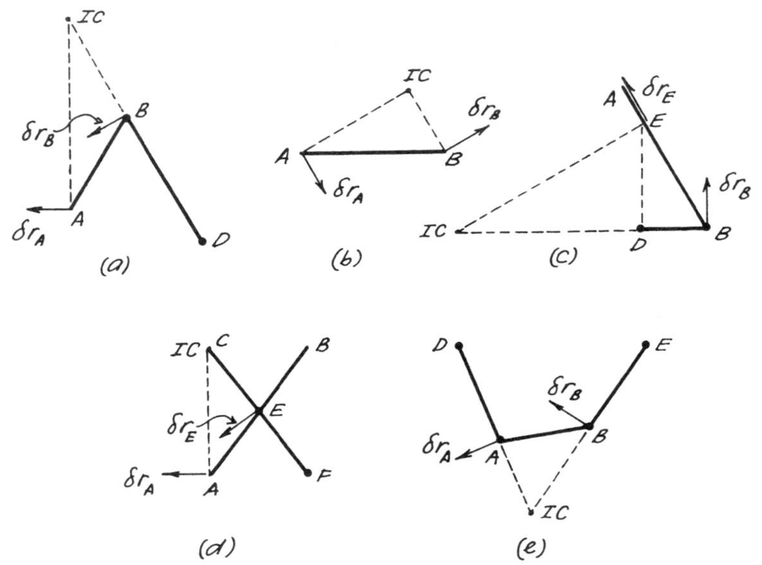

10.21

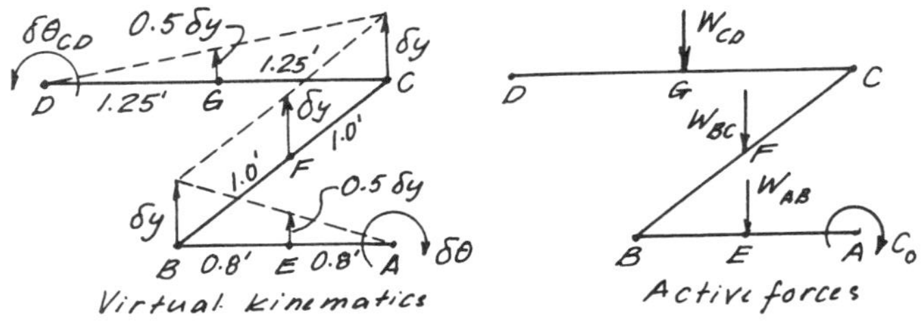

$W_{AB} = (12)(1.6) = 19.2$ lb $\quad W_{BC} = (12)(2) = 24$ lb $\quad W_{CD} = (12)(2.5) = 30$ lb

Note that bar BC translates. $\quad \therefore \delta y_B = \delta y_C = \delta y$

From motion of bar AB: $\delta y = 1.6\,\delta\theta$ ft

$\delta U = C_0\delta\theta - W_{AB}(0.5\,\delta y) - W_{BC}\delta y - W_{CD}(0.5\,\delta y)$

$= \left\{C_0 - 1.6\left[(19.2)(0.5) + 24 + (30)(0.5)\right]\right\}\delta\theta = (C_0 - 77.76)\delta\theta$

$\delta U = 0$: $C_0 = 77.8$ lb·ft ◆

10.22

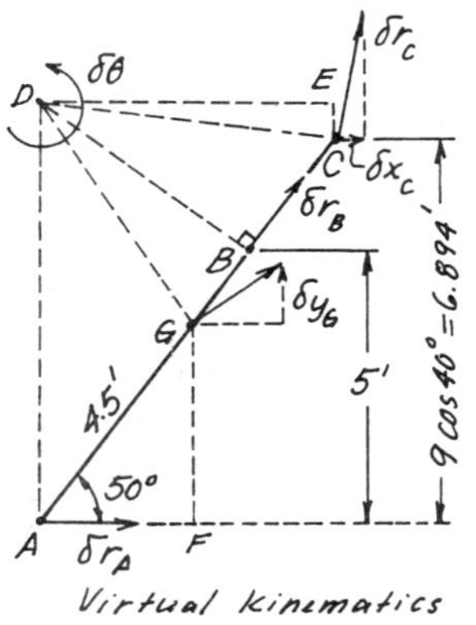

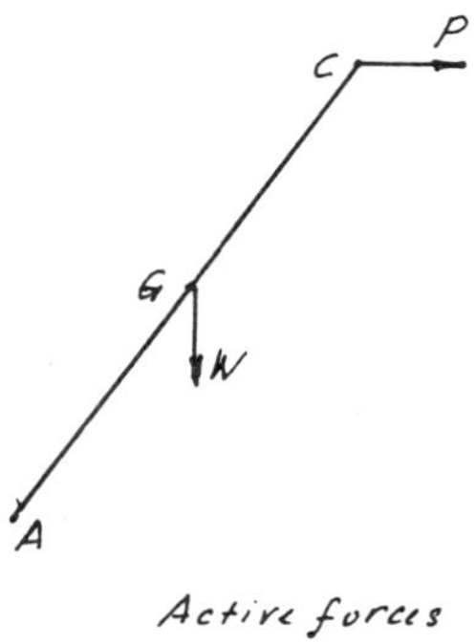

Instant center D is located from the known directions of δr_A and δr_B.

$\overline{AB} = \dfrac{5}{\cos 40°} = 6.527$ ft $\qquad \overline{AD} = \dfrac{\overline{AB}}{\cos 40°} = \dfrac{6.527}{\cos 40°} = 8.520$ ft

$\overline{EC} = \overline{AD} - 6.894 = 8.520 - 6.894 = 1.626$ ft $\qquad \overline{AF} = 4.5 \sin 40° = 2.893$ ft

$\delta y_G = \overline{AF}\ \delta\theta = 2.893\ \delta\theta \qquad \delta x_C = \overline{EC}\ \delta\theta = 1.626\ \delta\theta$

$\delta U = P\,\delta x_C - W\,\delta y_G = [1.626P - 40(2.893)]\delta\theta$

$\delta U = 0$: $1.626P - 40(2.893) = 0 \qquad \therefore P = \dfrac{40(2.893)}{1.626} = 71.2$ lb ◆

10.23

Release the cable, so that cable tension T becomes an active force.

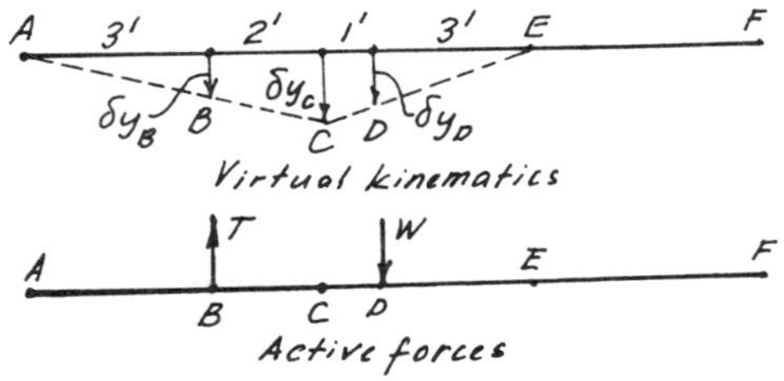

$\delta y_B = \dfrac{3}{5}\delta y_C \qquad \delta y_D = \dfrac{3}{4}\delta y_C$

$\delta U = -T\,\delta y_B + W\,\delta y_D$

$= \left[-\dfrac{3}{5}T + \dfrac{3}{4}(400)\right]\delta y_C$

$\delta U = 0$: $-\dfrac{3}{5}T + \dfrac{3}{4}(400) = 0 \qquad \therefore T = 500$ lb ◆

10.24

Release rotational constraint at F, so that the restraining couple C_F becomes active.

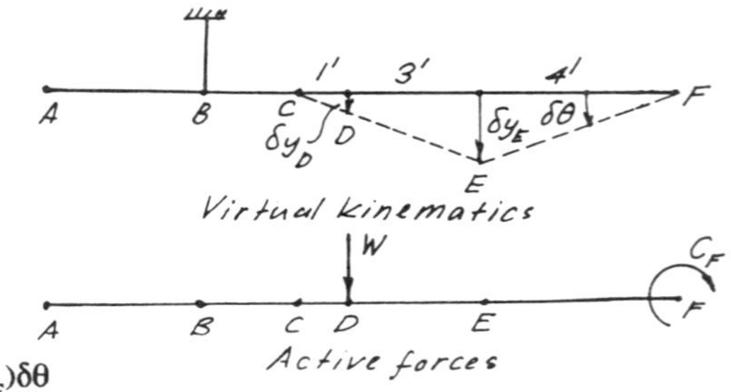

$\delta y_E = 4\ \delta\theta$ ft

$\delta y_D = \dfrac{1}{4}\delta y_E = 1.0\ \delta\theta$ ft

$\delta U = W\,\delta y_D - C_F\delta\theta$

$= 400(1.0\ \delta\theta) - C_F\delta\theta = (400 - C_F)\delta\theta$

$\delta U = 0$: $C_F = 400$ lb·ft ◆

10.25

Note that the scales form a parallelogram linkage.

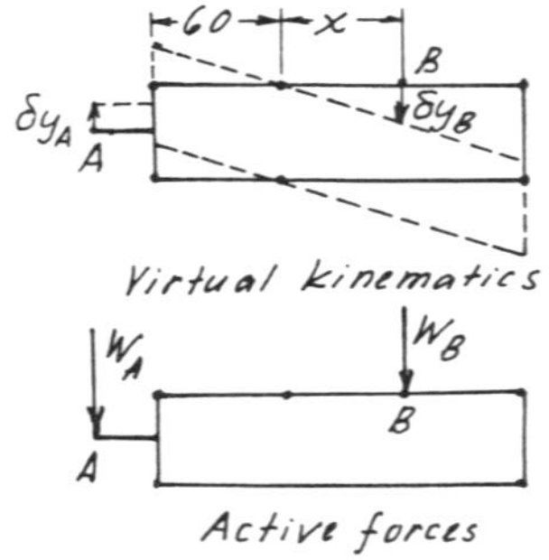

Kinematics: $\dfrac{\delta y_A}{60} = \dfrac{\delta y_B}{x} \qquad \therefore \delta y_B = \dfrac{x}{60}\delta y_A$

$\delta U = -W_A\delta y_A + W_B\delta y_B$

$= -0.4\ \delta y_A + 0.2\left(\dfrac{x}{60}\delta y_A\right) = \left(-0.4 + \dfrac{x}{300}\right)\delta y_A$

$\delta U = 0$: $-0.4 + \dfrac{x}{300} = 0 \qquad \therefore x = 120$ mm ◆

10.26

The I.C. of the plate is at E, as determined from the known directions of δr_A and δr_B.

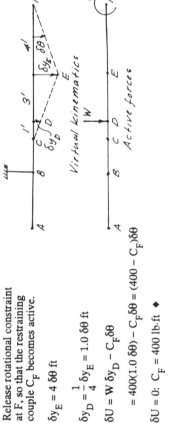

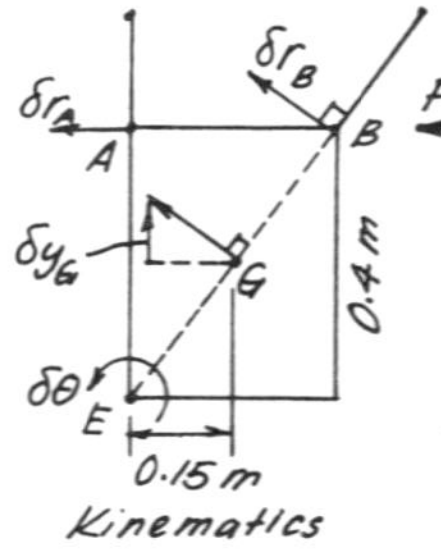

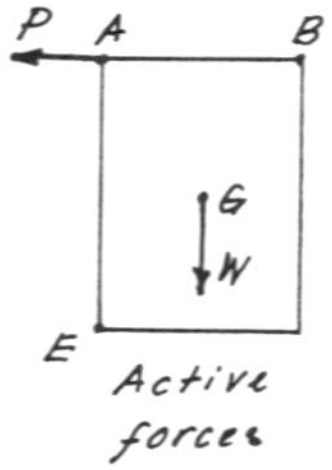

$\delta r_A = 0.4\ \delta\theta$ m

$\delta y_G = 0.15\ \delta\theta$ m

$\delta U = P\,\delta r_A - W\,\delta y_G$

$= P(0.4\ \delta\theta) - W(0.15\ \delta\theta)$

$\delta U = 0$: $0.4P - 0.15W = 0$

$\therefore P = \dfrac{0.15}{0.4}W = \dfrac{0.15}{0.4}(15 \times 9.81) = 55.2$ N ◆

10.27

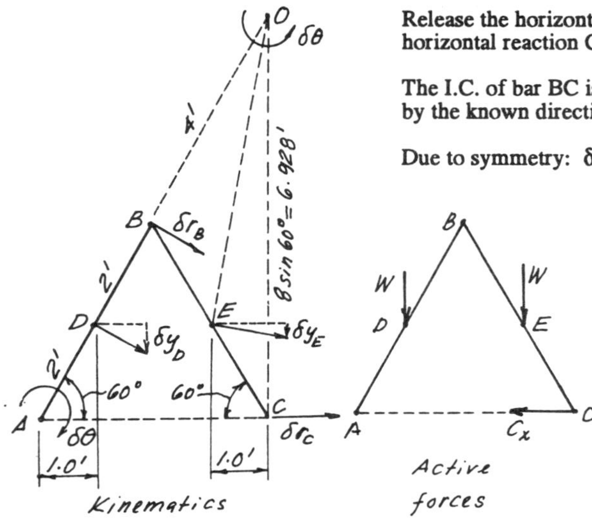

Release the horizontal constraint at C, so that the horizontal reaction C_x becomes an active force.

The I.C. of bar BC is located at O, as determined by the known directions of δr_B and δr_C.

Due to symmetry: $\delta\theta_{AB} = \delta\theta_{BC} = \delta\theta$

From motion of AB (rotation about A): $\delta y_D = 1.0\ \delta\theta$ ft

From motion of BC (rotation about O): $\delta y_E = 1.0\ \delta\theta$ ft, $\delta r_C = 6.928\ \delta\theta$ ft

$\delta U = W\,\delta y_D + W\delta y_E - C_x \delta r_C = (2.0W - 6.928C_x)\delta\theta$

$\delta U = 0$: $2.0W - 6.928C_x = 0 \quad \therefore C_x = 0.289W$ ◆

10.28

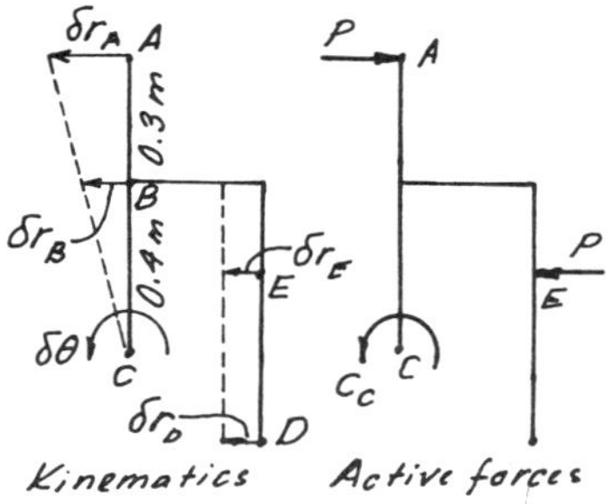

Release the rotational restraint at C, so that the couple C_C becomes active.

From motion of AC (rotation about C):

$\delta r_A = 0.7\ \delta\theta$ m, $\delta r_B = 0.4\ \delta\theta$ m

From motion of BD (translation):

$\delta r_E = \delta r_B = 0.4\ \delta\theta$ m

$\delta U = -P\,\delta r_A + P\,\delta r_E + C_C\delta\theta$

$= -P(0.7\ \delta\theta) + P(0.4\ \delta\theta) + C_C\delta\theta$

$= (-0.3P + C_C)\delta\theta \qquad \delta U = 0$: $-0.3P + C_C = 0 \quad \therefore C_C = 0.3P = 0.3(600) = 180$ N·m ◆

10.29

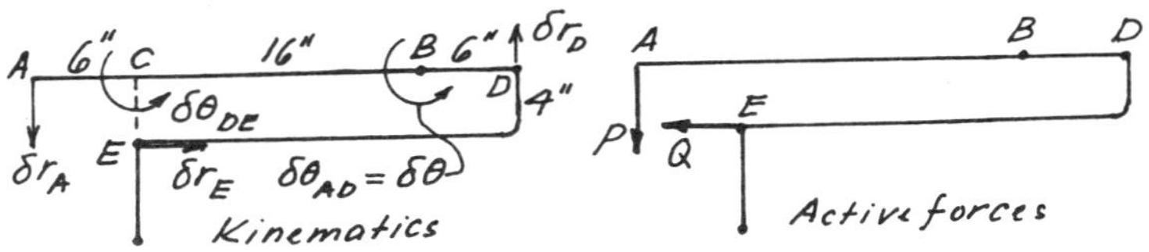

The I.C. of bar DE is at C, determined by the known directions of δr_D and δr_E.

From motion of AD (rotates about B): $\delta r_A = 22\ \delta\theta$ in, $\delta r_D = 6\ \delta\theta$ in

From motion of DE (rotates about C): $\delta r_D = 22\ \delta\theta_{DE}$ in, $\delta r_E = 4\ \delta\theta_{DE}$ in

Equating the two expressions for δr_D: $6\ \delta\theta = 22\ \delta\theta_{DE} \quad \therefore \delta\theta_{DE} = \frac{6}{22}\delta\theta = \frac{3}{11}\delta\theta$

$$\therefore \delta r_E = 4\left(\frac{3}{11}\delta\theta\right) = \frac{12}{11}\delta\theta \text{ in}$$

$$\delta U = P\,\delta r_A - Q\,\delta r_E = \left[P(22) - Q\frac{12}{11}\right]\delta\theta$$

$$\delta U = 0:\quad 22P - \frac{12}{11}Q = 0 \quad \therefore Q = \frac{(22)(11)}{12}P = \frac{(22)(11)}{12}(30) = 605 \text{ lb} \ ◆$$

10.30

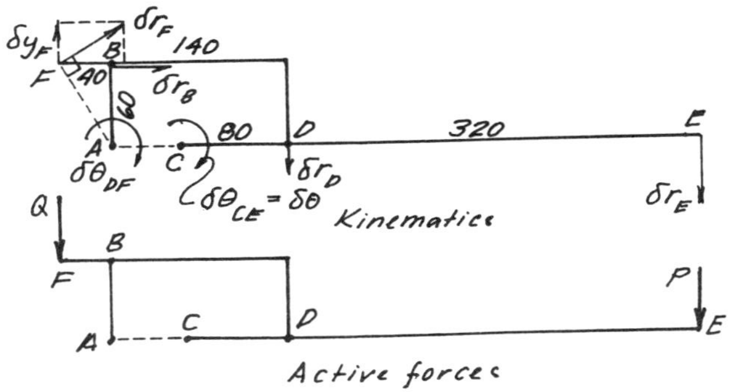

The I.C. of bar DF is located at A, as determined from the known directions of δr_B and δr_D.

(continued)

10.30 continued

From motion of bar CE (rotates about C): $\delta r_D = 80\ \delta\theta$ mm $\quad \delta r_E = 400\ \delta\theta$ mm

From motion of bar FD (rotates about A): $\delta r_D = 140\ \delta\theta_{DF} \quad \delta y_F = 40\ \delta\theta_{DF}$

Equating the expressions for δr_D: $80\ \delta\theta = 140\ \delta\theta_{DF} \quad \therefore \delta\theta_{DF} = \dfrac{80}{140}\delta\theta = 0.5714\ \delta\theta$

$\therefore \delta y_F = 40(0.5714\ \delta\theta) = 22.86\ \delta\theta$ mm

$\delta U = P\ \delta r_E - Q\ \delta y_F = P(400\ \delta\theta) - Q(22.86\ \delta\theta)$

$\delta U = 0$: $\quad 400P - 22.86Q = 0 \quad \therefore P = 0.05715Q = 0.05715(4200) = 240$ N ◆

10.31

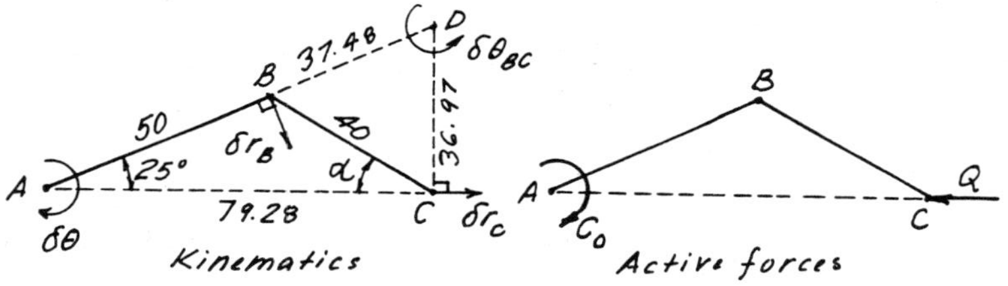

The I.C. of bar BC is located at D, as determined by the known directions of δr_B and δr_C.

Geometry: $\dfrac{\sin\alpha}{50} = \dfrac{\sin 25°}{40} \quad \therefore \alpha = \sin^{-1}\dfrac{50 \sin 25°}{40} = 31.89°$

$\overline{AC} = 50 \cos 25° + 40 \cos\alpha = 50 \cos 25° + 40 \cos 31.89° = 79.28$ mm

$\overline{CD} = \overline{AC} \tan 25° = 79.28 \tan 25° = 36.97$ mm

$\overline{AD} = \overline{AC}/\cos 25° = 79.28/\cos 25° = 87.48$ mm

$\overline{BD} = \overline{AD} - \overline{AB} = 87.48 - 50 = 37.48$ mm

From motion of bar AB (rotates about A): $\delta r_B = 50\ \delta\theta$ mm

From motion of bar BC (rotates about D): $\delta r_B = 37.48\ \delta\theta_{BC}$ mm, $\delta r_C = 36.97\ \delta\theta_{BC}$ mm

Equating the expressions for δr_B: $50\ \delta\theta = 37.48\ \delta\theta_{BC} \quad \therefore \delta\theta_{BC} = 1.3340\ \delta\theta$

$\therefore \delta r_C = 36.97(1.3340\ \delta\theta) = 49.32\ \delta\theta$ mm

$\delta U = C_0\delta\theta - Q\ \delta r_C = C_0\delta\theta - 200(49.32\ \delta\theta) = (C_0 - 9864)\delta\theta$

$\delta U = 0$: $C_0 - 9864 = 0 \quad \therefore C_0 = 9864$ N·mm $= 9.86$ N·m ◆

10.32

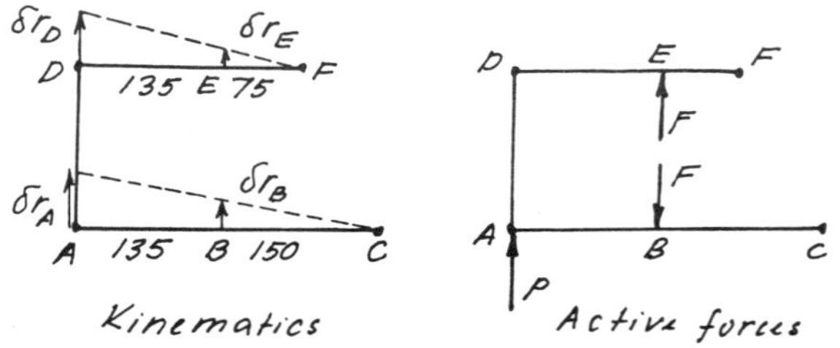

Choose δr_A as the kinematically independent variable.

From motion of bar AC (rotates about C): $\delta r_B = \dfrac{150}{285}\delta r_A = 0.5263\ \delta r_A$

From motion of bar AD (translates): $\delta r_D = \delta r_A$

From motion of bar DF (rotates about F): $\delta r_E = \dfrac{75}{210}\delta r_D = 0.3571\ \delta r_D = 0.3571\ \delta r_A$

$\delta U = P\ \delta r_A - F(\delta r_B - \delta r_E) = \left[P - F(0.5263 - 0.3571)\right]\delta r_A = (P - 0.1692\ F)\delta r_A$

$\delta U = 0$: $\quad P - 0.1692\ F = 0 \quad \therefore F = \dfrac{P}{0.1692} = \dfrac{2600}{0.1692} = 15\ 370$ N $= 15.37$ kN ◆

10.33

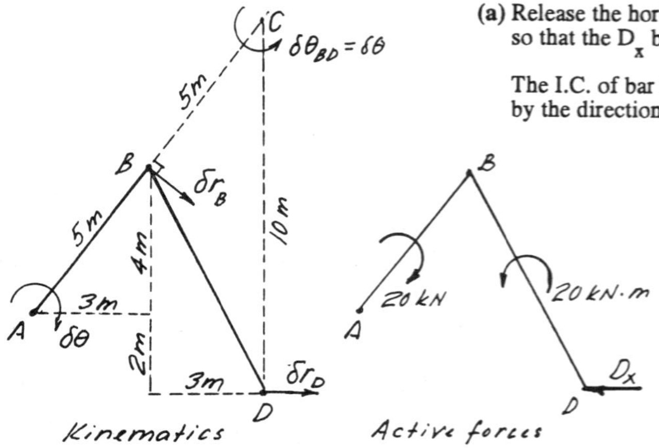

(a) Release the horizontal constraint at D, so that the D_x becomes an active force.

The I.C. of bar BD is at C, determined by the directions of δr_B and δr_D.

(continued)

10.33 continued

From motion of bar AB (rotates about A): $\delta r_B = 5\,\delta\theta$ m

From motion of bar BD (rotates about C): $\delta r_B = 5\,\delta\theta_{BD}$ m, $\delta r_D = 10\,\delta\theta_{BD}$ m

Equating the expressions for δr_B: $5\,\delta\theta_{BD} = 5\,\delta\theta \quad \therefore \delta\theta_{BD} = \delta\theta \quad \therefore \delta r_D = 10\,\delta\theta$ m

$\delta U = 20\,\delta\theta + 20\,\delta\theta_{BD} - D_x \delta r_D = (20\,\delta\theta + 20\,\delta\theta - D_x(10\,\delta\theta) = (40 - 10D_x)\delta\theta$

$\delta U = 0$: $40 - 10D_x = 0 \quad \therefore D_x = 4.0$ kN ◆

(b) Release the vertical constraint at D, so that D_y becomes an active force.

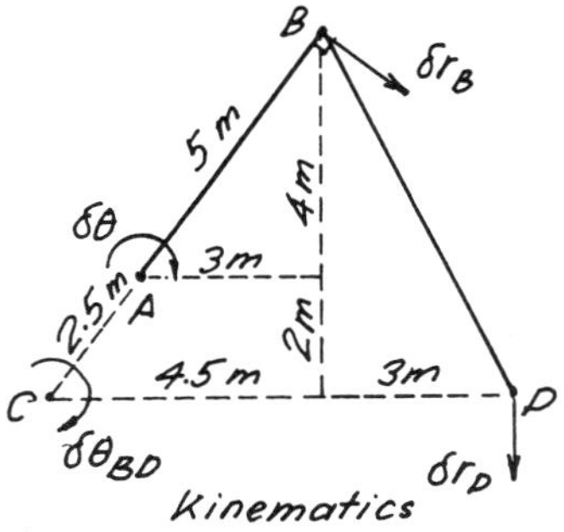

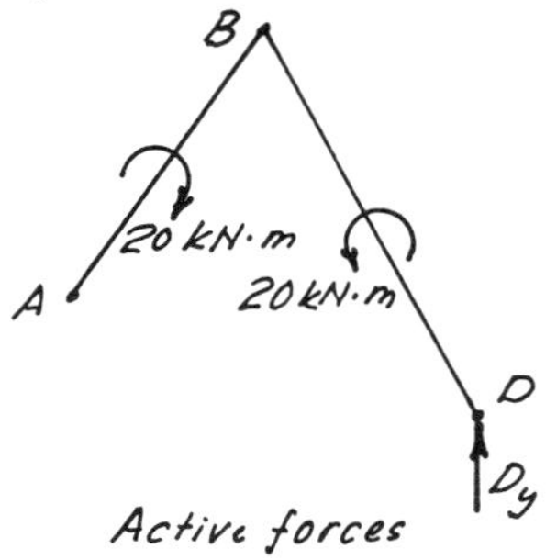

The I.C. of bar BD is at C, determined by the directions of δr_B and δr_D.

From motion of AB (rotates about A): $\delta r_B = 5\,\delta\theta$ m

From motion of BD (rotates about C): $\delta r_B = 7.5\,\delta\theta_{BD}$ m, $\delta r_D = 7.5\,\delta\theta_{BD}$ m

Equating the xpressions for δr_B: $5\,\delta\theta = 7.5\,\delta\theta_{BD} \quad \therefore \delta\theta_{BD} = 2/3\,\delta\theta \quad \therefore \delta r_D = 5\,\delta\theta$ m

$\delta U = 20\,\delta\theta - 20\,\delta\theta_{BD} - D_y \delta r_D = 20\,\delta\theta - 20(2/3)\delta\theta - D_y(5\,\delta\theta) = (6.667 - 5D_y)\delta\theta$

$\delta U = 0$: $6.667 - 5\,D_y = 0 \quad \therefore D_y = 1.333$ kN ◆

10.34

Release the cable at E, so that cable tension T becomes an active force.

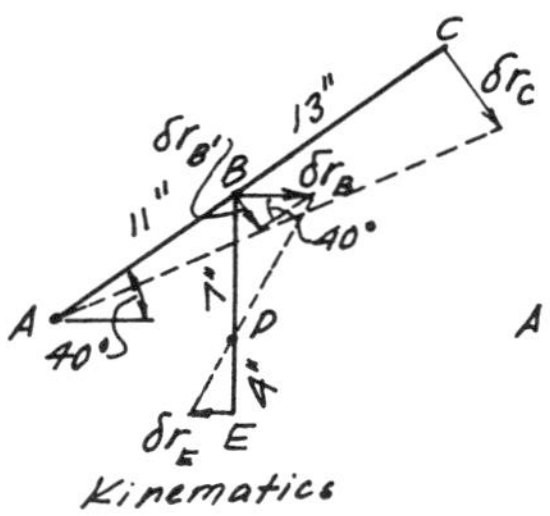

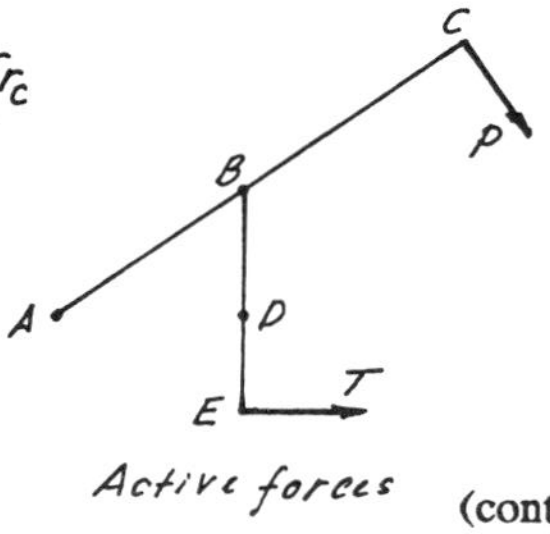

(continued)

10.34 continued

Notation:

δr_B = virtual displacement of point B <u>on bar BE</u> (virtual displacement of the collar)

$\delta r_{B'}$ = virtual displacement of point B <u>on bar AC</u>

Choose δr_B as the independent virtual displacement. Note that $\delta r_{B'} = \delta r_B \sin 40^\circ$

From motion of AC (rotates about B): $\delta r_C = \dfrac{24}{11}\delta r_{B'} = \dfrac{24}{11}(\delta r_B \sin 40^\circ) = 1.4024\,\delta r_B$

From motion of bar BE (rotates about D): $\delta r_E = \dfrac{4}{7}\delta r_B = 0.5714\,\delta r_B$

$\delta U = P\,\delta r_C - T\,\delta r_E = (1.4024\,P - 0.5714\,T)\delta r_B$

$\delta U = 0$: $1.4024\,P - 0.5714\,T = 0 \quad \therefore P = \dfrac{0.5714}{1.4024}T = \dfrac{0.5714}{1.4024}(25) = 10.19$ lb◆

10.35

The I.C. of rod AB is located at D, determined by the directions of δr_A and δr_B.

Geometry:

$\dfrac{\sin 30^\circ}{136} = \dfrac{\sin\alpha}{58} \quad \therefore \alpha = 12.31^\circ$

$\beta = 180^\circ - (30^\circ + 12.31^\circ) = 137.69^\circ$

$\dfrac{\sin\beta}{\overline{AC}} = \dfrac{\sin 30^\circ}{136} \quad \therefore \overline{AC} = 183.09$ mm

$\overline{AD} = \overline{AC}\tan 30^\circ = = 105.71$ mm

$\overline{BD} = \overline{AC}/\cos 30^\circ - 58 = 153.43$ mm

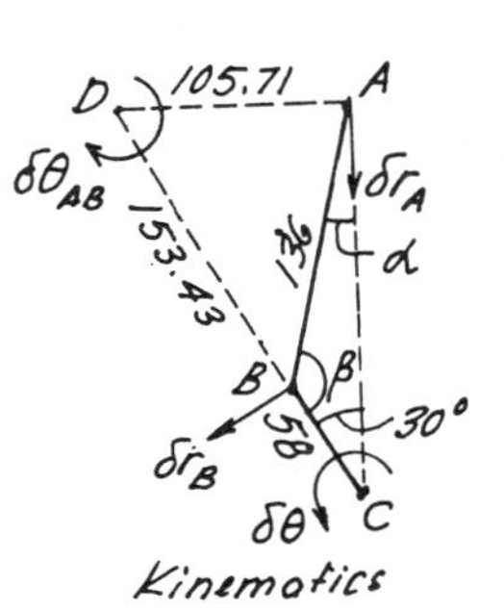

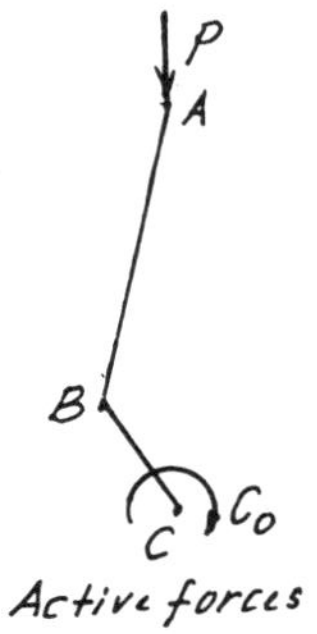

From motion of BC (rotates about C): $\delta r_B = 58\,\delta\theta$ mm

From motion of AB (rotates about D): $\delta r_B = 153.43\,\delta\theta_{AB}$ mm, $\delta r_A = 105.71\,\delta\theta_{AB}$ mm

Equating the expressions for δr_B: $58\,\delta\theta = 153.43\,\delta\theta_{AB} \quad \therefore \delta\theta_{AB} = 0.3780\,\delta\theta$

$\therefore \delta r_A = 105.71(0.3780\,\delta\theta) = 39.96\,\delta\theta$ mm

$\delta U = P\,\delta r_A - C_0\,\delta\theta = (39.96\,P - C_0)\delta\theta$

$\delta U = 0$: $39.96\,P - C_0 = 0 \quad \therefore C_0 = 39.96\,P = (39.96)(1600) = 63\,900$ N·mm $= 63.9$ N·m ◆

10.36

The I.C. of member CDF is G, found from the directions of δr_C and δr_D.

From similar triangles ABG and CDG:

$$\frac{1.2 + \overline{CG}}{3} = \frac{\overline{CG}}{1.0} \quad \therefore \overline{CG} = 0.6 \text{ in}$$

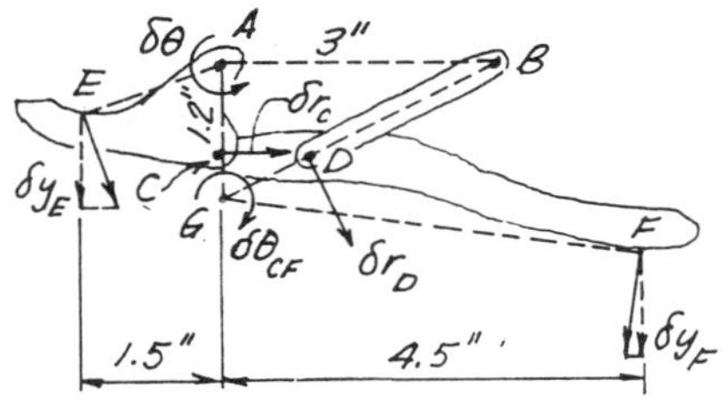

Kinematics

From motion of member CDF (rotates about G):

$$\delta r_C = \overline{CG}\,\delta\theta_{CF} = 0.6\,\delta\theta_{CF} \text{ in}$$

$$\delta y_F = 4.5\,\delta\theta_{CF} \text{ in}$$

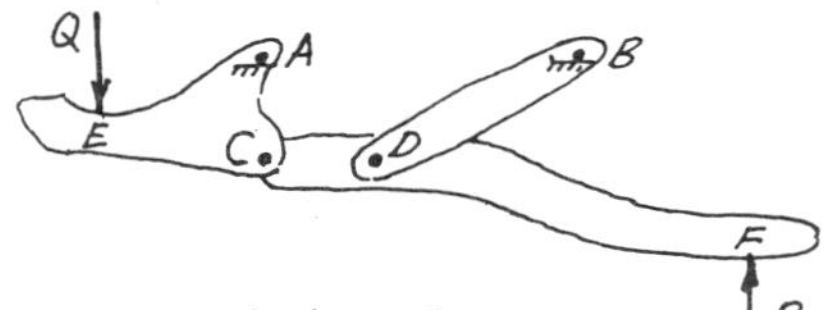

Active forces

From motion of member ACE (rotates about A):

$$\delta r_C = 1.2\,\delta\theta \text{ in}, \quad \delta y_E = 1.5\,\delta\theta \text{ in}$$

Equating the expressions for δr_C:

$$0.6\,\delta\theta_{CF} = 1.2\,\delta\theta \quad \therefore \delta\theta_{CF} = 2\,\delta\theta$$

$$\therefore \delta y_F = 4.5(2\,\delta\theta) = 9\,\delta\theta \text{ in}$$

$$\delta U = Q\,\delta y_E - P\,\delta y_F = (1.5Q - 9P)\delta\theta$$

$$\delta U = 0\text{:}\quad 1.5Q - 9.0P = 0 \quad \therefore Q = 6.0\,P \;\blacklozenge$$

10.37

Consider half of the mechanism. The I.C. of link AB is located at E, determined by the directions of δr_A and δr_B.

Geometry:

$$\overline{BC} = \frac{160}{\cos 35^\circ} = 195.32 \text{ mm}$$

$$\overline{EB} = \frac{52}{\cos 35^\circ} = 63.48 \text{ mm}$$

$$\overline{EA} = \frac{52}{\tan 25^\circ} + 52 \tan 35^\circ$$

$$= 147.93 \text{ mm}$$

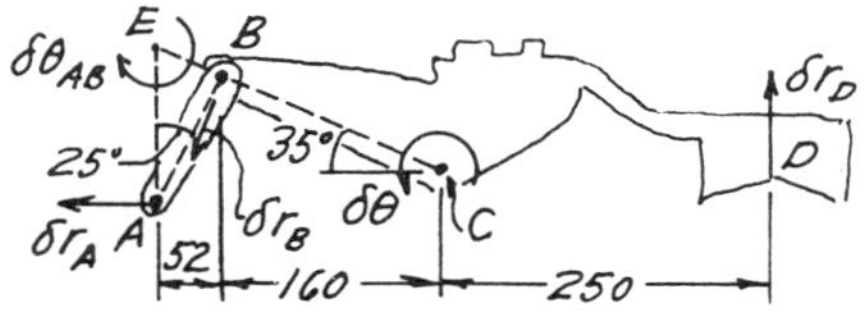

Kinematics

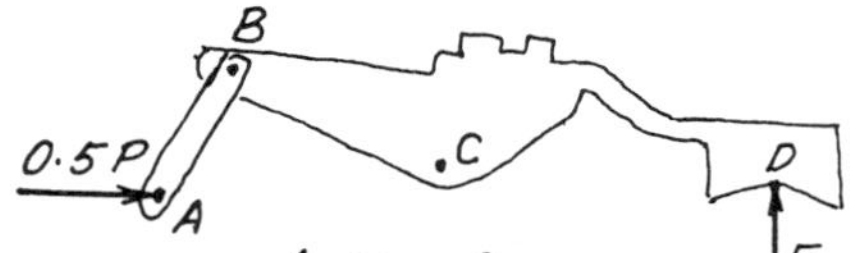

Active forces

(continued)

10.37 continued

From motion of link AB (rotates about E):

$$\delta r_B = \overline{EB}\,\delta\theta_{AB} = 63.48\,\delta\theta_{AB} \text{ mm}, \quad \delta r_A = \overline{EA}\,\delta\theta_{AB} = 147.93\,\delta\theta_{AB} \text{ mm}$$

From motion of part BCD (rotates about C):

$$\delta r_B = \overline{BC}\,\delta\theta = 195.32\,\delta\theta \text{ mm}, \quad \delta r_D = 250\,\delta\theta \text{ mm}$$

Equating the expressions for δr_B: $63.48\,\delta\theta_{AB} = 195.32\,\delta\theta \quad \therefore \delta\theta_{AB} = 3.077\,\delta\theta$

$$\therefore \delta r_A = 147.93(3.077\,\delta\theta) = 455.2\,\delta\theta \text{ mm}$$

$$\delta U = -0.5P\,\delta r_A + F\,\delta r_D = \left[-0.5P(455.2) + F(250)\right]\delta\theta$$

$$\delta U = 0\text{:}\quad -0.5P(455.2) + 250F = 0 \quad \therefore F = \frac{0.5(455.2)}{250} P = \frac{0.5(455.2)}{250}(120) = 109.2 \text{ N} \;\blacklozenge$$

10.38

(a) The I.C. of rod AB, located at D, was determined from the known directions of δr_A and δr_B.

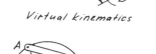

By measuring the drawing, we get $\overline{AD} = 35.5$ in and $\overline{BD} = 27.5$ in.

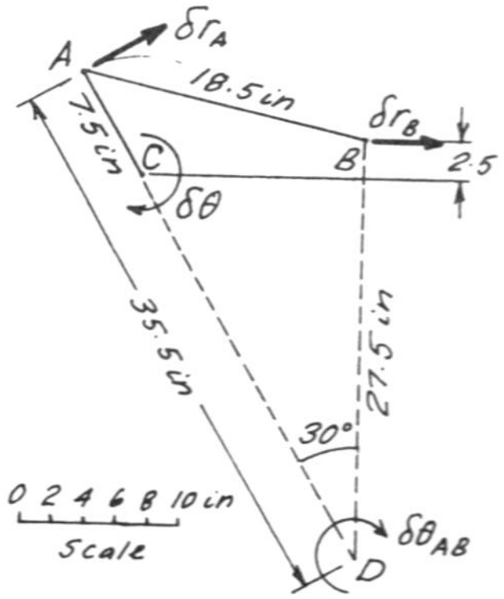

Virtual kinematics

(b)

From motion of flywheel radius AC (rotates about C):

$$\delta r_A = 7.5\,\delta\theta \text{ in}$$

From motion of connecting rod AB (rotates about D):

$$\delta r_A = 35.5\,\delta\theta_{AB} \text{ in}, \quad \delta r_B = 27.5\,\delta\theta_{AB} \text{ in}$$

Equating the expressions for δr_A: $7.5\,\delta\theta = 35.5\,\delta\theta_{AB}$

$$\therefore \delta\theta_{AB} = 0.211\,\delta\theta$$

$$\therefore \delta r_B = 27.5\,(0.211\,\delta\theta) = 5.80\,\delta\theta$$

$$\delta U = C_0\,\delta\theta - P\,\delta r_B = (C_0 - 5.80\,P)\delta\theta$$

$$\delta U = 0\text{:}\quad C_0 - 5.80\,P = 0$$

$$\therefore C_0 = 5.80\,P = (5.80)(120) = 696 \text{ lb·in} \approx 700 \text{ lb·in} \;\blacklozenge$$

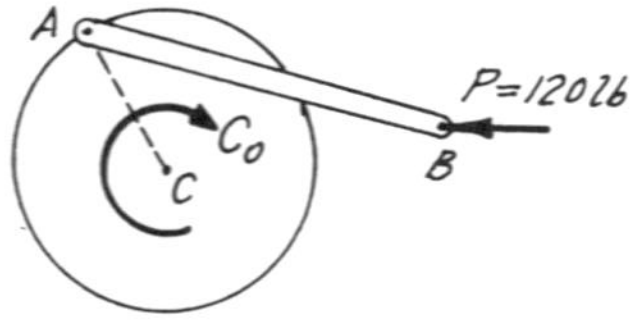

Active forces

10.39

1) Member ABF rotates about F, which determines the directions of δr_A and δr_B.

2) Since ABDE is a parallelogram linkage, $\delta r_D = \delta r_A$ and $\delta r_E = \delta r_B$.

3) The directions of δr_D and δr_E determine the location of H, the I.C. of the door.

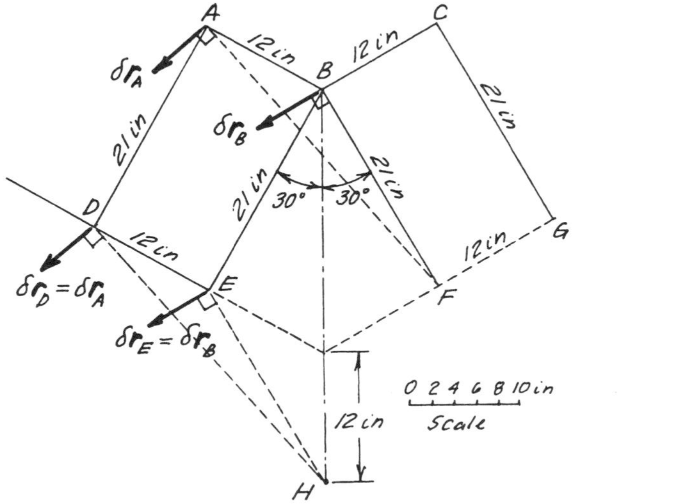

10.40

Since G is the mid-point of AB, we have

$$h_G = \frac{1}{2}(h_A + h_B)$$

From geomerty:

$$L\cos\theta = \overline{CD} + \overline{DE} = \frac{h_A}{\tan\alpha} + \frac{h_B}{\tan\alpha}$$

$$\therefore\ h_A + h_B = L\cos\theta\tan\alpha$$

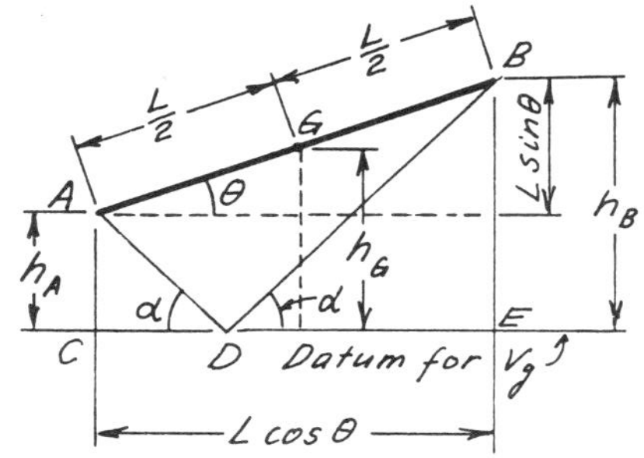

$$V_g = Wh_G = W\frac{h_A + h_B}{2} = \frac{WL}{2}\cos\theta\tan\alpha$$

$$\frac{dV_g}{d\theta} = -\frac{WL}{2}\sin\theta\tan\alpha \qquad \frac{dV_g}{d\theta} = 0 \text{ only if } \theta = 0 \ \blacklozenge$$

$$\frac{d^2V_g}{d\theta^2} = -\frac{WL}{2}\cos\theta\tan\alpha \qquad \frac{d^2V_g}{d\theta^2} < 0 \text{ when } \theta = 0 \quad \therefore \text{ \underline{The equilibrium is unstable}} \ \blacklozenge$$

10.41

Geometry: $h = 2\sin\theta - \tan\theta$

$V_g = Wh = W(2\sin\theta - \tan\theta)$

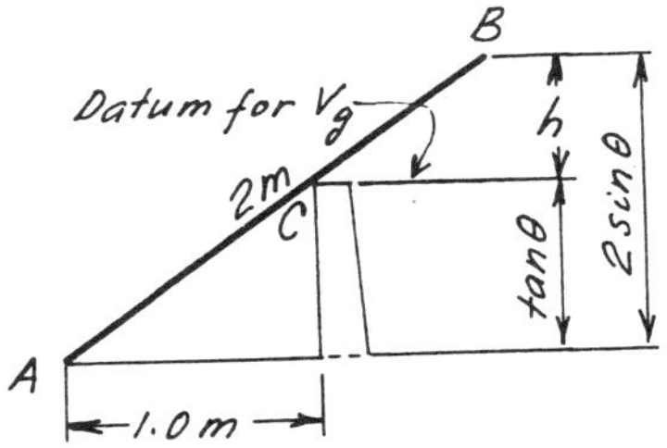

$$\therefore\ \frac{dV_g}{d\theta} = W(2\cos\theta - \sec^2\theta)$$

$$\frac{dV_g}{d\theta} = 0\text{:}\ \ 2\cos\theta - \sec^2\theta = 0$$

$$\therefore\ \cos^3\theta = \frac{1}{2} \quad \therefore\ \theta = 37.5^\circ \ \blacklozenge$$

$$\frac{d^2V_g}{d\theta^2} = W(-2\sin\theta - 2\sec^2\theta\tan\theta)$$

When $\theta = 37.5^\circ$: $\dfrac{d^2V_g}{d\theta^2} = -3.66\ W < 0$ $\therefore$ <u>The equlibrium is unstable</u> ◆

10.42

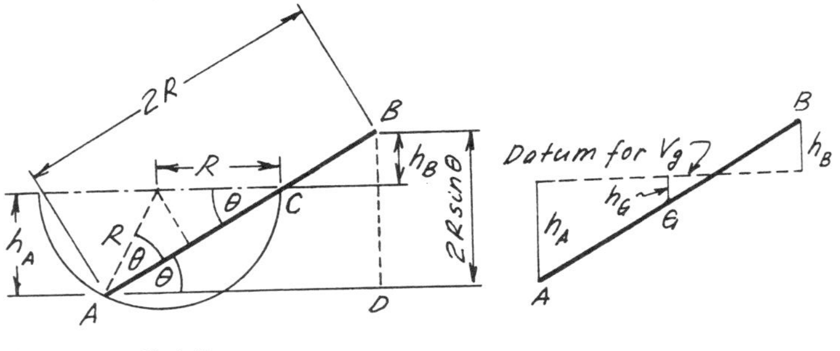

$h_A = \overline{AC}\sin\theta = (2R\cos\theta)\sin\theta$

$h_B = \overline{BD} - h_A = 2R\sin\theta - 2R\sin\theta\cos\theta = 2R\sin\theta\,(1 - \cos\theta)$

$h_G = \frac{1}{2}(h_A - h_B) = \frac{1}{2}2R\sin\theta\left[\cos\theta - (1 - \cos\theta)\right] = R\sin\theta\,(2\cos\theta - 1)$

$V_g = -Wh_G = -WR\sin\theta\,(2\cos\theta - 1)$

(continued)

10.42 continued

$$\therefore \frac{dV_g}{d\theta} = -WR\left[\cos\theta\,(2\cos\theta - 1) + \sin\theta\,(-2\sin\theta)\right] = -WR(2\cos^2\theta - 2\sin^2\theta - \cos\theta)$$

$$= -WR(4\cos^2\theta - \cos\theta - 2)$$

$\frac{dV_g}{d\theta} = 0$: $4\cos^2\theta - \cos\theta - 2 = 0$ The positive root is $\cos\theta = 0.8431$ $\therefore \theta = 32.5^o$ ◆

$\frac{d^2V_g}{d\theta^2} = -WR(-8\cos\theta\sin\theta + \sin\theta)$ When $\theta = 32.5^o$, $\frac{d^2V_g}{d\theta^2} = 3.09\,WR > 0$

∴ <u>The equilibrium is stable</u> ◆

10.43

The center of gravity G of the bar can be found by inspection.

$$h_G = \overline{OA}\sin\theta + \overline{AB}\cos\theta - \overline{BG}\sin\theta$$

$$= R\sin\theta + \left(R - \frac{b}{4}\right)\cos\theta - \frac{b}{4}\sin\theta$$

$$= \left(R - \frac{b}{4}\right)(\sin\theta + \cos\theta)$$

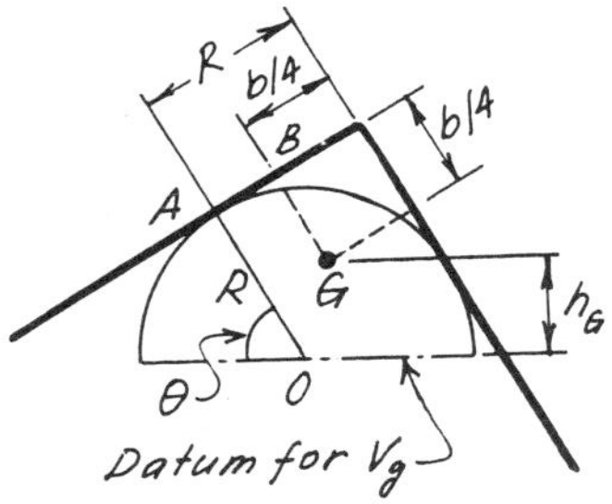

$$V_g = Wh_G = W\left(R - \frac{b}{4}\right)(\sin\theta + \cos\theta)$$

$$\therefore \frac{dV_g}{d\theta} = W\left(R - \frac{b}{4}\right)(\cos\theta - \sin\theta)$$

$$\frac{d^2V_g}{d\theta^2} = W\left(R - \frac{b}{4}\right)(-\sin\theta - \cos\theta)$$

<u>When $\theta = 45^o$</u>: $\frac{dV_g}{d\theta} = 0$ and $\frac{d^2V_g}{d\theta^2} = W\left(R - \frac{b}{4}\right)(-\sqrt{2})$

Equilibrium position $\theta = 45^o$ is stable when $d^2V_g/d\theta^2 > 0$, i.e. $b/4 > R$, or $b/R > 4$ ◆

10.44

$h_1 = R + \frac{R}{2}\cos\theta$ $\quad h_2 = R - \frac{R}{2}\cos\theta$

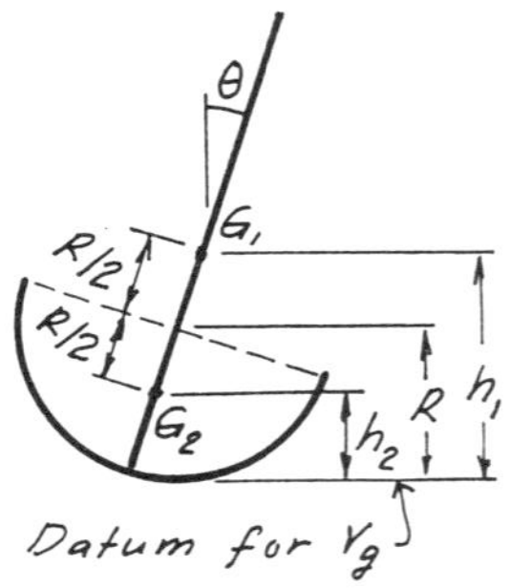

$$V_g = W_1h_1 + W_2h_2$$

$$= R\left[W_1\left(1 + \frac{1}{2}\cos\theta\right) + W_2\left(1 - \frac{1}{2}\cos\theta\right)\right]$$

$$= R\left[(W_1 + W_2) + \frac{1}{2}(W_1 - W_2)\cos\theta\right]$$

$$\therefore \frac{dV_g}{d\theta} = -\frac{R}{2}(W_1 - W_2)\sin\theta$$

$$\therefore \frac{d^2V_g}{d\theta^2} = -\frac{R}{2}(W_1 - W_2)\cos\theta$$

<u>At $\theta = 0$</u>: $\frac{d^2V_g}{d\theta^2} = -\frac{1}{2}R(W_1 - W_2)$ $\quad\therefore$ Equilibrium is stable if $\frac{W_1}{W_2} < 1$ ◆

10.45

$$h_G = R\cos\theta + R\theta\sin\theta + h\cos\theta$$

$$= (R + h)\cos\theta + R\theta\sin\theta$$

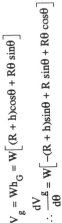

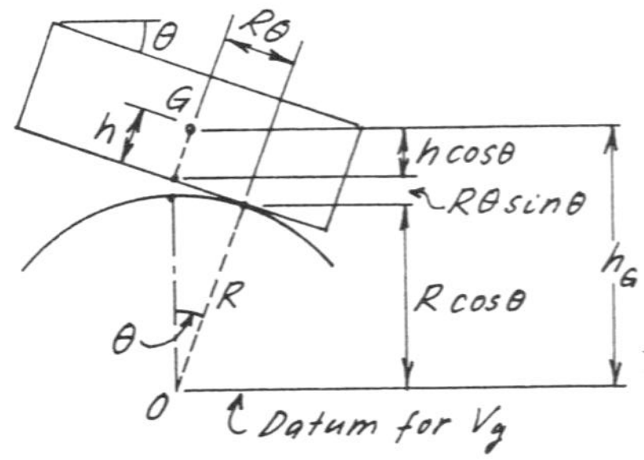

$$V_g = Wh_G = W\left[(R + h)\cos\theta + R\theta\sin\theta\right]$$

$$\therefore \frac{dV_g}{d\theta} = W\left[-(R + h)\sin\theta + R\sin\theta + R\theta\cos\theta\right]$$

$$= W(-h\sin\theta + R\theta\cos\theta)$$

$$\therefore \frac{d^2V_g}{d\theta^2} = W(-h\cos\theta + R\cos\theta - R\theta\sin\theta)$$

<u>At $\theta = 0$</u>: $\frac{d^2V_g}{d\theta^2} = W(-h + R)$ $\quad\therefore$ The equilibrium position is stable if $R > h$ ◆

10.46

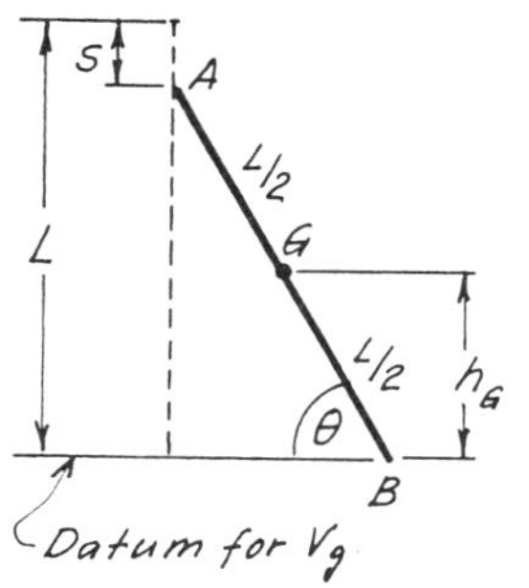

$y_G = \frac{L}{2}\sin\theta \qquad s = L - L\sin\theta = L(1-\sin\theta)$

$V_g = Wy_G = \frac{1}{2}WL\sin\theta = \frac{1}{2}(12)(2)\sin\theta = 12\sin\theta$ lb•ft

$V_e = \frac{1}{2}ks^2 = \frac{1}{2}kL^2(1-\sin\theta)^2 = \frac{1}{2}(6)(2)^2(1-\sin\theta)^2$

$= 12(1-\sin\theta)^2$ lb•ft

$V = V_g + V_e = 12(1 - \sin\theta + \sin^2\theta)$

$\therefore dV/d\theta = 12(-\cos\theta + 2\sin\theta\cos\theta) = 12\cos\theta\,(2\sin\theta - 1)$

$\therefore d^2V/d\theta^2 = 12\left[\sin\theta + 2(\cos^2\theta - \sin^2\theta)\right]$

$dV/d\theta = 0$ when $\cos\theta = 0$ or $2\sin\theta = 1$, i.e. $\theta = 90^\circ$ or $\theta = 30^\circ$

<u>At $\theta = 90^\circ$</u>: $d^2V/d\theta^2 = -12 < 0$ $\therefore$ the position is <u>unstable</u> ◆

<u>At $\theta = 30^\circ$</u>: $d^2V/d\theta^2 = 18 > 0$ $\therefore$ the position is <u>stable</u> ◆

10.47

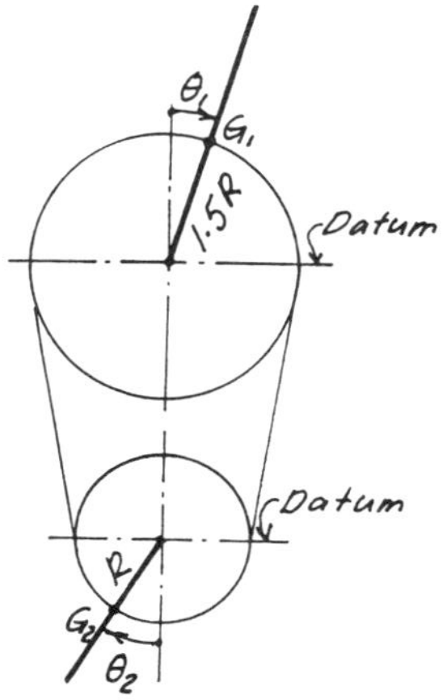

Kinematics: $1.5R\theta_1 = R\theta_2 \quad \therefore \theta_2 = 1.5\theta_1$

$V_g = W_1(1.5R\cos\theta_1) - W_2(R\cos\theta_2)$

$= R\left[1.5W_1\cos\theta_1 - W_2\cos(1.5\theta_1)\right]$

$\therefore dV_g/d\theta_1 = R\left[-1.5W_1\sin\theta_1 + 1.5W_2\sin(1.5\theta_1)\right]$

$\therefore d^2V_g/d\theta_1^2 = 1.5R\left[-W_1\cos\theta_1 + 1.5W_2\cos(1.5\theta_1)\right]$

<u>At $\theta_1 = 0$</u>: $d^2V_g/d\theta_1^2 = 1.5R(-W_1 + 1.5W_2)$

$\therefore$ Equilibrium is stable if $W_1/W_2 < 1.5$ ◆

10.48

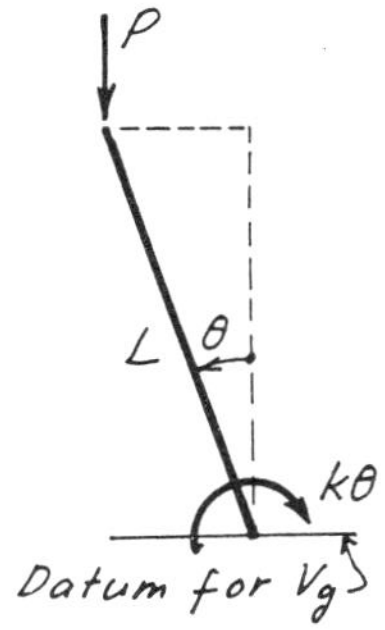

$V_g = P(L\cos\theta) \quad V_e = \frac{1}{2}k\theta^2 \quad V = V_g + V_e = PL\cos\theta + \frac{1}{2}k\theta^2$

$\therefore \frac{dV}{d\theta} = -PL\sin\theta + k\theta \quad \therefore \frac{d^2V}{d\theta^2} = -PL\cos\theta + k$

<u>At $\theta = 0$:</u> $\frac{d^2V}{d\theta^2} = -PL + k$

$\therefore$ Equilibrium is stable if $P < \frac{k}{L}$ ◆

10.49

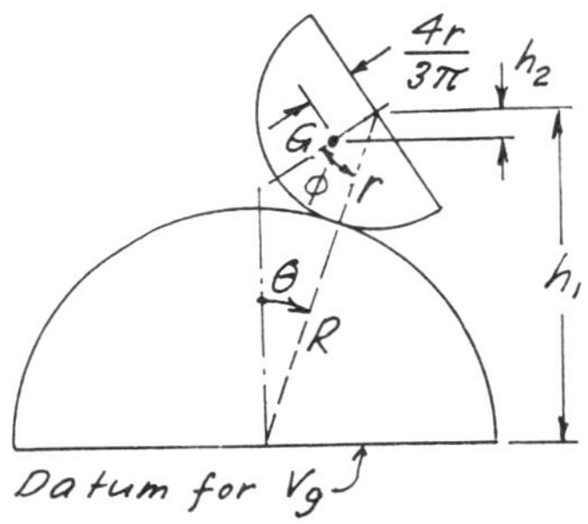

Kinematics: $R\theta = r\phi \quad \therefore \phi = \frac{R}{r}\theta$

Geometry: $h_1 = (R+r)\cos\theta$

$h_2 = \frac{4r}{3\pi}\cos(\theta + \phi) = \frac{4r}{3\pi}\cos\left[\left(1 + \frac{R}{r}\right)\theta\right]$

$V_g = W(h_1 - h_2) = W\left\{(R+r)\cos\theta - \frac{4r}{3\pi}\cos\left[\left(1+\frac{R}{r}\right)\theta\right]\right\}$

$= Wr\left\{\left(1+\frac{R}{r}\right)\cos\theta - \frac{4}{3\pi}\cos\left[\left(1+\frac{R}{r}\right)\theta\right]\right\}$

$\therefore \frac{dV_g}{d\theta} = Wr\left\{-\left(1+\frac{R}{r}\right)\sin\theta + \frac{4}{3\pi}\left(1+\frac{R}{r}\right)\sin\left[\left(1+\frac{R}{r}\right)\theta\right]\right\}$

$= Wr\left(1+\frac{R}{r}\right)\left\{-\sin\theta + \frac{4}{3\pi}\sin\left[\left(1+\frac{R}{r}\right)\theta\right]\right\}$

$\therefore \frac{d^2V_g}{d\theta^2} = Wr\left(1+\frac{R}{r}\right)\left\{-\cos\theta + \frac{4}{3\pi}\left(1+\frac{R}{r}\right)\cos\left[\left(1+\frac{R}{r}\right)\theta\right]\right\}$

<u>When $\theta = 0$:</u> $\frac{d^2V_g}{d\theta^2} = Wr\left(1+\frac{R}{r}\right)\left[-1 + \frac{4}{3\pi}\left(1+\frac{R}{r}\right)\right]$

$\therefore$ Equilibrium is stable if $-1 + \frac{4}{3\pi}\left(1+\frac{R}{r}\right) > 0$, or $\frac{R}{r} > \frac{3\pi}{4} - 1 = 1.356$ ◆

10.50

$$h = \frac{L-3}{2}\cos\theta \approx \frac{L-3}{2}\left(1 - \frac{1}{2}\theta^2\right) \text{ m}$$

Elongation of spring: $s = 3\sin\theta \approx 3\theta$ m

Weight of bar: $W = (150)(L+3)(9.81)$

$= 1471.5\,(L+3)$ N $= 1.4715(L+3)$ kN

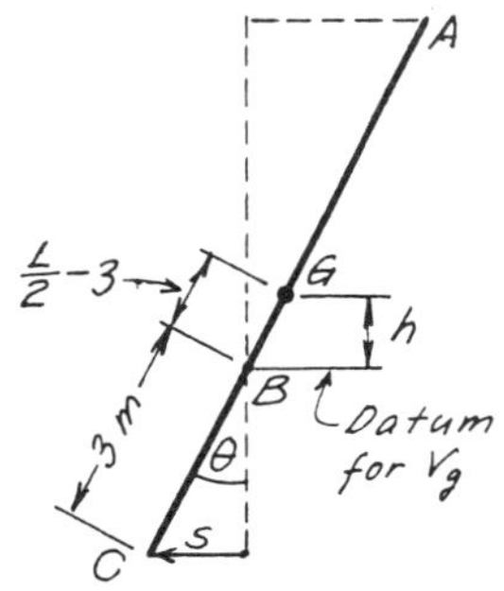

$$V = V_g + V_e = \frac{1}{2}ks^2 + Wh$$

$$= \frac{1}{2}(6)(3\theta)^2 + 1.4715(L+3)\frac{L-3}{2}\left(1 - \frac{\theta^2}{2}\right)$$

$$= \left[27 - 0.3679(L^2-9)\right]\theta^2 + 0.7358(L^2-9)$$

$$\therefore \frac{d^2V}{d\theta^2} = 2\left[27 - 0.3679(L^2-9)\right]$$

$\therefore$ Equilibrium is stable if $27 - 0.3679(L^2 - 9) > 0$, or $L < 9.08$ m ◆

10.51

Deformation of spring: $s = a\sin\theta = b\sin\phi$

For small angles: $s \approx a\theta = b\phi \quad \therefore \phi = \frac{a}{b}\theta$

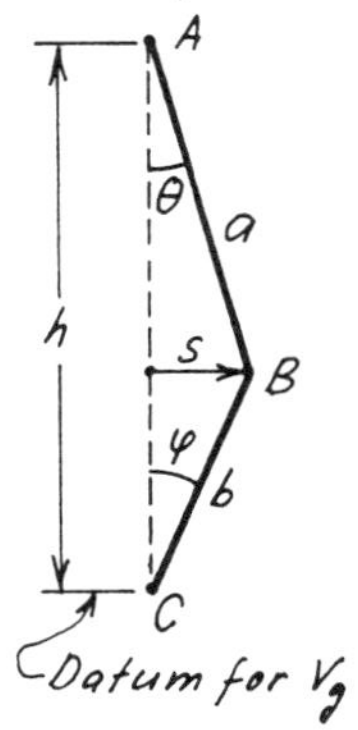

$$h = a\cos\theta + b\cos\phi \approx a\left(1 - \frac{1}{2}\theta^2\right) + b\left(1 - \frac{1}{2}\phi^2\right)$$

$$= a + b - \frac{1}{2}\left[a\theta^2 + b\left(\frac{a}{b}\theta\right)^2\right] = (a+b)\left(1 - \frac{a}{2b}\theta^2\right)$$

$$V = V_g + V_e = Wh + \frac{1}{2}ks^2 = W(a+b)\left(1 - \frac{a}{2b}\theta^2\right) + \frac{1}{2}k(a\theta)^2$$

$$\frac{dV}{d\theta} = W(a+b)\left(-\frac{a}{b}\theta\right) + ka^2\theta \qquad \frac{d^2V}{d\theta^2} = -W(a+b)\frac{a}{b} + ka^2$$

$\therefore$ Equilibrium is stable if $-W(a+b)\frac{a}{b} + ka^2 > 0$, or $W < k\frac{ab}{a+b}$

$\therefore$ Largest weight for which the equilibrium position is stable is $W = k\frac{ab}{a+b}$ ◆

10.52

Let the $\theta = 0$ position be the datum position.

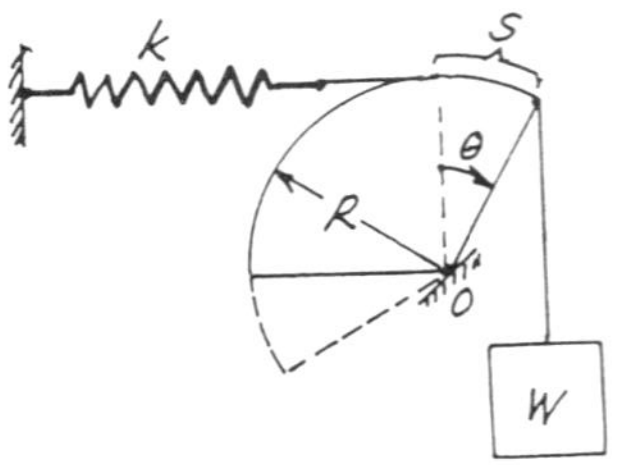

$$V_g = -WR(1-\cos\theta) \qquad V_e = \frac{1}{2}ks^2 = \frac{1}{2}k(R\theta)^2$$

$$V = V_g + V_e = -WR(1-\cos\theta) + \frac{1}{2}kR^2\theta^2$$

$$\therefore \frac{dV}{d\theta} = -WR\sin\theta + kR^2\theta$$

$\frac{dV}{d\theta} = 0$ when $\theta = 30°$ ($\pi/6$ rad): $-WR\sin 30° + kR^2\frac{\pi}{6} = 0 \qquad \therefore \frac{kR}{W} = \frac{6\sin 30°}{\pi} = 0.9549$

$$\therefore \frac{d^2V}{d\theta^2} = -WR\cos\theta + kR^2 = WR\left(-\cos\theta + \frac{kR}{W}\right) = WR(-\cos\theta + 0.9549)$$

When $\theta = 30°$: $\frac{d^2V}{d\theta^2} = WR(-\cos 30° + 0.9549) = 0.0889WR > 0 \quad \therefore$ Equilibrium is stable ◆

10.53

Let the $\theta = 0$ position be the datum position.

Let L_0 be the length of cable BED.

Note that weight D drops the distance

$(L_0 - s) - (L_0 - L) = L - s$

from its datum position.

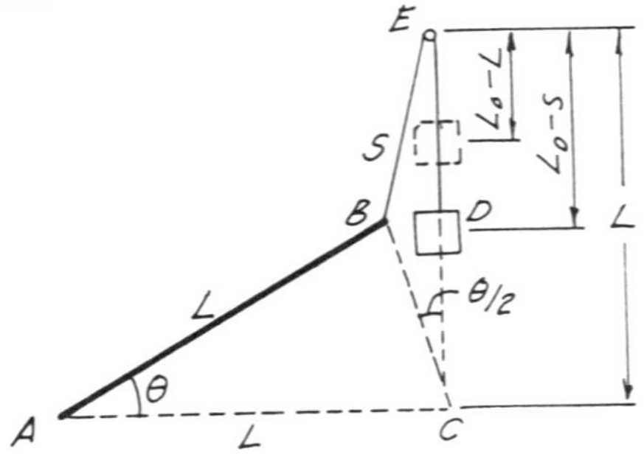

$$\therefore V_g = Wy_G - \left(\frac{3}{4}W\right)(L-s)$$

Geometry: $y_G = \frac{L}{2}\sin\theta$

From triangle ABC:

$$\overline{BC}^2 = L^2 + L^2 - 2L^2\cos\theta = 2L^2(1-\cos\theta)$$

From triangle BCE:

$$s^2 = L^2 + \overline{BC}^2 - 2L(\overline{BC})\cos\frac{\theta}{2} = L^2 + 2L^2(1-\cos\theta) - 2L^2\sqrt{2(1-\cos\theta)}\cos\frac{\theta}{2}$$

(continued)

10.53 continued

Substitute $\cos\dfrac{\theta}{2} = \sqrt{\dfrac{1+\cos\theta}{2}}$ in the last term:

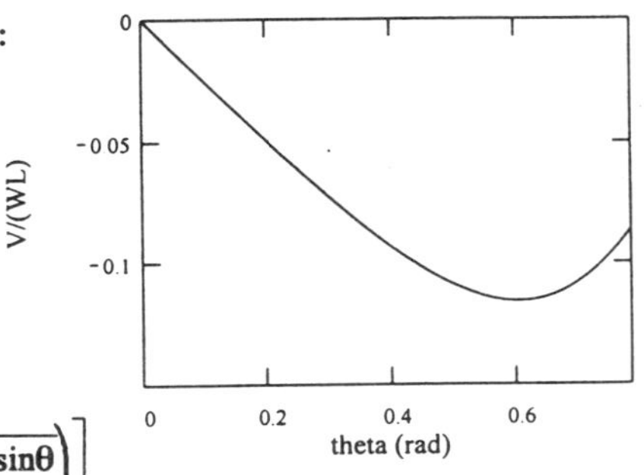

$$2L^2\sqrt{2(1-\cos\theta)}\cos\frac{\theta}{2} = 2L^2\sqrt{1-\cos^2\theta}$$

$$= 2L^2 \sin\theta$$

$\therefore s^2 = L^2(3 - 2\cos\theta - 2\sin\theta)$

$\therefore s = L\sqrt{3 - 2\cos\theta - 2\sin\theta}$

$\therefore V_g = WL\left[\dfrac{1}{2}\sin\theta - \dfrac{3}{4}\left(1 - \sqrt{3 - 2\cos\theta - 2\sin\theta}\right)\right]$

The plot shows that there is a stable equilibrium position at $\theta \approx 0.60$ rad $= 34^o$ ◆

10.54

Let L be the length of the rope CDE.

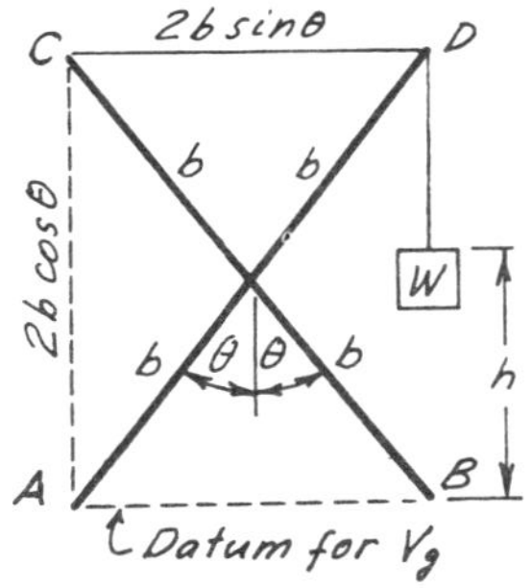

$\therefore L = \overline{CD} + \overline{DE} = 2b\sin\theta + (2b\cos\theta - h)$

$\therefore h = 2b(\sin\theta + \cos\theta) - L$

$V_g = Wh = W\left[2b(\sin\theta + \cos\theta) - L\right]$

$\dfrac{dV_g}{d\theta} = 2Wb(\cos\theta - \sin\theta)$

$\dfrac{d^2V_g}{d\theta^2} = 2Wb(-\sin\theta - \cos\theta)$

$\dfrac{dV_g}{d\theta} = 0$: $\cos\theta - \sin\theta = 0 \quad \therefore \tan\theta = 1 \quad \therefore \theta = 45^o$ ◆

When $\theta = 45^o$, $\dfrac{d^2V_g}{d\theta^2} = -2\sqrt{2}\,Wb < 0 \quad \therefore$ Equilibrium is unstable

10.55

From solution of Prob. 10.54 we have

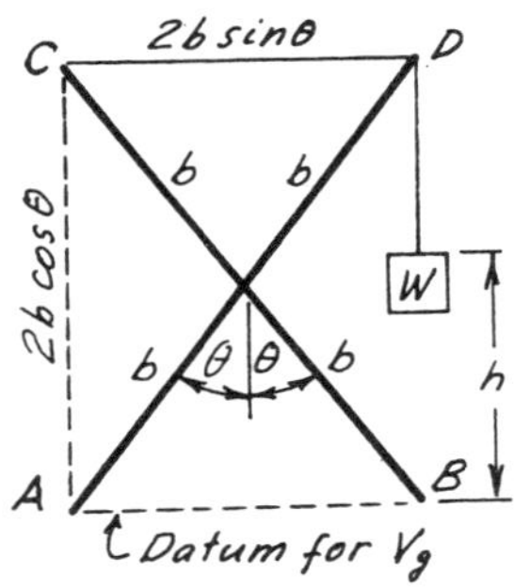

$h = 2b(\sin\theta + \cos\theta) - L$

where L is the length of the rope CDE.

Deformation of the spring AB is

$s = \overline{AB} - b = 2b\sin\theta - b$

$V = V_g + V_e = Wh + \dfrac{1}{2}ks^2$

$= W\left[2b(\sin\theta + \cos\theta) - L\right] + \dfrac{1}{2}\left(0.3\dfrac{W}{b}\right)(2b\sin\theta - b)^2$

$= Wb(0.15 + 1.4\sin\theta + 2\cos\theta + 0.6\sin^2\theta) - WL$

$\dfrac{dV}{d\theta} = Wb(1.4\cos\theta - 2\sin\theta + 1.2\sin\theta\cos\theta) = Wb(1.4\cos\theta - 2\sin\theta + 0.6\sin 2\theta)$

$\dfrac{d^2V}{d\theta^2} = Wb(-1.4\sin\theta - 2\cos\theta + 1.2\cos 2\theta)$

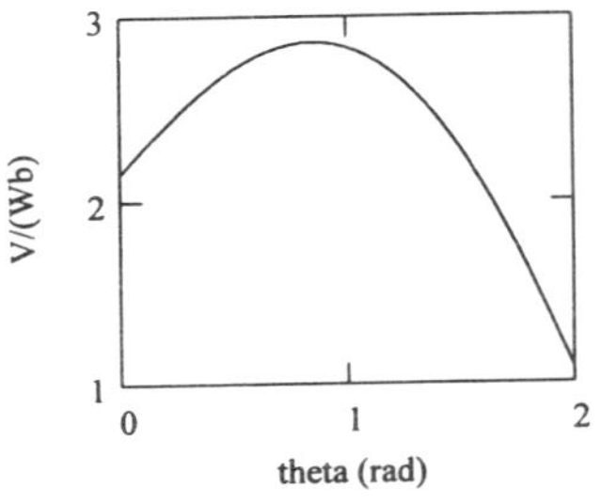

Plot of V/(Wb) indicates an unstable equilibrium position at $\theta \approx 0.9$ rad (the plot neglects the constant term WL). A more precise value is obtained by solving $dV/d\theta = 0$ by Newton's method: $\theta \leftarrow \theta - \dfrac{dV/d\theta}{d^2V/d\theta^2}$. Starting with $\theta =$ 0.9, Newton's method converges after only two iterations to $\theta = 0.8565$ rad $= 49.1^o$ (unstable equilibrium) ◆

10.56

Deformation of spring:

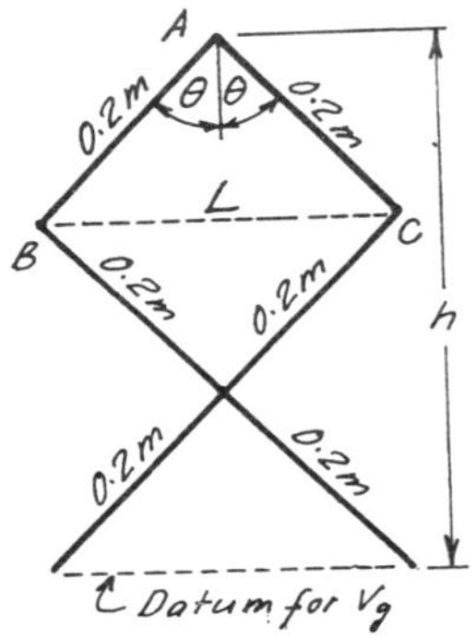

$s = L - L_0 = 2(0.2\sin\theta) - 2(0.2\sin 20^o)$

$= 0.4(\sin\theta - \sin 20^o)$

$h = 3(0.2\cos\theta) = 0.6\cos\theta$

$V = V_g + V_e = mgh + \dfrac{1}{2}ks^2$

$= m(9.81)(0.6\cos\theta) + \dfrac{1}{2}(250)(0.4)^2(\sin\theta - \sin 20^o)^2$

$= 5.886m\cos\theta + 20(\sin\theta - 0.3420)^2$ N·m

(continued)

10.56 continued

$$\therefore \frac{dV}{d\theta} = -5.886m\sin\theta + 40(\sin\theta - 0.3420)\cos\theta \quad N\cdot m$$

$$\therefore \frac{d^2V}{d\theta^2} = -5.886m\cos\theta - 40(\sin\theta - 0.3420)\sin\theta + 40\cos^2\theta \quad N\cdot m$$

<u>At $\theta = 60^o$</u>

$$\frac{dV}{d\theta} = 0: \; -5.886m\,(0.8660) + 40(0.8660 - 0.3420)(0.5) = 0$$

$$\therefore -5.097m + 10.480 = 0 \quad \therefore m = 2.06 \text{ kg} \; \blacklozenge$$

$$\frac{d^2V}{d\theta^2} = -5.886(2.06)(0.5) - 40(0.8660 - 0.3420)(0.8660) + 40\,(0.5)^2 = -14.2 \;\; N\cdot m < 0$$

$\therefore$ The equilibrium is <u>unstable</u>. ◆

10.57

From the solution of Prob. 10.56:

$$V = 5.886m\cos\theta + 20(\sin\theta - 0.3420)^2 = 5.886(2.06)\cos\theta + 20(\sin\theta - 0.3420)^2$$

$$= 12.125\cos\theta + 20(\sin\theta - 0.3420)^2 \quad N\bullet m$$

$$\therefore \frac{dV}{d\theta} = -\,12.125\sin\theta + 40(\sin\theta - 0.3420)\cos\theta \quad N\cdot m$$

$$\therefore \frac{d^2V}{d\theta^2} = -12.125\sin\theta - 40(\sin\theta - 0.3420)\sin\theta + 40\cos^2\theta$$

$$= 40(\cos^2\theta - \sin^2\theta) + 1.555\sin\theta \quad N\cdot m$$

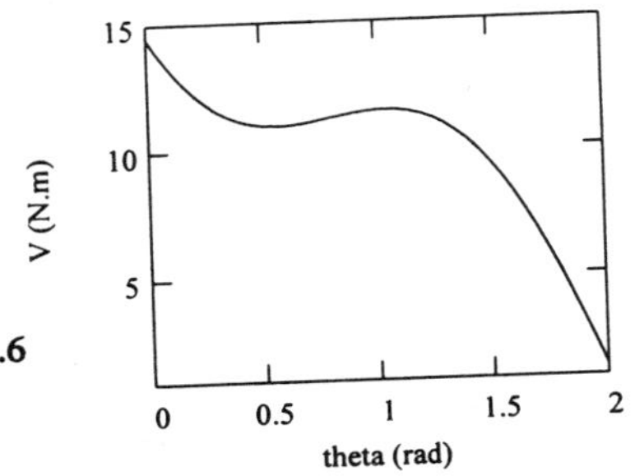

From plot of V vs. θ we see that there is a stable equilibrium position at $\theta \approx 0.6$ rad. An accurate value of θ can be computed by Newton's method:

$$\theta \leftarrow \theta - \frac{dV/d\theta}{d^2V/d\theta^2}$$

This yields after two iterations, starting with $\theta = 0.6$

$$\theta = 0.5620 \text{ rad} = 32.2^o \; \blacklozenge$$

10.58

Geometry: $h_G = \frac{L}{2}\sin\theta$

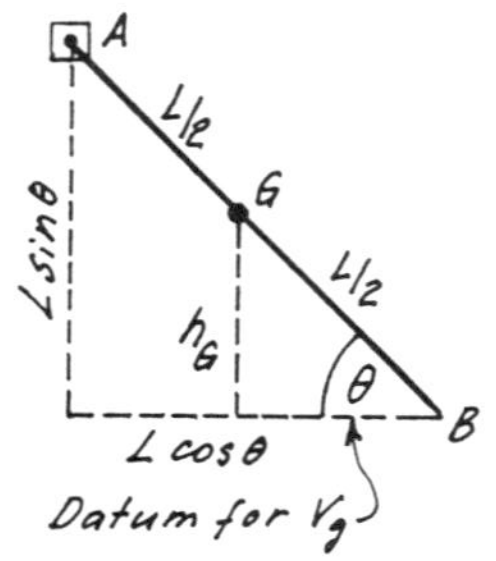

Let $\theta = \theta_0$ when the spring is undeformed. Thus the deformation of the spring is

$$s = L(\cos\theta - \cos\theta_0)$$

$$V = V_g + V_e = Wh_G + \frac{1}{2}ks^2$$

$$= (kL)\left(\frac{L}{2}\sin\theta\right) + \frac{1}{2}kL^2(\cos\theta - \cos\theta_0)^2$$

$$= \frac{1}{2}kL^2\left[\sin\theta + (\cos\theta - \cos\theta_0)^2\right]$$

$$\therefore \frac{dV}{d\theta} = \frac{1}{2}kL^2\left[\cos\theta - 2(\cos\theta - \cos\theta_0)\sin\theta\right]$$

$$\therefore \frac{d^2V}{d\theta^2} = \frac{1}{2}kL^2\left[-\sin\theta - 2(\cos\theta - \cos\theta_0)\cos\theta + 2\sin^2\theta\right]$$

<u>When $\theta = 65^o$</u>:

$$\frac{dV}{d\theta} = 0: \; \cos 65^o - 2(\cos 65^o - \cos\theta_0)\sin 65^o = 0$$

$$\therefore -0.3434 + 1.8126\cos\theta_0 = 0 \quad \therefore \theta_0 = 79.1^o \; \blacklozenge$$

$$\frac{d^2V}{d\theta^2} = \frac{1}{2}kL^2\left[-\sin 65^o - 2(\cos 65^o - \cos 79.1^o)\cos 65^o + 2\sin^2 65^o\right]$$

$$= \frac{1}{2}kL^2\,(0.539) > 0 \quad \therefore \text{Equilibrium is } \underline{\text{stable}} \;\therefore$$

10.59

From solution of Prob. 10.58 we get, after substituting $\theta_0 = 80^o$:

$$V = \frac{1}{2}kL^2\left[\sin\theta + (\cos\theta - \cos 80^o)^2\right] \qquad \frac{dV}{d\theta} = \frac{1}{2}kL^2\left[\cos\theta - 2(\cos\theta - \cos 80^o)\sin\theta\right]$$

$$\frac{d^2V}{d\theta^2} = \frac{1}{2}kL^2\left[-\sin\theta - 2(\cos\theta - \cos 80^o)\cos\theta + 2\sin^2\theta\right]$$

(continued)

10.59 continued

The plot of V vs. θ shows that there is a stable equilibrium position at $\theta \approx 1.2$ rad. A more accurate result can be obtained by solving $dV/d\theta = 0$ by Newton's method using the iterative formula

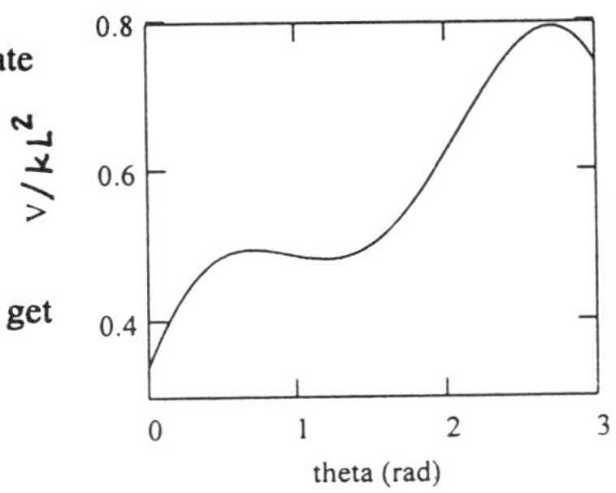

$$\theta \leftarrow \theta - \frac{dV/d\theta}{d^2V/d\theta^2}$$

After two iterations, starting from $\theta = 1.2$ rad, we get

$$\theta = 1.184 \text{ rad} = 67.8^\circ \ ◆$$

10.60

Geometry: $h = 10 \sin\theta$ in

Deformation of spring: $s = L - L_0 = 5\cos\theta - 2$ in

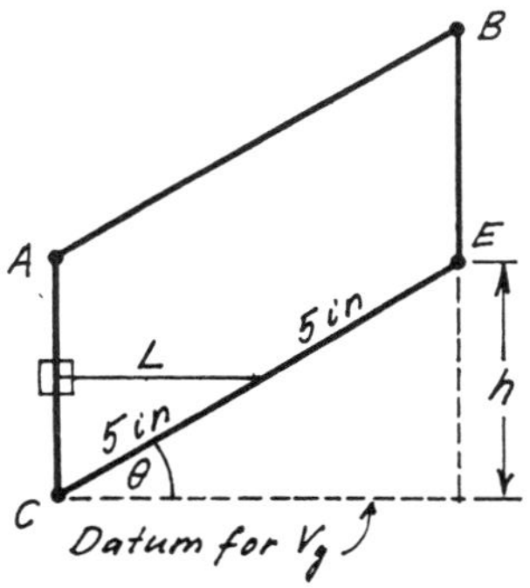

$$V = V_g + V_e = Wh + \frac{1}{2}ks^2$$

$$= (5)(10\sin\theta) + \frac{1}{2}(7.5)(5\cos\theta - 2)^2$$

$$= 50\sin\theta + 3.75(5\cos\theta - 2)^2 \quad \text{lb·in}$$

$$\therefore \frac{dV}{d\theta} = 50\cos\theta + 7.5(5\cos\theta - 2)(-5\sin\theta)$$

$$= 50\cos\theta + 75\sin\theta - 187.5\sin\theta\cos\theta \quad \text{lb·in}$$

$$\therefore \frac{d^2V}{d\theta^2} = -50\sin\theta + 75\cos\theta + 187.5(\sin^2\theta - \cos^2\theta) \text{ lb•in}$$

The plot of V vs. θ shows an unstable equilibrium position at $\theta \approx 0.5$ rad, and a stable one at $\theta \approx 0.9$ rad. Using these angles as the starting values, Newton's method

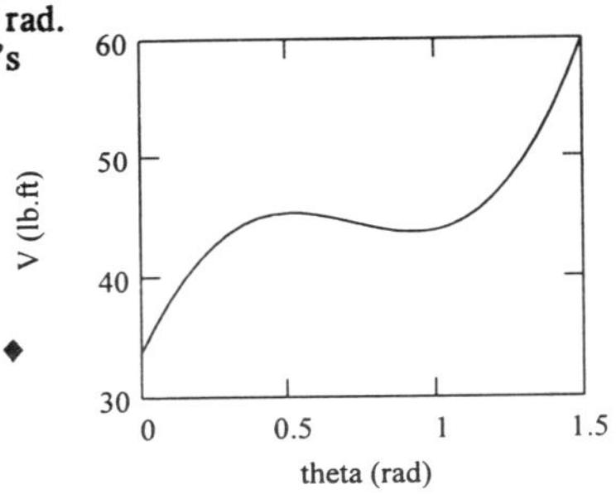

$$\theta \leftarrow \theta - \frac{dV/d\theta}{d^2V/d\theta^2}$$

yields after a few iterations:

$$\theta = 0.5165 \text{ rad} = 29.6^\circ \text{ (unstable equlibrium)} \ ◆$$

$$\theta = 0.9273 \text{ rad} = 53.1^\circ \text{ (stable equlibrium)} \ ◆$$

10.61

Geometry: $h = L(\sin\theta_1 + \sin\theta_2)$

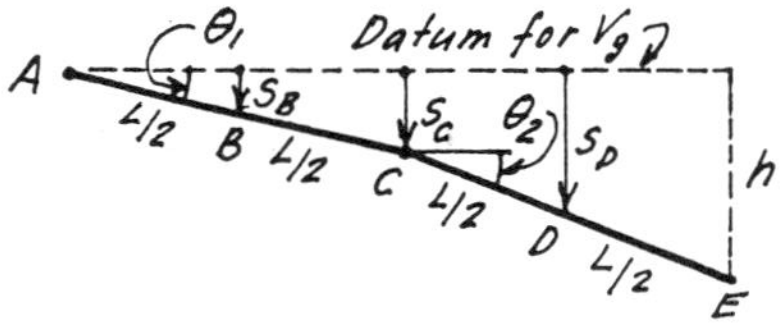

$$s_B = \frac{L}{2}\sin\theta_1 \qquad s_C = L\sin\theta_1$$

$$s_D = L\sin\theta_1 + \frac{L}{2}\sin\theta_2$$

$$V = V_g + V_e = -Wh + \frac{k}{2}(s_B^2 + s_C^2 + s_D^2)$$

$$= -\left(\frac{kL}{10}\right)L(\sin\theta_1 + \sin\theta_2) + \frac{kL^2}{2}\left[\frac{1}{4}\sin^2\theta_1 + \sin^2\theta_1 + \left(\sin\theta_1 + \frac{1}{2}\sin\theta_2\right)^2\right]$$

$$= kL^2\left[-\frac{1}{10}(\sin\theta_1 + \sin\theta_2) + \frac{9}{8}\sin^2\theta_1 + \frac{1}{8}\sin^2\theta_2 + \frac{1}{2}\sin\theta_1\sin\theta_2\right]$$

$$\therefore \frac{dV}{d\theta_1} = kL^2\left(-\frac{1}{10}\cos\theta_1 + \frac{9}{4}\sin\theta_1\cos\theta_1 + \frac{1}{2}\cos\theta_1\sin\theta_2\right)$$

$$\therefore \frac{dV}{d\theta_2} = kL^2\left(-\frac{1}{10}\cos\theta_2 + \frac{1}{4}\sin\theta_2\cos\theta_2 + \frac{1}{2}\sin\theta_1\cos\theta_2\right)$$

Discarding the obvious equilibrium position $\cos\theta_1 = \cos\theta_2 = 0$ ($\theta_1 = \theta_2 = 90^\circ$), we get

$$\frac{dV}{d\theta_1} = 0: \ \frac{9}{4}\sin\theta_1 + \frac{1}{2}\sin\theta_2 = \frac{1}{10} \qquad \frac{dV}{d\theta_2} = 0: \ \frac{1}{2}\sin\theta_1 + \frac{1}{4}\sin\theta_2 = \frac{1}{10}$$

The solution is: $\sin\theta_1 = -0.0800$, $\sin\theta_2 = 0.5600$ $\therefore \theta_1 = -4.6^\circ$, $\theta_2 = 34.1^\circ$ ◆

10.62

Choose s_A and θ as the kinematically independent variables.

$$\therefore s_B = s_A + \frac{L}{3}\sin\theta$$

$$\therefore s_C = s_A + L\sin\theta$$

$$\therefore h = s_A + \frac{L}{2}\sin\theta$$

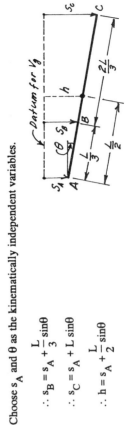

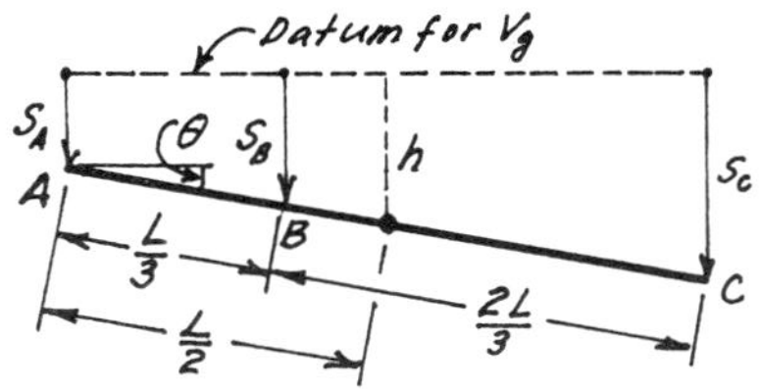

(continued)

10.62 continued

$$V = V_g + V_e = -Wh + \frac{k}{2}(s_A^2 + s_B^2 + s_C^2)$$

$$= -(kL)\left(s_A + \frac{L}{2}\sin\theta\right) + \frac{k}{2}\left[s_A^2 + \left(s_A + \frac{L}{3}\sin\theta\right)^2 + (s_A + L\sin\theta)^2\right]$$

$$= k\left(-Ls_A - \frac{1}{2}L^2\sin\theta + \frac{3}{2}s_A^2 + \frac{4}{3}Ls_A\sin\theta + \frac{5}{9}L^2\sin^2\theta\right)$$

$$\therefore \frac{dV}{d\theta} = k\left(-\frac{1}{2}L^2\cos\theta + \frac{4}{3}Ls_A\cos\theta + \frac{10}{9}L^2\sin\theta\cos\theta\right)$$

$$\therefore \frac{dV}{ds_A} = k\left(-L + 3s_A + \frac{4}{3}L\sin\theta\right)$$

Discarding the $\cos\theta = 0$ ($\theta = 90^\circ$) equilibrium position, the equilibrium equations are

$$\frac{dV}{d\theta} = 0: \quad \frac{4}{3}s_A + \frac{10}{9}L\sin\theta = \frac{1}{2}L \qquad \frac{dV}{ds_A} = 0: \quad 3s_A + \frac{4}{3}L\sin\theta = L$$

The solution is: $s_A = \frac{2}{7}L$, $\sin\theta = \frac{3}{28}$ $\quad\therefore \theta = 6.15^\circ$ ◆